PRENTICE HALL Geometry

- *The problem solving approach that relates geometry to algebra*
- *Provides the tools to implement the NCTM Curriculum and Professional Standards*

Comprehensive Coverage

Student Text
- Cohesive course written in "user friendly" language to ensure student success
- Allows students to become involved in the development of their own mathematical understandings
- Balance of solid mathematics with contemporary approaches

Problem Solving
- Complete Strategy lessons in each chapter develop skills to think critically, develop strategies, and choose a successful approach to solve proof and any problem

Communication
- Provides the opportunity to communicate mathematics in a variety of ways; Writing and Reading in Geometry

Reasoning
- Involvement in constructing and applying mathematical concepts; Thinking Critically

Connections
- Connects geometry to daily life
- Integrates related topics and other disciplines
- Develops students' mathematical power
- Students gain the ability to use mathematics in today's world

Technology
- Develops and explores concepts using multiple forms of technology

Review and Assessment
- Ongoing review and self-evaluation ensure success, including Algebra Review, Mixed Review, Chapter Summary and Review, Cumulative Review, Test Yourself, Chapter Test

Addresses Current Curriculum Issues . . .
- Alternative Assessment, Alternative Learning Styles, Cooperative Learning, Technology use, Multicultural Opportunities, Lesson-by-lesson implementation of the NCTM Curriculum Standards

PLUS...Superior and Flexible Support

Teacher's Edition
- Chapter Overviews, Lesson Plan for every lesson including background information, suggestions, examples, quizzes, enrichment; Pacing Chart, Resource Chart, and NCTM lesson-by-lesson correlation

Teacher's Resource Book
- Organized by chapter
- Investigation, Practice, Enrichment for every lesson
- Applications, Technology, Student and Teacher Aids
- Current Testing Program
- Graphing Utility

Teaching Transparencies
- Addresses Alternative Learning Styles
- One or more full-color transparencies per lesson
- Critical Thinking suggestions

Computer Test Bank with GRAPHICS
- 1000s of exercises to create multiple forms of tests
- Multiple Choice/Open-Ended Formats
- Choice of IBM, MAC, Apple II software
- Dial-a-Test
- Classroom Management system

Connections
- 48 pages of lessons and full-color poster
- Critical Thinking—Cooperative Learning
- Using technology as a discovery tool

Overhead Manipulatives Kit
- Tools for the classroom
- Algebra tiles—Geoboard—Tangrams—Spinner—Protractor

Solutions Manual
- Complete solutions to all Student Text exercises

THE APPROACH THAT MAKES THE DIFFERENCE...

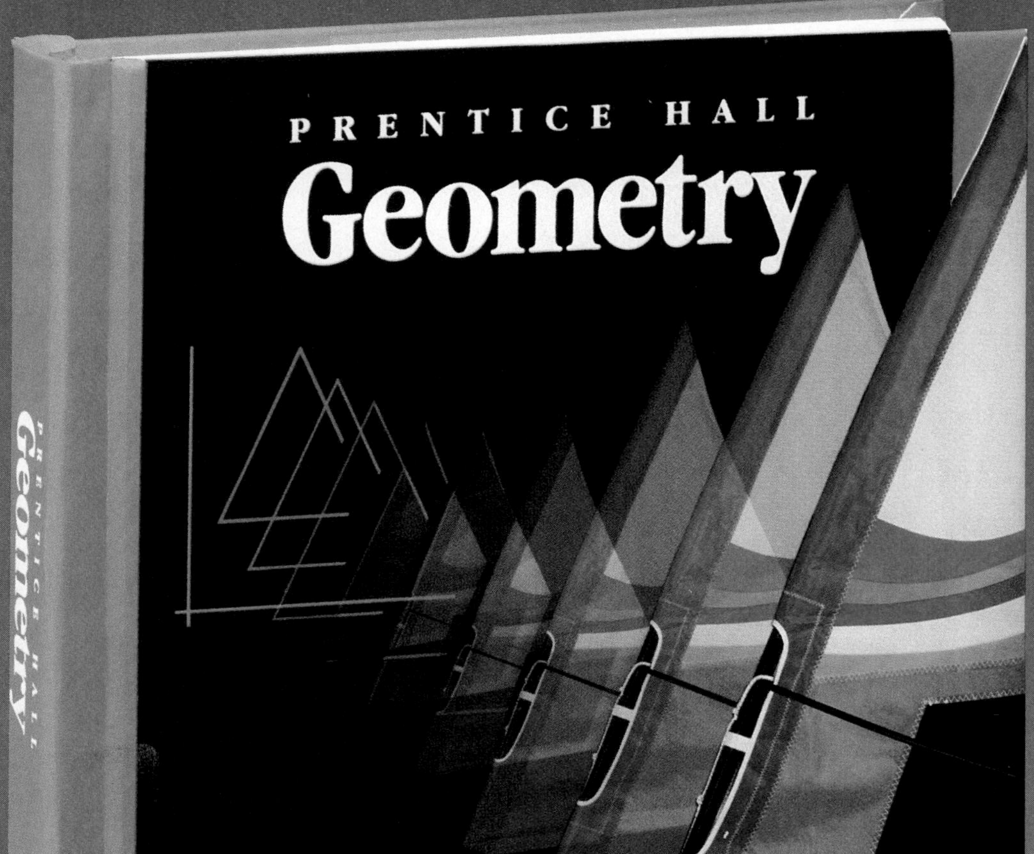

PRENTICE HALL

Geometry

Investigative...
Traditional...
Relevant...

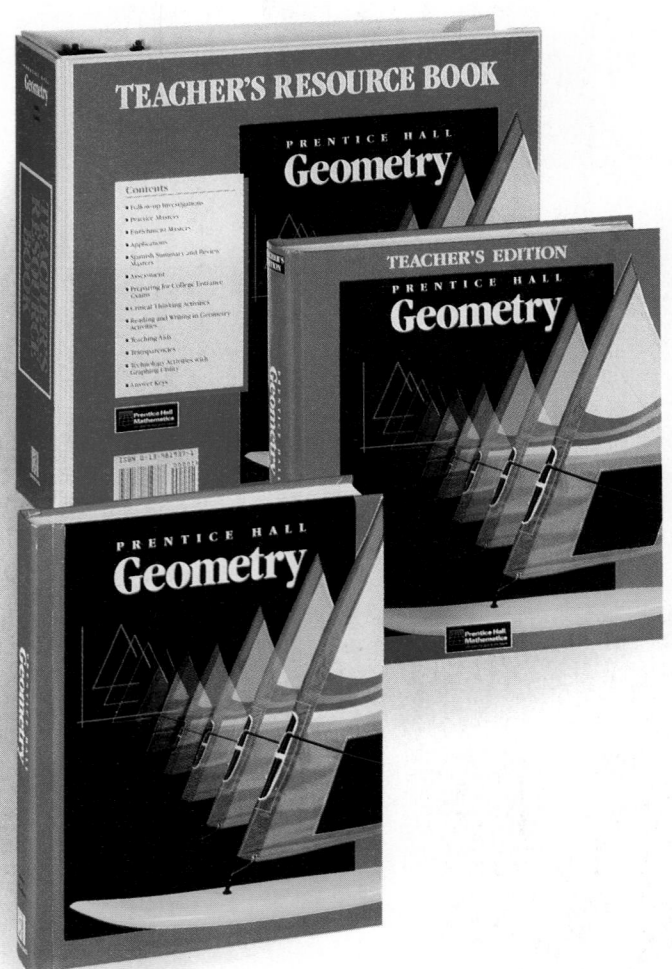

STUDENT TEXT

The problem-solving approach that relates geometry to algebra

- Develops strategies for problem solving and proof
- Connects geometry to daily life
- Integrates related topics and other disciplines
- Provides opportunities to communicate mathematically
- Enhances the development of concepts using technology
- Provides on-going review and self-evaluation
- Implements the NCTM Curriculum Standards

TEACHER'S EDITION

Support to help meet the challenges of teaching

- Chapter Overviews, suggestions, examples, quizzes, and enrichment
- Addresses current curriculum issues...
    Authentic Assessment — Alternative Learning Styles
    Cooperative Learning Techniques — Multicultural Connections
- Technology use and instruction
- Lesson-by-lesson implementation of the NCTM Curriculum Standards
- Tools to implement the NCTM Professional Standards

TEACHER'S RESOURCE BOOK

Wealth of ideas and support materials

- Organized by Chapter for convenient access
- Investigation, Practice, Enrichment for every lesson
- Applications, Technology, Teacher and Student Aids
- Current Testing program...including
    Authentic and Performance Assessment
    Up-to-date College Entrance Exam Reviews
- Graphing Utility included for use with program

TEACHING TRANSPARENCIES

*Address alternative
learning styles*

- One or more full-color transparencies per lesson
- Critical Thinking suggestions

COMPUTER TEST BANK WITH GRAPHICS

*The convenience of technology
at your fingertips*

- 1000s of exercises to create multiple forms of tests
- Multiple Choice/Open-Ended Formats
- Choice of IBM, MAC, Apple II software
- Dial-a-Test
- Classroom Management system

CONNECTIONS

*Color poster and a variety
of activities*

- Critical Thinking — Cooperative Learning — Informal Discourse
- Investigations outside the classroom
- Using technology as a discovery tool

OVERHEAD MANIPULATIVES KIT

Tools for the classroom

- Algebra Tiles — Geoboard (with bands)
- Tangrams — Spinner — Protractor

SOLUTIONS MANUAL

Covers every exercise

- Complete solutions to all Student Text exercises

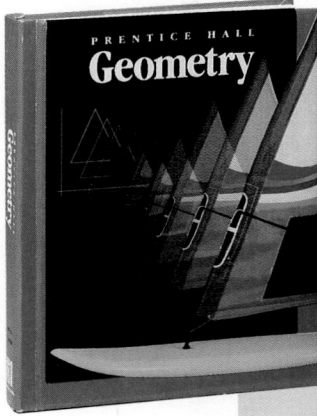

P R E N T I C E   H A L L

Geometry

STUDENTS DEVELOP THEIR MATHEMATICAL POWER

- Developing techniques and problem solving strategies to solve proof and in a variety of situations
- Gaining the ability to use mathematics in today's world
- Learning to communicate mathematics both orally and in writing
- Improving their thinking critically skills
- Connecting and integrating mathematics in real-life situations
- Using technology to develop concepts therefore enhancing their understanding of mathematics
- Benefiting from on-going review and self-evaluation

TEACHERS DEVELOP THEIR MATHEMATICAL POWER

- Tools to implement the NCTM Curriculum Professional Standards
- A lesson-by-lesson correlation to the NCTM Curriculum Standards
- A curriculum that addresses current issues
- Authentic Assessment Projects
- Cooperative Learning Techniques
- Strategies to address Alternative Learning Styles
- Suggestions for using technology to develop concepts
- Multicultural Connections

PRENTICE HALL

Geometry

Robert Kalin
Mary Kay Corbitt

Consulting Authors

Jan Fair ❖ Bettye C. Hall

Sadie C. Bragg ❖ Mona Fabricant

Jerome D. Hayden

Prentice Hall dedicates this
mathematics program to
all mathematics educators
and their students.

PRENTICE HALL
Englewood Cliffs, New Jersey
Needham, Massachusetts

Contents

Organization of The Geometry Program T7–T9

The NCTM Standards
About the Program
The Student Text
The Teacher's Edition
Superior and Flexible Support

Developing Mathematical Power T10–T18

Problem Solving
Communication
Reasoning
Connections
Technology
Assessment
Multicultural Opportunities
Cooperative Learning
Learning Styles
Resources

Pacing Geometry T19

Chapter 1	Overview	1A
Chapter 2	Overview	44A
Chapter 3	Overview	78A
Chapter 4	Overview	126A
Chapter 5	Overview	172A
Chapter 6	Overview	216A
Chapter 7	Overview	260A
Chapter 8	Overview	304A
Chapter 9	Overview	350A
Chapter 10	Overview	394A
Chapter 11	Overview	438A
Chapter 12	Overview	488A
Chapter 13	Overview	534A
Chapter 14	Overview	584A
Additional Answers		702

ISBN 0-13-353061-2

2 3 4 5 6 7 8 9 10   97 96 95 94 93

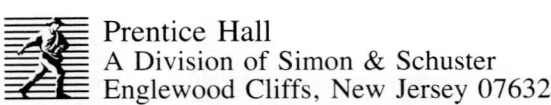
Prentice Hall
A Division of Simon & Schuster
Englewood Cliffs, New Jersey 07632

ORGANIZATION • OF • THE • PROGRAM

THE NCTM STANDARDS

Teaching mathematics continues to undergo change since the National Council of Teachers of Mathematics published its Curriculum and Evaluation Standards in 1989 and its Professional Standards in 1991.

The Curriculum and Evaluation Standards have provided a vision of what mathematics curriculum should include, and the Professional Standards are providing the same vision of teaching. Prentice Hall is committed to providing teachers with the support they need to help create that vision.

We are also committed to helping you create a learning environment in which students have access to experiences and challenges that lead to their development of mathematical power. Solid lesson development, critical thinking and discussion activities, application-based lessons, and writing in geometry activities make it easier for teachers to foster students' understanding of concepts and procedures.

Throughout its mathematics programs, Prentice Hall provides you with the tools for discourse…integration of technology, critical thinking activities, manipulatives, and opportunities for students to communicate mathematics in a variety of ways.

In this Teacher's Edition, current issues are addressed (pp. T10–T17) to help you implement the NCTM Curriculum Standards. Each Chapter Overview provides a lesson-by-lesson correlation to the Standards.

The National Council of Teachers of Mathematics
CURRICULUM STANDARDS

1 Mathematics as Problem Solving
2 Mathematics as Communication
3 Mathematics as Reasoning
4 Mathematics as Connections
5 Algebra
6 Functions
7 Geometry from a Synthetic Perspective
8 Geometry from an Algebraic Perspective
9 Trigonometry
10 Statistics
11 Probability
12 Discrete Mathematics
13 Conceptual Underpinning of Calculus
14 Mathematical Structure

In addition, side column commentary addresses Alternative Assessment (p. 76), Alternative Learning Styles (p. 51), Cooperative Learning (p. 46), Critical Thinking (p. 49), Multicultural Opportunities (p. 62), and Technology (p. 51).

ABOUT THE PROGRAM

The initial planning and subsequent development of *Prentice Hall Geometry* was done with input from more than 5000 teachers and supervisors, along with recommendations from subject matter scholars and consultants. The result is that our secondary mathematics programs are designed by teachers for teachers.

During each development phase, field testing and pilots were implemented for ongoing review and evaluation of the programs. Teachers and subject matter scholars assessed content, factual accuracy, conceptual integrity, and value. Thousands of teachers have piloted our programs, and tens of thousands of students are currently using *Prentice Hall Geometry*.

Each of the components received the same careful research and development as did the Student Text. Prentice Hall is creating and publishing materials that work in the classroom. The cooperation and involvement between publisher and teacher is a continual process. Students, along with teachers, provide us with insight into new and creative ideas that will ensure that every student can succeed. Planning, writing, editing, and evaluation personally involve all school personnel.

THE STUDENT TEXT

This comprehensive program allows students to investigate and discover lesson concepts in a variety of ways, before they are formally developed. The flexibility of the program provides teachers with a variety of approaches to make geometry

work. *Prentice Hall Geometry* actively involves students in their learning to develop their mathematical power through Problem Solving strategies, Cooperative Learning Projects, Critical Thinking and Reasoning Activities, Using Manipulatives and Technology to explore and develop concepts, and Connecting geometry to daily life.

In this program, students will develop and remember the skills and strategies necessary to select a successful approach to construct a proof and solve any problem. Our unique four-step method (*Understand the Problem, Plan the Approach, Complete the Work,* and *Interpret the Results*) guides students on a basis through all the conceptual levels of geometry...visualization, analysis, informal reasoning, and deduction where students can work in an axiomatic system.

The strategies that are developed provide students with the tools necessary to attack problems in an organized way. *Prentice Hall Geometry* provides the power for students to interpret statistical data, operate computers and calculators, use Logo to explore geometry concepts, construct proofs using an approach that relates geometry to algebra, and solve complex problems that relate to real-world situations.

Prentice Hall Geometry has been developed to help you to develop your students' mathematical power.

◆ Each *Chapter* begins with an introduction that connects geometry to a familar topic, and it also provides a *Project* for students to complete independently or in a cooperative learning situation.

◆ Each lesson begins with *Lesson Objectives* that tell students what is expected of them and *Investigations* that present you with a variety of ways to explore geometry.

◆ *New theorems, postulates,* and *concepts* are highlighted to emphasize their importance and for easy reference.

◆ *Completely worked-out examples* and *Proofs* provide instruction to help your students successfully complete their assignments. Solutions are given step-by-step with the reason for each step shown in blue type.

◆ The *Technology* logo [logo] identifies when using technology is beneficial to and appropriate for the development of concepts. In addition, *Technology Lessons* using Logo language provide you with alternative methods for exploring geometry.

◆ *Strategy* lessons, identified by blue borders, help students develop techniques and strategies for constructing proofs and solving problems in a variety of situations.

◆ *Class Exercises* include *Thinking Critically* to assess students' understanding of lesson concepts.

◆ Practice Exercises build a solid foundation of geometry skills . . .
  • *Thinking Critically*—helps improve reasoning skills
  • *Applications*—connects geometry to daily life and to other topics
  • *Developing Mathematical Power*—provides activities that may take students outside the classroom, exploring and using mathematics in today's world
  • *Mixed* and *Algebra Reviews*—will help students to remember the skills and concepts already learned

◆ *Writing, Reading,* and *Drawing in Geometry* activities help students to acquire communication skills.

◆ *Integrating Geometry* and *Career* features provide a look at how geometry is used in daily life.

◆ *Historical, Biographical Notes,* and *Careers* provide multicultural connections.

The complete review and assessment program provides opportunities for student self-evaluation, along with alternative assessment projects.

◆ *Chapter Summary and Review.* Two-page review of chapter content including important vocabulary

◆ *Cumulative Review.* One- to three-page review after all even numbered chapters that reviews concepts cumulatively from Chapter 1

◆ *Algebra Review.* Reviews basic math and algebra skills at the end of lessons and after all chapters that do not contain a Cumulative Review.

◆ *Test Yourself.* Midway and at the end of each chapter

◆ *Chapter Test.* One-page test at the end of each chapter

◆ *College Entrance Exam Review.* A review patterned to reflect the actual Scholastic Aptitude Test (SAT) and Achievement Test (Levels I and II) in mathematics

◆ *Chapter Project.* Each chapter introduction provides a project that can be used for performance assessment.

◆ *Extra Practice.* One page of additional exercises for each chapter in the back of the book.

THE TEACHER'S EDITION

The Teacher's Edition is designed to provide both the experienced and novice geometry teacher with more features than ever before to help them meet the challenges of teaching, to plan effectively, and to implement the NCTM Curriculum and Evaluation Standards.

◆ A *Pacing Chart* suggests how many days might be allocated to each lesson for three possible courses of study in a two-semester course.

◆ A *Chapter Overview* precedes each chapter with the following:

  • *Summary.* A brief description of the chapter content
  • *Chapter Objectives.* A listing of the lesson objectives
  • *Chapter Highlights.* Addresses Problem Solving, Communication, Reasoning, Connections, and Technolgy in the chapter
  • *Assignment Guide.* A chart that provides suggested assignments, an NCTM Curriculum Standards correlation on a lesson-by-lesson basis, plus chapter features and a *Resource Guide* that provides *Prentice Hall Geometry program resources* for the chapter

Throughout the book, nearly full-sized student text pages have answers in place and teaching suggestions that address current curriculum issues alongside. Each *Lesson Plan* contains the following.

  • *Vocabulary.* A list of important terms introduced in the lesson
  • *Materials/Manipulatives.* Materials and program resources that may be used to develop lesson concepts
  • *Technology.* Technological tools and program resources that may be used to develop lesson concepts
  • *Lesson Focus.* Includes suggestions, Alternative Learning Styles, Developing Mathematical Power, Critical Thinking, Cooperative Learning, Common Errors, Multicultural Opportunities, and Chalkboard Examples
  • *Follow-Up.* Includes Assignment Guide, Lesson Quiz, Alternative Assessment, and reduced pages from the *Teacher's Resource Book*
  • *Labeled exercises.* Labels indicating degree of difficulty of exercise sets noted only in the Teacher's Edition

SUPERIOR AND FLEXIBLE SUPPORT

TEACHER'S RESOURCE BOOK

◆ Organized by chapter
◆ Follow-up Investigation, Practice, Enrichment for every lesson
◆ Applications, Technology, Teacher and Student Aids
◆ Current Testing program . . . including Authentic and Performance Assessment and Up-to-date College Entrance Exam Reviews
◆ Graphing Utility included

COMPUTER TEST BANK with GRAPHICS

◆ Thousands of exercises to create multiple forms of tests
◆ Multiple Choice/Open-Ended Formats
◆ Choice of IBM, MAC, or Apple II series software
◆ Dial-a-Test
◆ Classroom Management system

TEACHING TRANSPARENCIES

◆ One or more full-color transparencies per lesson
◆ Critical Thinking suggestions

CONNECTIONS

◆ Color poster and 48 pages of activities
◆ Critical Thinking—Cooperative Learning—Informal Discourse
◆ Investigations outside the classroom
◆ Using technology as a discovery tool

OVERHEAD MANIPULATIVES KIT

◆ Tools for the classroom
◆ Algebra Tiles—Geoboard (with bands)
◆ Tangrams—Spinner—Protractor

SOLUTIONS MANUAL

◆ Complete solutions to all Student Text exercises

DEVELOPING · MATHEMATICAL · POWER

One of the primary goals of the Prentice Hall mathematics programs is to help students gain mathematical power. What is mathematical power? The NCTM *Curriculum and Evaluation Standards* states that mathematical power means

> **an individual's abilities to explore, conjecture, and reason logically, as well as the ability to use a variety of mathematical methods effectively to solve nonroutine problems. This notion is based on the recognition of mathematics as more than a collection of concepts and skills to be mastered; it includes methods of investigating and reasoning, means of communication, and notions of context. In addition, for each individual, mathematical power involves the development of personal self-confidence.**

Mathematical power is not acquired quickly or easily. It is built over time, through hard work and determination on the student's part, through patience and encouragement on the teacher's part. There are many aspects to be considered in developing mathematical power. The following pages are designed to help you explore some of the critical issues that affect mathematical teaching today. *Prentice Hall Geometry* is designed to help you incorporate these ideas into your own teaching style. References are made to specific features of the text and to their use in building mathematical power.

PROBLEM SOLVING

Solving problems is not only the goal of mathematics education—it is usually the method as well. Solving problems helps students understand ideas, and it gives them practice with procedure. When students practice problem solving, they are looking at a situation in different ways; they are weighing both sides of an argument; they are exploring new approaches to old questions. These are skills not just for math, not just for history, literature, science—these are life skills.

Varied problems require varied approaches. You can use the *Strategy* lessons found in each chapter to show students the kinds of things to look for in a problem, and you can encourage them to try their hand at adapting these strategies to new situations. Each of these lessons includes a list of *Problem Solving Reminders* tailored to the lesson topic. These are

the strategy lessons that are found in the text:

Analyze a Figure
Use Logical Reasoning
Use Inductive Reasoning
Identify Intermediate Goals
Recognize Underdetermined and Overdetermined
    Figures
Use Indirect Proof
Recognize Minimal Conditions
Find Inaccessible Distances
Estimate and Calculate Roots
Use Trigonometric Ratios
Use an Auxiliary Figure
Use Locus in Solving Construction Problems
Find Limits
Analyze Cross Sections of Solids
Use Coordinate Geometry in Proofs
Use Transformations

Long-term projects can bring together a combination of strategies, encouraging students to develop their own lines of reasoning and their own methods of organization. Each chapter contains a *Chapter Project*, found on the first page of the chapter. This project, in combination with the corresponding *Assessment* page in the *Teacher's Resource Book*, provides students with an ongoing assignment as they work through the chapter material. Thus, the project can also help you to assess a student's grasp of the chapter material and its application to the real world.

One of the traditionally "difficult" areas of geometry is creating proofs. In *Prentice Hall Geometry,* proofs are taken as problems to be solved using a variety of solutions—paragraph proofs, two-column proofs, indirect proofs—and a variety of strategies as well.

Group learning is a strategy in and of itself. The *Class Exercises* are an opportunity to practice new material in a group setting; very often a direction taken by one student can lead another on a new path, and these exercises may provide that chance. On the other hand, the Practice Exercises are for the most part designed to be completed by the students individually, to reinforce techniques, to extend ideas, and to show them—and you—which areas need further review. When problems from the *Practice Exercises* are particularly adaptable to group work, it is noted in the side column commentary of your Teacher's Edition.

When you teach problem solving to students, you can provide them with a wide range of problems. Students who achieve mathematical power are not afraid to try unfamiliar problems because they have already tried so many different types in the classroom and at home: one-step problems, problems that require extensive explanations or experimentation with technology and long-range problems like those posed in the *Chapter Projects*. When students have experience tackling varied, nonroutine problems in class, they are that much better equipped to deal with the problems that face them in the real world.

COMMUNICATION

Communication is essential to life, yet it is an ongoing process and a challenge for each of us. The process of mathematical communication, both in and out of the classroom, is no different. Working out a problem and explaining the method helps teach students the language of math, and as students become more comfortable with that language, their explanations and methods become clearer. Any vocabulary can be made stronger with regular practice, and the Prentice Hall approach weaves the mathematical vocabulary through each page of each lesson. A *Vocabulary* section is also included in the two-page *Chapter Summary and Review*.

Learning mathematics is a matter of building on what is already understood, and the stronger the structure, the longer it will stand. Communication is an important part of that structure. Frequently, students understand the idea behind a concept, yet it is not until they put it into words that it crystallizes in their minds. It is at that point that the concept becomes a part of their own mathematical reference. To aid in the development of this "concept crystallization," exercises and features requiring class discussion, *Writing in Mathematics,* and *Thinking Critically* are intertwined throughout the student text. In addition, many of the *Developing Mathematical Power* exercises, which are found at the end of the *Practice Exercise* sets, can be adapted as writing assignments. The side column of your Teacher's Edition also includes *Keeping a Portfolio,* a feature found in many lessons of the text.

When students are more comfortable speaking mathematically, they are more likely to ask probing questions. A vocabulary that expands inquiry also allows for more sophisticated responses. When homework assignments challenge students to speculate and imagine, the results are often surprising. In the words of the NCTM *Curriculum and Evaluation Standards,* "facility with the language of mathematics is an integral part of thinking mathematically, solving problems, and reflecting on one's own mathematical experiences."

REASONING

Every teacher has had students show up in class with a whole section of homework missing. Maybe the problems were worded differently from the ones the day before, or they did not ask for exactly the same thing; one way or another, some students will say, "we never went over these in class!" *You* know you went over that material; the problem is, *they* do not. In the classroom, teachers have the chance to express a problem in a variety of ways, to change parameters, and to help students find their way through to the result. At home, students may need the same sort of directed questioning that you are able to provide in the classroom. The *Thinking Critically* questions incorporated into the exercise sets will help to focus attention on the mathematics rather than on the "right answer." Exercises like these establish the habit of analyzing problems; and when students start thinking about old problems, picking them apart and examining their logic, they are less afraid to tackle new ones.

In mathematics courses, the logic that leads to an answer is usually more important than the answer itself. The right answer is no guarantee that students know what a problem is all about. The challenge is to involve students constantly in logical thinking, deciding when an alternate method is valid and when it is not. When students are given an assignment in which a number of open-ended questions are included, there is opportunity to shift the emphasis from rote learning to method and reasoning. The *Developing Mathematical Power* exercises found at the end of the *Practice Exercise* sets offer thought-provoking questions designed to stimulate the student's reasoning ability.

CONNECTIONS

Every teacher has a private list of perfect examples, foolproof analogies, favorite stories, and jokes for drawing a parallel and illustrating a concept for students. These are mathematical connections. By focusing on these connections, the student recalls something familiar—a shape, a process, an experience—and uses that as a springboard to understanding a new mathematical idea. Teachers are constantly looking for these springboards, and the Prentice Hall teaching program provides them with many opportunities to "make new connections."

The *Chapter Project* on the opening page of each chapter provides an opportunity for using the real world to illuminate the world of mathematics. Students use the math they are learning to accomplish the project; and in the process, the new mathematical ideas take on shape and meaning. In the Table of Contents you will find a list of careers, disciplines, and activities beneath each chapter title. These topics are all explored in the features and exercises of the chapter, and they provide a connection between the chapter material and real life.

Connections within mathematics can offer an alternative approach for a student struggling with the subject. "Seeing" the real solutions of a polynomial equation at the *x*-intercepts on a graphing calculator can wake up students who have slept through hours of factoring. A coordinate or transformational proof may give some students a sense of a theorem that the traditional approach could not supply.

Connections with other disciplines or with daily experience allow students of all abilities and interests to contribute to the class. When students demonstrate wave length with guitar frets, infinite series with a bouncing basketball, or line symmetry with paper airplanes, they are creating a memorable class and an indelible basis for understanding. Connections to other disciplines are also a chance to remind students that the subjects they learn in school are not isolated events, but part of a unified whole. The *Applications* section at the end of each exercise set provides connections with a varied assortment of activities, careers, and disciplines. When students find connections to mathematics, they answer the age-old question, "What will we ever use this for?"

TECHNOLOGY

The use of technology has changed the math classroom. Thanks to calculators, time that used to be spent poring through trig tables and log tables can now be used to explore mathematical relationships. Using technology, students can solve many problems in a short time, allowing them to watch patterns emerge. Graphing utilities let students compare twenty hyperbolas in the time it once took to graph one by hand. Spreadsheet programs encourage students to ask "What if?" rather than "What next?"

The expanding role of technology in the classroom poses difficult questions. An earlier generation wondered whether there were real benefits in working out square roots "the long way." Teachers have voiced similar concerns, more recently, about interpolation. Now they must reconsider the role of factoring techniques in the classroom, when a simple software command automatically factors polynomials. How much time should be spent teaching students to find the zeros of a function, when the SOLVE command provides real and imaginary solutions?

It becomes more and more important to explore and understand the implications of today's technology on the mathematical learning experience. Less computation time means more thinking time—how can that time be put to use? Instead of seeing mathematics in the classroom as a collection of already-discovered inert pieces of data, students need help exploring mathematics as the vast domain of inquiry it really is, where terms are redefined, relationships are explored, and information is constantly changing.

Logo is used as the technology medium for this text for several reasons. First, Logo allows us to try different definitions of the same term and examine the implications of each definition. Another reason is Logo's ability to integrate mathematical concepts.

Logo, with its powerful recursion tools, helps us begin to experience fractal geometry, a new kind of measurement theory. With Logo, we can test a variety of transformations and their compositions to discover the underlying structure of transformations. Furthermore, Logo can be used to generate a visual understanding of non-Euclidean geometry, one basis of modern computer graphics.

The [symbol] symbol is found throughout the student text, in *Examples* or *Practice Exercise* sets that work particularly well with calculators or utilities. Several chapters end with *Technology* features that focus on some specific aspect of technology today, and many of the *Applications* within the *Practice Exercises* contain detailed, step-by-step instructions for using Logo or some other form of technology.

ASSESSMENT

How do teachers know when their students understand the material? How do the students know? Both usually rely on the results of tests and quizzes, performance on homework, and that hazy yardstick called "class participation." These are all forms of assessment—but they are not the only forms. Most teachers know that traditional tests alone fail to give a complete picture of students' mathematical reasoning ability. The NCTM *Curriculum and Evaluation Standards* recommend "using multiple assessment techniques, including written, oral, and demonstration formats." Alternative forms of assessment are *not* just for the student who "does not test well"—they are for everyone.

One of the options available to teachers who want to test

"the whole student" is the systematic use of observations. These are a few of the questions you may want to ask yourself as you evaluate a student's progress. Does the student

work better alone or in a group?
help others?
listen to the ideas of others?
organize information?
verbalize and define concepts?
finish tasks?
accept guidance and/or corrections from others?
use a variety of strategies to solve problems?

Another way to evaluate a student's thinking process is to interview the student individually. This gives the student the opportunity to show you areas of real achievement that you may not have focused on. At the same time it may alert you to a false sense of security on the student's part. Here are some types of questions you may find helpful in an interview with a student:

What did you learn?
Where do you think you had difficulty?
What parts do you think you handled well?
What skills do you need to practice more?
Is there a project you would especially like to work on?
What steps did you take to solve the problem?
What other approach could you have used?
How did you check your answer?

More and more, students are finding that one path to success is keeping a portfolio. This is a collection of work the student has produced over a period of time, material that exhibits creativity, organization, accuracy, thoroughness, synthesis, or any of a hundred other characteristics that make good math. Assessing a student's portfolio is a valuable way to evaluate the student's

ability to think and work independently;
ability to use mathematics creatively;
willingness to apply mathematics to real-life situations;
and pride in accomplishment.

Performance assessment allows you to evaluate students as they work to complete a multi-step project or task. The performance itself could take a variety of forms, whether initiated by student or teacher. It may be an exhibit, a play, a project, an investigation. It could be a report, a set of interviews, a piece of construction. The actual form is not important; what is important is what the performance tells about the student's progress.

An authentic assessment uses a wide range of methods to measure a wide range of learning experience. Each chapter in this textbook provides a choice of three forms of assessment. The *Chapter Test* at the end of the chapter is a traditional form of assessment. In the Teacher's Edition side column is an *Alternative Assessment* providing a different perspective on the student's progress through the chapter. Finally, the *Chapter Project*, when completed with the corresponding *Assessment* page in the *Teacher's Resource Book*, presents an ideal opportunity for performance assessment.

MULTICULTURAL OPPORTUNITIES

One of the greatest challenges of the nineties is to improve student awareness of the contributions of cultures other than their own to mathematics. In order to meet the challenge of the NCTM's *Curriculum and Evaluation Standards*, students need to appreciate mathematics in its historical context. Mathematics has had its roots in different parts of the world, and contributions made by many scholars have lasted through centuries. Recognizing these facts can bring the vitality of ethnic and cultural diversity to the curriculum. More important, students can come to understand that the present body of mathematics knowledge is the result of many years of input from culturally different people.

Throughout the Teacher's Edition you will find *Multicultural Opportunities* detailed in the side column. These features point out areas within the text where contributions from a variety of cultural backgrounds are described. In addition, the *Overview* pages that precede each chapter in the Teacher's Edition often contain references to multicultural opportunities within the chapter. The Resource list at the end of this section offers a sample of the many available resources for providing multicultural opportunities to your students.

COOPERATIVE LEARNING

Cooperative learning has power to motivate students and stimulate learning.

In some places, people use cooperative learning just for learning basic algorithms; in other places, people use it just for complex problem solving. It's fine for both. In either case, it is important for you to be prepared.

Cooperative Learning Tips

◆ Create heterogeneous teams of students. Identify the six highest achievers and six lowest achievers in class; assign one of each to a group. Assign others to create a cross-section of gender, past performance levels, and ethnicity. Keep groups long enough for students to feel like a team—six to eight weeks.

◆ Take time to explain what you are doing and why. Emphasize that the primary goal is to learn a concept. Use groups for both one-day and multi-day discussions and problem solving.

◆ Give teams a get-acquainted activity, such as planning an imaginary party with limited resources. Allow time for students to organize and pick team names.

◆ Explain when you will assist. Monitor by walking around and listening, but try not to intervene too quickly if students encounter difficulties. The goal is for groups to work through ideas themselves. Ask how they chose strategies, what difficulties they encountered, how they decided if answers were reasonable.

◆ Individual accountability can take many forms, such as quizzes or written explanations. Base group scores on individual improvement over previous performance. Group scores accumulate toward reward levels.

◆ Establish a signal for quiet, but expect a more lively atmosphere. Your goal is to generate the kind of peer support, excitement, and camaraderie of sports teams. With that, you've got some of the most powerful motivating qualities known in social psychology.

LEARNING STYLES

Experienced teachers know that no single approach to a given topic will work with all of their students, all of the time. Some students understand ideas best when they are shown one clear definition, while some need multiple examples. For some students, the most meaningful examples are those put into words; for others, a series of images brings a point across more clearly. In order to teach to the whole group, teachers usually find it necessary to vary their approach—that is, to teach material with an eye toward the different learning styles of their students.

Researchers have identified many different learning styles. One school of thought divides learners into those who are "field-dependent" and "field-independent," sometimes categorized as "whole-to-part" and "part-to-whole," respectively. The field-dependent learner is most comfortable when

shown "the big picture" first, leaving the details for later. The field-independent learner, on the other hand, learns best in an analytic, sequential fashion, mastering one step before progressing to the next.

The traditional approach to teaching mathematics has been the field-independent approach, taking the subject a unit at a time and building on the foundation thus established. *Prentice Hall Geometry* follows this approach and structure. However, to accommodate the needs of the field-dependent learner as well, Prentice Hall *Geometry* contains the following whole-to-part, field-dependent features:

A list of *Objectives* at the beginning of each lesson, showing the student what to expect from the lesson.

A variety of *Applications* at the end of each lesson, to show the student a "purpose" of the mathematics of the problem.

A list of topics for *Keeping a Portfolio* in each lesson, many of which suggest ways for the students to understand the specifics of the lesson in the context of a larger concept.

A *Summary and Review* at the end of each chapter to allow students to get an idea of the chapter as a whole.

A *Chapter Project* explained at the opening of each chapter, designed to bring much of the chapter material together toward a common real-world goal.

Beyond these specific features, the Prentice Hall approach offers opportunities for both types of learners. The *Strategy* lessons stress the four-step approach to solving problems, with a field-independent emphasis on sequence and cause-and-effect. The *Examples* provide a total picture of how a problem is solved for the field-dependent learner: the student can see the entire problem completely worked out and can focus on the specific steps. This combined approach is used throughout the text, providing a detailed, step-by-step explanation of the logic behind an idea, and showing an example of how that idea is put into play.

In addition to the dual categories of field dependence and independence, researchers have further categorized learning styles based on the medium or modality of learning—that is, the physical method used in learning, as opposed to the philosophical approach used. Some of the modalities frequently listed are the auditory, the visual, the tactile, the kinesthetic, and the linguistic.

The auditory learner may be more successful with a lecture than a demonstration or may find that music can help bring meaning to a topic. This student, like the linguistic learner, is likely to be creative in using mnemonic devices, and may

have a good memory for vocabulary, dates, formulas, names, and lists in general.

The visual learner, as expected, is likely to succeed in constructions, graphs, and diagrams. Often an idea that is unclear when expressed in words makes sense when drawn as a diagram on the chalkboard. Projects that allow such students to create a visual display help not only the students who create the project, but also those who examine it later on display.

The tactile and kinesthetic learners are more comfortable with hands-on approaches to instruction, such as modeling, using manipulatives like algebra tiles, geoboards, and geometric solids.

The list of modalities is endless, depending on the researchers. You, as an observant teacher, are the most important researcher when it comes to analyzing the learning styles of your own students. The needs of these students may be partly met by using the *Alternative Learning Styles* suggestions found throughout the side columns of the Teacher's Edition.

RESOURCES

General

Booklets and Periodicals

National Council of Teachers of Mathematics. *An Agenda for Action: Recommendations for School Mathematics of the 1980's.* Reston, VA: NCTM, 1980.

National Council of Teachers of Mathematics. *Curriculum and Evaluation Standards for School Mathematics.* Reston, VA: NCTM, 1989.

National Council of Teachers of Mathematics. *Journal for Research in Mathematics Education,* January, March, May, July, and November. Reston, VA: NCTM.

National Council of Teachers of Mathematics. *The Mathematics Teacher.* Monthly September through May. Reston, VA: NCTM. Annually since 1926.

National Council of Teachers of Mathematics. *Professional Standards for Teaching Mathematics.* Reston, VA: NCTM, 1991.

Books

Abbot, Edwin A. *Flatland.* New York: Barnes and Noble, 1963.

Barnsley, Michael. *Fractals Everywhere.* San Diego, CA: Academic Press, Inc., 1988.

Bell, Eric Temple. *Mathematics: Queen & Servant of Science.* Washington, DC: Mathematical Association of America, 1979.

Boles, Martha, and Newman, Rochelle. *The Golden Relationship: Art, Math, Nature.* Bradford, MA: Pythagorean Press, 1983.

Clemens, Stanley R., Thomas J. Cooney, and Phares G. O'Daffer. *Geometry with Applications and Problem Solving.* Menlo Park, CA: Addison-Wesley, 1983.

College Entrance Examination Board. *Academic Preparation in Mathematics: Teaching for Transition from High School to College.* New York: CEBB, 1985.

Cooney, Thomas J., Edward J. Davis, and K. B. Henderson. "Teaching and Understanding of Proof." *Dynamics of Teaching Secondary School Mathematics.* Prospect Heights, IL: Waveland Press, Inc., 1975.

Davison, David M., Marsha Landau, Leah McCracken, Linda Thompson. *Prentice Hall Pre-Algebra.* Needham, MA: Prentice Hall, 1992.

Eves, Howard. *An Introduction to the History of Mathematics.* New York: Holt Rinehart and Winston, 1976.

Gardner, Martin. *The Second Scientific American Book of Mathematical Puzzles and Diversions.* Chicago: University of Chicago Press, 1987.

"Geometry in the Mathematics Curriculum." *Thirty-Sixth Yearbook of the National Council of Teachers of Mathematics.* Reston, VA: NCTM, 1973.

Graham, Neill. *Computers and Computing.* St. Paul, MN: West Publishing Company, 1983.

Grinstein, Louise S., and Paul J. Campbell. *Women of Mathematics: A Bibliographic Sourcebook.* Westport, CT: Greenwood Press, 1987.

"Historical Topics for the Mathematics Classroom." *Thirty-first Yearbook of the National Council of Teachers of Mathematics.* Reston, VA: NCTM, 1969.

"The Ideas of Algebra, K-12." *The 1988 Yearbook of the National Council of Teachers of Mathematics.* Reston, VA: NCTM, 1988.

Jacobs, Harold R. *Mathematics: A Human Endeavor.* 2nd ed. San Francisco: W. H. Freeman & Company, 1982.

James, Glenn, and Robert C., eds. *Mathematics Dictionary.* New York: Van Nostrand Reinhold, 1976.

Johnson, David R. *Making Minutes Count Even More: A Sequel to Every Minute Counts.* Palo Alto, CA: Dale Seymour Publications, 1986.

Krulik, Stephen, ed. "Problem Solving in School Mathematics." *1980 Yearbook of the National Council of Teachers of Mathematics.* Reston, VA: NCTM, 1980.

"Learning and Teaching Geometry, K-12." *1987 Yearbook of the National Council of Teachers of Mathematics.* Reston, VA: NCTM, 1987.

Mathematical Sciences Education Board. *Reshaping School Mathematics: A Philosophy and Framework for Curriculum.* Washington, DC: National Academy Press, 1990.

O'Daffer, Phares G., and Stanley R. Clemens. *Geometry: An Investigative Approach.* Reading, MA: Addison-Wesley, 1977.

Olds, C. D. "Continued Fractions." Vol. 9 of *New Mathematical Library,* Mathematical Association of America, Washington, DC.

Papert, Seymour. *Mindstorms: Children, Computers, and Powerful Ideas.* New York: Basic Books, 1980.

Perl, T. *Math Equals: Biographies of Women Mathematicians and Related Activities.* Menlo Park, CA: Addison-Wesley Publishing Co., 1978.

Peterson, Ivars. *The Mathematical Tourist.* New York: W.H. Freeman, 1988.

Polya, George. *How to Solve It: A New Aspect of Mathematical Method.* 2nd ed. Princeton, NJ: Princeton University Press, 1973.

Sobel, Max, and Evan M. Maletsky. *Teaching Mathematics: A Sourcebook of Aids, Activities, and Strategies.* 2nd ed. Englewood Cliffs, NJ: Prentice Hall, 1988.

Tobias, Sheila. *Overcoming Math Anxiety.* New York: W. W. Norton Company, 1978.

Usiskin, Zalman. *Van Hiele Levels and Achievement in Secondary School Geometry,* Department of Education, University of Chicago, ERIC Document No. SE 038 813.

West, Beverly H., et al. *The Prentice-Hall Encyclopedia of Mathematics.* Englewood Cliffs, NJ: Prentice-Hall, Inc., 1982.

Wirszup, Izaak. "Breakthroughs in the Psychology of Learning and Teaching Geometry" in Martin, J. Larry (ed.), *Space and Geometry.* ERIC Center for Science, Mathematics and Environmental Education, 1976.

Assessment

Designing District Evaluation Instruments for Math and Science Process Skills, an educators' network established in 1987 by the Association for Supervision and Curriculum Development. Contact Shelley Lipowich, 6321 N. Canon Del Pajaro, Tucson, AZ 85715.

"Educational Assessment—Policy and Use." No, 8, March 1990. American Education Research Association, 1310 South 6th Street, Champaign, IL 61820.

Kulm, Gerald (ed.). *Assessing Higher Order Thinking in Mathematics.* Washington, DC: American Association for the Advancement of Science, 1990.

Mathematics Portfolio Project, Vermont Department of Education, 120 State St., Montpelier, VT 05602.

Mitchell, Ruth. "A Caveat For Test Publishers," Basic Education, Vol. 31, No. 8. Washington, DC: Council for Basic Education, 1990.

"New Math Assessment," Instructor, April 1991.

Resnick, Lauren, and Daniel Resnick, "Tests as Standards of Achievement in Schools," *The Uses of Standardized Tests in American Education.* Princeton, NJ: Educational Testing Service, 1989.

Stenmark, Jean (ed.). Mathematics Assessment: *Myths, Models, Good Questions, and Practical Suggestions.* Reston, VA: NCTM, 1991.

"Testing: Where We Stand." Arlington, VA: American Association of School Administrators, 1989.

Cooperative Learning

Davidson, Neil, ed. *Cooperative Learning in Mathematics: A Handbook for Teachers.* Menlo Park, CA: Addison-Wesley, 1990.

Good, Thomas L., and others. "Using Work-groups in Mathematics Instruction," *Educational Leadership.* December 1989/January 1990.

Graves, N., and T. Graves. *Cooperative Learning: A Resource Guide.* Santa Cruz: The International Association for the Study of Cooperation in Education, 1990.

Kagan, S. *Cooperative Learning Resources for Teachers.* San Juan Capistrano: Resources for Teachers, 1990.

Newmann, F.M., and J.A. Thompson. *Effects of Cooperative Learning on Achievement in Secondary Schools: A Summary of Research.* Madison, WI: National Center for Effective Secondary Schools, 1987.

Slavin, R. *Cooperative Learning: Theory, Research, and Practice.* Englewood Cliffs, NJ: Prentice Hall, 1988.

Team Learning Project, Center for Research on Elementary and Middle Schools, The Johns Hopkins University, 3505 N. Charles St., Baltimore, MD 21218.

Multicultural Concerns

Browne, J. and J. P. Perez. *Multicultural Education Course of Study for Grades Kindergarten Through Twelve 1979–1981.* Los Angeles, CA: Los Angeles County School District.

Careccio, John. "Mathematical Heritage of Zambia," *The Arithmetic Teacher,* May 1970, pp. 391-395.

Cocking, Rodney, and Jose Mestre, ed. *Linguistic and Cultural Influences on Learning Mathematics.* Hillsdale, NJ: Lawrence Erlbaum Associates, 1988.

Fitzgerald, Frances. *America Revised: History Schoolbooks in the Twentieth Century.* Boston: Little, Brown, 1979.

Gilligan, Carol. *In a Different Voice.* Cambridge, MA: Harvard University Press, 1982.

Guild and Garger. *Marching to Different Drummers.* ASCD, 1985. Write to: Pat Guild Associates, PO BOX 99131, Seattle, WA 98119.

Kenschaft, Patricia C. "Black Men and Women in Mathematical Research", *Journal of Black Studies,* December, 1987, pp. 170-190.

Making Mathematics Work for Minorities. Washington DC: Mathematical Sciences Education Board, 1990.

Mallory, Garrick. *Picture Writing of the American Indians.* Dover, 1972.

A Nation at Risk: The Imperative for Educational Reform. U.S. Government Printing Office, 1983.

Neugebauer, O. *The Exact Science in Antiquity.* Dover, 1972.

Newell, Gipson, Rich, Stubblefield. *Black Mathematicians and Their Work.* Ardmore, PA: Dorrance and Company, 1980.

Newman, James. *The World of Mathematics.* New York: Simon & Schuster, 1956.

"The Rhind Papyrus," *Scientific American,* August 1952.

Takaki, Ronald. *Strangers from a Different Shore.* Boston: Little, Brown, 1989.

Zaslavsky, Claudia. *Africa Counts.* Prindle, Weber & Schmidt, 1973.

Learning Styles

Allen, W.H., and R.L. Van Sickle. "Learning Teams and Low Achievers." *Social Education,* 1984.

Faggella, Kathy, and Janet Horowitz. "Different Child, Different Style: Seven Ways to Reach and Teach All Children," *Instructor,* September 1990.

Feldman, Edmund Burke. *Varieties of Visual Experience.* New York: Harry N. Abrams, 1981.

Guild and Garger. Marching to Different Drummers. ASCD, 1985.

Guild, Pat and Louise McKinney. *Using Learning Styles to Help Students Be Successful.* Write to: Pat Guild Associates, PO Box 99131, Seattle, WA 98119.

Kim, Scott. *Inversions.* New York: W.H. Freeman, 1989.

Moore, David W., Sharon A. Moore, Patricia M. Cunningham, James W. Cunningham. *Developing Readers and Writers in the Content Areas.* New York: Longman, 1986.

Romberg, Thomas A., Thomas P. Carpenter, Richard T. White, Richard P. Tisher. *Research in Teaching and Learning, Vol. 4; Mathematics and Natural Sciences.* New York: Macmillan, 1990.

Skemp, Richard R. *The Psychology of Learning Mathematics.* Middlesex, England: Penguin Books, 1971.

Slawsky, Norman. "The Artist as Mathematician," *Mathematics Teacher,* April, 1977.

Tufte, Edward R. *Envisioning Information.* Cheshire, CT: Graphics Press, 1990.

Technology

Borenson, Henry. "The Graphics Calculator: A Helpful Tool," *Mathematics Teacher,* November 1990.

Coburn, Terrence G., Shirley Hoogenboom, and Judy Goodnow. *The Problem Solver with Calculators.* Sunnyvale, CA: Creative Publications, Inc., 1989.

Devaney, Robert L. *Chaos, Fractals, and Dynamics: Computer Experiments in Mathematics.* Menlo Park, CA: Addison-Wesley, 1990.

Devlin, Keith. *Microchip Mathematics—Number Theory for Computer Users.* Cheshire, England: Shiva Publishing, 1984.

The Elementary Mathematician, COMAP, Inc., 60 Lowell street, Arlington, MA 02174.

Graham, Neill. *Computers and Computing.* St. Paul, MN: West Publishing Company, 1983.

Graham, Ronald Lewis, Donald Ervin Knuth, Oren Patashnik. *Concrete Mathematics: A Foundation for Computer Science.* Menlo Park, CA: Addison-Wesley, 1989.

Papert, Seymour. *Mindstorms: Children, Computers, and Powerful Ideas.* New York: Basic Books, 1980.

Swadener, Mar, and William Blubaugh. "Teaching Mathematics with a Vision: Integrating Computers into Instruction," *Teaching and Learning Mathematics in the 1990s.* Reston, VA: NCTM, 1990.

Warger, Cynthia (ed.). *Technology in Today's Schools.* Alexandria, VA: Association for Supervision and Curriculum Development, 1990.

Videotapes

For All Practical Purposes: Size and Shape (Annenberg)

Future Series (PBS)

Landscape of Geometry (TVO Video)

Patterns AGSS259 (MTI)

Project Mathematics (Caltech)

Shape Hunting Series (Coronet)

A selected list of available software packages:

Apple 128K	Macintosh	IBM PC
for Algebra and Trigonometry:		
Algeblaster	Algeblaster	Algeblaster
Algebra Drill	Bradford Graph Wiz	Graphing Equations
Algebra Drill & Practice 1		Algebra Drill & Practice 1
Algebra Drill & Practice 2		Algebra Drill & Practice 2
ARBPLOT		ARBPLOT
Interpreting Graphs		Interpreting Graphs
NCTM Short Programs Disks		NCTM Short Programs
Chalkboard Graphics		Disks
Disk Learning in Trigonometry		MathCad
TI Emulation		TI Emulation
for Geometry:		
Logic and Euclidean Geometry		
Geometric Presupposer		Geometric Presupposer
Geometric Supposer:	Geometric Supposer:	Geometric Supposer:
Triangles	Triangles	Triangles
Quadrilaterals	Quadrilaterals	Quadrilaterals
Circles		Circles
	Bradford 3D Images	
LogoWriter	LogoWriter	LogoWriter
	Geometer's Sketchpad	
symbolic manipulators:		
	Maple	
	Theorist	
	Mathematica	Mathematica
		Derive
spreadsheets:		
Appleworks		
	Excel	
	Microsoft Works	
		Quattro
		Lotus

PACING GEOMETRY

The following three charts suggest how a total of 170 class days may be allocated by chapter for three different levels of ability.

BASIC COURSE

Chapter	1	2	3	4	5	6	7	8	9	10	11	12	13	14
Days	12	10	16	14	10	14	13	14	11	13	13	11	13	6
Section	all	all	all	all	all	all	all	all	all	all	all	all	all	some

AVERAGE COURSE

Chapter	1	2	3	4	5	6	7	8	9	10	11	12	13	14
Days	10	10	14	13	10	11	11	11	11	13	11	11	12	22
Section	all	all	all	all	all	all	all	all	all	all	all	all	all	all

ENRICHED COURSE

Chapter	1	2	3	4	5	6	7	8	9	10	11	12	13	14
Days	10	10	14	13	10	11	11	11	11	13	11	11	12	22
Section	all	all	all	all	all	all	all	all	all	all	all	all	all	all

A more detailed pacing chart is provided on the following pages. It is based on the number of days allocated per chapter suggested in the above three charts. Each of the 170 class days is represented (including reviews and tests) with text pages and practice exercises to be assigned.

PACING CHART FOR GEOMETRY

Day	Basic Course		Average Course		Enriched Course	
1	1.1	5/1–14, 15–25 odd, 39, 40	1.1	5/1–14, 15–25 odd, 26–32, 38–40	1.1	5/1–25 odd, 26–37, 38
2	1.2	10/1–10, 11–17 odd, 38, 43, 11/ Algebra Review	1.2	10/1–10, 11–27 odd, 37, 38, 43 11/Algebra Review	1.2	10/1–10, 19–29 odd, 31–38, 43 11/Algebra Review
3	1.3	15/1–16, 43	1.3	15/1–21, 22–28 even, 43–50	1.3	15/1–21, 22–36 even, 38–44
4	1.3	16/17–29 17/Algebra Review	1.4	21/1–15, 16–22 even, 28, 29 22/Test Yourself	1.4	21/1, 9–15, 16–26 even, 27–29 22/Test Yourself

Day	Basic Course	Average Course	Enriched Course
5	**1.4** 21/1–15, 16–22 even, 28 22/Test Yourself	**1.5** 26/1–6, 7–21 odd, 22–26, 31	**1.5** 26/1–6, 13–26, 27–31 odd
6	**1.5** 26/1–4, 7–17 odd, 31, 32	**1.6** 31/1–4, 5–15 odd, 17–28, 33	**1.6** 31/5–19 odd, 21–34
7	**1.6** 31/1–12, 33	**1.7** 36/1–10 37/Test Yourself	**1.7** 36/1–13 37/Project 37/Test Yourself
8	**1.6** 31/13–20, 34	38/Technology: Constructing Geometric Shapes Using Logo	38/Technology: Constructing Geometric Shapes Using Logo
9	**1.7** 36/1–7 37/Test Yourself	40/Summary and Review 42/Chapter 1 Test	40/Summary and Review 42/Chapter 1 Test
10	38/Technology: Constructing Geometric Shapes Using Logo	43/College Entrance Exam Review 44/Algebra Review	43/College Entrance Exam Review 44/Algebra Review
11	40/Summary and Review 42/Chapter 1 Test	**2.1** 49/1–11, 10–18 even, 25, 26, 30 50/Algebra Review	**2.1** 49/1–6, 12–26, 30, 31 50/Algebra Review
12	43/College Entrance Exam Review 44/Algebra Review	**2.2** 54/1–14, 15, 17, 19, 25, 33, 35 55/Mixed Review	**2.2** 54/1–19 odd, 21–25, 33–39 55/Mixed Review
13	**2.1** 49/1–11 odd, 26, 30 50/Algebra Review	**2.3** 58/1–4, 14–25, 31–35 61/Test Yourself	**2.3** 58/14–25, 28, 29, 31–35 61/Test Yourself
14	**2.2** 54/1–13 odd, 25, 33–35 55/Mixed Review	**2.4** 64/1–5, 7, 9	**2.4** 64/1–5, 8–18 even
15	**2.3** 58/1–13, 31, 33–35 61/Test Yourself	**2.4** 66/Project	**2.4** 66/Project
16	**2.4** 64/1–5, 7	**2.5** 70/1–9	**2.5** 70/1–9
17	**2.4** 66/Project	**2.5** 71/10–12, 15, 18 72/Test Yourself	**2.5** 71/10–14, 16, 18 72/Test Yourself
18	**2.5** 70/1–4	73/Technology: Solving Problems Using Logo	73/Technology: Solving Problems Using Logo
19	**2.5** 70/5–9, 15, 17 72/Test Yourself	74/Summary and Review 76/Chapter 2 Test	74/Summary and Review 76/Chapter 2 Test
20	73/Technology: Solving Problems Using Logo	77/College Entrance Exam Review 78/Cumulative Review	77/College Entrance Exam Review 78/Cumulative Review
21	74/Summary and Review 76/Chapter 2 Test	**3.1** 83/9–29, 37, 38	**3.1** 83/1–8, 14–29, 35–38

Day	Basic Course		Average Course		Enriched Course	
22		77/College Entrance Exam Review 78/Cumulative Review	3.2	89/1–20, 33	3.2	89/1–20, 33
23	3.1	83/1–13, 37	3.2	90/21–30, 34, 49 91/Mixed Review	3.2	90/21–32, 34, 49 91/Mixed Review
24	3.1	83/14–23, 38	3.3	95/1–7, 8–20 even, 24	3.3	95/5–12, 14–22 even, 23–25
25	3.2	89/1–10, 33	3.4	101/1–16, 32	3.4	101/3–22
26	3.2	89/11–18, 34, 49 91/Mixed Review	3.4	102/17–28, 34–36 103/Test Yourself	3.4	102/25–36 103/Test Yourself
27	3.3	95/1–8, 23	3.5	107/1–24	3.5	107/1–5, 11–24
28	3.4	101/1–12, 32	3.5	108/25–27, 31–33, 55–57 109/Algebra Review	3.5	108/25–33, 55–57 109/Algebra Review
29	3.4	101/13–18, 35 103/Test Yourself	3.6	112/1–19	3.6	112/1–20 113/Project
30	3.5	107/1–14, 55, 56	3.7	117/4–19, 37, 38	3.7	117/4–19, 37, 38
31	3.5	107/15–22, 57 109/Algebra Review	3.7	118/20–30, 39 119/Test Yourself	3.7	118/20–36, 39 119/Test Yourself
32	3.6	112/1–4		120/Integrating Geometry: Longitude and Latitude		120/Integrating Geometry: Longitude and Latitude
33	3.6	113/5–10		122/Summary and Review 124/Chapter 3 Test		122/Summary and Review 124/Chapter 3 Test
34	3.6	117/5–19 odd, 37		125/College Entrance Exam Review 126/Algebra Review		125/College Entrance Exam Review 126/Algebra Review
35	3.7	117/4–18 even 119/Test Yourself	4.1	131/1–15, 19, 37, 39	4.1	131/6–21, 28–39
36		120/Integrating Geometry: Longitude and Latitude	4.2	136/5–14, 27, 29, 35, 42	4.2	137/15–28
37		122/Summary and Review 124/Chapter 3 Test	4.2	137/15–26, 28, 30, 36, 43 138/Mixed Review	4.2	137/29–36, 42–43 138/Mixed Review
38		125/College Entrance Exam Review 126/Algebra Review	4.3	141/1–16	4.3	141/1–16
39	4.1	131/1–19	4.3	143/17–25, 29, 30 144/Test Yourself	4.3	143/17–30 144/Test Yourself
40	4.1	131/20–27, 37–39	4.4	148/1–6 148/Project	4.4	148/1–8 148/Project
41	4.2	136/1–14	4.5	152/7–14, 15–23 odd, 26–29	4.5	153/9–21, 24–29

Day	Basic Course	Average Course	Enriched Course
42	**4.2** 137/15–21, 35–36, 42–43 138/Mixed Review	**4.6** 157/1–10, 14 158/Project	**4.6** 157/1–10, 11–17 odd 158/Project
43	**4.3** 141/1–10	**4.7** 161/1–16	**4.7** 161/7–18
44	**4.3** 142/11–16, 29–30 144/Test Yourself	**4.7** 162/17–22, 26–28 163/Algebra Review 163/Test Yourself	**4.7** 162/19–28 163/Algebra Review 163/Test Yourself
45	**4.4** 148/1–5	164/Integrating Geometry: Precision and Accuracy	164/Integrating Geometry: Precision and Accuracy
46	**4.5** 152/1–8, 9–17 odd, 26–29	166/Summary and Review 168/Chapter 4 Test	166/Summary and Review 168/Chapter 4 Test
47	**4.6** 157/1–10	169/College Entrance Exam Review 170/Cumulative Review	169/College Entrance Exam Review 170/Cumulative Review
48	**4.7** 161/1–11	**5.1** 177/1–9, 10–20 even, 28, 29, 36, 37 178/Mixed Review	**5.1** 177/1–21, 22–26 even, 28, 29, 36, 37 178/Mixed Review
49	**4.7** 161/12–18, 26–28 163/Algebra Review 163/Test Yourself	**5.2** 182/1–14, 18–22	**5.2** 182/1–14, 18–23, 27–29
50	164/Integrating Geometry: Precision and Accuracy	**5.3** 187/1–5, 7, 8, 11 188/Project	**5.3** 187/1–5, 7, 8, 10–12 188/Project
51	166/Summary and Review 168/Chapter 4 Test	**5.4** 192/1–6, 13–22, 28, 29 193/Test Yourself	**5.4** 192/1–6, 13–22, 27–29 193/Test Yourself
52	169/College Entrance Exam Review 170/Cumulative Review	**5.5** 197/1–23 odd, 28, 32 198/Algebra Review	**5.5** 197/1–17, 18–24 even, 25–28, 32 198/Algebra Reivew
53	**5.1** 177/1–9, 10–20 even, 28, 36 178/Mixed Review	**5.6** 202/1–16, 22–24	**5.6** 202/1–16, 20, 22–24
54	**5.2** 182/1–14, 18, 19	**5.7** 207/1–21, 24–28 209/Test Yourself	**5.7** 207/1–28 209/Test Yourself
55	**5.3** 187/1–5, 7	210/Technology: Recursion and Tessellations	210/Technology: Recursion and Tessellations
56	**5.4** 192/1–23 odd 193/Test Yourself	212/Summary and Review 214/Chapter 5 Test	212/Summary and Review 214/Chapter 5 Test
57	**5.5** 197/1–8, 13–15, 28, 32 198/Algebra Review	215/College Entrance Exam Review 216/Algebra Review	215/College Entrance Exam Review 216/Algebra Review
58	**5.6** 202/1–11, 22–24	**6.1** 221/1–13, 22–30, 37, 38 222/Mixed Review	**6.1** 221/1–29, 30–36 even, 37, 38 222/Mixed Review
59	**5.7** 207/1–14, 24–28 209/Test Yourself	**6.2** 225/1–16, 17–23 odd, 29	**6.2** 226/6–25, 29–32
60	210/Technology: Recursion and Tessellations	**6.3** 230/1–19, 20–26 even 232/Mixed Review	**6.3** 230/1–19, 20–30 even

Day	Basic Course		Average Course		Enriched Course	
61		212/Summary and Review 214/Chapter 5 Test	**6.4**	236/1–13, 14–24 even, 35 238/Test Yourself	**6.4**	236/1–24, 25–33 odd, 34, 35 238/Test Yourself
62		215/College Entrance Exam Review 216/Algebra Review	**6.5**	242/1–22, 23–27 odd, 32, 33 243/Algebra Review	**6.5**	242/1–22, 23–29 odd, 32, 33 243/Algebra Review
63	**6.1**	221/1–13	**6.6**	246/1, 2, 3–13 odd	**6.6**	246/1, 2, 3–13 odd
64	**6.1**	221/14–23, 37, 38 222/Mixed Review	**6.6**	247/Project	**6.6**	247/Project
65	**6.2**	225/1–13	**6.7**	250/1, 11–33, 40–42 253/Test Yourself	**6.7**	251/11–28, 34–42 253/Test Yourself
66	**6.2**	226/14–19		254/Integrating Geometry: Vectors and Scalars		254/Integrating Geometry: Vectors and Scalars
67	**6.3**	230/1–12		256/Summary and Review 258/Chapter 6 Test		256/Summary and Review 258/Chapter 6 Test
68	**6.3**	230/13–19, 31, 32 232/Mixed Review		259/College Entrance Exam Review 260/Cumulative Review		259/College Entrance Exam Review 260/Cumulative Review
69	**6.4**	236/1, 2, 3–15 odd, 34 238/Test Yourself	**7.1**	265/1–22, 33–35, 46 266/Mixed Review	**7.1**	265/15–21 odd, 23–35, 46 266/Mixed Review
70	**6.5**	242/1–11	**7.2**	269/1–16, 19–22, 31–36	**7.2**	269/1–22, 25–28, 31–36
71	**6.5**	242/12–19, 32 243/Algebra Review	**7.3**	273/1–10, 18–25, 30–32 276/Test Yourself	**7.3**	273/1–17 odd, 18–22, 26–32 276/Test Yourself
72	**6.6**	246/1, 2, 3–13 odd	**7.4**	279/1–16, 23–25, 34 281/Algebra Review	**7.4**	279/1–16, 21–25, 34, 35 281/Algebra Review
73	**6.7**	251/2–20, 40 253/Test Yourself	**7.5**	284/1–20, 30–32	**7.5**	284/1–20, 27–32
74		254/Integrating Geometry: Vectors and Scalars	**7.6**	289/1–9 291/Project	**7.6**	289/1–13 291/Project
75		256/Summary and Review 258/Chapter 6 Test	**7.7**	295/5–25 odd	**7.7**	295/5–29 odd
76		259/College Entrance Exam Review 260/Cumulative Review	**7.7**	295/4–24 even, 29, 30 297/Mixed Review 297/Test Yourself	**7.7**	295/4–28 even, 29, 30 197/Mixed Review 297/Test Yourself
77	**7.1**	265/1–10		298/Technology: Similarity in Computer Graphics		298/Technology: Similarity in Computer Graphics
78	**7.1**	265/11–17, 33, 46 266/Mixed Review		300/Summary and Review 302/Chapter 7 Test		300/Summary and Review 302/Chapter 7 Test
79	**7.2**	269/1–16, 32		303/College Entrance Exam Review 304/Algebra Review		303/College Entrance Exam Review 304/Algebra Review

Day	Basic Course		Average Course		Enriched Course	
80	**7.3**	273/1–10	**8.1**	308/1–24, 43	**8.1**	308/15–25, 38–41
81	**7.3**	274/11–17, 30–32 276/Test Yourself	**8.1**	309/25–34, 44, 45	**8.1**	309/26–34, 42–45
82	**7.4**	279/1–12 281/Mixed Review	**8.2**	314/1–22, 28, 29 315/Mixed Review	**8.2**	314/1–20, 26–29 315/Mixed Review
83	**7.5**	284/1–11, 30	**8.3**	318/1–23, 32–38 320/Test Yourself	**8.3**	318/1–21, 29–38 320/Test Yourself
84	**7.6**	289/1–8	**8.4**	324/1–20, 29, 30 325/Algebra Review	**8.4**	324/1–30 325/Algebra Review
85	**7.7**	295/1–15 odd	**8.5**	329/1–21 odd 330/Project	**8.5**	329/1–25 odd 330/Project
86	**7.7**	295/2–14 even, 30 297/Mixed Review 297/Test Yourself	**8.6**	335/1–14, 20–26, 31–34	**8.6**	335/1–14, 20–34
87		298/Technology: Similarity in Computer Graphics	**8.7**	339/1–10 341/Project 341/Test Yourself	**8.7**	339/1–12 341/Project 341/Test Yourself
88		300/Summary and Review 302/Chapter 7 Test		342/Integrating Geometry: Astronomy		342/Integrating Geometry: Astronomy
89		303/College Entrance Exam Review 304/Algebra Review		344/Summary and Review 346/Chapter 8 Test		344/Summary and Review 346/Chapter 8 Test
90	**8.1**	308/1–14, 25, 43		347/College Entrance Exam Review 348/Cumulative Review		347/College Entrance Exam Review 348/Cumulative Review
91	**8.1**	308/15–24	**9.1**	355/1–21, 31	**9.1**	355/1–23, 27–32
92	**8.2**	314/1–14	**9.2**	360/1–21, 30–32	**9.2**	360/1–21, 25–32
93	**8.2**	314/15–20, 28 315/Mixed Review	**9.3**	365/4–25, 35, 36 367/Mixed Review 367/Test Yourself	**9.3**	365/8–30, 35, 36 367/Mixed Review 367/Test Yourself
94	**8.3**	318/1–16	**9.4**	371/1–22, 33–36	**9.4**	371/1–29, 33–36
95	**8.3**	318/17–24, 32, 38 320/Test Yourself	**9.5**	375/1–15, 23, 24 377/Algebra Review	**9.5**	375/1–15, 20–24 377/Algebra Review
96	**8.4**	324/1–17, 29 325/Algebra Review	**9.6**	381/1–5	**9.6**	381/1–5
97	**8.5**	329/1–17 odd	**9.6**	381/6–8 381/Project	**9.6**	381/6–8 381/Project
98	**8.6**	335/1–10	**9.7**	385/1–18, 22–24 387/Test Yourself	**9.7**	385/1–24 387/Test Yourself
99	**8.6**	335/11–16, 33		388/Technology: Using Logo to Create Geometric Marks and Mandalas		388/Technology: Using Logo to Create Geometric Marks and Mandalas

Day	Basic Course		Average Course	Enriched Course
100	**8.7**	339/1–8 341/Test Yourself	390/Summary and Review 392/Chapter 9 Test	390/Summary and Review 392/Chapter 9 Test
101		342/Integrating Geometry: Astronomy	393/College Entrance Exam Review 394/Algebra Review	393/College Entrance Exam Review 394/Algebra Review
102		344/Summary and Review 346/Chapter 8 Test	**10.1** 400/1–19 odd, 21–26, 38, 39, 46, 47 402/Algebra Review	**10.1** 400/1–31 odd, 32–39, 46–48 402/Algebra Review
103		347/College Entrance Exam Review 348/Cumulative Review	**10.2** 405/1–24 even, 28–33	**10.2** 405/1–26 even, 28–33
104	**9.1**	355/1–15, 20, 21, 31	**10.3** 410/1–16, 31, 32	**10.3** 410/1–20
105	**9.2**	360/1–16, 28	**10.3** 410/17–27 411/Test Yourself	**10.3** 410/21–25, 28–32 411/Test Yourself
106	**9.3**	365/1–15, 35 367/Mixed Review 367/Test Yourself	**10.4** 415/1–12, 23–25	**10.4** 415/1–14
107	**9.4**	371/1–14, 33, 36	**10.4** 415/13–18	**10.4** 415/15–25
108	**9.5**	375/1–10, 24 377/Algebra Review	**10.5** 419/1–23 odd, 27, 28, 36–37 421/Mixed Review	**10.5** 419/1–23 odd, 24–28, 36, 37 421/Mixed Review
109	**9.6**	381/1–4	**10.6** 424/1–10, 17–27 odd, 35	**10.6** 424/1–10, 17–33 odd, 36
110	**9.6**	381/5–8	**10.7** 430/1–4, 11	**10.7** 430/1–4, 11
111	**9.7**	385/1–11, 22 387/Test Yourself	**10.7** 431/5–6, 9–10, 12 431/Test Yourself	**10.7** 431/5–6, 9–10, 12–14 431/Test Yourself
112		388/Technology: Using Logo to Create Geometric Marks and Mandalas	432/Technology: Using Logo in Constructions	432/Technology: Using Logo in Constructions
113		390/Summary and Review 392/Chapter 9 Test	434/Summary and Review 436/Chapter 10 Test	434/Summary and Review 436/Chapter 10 Test
114		393/College Entrance Exam Review 394/Algebra Review	437/College Entrance Exam Review 438/Cumulative Review	437/College Entrance Exam Review 438/Cumulative Review
115	**10.1**	400/1–10, 13–16, 38, 46, 47 402/Algebra Review	**11.1** 442/1–19, 24–26, 30–31	**11.1** 442/1–19, 24–31
116	**10.2**	405/1–11, 15, 28, 30	**11.2** 447/1–18, 23–29, 35–38	**11.2** 447/1–18, 23–32, 35–38
117	**10.3**	410/1–17 odd, 31	**11.3** 452/1–15, 20–23, 28, 29 454/Mixed Review	**11.3** 452/1–15, 24–29 454/Mixed Review
118	**10.3**	410/2–16 even 411/Test Yourself	**11.4** 457/1–18, 25–27, 34–38 460/Test Yourself	**11.4** 457/1–18, 26–38 460/Test Yourself
119	**10.4**	415/2–8, 23	**11.5** 464/1–10 465/Project	**11.5** 464/1–10, 13 465/Project
120	**10.4**	415/9–12	**11.6** 468/1–25, 35–37	**11.6** 468/1–25, 30–37

Day	Basic Course	Average Course	Enriched Course
121	**10.5** 419/1–10, 27, 37 421/Mixed Review	**11.7** 474/1–9, 12–17, 22–23 475/Algebra Review	**11.7** 474/1–15, 20–23 475/Algebra Review
122	**10.6** 424/1–12, 34	**11.8** 478/1–28, 34, 35 481/Test Yourself	**11.8** 478/1–29 odd, 30–35 481/Test Yourself
123	**10.7** 430/1–3, 11	482/Integrating Geometry: Approximation of Area	482/Integrating Geometry: Approximation of Area
124	**10.7** 430/4–6 431/Test Yourself	484/Summary and Review 486/Chapter 11 Test	484/Summary and Review 486/Chapter 11 Test
125	432/Technology: Using Logo in Constructions	487/College Entrance Exam Review 488/Algebra Review	487/College Entrance Exam Review 488/Algebra Review
126	434/Summary and Review 436/Chapter 10 Test	**12.1** 493/1–13, 17–20, 27–30	**12.1** 493/1–13, 21–30
127	437/College Entrance Exam Review 438/Cumulative Review	**12.2** 498/1–17, 28–30	**12.2** 498/1–17, 24–30
128	**11.1** 442/1–14, 30	**12.3** 504/1–7, 13–20, 25–27 506/Test Yourself	**12.3** 504/1–13 odd, 17–27 506/Test Yourself
129	**11.2** 447/1–11	**12.4** 510/1–4 510/Project	**12.4** 510/1–6 510/Project
130	**11.2** 447/12–18, 35	**12.5** 513/1–18, 24–29 515/Mixed Review	**12.5** 513/1–20, 24–29 515/Mixed Review
131	**11.3** 452/2–11, 28	**12.6** 518/1–13, 22, 23 520/Algebra Review	**12.6** 518/1–13, 20–23 520/Algebra Review
132	**11.3** 452/1, 12–15, 29 454/Mixed Review	**12.7** 523/1–29, 34, 35 525/Test Yourself	**12.7** 523/1–7, 12–35 525/Test Yourself
133	**11.4** 457/1–10, 34, 35, 37 460/Test Yourself	526/Technology: The Coordinate System in Logo	526/Technology: The Coordinate System in Logo
134	**11.5** 464/1–8	528/Summary and Review 530/Chapter 12 Test	528/Summary and Review 530/Chapter 12 Test
135	**11.6** 468/2–5, 10–19, 36	531/College Entrance Exam Review	531/College Entrance Exam Review
136	**11.7** 474/3–11 odd, 22 475/Algebra Review	532/Cumulative Review	532/Cumulative Review
137	**11.8** 478/1–20, 35 481/Test Yourself	**13.1** 538/1–29	**13.1** 538/10–37, 58
138	482/Integrating Geometry: Approximation of Area	**13.1** 539/30–49, 56–58	**13.1** 539/38–48 even, 50–57
139	484/Summary and Review 486/Chapter 11 Test	**13.2** 543/1–26, 40–43	**13.2** 543/1–31 odd, 37–43

Day	Basic Course	Average Course	Enriched Course
140	487/College Entrance Exam Review 488/Algebra Review	**13.3** 548/1–24, 35, 45 550/Mixed Review 551/Test Yourself	**13.3** 548/1–29 odd, 30–36, 45 550/Mixed Review 551/Test Yourself
141	**12.1** 493/1–13, 27, 30	**13.4** 555/1–20, 21–39 odd, 45–48 557/Mixed Review	**13.4** 555/1–39 odd, 40–48 557/Mixed Review
142	**12.2** 498/1–9, 28, 30	**13.5** 561/1–24, 25–35 odd, 37–48, 56–58	**13.5** 561/1–24, 25–47 odd, 49–58
143	**12.3** 504/1–7, 11–14, 25 506/Test Yourself	**13.6** 567/1–24, 29–34, 41, 42 569/Algebra Review	**13.6** 567/1–14, 15–33 odd, 35–42 569/Algebra Review
144	**12.4** 510/1–4 510/Project	**13.7** 574/1–15 odd	**13.7** 574/10–26 even
145	**12.5** 513/1–8, 10, 27 515/Mixed Review	**13.7** 576/17–26 577/Project 577/Test Yourself	**13.7** 576/27–32 577/Project 577/Test Yourself
146	**12.6** 518/3–7, 22 520/Algebra Review	578/Technology: Embedded Recursion and Dragon Curves	578/Technology: Embedded Recursion and Dragon Curves
147	**12.7** 523/4–20, 24 525/Test Yourself	580/Chapter Summary and Review 582/Chapter 13 Test	580/Chapter Summary and Review 582/Chapter 13 Test
148	526/Technology: The Coordinate System in Logo	583/College Entrance Exam Review 584/Algebra Review	583/College Entrance Exam Review 584/Algebra Review
149	528/Summary and Review 530/Chapter 12 Test	**14.1** 589/1–6	**14.1** 589/1–10
150	531/College Entrance Exam Review	**14.1** 590/7–12, 16 590/Mixed Review	**14.1** 590/11–16 590/Mixed Review
151	532/Cumulative Review	**14.2** 594/1–14, 28, 30	**14.2** 594/1–19, 28, 30
152	**13.1** 538/1–21, 56	**14.2** 595/15–24, 29, 31	**14.2** 595/20–27, 29, 31
153	**13.1** 539/22–37, 58	**14.3** 598/1–14, 24	**14.3** 598/1–14, 24
154	**13.2** 543/1–18, 40	**14.3** 599/15–19, 25	**14.3** 599/15–23, 25
155	**13.3** 548/1–14, 35 550/Mixed Review 551/Test Yourself	**14.4** 603/1–15, 40	**14.4** 603/1–21, 40
156	**13.4** 555/1–22, 46–48 557/Mixed Review	**14.4** 604/16–32, 41 606/Test Yourself	**14.4** 605/22–39, 41 606/Test Yourself
157	**13.5** 561/1–28, 56	**14.5** 609/1–18, 31	**14.5** 609/1–18, 31
158	**13.6** 567/1–10, 41	**14.5** 610/19–28, 32, 42–46 611/Algebra Review	**14.5** 610/19–30, 32, 42–46 611/Algebra Review
159	**13.6** 568/11–24 569/Algebra Review	**14.6** 615/1–10, 20, 21, 26	**14.6** 615/1–10, 20, 21, 26

Day	Basic Course	Average Course	Enriched Course
160	**13.7** 574/1–11	**14.6** 615/11–19, 22, 23, 27	**14.6** 11–19, 22–25, 27
161	**13.7** 575/12–16 577/Project 577/Test Yourself	**14.7** 619/1–20, 44	**14.7** 619/1–23, 44
162	578/Technology: Embedded Recursion and Dragon Curves	**14.7** 620/21–38, 45, 46	**14.7** 620/24–43, 45, 46
163	580/Chapter Summary and Review 582/Chapter 13 Test	**14.8** 624/1–4	**14.8** 624/3–8
164	583/College Entrance Exam Review 584/Algebra Review	**14.8** 625/5–7 625/Project	**14.8** 625/9–11 625/Project
165	**14.1** 589/3–8, 16 590/Mixed Review	**14.9** 628/1–16, 31	**14.9** 628/1–16, 31
166	**14.2** 594/1–9, 28, 30	**14.9** 629/17–26, 32 631/Test Yourself	**14.9** 629/17–30, 32 631/Test Yourself
167	**14.3** 598/1, 3–10, 24 **14.4** 603/3–15, 40, 41	632/Technology: Fractals	632/Technology: Fractals
168	**14.5** 609/1–14, 31, 42–44 611/Algebra Review **14.7** 619/1–16, 44, 46	634/Chapter Summary and Review 636/Chapter 14 Test	634/Chapter Summary and Review 636/Chapter 14 Test
169	634/Chapter Summary and Review 638/Cumulative Review	637/College Entrance Exam Review 638/Cumulative Review	637/College Entrance Exam Review 638/Cumulative Review
170	Final Exam	Final Exam	Final Exam

PRENTICE HALL

Geometry

Robert Kalin
Mary Kay Corbitt

Consulting Authors

Jan Fair ❖ Bettye C. Hall
Sadie C. Bragg ❖ Mona Fabricant
Jerome D. Hayden

*Prentice Hall dedicates this
mathematics program to
all mathematics educators
and their students.*

PRENTICE HALL
Englewood Cliffs, New Jersey
Needham, Massachusetts

PRENTICE HALL
Geometry

AUTHORS

Robert Kalin
Professor Emeritus
Florida State University
Mathematics Education Program
Tallahassee, Florida

Mary Kay Corbitt
Associate Professor of Mathematics
Valdosta State College
Valdosta, Georgia

CONSULTING AUTHORS

Jan Fair
Director, CAPP Project SUCCESS
A Math/Science California Academic
  Partnership Program
Lompoc/San Luis Obispo/Santa Maria,
  California

Bettye C. Hall
Director of Mathematics
Houston Independent School
  District
Houston, Texas

Jerome D. Hayden
Mathematics Department Chairman, K-12
McLean County Unit District 5
Normal, Illinois

Sadie C. Bragg
Professor of Mathematics and Associate
  Dean of Curriculum
Borough of Manhattan Community College
The City University of New York
New York, New York

Mona Fabricant
Professor of Mathematics
Queensborough Community College
Bayside, New York

CONSULTANTS

Sylva D. Cohn
Formerly Associate Professor
  of Mathematics
State University of New York
  at Stony Brook
Stony Brook, New York

Beva Eastman
Associate Professor of Mathematics
William Paterson College
Wayne, New Jersey

Mary Dell Morrison
Mathematics Instructor (Retired)
Columbia High School
Maplewood, New Jersey

REVIEWERS

Keith F. Bond
Mathematics Department Chairman
Housatonic Valley Regional High School
Falls Village, Connecticut

Herbert Hollister
Professor of Mathematics
Bowling Green State University
Bowling Green, Ohio

Eleanor Pearson
Mathematics Department Chairman
Woodrow Wilson High School
Dallas, Texas

Prentice Hall
A Division of Simon & Schuster
Englewood Cliffs, New Jersey
07632

Cover Design: Martucci Studio

Chapter Opener Design: Function Thru Form

Staff Credits
Editorial: Rosemary Calicchio, Enid Nagel, Debra Berger, Mary Ellen
Cheasty, Michael Ferejohn, Tony Maksoud, John Nelson, Alan MacDonell,
Ann Fattizzi
Design: Laura Jane Bird, Art Soares
Production: Amy Fleming, Lorraine Moffa, Suse Cioffi
Photo Research: Libby Forsyth, Emily Rose, Martha Conway
Publishing Technology: Andrew Grey Bommarito, Gwendollynn Waldron,
Deborah Jones, Monduane Harris, Michael Colucci, Gregory Myers, Cleasta
Wilburn
Marketing: Everett Draper, Julie Scarpa, Michelle Sergi
Pre-Press Production: Laura Sanderson, Natalia Bilash, Denise Herckenrath
Manufacturing: Rhett Conklin, Gertrude Szyferblatt
National Consultants: Susan Berk, Charlotte Mason

Contents

1 The Language of Geometry

CONNECTIONS. *Architecture • Travel • Cartography • Carpentry • Sports • Transportation • Technology • Navigation • Meteorology*

Developing Mathematical Power   1

1.1	Points, Lines, and Planes	2
1.2	Some Relationships Among Points, Lines, and Planes	7
1.3	Segments and Rays	12
1.4	Angles	18
1.5	Angle Pairs	23
1.6	Perpendicular Lines	28
1.7	Strategy: Analyze a Figure	33

Review

Algebra Review   11, 17, 44
Summary and Review   40
College Entrance Exam Review   43
Extra Practice   643

Assessment

Test Yourself   22, 37
Chapter Test   42
Chapter Project   1

2 The Logic of Geometry

CONNECTIONS: *Law • Meteorology • Sports • Entertainment • Finance • Science • Algebra*

Developing Mathematical Power   45

2.1	Conditional Statements	46
2.2	Converses, Inverses, and Contrapositives	51
2.3	Properties from Algebra	56
2.4	Strategy: Use Logical Reasoning	62
2.5	Proving Theorems	67

Review

Algebra Review   50
Mixed Review   55
Summary and Review   74
College Entrance Exam Review   77
Cumulative Review (1–2)   78
Extra Practice   644

Assessment

Test Yourself   61, 72
Chapter Test   76
Chapter Project   45

3 Parallelism

CONNECTIONS: *Technology • Navigation • Maintainance • Architecture • Surveying • Sports • Art*

Developing Mathematical Power   79
3.1   Lines, Planes, and Transversals   80
3.2   Properties of Parallel Lines   85
3.3   Proving Lines Parallel   92
3.4   Parallel Lines and Triangles   97
3.5   Polygons   104
3.6   Strategy: Use Inductive Reasoning 110
3.7   Angles of a Polygon   114

Review
Algebra Review, 109, 126
Mixed Review 91
Summary and Review 122
College Entrance Exam Review 125
Extra Practice 645

Assessment
Test Yourself 102, 119
Chapter Test 124
Chapter Project 79

4 Congruent Triangles

CONNECTIONS: *Architecture • Probability • Technology • Carpentry • Maps • Design • Construction*

Developing Mathematical Power   127
4.1   Correspondence and Congruence   128
4.2   Proving Triangles Congruent   133
4.3   Using Congruent Triangles   139
4.4   Strategy: Identify Intermediate Goals 145
4.5   Medians, Altitudes, and Bisectors 149
4.6   Strategy: Recognize Underdetermined
      and Overdetermined Figures   155
4.7   Proving Right Triangles Congruent 159

Review
Algebra Review 163
Mixed Review 138
Summary and Review 166
College Entrance Exam Review 169
Cumulative Review (1–4) 170
Extra Practice 646

Assessment
Test Yourself 144, 163
Chapter Test 168
Chapter Project 127

5 Inequalities in Triangles

CONNECTIONS: *Technology • Design • Construction • Navigation • Law • Art • Architecture*

Developing Mathematical Power　173

5.1　Congruence in a Single Triangle:
　　　Isosceles Triangle Theorem　174
5.2　Properties of Inequality　179
5.3　Strategy: Use Indirect Proof　184
5.4　Indirect Proof and Inequalities　189
5.5　Inequalities in One Triangle　194
5.6　More on Inequalities　199
5.7　Congruence in Space: Dihedral Angles　204

Review

Algebra Review　198, 216
Mixed Review　178
Summary and Review　212
College Entrance Exam Review　215
Extra Practice　647

Assessment

Test Yourself　193, 209
Chapter Test　214
Chapter Project　173

6 Quadrilaterals

CONNECTIONS: *Technology • Construction • Hobbies • Art • Architecture*

Developing Mathematical Power　217

6.1　The Parallelogram—A Special
　　　Quadrilateral　218
6.2　Finding Quadrilaterals That Are
　　　Parallelograms　223
6.3　Parallel Lines and Midpoints　228
6.4　Special Parallelograms　233
6.5　Trapezoids　239
6.6　Strategy: Recognize Minimal
　　　Conditions　244
6.7　Congruent Quadrilaterals　248

Review

Algebra Review　243
Mixed Review　222, 232
Summary and Review　256
College Entrance Exam Review　259
Cumulative Review (1–6)　260
Extra Practice　648

Assessment

Test Yourself　238, 253
Chapter Test　258
Chapter Project　217

7 Similarity

CONNECTIONS: *Recreation • Construction • Technology • Algebra • Typing • Scale Drawing • Photography • Surveying • Finding Inaccessible Distances*

Developing Mathematical Power		261
7.1	Ratio and Proportion	262
7.2	Properties of Proportions	267
7.3	Similar Polygons	271
7.4	Similar Triangles	277
7.5	More on Similar Triangles	282
7.6	Strategy: Find Inaccessible Distances	287
7.7	Proportional Segments	292

Review

Algebra Review   281, 304
Mixed Review   266, 297
Summary and Review   300
College Entrance Exam Review   303
Extra Practice   649

Assessment

Test Yourself   276, 297
Chapter Test   302
Chapter Project   261

8 Right Triangles

CONNECTION: *Recreation • Technology • Navigation • Carpentry • Physics*

Developing Mathematical Power		305
8.1	Right Triangle Similarity	306
8.2	Pythagorean Theorem	311
8.3	Converse of the Pythagorean Theorem	316
8.4	Special Right Triangles	321
8.5	Strategy: Estimate and Calculate Roots	326
8.6	Trigonometric Ratios	331
8.7	Strategy: Use Trigonometric Ratios	337

Review

Algebra Review   325
Mixed Review   315
Summary and Review   344
College Entrance Exam Review   347
Cumulative Review (1–8)   348
Extra Practice   650

Assessment

Test Yourself   320, 341
Chapter Test   346
Chapter Project   305

9 Circles

CONNECTIONS: *Astronomy • Technology • Gardening • Industry • Design • Sports • Measurement • Architecture*

Developing Mathematical Power		351
9.1	Circles, Segments, and Congruency	352
9.2	Properties of Tangents	357
9.3	Arcs, Chords, and Central Angles	362
9.4	Inscribed Angles	368
9.5	Tangents, Secants, and Angles	373
9.6	Strategy: Use an Auxiliary Figure	378
9.7	Circles and Segment Lengths	382

Review
Algebra Review   377, 394
Mixed Review   367
Summary and Review   390
College Entrance Exam Review   393
Extra Practice   651

Assessment
Test Yourself   367, 387
Chapter Test   392
Chapter Project   351

10 Constructions and Loci

CONNECTIONS: *Technology • Architecture • Drawing • Landscaping • Navigation*

Developing Mathematical Power		395
10.1	Beginning Constructions	396
10.2	Constructing Perpendiculars and Parallels	403
10.3	Concurrent Lines	407
10.4	Circles	412
10.5	Special Segments	417
10.6	Loci	422
10.7	Strategy: Use Loci in Solving Construction Problems	427

Review
Algebra Review   402
Mixed Review   421
Summary and Review   434
College Entrance Exam Review   437
Cumulative Review (1–10)   438
Extra Practice   652

Assessment
Test Yourself   411, 431
Chapter Test   436
Chapter Project   395

11 Area

CONNECTIONS: *Design • Technology • Quilting • City Planning • Carpentry • Landscaping • Traffic Engineering • Architecture • Computer Graphics • Automobiles • Manufacturing • Hobbies*

Developing Mathematical Power   439

11.1   Area of Squares and Rectangles   440

11.2   Area of Parallelograms and Triangles   445

11.3   Area of Trapezoids   450

11.4   Area of Regular Polygons   455

11.5   Strategy: Find Limits   461

11.6   Circumference and Arc Length   466

11.7   Area of Circles, Sectors, and Segments   471

11.8   Areas of Similar Figures   476

Review

Algebra Review   475, 488

Mixed Review   454

Summary and Review   484

College Entrance Exam Review   487

Extra Practice   653

Assessment

Test Yourself   460, 481

Chapter Test   486

Chapter Project   439

12 Area and Volume of Solids

CONNECTIONS: *Package Design • Ranching • Technology • Archaeology • Packing • Water Management • Metallurgy • Architecture • Sewing • Consumer Math*

Developing Mathematical Power   489

12.1   Prisms   490

12.2   Pyramids   495

12.3   Cylinders   502

12.4   Strategy: Analyze Cross Sections of Solids   507

12.5   Cones   511

12.6   Spheres   516

12.7   Areas and Volumes of Similar Solids   521

Review

Algebra Review   520

Mixed Review   515

Summary and Review   528

College Entrance Exam Review   531

Cumulative Review (1–12)   532

Extra Practice   654

Assessment

Test Yourself   506, 525

Chapter Test   530

Chapter Project   489

13 Coordinate Geometry

CONNECTIONS: *Interior Design • Technology • Recreation • Sports • Construction • Numerical Analysis • Science • Crafts*

Developing Mathematical Power 535

13.1 The Distance Formula 536
13.2 The Equation of a Circle 541
13.3 The Midpoint Formula 546
13.4 Slope of a Line 552
13.5 Equations of a Line 558
13.6 Slopes of Parallel and Perpendicular Lines 565
13.7 Strategy: Use Coordinate Geometry in Proofs 570

Review

Algebra Review 569, 584
Mixed Review 550, 557
Summary and Review 580
College Entrance Exam Review 583
Extra Practice 655

Assessment

Test Yourself 551, 577
Chapter Test 582
Chapter Project 535

14 Transformational Geometry

CONNECTIONS: *Cartography • Technology • Sports • Art • Astronomy • Recreational Mathematics • Optics • Design • Numerical Analysis • Linguistics*

Developing Mathematical Power 585

14.1 Mappings 586
14.2 Reflections 591
14.3 Translations 596
14.4 Rotations 601
14.5 Dilations 607
14.6 Composition of Mappings 612
14.7 Identity and Inverse Transformations 617
14.8 Strategy: Use Transformations 622
14.9 Symmetry 626

Review

Algebra Review 611
Mixed Review 590
Summary and Review 634
College Entrance Exam Review 637
Cumulative Review (1–14) 638
Extra Practice 656

Assessment

Test Yourself 606, 631
Chapter Test 636
Chapter Project 585

Tables 657
Symbols and Abbreviations 659
Answers to Selected Exercises 661

Postulates, Theorems, and Constructions 675
Glossary 687
Index 694

ix

Developing Mathematical Power

Problem Solving 33–37, 62–66, 110–113, 145–148, 155–158, 184–188, 244–247, 287–291, 326–329, 337–341, 378–382, 427–431, 461–465, 507–510, 570–577, 622–625

Communication **Writing in Mathematics** 5, 10, 11 50, 61, 71, 72, 91, 103, 227, 232, 250, 314, 361, 377, 402, 410, 415, 426, 442, 545

Reading in Geometry 132, 138, 208, 281, 460, 501, 600, 621

Drawing in Geometry 4, 9, 21, 26, 31, 82, 100, 101, 103, 105, 106, 108, 109, 117, 155-158, 179, 183, 206, 225, 236, 247, 318, 355, 364, 478

Reasoning—Thinking Critically 15, 16, 46, 51, 53, 55, 56, 61, 72, 88, 138, 176, 178, 181, 187, 194, 201, 203, 230, 241, 248, 253, 266, 267, 273, 281, 286, 289, 292, 294, 306, 313, 357, 368, 373, 399, 402, 405, 415, 416, 442, 447, 452, 455, 466, 468, 470, 476, 478, 493, 501, 504, 513, 523, 543, 546, 554, 555, 558, 561, 567, 573, 586, 595, 598, 603

Connections **Applications** 6, 11, 17, 22, 27, 32, 50, 55, 60, 71, 84, 90, 96, 102, 109, 119, 132, 138, 144, 154, 163, 178, 183, 193, 198, 203, 208, 222, 227, 232, 238, 243, 253, 266, 270, 276, 281, 286, 297, 310, 315, 320, 325, 336, 356, 361, 366, 372, 377, 386, 387, 402, 406, 411, 416, 421, 426, 444, 449, 454, 460, 470, 475, 481, 494, 501, 506, 515, 520, 540, 545, 550, 557, 564, 569, 590, 595, 600, 606, 611, 616, 621

Integrating Geometry 94, 95, 102, 119, 120–121, 128, 144, 149, 164–165, 194, 200, 204, 218, 254–255, 266, 267, 270, 275, 276, 277, 280, 292, 297, 310, 325, 331, 336, 337, 342–343, 352, 356, 361, 366, 377, 386, 416, 426, 444, 449, 476, 482–483, 499, 525, 558, 590, 611, 630–631

Projects 1, 37, 45, 66, 79, 113, 127, 138, 148, 158, 173, 188, 217, 247, 262, 281, 291, 305, 341, 351, 381, 395, 439, 465, 489, 510, 535, 577, 585, 625

Careers 6, 7, 8, 11, 12, 18, 22, 23, 28, 32, 46, 50, 55, 80, 102, 128, 162, 193, 204, 232, 248, 281, 316, 343, 442, 521

Developing Mathematical Power

Investigations

Biographical Note   84, 92, 311, 426, 475, 482, 520, 540, 545, 564, 616

Historical Note   84, 92, 132, 208, 228, 238, 311, 420, 421, 475, 482, 501, 520, 540, 545, 564, 616

Investigation   103, 138, 208, 270, 320, 372, 402, 421, 460, 494, 520, and at the beginning of every non-strategy lesson

Extension   198, 227, 270, 336, 372, 406, 421, 449, 540, 545, 550, 611, 616

Thinking Critically   46, 51, 56, 194, 248, 267, 292, 306, 357, 368, 373, 445, 466, 476, 546, 558, 586

Visualizing the Concept   2, 7, 12, 18, 23, 28, 80, 85, 104, 128, 149, 159, 179, 199, 204, 218, 228, 239, 263, 271, 277, 311, 316, 321, 331, 352, 362, 382, 417, 422, 440, 471, 490, 521, 541, 552, 591, 596, 601, 612, 617, 626

Using Manipulatives   92, 97, 114, 131, 139, 152, 162, 174, 223, 396, 403, 412, 450, 495, 502, 511, 516

Coordinate Geometry   133, 189, 233, 324, 455, 536, 565, 607

Constructions   67, 282, 407, 444

Technology

15–17, 38–39, 73, 83–84, 89–90, 95–96, 105–109, 117–119, 131–132, 136–138, 152–154, 161–163, 177–178, 182–183, 197–198, 202–203, 210–211, 221–222, 225–227, 236–238, 242–243, 250–253, 264, 265–266, 269–270, 273–276, 279–281, 284–286, 289–291, 295–297, 298–299, 308–310, 314–315, 318–320, 324–325, 327–329, 335–336, 337–341, 342–343, 355–356, 365–367, 371–372, 375–377, 385–387, 388–389, 432–433, 400–402, 405–406, 410–411, 415–416, 419–421, 424–426, 442–444, 447–449, 452–454, 457–460, 463–465, 468–470, 474–475, 478–481, 493–494, 498–501, 504–506, 513–515, 518–520, 523–525, 526–527, 538–540, 543–545, 548–550, 555–557, 561–564, 567–569, 578–579, 589–590, 594–595, 598–600, 609–611, 615–616, 628–631, 632–633

*G*eometry is a vital part of mathematics, and mathematics is a vital part of your life. Changes in society and in the use of technology require that you have a strong background in mathematics. The emphasis is not only on geometry skills, but on developing your *mathematical power*. What is mathematical power?

- The knowledge and understanding of mathematical ideas, concepts, and procedures
- The ability to solve problems within mathematics and in other subject areas
- The ability to use mathematical tools and techniques
- The ability to use mathematics in your world beyond the classroom
- The ability to use mathematics to communicate
- The ability to reason and think critically
- The understanding and appreciation of the nature and beauty of mathematics

Using your geomety book effectively will help you to develop your mathematical power. Let us introduce you to the parts of your geometry book that can help you to develop the aspects of mathematical power.

Each chapter begins with an introduction that connects geometry to a familiar topic, and it also provides you with a project to complete independently or with classmates.

Investigations begin each lesson. These activities present you with a variety of ways to explore geometry.

Completely worked-out examples and proofs contain instruction to help you to successfully complete your assignments.

New theorems, postulates, and concepts are highlighted for easy reference.

The **Technology** logo throughout the book identifies when using technology is beneficial to and appropriate for the development of concepts. In addition, **Technology Lessons** using Logo language provide you with alternative methods for exploring geometry.

Strategy lessons, identified by blue borders, help you to develop techniques and strategies for constructing proofs and solving problems in a variety of situations.

Practice Exercises build a solid foundation of geometry skills . . .

Thinking Critically—helps improve your reasoning skills.

Applications—connects geometry to daily life and to other topics.

Developing Mathematical Power—provides you with activities that may take you outside your classroom, exploring and using mathematics in today's world.

Mixed and **Algebra Reviews**—will help you to remember the skills and concepts already learned.

Writing, Reading, and **Drawing in Geometry** activities help you to acquire communication skills.

Integrating Geometry features provide a look at how geometry is used in daily life.

Test Yourself provides you with a tool for self-evaluation. Answers to these and other selected exercises can be found in the back of the book.

*R*emember . . . Mathematics is not a spectator sport! Actively participating, reading carefully, and completing your assignments will contribute to your success in geometry and in other mathematics courses you take in the future.

OVERVIEW • Chapter 1

SUMMARY

In Chapter 1, students define geometry terms using the undefined terms. The concepts of distance, segment, ray, and midpoint are developed, and students are introduced to mathematical symbols. They learn to draw and interpret figures, to measure angles, to classify angles, and to define and recognize special angle pairs.

The chapter helps the student to develop an intuitive feeling for proof and for the nature of a deductive system by stressing pre-proof activities. For example:
1. Statements are presented, and students are asked to draw conclusions.
2. Students use definitions, postulates, and theorems as reasons to justify conclusions.

CHAPTER OBJECTIVES

- To use undefined terms to define basic geometric terms

- To use certain postulates and theorems that relate points, lines, and planes

- To identify and use the symbols for segments, rays, perpendicular lines, and angles

- To find the distance between two points on a number line and the coordinate of the midpoint of a segment

- To classify, identify, and measure types of angles and angle pairs

- To state and apply theorems about midpoints, angle bisectors, vertical angles, perpendicular lines, complementary, and supplementary angles

- To use the information conveyed by a figure to help solve a problem

CHAPTER HIGHLIGHTS

DEVELOPING MATHEMATICAL POWER

Problem Solving

The four-step problem solving process is introduced in Lesson 1.7, which presents the strategy of analyzing a figure. The strategy lesson has a follow-up project.

Communication

The side column offers suggestions for cooperative learning activities, alternative learning opportunities, and topics such as star-gazing for journal entries in students' portfolios. The *Teacher's Resource Book* contains a Chapter Summary and Review in Spanish.

Reasoning

Students analyze basic geometric terms in preparation for upcoming proofs. Existence and uniqueness statements are compared and contrasted.

Connections

Each lesson contains real-world applications such as cartography, carpentry, and transportation. Algebra is integrated for calculating angle pairs and midpoints of segments. The Chapter Project provides another opportunity for students to apply chapter concepts.

Technology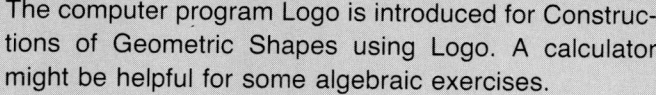

The computer program Logo is introduced for Constructions of Geometric Shapes using Logo. A calculator might be helpful for some algebraic exercises.

ASSIGNMENT GUIDE   Meeting Student Needs

STUDENT TEXT

Chapter Content	Basic	Average	Enriched	NCTM STANDARDS*
1.1 Points, Lines and Planes	D: 5/1-14, 15-25 odd, 39, 40	D: 5/1-14, 15-25 odd, 26-32, 38-40	D: 5/1-25 odd, 26-37, 38-40	2, 3
1.2 Some Relationships Among Points, Lines, and Planes	D: 10/1-10, 11-18 odd, 38, AR R: 5/15-25 even	D: 10/1-10, 11-28 odd, 37, 38, 43, AR R: 5/15-25 even	D: 10/1-10, 19-30 odd, 31-38, 43, AR R: 5/1-25 even	2, 3, 4
1.3 Segments and Rays	D: 15/1-10, 11-16 odd, 17-21, 43, AR R: 10/11-18 even	D: 15/1-21, 22-29 even, 43, AR R: 10/11-28 even	D: 15/1-21, 22-37 even, 38-44, AR R: 10/19-30 even	2, 3, 4, 5
1.4 Angles	D: 21/1-15, 16-22 even, 28 R: 15/11-16 even	D: 21/1-15, 16-22 even, 28, 29 R: 15/22-29 odd	D: 21/1, 9-15, 16-26 even, 27-29 R: 15/22-37 odd	2, 3, 4, 8
1.5 Angle Pairs	D: 26/1-4, 7-18 odd, 31, 32 R: 21/16-22 odd	D: 26/1-6, 7-21 odd, 22-26, 31 R: 21/16-22 odd	D: 26/1-6, 13-26, 27-32 odd R: 21/16-26 odd	2, 3, 4, 5
1.6 Perpendicular Lines	D: 31/1-4, 5-16 odd, 17-20, 33 R: 26/7-18 even	D: 31/1-4, 5-16 odd, 17-28, 33 R: 26/7-21 even, 32	D: 31/5-20 odd, 21-34 R: 26/27-32 even	2, 3
1.7 Strategy—Analyze a Figure	D: 36/1-7 R: 31/5-16 even	D: 36/1-10 R: 31/5-16 even	D: 36/1-13 R: 31/5-20 even	1, 2, 3,7

D = Daily   R = Review   AR = Algebra Review

*For a complete list of NCTM Standards, see p. T7.

STUDENT TEXT

Review/Assessment
Algebra Review 11, 17, 44

Summary and Review 40

College Ent. Exam Rev. 43

Extra Practice 643

Test Yourself 22, 37

Chapter Test 42

Chapter Project 1

Special Features
Constructions 17, 27, 32

Career 6

Technology 17, 38-39

Devel. Math. Power 11

Applications 6, 11, 17, 22, 27, 32

Project 37

RESOURCES

Teacher's Resource Book
Ch. 1: Investigation/Practice/ Enrichment 1-20

Spanish Sum. and Rev. 1-2

Quizzes 5-8

Chapter Tests 9-12

Perf. Assessment Proj. Ch. 1

Critical Thinking 1

Reading and Writing in Geom. 1

Technology 1-2

Teaching Aid 1

Transparency 1

Teaching Transparencies 1-7

Computer Test Bank 23-88

Connections 3-4

PH Graph. Utility

Overhead Manip. Kit

The Language of Geometry

Follow your star?

- - - - - - - - - - -

Developing Mathematical Power

Although sophisticated electronic navigation equipment is now available, some sailors still use sextants to navigate by the North Star, Polaris. Polaris lies almost on the line containing the axis of the Earth's rotation. Thus, Polaris always appears to be due north.

Project

Suppose you are the navigator for a boat sailing in a race from Newport, RI, to Hamilton, Bermuda. How could you use Polaris to plot your course? What effect will the ocean currents have on your course?

ME
NH
MA
T
Newport, Rhode Island
ATLANTIC OCEAN
Hamilton, Bermuda

1

LESSON PLAN

Vocabulary

Collinear	Noncollinear
Coplanar	Noncoplanar
Edge	Opposite
Half-plane	half-planes
Intersect	Plane
Intersection	Point
Line	Space

Materials/Manipulatives

Models of geometric figures
Grid paper
Teacher's Resource Book,
   Teaching Aid 1
   Transparency 1
Teaching Transparencies 1
   and 2

Technology

Computer Test Bank, pp. 23–33

LESSON FOCUS

Review

In the lesson, the basic geometric terms *point, line,* and *plane* are reviewed and then expanded upon.

Alternative Learning Styles

- Use the Investigation and Teaching Transparency 2 to help students visualize and understand the terms *point* and *line.*
- Encourage students who have difficulty drawing planes to use grid paper. Have them locate a point at the intersection of two grid lines and count *y* units up or down and *x* units right or left. With this as the slope and direction of their plane, have them connect the boundary points.

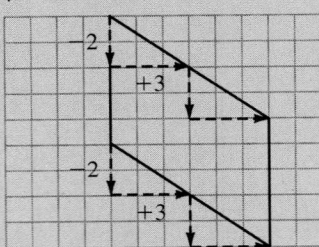

1.1

Points, Lines, and Planes

Objectives: To identify and draw representations of points, lines, and planes

To use undefined terms to define some basic geometric terms

When you look at the night sky how many stars do you see? Actually, there are billions of stars, each represented as a small dot of light in the sky. Each dot of light suggests a *point*, the simplest figure in geometry.

Investigation—*Visualizing the Concept*

The bright stars at the right form the constellation, the Big Dipper. You can think of the stars as *points.* Copy or trace the points on a sheet of paper. Connect the points with *lines* to illustrate the constellation.

1. How many stars form the constellation? 7
2. How many lines connect two points? 1
3. How many points are on a line? infinitely many
4. How many lines are in space? infinitely many

Point is one of three basic undefined terms in geometry. A **point** has no size and no dimension, merely position. A point is usually represented in a drawing by a dot and named with a capital letter. For example, the point represented in the circle at the right is called point *P.*

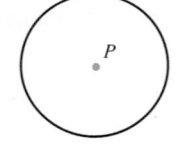

Line is also undefined in geometry. A **line** consists of infinitely many points extending without end in both directions. A line is usually named by any two of its points or by a lowercase letter. Line *SL,* written $\overleftrightarrow{SL}$ or $\overleftrightarrow{LS}$, can also be named line *k.*

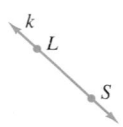

Plane is a third undefined term. A **plane** can be thought of as a flat surface with no thickness that extends without end in all directions. Although a plane has no boundaries, it is usually pictured by a four-sided figure. Planes are named by a capital letter, or by three points in the plane that are not on the same line. Thus, plane *X* can also be named plane *RST.*

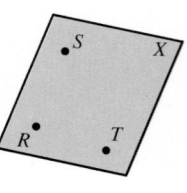

2   Chapter 1 The Language of Geometry

Developing Mathematical Power

Cooperative Learning   Have students study the Dutch artist Maurice C. Escher. Each group should choose and photocopy one of his lithographs. After using colored pencils to show the direction of the lines and planes, students could create a bulletin board display of their work.

EXAMPLE 1 **Name a point, line, or plane suggested by each indicated part of the figure.**
   a. floor   **b.** rear wall corners
   c. front wall   **d.** ceiling boundaries

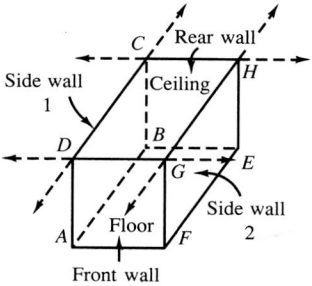

   a. plane *ABE*, *ABF*, *AEF*, or *BEF*
   b. points *B*, *C*, *E*, and *H*
   c. plane *AFG*, *FGD*, *GDA*, or *DAF*
   d. $\overleftrightarrow{CD}$, $\overleftrightarrow{DG}$, $\overleftrightarrow{GH}$, and $\overleftrightarrow{HC}$

In the figure at the right all points and lines are contained in plane *P*. Point *D is in* (or *is on*) both lines *m* and *l*. Line *m contains* points *E*, *F*, and *D*, but *does not contain* points *I*, *J*, *G*, or *H*. Plane *P contains* points *I*, *E*, *J*, *F*, *G*, *D*, and *H*. Lines *m*, *k*, and *l lie* in plane *P*.

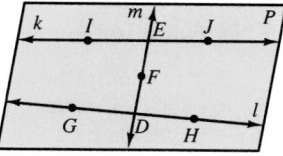

The undefined terms point, line, and plane are used to define the following important concepts. The phrase "if and only if" is often used to combine the two ways of wording a definition. For example, "points are **collinear** *if and only if* they lie on the same line" means:

1. Points are collinear *if* they lie on the same line.
2. Points lie on the same line *if* they are collinear.

Points that are *not collinear* are called **noncollinear.**

Points are **coplanar** if and only if they lie on the same plane. Otherwise, they are **noncoplanar. Space** is the set of all points. A set of points is the **intersection** of two figures if and only if the points lie in both figures. The figures *intersect* at that point or set of points.

EXAMPLE 2 The Great Pyramid of Khufu consists of four triangular faces and a square base. In the figure, *S* and *T* represent openings to the pyramid's ventilation shafts.

Use the figure to give an example of each.

   a. three collinear points   **b.** three noncollinear points
   c. six coplanar points   **d.** four noncoplanar points
   e. intersection of the edges   **f.** a point collinear with *T* and *D*
       that lie in $\overleftrightarrow{CB}$ and $\overleftrightarrow{BA}$

a. *B*, *Y*, *A*   **b.** *C*, *X*, *B*   **c.** *B*, *Y*, *A*, *D*, *T*, *C*   **d.** *A*, *B*, *C*, *X*   **e.** *B*   **f.** *A*

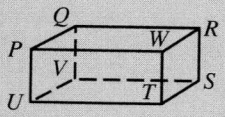
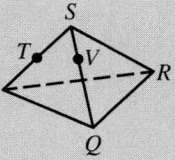
3

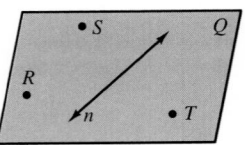

Line *n* is contained in plane *Q*. Line *n* separates *Q* into three sets of infinitely many points. One of the sets is *n* itself. The other two sets are called **half-planes.** *n* is the **edge** of each half-plane but is not contained in either half-plane. *R* and *S* are on the same side of *n* and thus lie in the same half-plane. *S* and *T* are on opposite sides of *n* and thus lie in *opposite half-planes*.

CLASS EXERCISES

Drawing in Geometry

1. Here are pictures of a horizontal plane, a vertical plane, and intersecting horizontal and vertical planes. Practice drawing these. When are dashed lines used? to represent hidden parts of a figure

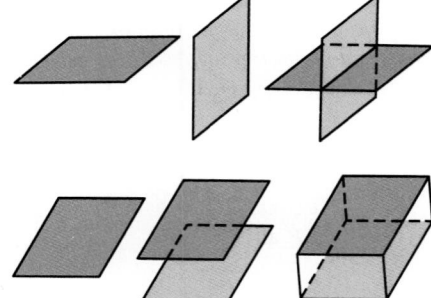

2. Follow these drawings to make a picture of a box. Note the dashed lines.

Name the following.

3. Corners of the right face
   K, L, P, O

4. Point coplanar with *I*, *J*, and *K* L

5. Plane of the front face
   MPI; answers may vary.

6. Intersection of $\overleftrightarrow{IM}$ and $\overleftrightarrow{FP}$ M

7. Three collinear points
   M, F, P or P, R, O

8. Three noncollinear points
   J, L, R; answers may vary.

9. Six coplanar points
   M, F, P, R, O, N

10. Four noncoplanar points
    I, J, K, P; answers may vary.

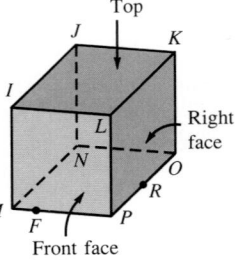

Complete. Use the figure above and these words: *contains, collinear, noncollinear, coplanar, intersection, half-plane, opposite half-planes.*

11. *I* is the _?_ of $\overleftrightarrow{IJ}$ and $\overleftrightarrow{IM}$.
    intersection

12. *R*, *P*, and *O* are coplanar and _?_.
    collinear

13. *R*, *M*, and *N* are coplanar but _?_.
    noncollinear

14. Plane *MNO* _?_ *R*, *P*, and *F*.
    contains

15. $\overleftrightarrow{PR}$ _?_ *O*.
    contains

16. If $\overleftrightarrow{JL}$ is drawn, $\overleftrightarrow{JL}$ becomes the edge of two _?_. half-planes

17. If $\overleftrightarrow{JL}$ is drawn, points *K* and *I* lie in _?_. opposite half-planes

18. *R*, *F*, and *P* are _?_ and noncollinear. coplanar

4

PRACTICE EXERCISES

A Use the drawing to complete each sentence with these words: *contain(s), intersection, collinear, noncollinear, coplanar.*

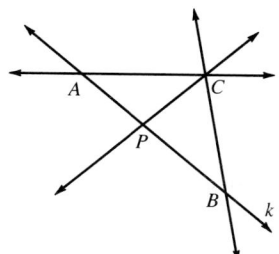

1. *P* is the _?_ of $\overleftrightarrow{CP}$ and *k*. intersection

2. The _?_ of $\overleftrightarrow{AB}$ and $\overleftrightarrow{AC}$ is *A*. intersection

3. *A, B,* and *C* are _?_. noncollinear; also coplanar

4. *C, B,* and *P* are _?_. noncollinear; also coplanar

5. *A, C,* and *P* are _?_ and _?_. coplanar noncollinear

6. *A, B,* and *P* are _?_ and _?_. collinear coplanar

Draw and label each figure. Answers may vary. See below.

7. $\overleftrightarrow{AB}$

8. plane *R*

9. Three coplanar points: *X, Y,* and *Z*

10. The intersection of $\overleftrightarrow{CD}$ and $\overleftrightarrow{EF}$

11. Line *l* containing points *P* and *R*, but not point *S*

12. Plane *N* containing $\overleftrightarrow{GH}$, and point *T* not on $\overleftrightarrow{GH}$

13. Three collinear points: *L, M,* and *N*

14. A cube

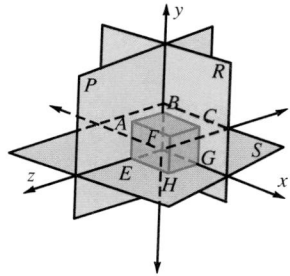

This figure shows a box that is set in a corner formed by three intersecting planes, *P, R,* and *S*. The bottom face of the box lies in horizontal plane *S*; the left rear face lies in vertical plane *P*; the right rear face lies in vertical plane *R*.

True or false? If false, explain why.

15. Plane *P* contains *A, B,* and *E*. true

16. Plane *R* contains *B, C,* and *H*. False; *H* is not in *R*.

17. *E, F, G,* and *H* are coplanar. true

18. *E, F, G,* and *H* lie in plane *S*. true

B **19.** *E* and *F* lie in *z*. true

20. *E* and *B* lie in *z*. False; *B* is not on *z*.

21. Plane *BCG* contains *H*. False; *H* is in face *FEG, AEH,* and *CGH*.

22. *H* lies in plane *S*. true

23. *F* is the intersection of *y* and *x*. true

24. *A* and *C* lie in opposite half-planes of *R*. False; *P* and *R* are not opposite half-planes.

25. Writing in Mathematics Use the geometric terms from this lesson to describe your classroom. Answers may vary.

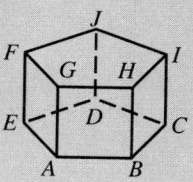

This hat box pictured has a top and bottom and 5 side faces.

1. Name the plane that contains the top of the box. plane *FGH* (Answers may vary.)

2. Name the intersection of *FGH* and *HBC*. $\overleftrightarrow{HI}$

3. Name the intersection of $\overleftrightarrow{FE}$ and $\overleftrightarrow{AE}$. point *E*

4. *D* lies in 3 planes shown. Name them. *DEF, CDJ, CDE* (Answers may vary.)

5. Complete the sentence: *G, H,* and *B* are points that are _?_ but _?_. coplanar; noncollinear

Enrichment

Distribute to students a larger version of the figure shown below.

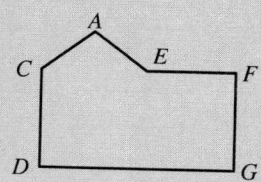

Ask students to consider how they could make one cut and rearrange the parts to form a square. Have students label points in the diagram to enable them to describe the solution to the problem without actually cutting the figure. Cut along a ⊥ line from *A* to $\overline{DG}$. Match *A* to *A, C* to *E,* and *D* to *F*.

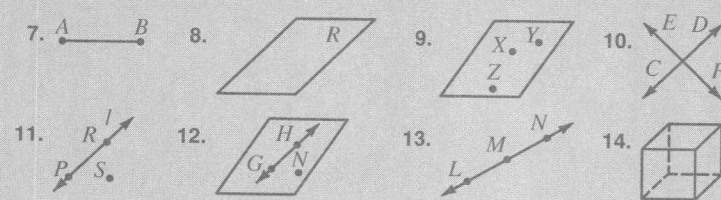

7. *A* ——— *B*

8. *R*

9. *X.* *Y.* *Z.*

10. *E D* *C* *F*

11. *R* *l* *P* *S.*

12. *H* *G* *N*

13. *N* *M* *L*

14.

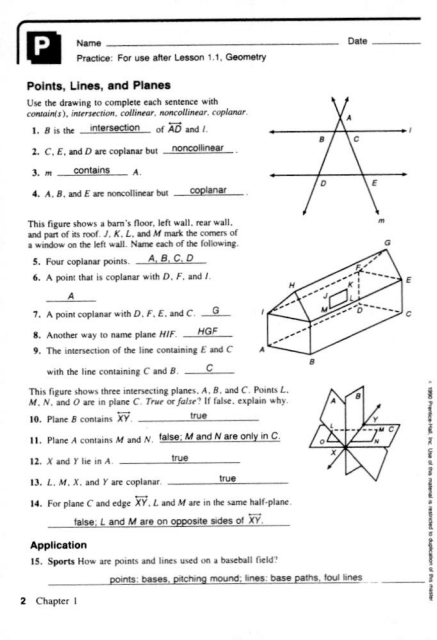

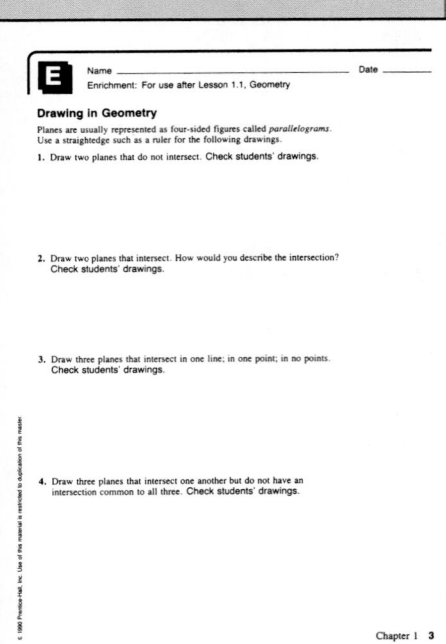

Refer to the pyramid for Exercises 26–32.

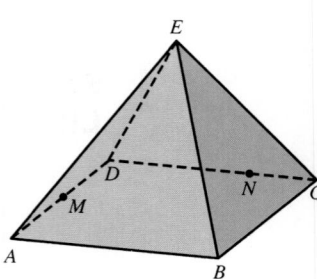

26. Each face of a pyramid is part of a plane. How many planes are shown? Name them. 5: *EAB, EAD, EBC, EDC, ABD*

27. Each edge is part of a line. How many lines contain *E*? Name them. 4: $\overleftrightarrow{AE}$, $\overleftrightarrow{BE}$, $\overleftrightarrow{CE}$, $\overleftrightarrow{DE}$

28. Give the intersection of the line containing *A* and *M* and the line containing *N* and *C*. *D*

29. Name the planes that contain *A*. *ABD, ABE, ADE*

30. Name the plane that does not contain *E*. *ABC*

31. Name the two planes that contain points *A*, *M*, and *D*. *ADE, ABD*

32. Do $\overleftrightarrow{AD}$ and $\overleftrightarrow{BE}$ intersect? If so, name the intersection. They do not intersect.

Sketch a pyramid with a five-sided base. Use dashed lines for parts hidden from view. Label the points where three or more faces intersect.

C **33.** How many points did you label? See side column. 6: *A B C D E T*
Answers for Ex. 34–35 vary with student sketches.

34. How many edges are there? Name the lines that contain them. 10; $\overleftrightarrow{TA}$, $\overleftrightarrow{TB}$, $\overleftrightarrow{TC}$, $\overleftrightarrow{TD}$, $\overleftrightarrow{TE}$, $\overleftrightarrow{AB}$, $\overleftrightarrow{BC}$, $\overleftrightarrow{CD}$, $\overleftrightarrow{DE}$, $\overleftrightarrow{EA}$

35. Name a point that is contained in five planes; name the five planes. *T; TAB, TBC, TCD, TDE, TAE*

36. Consider the base and any other face. What is the intersection of the planes that contain them? a line that contains an edge of the base

37. Are any of the faces opposite half-planes? Explain your answer. No; they are noncoplanar.

Applications

38. Architecture Find a photo of the Hancock Tower in Chicago. Sketch the lines and planes that are suggested in the photo. Answers may vary.

39. Travel How are points and lines used on a road map? points: cities and places of interest, intersections of roads; lines: boundaries, roads, and scales

40. Cartography How are lines used on a world map? How are these lines related? Answers may vary. For example, lines of latitude and longitude are used to locate points on a map. These two kinds of lines intersect.

Developing Mathematical Power

41. Investigation Drawing is a skill, an art, and a science. Beyond its importance to *painters, cartoonists,* and *sculptors,* it plays a major role in various industries. *Designers* sketch items such as clothing, fabrics, landscapes, and buildings. *Draftspersons* and *engineers* develop blueprints and structural designs. Many graphics are composed with computers. Choose one of the careers mentioned and make a report. Create an appropriate drawing as part of your report. Answers may vary.

6 Chapter 1 The Language of Geometry

33.–37.

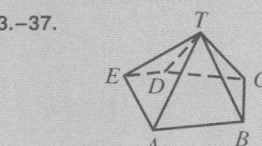

1.2 Some Relationships Among Points, Lines, and Planes

Objective: To use some postulates and theorems that relate points, lines, and planes

Statements accepted as true are called *postulates* or *axioms*. In geometry, **postulates** are accepted as true statements and are used to justify conclusions.

Investigation—*Visualizing the Concept*

A surveying team is locating boundary lines on a lot. They find the post marking one corner and call it *K*. 50 ft north along the line of sight they mark a second corner post *P*. *K* and *P* determine $\overleftrightarrow{KP}$.

1. If they had found *P* first and then *K*, would $\overleftrightarrow{PK}$ be the same line as $\overleftrightarrow{KP}$? yes

2. Can you visualize another surveyor's line that contains both points *P* and *K*? Explain. No; only one line can contain both points *P* and *K*.

Geometricians need a place from which they can begin to prove statements. Thus, they make the following assumption.

> **Postulate 1** A line contains at least two distinct points. A plane contains at least three noncollinear points. Space contains at least four noncoplanar points.

Since straightness is a property of a line, *m* is the only line in this drawing, and the only line that contains both *R* and *S*. This concept is formally stated as Postulate 2.

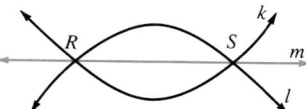

> **Postulate 2** If two distinct points are given, then a unique line contains them.

Another way to express Postulate 2 is: *Two distinct points determine a unique line*.

The word *unique* throughout this text means *exactly one*, or *one and only one*.

LESSON PLAN

Vocabulary
Postulate
Theorem
Unique

Materials/Manipulatives
Rope
Straws
Boxes with straight edges
Teacher's Resource Book,
  Teaching Aid 1
Teaching Transparencies 1 and 2

Technology
Computer Test Bank, pp. 33–38

LESSON FOCUS

Review
Absolute value is reviewed in Exercises 39–42 to prepare students for the Ruler Postulate in Lesson 1.3.

Alternative Learning Styles
In order to develop an understanding of the relationship between two points and a line, some students may need to act out the situation in the Investigation, which is an informal presentation of Postulate 2. Students should recognize that there is exactly one line through any two points. Have students identify points in the classroom from which they could make sightings to measure distances. Use string to illustrate the distance between the two points. You may wish to do this activity outdoors.

Developing Mathematical Power

Keeping a Portfolio Have students use Reading and Writing in Geometry, p. 1, in the *Teacher's Resource Book* as the format for their journal entries. This gives them an excellent opportunity to summarize their understanding of geometric statements.

7

It is important that students study each postulate and theorem in terms of concrete objects and experiences. Simple objects like rope, straws, and edges of boxes can represent lines; walls and cardboard can represent planes. Examples are given below for Postulates 2 and 3.

Postulate 2: Two consecutive corners (points) of a box determine only the edge (line) joining them.

Postulate 3: Two fingertips (points), fixed in position, can hold a piece of cardboard (plane) in many different positions so as to represent many planes. A third fingertip changes nothing if it is collinear with the other two. But three noncollinear fingertips can balance the cardboard piece in exactly one position, much as a waiter balances a tray.

Tell students that they will prove theorems formally later in the course.

Critical Thinking
Creative Thinking Ask students to demonstrate postulates and theorems using concrete items.

Common Error
• Some students will lack strong memorization skills. Since students' ability to make effective use of these postulates and theorems will depend on their ability to remember them, these students will benefit from stating the postulates and theorems in full each time they are used in exercises. Have students write theorems and postulates as they are presented in class, and maintain a record of them.
• See *Teacher's Resource Book* for additional remediation.

Planes X, Y, and Z are only three of the infinitely many planes that contain points A and B. Point C is collinear with A and B. Thus, all the planes that contain A and B also contain C. However, only plane Z contains noncollinear points D, A, and B. This concept is stated in the next postulate.

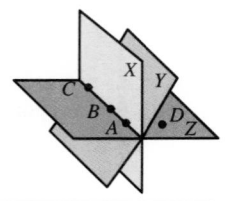

Postulate 3   Through any two points there are infinitely many planes. Through any three points there is at least one plane. Through any three noncollinear points there is exactly one plane.

From Postulate 2 it is known that only one line contains both J and K. Consider the infinitely many points in $\overleftrightarrow{JK}$. Experience suggests that all points of $\overleftrightarrow{JK}$ lie in plane P. This is the assumption made by an artist who draws linear designs. Postulate 4 is a formal statement of this assumption.

Postulate 4   If two points are in a plane, then the line that contains those points lies entirely in the plane.

An architect might sketch a drawing showing vertical plane A and horizontal plane B intersecting. There are infinitely many points in the intersection, $\overleftrightarrow{PT}$. In fact, for any two intersecting planes, the following postulate holds true.

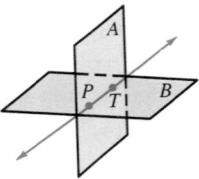

Postulate 5   If two distinct planes intersect, then their intersection is a line.

Using these postulates as starting points, it is possible to conclude that certain statements are true. Such statements are called *theorems*. Unlike postulates, which are statements that are accepted as true, **theorems** are statements that must be proven true by citing undefined terms, definitions, and postulates.

Theorem 1.1   If two distinct lines intersect, then they intersect in exactly one point.

Lines *l* and *m* intersect at *K*. If *l* and *m* were to intersect at a second point, then both would contain the same two points. By Postulate 2, that is impossible. Therefore, *K* is the only point of intersection for lines *l* and *m*.

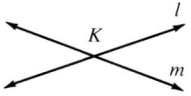

> **Theorem 1.2** If there is a line and a point not in the line, then there is exactly one plane that contains them.

Let *r* and *D* represent the line and point of this theorem. Postulate 1 says that *r* has at least two distinct points such as *F* and *G*. Points *D*, *F*, and *G* are noncollinear, so by Postulate 3 there is exactly one plane that contains them. Postulate 4 says that all the other points in *r* must be in this plane as well. Hence, this is the one plane that contains *r* and *D*.

> **Theorem 1.3** If two distinct lines intersect, then they lie in exactly one plane.

Lines *k* and *m* intersect in point *P*. Consider another point *Q* on *k*. From Theorem 1.2, it is known that exactly one plane contains both *m* and *Q*. Postulate 4 says that since *k* contains *P* and *Q*, *k* lies in the same plane as *P* and *Q* and hence in the same plane as *m*.

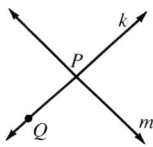

"Exactly one" in Theorem 1.3 involves *existence* and *uniqueness* statements:

1. There *exists at least one* plane that contains the intersecting lines.

2. There is *only one* plane that contains the intersecting lines.

The first statement is for the *existence* of the plane, and the second is for the *uniqueness* of the plane. "Exactly one" implies existence and uniqueness.

The *undefined terms* and the beginning *definitions* were used to formulate:
    Postulates: statements *accepted* without proof
    Theorems: statements that must be *proven*

CLASS EXERCISES

Use a straightedge when drawing lines for these exercises.

1. Mark any two points *R* and *S* on the paper. Draw a line *m* through *R* and *S*. Which postulate tells how many lines are determined by *R* and *S*? Post. 2

2. Which postulate states how many points of $\overleftrightarrow{RS}$ lie in the plane of the paper? Post. 4

1.2 Some Relationships Among Points, Lines, and Planes   9

True or false? If false, rewrite as a true statement.

1. If 2 planes intersect, then their intersection is a <u>point</u>. false; line
2. Three points are always coplanar. true
3. Three <u>collinear</u> points determine exactly one plane. false; noncollinear
4. A line and a point not on that line determine exactly one plane. true
5. The line determined by points A and B lies in more than one plane. true
6. Through any two points there is exactly one line. true
7. A plane contains at <u>most</u> 3 noncollinear points. false; least

Enrichment

How many lines are determined by 3 noncollinear points? By 4 points, no 3 of which are collinear? By 5 such points? By 6 such points? By n such points? 3; 6; 10; 15; $\frac{n(n-1)}{2}$

In Exercises 3–6, make a drawing and use it to answer each question.

3. Points A, B, and C are noncollinear. How many lines do they determine? How many planes do they determine? 3; 1

4. Points A, B, and C are collinear. How many lines do they determine? How many planes do they determine? 1; infinitely many

5. Point C is not on $\overleftrightarrow{AB}$. How many planes contain both $\overleftrightarrow{AB}$ and C? 1

6. Distinct lines k and l intersect. What is their intersection? a point

7. How many planes contain both lines l and k? 1

8. **Writing in Mathematics** Look around the classroom for an illustration of a theorem from this lesson. Explain how the theorem is illustrated. Answers may vary.

PRACTICE EXERCISES

In Exercises 1–4, make a drawing and use it to answer each question.

A 1. Given two points P and Q, draw $\overleftrightarrow{PQ}$. Does $\overleftrightarrow{PQ}$ lie entirely in the plane of the paper? Which postulate or theorem justifies your answer? Post. 4

2. Given any point R, draw two lines k and l through R. Do they seem to intersect in another point? Which theorem justifies your answer? Th. 1.1

3. Given three noncollinear points S, T, and U, draw $\overleftrightarrow{ST}$. Does U lie on $\overleftrightarrow{ST}$? The definition of what word justifies your answer? no; noncollinear

4. Draw line m. Mark three points V, W, and X that lie on m. How many planes pass through V and W? Which postulate justifies your answer? infinitely many; Post. 3

Add the key word or words that make each statement always true.

5. _?_ points determine a line. Two

6. Three _?_ points lie on a line. collinear

7. Three _?_ points determine a plane. noncollinear

8. _?_ lines l and k determine a plane. intersecting

9. Four _?_ points determine space. noncoplanar

10. _?_ planes R and T determine a line. intersecting

Briefly describe one model for each. Answers may vary.

11. In a classroom: 2 intersecting lines
12. On a ball field: 2 intersecting lines
13. On a city map: Postulate 2
14. On a dining table: Postulate 2
15. In a home: 2 intersecting planes
16. Outside: 2 intersecting planes

Tell which postulate or theorem is illustrated.

17. Ramón cannot find the northwest corner of his lot until he finds where ropes along the west and north lot lines cross. Th. 1.1

18. A ruler placed between two nails on a wall lies flat against the wall. Post. 5

Imagine three noncollinear points *A*, *B*, and *C*. State the definition, postulate, or theorem that makes each statement true.

B
19. *ABC* is a unique plane. Post. 3
20. $\overleftrightarrow{BC}$ is a unique line. Post. 2
21. $\overleftrightarrow{AB}$, $\overleftrightarrow{BC}$, and $\overleftrightarrow{AC}$ each lie in *ABC*. Post. 4
22. *QBC* and *ABC* intersect in $\overleftrightarrow{BC}$. Post. 5
23. $\overleftrightarrow{AB}$ and $\overleftrightarrow{BC}$ intersect in *B* and only in *B*. Th. 1.1
24. $\overleftrightarrow{AB}$ and $\overleftrightarrow{AC}$ intersect in *A* and only in *A*. Th. 1.1

Give the number of lines determined for each situation.

25. Three noncollinear points 3
26. Two intersecting planes 1
27. Four coplanar points, three of which are collinear 4
28. Four coplanar points, no three of which are collinear 6
29. Write the existence and uniqueness statements for Theorem 1.1.
Two distinct lines intersect in at least one point. Two distinct lines intersect in only one point.
30. Write the existence and uniqueness statements for Theorem 1.2.
At least one plane contains a line and a point not on the line. Only one plane contains a line and a point not on the line.

How many lines are determined by the given condition?

C
31. Five coplanar points, no three of which are collinear 10
32. Six coplanar points, no three of which are collinear 15
33. Three planes whose intersection is a point 3
34. Three planes, each of which intersects the other two at different places 3

How many planes are determined by the given condition?

35. Four noncoplanar points, no three of which are collinear 4
36. Five noncoplanar points, exactly three of which are collinear 5

Applications

37. Carpentry Explain why a four-legged stool may wobble and a three-legged stool will not. Four noncollinear points may be noncoplanar.
38. Sports Which concept(s) of this lesson can be applied to the situation of two athletes playing tug of war? If two distinct points are given, then a unique line contains them.

Algebra Review

Evaluate.

39. $|-5|$ 5
40. $|3-6|$ 3
41. $|12-3|$ 9
42. $|-2-(-3)|$ 1

Developing Mathematical Power

43. Writing in Mathematics Lines are assumed to be straight. Describe what might happen if some lines were straight and some were not. Answers may vary.

1.2 Some Relationships Among Points, Lines, and Planes   **11**

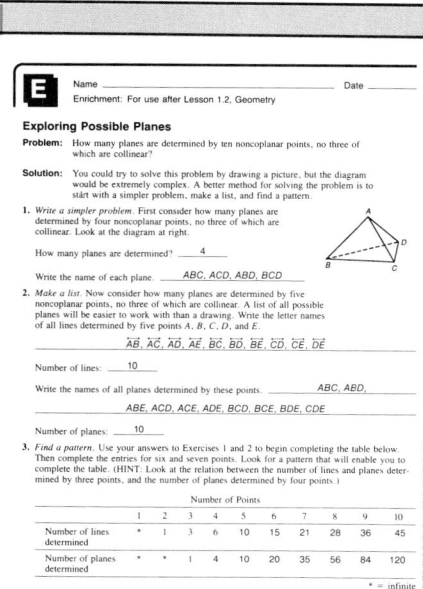

Vocabulary

Between (points)	Length of a segment
Congruent segments	Midpoint
Coordinate	Opposite rays
Corollary	Ray
Distance	Segment
Endpoint(s)	Segment bisector

Materials/Manipulatives

Compasses and straightedges
Teaching Transparency 3

Technology

Calculator
Computer Test Bank, pp. 38–53

LESSON FOCUS

Review

• Review the use of a number line. Draw a number line on the chalkboard. Count units to determine the distance between points. Absolute value is used to guarantee a positive result.
• The Algebra Review in Exercises 45–50 reviews translating word sentences to equations and solving simple linear equations.

Alternative Learning Styles

• Have students take measurements of the distance between pairs of points in the classroom. They can use string to represent the segment between any two points. The Investigation also shows this, an application of the Ruler Postulate.
• Assign zero to a point in the classroom and have students find the measure of distances to the right and to the left of that point. Then tell students to fold the string in half to find the midpoint.

1.3

Segments and Rays

Objectives: To distinguish between segments, rays, and lines
To find the distance between two points on a number line
To find the coordinate of the midpoint of a segment

The *number line* is an important mathematical model that integrates arithmetic, algebra, and geometry. On a number line the real numbers are placed in a one-to-one correspondence with all the points on the line. Each number is called the **coordinate** of the point with which it is paired.

Investigation—*Visualizing the Concept*

Archaeologists on a "dig" use measuring tapes and magnetic compasses to map out the locations of their "finds."

At this site archaeologists have uncovered artifacts at points L, V, Y, and Z and at the corner of an ancient building at O. They look for a second corner along an east-west line. They find it 15 ft to the east at N. Building supports are found between O and N at B and at M.

This picture shows the archaeologists at work.

Use the information in the picture to find the distance between the given points.

1. O to B 4.5 ft **2.** B to N 10.5 ft **3.** L to O 3 ft **4.** M to N 6 ft **5.** L to B 7.5 ft

When using a number line, assume these statements.

> **Postulate 6** Given any two points there is a unique distance between them.
>
> **Postulate 7** **The Ruler Postulate** There is a one-to-one correspondence between the points of a line and the set of real numbers such that the **distance** between two distinct points of the line is the absolute value of the difference of their coordinates.

12 Chapter 1 The Language of Geometry

Developing Mathematical Power

Cooperative Learning Provide each small group with magazines. Direct them to find pictures that illustrate the geometric concepts they have learned thus far. Have them mark these pictures as shown in the Investigation and create a collage.

Since distances are positive, it is necessary in geometry to use the algebraic concept of absolute value to guarantee a positive result. Use the symbol AB or BA to represent the distance between points A and B.

EXAMPLE 1   **Use the Ruler Postulate to find AB.**

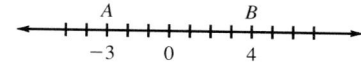

$$AB = |-3 - (+4)| \qquad \text{or} \qquad AB = |(+4) - (-3)|$$
$$= |-7| = 7 \qquad\qquad\qquad\qquad = |7| = 7$$

The following definition uses the idea of distance between points to determine when one of three collinear points is *between* the other two.

Definition   Given three collinear points X, Y, and Z, Y is **between** X and Z if and only if $XY + YZ = XZ$.

EXAMPLE 2   **K is between J and L.**
Find JK, KL, and JL.

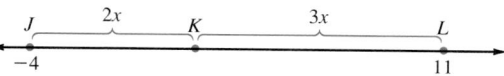

			Check:
$JL = |-4 - (+11)| = 15$	*Ruler Postulate*		$2(3) + 3(3) \overset{?}{=} 15$
$JK + KL = JL$	*Definition of betweenness*		$6 + 9 \overset{?}{=} 15$
$2x + 3x = 15$	*Substitution property*		$15 = 15$ ✔
$5x = 15$	*Distributive property*		
$x = 3$	*Division property*		

Thus, $JK = 2(3) = 6$, $KL = 3(3) = 9$, and $JL = 5(3) = 15$.

Betweenness of points and the Ruler Postulate suggest these **definitions.**

A set of points on a line is a **segment** if and only if it consists of two points, called the *endpoints,* and all points between them. Segment ST, written as $\overline{ST}$, has endpoints S and T.

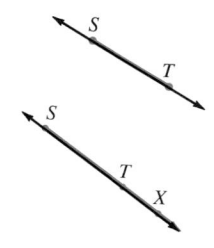

A set of points is a **ray** if and only if it consists of a segment, $\overline{ST}$, and all points X such that T is between X and S. S is the *endpoint* of ray SX, written as $\overrightarrow{SX}$. $\overrightarrow{TX}$ and $\overrightarrow{TS}$ are called **opposite rays** if T is between S and X.

The *length* or **measure, ST, of a segment, $\overline{ST}$,** is the distance between S and T.

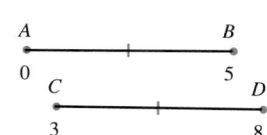

Two **segments** are **congruent** if and only if they have equal measures. $\overline{AB} \cong \overline{CD}$ if and only if $AB = CD$. (*Tick marks* indicate equal measure and the fact that the segments can be made to coincide.)

1.3 Segments and Rays   **13**

TEACHING SUGGESTIONS

- To help students learn to find the coordinate of a midpoint, provide many exercises where the coordinates of the endpoints differ by an even number of units, then by an odd number of units. Help students develop a formula for the coordinate of the midpoint of a segment whose endpoints have coordinates a and b. $\frac{a+b}{2}$
- Have students calculate several distances by subtracting coordinates both ways:

$$|-3 - (4)| = |-7| = 7$$
$$|4 - (-3)| = |4 + 3| = 7$$

Students should notice that the same answer is obtained both ways. If students do their work carefully, they need to do only *one* calculation.

Critical Thinking
1. *Generalization* Ask students to develop a general formula for the coordinate of a midpoint.
2. *Comparing-Contrasting* Have students determine the equivalence of $|a - b|$ and $|b - a|$.

CHALKBOARD EXAMPLES

- **For Example 1**
  Points A, B, C, and D are collinear points with coordinates 7, 2, −1, and −6, respectively. Use the Ruler Postulate to find AB, BC, and CD.
  $AB = |7 - 2| = |5| = 5$
  $BC = |2 - (-1)| = |3| = 3$
  $CD = |-1 - (-6)| = |5| = 5$

- **For Example 2**
  Points G, H, and K are collinear, with K between G and H. If $\overline{GH}$ is five times as long as $\overline{HK}$ and $GK = 20$, find the length of $\overline{GH}$.
  Let $x = HK$. Then $GH = 5x$.
  $GK + KH = GH$
  $20 + x = 5x$
  $5 = x$
  Then $GH = 5x = 25$.

13

A point of a segment is its **midpoint** if and only if it divides the segment into two congruent segments. M is the midpoint of $\overline{AB}$ if and only if $\overline{AM} \cong \overline{MB}$.

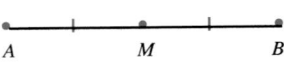

A **corollary** is a theorem whose justification follows from *another* theorem. The Ruler Postulate justifies the following theorem and its corollary.

Theorem 1.4   On a ray there is exactly one point that is at a given distance from the endpoint of the ray.

Corollary   Each segment has exactly one midpoint.

Any line, segment, ray, or plane that intersects a segment at its midpoint is called a **bisector of the segment.** If M is the midpoint of $\overline{XY}$, then line k, plane Z, $\overrightarrow{MR}$ and $\overrightarrow{MT}$ all bisect $\overline{XY}$.

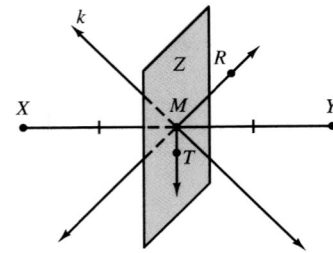

The Midpoint Theorem can be justified by applying the definition of a midpoint.

Theorem 1.5   Midpoint Theorem   If M is the midpoint of a segment $\overline{AB}$, then

$$2AM = AB \qquad\qquad 2MB = AB$$
$$AM = \frac{1}{2}AB \quad \text{and} \quad MB = \frac{1}{2}AB$$

Justified in Practice Exercise 38

EXAMPLE 3 $\overline{DB} \cong \overline{BE}$, $\overline{AB} \cong \overline{BC}$, $\overline{FB} \cong \overline{BG}$, $AB = 3$, $FB = 2$, and $DB = 1$

a. What is the midpoint of $\overline{FG}$?

b. Name four bisectors of $\overline{FG}$.

c. Name the coordinate of the midpoint of $\overline{IB}$.

d. What segment is congruent to $\overline{HJ}$?

e. $IB + BD = \underline{\ ?\ }$ Is B between I and D?

a. B b. $\overleftrightarrow{DE}, \overleftrightarrow{AC}, \overrightarrow{BJ}, \overline{IJ}$ c. -1.5 d. $\overline{DB}$ or $\overline{BE}$ e. 4; no

Other answers are poss.

You have seen how the algebraic concepts of number line and absolute value lead to the geometric concepts of distance, segment, and midpoint.

CLASS EXERCISES

Use this number line for Exercises 1–10. Justify each answer in terms of the definitions and theorems of this lesson.

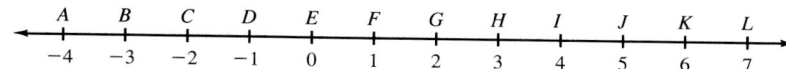

1. How far is it from A to E? 4 units; Post. 7
2. How far is it from K to B? 9 units; Post. 7
3. Find DJ. 6; Post. 7
4. Find AD. 3 units; Post. 7
5. Name the points that are a distance of 4 units from G. C, K; Post. 7
6. Name the points that are a distance of 5 units from G. B, L; Post. 7
7. Is $BD + DH = BH$? yes; def. of betweenness
8. Is $EA + AB = EB$? no; def. of betweenness
9. What is the midpoint of $\overline{EI}$? G; def. of midpt.
10. What is the midpoint of $\overline{BL}$? G; def. of midpt.
11. If X is the midpoint of $\overline{PM}$, what is true about $\overleftrightarrow{RT}$? $\overleftrightarrow{RT}$ is a bisector of $\overline{PM}$.
12. If X is the midpoint of $\overline{RT}$, write an equation relating RX and RT. $RX = \frac{1}{2}RT$

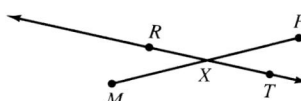

PRACTICE EXERCISES Use technology where appropriate.

Refer to this number line for Exercises 1–10.

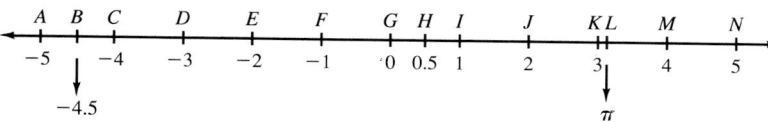

A
1. DG 3
2. JG 2
3. DJ 5
4. BI 5.5
5. BH 5
6. GL π
7. $FM + DF = \underline{\ ?\ }$ 7
8. $HF + CF = \underline{\ ?\ }$ 4.5
9. $FL + LN$ 6
10. **Thinking Critically** Explain how you would find $CG - GF$; $DJ - DG$. Answers may vary. $|-4 - 0| - |0 - (-1)| = 3$; $|-3 - 2| - |-3 - 0| = 2$

Study this number line.

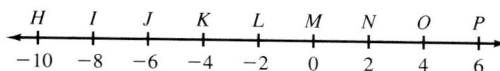

11. Find MO; JN; HL. 4; 8; 8
12. Find IM; KN; IK. 8; 6; 4
13. Name the congruent segments in Exercise 11. $\overline{JN} \cong \overline{HL}$
14. Name the congruent segments in Exercise 12. none
15. What is the coordinate of the midpoint of $\overline{IO}$? of $\overline{KP}$? −2; 1
16. Name the segment with endpoint I and midpoint K; with endpoint N and midpoint L. $\overline{IM}$; $\overline{JN}$

1.3 Segments and Rays   **15**

In this figure, M is between R and P. Find the following.

17. RM 16   **18.** MP 12   **19.** RP 28   **20.** The coordinate of M 6

21. Thinking Critically What is the difference between $\overrightarrow{AB}$ and $\overrightarrow{BA}$?
$\overrightarrow{AB}$ has endpoint A and passes through B, while $\overrightarrow{BA}$ has endpoint B and passes through A.

Study this number line.

$$\underset{-2}{C}\ \underset{-1.75}{D}\quad \underset{-1}{E}\qquad \underset{0}{F}\qquad\qquad \underset{1}{G}\qquad\qquad \underset{2}{H}\ \underset{2.25}{I}\ \underset{2.75}{J}$$

B **22.** Give another name for $\overrightarrow{FH}$. $\overrightarrow{FI}$, $\overrightarrow{FJ}$, or $\overrightarrow{FG}$

23. Give another name for $\overrightarrow{FC}$. $\overrightarrow{FD}$ or $\overrightarrow{FE}$

24. Do $\overrightarrow{EF}$ and $\overrightarrow{EI}$ represent the same points? yes

25. Do $\overrightarrow{EF}$ and $\overleftrightarrow{EI}$ represent the same points? no

26. What is the length of $\overline{EG}$? $\overline{CF}$? $\overline{GI}$?
2; 2; 1.25

27. What is the length of $\overline{DC}$? $\overline{IJ}$? $\overline{GJ}$?
0.25; 0.50; 1.75

28. Name the congruent segments in Exercise 26. $\overline{EG} \cong \overline{CF}$

29. Name the congruent segments in Exercise 27. none

Points A, B, C are collinear; B is between A and C.

30. $AC = 24$, $AB = \frac{3}{4}AC$. $AB = \underline{\ ?\ }$. 18

31. $AB = 24$, $AB = \frac{2}{3}AC$. $AC = \underline{\ ?\ }$. 36

In this figure $\overleftrightarrow{VS}$ is a bisector of $\overline{RT}$.

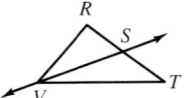

32. $RS = \frac{1}{2} \cdot \underset{RT}{\underline{\ ?\ }}$ **33.** $RT = 2 \cdot \underset{RS}{\underline{\ ?\ }}$ or $2 \cdot \underset{ST}{\underline{\ ?\ }}$

If A, X, and B are collinear, which point is between the other two? Explain.

C **34.** $AX = 11$, $XB = 1$, $AB = 12$
X; AX + XB = AB

35. $AX = 24$, $XB = 2$, and $AB = 22$
B; AB + BX = AX

36. $AX = 0.3$, $XB = 4$, and $AB = 3.7$
A; AB + AX = BX

37. $AX = XB$
X; AX + XB = AB

38. This logical argument proves the first conclusion of Theorem 1.5. Give the definition or property that justifies each statement.

   1. If M is the midpoint of $\overline{AB}$, then $\overline{AM} \cong \overline{MB}$. def. of midpt.
   2. If $\overline{AM} \cong \overline{MB}$, then $AM = MB$. def. of ≅ segments
   3. $AM + MB = AB$ def. of betweenness
   4. $AM + AM = AB$ subst. prop.
   5. $2AM = AB$ distrib. prop.

39. Write the existence and uniqueness statements for Theorem 1.4. On a ray there exists at least one point that is a given distance from the endpoint of the ray. On a ray there is only one point that is a given distance from the endpoint of the ray.

In this figure, $\overline{MP}$ bisects $\overline{CA}$ at M and $\overline{AB}$ at P.

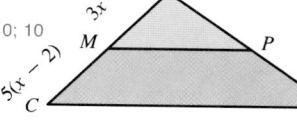

40. Find AC. 20   **41.** Find AM and MC. 10; 10

42. If $AP = \frac{3}{2}AM$, find AB. 30

Applications

43. Transportation On a train line three towns are represented by collinear points A, B, and C. Town A is 45 mi north of B, and C is 10 mi south of A. Which town is between the other two? c

44. Technology Use a calculator to find the coordinate of the midpoint of a segment whose endpoints have coordinates $\sqrt{3.13}$ and $\sqrt{102.5}$. 5.95

Algebra Review

Write an equation for each sentence.

45. Five less than 4 times a number is 19. $4x - 5 = 19$

46. Twice the sum of a number and 3 is 20. $2(x + 3) = 20$

47. A number is equal to 90 minus the number itself. $x = 90 - x$

Solve.

48. $9x + 7 = 115$ 12   **49.** $3(x - 4) = 15$ 9   **50.** $3(4 - x) = 15$ −1

CONSTRUCTION

Using only a *compass* and a *straightedge*, you can *construct* a segment congruent to a given segment.

Given: $\overline{AB}$ *Construct:* $\overline{DE}$, such that $\overline{DE} \cong \overline{AB}$

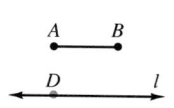

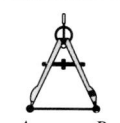

1. Draw line *l*. On *l*, locate and label a point *D*.

2. Place the compass point on *A*. Adjust the opening so that the pencil point lies on *B*.

3. Place the compass point on *D* and move the compass so the pencil makes an arc that intersects *l*. Label that point *E*. Now $\overline{DE} \cong \overline{AB}$. Why? Compass opening was fixed so that $DE = AB$.

EXERCISE *Given:* $\overline{TR}$ *Construct:* $\overline{MN}$, such that $\overline{MN} \cong \overline{TR}$. To check your construction compare TR and MN. Check students' constructions.

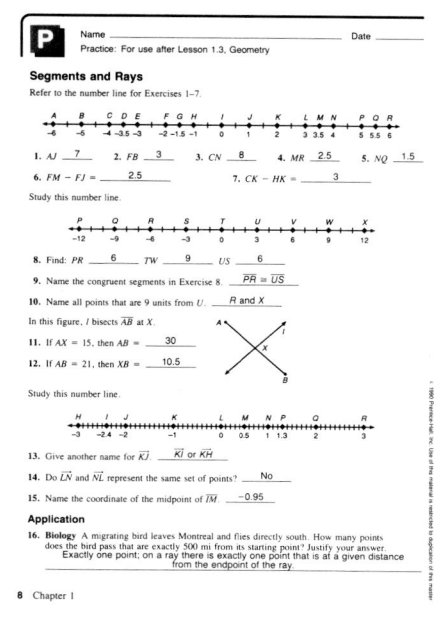

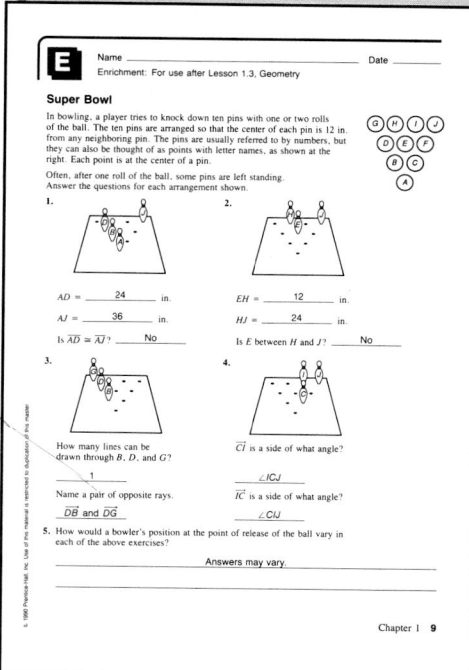

1.3 Segments and Rays   **17**

Angles

Objectives: To identify opposite rays and angles
To measure, classify, and identify types of angles

A basic figure of geometry is the *angle*. Surveyors use an instrument called a *transit* to measure angles.

Investigation—*Visualizing the Concept*

A new house lot has a 200 ft left-side boundary that is at an angle of 90° from the street. To establish a line of sight along the street boundary, $\overleftrightarrow{PT}$, the surveyors set the transit at corner point *S* and sight along $\overrightarrow{ST}$. They use a line of sight 90° to the left of $\overrightarrow{ST}$. They fix a stake 200 ft from *S*. This is *R* on the city map.

1. What does $\overrightarrow{SR}$ represent on the city map?
   SR is the boundary of the lot from corner to corner.
2. How can you find the lot boundary by starting with $\overrightarrow{SP}$? *Use a line of sight 90° to the right of SP.*

Definition A figure is an **angle** if and only if it is the union of two noncollinear rays, the **sides,** with a common endpoint, the **vertex.**

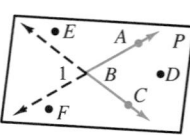

The sides and the vertex are used to name the angle.
Sides: $\overrightarrow{YX}, \overrightarrow{YZ}$ *Vertex: Y   Name:* angle *XYZ,* written as ∠*XYZ.*

All the points of $\overrightarrow{BA}$ and $\overrightarrow{BC}$ are on the angle. A point is an *interior point* of ∠*ABC* if it lies in the intersection of the half-plane that contains *A* and has edge $\overleftrightarrow{BC}$ and the half-plane that contains *C* and has edge $\overleftrightarrow{AB}$. If a point in plane *P* is neither on nor in the interior of the angle, then the point is an *exterior point.* Thus, *D* is an interior point and *E* and *F* are exterior points.

An angle can also be named by a number or by its vertex. In the figure, no angle can be named ∠*B* since all four angles have vertex *B*. The dashed angle is named ∠1.

Definition Two coplanar angles are **adjacent** if and only if they satisfy three conditions: (1) they have a *common* vertex, (2) they have a *common* side, and (3) they have *no common* interior points.

18   Chapter 1 The Language of Geometry

Developing Mathematical Power

Keeping a Portfolio Have students write in their math journals a paragraph that explains and compares the Ruler Postulate and the Protractor Postulate. Have them do the same for the Midpoint and Angle Bisector Theorems.

EXAMPLE 1   Use the figure to name the following.

a. An angle named by one letter
b. ∠1 and ∠2 with letters
c. The sides of ∠3
d. An angle adjacent to ∠1

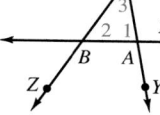

a. ∠C   b. ∠CAB; ∠ABC   c. $\overrightarrow{CZ}$ and $\overrightarrow{CY}$ d. ∠BAY or ∠CAX

You can find the degree **measure of an angle** with a **protractor.** Using the *black* scale, the measure of ∠CSA = 35. This is written $m\angle CSA = 35$. The *blue* scale gives the same measure, since $180 - 145 = 35$. In this text, the measure of an angle will always represent a number of degrees.

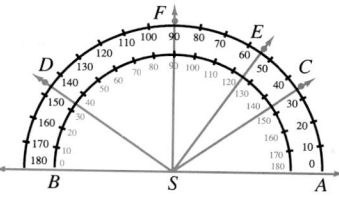

Definitions   ∠A is an **acute angle** if and only if $0 < m\angle A < 90$
                  ∠A is a **right angle** if and only if $m\angle A = 90$
                  ∠A is an **obtuse angle** if and only if $90 < m\angle A < 180$

Postulate 8   Given any angle, there is a unique real number between 0 and 180 known as its degree measure.

Postulate 9   The Protractor Postulate   In a half-plane with edge $\overleftrightarrow{AB}$ and any point S between A and B, there exists a one-to-one correspondence between the rays that originate at S in that half-plane and the real numbers between 0 and 180. To measure an angle formed by two of these rays, find the absolute value of the difference of the corresponding real numbers.

Thus, on the protractor above, $m\angle DSC = |35 - 145|$ or $|145 - 35|$ or 90.

The Protractor Postulate justifies the following theorem.

Theorem 1.6   In a half-plane, through the endpoint of a ray lying in the edge of the half-plane, there is exactly one other ray such that the angle formed by the two rays has a given measure between 0 and 180.

EXAMPLE 2   Use a protractor to find each measure.
a. $m\angle ASX$ b. $m\angle PSX$

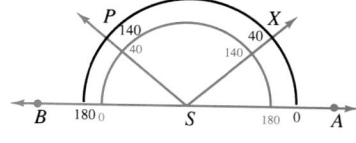

a. $|40 - 0| = 40$ or $|180 - 140| = 40$; $m\angle ASX = 40$
b. $|140 - 40| = 100$ or $|40 - 140| = 100$; $m\angle PSX = 100$

1.4 Angles   **19**

- Point out that the definition of an angle (the union of two *noncollinear* rays) means that straight angles, which students may have studied in earlier courses, will not be included in this course.

- Students should understand that in the diagram $\overrightarrow{OC}$ is *not* between $\overrightarrow{OA}$ and

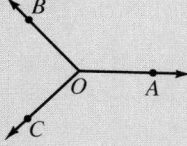

$\overrightarrow{OB}$, and it is *not* true that $m\angle AOC + m\angle COB = m\angle AOB$.

CHALKBOARD EXAMPLES

- **For Example 1**
  a. Name the sides of ∠1.

  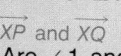
  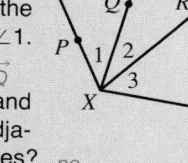

  $\overrightarrow{XP}$ and $\overrightarrow{XQ}$
  b. Are ∠1 and ∠PXR adjacent angles?   no
  c. Name all pairs of adjacent angles shown.

  ∠1 and ∠2; ∠1 and ∠QXS; ∠2 and ∠3; ∠PXR and ∠3

- **For Example 2**
  When a protractor is used to measure ∠FOG, $\overrightarrow{OF}$ corresponds to 50 and $\overrightarrow{OG}$ to 120 on the same scale. What is the measure of ∠FOG?
  $|120 - 50| = |70| = 70$
  $m\angle FOG = 70$

Common Error

- Some students will read the wrong protractor scale when measuring angles. Have them always estimate the size of the angle before measuring. Also remind students to place the center of the protractor on the vertex of the angle.

- See *Teacher's Resource Book* for additional remediation.

Definition   Two **angles** are **congruent** if and only if they have equal measures. In symbols, $\angle X \cong \angle Y$ if and only if $m\angle X = m\angle Y$.

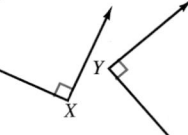

The ⌐ symbol indicates that angles X and Y are right angles. Thus, $m\angle X = 90$ and $m\angle Y = 90$. So, $m\angle X = m\angle Y$ and $\angle X \cong \angle Y$. This leads to an important theorem.

> **Theorem 1.7**   All right angles are congruent.

Given three coplanar rays $\overrightarrow{OA}$, $\overrightarrow{OT}$, and $\overrightarrow{OB}$, $\overrightarrow{OT}$ is **between** $\overrightarrow{OA}$ and $\overrightarrow{OB}$ if and only if $m\angle AOT + m\angle TOB = m\angle AOB$. A ray is a **bisector of an angle** if and only if it divides the angle into two congruent angles, thus angles of equal measure. If $\overrightarrow{OX}$ bisects $\angle AOB$, then $m\angle AOX = m\angle XOB$.

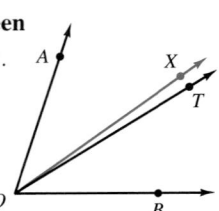

> **Theorem 1.8   Angle Bisector Theorem**   If $\overrightarrow{OX}$ is a bisector of $\angle AOB$, then
>
> $$2m\angle AOX = m\angle AOB \qquad \qquad 2m\angle XOB = m\angle AOB$$
> $$m\angle AOX = \tfrac{1}{2}m\angle AOB \quad \text{and} \quad m\angle XOB = \tfrac{1}{2}m\angle AOB$$
> Justified in Practice Exercises 9–15

CLASS EXERCISES

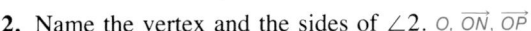

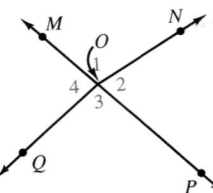

1. **a.** Which rays *appear* to be opposite rays? *OM and OP*
   b. What information must be given for you to accept that conclusion? *M, O, and P are collinear.*

2. Name the vertex and the sides of $\angle 2$. *O, ON, OP*

3. Name an interior point of $\angle NOQ$. *P*

Use this figure for Exercises 4–7. Redraw it, if necessary.

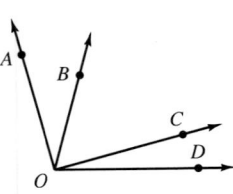

4. How many pairs of adjacent angles are there? *4*

5. If $\overrightarrow{OB}$ bisects $\angle AOC$, what must be true?
   m∠AOB = m∠BOC

6. If $m\angle AOB = 25$ and $\angle AOB \cong \angle COD$, what can you conclude about $\angle COD$? *m∠COD = 25*

7. If $m\angle AOC = 90$ and $m\angle AOB = 20$, what can you conclude about $\angle BOC$? *m∠BOC = 70*

PRACTICE EXERCISES

A **1. Drawing in Geometry** Using a straightedge, estimate and draw angles with the following measures: 90, 45, 60, 30, 135. Check by measuring each angle with a protractor. See side column.

In Exercises 2–7, classify each angle as acute, right, or obtuse.

2. $\angle EOF$ acute   **3.** $\angle BOF$ obtuse   **4.** $\angle AOC$ right

5. $\angle DOA$ obtuse   **6.** $\angle EOB$ right   **7.** $\angle BOX$ acute

8. $\angle EOB$ is adjacent to $\angle \underline{?}$ and $\angle \underline{?}$. possible
answers: EOF, BOX, BOA

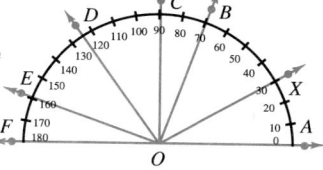

Complete this justification of the Angle Bisector Theorem (Theorem 1.8).

If $\overrightarrow{OX}$ is the bisector of $\angle AOB$, then there are four conclusions:

a. $2m\angle AOX = m\angle AOB$ b. $2m\angle XOB = m\angle AOB$

c. $m\angle AOX = \frac{1}{2}m\angle AOB$ d. $m\angle XOB = \frac{1}{2}m\angle AOB$

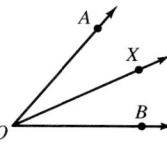

Justification

9. Since $\overrightarrow{OX}$ bisects $\angle AOB$, then $m\angle AOX = \underline{?}$. m∠XOB

10. Since $\overrightarrow{OX}$ is between $\overrightarrow{OA}$ and $\overrightarrow{OB}$, then $\underline{?}$. m∠AOX + m∠XOB = m∠AOB

11. By substituting from Exercise 4 into the equation in Exercise 5, $\underline{?}$.
m∠AOX + m∠AOX = m∠AOB

12. Using the $\underline{?}$ property, $2m\angle AOX = m\angle AOB$ (conclusion *a*). distributive

13. Using Exercises 4–7, it follows that $2m\angle XOB = \underline{?}$ (conclusion *b*).
m∠AOB

14. Multiplying both sides of $2m\angle AOX = \underline{?}$ (conclusion *a*) by $\underline{?}$
gives this equation: $m\angle AOX = \frac{1}{2}m\angle AOB$ (conclusion *c*) m∠AOB; $\frac{1}{2}$

15. Multiplying both sides of $2m\angle XOB = m\angle AOB$ (conclusion *b*) by $\underline{?}$
gives this equation: $m\angle XOB = \frac{1}{2}m\angle AOB$ (conclusion *d*) $\frac{1}{2}$

16. Give three names for the angle with vertex *C*.
Answers may vary; ∠C, ∠4, ∠ACG

17. Give a three-letter name for $\angle 1$; for $\angle 2$.
∠DAB; ∠ADB

18. $m\angle \underline{?} + m\angle DBC = m\angle ABC$. ABD

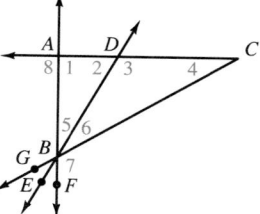

B **19.** If $m\angle 6 = 35$ and $m\angle 7 = 110$, then
$m\angle DBF = \underline{?}$. 145

20. If $m\angle 5 = 30$ and $m\angle ABC = 75$, then
$m\angle 6 = \underline{?}$. 45

21. If $\overrightarrow{BE}$ bisects $\angle GBF$, which angles have equal measures? ∠GBE, ∠FBE

22. If $\angle 1$ and $\angle 8$ are right angles, then $\angle 1 \cong \angle 8$. Why? All right angles are ≅.

1.4 Angles   **21**

Test Yourself

See *Teacher's Resource Book*, Tests, pp. 5–6.

Lesson Quiz

1. Give another name for $\angle 6$. ∠ADB
2. Name the sides of $\angle 7$. $\overrightarrow{DC}$ and $\overrightarrow{DB}$

Identify the numbered angles that appear to be:

3. two right angles   ∠3 and ∠4
4. one obtuse angle   ∠1
5. four acute angles   ∠2, ∠6, ∠7, ∠5
6. Identify three pairs of adjacent angles.   ∠1 and ∠2; ∠6 and ∠7; ∠3 and ∠4
7. If $m\angle 6 = 45$ and $m\angle ADC = 100$, then $m\angle 7 = \underline{?}$ 55
8. Suppose $\overrightarrow{DB}$ is the bisector of $\angle ADC$, and $m\angle 6 = 55$. Then $m\angle ADC = \underline{?}$ 110

Enrichment

$\overrightarrow{OB}$ bisects $\angle AOC$.
$m\angle AOB = 6x$
$m\angle AOC = 2x + 2y$
$m\angle BOC = y + 5$
Find the values of *x* and *y* and find $m\angle AOC$. x = 5; y = 25; m∠AOC = 60

Additional Answers

1.   90°
45°
60°
30°
135°

21

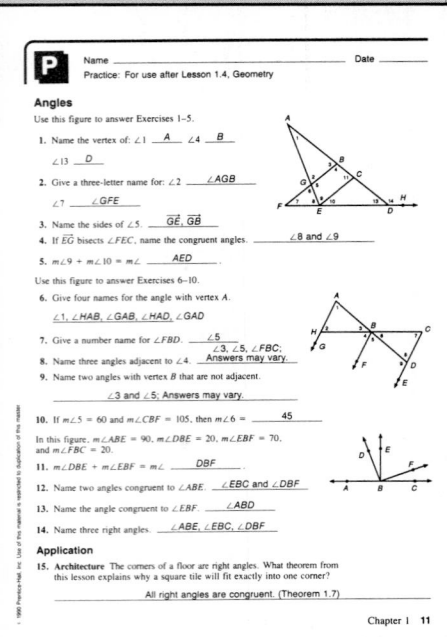

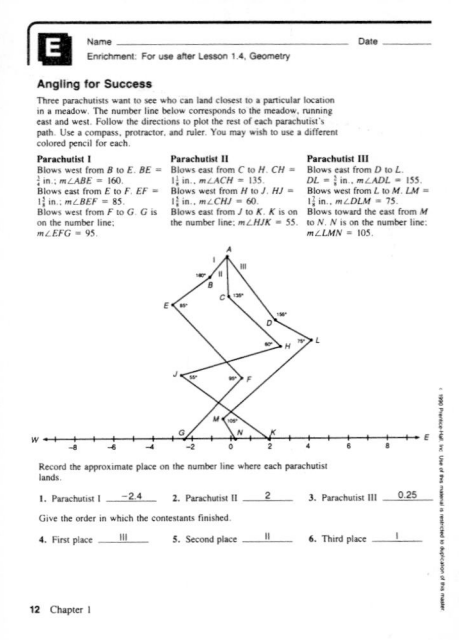

In this figure, $m\angle ABC = 72$. Find $m\angle 1$ and $m\angle 2$, using the information given in each exercise.

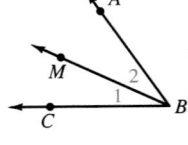

C **23.** $\overrightarrow{BM}$ bisects $\angle ABC$. 36; 36

24. $m\angle 1 = 3m\angle 2$
$m\angle 1 = 54; m\angle 2 = 18$

25. $m\angle 2$ is 10 more than $m\angle 1$. $m\angle 1 = 31; m\angle 2 = 41$

26. $m\angle 2$ is 50 more than three times $m\angle 1$.
$m\angle 1 = 5.5; m\angle 2 = 66.5$

27. Find the measure of the angle formed by the hands of a clock at 5:30. 15

Applications

See side column.

28. Navigation The course of an aircraft is the direction of its flight. It is represented by an angle. This angle is measured clockwise from north. Draw an angle to represent a course of 105°.

29. Meteorology The wind blowing from the southwest points a weather vane 45° east of north. Sketch the angle.

TEST YOURSELF

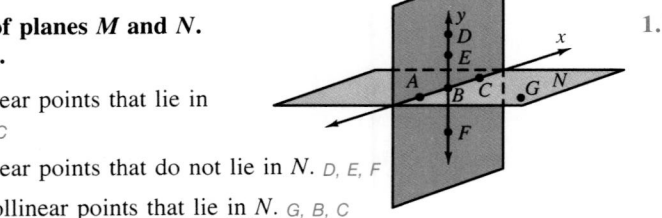

x is the intersection of planes M and N. 1.1
y lies in M. G is in N.

1. Name three collinear points that lie in both planes. A, B, C

2. Name three collinear points that do not lie in N. D, E, F

3. Name three noncollinear points that lie in N. G, B, C

Complete each statement. Then tell whether it is a postulate, theorem, or definition. 1.2

4. If two points are given, then they determine a ?. line; postulate

5. If there is a line and a point not on the line, then there is exactly ? that contains them. one plane; theorem

6. Given three collinear points X, Y, and Z, Y is between X and Z if and only if ?. XY + YZ = XZ; definition

The coordinates of A and B are -3 and 6, respectively. 1.3–1.4

7. Find AB, and the coordinate of the midpoint of $\overline{AB}$. 9; 1.5

8. Name the angle's vertex and its sides. W; $\overrightarrow{WA}$, $\overrightarrow{WB}$

9. Name an exterior point and an interior point of the angle. I; E

10. If $\overrightarrow{WE}$ bisects the angle shown, which angles are congruent? $\angle AWE \cong \angle BWE$

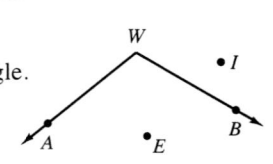

22 Chapter 1 The Language of Geometry

28. *North*
105°
East

29.
N 45°
W — E
S

1.5 Angle Pairs

Objectives: To classify and apply definitions of various types of angle pairs

To apply the theorem about vertical angles

Special relationships between pairs of angles are useful in the application of geometry.

Investigation—*Visualizing the Concept*

Pilots use magnetic compasses to determine direction. East is 90° clockwise from north. South is 180° clockwise from north. West is 90° counterclockwise from north. Setting a *direction* of 60° east of north heads a ship or plane along $\overrightarrow{OP}$. This means that $m\angle NOP = 60$.

1. Find $m\angle POE$ and $m\angle POS$. 30; 120

2. Find the sum of the measures of $\angle NOP$ and $\angle POE$; of $\angle NOP$ and $\angle POS$. 90; 180

Two angles may form a special *angle pair*, as noted in the definitions below.

Definitions   Two angles are **complementary angles** if and only if the sum of their measures is 90. Each is called a *complement* of the other. Two angles are **supplementary angles** if and only if the sum of their measures is 180. Each is called a *supplement* of the other. Two angles form a **linear pair** if and only if they are adjacent angles whose noncommon sides are opposite rays.

Study the special angle relationships in each figure.

$m\angle A + m\angle B$
$= 40 + 50 = 90$

$\angle B$ is a complement of $\angle A$. The adjacent angles at C are complements. Why? The sum of their measures is 90.

$m\angle FOQ + m\angle EQI$
$= 110 + 70 = 180$

$\angle FOQ$ is a supplement of $\angle EQI$. $\angle FOQ$ and $\angle EOF$ are adjacent and supplementary. Why? They form a linear pair, and the sum of their measures is 180.

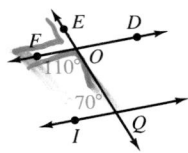

> **Postulate 10   Linear Pair Postulate**   If two angles form a linear pair, then they are supplementary angles.

1.5 Angle Pairs   **23**

Developing Mathematical Power

Keeping a Portfolio   Have students write an argument similar to that on the top of page 25 to show that the vertical angles 2 and 4 are congruent.

LESSON PLAN

Vocabulary
Complement
Complementary angles
Linear pair
Supplement
Supplementary angles
Vertical angles

Materials/Manipulatives
Compasses and straightedges
Teaching Transparency 5

Technology
Computer Test Bank, pp. 63–70

LESSON FOCUS

Review
Review solving simple algebraic equations. Be sure that students understand how to solve an equation when it has the variable on both sides.

Solve.
1. $3x - 120 = 30 - 2x$
2. $90 + 2x = 3x - 40$
3. $4(30 - x) = 60 + 2x$
1. 30   2. 130   3. 10

Alternative Learning Styles
- The Investigation presents a concrete situation involving complementary and supplementary angles. Have students use compasses to determine the locations of various objects in the classroom, relative to the students' desks, and have them record the locations using degree measure.
- Have students use protractors to draw pairs of nonadjacent complementary angles. Have them cut out each angle and place the angle pairs next to each other to show that the pairs form 90° angles. Direct a similar activity for supplementary angles.

23

- The concept of a linear pair is likely to be new to students. The concept is necessary because our geometry does not include straight angles. Make sure that students understand that the angles in a linear pair must be supplementary, but two supplementary angles do not necessarily form a linear pair.
- Students should understand that *three* angles cannot be complementary or supplementary. Tell them that $m\angle 1 = 20$, $m\angle 2 = 30$, and $m\angle 3 = 40$. Ask if $\angle 1$, $\angle 2$, and $\angle 3$ are complementary.

CHALKBOARD EXAMPLES

- **For Example 1**

  In a certain linear pair, one angle measures three times as much as the other. What is the measure of each angle?

  Let $x =$ the measure of the
        smaller angle.
  Let $3x =$ the measure of the
        larger angle.
  $x + 3x = 180$
  $4x = 180$
  $x = 45$
  $3x = 135$

- **For Example 2**

  Four times the measure of a complement of a certain angle is equal to 45 less than the measure of the supplement of that angle. Find the measure of each angle.

  Let $x =$ the measure of the angle.
  Then $90 - x =$ the measure of the
        complement.
  and $180 - x =$ the measure of the
        supplement.
  $4(90 - x) = (180 - x) - 45$
  $360 - 4x = 135 - x$
  $225 = 3x$
  $75 = x$
  The complement is $15°$.
  The supplement is $105°$.
  Check: $4(15) = 105 - 45$

EXAMPLE 1 In a certain linear pair, one angle measures twice as much as the other. What is the measure of each angle?

Let $x =$ measure of the smaller angle, then $2x =$ measure of the larger angle.

$x + 2x = 180$	*Linear Pair Postulate*	**Check:**
$3x = 180$	*Distributive property*	$60 + 2(60) \stackrel{?}{=} 180$
$x = 60$	*Division property*	$3(60) \stackrel{?}{=} 180$
		$180 = 180$ ✔

The angle measures are 60 and 120.

EXAMPLE 2 Three times the measure of a complement of a certain angle is equal to 30 more than the measure of a supplement of that angle. Find the measure of each angle.

Let $x =$ the measure of the angle, $90 - x =$ the measure of a complement (since $x + 90 - x = 90$), and $180 - x =$ the measure of a supplement.

Then, $3(90 - x) =$ three times the measure of a complement, and $30 + (180 - x) = 30$ more than the measure of a supplement

$3(90 - x) = 30 + (180 - x)$	**Check:**
$270 - 3x = 210 - x$	$3(90 - 30) \stackrel{?}{=} 30 + (180 - 30)$
$-2x = -60$	$270 - 90 \stackrel{?}{=} 30 + 150$
$x = 30$, $90 - x = 60$, and	$180 = 180$ ✔
$180 - x = 150$.	

The angle measures are 30, 60, and 150.

In this figure, lines n and k intersect. Two pairs of *vertical angles* are formed: $\angle 1$ and $\angle 3$, $\angle 2$ and $\angle 4$.

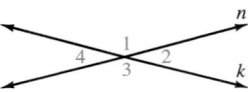

Definition Two angles are called **vertical angles** if and only if they are two nonadjacent angles formed by two intersecting lines.

EXAMPLE 3 In this figure, r intersects s and t.

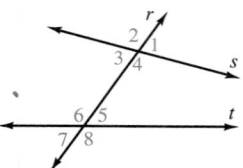

  a. Name four pairs of vertical angles.

  b. $m\angle 1 = 30$. Find $m\angle 2$, $m\angle 3$, and $m\angle 4$.

  a. $\angle 1$ and $\angle 3$; $\angle 2$ and $\angle 4$; $\angle 5$ and $\angle 7$; $\angle 6$ and $\angle 8$.

  b. Since r and s form four linear pairs and $m\angle 1 = 30$; then $m\angle 2 = 150$, $m\angle 3 = 30$, and $m\angle 4 = 150$.

Note that in Example 3b, vertical angles $\angle 1$ and $\angle 3$ both have measures of 30 and vertical angles $\angle 2$ and $\angle 4$ both have measures of 150. These results suggest the following theorem.

24 Chapter 1 The Language of Geometry

Developing Mathematical Power
Cooperative Learning Draw the figure at right on the chalkboard. Have groups of students use their new vocabulary to describe all the relationships they see.

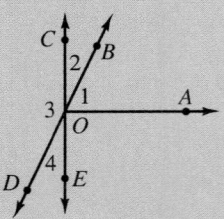

Theorem 1.9   If two angles are vertical, then they are congruent.

After you read this argument, tell whether or not you are convinced that it justifies Theorem 1.9.

Since lines *l* and *m* intersect, vertical angles are formed. Angles 1 and 3 form one pair of vertical angles.

$\angle 1$ and $\angle 2$ form a linear pair.	$\angle 3$ and $\angle 2$ form a linear pair.
$m\angle 1 + m\angle 2 = 180$	$m\angle 3 + m\angle 2 = 180$
$m\angle 1 = 180 - m\angle 2$	$m\angle 3 = 180 - m\angle 2$

Therefore, $\angle 1$ and $\angle 3$ are equal in measure and must be congruent.

CLASS EXERCISES

Answers may vary.

1. Identify four pairs of complementary angles. $\angle A$ and $\angle B$; $\angle CED$ and $\angle CDE$; $\angle A$ and $\angle CDE$; $\angle B$ and $\angle CED$
2. Identify two linear pairs. $\angle CED$ and $\angle DEA$; $\angle CDE$ and $\angle EDB$
3. Identify four pairs of supplementary angles.

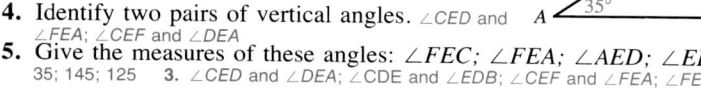

4. Identify two pairs of vertical angles. $\angle CED$ and $\angle FEA$; $\angle CEF$ and $\angle DEA$
5. Give the measures of these angles: $\angle FEC$; $\angle FEA$; $\angle AED$; $\angle EDB$. 145; 35; 145; 125   **3.** $\angle CED$ and $\angle DEA$; $\angle CDE$ and $\angle EDB$; $\angle CEF$ and $\angle FEA$; $\angle FEA$ and $\angle AED$

True or false. Justify each answer.

6. Complementary angles are always adjacent. false; they may lie anywhere

7. Supplementary angles are always adjacent. false; they may lie anywhere

8. The angles of a linear pair are always adjacent. true; def. of linear pair

9. A complement of an acute angle is acute. true; each $\angle$ in the pair is acute

10. A supplement of an obtuse angle is acute. true; if $x > 90$, then $180 - x < 90$

11. A supplement of an acute angle is acute. false; if $x < 90$, then $180 - x > 90$

12. A supplement of a right angle is a right angle. true; $180 - 90 = 90$

13. Vertical angles are sometimes adjacent. false; def. of ver. $\angle$s

14. If two angles are vertical, they are either both acute or both obtuse. false; they could be right angles

Find the measures of a complement and a supplement, if possible.

15. $m\angle A = 35$ comp.: 55 supp.: 145
16. $m\angle B = 135$ no comp. supp.: 45
17. $m\angle C = x$ comp.: $90 - x$ if $x < 90$ supp.: $180 - x$

18. What are the measures of a linear pair of angles if the measure of one angle is five times that of the other? 30, 150

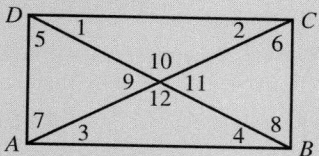

$\angle 1 \cong \angle 2 \cong \angle 3 \cong \angle 4$
$\angle DAB, \angle ABC, \angle BCD, \angle CDA$ are right angles.
$m\angle 1 = 29$ and $m\angle 9 = 58$.
Find the measures of all numbered angles.
$m\angle 1 = m\angle 2 = m\angle 3 = m\angle 4 = 29$
$m\angle 5 = m\angle 6 = m\angle 7 = m\angle 8 = 61$
$m\angle 9 = m\angle 11 = 58$
$m\angle 10 = m\angle 12 = 122$

Common Error

• Students may assume that in order to be complementary and supplementary pairs, angles must be adjacent. Provide examples of nonadjacent angles that are complementary or supplementary.
• See *Teacher's Resource Book* for additional remediation.

LESSON FOLLOW-UP

Critical Thinking

1. *Causal Explanation* Have students explain the various types of angle pairs.
2. *Classification* Ask students to distinguish the similarities and differences among the relationships of the lines and angles in each pair.

Assignment Guide

See p.1B for assignments.

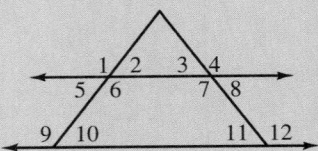
PRACTICE EXERCISES

See side column.

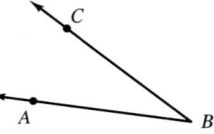

A **1. Drawing in Geometry** Copy $\angle ABC$. Draw $\overrightarrow{CB}$ and $\overrightarrow{AB}$. Label a point D so that B is between A and D. Label a point E so that B is between C and E.

2. Name the vertical angle to $\angle ABC$. Name the other pair of vertical angles. $\angle DBE$; $\angle DBC$ and $\angle ABE$

If possible, find the measures of a complement and a supplement for each.

3. $m\angle A = 38$
complement: 52
supplement: 142

4. $m\angle C = 95$
complement: none
supplement: 85

5. $m\angle E = x$
complement: $90 - x$ if $x < 90$
supplement: $180 - x$

6. $m\angle Y = x + 15$
complement: $75 - x$
supplement: $165 - x$

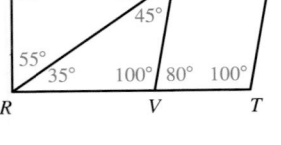

7. Name one pair of adjacent complementary angles; of nonadjacent complementary angles. $\angle WRU$ and $\angle URV$; $\angle RUV$ and $\angle S$ or $\angle WRU$ and $\angle WUR$

8. Name one pair of adjacent supplementary angles; of nonadjacent supplementary angles. $\angle RVU$ and $\angle UVT$ or $\angle RUV$ and $\angle VUS$; $\angle UVT$ and $\angle T$ or $\angle VUS$ and $\angle S$

9. Name an angle congruent to $\angle T$; to $\angle WUR$. $\angle RVU$; $\angle URV$

10. Name an angle congruent to $\angle WUV$. $\angle UVT$

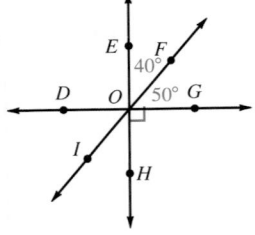

11. Name the vertical angle to $\angle 1$; $\angle 2$; $\angle 3$; $\angle 4$. $\angle 7$; $\angle 8$; $\angle 5$; $\angle 6$

12. Name the vertical angle to $\angle 5$; $\angle 6$; $\angle 7$; $\angle 8$. $\angle 3$; $\angle 4$; $\angle 1$; $\angle 2$

13. If $m\angle 2 = 87$, find the measures of $\angle 1$, $\angle 7$, and $\angle 8$. 93, 93, 87

14. If $m\angle 4 = 105$, find the measures of $\angle 3$, $\angle 5$, and $\angle 6$. 75, 75, 105

$\overleftrightarrow{DG}$, $\overleftrightarrow{EH}$, and $\overleftrightarrow{FI}$ intersect at O.

B **15.** Name two linear pairs of angles. $\angle DOE$ and $\angle EOG$; $\angle EOF$ and $\angle FOH$; answers may vary.

16. Name a supplement of $\angle FOH$. $\angle EOF$ or $\angle IOH$

17. Name a supplement of $\angle GOI$. $\angle DOI$ or $\angle GOF$

18. $\angle DOE$ and $\angle GOH$ are supplementary, but do not form a linear pair. Explain. They are not adj.

Write an equation. Use it to find the measures of the angles.

19. Three times the measure of an angle is 15 less than the measure of its complement. $3x = (90 - x) - 15$; $x = 18.75$; $90 - x = 71.25$

20. Five times the measure of an angle is 48 more than the measure of its supplement. $5x = (180 - x) + 48$; $x = 38$; $180 - x = 142$

21. The measure of an angle is 30 more than half the measure of its supplement. $x = 30 + \frac{1}{2}(180 - x)$; $x = 80$, $180 - x = 100$

1–2.

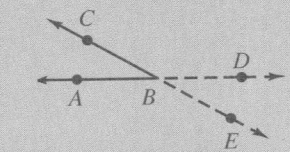

Complete this argument: If ∠2 and ∠4 are vertical angles, then ∠2 ≅ ∠4.

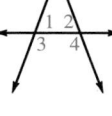

22. ∠2 and ∠3 form a <u>?</u> pair, and ∠4 and ∠3 form a <u>?</u> pair.
   linear — linear

23. Thus, $m\angle 2 + m\angle 3 = 180$ and <u>?</u>, by the <u>?</u>.
   $m\angle 4 + m\angle 3 = 180$ Linear Pair Postulate

24. Then, $m\angle 2 = $ <u>?</u> and <u>?</u>, by <u>?</u>.
   $180 - m\angle 3$ $m\angle 4 = 180 - m\angle 3$ subtraction property

25. Therefore, the <u>?</u> property justifies that $m\angle 2 = m\angle 4$.
   transitive

26. By <u>?</u>, ∠2 ≅ ∠4.
   def. of ≅ ∠s

Find the measures of the angle, its complement, and its supplement.

C 27. Three times the supplement equals seven times the complement
   22.5, 67.5, 157.5

28. Four times the complement equals $\frac{2}{3}$ of the supplement
   72, 18, 108

Write an argument to support your conclusion.

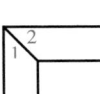

29. If ∠1 ≅ ∠2, what conclusion can you draw about ∠3 and ∠4?
   See side column.

30. If $m\angle 3 > m\angle 4$, what conclusion can you draw about ∠1 and ∠2?
   $m\angle 1 + m\angle 3 = 180$ and $m\angle 2 + m\angle 4 = 180$
   $m\angle 3 = 180 - m\angle 1$ and $m\angle 4 = 180 - m\angle 2$

Applications
   $180 - m\angle 1 > 180 - m\angle 2$
   Conclusion: $m\angle 1 < m\angle 2$

31. **Carpentry** Two pieces of molding are cut to size for framing a doorway. What must be true about ∠1 and ∠2? ∠1 and ∠2 must be complementary.

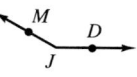

32. **Navigation** A plane is heading 25° west of north. Find the heading of a second plane flying in the opposite direction. 155° E of N

CONSTRUCTION

Given: ∠O   *Construct:* ∠RST ≅ ∠O

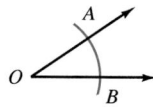

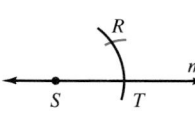

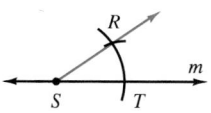

1. Draw line m. On m, pick any point and name it S. Put the compass point on O. Draw an arc intersecting ∠O at A and B. With the same compass opening and with the point at S, draw an arc intersecting m at T.

2. Adjust the compass opening to fit AB. With that opening and with the compass point on T, draw an arc intersecting the prior arc at R. Draw SR. Now ∠RST ≅ ∠O.

EXERCISE   *Given:* ∠MJD   *Construct:* ∠KPF ≅ ∠MJD
   Check students' constructions.

29. ∠1 and ∠3 and ∠2 and ∠4 are supplementary; $m\angle 1 + m\angle 3 = 180$ and $m\angle 2 + m\angle 4 = 180$, $m\angle 3 = 180 - m\angle 1$;
   $m\angle 4 = 180 - m\angle 2$ or $m\angle 4 = 180 - m\angle 1$
   Conclusion: ∠3 ≅ ∠4

Vocabulary

Perpendicular
Perpendicular bisector of a
segment

Materials/Manipulatives

Compasses and straightedges
Teaching Transparency 6
Connections, pp. 3 and 4

Technology

Computer Test Bank, pp. 71–82

LESSON FOCUS

Review

- Draw this figure on the chalkboard.

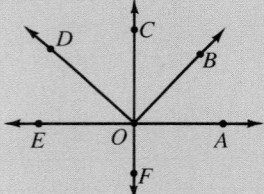

If ∠*AOC* is a right angle and
m∠*AOB* = 25, ask students what other angle measures they can find.
m∠*AOC* = *m*∠*COE* = *m*∠*EOF* =
m∠*FOA* = 90; *m*∠*BOC* = 65

- The Chapter Summary and Review, pp. 40 and 41, gives vocabulary, concepts, and review exercises by lesson.
- The end of the chapter features an
  Algebra Review on p. 44.

Alternative Learning Styles

Perpendicular lines and right angles
are two of the elements of geometry
that are often encountered in everyday life. Ask students to look at one
corner of the classroom and give the
number of right angles. 3 the number of pairs of perpendicular lines. 3
Have students make a T square from
two pieces of cardboard and use it to
draw perpendicular lines and to check
to see if lines are perpendicular.

28

1.6 Perpendicular Lines

Objectives: To identify perpendicular lines, rays, and segments
To state and apply theorems about perpendicular lines,
supplementary angles, and complementary angles

Lines that intersect at right angles are often
used by navigators, map makers, architects,
and carpenters.

Investigation—*Visualizing the Concept*

A plumb line is a weighted line that is used
to show vertical direction. Construction
workers use *T squares, plumb lines,* and
levels to ensure right angles.

Which lines and/or surfaces in this house
frame probably form right angles?
Most of the pieces of wood intersect to form rt. ∠s.

Recall that the symbol ⌐ is used to denote a right angle. It is used here to
show that ∠1, ∠*C*, and ∠*HOM* are right angles.

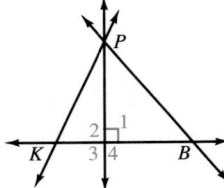 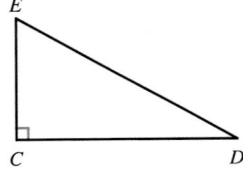 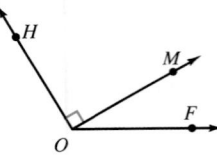

Definition Two lines are **perpendicular** (⊥) if and only if they intersect to
form a right angle. Two segments or rays are perpendicular if and only if they
have a point in common and the lines they determine intersect to form a right
angle. A line is perpendicular to a plane at a point *P* if and only if it is
perpendicular to every line in the plane that passes through *P*. Two planes are
perpendicular if and only if one plane contains a line that is perpendicular to
the other plane.

> **Theorem 1.10** If two lines are perpendicular, then the pairs of
> adjacent angles they form are congruent.

28 Chapter 1 The Language of Geometry

Developing Mathematical Power

Keeping a Portfolio Have students create a set of index cards for the theorems
and corollaries. On one side have them write the if statement (condition) and on the
other side write the then statement (conclusion).

Since $r \perp t$ and $\angle 1$ is a right angle, $m\angle 1 = 90$. $\angle 1$ and $\angle 2$ form a linear pair; thus $\angle 2$ is a supplement of $\angle 1$. Therefore, $m\angle 2 = 90$, and hence $\angle 2 \cong \angle 1$. The same reasoning applies to the other three pairs of adjacent angles.

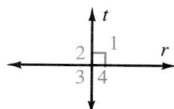

Corollary 1   If two lines are perpendicular, then all four angles they form are congruent.

Corollary 2   If two lines are perpendicular, then all four angles they form are right angles.

Theorem 1.11   If two lines intersect to form a pair of congruent adjacent angles, then the lines are perpendicular.

Theorems 1.10 and 1.11 can be rewritten in this form.

If: two lines are perpendicular	If: adjacent angles formed by
then: adjacent angles formed by the	two lines are congruent
two lines are congruent.	then: the two lines are perpendicular.

Study this argument for the justification of Theorem 1.11. Both $\angle 1$ and $\angle 2$ are marked with a tick mark, indicating that $\angle 1 \cong \angle 2$. Hence, $m\angle 1 = m\angle 2$. But $\angle 1$ and $\angle 2$ are a linear pair and therefore supplementary. Since their measures are equal, each must measure 90° and be a right angle. Thus, by the definition of perpendicular lines, $k \perp m$.

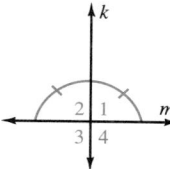

$\overleftrightarrow{PM}$, the line determined by the following paper folding, is called the *perpendicular bisector* of $\overline{AB}$.

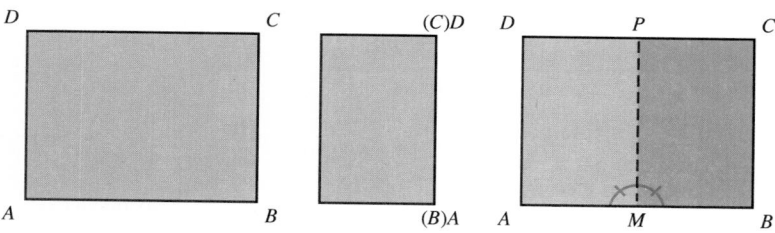

Since the paper is folded so that $AM = MB$, M must be the midpoint of $\overline{AB}$. The fold creates congruent adjacent angles, so $\overleftrightarrow{MP}$ must be perpendicular to $\overline{AB}$.

Definition   A line, ray, segment, or plane is a **perpendicular bisector of a segment** if and only if the line, ray, segment, or plane is perpendicular to the segment at its midpoint.

- Help students identify perpendicular lines in the classroom, the school grounds, or on an athletic field.
- The discussion following the statement of Theorem 1.11 shows how Theorem 1.10 and its converse, Theorem 1.11, can be combined as a biconditional. Converses and biconditionals will be introduced formally in Lesson 2.2.
- Actually carrying out the paper-folding experiment described at the bottom of p. 29 may help some students to better understand the concept of perpendicular bisector.
- At this point students are only asked to give brief justifications for statements. The ability to prove theorems will be developed beginning with Chapter 2.
- Encourage students to give complete statements of theorems as justifications rather than referring to the theorems by number.
- For Practice Exercise 32, the theorem can be properly justified in Chapter 5 where students are introduced to indirect proofs.

Developing Mathematical Power

Cooperative Learning   Have groups of students work on Enrichment, p. 18, in the *Teacher's Resource Book* (see p. 32). Encourage them to draw as many sketches as they can that satisfy all the conditions for each question. Provide time for them to share their answers.

- **For the Example**

  Justify each statement.

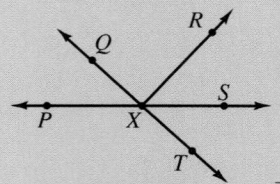

a. If ∠QXR is a right angle, then $\overrightarrow{XR}$ ⊥ $\overleftrightarrow{QT}$.

b. If $\overrightarrow{XR}$ ⊥ $\overleftrightarrow{QT}$, then ∠RXQ ≅ ∠RXT.

c. If $\overrightarrow{XR}$ ⊥ $\overleftrightarrow{QT}$, then ∠RXS and ∠SXT are complementary angles.

d. If $\overrightarrow{XR}$ ⊥ $\overleftrightarrow{QT}$, then ∠QXR and ∠RXT are right angles.

e. If $\overrightarrow{XR}$ ⊥ $\overleftrightarrow{QT}$ and $\overline{QX}$ ≅ $\overline{XT}$, then $\overrightarrow{XR}$ is the perpendicular bisector of $\overline{QT}$.

f. ∠SXT ≅ ∠PXQ

Theorem 1.12 If there is given any point on a line in a plane, then there is exactly one line in that plane perpendicular to the given line at the given point.

The *existence* and *uniqueness* statements must be considered in the justification. $\overleftrightarrow{AB}$ lies in plane R and contains point P.

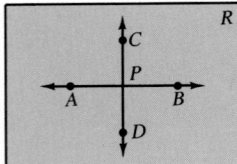

1. There exists $\overrightarrow{CD}$ in R such that $\overleftrightarrow{CD}$ contains P and $\overleftrightarrow{CD}$ ⊥ $\overleftrightarrow{AB}$. (*existence*)

2. Only one line $\overleftrightarrow{CD}$ in R is perpendicular to $\overleftrightarrow{AB}$ at P. (*uniqueness*)

Corollary If there is given any segment in a plane, then in that plane there is exactly one line that is a perpendicular bisector of the segment.

Theorem 1.13 If the exterior sides of two adjacent acute angles are perpendicular, then the angles are complementary.

You can use a compass to visualize Theorem 1.13, since the lines representing the directions are perpendicular. Thus, $\overleftrightarrow{NS}$ ⊥ $\overleftrightarrow{EW}$, and $m∠NOE = 90$. Any ray $\overrightarrow{OP}$ between $\overrightarrow{ON}$ and $\overrightarrow{OE}$ will form two adjacent angles. These angles will be complementary, since the sum of their measures will be 90.

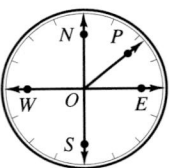

Theorem 1.14 If there is a point not on a line, then there is exactly one line perpendicular to the given line through the given point. Justified in Practice Exercise 32

EXAMPLE **Justify each statement.**

a. If $\overleftrightarrow{XM}$ ⊥ $\overline{CD}$, then ∠1 ≅ ∠4.

b. If ∠XPB ≅ ∠XPA, then $\overleftrightarrow{XM}$ ⊥ $\overline{AB}$.

c. If $\overline{CD}$ ⊥ $\overline{BC}$, then $\overleftrightarrow{CD}$ is the only line in this plane perpendicular to $\overline{BC}$ at C.

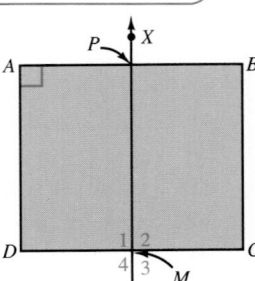

a. If lines are ⊥, then the adjacent angles formed are ≅.

b. If adjacent angles are ≅, then the lines are ⊥.

c. There is only one line in a plane ⊥ to another line at a given point.

CLASS EXERCISES

Justify each statement.

1. If $m \perp k$, then m is the only line in the plane perpendicular to k at point P. Th. 1.12

2. If $m \perp k$, then $\angle 3$, $\angle 4$, $\angle 5$, and $\angle 6$ are all right angles. cor. 2 of Th. 1.10

3. If $\overline{AP} \cong \overline{PB}$ and $m \perp k$, then m is the perpendicular bisector of $\overline{AB}$. def. of $\perp$ bisector

4. If $m \perp k$, then $\angle 3 \cong \angle 4 \cong \angle 5 \cong \angle 6$. cor. 1 of Th. 1.10

5. If $\angle 1 \cong \angle 2$, then $k \perp l$. Th. 1.11   6. If $m \perp k$, then $\angle 4 \cong \angle 3$. Th. 1.10

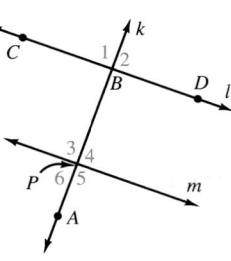

PRACTICE EXERCISES

Drawing in Geometry   Use the figure to draw and label rays for the directions given below. In each case, a complementary adjacent angle is formed. Rename the direction in terms of the complement.

A   1. $\overrightarrow{OP}$: 45° E of N   2. $\overrightarrow{OQ}$: 30° E of S
3. $\overrightarrow{OR}$: 22.5° N of W   4. $\overrightarrow{OT}$: 55° W of S   See side column.

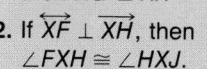
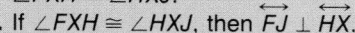

If possible, justify each statement.

5. If $\overrightarrow{AP} \perp m$ and $\overline{CP} \cong \overline{PB}$, then $\overrightarrow{AP}$ lies in the only line that is the perpendicular bisector of $\overline{CB}$. cor. of Th. 1.12

6. If $\overleftrightarrow{AC} \perp l$, then in the plane of this figure, $\overleftrightarrow{AC}$ is the only line perpendicular to l at A. Th. 1.12

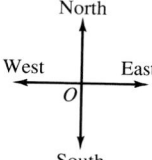

7. If $l \perp k$, then $\angle 6$ is a right angle. def. of $\perp$

8. If $\overleftrightarrow{AC} \perp \overleftrightarrow{AB}$, then $\angle CAB$ is a right angle. def. of $\perp$

9. If $l \perp k$, then $\angle 1$ and $\angle 2$ are complementary. Th. 1.13

10. If $\angle 1$ and $\angle 3$ are complementary, then $k \perp m$. impossible

11. If $\angle 2$ and $\angle 5$ are complements, then $\overrightarrow{AP} \perp l$. impossible

12. If $\angle 6$ is a right angle, then $k \perp l$. def. of $\perp$

13. If $\angle 4 \cong \angle 5$, then $\overrightarrow{AP} \perp m$. Th. 1.11

14. If $\angle 6 \cong \angle CAB$, then $k \perp l$. Th. 1.11

15. If $m \angle 5 = 90$, then $\overrightarrow{AP} \perp m$. def of $\perp$ and def. of rt. $\angle$

16. If $\overrightarrow{AP} \perp m$, then $\angle 4 \cong \angle 5$. Th. 1.10

If $\overrightarrow{SW} \perp \overleftrightarrow{RT}$, write an algebraic expression for:

B   17. $\angle YSW$ in terms of x 90 − x   18. $\angle VSW$ in terms of y 90 − y

19. $\angle YSV$ in terms of x and y 20. $\angle YST$ in terms of x 180 − x
180 − x − y

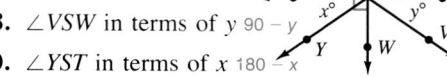

1.6 Perpendicular Lines   **31**

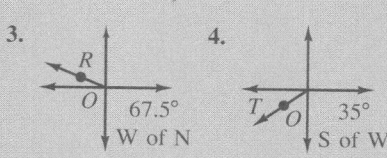

LESSON FOLLOW-UP

Critical Thinking
Observation Ask students to describe lines or planes related to real-world situations that form a right angle.

Assignment Guide
See p. 1B for assignments.

Construction
Challenge students to construct a square by combining the constructions on pp. 17 and 32.

Begin with $\overline{AB}$. Construct a $\perp$ to $\overline{AB}$ at B. On this $\perp$, let C be the point such that $\overline{BC} \cong \overline{AB}$. Continue by constructing a $\perp$ to $\overline{BC}$ at C and marking off D on this $\perp$ so that $\overline{CD} \cong \overline{BC}$ (or $\overline{AB}$). Connect points A and D.

Lesson Quiz
Justify each statement.

1. If $\angle GXI$ is a rt. $\angle$, then $\overleftrightarrow{XG} \perp \overleftrightarrow{XI}$.

2. If $\overleftrightarrow{XF} \perp \overleftrightarrow{XH}$, then $\angle FXH \cong \angle HXJ$.

3. If $\angle FXH \cong \angle HXJ$, then $\overleftrightarrow{FJ} \perp \overleftrightarrow{HX}$.

4. If $\overline{FX} \cong \overline{XJ}$ and $\overleftrightarrow{HX} \perp \overleftrightarrow{FJ}$, then $\overleftrightarrow{HX}$ is the perpendicular bisector of $\overline{FJ}$.

5. If $\overleftrightarrow{XH} \perp \overleftrightarrow{XJ}$, then $\angle HXI$ and $\angle IXJ$ are complementary angles.

1. Def. of $\perp$ rays
2. If two lines are $\perp$, then the pairs of adj. $\angle$s they form are $\cong$.
3. If two lines intersect to form a pair of $\cong$ adj. $\angle$s, the lines are $\perp$.
4. Def. of $\perp$ bisector
5. If the ext. sides of two adj. acute $\angle$s are $\perp$, then the $\angle$s are comp.

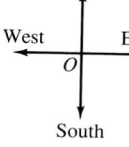

Lines a and b meet to form congruent adjacent angles, $\angle 1$ and $\angle 2$. If $m\angle 1 = x^2 + 9$ and $m\angle 2 = y^2 - 10$, find the values of x and y.
$$x^2 + 9 = 90 \qquad y^2 - 10 = 90$$
$$x = \pm 9 \qquad y = \pm 10$$

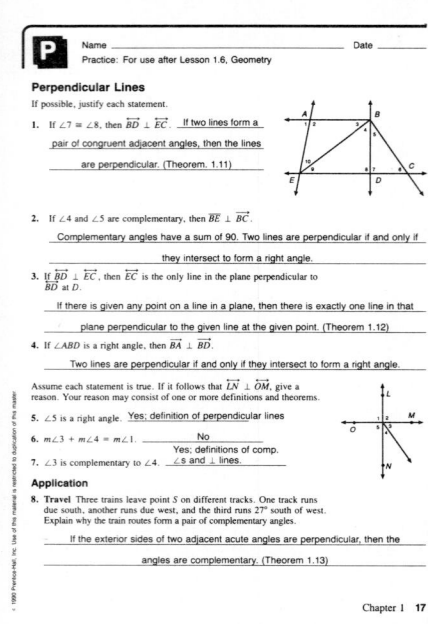

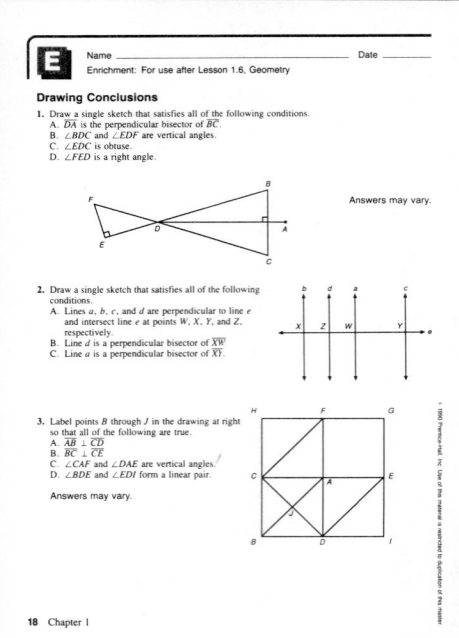

Assume each statement is true. If it follows that $\overleftrightarrow{AB}$ is perpendicular to $\overleftrightarrow{CD}$, give a reason. Your reason may consist of one or more definitions and theorems.

21. $\angle 1$ is a right angle. no

22. $m\angle 1 + m\angle 2 = m\angle 3$ yes; def. of between ray, def. of $\cong \angle$s, and Th. 1.11

23. $m\angle 1 + m\angle 2 + m\angle 3 = 180$ no

24. $m\angle 3 + m\angle 5 = 180$ yes; vert. $\angle$s Th., def. of rt. $\angle$, and def. of $\perp$

25. $m\angle 1 + m\angle 2 + m\angle 4 = 180$ yes; same as Ex. 20 plus def. of between ray

26. $m\angle 4 = m\angle 1 + m\angle 2$ no

27. $m\angle 2 + m\angle 1 = m\angle 5$ yes; def. of between ray, def. of $\cong \angle$s, and Th. 1.11

28. $m\angle 1 = m\angle 5 - m\angle 2$ yes; addition plus Ex. 23

Find the measures of all the numbered angles.

C **29.** $\overline{AB} \perp \overline{BC}$; $m\angle 1 = 9m\angle 2$, $\angle 1 \cong \angle 3$ and $\angle 2 \cong \angle 6$, $m\angle 4 = 2m\angle 6$ and $m\angle 5 = 2m\angle 1$ $m\angle 1 = 81$, $m\angle 2 = 9$ $m\angle 3 = 81$, $m\angle 4 = 18$ $m\angle 5 = 162$, $m\angle 6 = 9$

30. Suppose $\overline{AB} \perp \overline{BC}$, $\overline{BD} \perp \overline{AC}$, $m\angle 1 = 3m\angle 2$, $\angle 1$ and $\angle 3$ are complementary as are $\angle 2$ and $\angle 6$. $m\angle 1 = 67.5$, $m\angle 2 = 22.5$, $m\angle 3 = 22.5$ $m\angle 4 = 90$, $m\angle 5 = 90$, $m\angle 6 = 67.5$

31. Give the postulate that justifies the existence statement on page 30. Restate the postulate in terms of the figure. See side column.

32. What statements must be considered to justify Theorem 1.14? Through a given pt. not on a line there exists one line $\perp$ to the given line. Through a given pt. not on a line there is only one line $\perp$ to the given line.

Applications

33. Navigation A navigator changes heading to a flight path that is perpendicular to 35°E of N. Give the two possible new directions. 35° S of E (or 125° E of N); 55° W of N

34. Cartography Find and describe lines that appear on maps. Answers may vary.

CONSTRUCTION

Given: line l with point O on l *Construct:* $m \perp l$ at O

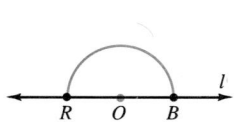

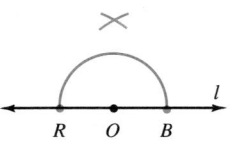

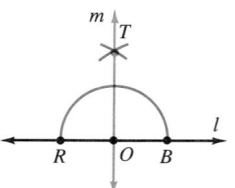

1. *Use O as a center point and draw an arc through line l. Mark the points of intersection R and B.*

2. *Use R as a center point. Using a compass opening greater than RO, draw an arc above l; do the same using B as a center point.*

3. *Call the intersection of the arcs T. Draw $\overline{TO}$. Call it m. Now $m \perp l$ at O.*

EXERCISE   *Given:* line t with point P on t *Construct:* $r \perp t$ at P Check students' constructions.

31. Protractor Postulate; in a half-plane with edge $\overleftrightarrow{AB}$ and P between A and B, there exists a one-to-one correspondence between the rays that originate at P in that half-plane and the real numbers between 0 and 180.

Strategy: Analyze a Figure

You have probably had experience with problem solving in your previous mathematics courses. Solving problems can be fun, but if you don't know where to begin, it can be frustrating. Often the first step in solving a geometry problem requires that you *study a given figure* or *draw a suitable figure*.

Figures allow you to determine information regarding betweenness relationships of segments and angles and interior and exterior points of an angle. Segment lengths and angle measures can also be determined *if specific markings* appear in the figure. For example, *tick marks* convey *congruence* and the symbols ⊥ and ⌐ respectively convey *perpendicular lines* and *right angles*.

Problem solving is a process consisting of several steps that are applied sequentially.

Understand the Problem	**Read the problem.**
	Study the figure given or draw a suitable figure.
	Label the figure.
	What information is given?
	What are you asked to find?
	Identify important mathematical ideas.
	Is there any excess information?
Plan Your Approach	**Choose a method.**
	Recall related problems.
	Decide how definitions, postulates, and theorems can be applied.
Implement the Plan	Assign symbols and write a word equation.
	Apply the mathematics.
	Solve any equations that you used.
	Keep an open mind and change your method if necessary.
Interpret the Results	**State and check your conclusion.**
	What generalizations can you make?

Strategy: Analyze a Figure **33**

LESSON PLAN

Materials/Manipulatives
Teaching Transparency 7

Technology
*Computer Test Bank, pp. 83–87
Teacher's Resource Book,
Technology, p. 2*

LESSON FOCUS

This lesson introduces students to the 4-phase approach to problem solving based on the work of Polya. The model relies on the use of *heuristics*—general problem solving strategies—that may be useful at various points during the problem solving process. Tell students that they should learn to ask themselves various questions that represent things to think about, or try at each phase, as they attempt to solve a problem.

Alternative Learning Styles

Encourage students to mark the diagram for what they are asked to find. By isolating the part they need first, they can then look at it in relationship to the whole figure.

Critical Thinking

Analysis Ask students to analyze the problem solving process, to recognize various phases of this process and various strategies that may be applicable at each phase.

Developing Mathematical Power

Keeping a Portfolio Provide students with copies of Critical Thinking, p. 1, in the *Teacher's Resource Book.* Have them complete it and include it in their math journals. Allow time for them to share responses with the rest of the class.

TEACHING SUGGESTIONS

- Provide many opportunities for students to solve problems as they learn to apply the problem solving process. Remind them that they will become adept at solving problems only through practice.
- Remind students of what can and cannot be assumed from a given figure. Have them identify characteristics and relationships based on a variety of given diagrams.
- One of the most difficult aspects of problem solving is to teach students how to try a different approach when their chosen approach fails. Encourage students to think of as many ways to approach a problem as they can, and demonstrate your own willingness to try different approaches when your original method fails.

CHALKBOARD EXAMPLES

- **For Example 1**

Find $m\angle AOB$ and $m\angle AOD$.

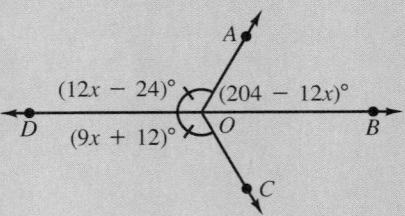

Understand the Problem:
Study the figure. What are you asked to find? Find the measures of ∠s *AOB* and *AOD*. What facts can you determine?
Linear pairs: ∠*AOD* and ∠*AOB*; ∠*DOC* and ∠*BOC*
Congruent pair: ∠*AOD* and ∠*COD*
$m\angle AOD = 12x - 24$; $m\angle AOB = 204 - 12x$; $m\angle COD = 9x + 12$

Plan Your Approach:
Write the appropriate equations.
$(12x - 24) + (204 - 12x) = 180$
$12x - 24 = 9x + 12$

EXAMPLE 1   On the blueprint, find the measure of the angle formed by the rear wall of the house and the southern boundary.

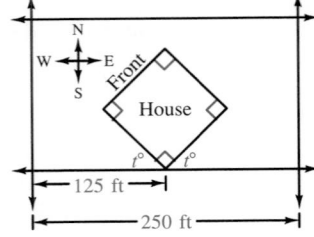

☐ **Understand the Problem**

Study the figure given.

Label the figure.

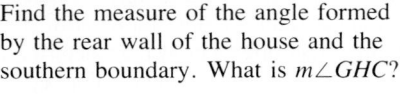

What are you asked to find?
Find the measure of the angle formed by the rear wall of the house and the southern boundary. What is $m\angle GHC$?

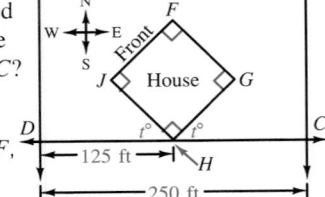

What facts can you determine?
Right angles: ∠*FJH*, ∠*JHG*, ∠*HGF*, ∠*GFJ*
Adjacent angles: ∠*DHJ* and ∠*JHG*,
  ∠*DHJ* and ∠*JHC*,
  ∠*DHG* and ∠*GHC*,
  ∠*JHG* and ∠*GHC*
Linear pairs: ∠*DHJ* and ∠*JHC*, ∠*DHG* and ∠*GHC*
Between points: *H* is between *D* and *C*.
Angle measures: $m\angle DHJ = t$, $m\angle GHC = t$
Segment lengths: $DC = 250$ ft, $DH = 125$ ft

Which facts are necessary to solve this problem?
Right angle ∠*JHG*, both linear pairs, between point *H*, and angle measures $m\angle DHJ = t$ and $m\angle GHC = t$

Is there any excess information?
Yes, since only the angles with vertex *H* are necessary to solve the problem.

☐ **Plan Your Approach**

Apply the definitions and postulates.

Write the appropriate equations.

$m\angle DHJ + m\angle JHG = m\angle DHG$	*Definition of a between ray*
∠*DHG* and ∠*GHC* are supplementary.	*Linear Pair Postulate*
$m\angle DHG + m\angle GHC = 180$	*Definition of supplementary angles*
$m\angle JHG = 90$	*Definition of right angle*

Implement the Plan	**Solve the equation.** $m\angle DHG + m\angle GHC = 180$ $m\angle DHJ + m\angle JHG + m\angle GHC = 180$ $\qquad t \quad + \quad 90 \quad + \qquad t = 180$ $\qquad\qquad\qquad\qquad\qquad 2t = 90$ $\qquad\qquad\qquad\qquad\qquad\; t = 45$
Interpret the Results	The measure of the angle formed by the rear wall of the house and the southern boundary is 45.

Problem Solving Reminders

- In a problem, identify the information that the given figure conveys. If no figure is given, it might be helpful to draw a suitable figure.
- Be sure that the conclusions that you draw regarding the figure can be justified.
- Be sure that your conclusion answers the question asked in the problem.

EXAMPLE 2   Find the length of $\overline{MR}$.

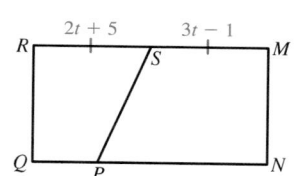

Understand the Problem	**Study the figure.** MR is a segment with between point S. S is also the midpoint of $\overline{MR}$ since the tick marks show that $MS = SR$. $MS = 3t - 1$ and $SR = 2t + 5$.
Plan Your Approach	**Use the definitions and theorems concerning midpoints to set up the appropriate equations.** **a.** $MS = SR$ *Definitions of midpoint and congruence* **b.** $MR = 2(MS)$ *Midpoint Theorem*

Implement the Plan	**Solve the equations.**
	a. $MS = SR$ **b.** $MR = 2(MS)$
	      $3t - 1 = 2t + 5$ $= 2(3t - 1)$
	            $t = 6$ $= 2(17) = 34$

Interpret the Results	$\overline{MS}$ and $\overline{SR}$ each have length 17 units. Thus the length of $\overline{MR}$ is 34 units.

Implement the Plan:
Solve the equations.
$(12x - 24) + (204 - 12x) = 180$
$\qquad\qquad\qquad\qquad\quad 180 = 180$
Since this equation is true for all values of x, the measures of $\angle$s AOB and AOD cannot be determined.

$12x - 24 = 9x + 12$
$x = 12$
$m\angle AOB = 204 - 12(12) = 60$
$m\angle AOD = 12(12) - 24 = 120$

Interpret the Results:
State and check your conclusion. Since $m\angle COD = 9x + 12 = 120$, the $\cong \angle$s have equal measures. Also, the sum of the measures of the supp. $\angle$s is 180, so $m\angle AOB = 60$ and $m\angle AOD = 120$.

- **For Example 2**

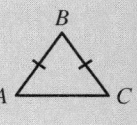

  If $AB = 5x + 7$,
  $BC = 10x - 3$, and the
  perimeter of $\triangle ABC$
  is 50, find AC.

  Understand the Problem:
  To find: AC
  Given: $\overline{AB} \cong \overline{BC}$; $AB = 5x + 7$; $BC = 10x - 3$, perimeter of $\triangle ABC = 50$.

  Plan Your Approach:
  $AB + BC + AC = 50$
  $AB = BC$

  Implement the Plan:
  $AB = BC$
  $5x + 7 = 10x - 3$
  $\qquad\; x = 2$

  Thus, $AB = 17$ and $BC = 17$. Since $17 + 17 + AC = 50$, $AC = 16$.

  Interpret the Results:
  $AC = 16$

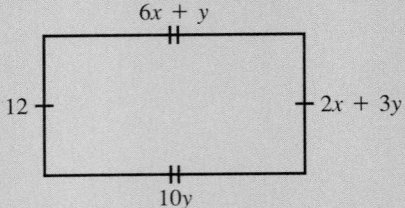
CLASS EXERCISES

Use the figure to determine each measure.

1. *RM* 4
2. *FM* 12
3. *RT* 16
4. *FT* 24

5. Find the measure of $\angle GJH$.
$5x - 5 = 90$, $x = 19$, $m\angle GJH = 57$

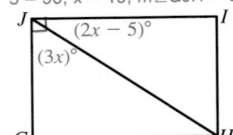

6. The perimeter is 48 in. Find *AB*.
$AB = 12$ in.

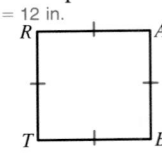

PRACTICE EXERCISES

A

1. Find $m\angle QMP$ if $m\angle LMA = 63$.
$m\angle QMP = \frac{2}{3}m\angle LMP = \frac{2}{3} \cdot 117 = 78$

2. Find *XY* if $YZ = \frac{1}{3}(XY)$.
$t + 2 = \frac{1}{3}(4t - 6)$, $t = 12$, $XY = 42$

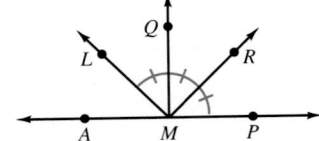

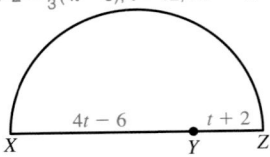

Use this figure for Exercises 3–5.

3. Find $m\angle EBC$.
$(t - 15) + (t + 5) = 90$
$t = 50$
$m\angle EBC = 55$

4. Find $m\angle ABE$ 125

5. Find $m\angle DBC$. $m\angle DBC = 90 + 55 = 145$

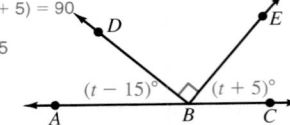

6. Find *DC* if $AC = 10$. $AD = DC$
$DC = 5$

7. Find $m\angle TRW$ if $\angle TRW \cong \angle URS$.
21

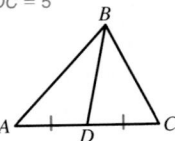

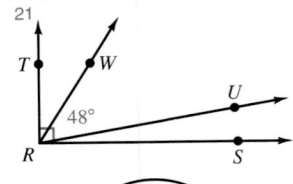

Use this figure for Exercises 8–10.

B

8. Find $m\angle ABC$ if $m\angle DBC = 28$.
$m\angle ABC = 56$

9. If $m\angle ABC = 75$, find $m\angle OBC$.
$2m\angle OBC = m\angle ABC$ $m\angle OBC = 37.5$

10. If $m\angle CBA = 5a - 8b$, find $m\angle ABD$.
$2.5a - 4b$

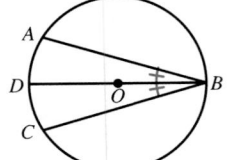

Use this figure for Exercises 11–13.

C   **11.** Find *IK* if *ML* = 12. *IK* = 2*ML* = 24

12. Find $m\angle NJM$ if $\angle IHN$ and $\angle KLM$ are complementary. $m\angle NJM$ = 90 if *I*, *J*, and *K* are coll.

13. If $m\angle IJN = \frac{1}{2}m\angle KJM$ and the angles are complementary, find $m\angle H$. 30

PROJECT

Use any of the instruments for drawing or measuring that were mentioned in this chapter (compass, straightedge, protractor) to draw a picture of the place where you live. Bring your drawing to class and have classmates describe your home from the drawing. What kinds of assumptions might be made from your drawing? Answers may vary.

TEST YOURSELF

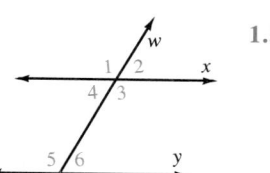

1. Name all the angles vertical to $\angle 1$. $\angle 3$ **1.5**

2. Name the four linear pairs formed by the intersection of lines *w* and *x*. $\angle 1$ and $\angle 2$, $\angle 2$ and $\angle 3$, $\angle 3$ and $\angle 4$, $\angle 4$ and $\angle 1$

3. Name two supplements to $\angle 1$. $\angle 2$, $\angle 4$

4. If $\angle 3$ and $\angle 6$ are supplementary, and $m\angle 3 = 125$, find the measures of $\angle 6$, $\angle 7$, and $\angle 8$. 55, 55, 125

If the statement is true, does it follow that $y \perp x$? If so, give a reason.

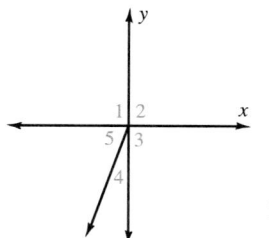

5. $\angle 1 \cong \angle 2$ yes; Th. 1.11   **1.6**

6. $\angle 1 \cong \angle 3$ no

7. $m\angle 1 + m\angle 2 = 180$ no

8. $m\angle 3 = 90$ yes; defs. of rt. $\angle$ and $\perp$

9. $\angle 5$ is a complement of $\angle 4$. yes; def. of comp. $\angle$, rt. $\angle$, and $\perp$

10. If a figure shows $\overrightarrow{OT}$ between $\overrightarrow{OR}$ and $\overrightarrow{OM}$, what conclusions must be true? $\angle ROT$ and $\angle TOM$ are adj. $\angle$s.   **1.7**
T is an interior pt. of $\angle ROM$; $m\angle ROT + m\angle TOM = m\angle ROM$.

1.7 Strategy: Analyze a Figure   **37**

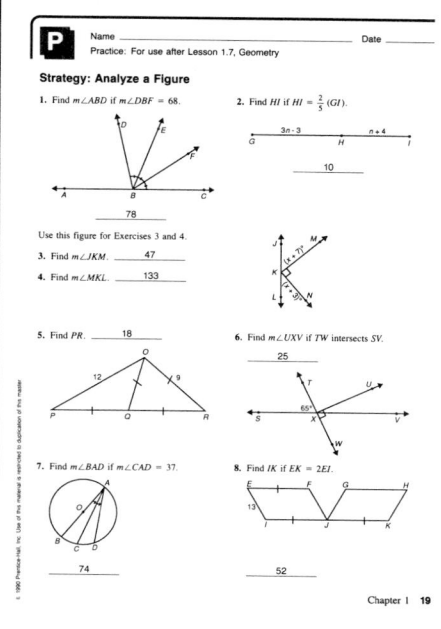
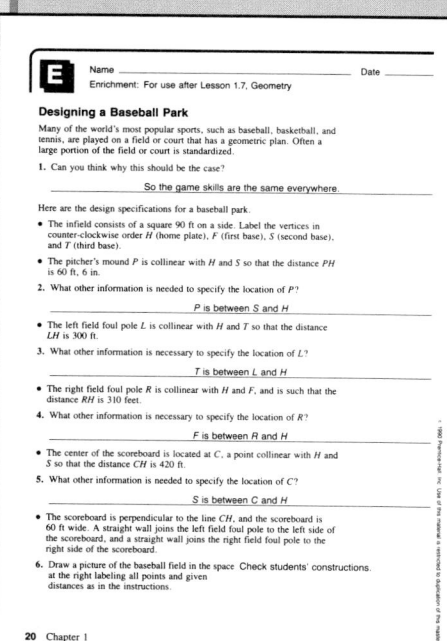

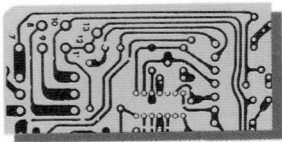

TECHNOLOGY: Constructing Geometric Shapes Using Logo

Logo is a family of computer languages designed to help people investigate geometry by experiment and exploration. Logo activities provide direct experiences that will help you to understand the geometric concepts that you are learning. In this text, the LogoWriter version of Logo will be used.

You can think of Logo as a geometric construction tool. To construct geometric figures, you give instructions to an imaginary robot called a *turtle.* The Logo turtle understands a few simple **commands** called **primitives** that are built into the language.

The turtle recognizes the next four basic commands by their full or abbreviated name, and each command is followed by an input number.

Command	Input	Output
forward	fd 10	Moves the turtle forward 10 turtle steps.
back	bk 15	Moves the turtle back 15 turtle steps.
right	rt 40	Turns the turtle right 40 degrees.
left	lt 7	Turns the turtle left 7 degrees.

The following table lists six more useful Logo commands.

Command	Input	Output
penup	pu	Allows the turtle to move without drawing.
pendown	pd	Starts the turtle drawing again.
home	home	Returns the turtle to its beginning position in the middle of the screen.
stamp	stamp	Stamps a copy of the turtle on the screen; this cannot be seen until you move the turtle away (this is specific to LogoWriter).
repeat	repeat	Repeats a list of commands as often as you wish and needs two inputs: (1) a number and (2) a list of commands typed within square brackets [ ].
clear graphics	cg	Clears the screen.

38   Chapter 1 The Language of Geometry

You can define your own Logo commands called **procedures** using primitives or other procedures. Procedures are defined on the *flip side* of the page. To define a procedure:

1. Press the flip keys (open-apple F) to move to the flip side of the page.

2. Type the word *to* followed by a name of your choosing. The name of a Logo procedure can be any word (with no spaces) that is not a primitive or the name of a procedure.

3. Type in a series of commands. When your procedure is complete, type the word *end*.

4. Press the flip keys to return to the turtle screen.

5. Type the name of your new procedure to test it.

EXAMPLE   **Copy the following procedure. Use the repeat command to draw the figure six times, each time turning it 30°.**

to squiggle   *Commands can be written one after the*
fd 30 rt 45 bk 20   *other, each separated by a space.*
rt 45 fd 30
end

repeat 6 [squiggle lt 30]

EXERCISES   See Solutions Manual.

1. Explore the screen: Move the turtle to the top, bottom, right, and left edges. Determine the height and width of the screen.

2. Write the Logo commands that would be used to draw each of the following:
   a. a small square   **b.** a large square   **c.** your initials

3. Edit the *squiggle* procedure above by going back to the flip side. Use the cursor keys and the delete key to add new commands, delete old commands, or change one of the input numbers. Flip back to the turtle screen and test your procedure.

4. Write a procedure called *square* that uses the repeat command to draw a square with 40 turtle steps on a side.

5. Write a procedure called *triangle* that uses the repeat command to draw a triangle of 40 steps on each side.

- See *Teacher's Resource Book, Spanish Chapter Summary and Review,* pp. 1–2.
- See Extra Practice, p. 643.

CHAPTER 1 SUMMARY AND REVIEW

Vocabulary

acute angle (19)	edge (4)	plane (2)
adjacent angles (18)	half-plane (4)	point (2)
angle (18)	intersection (3)	postulate (7)
angle bisector (20)	line (2)	protractor (19)
between points (13)	linear pair (23)	ray (13)
between rays (20)	measure of angle (19)	right angle (19)
collinear (3)	measure of segment (13)	segment (13)
complementary angles (23)	midpoint (14)	segment bisector (14)
congruent angles (20)	noncollinear (3)	sides (18)
congruent segments (13)	noncoplanar (3)	space (3)
coordinate (12)	obtuse angle (19)	supplementary angles (23)
coplanar (3)	opposite rays (13)	theorem (8)
corollary (14)	perpendicular (28)	vertex (18)
distance (12)	perpendicular bisector (29)	vertical angles (24)

Using and Relating Points, Lines, and Planes Postulates are   **1.1–1.2**
statements that are accepted as true. Theorems are statements that must be
proven as true.

Justify each answer with a definition, postulate, or theorem.

1. What figure is determined by points D and E? $\overleftrightarrow{DE}$; Post. 2

2. A and B are in plane Q. How many other points
   of $\overleftrightarrow{AB}$ are in Q? all of them; Post. 4

3. Name the plane that contains points D, B, and C. Q; Post. 3

4. What is the intersection of planes M and P? $\overleftrightarrow{DE}$; Post. 5

5. Name the plane determined by $\overleftrightarrow{DE}$ and A. Q; Th. 1.2

6. Name the plane in which lines $\overleftrightarrow{AC}$ and $\overleftrightarrow{DE}$ lie. Q; Th. 1.3

Segments and Rays Line segment XY, $\overline{XY}$, can be measured by using a   **1.3**
number line and the Ruler Postulate. Its length, or distance, is written as XY.

7. Find AB. What is its midpoint? 4, Y

8. Name the coordinates of the
   points that are 3.5 units from Y. −1, −8

9. Name the segments with endpoint X that are congruent to $\overline{BC}$. $\overline{XZ}$, $\overline{XB}$

Angles An angle is the union of two rays with a common endpoint. Angles can be classified according to their measures.

1.4

10. Are $\angle 1$ and $\angle 3$ adjacent? Explain your answer.
No; they do not have a common side.

11. Name the sides and vertex of $\angle 2$. $\overrightarrow{OX}, \overrightarrow{OY}, O$

12. Name the ray opposite to $\overrightarrow{OW}$. $\overrightarrow{OZ}$

13. If $\overrightarrow{OP}$ bisects $\angle WOX$, what angles are congruent?
$\angle POW \cong \angle XOP$

14. If $m\angle 2 = 91$ and $m\angle WOY = 116$, find $m\angle 1$. 25

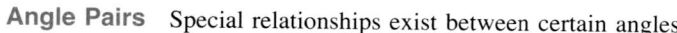

Angle Pairs Special relationships exist between certain angles.

1.5

15. Name the two angles that can each form a linear pair with $\angle PQT$. What other kind of angle pair does each form with $\angle PQT$? $\angle PQV$ and $\angle TQR$; supplementary $\angle$s

16. Suppose $\angle RQT$ is a supplement of $\angle QTU$. $m\angle QTU = 60$, $m\angle RQT = 120$, Find the measures of all 8 angles shown. $m\angle RQV = 60$, $m\angle PQV = 120$, $m\angle PQT = 60$, $m\angle QTS = 120$, $m\angle STW = 60$, $m\angle WTU = 120$

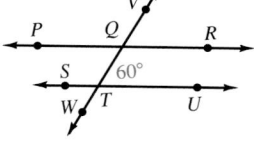

Perpendicular Lines A line (or ray or segment) is the perpendicular bisector of a segment if and only if the line (or ray or segment) is perpendicular to the segment at its midpoint.

1.6

Justify each true statement.

17. If $\angle 3$ is a right angle, then $k \perp l$. def. of $\perp$

18. If $k \perp l$ at B, then w is NOT perpendicular to l. Th. 1.12

19. If $\overrightarrow{BD}$ is perpendicular to $\overrightarrow{BC}$, then $\angle 4$ is a complement of $\angle 5$. Th. 1.13

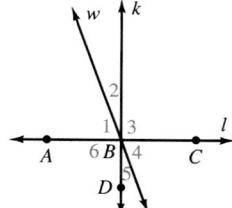

Strategy: Analyze a Figure

1.7

| Understand the Problem | Plan Your Approach | Implement the Plan | Interpret the Results |

$\overline{AN}$ is the perpendicular bisector of $\overline{MY}$.

20. Find t. 3
21. Find MY. 58
22. Find AM. 33
23. Find $m\angle ANY$. 90
24. Find AY. 33
25. Find MN. 29

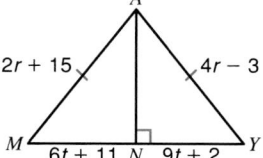

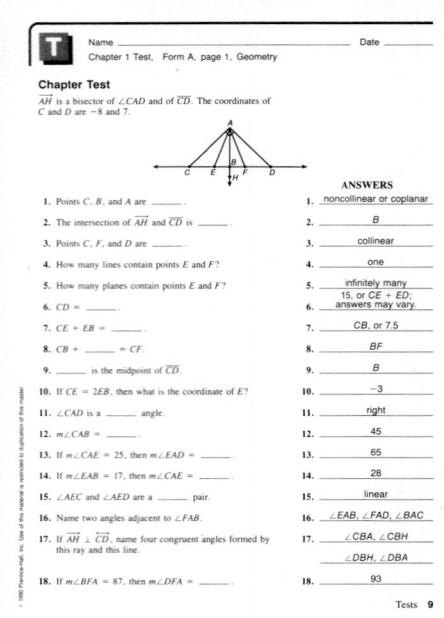

See *Teacher's Resource Book, Tests,* pp. 9–12.

Chapter 1 TEST

$\overrightarrow{CF}$ is the bisector of $\angle ACB$. $\overline{AE}$ bisects $\overline{CB}$. The coordinates of C and B are -5 and 7, respectively.

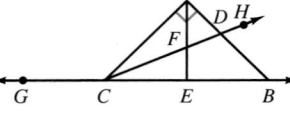

1. Name three collinear points. any 3 points on $\overleftrightarrow{GB}$, $\overleftrightarrow{AE}$, $\overleftrightarrow{AB}$, or $\overleftrightarrow{CH}$

2. The intersection of $\overrightarrow{CF}$ and $\overleftrightarrow{AE}$ is $\underline{\ ?\ }$. F

3. Points C, F, and E are $\underline{\ ?\ }$. noncollinear, coplanar

4. How many planes contain points C, A, and B? 1

5. $CF + \underline{\ ?\ } = CD$ FD

6. $CB = \underline{\ ?\ }$ 12, CE + EB or GB − GC

7. $\underline{\ ?\ }$ is the midpoint of $\overline{CB}$ and has coordinate $\underline{\ ?\ }$. E, 1

8. If $\angle DFA$ is acute, then $\angle CFA$ is $\underline{\ ?\ }$. obtuse

9. $\angle\ \underline{\ ?\ }$ is a supplement of $\angle AEB$. $\angle AEC$

10. Two angles adjacent to $\angle ACF$ are pictured. They are $\underline{\ ?\ }$ and $\underline{\ ?\ }$. $\angle ACG$ $\angle ECF$

11. If $m\angle CAF = 50$, then $m\angle FAD = \underline{\ ?\ }$. 40

12. $\angle ADF$ and $\angle\ \underline{\ ?\ }$ form a linear pair. ADH or FDB

13. $\angle\ \underline{\ ?\ }$ is a right angle. CAB

14. Name a pair of congruent angles. $\angle ACF \cong \angle FCB$

15. CB is $\frac{3}{4}GB$. What is the coordinate of G? −9

16. If $\overline{CD} \perp \overline{AE}$, name four right angles. $\angle AFD$, $\angle DFE$, $\angle EFC$, $\angle CFA$

17. If $m\angle AEC = m\angle AEB$, then $\overline{AE}\ \underline{\ ?\ }\ \overline{CB}$. Justify with a theorem. $\perp$, Th. 1.11

18. Four times the complement of an angle is $20°$ less than the angle. Find the measure of the angle. 76

19. If $m\angle RND = 112$, find $m\angle RNB$. 158

20. If $m\angle RNB = 3t + 8$ and $m\angle BNA = 2t - 3$, find $m\angle AND$. 23

Challenge

On a segment with endpoints 2 and 17, find a point that separates the segment into two parts whose ratio is $3:2$. Is there more than one such point? points 11 and 8

42   Chapter 1 The Language of Geometry

Alternative Assessment As you describe the diagram at the top of the page, have students draw it from your description. After collecting the drawings, have them use the diagram in the textbook and state all the information they can about it. They should justify any statements they make with valid reasons. Statements could be about relationships, measures, and so on.

Select the best choice for each question.

1. If the points on the number line have
D   the indicated coordinates, find PQ.

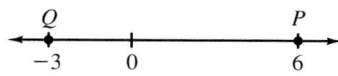

     -3 0 6

   A. -3 **B.** 3 **C.** 6
   D. 9 **E.** $|6 - 3|$

2. If $a = -2$, then $|3a + (a + 1)^2| =$
A
   A. 5 **B.** 7 **C.** 9
   D. 11 **E.** 15

3. If $3x + 7 = 17$, then $6x - 1 =$
B
   A. 20 **B.** 19 **C.** 18
   D. 17 **E.** 16

Use this number line for 4–5.

     A B C D E
   -10 -5 0 5 10

4. The midpoint of segment $\overline{AE}$ has
B   coordinate

   A. -2 **B.** -0.5 **C.** -1
   D. 1 **E.** 2

5. If D is the midpoint of segment $\overline{CX}$,
E   then X has coordinate

   A. -7 **B.** 3 **C.** 4.5
   D. 7 **E.** 9

6. If two complementary angles have
D   measures of $2x + 21$ and $3x - 26$,
   the smaller angle has a measure of

   A. 57 **B.** 43 **C.** 38
   D. 31 **E.** 19

7. Solve for x: $\dfrac{4}{x} = \dfrac{6}{23}$
D
   A. $\dfrac{23}{3}$ **B.** $\dfrac{23}{2}$ **C.** $\dfrac{43}{3}$

   D. $\dfrac{46}{3}$ **E.** $\dfrac{92}{3}$

8. If $3x - 2y = 14$ and $2x - 3y = 21$,
C   find the value of $x - y$.

   A. 5 **B.** -5 **C.** 7
   D. -7 **E.** 9

9. Three angles have measures of
B $2x + 5$, $3x + 1$, and $x - 10$. If their
   mean is 58, what is the measure of
   the largest angle?

   A. 91 **B.** 90 **C.** 72
   D. 65 **E.** 61

10. Star Video is advertising 20% off
D   on a \$17.85 package of 3 VHS
   video tapes. Twinkle Video has the
   same tapes at $\dfrac{1}{3}$ off the regular price
   of \$6.99 each. At which store
   would a purchase of 3 tapes cost
   less and by how much?

   A. Star, \$0.70 **B.** Twinkle, \$0.70
   C. Star, \$0.30 **D.** Twinkle, \$0.30
   E. They cost the same.

11. In $\angle WXZ$, Y is on $\overline{XZ}$ and T is on
E $\overleftrightarrow{WZ}$. Which of the following would
   determine a plane?

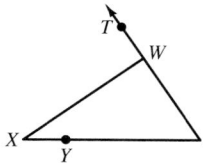

   A. $\overline{XY}$ and Z **B.** X,Y,Z **C.** T,Z,W
   D. $\overrightarrow{WT}$ and Z **E.** $\angle TWX$

The individual comments made for certain problems will help guide the students in solving them.

1. The scale marks on the number line have been omitted to encourage students to use subtraction instead of counting.
3. This problem could be solved by finding the value of x and substituting it into $6x - 1$, but it could also provide a simple example of how a problem itself can offer a quick solution for the alert student.
4–5. As a contrast to Exercise 1, both of these could be solved by simply counting along the number line.
8. As in Exercise 3, this can be solved by finding x and y and then substituting them into $x - y$. However, more work is involved in doing this, thus there are more chances of error.

See *Teacher's Resource Book* for *Preparing for College Entrance Exams*.

The following skills and concepts are reviewed:
Simplifying expressions
Solving equations

Simplify each expression.

Example $16 + 8(5 - 2) \div 4$
$= 16 + 8(3) \div 4$ *Simplify inside the parentheses.*
$= 16 + 24 \div 4$ *Perform multiplication and division*
$= 16 + 6$ *from left to right.*
$= 22$ *Add.*

1. $5 + 5 \div 5 \cdot 5$ 10

2. $4 + 2(5 + 7)$ 28

3. $\dfrac{2 \cdot 8 - 2 \cdot 10}{4} + 3 - 2 \cdot 5$ -8

4. $|5 - 7|$ 2

5. $-|5 - 7|$ -2

6. $|x|$ x if $x \geq 0$ $-x$ if $x < 0$

Solve.

Example $7x = 4(3x + 5)$
$7x = 12x + 20$ *Use the distributive property.*
$7x - 12x = 12x - 12x + 20$ *Use the addition property.*
$-5x = 20$ *Combine like terms.*
$x = -4$ *Divide each side by -5.*

7. $2(x + 7) = 20$ 3

8. $4x - 5 = 3x + 8$ 13

9. $24 = \dfrac{3}{4}x$ 32

10. $\dfrac{5}{9} = \dfrac{30}{x}$ 54

11. $|x| = 6$ ± 6

12. $\dfrac{1}{3}(180 - x) = 2(90 - x)$ 72

13. $|5x - 8| = -17$ no solution

14. $|3x - 4| = 5$ 3, $-\frac{1}{3}$

15. If $\dfrac{x}{y} = \dfrac{12}{7}$ and $y = 28$, find x. 48

16. If $x + 15y = 90$ and $y = \dfrac{x}{3}$, find x and y. $x = 15$ $y = 5$

17. Find two integers whose sum is 23 and whose product is 90. 5, 18

18. Find two integers whose sum is 49 and whose product is 180. 4, 45

19. The sum of two numbers is 90. Write an expression for each number. Use two variables. $x = 90 - y$; $y = 90 - x$

20. The difference of two numbers is 90. Write an expression for each number. Use two variables. $x = y + 90$; $y = x - 90$

21. One number is four times another number. The sum of the numbers is 90. Find each number. 72, 18

22. One number is six less than five times another number. The sum of the numbers is 180. Find each number. 149, 31

23. Thirty-six floors of a skyscraper are completed. This is two-thirds of the planned number of floors. How many floors will the building have? 54

OVERVIEW • Chapter 2

SUMMARY

In Chapter 2, students define the negation of a statement as well as conditionals, converses, inverses, contrapositives, and biconditionals. They learn to state a conditional in if-then form, and to recognize its hypothesis and conclusion. The concept of logically equivalent statements is explained. Students review basic algebraic properties. They use these together with the definitions of congruence properties to establish reflexive, symmetric, and transitive properties of congruence. Students will be introduced to the use of logical reasoning in planning and completing formal two-column proofs, including proofs of theorems.

CHAPTER OBJECTIVES

- To write the negation of a statement

- To state conditional statements in if-then form

- To recognize the hypothesis and conclusion of a conditional

- To state the converse, inverse, and contrapositive of a conditional

- To recognize logically equivalent statements

- To form biconditionals and identify definitions

- To recognize and use algebraic properties as reasons to justify steps in geometric proofs

- To use the reflexive, symmetric, and transitive properties for congruence

- To recognize the rudiments of logical reasoning

- To write formal proofs of theorems and other statements

CHAPTER HIGHLIGHTS

DEVELOPING MATHEMATICAL POWER

Problem Solving

The strategy lesson incorporates the four problem solving steps in writing flow proofs. The four-step process is used again in Lesson 2.5 to analyze writing formal proofs.

Communication

The side column suggests topics for writing and reading in geometry. Alternative learning styles are addressed through Venn diagrams and paper cut-outs. Enrichment exercises from the *Teacher's Resource Book* are suggested for cooperative learning endeavors. There is a Spanish version of the Chapter Summary and Review in the *Teacher's Resource Book*.

Reasoning

The side column suggests ways for analyzing logical and invalid reasoning. Students write flow proofs and formal proofs. Students compare and contrast three types of proofs. The Project in Lesson 2.4 involves completing truth tables.

Connections

Lesson 2.3 integrates the properties of algebra into geometry. The discussion of George Boole provides an example of the variety of cultural influences on mathematics. Numerous real-world applications are offered, such as meteorology, law, and finance.

Technology

Solving problems using Logo is the topic of the technology feature.

STUDENT TEXT

Chapter Content	Basic	Average	Enriched	NCTM STANDARDS*
2.1 Conditional Statements	D: 49/1-11 odd, 26, 27, AR	D: 49/1-11, 10-19 even, 24-27, 31, AR	D: 49/1-6, 12-27, 31, 32, AR	2, 3, 4, 12, 14
2.2 Converses, Inverses, and Contrapositives	D: 54/1-14 odd, 25, MR R: 49/1-11 even	D: 54/1-14, 15-20 odd, 24, 25, 33-35, MR R: 49/10-19 odd	D: 54/1-20 odd, 21-25, 33-39, MR R: 49/7-11	3, 4, 12, 14
2.3 Properties from Algebra	D: 58/1-13, 31, 33-35 R: 54/1-14 even	D: 58/1-4, 14-25, 31-35 R: 54/15-20 even	D: 58/14-25, 28, 29, 31-35 R: 54/1-20 even	3, 4, 5, 8, 14
2.4 Strategy: Use Logical Reasoning	D: 64/1-5, 7 R: 58/14-18	D: 64/1-5, 7, 9 R: 58/26, 27	D: 64/1-5, 8-18 even R: 58/26, 27, 30	1, 3, 7, 14
2.5 Proving Theorems	D: 70/1-9, 15, 17 R: 64/6, 8	D: 70/1-12, 15, 18 R: 64/6, 8	D: 70/1-14, 16, 18 R: 64/11-18 odd	1, 2, 3, 5, 7, 8

D = Daily   R = Review   AR = Algebra Review   MR = Mixed Review

*For a complete list of NCTM Standards, see p. T7.

STUDENT TEXT

Review/Assessment

Mixed Review 55

Algebra Review 50

Summary and Review 74

College Ent. Exam Rev. 77

Cumulative Review 78

Extra Practice 644

Test Yourself 61, 72

Chapter Test 76

Chapter Project 45

Special Features

Careers 50

Technology 73

Devel. Math. Power 50, 55, 61, 71

Applications 50, 55, 60, 71

Project 66

RESOURCES

Teacher's Resource Book

Ch. 2: Investigation/Practice/ Enrichment 1-13

Spanish Sum. and Rev. 3-4

Quizzes 13-16

Chapter Tests 17-20

Cumulative Tests 21-24

Perf. Assessment Proj. Ch. 2

Critical Thinking 2

Reading and Writing in Geom. 2

Technology 3-4

Teaching Aid 2

Transparency 2

Teaching Transparencies 8-12

Computer Test Bank 89-132

Connections 5

PH Graph. Utility

Overhead Manip. Kit

The Logic of Geometry

No passing zone?

Developing Mathematical Power

What do you call something that seems logical but is contradictory to common sense? Mathematicians call it a *paradox*. In the fifth century B.C., a Greek philosopher named Zeno posed a remarkable paradox.

In modern terms, this is Zeno's Paradox: Imagine a race between a racing car and a bicycle. Since the racing car is faster, the bicycle is given a head start. By the time the car reaches the bicycle's starting point, the bicycle will have moved on. Each time the car reaches a point where the bicycle has been, the bicycle will have moved on. Therefore, according to Zeno, the car will never pass the bicycle, and the bicycle will win the race!

Project

How would you prove that Zeno's reasoning was correct? How would you prove that the racing car will pass the bicycle at some point in the race? Write a convincing argument for both sides.

The rules of logic dictate that the racing car will pass the bicycle if the course is long enough. If one assumes that the bicycle is given a head start of 1000 meters and that the racing car can travel 10 times faster than the bicycle, the racing car will reach the bicycle in $1111\frac{1}{9}$ meters. If the race track is shorter than this, the bicycle will win. Otherwise, the racing car will pass the bicycle.

BACKGROUND

In the fifth century B.C., Zeno of Elea (in present-day Italy) proposed about forty paradoxes. The best known of these is the paradox of Achilles and the tortoise, restated for students as a paradox of a car and a bicycle. Using the assumptions made by the Pythagoreans about infinity, sequences, and partial sums, Zeno showed how they led to contradictions. Zeno's paradoxes were very upsetting to the Greek mathematicians of his day, and they remain controversial.

Instruction

Mathematics provides the power to state, analyze, and prove ideas through the rules of logic. This project involves analyzing a paradox. The project is developed by analyzing data and by using mathematical skills and logic.

Cooperative Learning

This project is accomplished through a succession of tasks, each of which is well-suited to a cooperative learning situation. These tasks include:

1. Applying concepts of logic.
2. Analyzing data.
3. Performing calculations on that data.
4. Analyzing results for accuracy and reasonableness.

Students should see that drawing a diagram may help them understand the conditions of the problem.

Alternative Assessment

See the *Teacher's Resource Book,* Assessment, Chapter 2. This project and the TRB page may be used as an alternative form of assessment for selected topics in Chapter 2.

Vocabulary

Conclusion	Hypothesis
Conditional	Negation
Counter-example	

Materials/Manipulatives

Teaching Transparency 8

Technology

Computer Test Bank, pp. 89–99

LESSON FOCUS

Review

• Ask students whether the following statements are true or not.

1. If $\angle A$ is a right angle, then $m\angle A = 90$.   true
2. If $\angle B$ is an acute angle, then $m\angle B = 45$.   false; e.g., 28°
3. If $m\angle C = 45$, then $\angle C$ is an acute angle.   true

• For the Algebra Review, Exercises 28–30, students solve 2-step equations.

Alternative Learning Styles

• The Investigation encourages the critical thinking process by providing students with the opportunity to classify conditional statements as true or false.

• Visualizing the hypothesis and the conclusion in a conditional often gives students a clearer understanding of that relationship. To help students visualize "if $m\angle ABC = 15$, then $\angle ABC$ is acute," use the Venn Diagram to show that because $\angle ABC$ is part of acute angles, it is a true conditional.

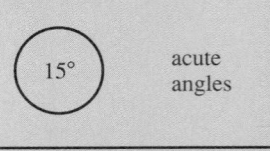

2.1

Conditional Statements

Objectives: To write the negation of a statement
To state conditional statements in if-then form
To recognize the hypothesis and conclusion of a conditional

Computer programmers, logicians, and mathematicians are some of the people who use the rules of logic. In mathematics, these rules can help you to determine whether a statement is true or false.

Investigation—*Thinking Critically*

Study these statements. Note that each contains two related clauses: an if-clause and a then-clause.

a. *If* a student scores higher than 95%, *then* the student earns an A.
b. *If* $12 + 3 = 15$, *then* $15 - 12 = 3$.
c. *If* $3x - 7 = 3$, *then* $x = 4$.
d. *If* a person gets a measles vaccination, *then* that person will not get measles.
Statement (a) is true in many schools; however, maybe not all. Statement (b) is always true.
Are the statements true or false? Justify your answer. Statement (c) is always false.
Statement *d* is probably true.

In mathematics, a statement, p, is either true or false.

p	True or False?
2 is the only solution of $3x - 6 = 0$.	True
2 is not the only solution of $3x - 6 = 0$.	False
All segments have more than one midpoint.	False
All segments have one midpoint.	True
If $3x = 39$, then $x = 13$.	True
If $3x = 39$, then $x \neq 13$.	False

The **negation** of any statement p can be formed by using the word *not*, changing $=$ to $\neq$, or some similar revision.

Here are the rules of logic for negations:

> **The negation of a true statement is always false.**
> **The negation of a false statement is always true.**

The negation of p in symbols is $\sim p$ (read "not p").

Developing Mathematical Power

Cooperative Learning   Provide each group with Enrichment, p. 3, in the *Teacher's Resource Book* (see side column, p. 50). Have them share their answers and create their own paradoxes. Encourage them to explore the concept of a paradox in the writings of G. K. Chesterton.

EXAMPLE 1 **Complete the table.**

p	True or False?	~*p*	True or False?
a. Two points determine a unique line.	?	?	?
b. $2 \cdot 5 = 7$	?	?	?
c. Acute angles measure 90° or more.	?	?	?

a. True; two points do not determine a unique line; false
b. False; $2 \cdot 5 \neq 7$; true
c. False; acute angles do not measure 90° or more; true

Many mathematical concepts are expressed as if-then statements, called *conditionals*. **Conditionals** are formed by joining two statements, *p* and *q*, with the words *if* and *then*: If *p*, then *q*. For example:

> *p*-statement: Two lines intersect.
> *q*-statement: Two lines intersect at a point.
> Conditional: If two lines intersect, then they intersect at a point.

The if-statement is the **hypothesis,** and the then-statement is the **conclusion.** Conditionals do not always appear in if-then form. Here is a conditional:

> All right angles are congruent.

To express this in if-then form, try using the subject of the sentence to form the hypothesis and the predicate of the sentence to form the conclusion.

Subject	**Predicate**
All right angles	are congruent
Hypothesis	**Conclusion**
If angles are right angles,	then they are congruent

EXAMPLE 2 **Write the conditionals in if-then form. Then, underline each hypothesis once and each conclusion twice.**

a. Vertical angles are congruent.   **b.** Two planes intersect in a line.

a. If two angles are vertical angles, then they are congruent.
b. If two planes intersect, then their intersection is a line.

Conditional statements are either *true conditionals* or *false conditionals*. A conditional is a false conditional when the conclusion is *false* and the hypothesis is *true*. Compare the following examples:

Conditional: If two angles are congruent, then they are vertical angles. In the figure $\angle POQ \cong \angle QOR$, yet $\angle POQ$ and $\angle QOR$ are not vertical angles. This one instance, called a *counterexample*, shows that this is a false conditional.

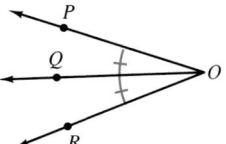

2.1 Conditional Statements   **47**

TEACHING SUGGESTIONS

- Point out that a conditional is a statement that *can* be written in if-then form. Ask for examples of sentences that can't be written in if-then form.   questions, commands
- Students can form the negation of statements involving inequalities without using "not." Point out that in Example 1c, the negation of "90° or more" could be written "less than 90°." Similarly, the negation of "less than" could be written "greater than or equal to."
- Ask students to form the negation of a sentence that involves "not." For example, the negation of "$\angle A$ is not a right angle" is "$\angle A$ is a right angle."

CHALKBOARD EXAMPLES

- **For Example 1**
  Tell whether each of the following statements is true or not. Give the negation, and state true or false.

  a. $\perp$ lines intersect at a 95° $\angle$.
  b. $48 \div 6 < 8$
  c. The sum of the $\angle$ measures of comp. $\angle$s is 90.

  a. False; $\perp$ lines do not intersect at a 95° $\angle$; true.
  b. False; $48 \div 6 \geq 8$; true.
  c. True; the sum of the $\angle$ measures of comp. $\angle$s is not 90; false.

- **For Example 2**
  State each conditional in if-then form. Then underline each hypothesis once and each conclusion twice.

  a. $\perp$ lines intersect at a 90° $\angle$.
  b. Two points determine a unique line.

  a. If two lines are $\perp$, then they intersect at a 90° $\angle$.
  b. If two points are given, then there is exactly one line that passes through both.

- **For Example 3**

  Are the following statements true or false? If true, verify. If false, give a counterexample.

  a. If an angle is a right angle, then it measures more than 50°.
  b. If two angles are supplementary, then they are right angles.

  a. True; by definition, the measure of a right angle is 90, and 90 > 50.
  b. False; $m\angle 1 = 100$ and $m\angle 2 = 80$.

Common Error
- Students might have difficulty in changing a statement to a conditional. Point out that statements often need to be manipulated into the conditional form by adding or deleting some words.
- See *Teacher's Resource Book* for additional remediation.

LESSON FOLLOW-UP

Assignment Guide
See p. 44B for assignments.

Developing Mathematical Power
Writing in Mathematics Students are asked for a negation that does not involve a negative and to write conditionals in if-then form.

Conditional: If two angles are vertical angles, then they are congruent.
This is a true conditional. It was justified as Theorem 1.9.

Conditional: If two angles form a linear pair, then they are supplementary.
This is a true conditional. It is the Linear Pair Postulate.

Conditional: If an angle is a right angle, then its measure is 90.
This is a true conditional. It is the definition of a right angle.

Note that there are no counterexamples for theorems, postulates, or definitions.

EXAMPLE 3 **Are these conditionals true or false? If true, verify. If false, give a counterexample.** Counterexamples can vary.

a. If $m\angle E = 37$, then $\angle E$ is an acute angle.
b. If $\angle E$ is an acute angle, then $m\angle E = 37$.
c. If a number is greater than 5, then the number is greater than 3.
d. If a number is greater than 3, then the number is greater than 5.
e. If two angles are congruent, then they are right angles.
f. If two angles are right angles, then they are congruent.

a. T; by definition of acute angle
b. F; $m\angle E$ might be 45.
c. T; by algebraic properties
d. F; the number might be 4.
e. F; both angles might be 85°
f. T; by Theorem 1.7

CLASS EXERCISES

Complete the table.

Statement (p)	True or False?	Negation (~p)	True or False?
1. $3 + 2 = 5$	? true	? $3 + 2 \neq 5$	? false
2. 4 is a solution of $3x < 7$.	? false	4 is not ? a solution of $3x < 7$.	? true
3. Right angles do not measure 90°.	? false	Rt. ? ∠s do measure 90°.	? true

Write in if-then form. Underline the hypothesis once, the conclusion twice.

4. The measure of a right angle is 90. If an ∠ is a rt. ∠, then its measure is 90.

5. Two intersecting lines lie in exactly one plane. If 2 lines intersect, then the lines lie in exactly one plane.

True or false? If true, verify. If false, give a counterexample.

6. If $\angle Y$ is an obtuse angle, then $m\angle Y = 178$. false; suppose $m\angle Y = 100$

7. If three points are given, then exactly one plane contains them. false; suppose the 3 points are collinear

8. If $m\angle 1 + m\angle 2 = 180$, then $\angle 1$ and $\angle 2$ are supplementary.
true; def. of supp. ∠s

A **Refer to the figure to complete Exercises 1–6.**

Statement (p)	True or False?	Negation (~p)	True or False?
1. $m\angle BAC = 90$	_?_ true	_?_ $m\angle BAC \neq 90$	_?_ false
2. $\angle B$ is obtuse.	_?_ true	_?_ $\angle B$ is not obt.	_?_ false
3. $\angle 1$ is a complement of $\angle 2$.	_?_ true	$\angle 1$ is _?_ not a comp. of $\angle 2$	_?_ false
4. $\angle 2$ is a supplement of $\angle B$.	_?_ false	$\angle 2$ is _?_ not a supp. of $\angle B$	_?_ true
5. $m\angle 1 + m\angle 2 = 180$	_?_ false	$m\angle 1 + \,$ _?_ $m\angle 2 \neq 180$	_?_ true
6. $\overrightarrow{AX}$ is a bisector of $\angle BAC$.	_?_ false	$\overrightarrow{AX}$ is _?_ not a bisector of $\angle BAC$.	_?_ true

Write each conditional in if-then form. Underline the hypothesis once, and the conclusion twice.

7. Two perpendicular lines form four right angles.
If 2 lines are ⊥, then the lines form 4 rt. ∠s.

8. The measure of an obtuse angle is greater than 90, but less than 180.
If an ∠ is obt., then its measure is greater than 90, and less than 180.

9. The sum of two even numbers is even.
If 2 numbers are even, then their sum is even.

True or false? If true, verify. If false, give a counterexample.

10. If two points are in a plane, then the line that contains those points lies entirely in that plane. true; Post. 4

11. If two pairs of angles formed by two intersecting lines are congruent, then the lines are perpendicular. false; vert. ∠s are ≅ but need not be rt. ∠s.

Write in if-then form. Identify the hypothesis and conclusion. See side column.

B **12.** Two points determine a unique line.   **13.** A prime integer has only two factors.

14. An even number is a multiple of 2.   **15.** A negative integer is less than 0.

True or false? If false, give a counterexample.

16. If two angles are complements, then they are both acute. true

17. If three points are collinear, then they determine a unique plane. false; they lie in the intersection of many planes

18. If two lines intersect, then they form two pairs of vertical angles. true

19. If two numbers are odd, then their sum is even. true

C **20.** There exist counting numbers x and y such that $y + x = 0$. false; let x = 3

21. If $a^2 = b^2$, then $a = b$. false; let a = −3 and b = 3

2.1 Conditional Statements   **49**

12. If 2 points are given, then there is a unique line through the two points.

13. If an integer is prime, then the integer has exactly two factors.

14. If a number is even, then the number is a multiple of 2.

15. If an integer is negative, then it is less than 0.

Careers: Lawyer

Students should observe that lawyers are trained to know the existing laws and to use logical reasoning. Thus, lawyers can claim to be especially qualified to revise old laws, or write new ones, to interpret existing laws, and to administer state and local affairs in accordance with the laws.

Lesson Quiz

In Exercises 1–3, write each statement in if-then form, and underline each hypothesis once and each conclusion twice.

1. Two intersecting lines that form two adjacent congruent angles are perpendicular.

2. The two angles in a linear pair are supplementary.

3. The sum of an odd and an even number is even.

4. Tell whether each conditional above is true or false. If true, verify. If false, give a counterexample.

1. If two intersecting lines form two adjacent congruent angles, then the lines are perpendicular.

2. If two angles form a linear pair, then the angles are supplementary.

3. If one number is odd and another is even, then their sum is even.

4. 1. True; Theorem 1.11
   2. True; Linear Pair Postulate
   3. False; the sum of 1 and 2 is 3.

Critical Thinking

1. *Translating* Have students express statements in if-then form.

2. *Classifying* Ask students to classify conditional statements as true or false and to construct counterexamples for false ones.

3. *Application* Have students construct the negation of a conditional statement.

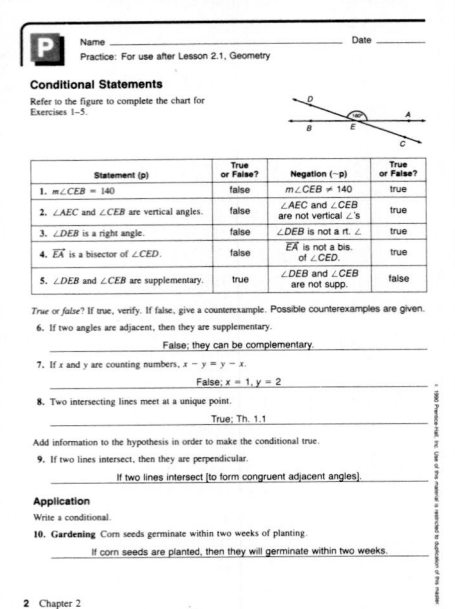

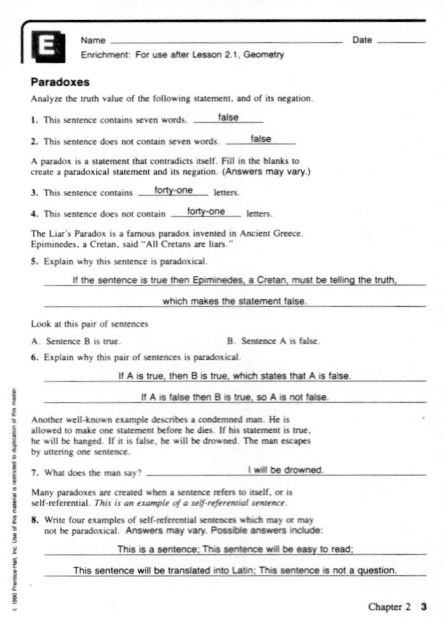

Add information to the hypothesis in order to make the conditional true.

22. If a number is a perfect square, then the square root is even.
If an even number . . .

23. If two angles are supplementary, then one is acute and one is obtuse.
If two ∠s are supp. and not ≅, . . .

Applications

Write a conditional that could apply to each situation.

24. Law The Constitution states these qualifications for becoming President: ''No person except a natural-born citizen, or a citizen of the United States at the time of the adoption of this Constitution, shall be eligible to the office of President; neither shall any person be eligible to that office who shall not have attained to the age of thirty-five years, and been fourteen years a resident within the United States.'' See side column.

25. Meteorology A weather forecaster predicts a snow storm and a possible accumulation of 3 to 5 inches. If it snows, then there will be an accumulation of 3 to 5 inches.

26. Sports The track team that finishes third wins a bronze medal. If the track team finishes third, then it will win a bronze medal.

Algebra Review

Solve.

27. $31 = 2x + 9$ 11

28. $8c - 6 = 3c + 14$ 4

29. $3(y - 2) = 15$ 7

Developing Mathematical Power

30. Writing in Mathematics Write a negation for Example 1c that does not involve the use of the word ''not.'' Explain. Acute angles measure less than 90°. Possible explanation: "less than" can be thought of as the negation of "equal to or more."

31. Writing in Mathematics If you were to form a math club, what would be the conditions for membership? Write five conditions in if-then form. Answers may vary.

CAREERS

The logical arguments presented in courts of law are well known to us via stories in movies, television programs, novels, and news reports. Lawyers must work with the laws and the conclusions drawn from these laws. Laws are the counterpart of postulates, and conclusions drawn are akin to theorems. When candidates send out their background information at election time, note how many are lawyers. Why might lawyers make good candidates?

Additional Answer
24. If a person is a natural-born citizen, or a citizen of the United States at the time of the adoption of this Constitution, and is at least 35 years old and has been a resident within the U.S. for 14 years, then the person is eligible to the office of President. (The converse is also acceptable.)

Converses, Inverses, and Contrapositives

Objectives: To state the converse, inverse, and contrapositive of a conditional
To recognize logically equivalent statements
To form biconditionals and identify definitions

Everyday life is filled with conditional statements. Related statements can be written by using the hypothesis and conclusion of a given conditional.

Investigation — *Thinking Critically*

Newspaper headlines are designed to convey a quick message. They often imply more than what is printed. In the newspaper headline, let *p* be the hypothesis, and let *q* be the conclusion. See page 702.

1. State the hypothesis.

2. State the conclusion.

3. Form each of the following statements.

    a. If *q*, then *p*.   **b.** If ~*p*, then ~*q*.   **c.** If ~*q*, then ~*p*.

4. Which of these statements does the headline imply is true?

5. Could each of these statements be true? Explain.

> **CALIFORNIA**
> ■ Break or Take?
>
> If Candidate Lee wins in California, she will win her party's presidential nomination.

Three related if-then statements are formed by switching and/or negating the hypothesis and conclusion of a conditional.

Table 1

Type	Form	Statement	True or False?
Conditional	If *p*, then *q*.	If two angles are vertical, then they are congruent.	True
Converse	If *q*, then *p*.	If two angles are congruent, then they are vertical.	False
Inverse	If ~*p*, then ~*q*.	If two angles are *not* vertical, then they are *not* congruent.	False
Contrapositive	If ~*q*, then ~*p*.	If two angles are *not* congruent, then they are *not* vertical.	True

Developing Mathematical Power

Cooperative Learning   Provide each group with Enrichment, p. 6, in the *Teacher's Resource Book* (see side column, p. 55). Have them complete the sheet and discuss their answers to questions 6–10. Each group can create a similar worksheet to share with the class.

LESSON PLAN

Vocabulary
Biconditional   Inverse
Contrapositive   Logically
Converse   equivalent

Materials/Manipulatives
Advertisements
Teacher's Resource Book,
  Teaching Aid 2
Teaching Transparency 9

Technology
Computer Test Bank, pp. 100–107

LESSON FOCUS

Review
- Put the following four sentences on the chalkboard. Ask which are true and how are they related.

1. If $m\angle A = 45$, then $\angle A$ is acute. true
2. If $\angle A$ is acute, then $m\angle A = 45$. false
3. If $m\angle A \neq 45$, then $\angle A$ is not an acute angle. false
4. If $\angle A$ is not an acute angle, then $m\angle A \neq 45$. true

In 1 and 2, the hyp. and concl. are interchanged. In 3, the hyp. and concl. are the negations of 1. Hyp. and concl. of 4 are the negations of 2. The hyp. and concl. of 3 and 4 are interchanged.

- The Mixed Review Exercises 26–32 involve concepts from Lessons 1.3 to 1.6.

Alternative Learning Styles
- Students visualize the implications of a newspaper headline in the Investigation.
- Have students choose one of their favorite ads and examine the conditional viewpoint and then discuss the relative merits of the ads.

CHALKBOARD EXAMPLES

- **For Example 1**

  State the following in if-then form. Give the converse, inverse, and contrapositive. Give the truth value of the four statements.

  Two lines that intersect to form a pair of congruent adjacent angles are perpendicular.

  If two lines intersect to form a pair of congruent adjacent angles, then the two lines are perpendicular. true
  Converse: If two lines are perpendicular, then the two lines intersect to form a pair of congruent adjacent angles. true
  Inverse: If two lines do not intersect to form a pair of congruent adjacent angles, then the two lines are not perpendicular. true
  Contrapositive: If two lines are not perpendicular, then the two lines do not intersect to form a pair of congruent adjacent angles. true

- **For Example 2**

  State the truth value of each conditional statement and its converse, inverse, and contrapositive.

  a. If two lines are perpendicular, then they form two pairs of congruent angles.
  b. If two angles are supplementary, then they are right angles.

  a. Conditional: true; Converse: false; Inverse: false; Contrapositive: true
  b. Conditional: false; Converse: true; Inverse: true; Contrapositive: false

EXAMPLE 1 **For the following conditional, write the converse, inverse, and contrapositive, and the truth values of all four statements.**

If an angle is a right angle, then it has a measure of 90.

Type	Statement	True or False?
Conditional	If an angle is a right angle, then it has a measure of 90.	True
Converse	If an angle has a measure of 90, then it is a right angle.	True
Inverse	If an angle is *not* a right angle, then it does *not* have a measure of 90.	True
Contrapositive	If an angle does *not* have a measure of 90, then it is *not* a right angle.	True

EXAMPLE 2 **State the truth values of each conditional statement and its converse, inverse, and contrapositive.**

a. If an angle is obtuse, then its measure is 130.
b. If an angle is acute, then its measure is 130.

a. Conditional: False
   Converse: True
   Inverse: True
   Contrapositive: False

b. Conditional: False
   Converse: False
   Inverse: False
   Contrapositive: False

Note the patterns in the truth values of the four related statements from Table 1 and Examples 1 and 2.

	Conditional If p, then q.	Converse If q, then p.	Inverse If $\sim p$, then $\sim q$.	Contrapositive If $\sim q$, then $\sim p$.
Table 1	True	False	False	True
Example 1	True	True	True	True
Example 2a	False	True	True	False
Example 2b	False	False	False	False

These patterns suggest the following rules of logic.

A conditional and its contrapositive have the same truth value.
The converse and inverse of any conditional have the same truth value.
The truth value of a converse *may* or *may not* be the same as that of its conditional.

Statements that have the same truth value are called **logically equivalent** statements. What types of statements are always logically equivalent?
a conditional and its contrapositive; its converse and its inverse

52 Chapter 2 The Logic of Geometry

A **biconditional** is an "if and only if" statement. It combines a conditional and its converse into one statement. Every *definition* is a biconditional. If and only if is abbreviated "iff."

Conditional	+	Converse	=	Biconditional
If p, then q.		If q, then p.		p if and only if q.
If two angles are congruent, then they have the same measure.		If two angles have the same measure, then they are congruent.		Two angles are congruent iff they have the same measure.

EXAMPLE 3   **State the truth value of the conditional, converse, and biconditional.**

      a. Two lines form congruent adjacent angles if and only if the two lines are perpendicular.

      b. Two angles are congruent iff the angles are right angles.

      a. True, true, true   **b.** False, true, false

The pattern discovered in Example 3 leads to two more rules of logic.

A biconditional is true when both its conditional and converse are true.
A biconditional is false when either its conditional or converse is false.

CLASS EXERCISES

Thinking Critically

Explain why these definitions are not satisfactory. Then, correct the definitions and restate them as biconditionals. See side column.

1. An angle is a set of points consisting of two noncollinear rays.

2. Adjacent angles are two coplanar angles that have a common side.

State the truth value for each conditional. Then form the converse, inverse, and contrapositive and give their truth values. See page 702.

3. If two angles are both acute, then the two angles are complementary.

4. If two nonright angles are supplementary, then one of the angles is obtuse and the other is acute.

5. If two angles are supplementary, then the sum of the measures of the two angles is 180.

6. If two angles are supplementary, then they form a linear pair.

State the biconditional for each and give its truth value.

7. Exercise 3   **8.** Exercise 4   **9.** Exercise 5   **10.** Exercise 6

1. The rays may not intersect at their endpoints; e.g., 2 noncollinear rays that are not an ∠. Add "with a common endpoint"; a set of points is an ∠ iff it consists of 2 noncollinear rays with a common endpoint.
2. The common side may not be between the ∠s. Add "between them"; two coplanar∠s are adjacent ∠s iff they have a common vertex and a common side between them.

PRACTICE EXERCISES

State the truth value for each conditional. Then form the converse, inverse, and contrapositive and give the truth value for each.
See Additional Answers, p. 702.

A
1. If two angles are adjacent angles, then they are complementary.

2. If two angles are congruent, then the two angles are right angles.

3. If two lines are perpendicular, then they intersect to form a right angle.

4. If two segments are congruent, then they have equal measures.

5. If $m\angle 1 = m\angle 2$, then $m\angle 2 = m\angle 1$.

6. If $m\angle 3 < m\angle 4$, then $m\angle 4 < m\angle 3$.

7. If Sam went to the prom, then he bought flowers.

Write the biconditional for each and give its truth value.

8. Exercise 1   9. Exercise 4   10. Exercise 7

State the true conditional and converse for each definition.

11. An angle is obtuse if and only if its measure is greater than 90 and less than 180. If the meas. of an $\angle$ is greater than 90 and less than 180, then the $\angle$ is obt. If an $\angle$ is obt., then its meas. is greater than 90 and less than 180.
12. Points are collinear if and only if the points lie on the same line. If 2 or more pts. lie in the same line, then the pts. are colli. If 2 or more pts. are colli., then the pts. lie on the same line.

Write a statement that is logically equivalent to each conditional.

13. If a youngster misbehaves, then his or her allowance is stopped. If a youngster's allowance is not stopped, then the youngster has not misbehaved.
14. If two lines are perpendicular, then the four angles formed are congruent. If the 4 $\angle$s formed by 2 intersecting lines are not $\cong$, then the lines are not $\perp$.

Write a pair of logically equivalent statements in if-then form.
See Additional Answers, p. 702.

B
15. The sum of two negative integers is negative.

16. Coplanar points lie in the same plane.

State the truth value for each conditional. Then write the related biconditional and give its truth value.

17. Two intersecting lines lie in exactly one plane. true; two lines lie in one plane iff they are intersecting; false
18. Adjacent complementary angles have exterior sides that are perpendicular. True; the noncommon sides of 2 adj. $\angle$s are $\perp$ iff the 2 $\angle$s are comp.; true.

Form the converse, inverse, and contrapositive and give their truth values.
See Additional Answers, p. 702.
19. If $3x - 7 = 11$, then $x = 6$.   20. If $y = 9$, then $y^2 - 1 = 80$.

Each statement represents the inverse of a conditional. State the conditional, the converse, and the contrapositive. See Additional Answers, p. 702.

C 21. If M is between X and Y but not the midpoint of $\overline{XY}$, then $XM \neq MY$.

22. If $\overrightarrow{OX}$ is the bisector of $\angle AOB$, then $2m\angle AOX = m\angle AOB$.

23. If two angles are not congruent, then the two angles are not vertical.

Applications

24. **Meteorology** The weather forecaster said that if the hurricane continues on its present course, people living near the ocean will have to be evacuated. If people living near the ocean were not evacuated, what conclusion can you draw? The hurricane did not continue on its course.

25. **Entertainment** A television studio will broadcast a movie if the baseball game is rained out. If the movie is not broadcast, what can you conclude? The baseball game was not rained out.

Mixed Review

H is between G and I. Find:

26. GH 3   27. HI 28. GI

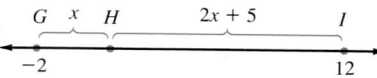

26. GH 3

Draw $\angle JKL$ with between ray, $\overrightarrow{KM}$. Find $m\angle JKM$ and $m\angle MKL$ using the information given.

29. $\overrightarrow{KM}$ bisects $\angle JKL$; $m\angle JKL = 48$. 24, 24

30. $m\angle JKM = 2m\angle MKL$; $m\angle JKL = 57$. 38, 19

31. $m\angle JKM = 3m\angle MKL$; $\angle JKM$ and $\angle MKL$ are complementary angles. 67.5, 22.5

32. $\overrightarrow{JK}$ and $\overrightarrow{KL}$ are perpendicular; $m\angle JKM = \frac{1}{2} m\angle MKL$. 30, 60

Developing Mathematical Power

Thinking Critically Determine if the resulting statement is the conditional, inverse, converse, or contrapositive.

33. The converse of the inverse contrapositive

34. The inverse of the contrapositive converse

35. The converse of the contrapositive inverse

36. The contrapositive of the inverse converse

37. The inverse of the converse contrapositive

38. The contrapositive of the converse inverse

39. The converse of the converse conditional

Teacher's Resource Book

Follow-Up Investigation—Chapter 2, p. 4

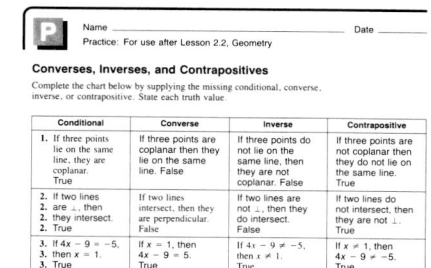

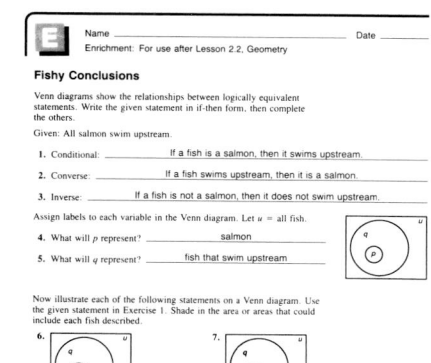

Vocabulary
Algebraic properties
Proof
Reflexive property
Symmetric property
Transitive property

Materials/Manipulatives
Teacher's Resource Book,
  Teaching Aid 2
Teaching Transparency 10

Technology
Computer Test Bank,
  pp. 107–118

LESSON FOCUS

Review
- Have students write the number that will make the conditional true.
  1. If $x = 3$, then $x + \underline{\ ?\ } = 4$.
  2. If $x = \underline{\ ?\ }$, then $3x = 12$.
  3. If $x = \underline{\ ?\ }$, then $\frac{2}{5}x = \frac{1}{5}$.
  4. If $x = 5$, then $x - 3 = \underline{\ ?\ }$.
  5. If $x = 9$, then $2x + 5 = \underline{\ ?\ }$.

  1. 1 2. 4 3. $\frac{1}{2}$ 4. 2 5. 23

Alternative Learning Styles
- In the Investigation, the algebraic properties are used in a logical sequence of steps to introduce students to the flow of a proof.
- Manipulation involving cut-outs, paper folding, and matching can be used to illustrate the properties of algebra. For example, for the addition property, students can draw a line segment 10 cm long, locate the midpoint, and cut the segment at the midpoint. Then, by labeling one piece of the line segment a and the other b, they can match the segments to show that $a = b$. By extending each segment 3 cm and matching the segments again, they will prove the addition property of equality.

2.3

Properties from Algebra

Objectives: To recognize and use algebraic properties as reasons to justify steps in geometric problems

To use the reflexive, symmetric, and transitive properties for congruence

In algebra, the facts about real numbers and equality are listed as "properties." The properties of geometry are assumed as *postulates* or proved as *theorems*.

Investigation—*Thinking Critically*

Study this logical sequence of statements.

$a = b$	Given (Assume the hypothesis true.)
$a + c = a + c$	Reflexive property
$a + c = b + c$	Substitution property

1. Can you find any real numbers a, b, and c which satisfy the first two lines of the sequence, but not the last line? no
2. Write the conditional statement that would summarize this sequence. If $a = b$, then $a + c = b + c$.
3. What algebraic property does that conditional statement represent? addition

The following properties are true for all real numbers, a, b, c, and d.

Properties of Equality

Addition: If $a = b$, then $a + c = b + c$.

Subtraction: If $a = b$, then $a - c = b - c$.

Multiplication: If $a = b$, then $ca = cb$.

Division: If $a = b$, and $c \neq 0$, then $\frac{a}{c} = \frac{b}{c}$.

Distributive: $a(b + c) = a \cdot b + a \cdot c$ and $a \cdot b + a \cdot c = a(b + c)$

Substitution: If $a + b = c$ and $b = d$, then $a + d = c$.

Reflexive: $a = a$

Symmetric: If $a = b$, then $b = a$.

Transitive: If $a = b$ and $b = c$, then $a = c$.

Note in Example 1 that these properties are used to justify algebraic statements.

Developing Mathematical Power

Keeping a Portfolio   Have students draw geometric examples for each of the following properties: substitution, reflexive, symmetric, and transitive. For each property, have them provide an example using line segments and an example using angles. Use Teaching Transparency 10 when discussing their work.

EXAMPLE 1   Given the following conditional, support each statement in this justification with a reason.

$$\text{If } 2(5x - 3) = 8 + 3x, \text{ then } x = 2.$$

$2(5x - 3) = 8 + 3x$	?
$10x - 6 = 8 + 3x$	Distributive property
$10x = 14 + 3x$	?
$7x = 14$	?
$x = 2$	?

Reasons: Given; Addition property; Subtraction property; Division property

The above properties can also be used to justify statements in geometry. A logical sequence of *statements* with their supporting *reasons* is called a **proof.**

> **Theorem 2.1**   Congruence of segments is reflexive, symmetric, and transitive.   Proved in Practice Exercises 19 and 20 and in Example 2

Example 2 is a *proof* of the transitive property of congruent segments.

EXAMPLE 2   Write a convincing argument, or proof, for this conditional:
If $\overline{AB} \cong \overline{CD}$ and $\overline{CD} \cong \overline{EF}$, then $\overline{AB} \cong \overline{EF}$.

$\overline{AB} \cong \overline{CD}$ and $\overline{CD} \cong \overline{EF}$	Given (Assume the hypothesis is true.)
$AB = CD$ and $CD = EF$	Definition of congruent segments
$AB = EF$	Transitive property of equality
$\overline{AB} \cong \overline{EF}$	Definition of congruent segments

> **Theorem 2.2**   Congruence of angles is reflexive, symmetric, and transitive.   Proved in Practice Exercises 21, 22, and 23

EXAMPLE 3   Write a proof for this conditional: If $\angle A$ and $\angle B$ are complements and $m\angle B = 4m\angle A$, then $m\angle A = 18$ and $m\angle B = 72$.

$\angle A$ and $\angle B$ are complements; $m\angle B = 4m\angle A$	Given (Assume the hypothesis.)
$m\angle A + m\angle B = 90$	Definition of complementary angles
$m\angle A + 4m\angle A = 90$	Substitution property
$5m\angle A = 90$	Distributive property
$m\angle A = 18$	Division property
$m\angle B = 4 \times 18 = 72$	Substitution property

Developing Mathematical Power

Cooperative Learning   Have each group work through Exercises 33–35 on p. 61. Encourage them to list their statements and reasons as in Example 1. When they share their answers, discuss different steps that were taken to reach the same conclusion. Is any one method more correct?

TEACHING SUGGESTIONS

- Illustrate the use of each property by having students use the property to solve an equation. For example, begin by using the addition property to solve $x - 3 = 29$. For the remainder of the properties, ask students to propose appropriate equations.

- Many students are puzzled by the reflexive property. Point out that later in the course they will use the reflexive property to show that in figures such as the one below, $\overline{AC} \cong \overline{AC}$ (or $AC = AC$).

  That will enable them to show that $\triangle ABC$ and $\triangle ADC$ have the same size and shape.

  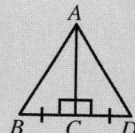

- Students may question the need for Theorems 2.1 and 2.2. Tell them that these theorems will shorten their work later in the course.

Critical Thinking

Classifying   Ask students to propose equations whose solution requires the use of specific algebraic properties.

CHALKBOARD EXAMPLES

- **For Example 1**
  In the following justification, support each statement with a reason.
  If $2x = 7(180 - x)$, then $x = 140$.
  $$2x = 7(180 - x)$$
  $$2x = 1260 - 7x$$
  $$2x + 7x = 1260$$
  $$9x = 1260$$
  $$x = 140$$

  Reasons: Given; Distributive property; Addition property; Distributive property; Division property

- **For Example 2**

  (Either demonstrate one of Practice Exercises 19–23, p. 59, or use the following to demonstrate the use of the transitive property of congruent segments.) Write a convincing argument, or proof, for this conditional: If $\overline{AB} \cong \overline{CD}$, $\overline{CD} \cong \overline{DE}$, and $\overline{DE} \cong \overline{FG}$, then $\overline{AB} \cong \overline{FG}$.

$\overline{AB} \cong \overline{CD}$,	
$\overline{CD} \cong \overline{DE}$	Given
$\overline{AB} \cong \overline{DE}$	Trans. prop. of $\cong$ seg.
$\overline{DE} \cong \overline{FG}$	Given
$\overline{AB} \cong \overline{FG}$	Trans. prop. of $\cong$ seg.

- **For Example 3**

  Write a convincing argument, or proof, for this conditional: If $\angle A$ and $\angle B$ are supplements and $m\angle B = 5m\angle A$, then $m\angle A = 30$ and $m\angle B = 150$.

$\angle A$ and $\angle B$ are supplements;	Given
$m\angle B = 5m\angle A$	
$m\angle A + m\angle B = 180$	Def. of supp. $\angle$s
$m\angle A + 5m\angle A = 180$	Subst. prop.
$6m\angle A = 180$	Distrib. prop.
$m\angle A = 30$	Div. prop.
$m\angle B = 5m\angle A = 150$	Subst. prop.

Common Error

- Some students may have trouble supplying reasons for statements. They may need to have a list of the algebraic properties and geometric definitions in front of them until they are memorized.
- See *Teacher's Resource Book* for additional remediation.

LESSON FOLLOW-UP

Assignment Guide
See p. 44B for assignments.

CLASS EXERCISES

Name the properties that justify the steps taken.

1. $x + 5 = -7$
$x = -12$ subtr.

2. $\dfrac{x}{5} = 10$
$x = 50$ mult.

3. $37 = x$
$x = 37$ sym.

4. $x = -4 - 2x$
$3x = -4$ add., distrib.

5. $3\left(\dfrac{x}{3} - 7\right) = \dfrac{2}{3}$
$x - 21 = \dfrac{2}{3}$ distrib.

6. $m\angle A + m\angle B = 180$
$180 = m\angle A + m\angle B$ sym.

Use the named property to complete the statement.

7. Subtraction: $m\angle A + m\angle B = m\angle C + m\angle B$, so $m\angle A = \underline{?}$ $m\angle C$
120

8. Substitution: $m\angle A = 90$ and $m\angle A + 30 = m\angle B$, so $m\angle B = \underline{?}$

Support each statement with a reason.

9. $\dfrac{x - 20}{5} = 10$ Given
$x - 20 = 50$ $\underline{?}$ Mult. prop.
$x = 70$ $\underline{?}$ Add. prop.

10. $18 - 3x = 0$ Given
$-3x = -18$ $\underline{?}$ Subtr. prop.
$x = 6$ $\underline{?}$ Div. prop.

PRACTICE EXERCISES

Name the properties that justify the steps taken.

A
1. $\overline{RS} \cong \overline{XY}$; thus, $\overline{XY} \cong \overline{RS}$ Sym. prop. of congruence
2. $AB = RS$; thus, $2AB = 2RS$ Mult. prop.
3. $m\angle P + m\angle Q = m\angle R + m\angle Q$; thus, $m\angle P = m\angle R$ Subtr. prop.
4. $\angle P \cong \angle Q$ and $\angle Q \cong \angle R$; thus, $\angle P \cong \angle R$ Trans. prop. of congruence

Support each statement with a reason.

5. $4\left(\dfrac{x}{2} - 6\right) = 8$ Given
$2x - 24 = 8$ $\underline{?}$ Distrib. prop.

6. $x = 7 - 3x$ Given
$4x = 7$ $\underline{?}$ Add. prop. Distrib. prop.

7. $m\angle A + m\angle B = 180$ Given
$m\angle B = 80$ Given
$m\angle A + 80 = 180$ $\underline{?}$ Subst. prop.

8. $m\angle A = 3m\angle B$ Given
$m\angle A + m\angle B = 180$ Given
$3m\angle B + m\angle B = 180$ $\underline{?}$ Subst. prop.

Use the named property to complete the statement.

9. Reflexive: $m\angle A + m\angle B = \underline{?}$
$m\angle A + m\angle B$
10. Division: $3m\angle A = 90$, so $m\angle A = \underline{?}$
30
11. Transitive: $\overline{AX} \cong \overline{BY}$ and $\overline{BY} \cong \overline{CZ}$, so $\overline{AX} \cong \underline{?}$ $\overline{CZ}$

58   Chapter 2 The Logic of Geometry

58

Support each statement with a reason.

12. $7 = 2x - 5$ Given
  $12 = 2x$ _?_ Add. prop.
  $6 = x$ _?_ Div. prop.
  $x = 6$ _?_ Sym. prop.

13. $1 = 3\left(x + \dfrac{8}{3}\right) - 1$ Given

  $2 = 3\left(x + \dfrac{8}{3}\right)$ _?_ Add. prop.

  $2 = 3x + 8$ _?_ Distrib. prop.
  $-6 = 3x$ _?_ Subtr. prop.
  $-2 = x$ _?_ Div. prop.
  $x = -2$ _?_ Sym. prop.

Use the given property to complete the statement.

14. Reflexive property: $HK = $ _?_ HK

15. Transitive property: If $\angle 1 \cong \angle 2$, and $\angle 2 \cong \angle 4$, then _?_. $\angle 1 \cong \angle 4$

16. Substitution property: If $m\angle 1 + m\angle 4 = 90$, and $m\angle 4 = m\angle 6$, then
_?_. $m\angle 1 + m\angle 6 = 90$

17. Subtraction property: If $RS + TP = MN + RS$, then _?_. $TP = MN$

18. Addition property: If $AB = VT$, and $CD = XY$, then _?_. $AB + CD = VT + XY$

In Exercises 19–23, complete the proofs for each part of Theorems 2.1 and 2.2. Support each statement with a reason.

19. Congruence of segments is reflexive.
If $\overline{AB}$ is a segment, then $\overline{AB} \cong \overline{AB}$.

$\overline{AB}$	_?_ Given
AB	_?_ Def. of seg. measure
$AB = AB$	_?_ Refl. prop.
$\overline{AB} \cong \overline{AB}$	_?_ Def. of $\cong$ segments

20. Congruence of segments is symmetric.
If $\overline{AB} \cong \overline{CD}$, then $\overline{CD} \cong \overline{AB}$.

$\overline{AB} \cong \overline{CD}$	_?_ Given
$AB = CD$	_?_ Def. of $\cong$ segments
$CD = AB$	_?_ Sym. prop.
$\overline{CD} \cong \overline{AB}$	_?_ Def. of $\cong$ segments

21. Congruence of angles is reflexive.
If A is an angle, then $\angle A \cong \angle A$.

$\angle A$	_?_ Given
$m\angle A$	_?_ Protractor Post.
$m\angle A = m\angle A$	_?_ Refl. prop.
$\angle A \cong \angle A$	_?_ Def. of $\cong \angle$s

22. Congruence of angles is symmetric.
If $\angle A \cong \angle B$, then $\angle B \cong \angle A$.

$\angle A \cong \angle B$	_?_ Given
$m\angle A = m\angle B$	_?_ Def. of $\cong \angle$s
$m\angle B = m\angle A$	_?_ Sym. prop.
$\angle B \cong \angle A$	_?_ Def. of $\cong \angle$s

23. Congruence of angles is transitive.
If $\angle A \cong \angle B$ and $\angle B \cong \angle C$, then $\angle A \cong \angle C$.

$\angle A \cong \angle B$ and $\angle B \cong \angle C$	_?_ Given
$m\angle A = m\angle B$ and $m\angle B = m\angle C$	_?_ Def. of $\cong \angle$s
$m\angle A = m\angle C$	_?_ Trans. prop.
$\angle A \cong \angle C$	_?_ Def. of $\cong \angle$s

Test Yourself

See *Teacher's Resource Book, Tests,* pp. 13–14.

Lesson Quiz

Supply the justification.

1. $6(\frac{x}{3} - 3) = 4$ Given
   $2x - 18 = 4$?

2. $x = 4x - 9$ Given
   $-3x = -9$?

3. $180 = m\angle 1 + m\angle 2$ Given
   $m\angle 1 + m\angle 2 = 180$?

4. $\angle 1 \cong \angle 2$ and $\angle 2 \cong \angle 3$ Given
   $\angle 1 \cong \angle 3$?

5. Supply the reasons for the justification: If $m\angle 1 + m\angle 2 = 100$ and $m\angle 2 = 4m\angle 1$, then $m\angle 1 = 20$ and $m\angle 2 = 80$.
   $m\angle 1 + m\angle 2 = 100; m\angle 2 = 4m\angle 1$?
   $m\angle 1 + 4m\angle 1 = 100$?
   $5m\angle 1 = 100$?
   $m\angle 1 = 20$?
   $m\angle 2 = 4m\angle 1 = 4(20) = 80$?

1. Distributive property
2. Subtraction property
3. Symmetric property
4. Transitive property of congruence
5. Given; Substitution; Distributive property; Division property; Substitution

Enrichment

State three pairs of congruences involving sides or angles of two triangles.

a.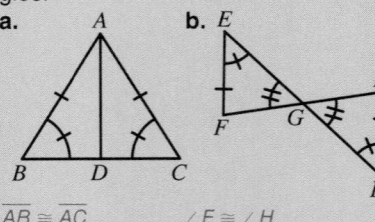

b. E

$\overline{AB} \cong \overline{AC}$ $\angle E \cong \angle H$
$\angle B \cong \angle C$ $\overline{EF} \cong \overline{HK}$
$\overline{AD} \cong \overline{AD}$ $\angle EGF \cong \angle HGK$

Supply the missing statements or reasons.

24. If $-6 = 2(x + 2)$, then $x = -5$.

$-6 = 2(x + 2)$? Given
$-6 = 2x + 4$?   ? Distrib. prop.
$-10 = 2x$? Subtr. prop.
$x = -5$ $-5 = x$? Div. prop.
           ?   ? Sym. prop.

25. If $-\frac{4}{3}(x - 2) = 8$, then $x = -4$.

$-\frac{4}{3}(x - 2) = 8$? Given
$x - 2 = -6$? Mult. prop.
      ?   ? Add. prop.
$x = -4$

26. If $\angle A$ and $\angle B$ are supplements and $m\angle A = 5m\angle B$, then $m\angle A = 150$ and $m\angle B = 30$.

$\angle A$ and $\angle B$ are supplements.   ? Given
$m\angle A = 5m\angle B$? Given
   ? $m\angle A + m\angle B = 180$ Definition of supplementary angles
$5m\angle B + m\angle B = 180$? Subst. prop.
   ? $6m\angle B = 180$? Distrib. prop.
$m\angle B = $? 30 ? Div. prop.
$m\angle A = $? $5m\angle B = 150$? Subst. prop.

27. Put these algebraic statements in logical order. Explain your answer.

$2x - 12 = 20; x = 16; \frac{2(x - 6)}{5} = 4; 2x = 32; 2(x - 6) = 20$ $\frac{2(x - 6)}{5} = 4$,

given; $2(x - 6) = 20$, mult. prop.; $2x - 12 = 20$, distrib. prop.; $2x = 32$, add. prop.; $x = 16$, div. prop.

Prove these conditionals with a sequence of statements and reasons.

See Additional Answers, p. 702.

C **28.** If $3x + 6y = 9$ and $6x - 5y = -33$, then $y = 3$. (Use substitution.)

29. If the measure of a supplement of $\angle R$ is seven times greater than the measure of its complement, then $m\angle R = 75$.

30. If the measure of a supplement of $\angle D$ is 15 greater than four times the measure of its complement, then $m\angle D = 65$.

Applications

31. Finance Fifty shares of stock X are worth 30 shares of stock B, and 30 shares of stock B are worth 20 shares of stock Y. Explain why 50 shares of stock X are worth 20 shares of stock Y.
If $50X = 30B$ and $30B = 20Y$, then $50X = 20Y$ by the trans. prop.

32. Science This pan balance scale was even until a 10-g weight was removed from the left pan. There are only these weights available: one 5-g, two 3-g, three 2-g. Give at least two possible ways to replace the 10-g weight and explain why your answers work. one 5-g, one 3-g, one 2-g or two 3-g, two 2-g; subst. prop.

Additional Answer for p. 61

14. $\angle A$ and $\angle B$ are complements.   Given
$m\angle A = 9m\angle B$ Given
$m\angle A + m\angle B = 90$ Def. of comp.
$9m\angle B + m\angle B = 90$ Subst. prop.

$10m\angle B = 90$ Distrib. prop.
$m\angle B = 9$ Div. prop.
$m\angle A = 81$ Subst. prop.

Developing Mathematical Power

Thinking Critically Apply the properties of equality to reason logically from the first equation to the second. Answers may vary.

33. $x = 3$; $3x - 7 = x - 1$ $x = 3, 2x = 6, 2x - 7 = -1, 3x - 7 = x - 1$

34. $x = -5$; $5x - 9 = 2(2x - 7)$ $x = -5, x - 9 = -14, 5x - 9 = 4x - 14, 5x - 9 = 2(2x - 7)$

35. $x = 16$: $1\frac{3}{4}x - 4 = 8 + x$ $x = 16, 3x = 48, \frac{3}{4}x = 12, 1\frac{3}{4}x = 12 + x, 1\frac{3}{4}x - 4 = 8 + x$

TEST YOURSELF

Tell whether the statement is true or false. Then, write the negation and tell whether it is true or false.

1. -4 is the solution of $-3x = 12$. true; -4 is not the solution of $-3x = 12$; false   2.1

2. A right angle has a measure of 90. true; a rt $\angle$ does not have a measure of 90; false

3. An odd integer is divisible by 2. false; an odd integer is not divisible by 2; true

4. The sum of the measures of two supplementary angles is 90. false; the sum of the measures of two supp. $\angle$s is not 90; true

Write each conditional in if-then form. Underline the hypothesis once and the conclusion twice. See side column.

5. A student whose average is above 70% passes the course.

6. Exactly one plane contains a given line and a point not on that line.

7. An even integer has an even ones digit.

8. A right angle has a measure less than 180.

True or false? If false, give a counterexample.

9. If an angle is obtuse, then its measure is greater than 100. false; an $\angle$ measuring between 90 and 100 is also ob.

10. If two angles are supplementary and adjacent, then they are right angles. false; the measures of any pair of noncongruent adj. $\angle$s whose sum is 180 could be used as a counterexample

11. State the truth value of the conditional. Then form the converse, inverse, and contrapositive and give the truth value of each.   2.2

If two angles have measures of 35 and 55, then they are complementary. true. See Additional Answers, p. 702.

12. Which pairs of statements in Exercise 11 are logically equivalent? cond. and contr.; conv. and inv.

13. Explain how a biconditional is formed and when it is true. See Additional Answers, p. 702.

14. Prove this conditional with a sequence of statements and reasons.   2.3

If $\angle A$ and $\angle B$ are complements and $m\angle A = 9m\angle B$, then $m\angle B = 9$ and $m\angle A = 81$. See side column page 60.

2.3 Properties from Algebra   **61**

---

5. If a student has an average above 70%, then the student passes the course.
6. If a set of points consists of a line and a point not on that line, then there is exactly one plane that contains the line and the point.
7. If a number is even, then it has an even ones digit.
8. If an angle is a right angle, then its measure is less than 180.

P Name _____ Date _____
Practice: For use after Lesson 2.3, Geometry

Properties of Algebra
Name the properties that justify the steps taken.

1. $AB = EF$; therefore $AB + CD = EF + CD$. ___ Add. prop.
2. $\angle ABC \cong \angle Q$; therefore $\angle Q = \angle ABC$. ___ Sym. prop. of congruence

Support each statement with a reason.

3. $5(y - x) = 20$ ___ Given
   $5y - 5x = 20$ ___ Distrib. prop.
4. $2x = m\angle C + x$ ___ Given
   $x = m\angle C$ ___ Subtr. prop.
5. $CD = AF - 2(CD)$ ___ Given
   $3(CD) = AF$ ___ Add. prop.
6. $(q - x) = r$ ___ Given
   $4(q - x) = 4r$ ___ Mult. prop.
7. $m\angle Q - m\angle R = 90$ ___ Given
   $m\angle Q = 4m\angle R$ ___ Given
   $4m\angle R - m\angle R = 90$ ___ Subst.
8. $m\angle AOX = 2m\angle XOB$ ___ Given
   $2m\angle XOB = 140$ ___ Given
   $m\angle AOX = 140$ ___ Trans. prop. or subst.

Supply the missing statements or reasons.

9. If $\angle P$ and $\angle Q$ are complements and $m\angle Q = 5m\angle P$, then $m\angle P = 15$ and $m\angle Q = 75$.

Statements	Reasons
1. $\angle P$ and $\angle Q$ are complements, $m\angle Q = 5m\angle P$	1. ___ Given
2. $m\angle P + m\angle Q = 90$	2. Definition of complementary angles
3. $m\angle P + 5m\angle Q = 90$	3. Substitution
4. $6m\angle P = 90$	4. Distributive Property
5. $m\angle P = 15$	5. ___ Division property
6. $m\angle Q = 5 \times 15 = 75$	6. Substitution

Application

10. **Sports** Two runners tie when running a race. If both runners improve their times by 5 s in the next race, how do you know they will tie again? ___ Subtraction property

8 Chapter 2

E Name _____ Date _____
Enrichment: For use after Lesson 2.3, Geometry

Changes
In the problems below, assume that you can use half-dollars, quarters, dimes, nickels, and pennies. Show key steps and justify your solution. Answers may vary.

1. What combination of 34 coins and nickels equals $2.40? $0.10a +$ $0.05b =$ ___ 2.40 ___ and $a + b =$ ___ 34 ___ . from the given conditions.
   $0.10a + 0.05(34 - a) = 2.40$, by substitution. $0.10a + 1.7 - 0.05a = 240$, by the distributive prop.; $a = 14$, $b = 20$ by subtr., distrib., div. and subst. prop.
   14 dimes and 20 nickels

2. If you have an equal number of each denomination of coins and the total is $4.55, how many coins do you have?
   $0.50a +$ ___ $0.25a + 0.10a + 0.05a + 0.01a$ ___ $= 4.55$ from the given conditions.
   $0.91a = 4.55$ so $a = 5$, by the distributive and division properties.
   Five of each denomination; twenty-five coins (since $5a = 25$)

3. Someone has suggested creating a new denomination of coin less than 50 cents. Five of the new coins will equal 10 of one existing coin and 20 of another. What is the denomination of the new coin? Explain how you arrived at your answer.
   If n = new coin, a, b existing coins, then by the given, $5n = 10a$ and $5n = 20b$.
   By the Symmetric and Transitive properties, $10a = 20b$. $a = 2b$ by division prop.
   $a = 10$, $b = 5$. a = dime, b = nickel, $5n = 20b$, $5n = 20 \times 5$, so $n = 20$.
   The new coin is 20¢.

4. What is the greatest number of coins that can be used to make change for a dollar? ___ 100 ___ the least? ___ 2 ___ How many ways are there to make change for a dollar that include at least one of each denomination of coin? List them.
   two: one of each plus a nickel and 4 pennies; one of each plus nine pennies.

Chapter 2 9

61

Vocabulary

Deductive   Given
  reasoning   Prove
Flow proof

Materials/Manipulatives

Teacher's Resource Book,
  Critical Thinking, p. 2
Teaching Transparency 11
Connections, p. 5

Technology

Computer Test Bank, pp.
  118–126

LESSON FOCUS

Review

Draw this figure on the chalkboard. Ask students to state and justify a conclusion they can reach, given each of the following conditions.

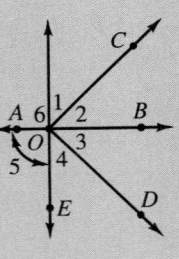

a. $\overrightarrow{OD}$ bisects ∠*BOE*.
b. ∠6 is a right angle.
c. $\overrightarrow{OD}$ is perpendicular to $\overrightarrow{OC}$.

a. ∠3 ≅ ∠4 (Def. of angle bisector)
b. $\overleftrightarrow{AO} \perp \overleftrightarrow{OE}$ (Def. of ⊥ lines)
c. ∠*COD* is a rt. ∠. (Def. of ⊥)

Alternative Learning Styles

Relating and comparing new concepts to familiar ones often clarifies them for students. If students create a flow chart for everyday experiences and see the necessity for *every* step, their transference of a flow process to flow proof will be facilitated.

Multicultural Opportunity

See Project, p. 65.

2.4   # Strategy: Use Logical Reasoning

When you reason logically from given statements to a desired conclusion, you are using **deductive reasoning.** In geometry, proving a conditional by deductive reasoning involves this process:

Assume the *hypothesis* (the **Given**) is true. ⟹ Apply appropriate postulates, proven theorems, and/or definitions in logical order. ⟹ Arrive at the *conclusion* (the **Prove**).

For example:

Given: Lines *k* and *l* intersect, and ∠1 ≅ ∠2

    ↓ *Use the theorem that states: If two lines intersect to form a pair of congruent adjacent angles, then the lines are perpendicular.*

Prove: $k \perp l$

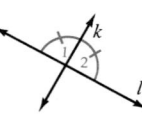

Given: $\overline{AB} \cong \overline{BC}$ and $\overline{BC} \cong \overline{DE}$

    ↓ *Use the theorem that states: Congruence of segments is transitive.*

Prove: $\overline{AB} \cong \overline{DE}$

You can use the problem solving guidelines to help you decide how to reason logically from a given statement to a desired conclusion.

EXAMPLE 1   **Given:** $\overline{AB}$
                 Prove: $AX + XY + YB = AB$

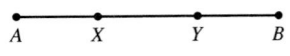

☐ **Understand the Problem**   **What information is given in the figure?** $\overline{AB}$; *X* is between *A* and *Y*, and *A* and *B*; *Y* is between *A* and *B*, and *X* and *B*.

☐ **Plan Your Approach**   **Look Back:** What postulates, proven theorems, or definitions have a conclusion that looks like the *Prove*?

     Look Ahead: What postulates, proven theorems, or definitions can take you from the *Given* to the *Prove*?

     Since between points are *Given* and the *Prove* has the form of a betweenness statement, apply the definition of betweenness.

62   Chapter 2 The Logic of Geometry

Developing Mathematical Power

Keeping a Portfolio   Have students write in their math journals the value of each of the four problem solving guidelines for doing a flow proof. What do they find most difficult in a flow proof?

Implement the Plan

Given: X is between A and B; Y is between X and B.

Use the definition of between points.

$$AX + XB = AB \qquad XY + YB = XB$$

Use the Substitution property.

Prove: $AX + XY + YB = AB$

Interpret the Results

If 2 points lie between the endpoints of a segment, then the sum of the 3 smaller segment lengths equals the length of the entire segment.

EXAMPLE 2

Given: $\overrightarrow{OB}$ is a bisector of $\angle AOC$;
$\angle 2 \cong \angle 3$
Prove: $\angle 1 \cong \angle 3$

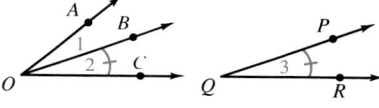

Understand the Problem

The bisector $\overrightarrow{OB}$ separates $\angle AOC$ into two adjacent angles, $\angle 1$ and $\angle 2$. The *Given* states that $\angle 2 \cong \angle 3$.

Plan Your Approach

Look Ahead: The definition of an angle bisector allows you to conclude that $\angle 1 \cong \angle 2$.

Look Back: Since the congruences involve three angles, the Transitive property might be applied.

Implement the Plan

Given: $\overrightarrow{OB}$ is a bisector of $\angle AOC$; $\angle 2 \cong \angle 3$

Use the definition of angle bisector.

$$\angle 1 \cong \angle 2$$

Use the Transitive property of congruent angles.

Prove: $\angle 1 \cong \angle 3$

Interpret the Results

If a given angle is congruent to one of the two angles formed by an angle bisector, then it is congruent to the other angle.

Examples 1 and 2 are illustrations of a type of proof called a *flow proof*.

Additional Answer for p. 64

1. Logic; A conditional statement is a declaration that something is true under certain conditions. Begin with postulates—statements that are assumed true. Given valid postulates, we interconnect two or more postulates and/or some definitions to form a theorem. If we accept as true the conditions of the theorem, we agree to the conclusion. If the correct postulates, definitions, previously-proven theorems or algebraic properties are chosen in the correct sequence, then the resulting conclusion must be true.

TEACHING SUGGESTIONS

- For some time to come, it may help students if you prominently display posters listing key postulates, definitions, and previously proven theorems.

- The *Look Ahead/Look Back* strategy described under Plan Your Approach is intended to help students see how to get from the hypothesis (*Given*) to the conclusion (*Prove*). In this lesson's short proofs, students will get more help from the *Look Ahead* part, but the *Look Back* strategy will prepare them for the longer proofs they will encounter later in the course.

- Under Implement the Plan, a flow-proof format is used to ease students' introduction to deductive reasoning. The next lesson will introduce the more formal two-column proof.

CHALKBOARD EXAMPLES

- **For Example 1**

  Given: B is between A and C, and $BC = BD$.

  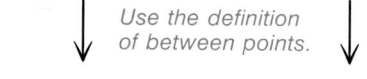

  Prove: $AC = AB + BD$

  Understand the Problem:
  B is between A and C.
  $BC = BD$

  Plan Your Approach:
  Apply the def. of betweenness of points.

  Implement the Plan:

  Given: B is between A and C. Use the def. of betweenness of points.
  $AC = AB + BC$

  Given: $BC = BD$
  Use substitution.

  Prove: $AC = AB + BD$

  Interpret the Results:
  If B is between A and C and $BC = BD$, then $AC = AB + BD$.

63

For Example 2

Given: $\overrightarrow{BX}$ between $\overrightarrow{BA}$ and $\overrightarrow{BC}$; $\overrightarrow{BY}$ between $\overrightarrow{BX}$ and $\overrightarrow{BC}$.

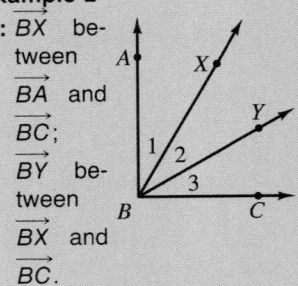

Prove: $m\angle 1 + m\angle 2 + m\angle 3 = m\angle ABC$

Understand the Problem:

$\overrightarrow{BX}$ is between $\overrightarrow{BA}$ and $\overrightarrow{BC}$.
$\overrightarrow{BY}$ is between $\overrightarrow{BX}$ and $\overrightarrow{BC}$.

Plan Your Approach:
Use the def. of betweenness.

Implement the Plan:

$\overrightarrow{BX}$ is between $\overrightarrow{BA}$ and $\overrightarrow{BC}$.

$\overrightarrow{BY}$ is between $\overrightarrow{BX}$ and $\overrightarrow{BC}$.

Use the def. of bet. of rays.

$m\angle 1 + m\angle XBC = m\angle ABC$

$m\angle 2 + m\angle 3 = m\angle XBC$

Use substitution.

$m\angle 1 + m\angle 2 + m\angle 3 = m\angle ABC$

Interpret the Results:
Measures of adjacent angles can be added.

Common Error

- Students sometimes try to get from the *Given* to the *Prove* without recognizing the significance of the intermediate steps. Stress the importance of *Plan Your Approach*.
- See *Teacher's Resource Book* for additional remediation.

LESSON FOLLOW-UP

Assignment Guide

See p. 44B for assignments.

64

CLASS EXERCISES

1. What guarantees that deductive reasoning leads to a correct conclusion? See side column, p. 63.

State the definition, postulate, or previously proven theorem that allows you to reason deductively from the *Given* to the *Prove*.

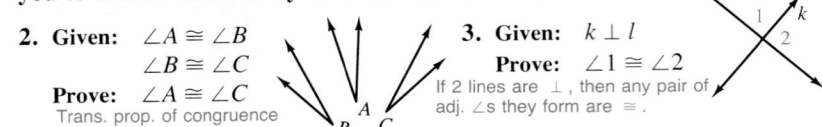

2. **Given:** $\angle A \cong \angle B$
   $\angle B \cong \angle C$
   Prove: $\angle A \cong \angle C$
   Trans. prop. of congruence

3. **Given:** $k \perp l$
   Prove: $\angle 1 \cong \angle 2$
   If 2 lines are $\perp$, then any pair of adj. $\angle$s they form are $\cong$.

4. **Given:** $m \perp n$
   Prove: $\angle 1, \angle 2, \angle 3,$ and $\angle 4$ are right angles.
   If 2 lines are $\perp$, then they form 4 rt. $\angle$s. (Cor. 2 to Th 1.10)

5. **Given:** M is the midpoint of $\overline{AB}$.
   Prove: $\overline{AM} \cong \overline{MB}$
   Def. of midpt.: point M is the midpt. of $\overline{AB}$ iff $\overline{AM} \cong \overline{MB}$.

Supply the justifications in this flow proof.

6. **Given:** M is the midpoint of $\overline{PQ}$; $MQ = QN$
   Prove: $PM = QN$

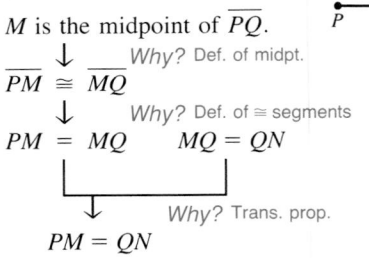

M is the midpoint of $\overline{PQ}$.
↓ *Why?* Def. of midpt.
$\overline{PM} \cong \overline{MQ}$
↓ *Why?* Def. of $\cong$ segments
$PM = MQ \qquad MQ = QN$
↓ *Why?* Trans. prop.
$PM = QN$

PRACTICE EXERCISES

State the definition, postulate, or previously proven theorem that allows you to reason deductively from the *Given* to the *Prove*.

A 1. **Given:** $\angle A$ and $\angle B$ are complements.
   Def. of comp. $\angle$s
   Prove: $m\angle A + m\angle B = 90$

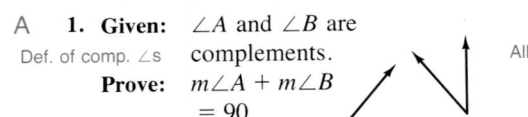

2. **Given:** $\angle G$ and $\angle H$ are right angles.
   All rt. $\angle$s are $\cong$.
   Prove: $\angle G \cong \angle H$

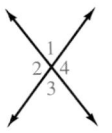

3. **Given:** p and q intersect.
   If 2 lines intersect, then they intersect in exactly one point.
   Prove: R is the only intersection.

4. **Given:** $\angle 2$ and $\angle 4$ are vertical angles.
   Vert. $\angle$s are $\cong$.
   Prove: $\angle 2 \cong \angle 4$

64 Chapter 2 The Logic of Geometry

---

7. Add $m\angle GOH$ to both sides of the given equation. Then use betweenness of rays to reach a conclusion.

8. Subtract $m\angle GOH$ from both sides of the given equation. Then use betweenness of rays to reach a conclusion.

9. $\angle 7 \cong \angle 1$ and $\angle 4 \cong \angle 6$ because vert. $\angle$s are $\cong$. Use the subst. prop. to show $\angle 1 \cong \angle 4$.

10. $\angle 5 \cong \angle 3$ and $\angle 2 \cong \angle 8$ because vert. $\angle$s are $\cong$. Use the subst. prop. to show $\angle 8 \cong \angle 3$.

Supply the justifications in the flow proofs.

5. Given: $\overline{RS} \cong \overline{TV}$

Prove: $RT = SV$

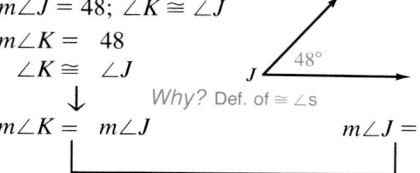

$\overline{RS} \cong \overline{TV}$ ↓ *Why?* Def. of ≅ segments → $RS = TV$

$\overline{ST} \cong \overline{ST}$ ↓ *Why?* Def. of ≅ segments → $ST = ST$

↓ *Why?* Add. Prop.

$RS + ST = TV + ST$ — *Why?* Def. of betweenness

Why? Def. of betweenness
$RS + ST = RT$ $TV + ST = SV$

↓ *Why?* Subst. prop.

$RT = SV$

6. Given: $m\angle J = 48$; $\angle K \cong \angle J$

Prove: $m\angle K = 48$

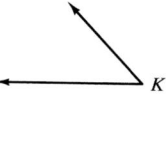

$\angle K \cong \angle J$ ↓ *Why?* Def. of ≅ ∠s → $m\angle K = m\angle J$

$m\angle J = 48$

↓ *Why?* Trans. prop.

$m\angle K = 48$

B **Reason deductively from the _Given_ to the _Prove_.** See side column.

7. Given: $m\angle FOG = m\angle HOK$

Prove: $m\angle FOH = m\angle GOK$

8. Given: $\angle HOF \cong \angle KOG$

Prove: $\angle GOF \cong \angle KOH$

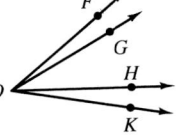

9. Given: $\angle 7 \cong \angle 6$ **10. Given:** $\angle 5 \cong \angle 2$

Prove: $\angle 1 \cong \angle 4$ **Prove:** $\angle 8 \cong \angle 3$

11. Given: $\angle 4 \cong \angle 7$ **12. Given:** $\angle 8 \cong \angle 5$

Prove: $\angle 1 \cong \angle 6$ **Prove:** $\angle 2 \cong \angle 3$

See side column.

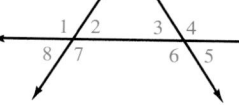

13. Given: M and X are midpoints of $\overline{AB}$ and $\overline{CD}$, respectively; $\overline{AM} \cong \overline{CX}$

Prove: $\overline{MB} \cong \overline{XD}$

See Additional Answers, p. 702.

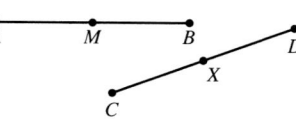

2.4 Strategy: Using Logical Reasoning   **65**

11. $\angle 1 \cong \angle 7$ and $\angle 6 \cong \angle 4$ because vert. ∠s are ≅ . Use the trans. prop. and the subst. prop. to show $\angle 1 \cong \angle 6$.

12. $\angle 2 \cong \angle 8$ and $\angle 3 \cong \angle 5$ because vert. ∠s are ≅ . Use the trans. prop. and the subst. prop. to show $\angle 2 \cong \angle 3$.

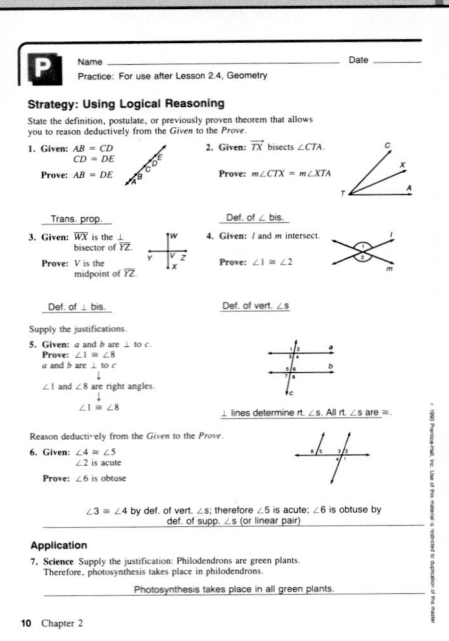

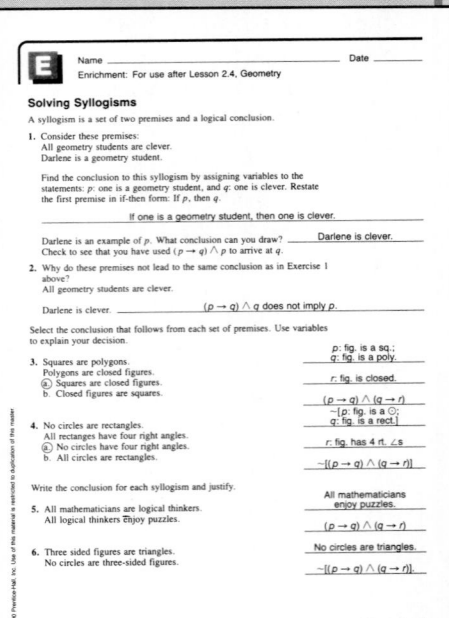

Use this figure for Exercises 14–18.
See Additional Answers, p. 702.

C **14. Given:** $\overrightarrow{XS}$ and $\overrightarrow{XW}$ are the bisectors of $\angle RXT$ and $\angle YXV$ respectively; $\angle 2 \cong \angle 3$
Prove: $\angle 1 \cong \angle 4$

15. Given: $\angle 4 \cong \angle 1$, $\angle 2 \cong \angle 3$
Prove: $\angle RXT \cong \angle YXV$

16. Given: $\angle YXS \cong \angle RXW$
Prove: $\angle 1 \cong \angle 4$

17. Given: $\angle 1 \cong \angle 4$, $\angle 2 \cong \angle 3$
Prove: $\angle RXV \cong \angle TXY$

18. Given: $\angle 1 \cong \angle 2$, $\angle 3 \cong \angle 4$, $\angle RXW \cong \angle YXS$
Prove: $\angle 1 \cong \angle 4$

PROJECT

Computer systems employ a logic based on exactly two states: true or false (yes or no, on or off). Boolean Algebra, named for George Boole, is used to work out problems in this system of logic. Letters and symbols represent statements and operations.

For example, if a statement represented by p is true, then its negation, $\sim p$, is false. Similarly, if the statement is false, then its negation is true. A *truth table* can be used to show this information:

p	$\sim p$
T	F
F	T

A *conjunction* is a compound sentence connecting the two parts with the word *and*. A *disjunction* connects the two parts with the word *or*.

EXAMPLE Let p represent "It is raining"; let q represent "I like school." Create the conjunction, p *and* q ($p \wedge q$), and the disjunction, p *or* q ($p \vee q$).

Conjunction: "It is raining *and* I like school."
Disjunction: "It is raining *or* I like school."

This information may also be put into a truth table. Four possible cases must be considered. A conjunction is true only when both parts are true, and a disjunction is true when either part is true.

p	q	$p \wedge q$	$p \vee q$
T	T	T	T
T	F	F	T
F	T	F	T
F	F	F	F

EXERCISE Research truth tables for a conditional statement ($p \rightarrow q$), its converse ($q \rightarrow p$), inverse ($\sim p \rightarrow \sim q$), and contrapositive ($\sim q \rightarrow \sim p$).

Proving Theorems

Objective: To write formal proofs of theorems and other statements

You have justified theorems and statements with paragraph proofs and flow proofs. Another method is a two-column form, called a *formal proof.*

Investigation—*Constructions*

1. Trace ∠ABC on a piece of paper.
2. Construct ∠RST congruent to ∠ABC. (Page 27)
3. Draw $\overrightarrow{BD}$ opposite $\overrightarrow{BC}$. What is the relationship between ∠ABC and ∠ABD? They are supplementary.
4. Draw $\overrightarrow{SV}$ opposite $\overrightarrow{SR}$. Give the relationship between ∠RST and ∠TSV. They are supplementary.
5. What appears to be the relationship between ∠ABD and ∠TSV? How could you verify your answer? They appear to be congruent. Answers may vary; measure each angle with a protractor.

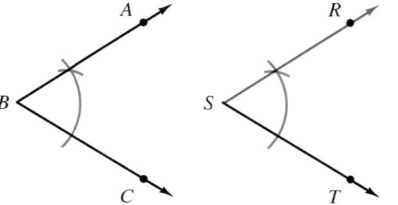

Most formal proofs consist of six steps.

I. Read the theorem or statement. Then draw a *figure.*

II. Determine the hypothesis. The information in the hypothesis is called the *Given.* State the *Given* in terms of the figure.

III. Determine the conclusion (the then-clause information, which is what you are to prove). State the conclusion in terms of the figure and label it *Prove.*

IV. Study the figure, *Given,* and *Prove* and write a *Plan* indicating which definitions, postulates, and/or previously-proven theorems you can use to reason logically from the figure and the *Given* to the *Prove.*

V. Write the *Proof* by listing in logical order each statement that you know to be true. Some will be Given statements; some will be arrived at through deductive reasoning. Each statement must be justified with a reason such as Given information, a definition, postulate, or previously-proven theorem.

VI. State the *Conclusion,* which is a restatement of what has been proven.

2.5 Proving Theorems **67**

Developing Mathematical Power

Cooperative Learning Have students experiment with paper proofs. Provide each group with Enrichment, p. 13, in the *Teacher's Resource Book* (see side column, p. 72). Have students fold the paper as directed to discover relationships between segments and angles. Encourage students to share ideas and strategies for each proof. Then have each group create a paper proof of its own to share.

LESSON PLAN

Vocabulary
Formal proof
Two-column proof

Materials/Manipulatives
Teacher's Resource Book,
 Transparency 2
Teaching Transparency 12

Technology
Computer Test Bank, pp.
 127–132

LESSON FOCUS

Review
- The Chapter Summary and Review, pp. 74–75, gives vocabulary and concepts and review exercises by lesson.
- The end of the chapter features a Cumulative Review on p. 78.

Alternative Learning Styles

Depending on their learning styles, different students may prefer different proof formats. Ask students to reconsider Theorem 1.7: All right angles are congruent. Contrast its proof in these three formats:

1. The paragraph form on page 20
2. The flow-proof format introduced in Lesson 2.4
    Given: ∠X and ∠Y are rt. ∠s.
    Prove: ∠X ≅ ∠Y

∠X is a rt. ∠.   ∠Y is a rt. ∠.
↓   Def. of a rt. ∠   ↓
m∠X = 90   m∠Y = 90
↓   Trans. prop.
m∠X = m∠Y
↓ Def. of ≅ ∠s
∠X ≅ ∠Y

See p. 68 for format 3.

3. A two-column proof

Statements	Reasons
1. $\angle X$ is a rt. $\angle$; $\angle Y$ is a rt. $\angle$.	1. Given
2. $m\angle X = 90$; $m\angle Y = 90$	2. Def. of a rt. $\angle$
3. $m\angle X = m\angle Y$	3. Trans. prop.
4. $\angle X \cong \angle Y$	4. Def. of $\cong \angle$s

TEACHING SUGGESTIONS

- Use the proof of Theorem 2.3 as a model for students to use as they start to do their own proofs. Point out Steps I–VI. Explain the two-column format.
- The proof of Theorem 2.3 in the student text is only for the case where two angles are supplements of congruent angles. Prove on the chalkboard the case where the two angles are supplements of the same angle.
- Some teachers prefer to have students do Step IV, the Plan, orally or on work paper, omitting it from their written work. Using work paper makes it easier to recover from false starts.
- Some teachers prefer to have students give Step VI, the statement of the conclusion, orally.

CHALKBOARD EXAMPLE

- **For the Example**

  If $\angle 3$ is a supplement of $\angle 2$, $m\angle 3 = x + 90$, and $m\angle 1 = 3x - 10$, find the measure of each angle.

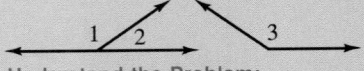

  Understand the Problem:
  $\angle 1$ and $\angle 2$ are a linear pair.
  $\angle 3$ and $\angle 2$ are supplementary.
  $m\angle 3 = x + 90$; $m\angle 1 = 3x - 10$
  Find $m\angle 1$, $m\angle 2$, $m\angle 3$.
  Plan Your Approach:
  Since $\angle 1$ and $\angle 2$ are a linear pair, they are supplementary. $\angle 1 \cong \angle 3$, since they are both supplements of $\angle 2$. Thus, $m\angle 1 = m\angle 3$ (Def. of $\cong \angle$s), and $x + 90 = 3x - 10$ (Substitution).

Note how the six steps are used in the proof of Theorem 2.3.

> **Theorem 2.3** If two angles are supplements of congruent angles or of the same angle, then the two angles are congruent.

I.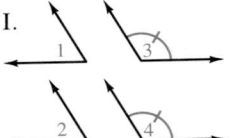

II. **Given:** $\angle 1$ is a supplement of $\angle 3$;
$\angle 2$ is a supplement of $\angle 4$;
$\angle 3 \cong \angle 4$

III. **Prove:** $\angle 1 \cong \angle 2$

IV. **Plan:** By the definition of supplementary angles, $m\angle 1 + m\angle 3 = 180$ and $m\angle 2 + m\angle 4 = 180$. Since $m\angle 3 = m\angle 4$, the algebraic properties can be used to show that $m\angle 1 = m\angle 2$.

V. **Proof:**

Statements	Reasons
1. $\angle 1$ and $\angle 3$ are supplementary; $\angle 2$ and $\angle 4$ are supplementary.	1. Given
2. $m\angle 1 + m\angle 3 = 180$; $m\angle 2 + m\angle 4 = 180$	2. Def. of supplementary $\angle$s
3. $\angle 3 \cong \angle 4$	3. Given
4. $m\angle 3 = m\angle 4$	4. Def. of congruent $\angle$s
5. $m\angle 1 + m\angle 3 = m\angle 2 + m\angle 4$	5. Transitive property
6. $m\angle 1 + m\angle 3 = m\angle 2 + m\angle 3$	6. Substitution property
7. $m\angle 1 = m\angle 2$	7. Subtraction property
8. $\angle 1 \cong \angle 2$	8. Def. of congruent $\angle$s

VI. **Conclusion:** If $\angle 1$ is a supplement of $\angle 3$, $\angle 2$ is a supplement of $\angle 4$, and $\angle 3 \cong \angle 4$, then $\angle 1 \cong \angle 2$. This also holds for supplements of the same angle.

You may find it helpful to relate the steps in writing a formal proof to the four problem solving steps that are used throughout this text.

Understand the Problem	Plan Your Approach	Implement the Plan	Interpret the Results
Read the problem; draw the figure; state the *Given* and *Prove*.	Analyze the figure, *Given* and *Prove*. Then write a *Plan*.	Write the *Proof* in two-column form.	State the *Conclusion*.

The next theorem can also be proven using the six-step method.

> **Theorem 2.4** If two angles are complements of congruent angles or of the same angle, then the two angles are congruent.
> Proved in Practice Exercise 12

Once a theorem has been proven, it can be used as a statement or as a reason in the proofs of other theorems. It can also be applied to figures to determine measures.

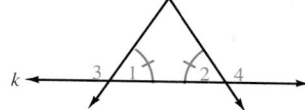

EXAMPLE If $\angle 1 \cong \angle 2$, $m\angle 3 = 5x + 30$, and $m\angle 4 = 9x - 50$, find $m\angle 3$ and $m\angle 4$.

Since $\angle 1 \cong \angle 2$ is given, $\angle 3 \cong \angle 4$ by Theorem 2.3. Thus, $m\angle 3 = m\angle 4$ by the definition of congruent angles. Use the algebraic properties and substitution to find the angle measures.

$$m\angle 3 = m\angle 4$$
$$5x + 30 = 9x - 50$$
$$80 = 4x$$
$$20 = x$$

Thus, $m\angle 3 = 5x + 30 = 100 + 30$, or 130
$m\angle 4 = 9x - 50 = 180 - 50$, or 130

Throughout this course you will be asked to *write proofs*. You should use the *problem solving guidelines* and relate them to the *six steps of a formal proof*. Remember: **Planning your approach is the key to writing a proof.**

CLASS EXERCISES

1. If a theorem to be proven is stated as a conditional, then the hypothesis is the __?__ and the conclusion is the __?__.
   Given   Prove

Use the figure, *Given*, and *Prove* for Exercises 2–4.

Given: $\overline{AB} \cong \overline{CD}$; B is between A and C;
C is between B and D.

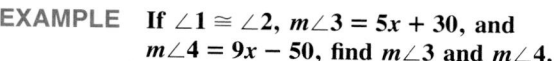

Prove: $\overline{AC} \cong \overline{BD}$

2. How does the figure suggest a way to prove this problem? Add BC to both AB and CD.

3. Use a **Look Back** technique: *Name a way to reach the conclusion, $\overline{AC} \cong \overline{BD}$, by reasoning from the Prove to the Given.* Go from $\overline{AC} \cong \overline{BD}$ to $AC = BD$ via def. of $\cong$ segments. Observe in the figure that $AC = AB + BC$ and $BD = CD + BC$. Thus, BC was added to both AB and CD.

4. Use a **Look Ahead** technique: *Name a way to use the hypothesis, $\overline{AB} \cong \overline{CD}$, to reason from the Given to the Prove.* Use the def. of $\cong$ segments to get $AB = CD$; then add BC to both AB and CD to get $AC = BD$. The conclusion follows by the def. of $\cong$ segments.

2.5 Proving Theorems   **69**

Implement the Plan:
$m\angle 1 = m\angle 3$
$x + 90 = 3x - 10$
$100 = 2x$
$50 = x$
$m\angle 1 = 3x - 10 = 140$
$m\angle 3 = x + 90 = 140$
$m\angle 2 = 180 - 140 = 40$

Interpret the Results:
$\angle 1$ and $\angle 3$, which are both supplements of $\angle 2$, each measure 140°. $\angle 2$ measures 40°.

Common Errors

- Some students have so much trouble setting up the format of a proof that they never get to the statements/reasons step. Using a one-page form with space provided for *Given, Prove,* figure, and the two columns can help students get used to the format. Separating out the Plan step as scratch work can also help, since students could then replan the proof, if their original approach did not lead to the desired conclusion.

- Some students list all the given information in the first step of a proof. Point out that a proof might be easier to follow if given information is listed at the point where it will be used in the proof.

- See *Teacher's Resource Book* for additional remediation.

LESSON FOLLOW-UP

Assignment Guide
See p. 44B for assignments.

Additional Answers for p. 71

9. Plan: $\angle AVR$ has between ray $\vec{VC}$. Thus, $m\angle AVR = m\angle AVC + m\angle CVR$. Similarly, $\angle DVC$ has between ray $\vec{VR}$, and so $m\angle DVC = m\angle RVD + m\angle RVC$. Since $m\angle AVR = m\angle DVC$, $m\angle AVC + m\angle CVR = m\angle DVR + m\angle CVR$. The concl. follows by algebraic properties.

10. Plan: Use the Linear Pair Postulate and Th 2.3 to show $\angle CBD \cong \angle ECB$. Then use the $\angle$ Bisector Th. and algebraic properties to show $\angle CBP \cong \angle BCP$.

Proof:

Statements	Reasons
1. $\angle ABC \cong \angle ACB$	1. Given
2. $\angle CBD$ and $\angle ABC$ are a linear pair. $\angle ECB$ and $\angle ACB$ are a linear pair.	2. Def. of linear pair
3. $\angle CBD$ and $\angle ABC$ are supplements; $\angle ECB$ and $\angle ACB$ are supplements.	3. Linear Pair Postulate
4. $\angle CBD \cong \angle ECB$	4. Suppl. of $\cong \angle$s are $\cong$.
5. $\vec{BP}$ is bisector of $\angle CBD$; $\vec{CP}$ is bisector $\angle ECB$.	5. Given
6. $m\angle CBP = \frac{1}{2}m\angle CBD$ $m\angle BCP = \frac{1}{2}m\angle ECB$	6. $\angle$ Bis. Th.
7. $m\angle CBD = m\angle ECB$	7. Def. of $\angle \cong$
8. $\frac{1}{2}m\angle CBD = \frac{1}{2}m\angle ECB$	8. Mult. prop.
9. $m\angle CBP = m\angle BCP$	9. Subst.
10. $\angle CBP \cong \angle BCP$	10. Def. of $\angle \cong$

Conclusion: In the given figure, if $\vec{BP}$ and $\vec{CP}$ are $\angle$ bisectors of $\angle DBC$ and $\angle ECB$ and $\angle ABC \cong \angle ACB$, then $\angle CBP \cong \angle BCP$.

PRACTICE EXERCISES

Supply the missing information.

A 1. Given: $\angle 3$ and $\angle 1$ are complementary; $m\angle 1 + m\angle 2 = 90$.

Prove: $\angle 3 \cong \angle 2$

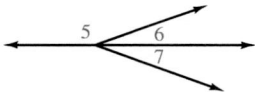

Plan: Since $m\angle 1 + m\angle 2 = 90$, $\angle 1$ and $\angle 2$ are $\underline{?}$. Since $\angle 3$ and $\angle 2$ are both complementary to $\underline{?}$, it follows that $\angle \underline{?} \cong \angle \underline{?}$.
compl.; $\angle 1$; 3; 2

Proof:

Statements	Reasons
1. $m\angle 1 + m\angle 2 = 90$	1. $\underline{?}$ Given
2. $\angle 1$ and $\angle 2$ are $\underline{?}$ compl.	2. $\underline{?}$ Def. of comp. $\angle$s
3. $\underline{?}$ $\angle 3$ and $\angle 1$ are compl.	3. Given
4. $\angle \underline{?}_3 \cong \angle \underline{?}_2$	4. Angles that are complements of the same angle are congruent.

complements

Conclusion: If $\angle 3$ and $\angle 2$ are both $\underline{?}$ of the same angle, then $\angle 3 \cong \angle 2$.

Use the figure and the *Given* and *Prove* to write a *Plan* for each.

2. Given: $\angle 4 \cong \angle 5$ **Prove:** $\angle 3 \cong \angle 6$
See below for 2 & 3.

3. Given: $\angle 4 \cong \angle 5$ **Prove:** $\angle 4$ and $\angle 6$ are supplementary.

4. Given: $\angle 4 \cong \angle 8$ **Prove:** $\angle 4 \cong \angle 5$
See side column, page 71.

B 5. $\angle 7$ is supplementary to $\angle 5$. If $m\angle 7 = 32$, $m\angle 6 = \underline{?}$. 32

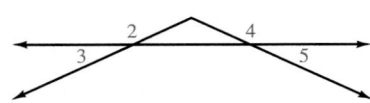

6. $\vec{JC} \perp \vec{JD}$ and $\angle K$ is complementary to $\angle CJE$. If $m\angle EJD = 37$, $m\angle K = \underline{?}$. 37

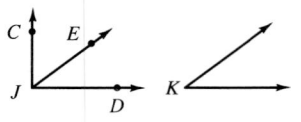

7. $\angle 3 \cong \angle 5$; $m\angle 3 = 3x + 4$; $m\angle 5 = 4x - 3$; find $m\angle 2$ and $m\angle 4$. $m\angle 2 = 155$, $m\angle 4 = 155$

8. $\overleftrightarrow{CD} \perp \overleftrightarrow{AB}$ and $\angle 1 \cong \angle 2$. $m\angle 1 = 3x - 2$; $m\angle 2 = 5(x - 2)$; find $m\angle 7$ and $m\angle 8$. $m\angle 7 = 80$, $m\angle 8 = 80$

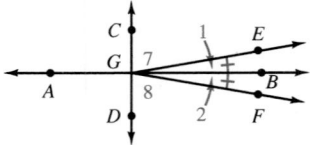

2. By the definition of linear pair and the Linear Pair Postulate, $m\angle 3 + m\angle 4 = 180$ and $m\angle 5 + m\angle 6 = 180$. Using the Transitive property and substitution of $m\angle 5$ for $m\angle 4$ gives $m\angle 3 + m\angle 5 = m\angle 5 + m\angle 6$. Then, by subtraction and Def. of $\cong \angle$s, $\angle 3 \cong \angle 6$.

3. By the definition of a linear pair and the Linear Pair Postulate, $m\angle 5 + m\angle 6 = 180$. Using the Given ($\angle 4 \cong \angle 5$), the definition of $\cong \angle$s ($m\angle 4 = m\angle 5$), and substitution gives $m\angle 4 + m\angle 6 = 180$. Then by Def. of supp. $\angle$s, $\angle 4$ is supplementary to $\angle 6$.

9. Given: $\angle AVR \cong \angle DVC$
Prove: $\angle AVC = \angle DVR$
Plan: ?

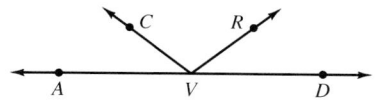

Write a proof. See side column page 70.

10. $\angle ABC \cong \angle ACB$. $\overrightarrow{BP}$ and $\overrightarrow{CP}$ are angle bisectors of $\angle DBC$ and $\angle ECB$.
Prove that $\angle CBP \cong \angle BCP$.

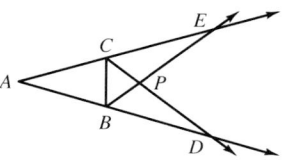

11. $\angle ABC \cong \angle ACB$. $\overrightarrow{BP}$ and $\overrightarrow{CP}$ are angle bisectors of $\angle DBC$ and $\angle ECB$.
Prove that $\angle ECP \cong \angle DBP$. See side column, p. 74.

12. Complete this proof of Theorem 2.4:
If two angles are complements of congruent angles or of the same angle,
then the two angles are congruent.

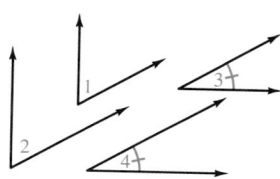

Given: $\angle 1$ is a complement of $\angle 3$;
$\angle 2$ is a complement of $\angle 4$; $\angle 3 \cong \angle 4$
Prove: $\angle 1 \cong \angle 2$

C **13.** $\overleftrightarrow{DE}$, $\angle 1 \cong \angle 2$, and $\overrightarrow{BP}$ is the angle bisector of $\angle ABC$.
Prove that $\overrightarrow{BP} \perp \overleftrightarrow{DE}$.

14. Assume that $\angle 3$ and $\angle 1$ are complementary angles.
Prove that $\angle 4$ and $\angle 2$ are complementary angles.

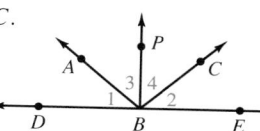

Applications

Algebra   The equations you studied in algebra can be solved by applying the techniques of formal proofs. The following algebraic sentences and their solutions are expressed as conditionals. Solve them as formal proofs. Proofs may vary, but should show the hypothesis as the Given, the conclusion as the Prove, a Plan, a step-by-step solution with supporting reasons, and a conclusion.

15. If $6(2n - 5) = -3(7 - 3n) + 2n$, then $n = 9$.
16. If $-5(3x - 2) + 6(2 - 2x) = 3x$, then $x = \frac{11}{15}$.

Developing Mathematical Power

17. Writing in Mathematics   Explain why a Plan can sometimes be considered a paragraph proof. If the Plan is detailed and includes supporting reasons, then it may be considered a paragraph proof.

2.5 Proving Theorems   **71**

4. Using the Given ($\angle 4 \cong \angle 8$), $\angle 8 \cong \angle 5$ (by Vertical $\angle$s $\cong$), and the Transitive property gives $\angle 4 \cong \angle 5$.

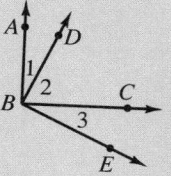

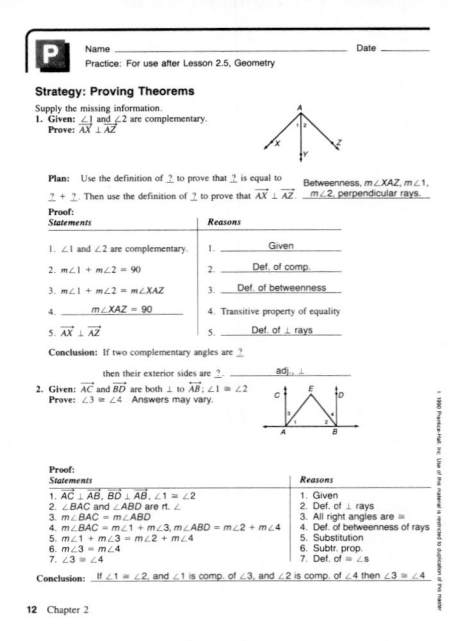

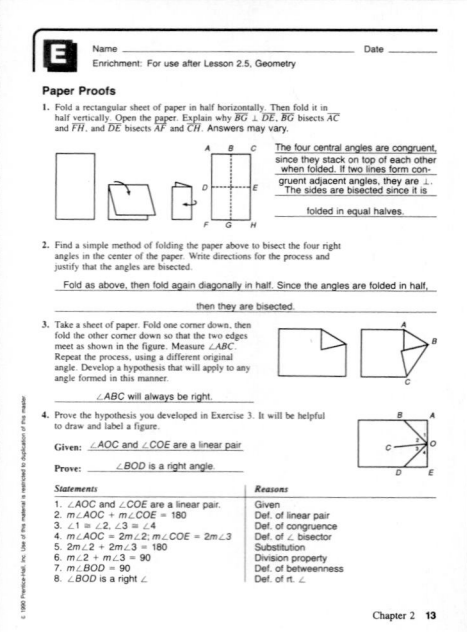

18. **Thinking Critically**   Choose a Practice Exercise for which you have written a formal proof. Apply the paragraph proof and flow proof methods to the same exercise. Then compare and contrast the three types of proof.

TEST YOURSELF

State the definition, postulate, or previously proven theorem that allows you to reason deductively from the *Given* to the *Prove*.

1. **Given:** $\overrightarrow{PQ} \perp \overrightarrow{PS}$
   Prove: $\angle 1$ and $\angle 2$ are complementary.
   If the ext. sides of 2 adj. acute $\angle$s are $\perp$, then the $\angle$s are comp.

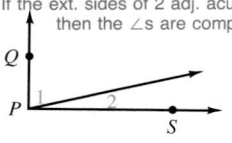

2. **Given:** $\overrightarrow{OT}$ bisects $\angle SOR$.   2.4
   Prove: $\angle 1 \cong \angle 2$ def. of $\angle$ bisector

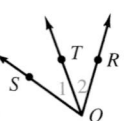

3. Supply the justifications for the statements.

   Given: $\angle LON \cong \angle DCF$;
   $\overrightarrow{OM}$ bisects $\angle LON$;
   $\overrightarrow{CE}$ bisects $\angle DCF$.
   Prove: $\angle 1 \cong \angle 3$

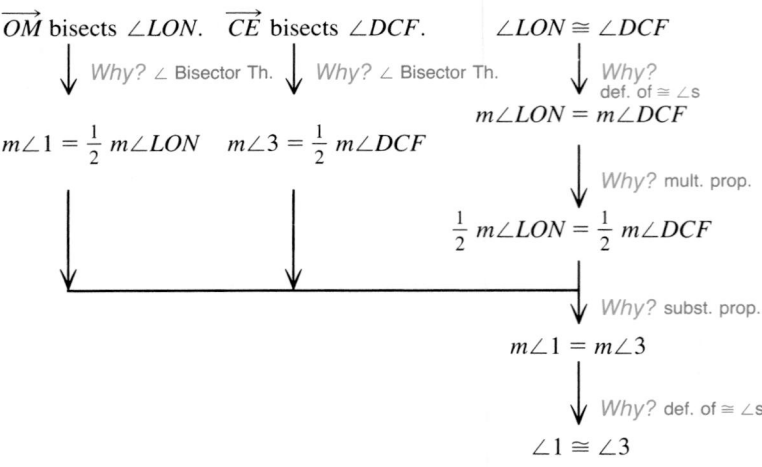

$\overrightarrow{OM}$ bisects $\angle LON$. $\overrightarrow{CE}$ bisects $\angle DCF$. $\angle LON \cong \angle DCF$

Why? $\angle$ Bisector Th.   *Why?* $\angle$ Bisector Th.   *Why?* def. of $\cong \angle$s
$m\angle LON = m\angle DCF$

$m\angle 1 = \frac{1}{2} m\angle LON$ $m\angle 3 = \frac{1}{2} m\angle DCF$

Why? mult. prop.
$\frac{1}{2} m\angle LON = \frac{1}{2} m\angle DCF$

Why? subst. prop.
$m\angle 1 = m\angle 3$

Why? def. of $\cong \angle$s
$\angle 1 \cong \angle 3$

2.5

4. **Given:** $\overleftrightarrow{BC} \perp \overrightarrow{AD}$; $\angle 2 \cong \angle 3$
   Prove: $\angle 1 \cong \angle 4$ See below.

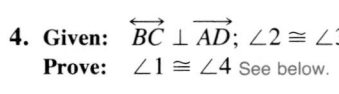

72   Chapter 2 The Logic of Geometry

4. **Plan:**   Use the Given to show that angle pairs, $\angle 1$ and $\angle 2$, and $\angle 4$ and $\angle 3$ are comp. Concl. follows by Th. 2.4.
Proof:

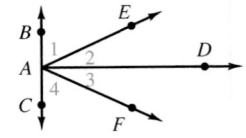

Statements	Reasons
1. $\overleftrightarrow{BC} \perp \overrightarrow{AD}$, $\angle 2 \cong \angle 3$	1. Given
2. $\angle 1$ compl. $\angle 2$, $\angle 4$ compl. $\angle 3$	2. If the ext. sides of 2 adj. $\angle$s are $\perp$, then the $\angle$s are comp.
3. $\angle 1 \cong \angle 4$	3. Comp. $\angle$s of $\cong \angle$s are themselves $\cong$.

Conclusion: In the given figure, if $\overleftrightarrow{BC} \perp \overrightarrow{AD}$ and $\angle 2 \cong \angle 3$, then $\angle 1 \cong \angle 4$.

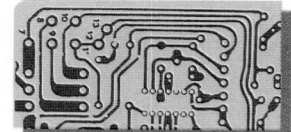

TECHNOLOGY:
Solving Problems Using Logo

Logo provides visual feedback as you work through a problem step by step.

A mistake or a misconception in a computer program is called a *bug*. You may believe that your *plan* is complete and accurate, but the *proof* (or drawing) shows that it was not. Thus, the program must be fixed, or **debugged.**

EXAMPLE   **Which of these drawings**

a. is obtained by using square and triangle procedures?
b. actually shows a picture of a house?

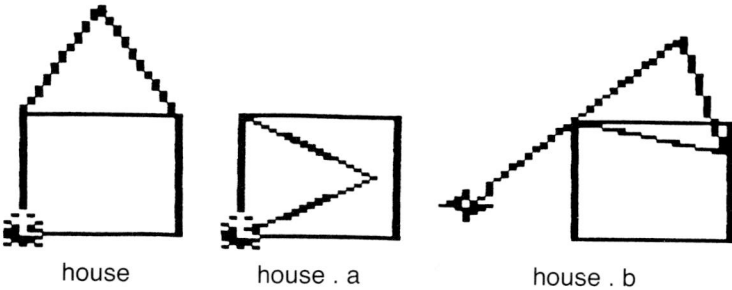

house   house . a   house . b

a. house, house.a, house.b   **b.** house

The bugs in the procedures for *house.a* and *house.b* concern the turtle's position and heading: where it is located on the screen and the direction in which it is pointing.

EXERCISES   See Solutions Manual.

Debug the following procedures for *house.a* and *house.b* shown above, so that each picture produced will be like the picture of *house*.

1. to house.a
   square
   triangle
   end

2. to house.b
   square
   forward 40 right 45
   triangle back 40
   end

Technology: Solving Problems Using Logo   **73**

Technology

Logo can be an excellent vehicle for practicing and understanding problem solving strategies. Have students explain how the concept of *debugging* a procedure might be applied when writing a two column proof.
See *Teacher's Resource Book*, Follow-up *Technology*, pp. 3–4.

- See *Teacher's Resource Book, Spanish Chapter Summary and Review* pp. 3–4.
- See Extra Practice, p. 644.

Additional Answers for p. 71

11. Plan: Use Linear Pair Post. and Th. 2.3 to show ∠ECB ≅ ∠DBC. Then use the ∠ Bis. Th. and the alg. prop. to show $m\angle ECP = m\angle DBP$. Concl. follows by def. of ≅ ∠s.

Proof:

Statements	Reasons
1. ∠ABC ≅ ∠ACB	1. Given
2. ∠DBC and ∠ABC are a linear pair; ∠ECB and ∠ACB are a linear pair.	2. Def. of linear pair
3. ∠DBC and ∠ABC are supplements; ∠ECB and ∠ACB are supplements.	3. Linear Pair Post.
4. ∠DBC ≅ ∠ECB	4. Suppl. of ≅ ∠s are ≅ .
5. $\vec{BP}$ is bis. of ∠DBC; $\vec{CP}$ is bis. of ∠ECB.	5. Given
6. $m\angle DBP = \frac{1}{2}m\angle DBC$ $m\angle ECP = \frac{1}{2}m\angle ECB$.	6. ∠ Bis. Th.
7. $m\angle DBC = m\angle ECB$	7. Def. of ≅ ∠s
8. $\frac{1}{2}m\angle DBC = \frac{1}{2}m\angle ECB$	8. Mult. prop.
9. $m\angle DBP = m\angle ECP$	9. Subst.
10. ∠ECP ≅ ∠DBP	10. Def. of ≅ ∠s.

Conclusion: In the given figure, if $\vec{BP}$ and $\vec{CP}$ are ∠ bisectors of ∠DBC and ∠ECB and ∠ABC ≅ ∠ACB, then

Vocabulary

biconditional (53)	inverse (51)
conclusion (47)	logically equivalent (52)
conditional (47)	negation (46)
contrapositive (51)	proof (57)
converse (51)	Prove (62)
counterexample (47)	real number properties (56)
deductive reasoning (62)	Reflexive property of congruence (57)
formal proof (67)	Symmetric property of congruence (57)
Given (62)	Transitive property of congruence (57)
hypothesis (47)	truth value (52)
If-then form (47)	

Conditional Statements Conditionals can be formed by joining two statements with the words if and then. The **if**-statement is called the hypothesis and the **then**-statement is called the conclusion.   2.1

True or false? Then give the negation and identify it as true or false.

1. ∠2 is a complement of ∠1.
   true; ∠2 is not a complement of ∠1; false
2. ∠*RST* is an obtuse angle.
   false; ∠*RST* is not an obtuse ∠; true
3. $m\angle 1 + m\angle 2 = 90$
   true; $m\angle 1 + m\angle 2 \neq 90°$; false

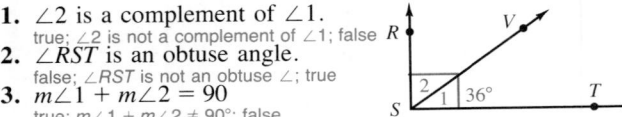

Rewrite these conditionals in if-then form. Then underline the hypothesis once and the conclusion twice.

4. The measure of an acute angle is less than 90. If <u>an ∠ is an acute ∠</u>, then <u>its measure is less than 90</u>.
5. Three noncollinear points determine a unique plane.
   If <u>3 points are noncollinear</u>, then <u>they determine a unique plane</u>.

Converses, Inverses, and Contrapositives A conditional and its contrapositive are logically equivalent; also a conditional's inverse and converse are logically equivalent. If a conditional and its converse are both true, a true biconditional can be formed.   2.2

6. Give the converse, inverse, contrapositive, and their truth values for:
   If two lines intersect, then they lie in exactly one plane. See side column.

7. If a true biconditional can be formed from the statements in Exercise 6, state it. If not, explain. It cannot, because the converse is false. Both the conditional and its converse must be true in order for the biconditional to be true.

6. Converse: If 2 lines lie in exactly one plane, then the lines intersect. False
   Inverse: If 2 lines do not intersect, then they do not lie in exactly one plane. False
   Contrapositive: If 2 lines do not lie in exactly one plane, then the two lines do not intersect. True

Properties from Algebra   Algebraic properties can be used to justify the statements made in geometry proofs.   2.3

8. Supply the missing reasons for the justification of:

*If ∠P and ∠Q are supplements and m∠P = 4m∠Q,
then m∠Q = 36 and m∠P = 144.*

∠P and ∠Q are supplements; m∠P = 4m∠Q   Given
$$m\angle P + m\angle Q = 180 \qquad \underline{?} \text{ Def. of supp. } \angle s$$
$$4m\angle Q + m\angle Q = 180 \qquad \underline{?} \text{ Subst. prop.}$$
$$5m\angle Q = 180 \qquad \underline{?} \text{ Distrib. prop.}$$
$$m\angle Q = 36 \qquad \underline{?} \text{ Div. prop.}$$
$$m\angle P = 144 \qquad \underline{?} \text{ Subst. prop.}$$

Use Logical Reasoning and Prove Theorems   Recall the problem solving guidelines.   2.4, 2.5

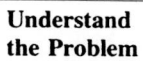

| Understand the Problem | Plan Your Approach | Implement the Plan | Interpret the Results |

Supply the missing reasons.

9. **Given:** ∠DAB ≅ ∠CAE
   Prove: ∠BAC ≅ ∠DAE

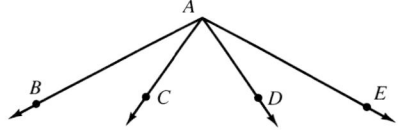

Proof:

Statements	Reasons
1. ∠DAB ≅ ∠CAE	1. <u>?</u> Given
2. m∠DAB = m∠CAE	2. <u>?</u> Def. of ≅ ∠s
3. ∠CAD ≅ ∠CAD	3. <u>?</u> Refl. prop. of ≅
4. m∠DAB = m∠BAC + m∠CAD m∠CAE = m∠DAE + m∠CAD	4. <u>?</u> Def. of betw. of rays
5. m∠BAC + m∠CAD = m∠DAE + m∠CAD	5. <u>?</u> Subst. prop.
6. m∠BAC = m∠DAE	6. <u>?</u> Subtr. prop.
7. ∠BAC ≅ ∠DAE	7. <u>?</u> Def. of ≅ ∠s

10. **Given:**   line *l*, ∠4 is supplementary to ∠3.
    Prove: ∠2 ≅ ∠4
    See side column.

10. Plan: Show ∠2 suppl. to ∠3. Since ∠4 is also supp. to ∠3, ∠2 ≅ ∠4.

Proof:

Statements	Reasons
1. ∠4 is suppl. to ∠3.	1. Given
2. ∠2 and ∠3 are a linear pair.	2. Def. of linear pair
3. ∠2 and ∠3 are supplementary.	3. Linear Pair Postulate
4. ∠4 ≅ ∠2	4. If two ∠s are supp. to the same ∠, they are ≅.

Conclusion: In the given figure, if ∠4 is supp. to ∠3, then ∠2 ≅ ∠4.

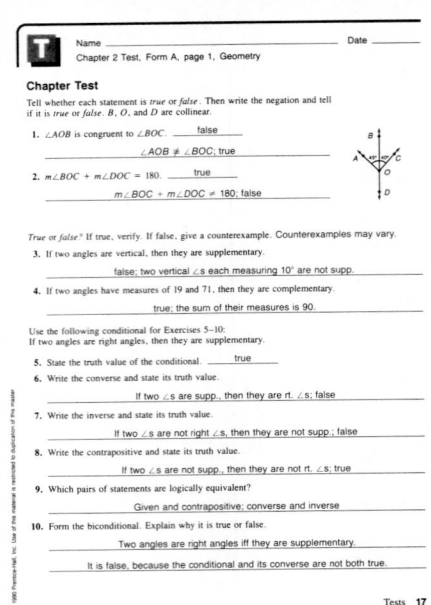

True or false? Then write the negation and tell if it is true or false.

1. $\angle 2$ and $\angle ACG$ are congruent.
   true; $\angle 2$ and $\angle ACG$ are not $\cong$; false
2. $\angle 1$ and $\angle ACG$ are not complements.
   false; $\angle 1$ and $\angle ACG$ are complements; true
3. $m\angle ACD + m\angle FCA = 180$
   true; $m\angle ACD + m\angle FCA \neq 180$; false

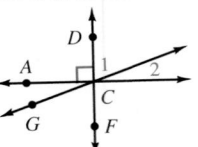

True or false? If true, verify. If false, give a counterexample.

4. If two angles have measures of 15 and 165, then they are supplementary.
   true; the sum of their measures is 180
5. If two angles are supplementary, then they have measures of 15 and 165.
   false; $\angle$s with measures of 25 and 155 are also supp.

In Exercises 6–9, write the indicated form for the following statement. Then state its truth value. See side column.

Two adjacent angles with noncommon sides that are perpendicular are complementary.

6. Conditional   7. Converse   8. Inverse   9. Contrapositive

10. Which pairs of statements in Exercises 6–9 are logically equivalent?
    The cond. and its contr.; the inv. and the conv.
11. Form the biconditional of the original statement above. Is it true or false?
    Two adj. $\angle$s are comp. iff their noncommon sides are $\perp$. It is true, because both the cond. and conv. are true.

12. If $\overrightarrow{RA} \perp \overrightarrow{RC}$, $\overrightarrow{OX} \perp \overrightarrow{OZ}$, $\angle ARB \cong \angle ZOY$, $m\angle YOX = 7x - 6$, and $m\angle BRC = 3x + 10$, find $m\angle ARB$ and $m\angle ZOY$. 68

13. If $\angle BRD$ and $\angle WOZ$ are both supplements of $\angle BRC$, and $m\angle BRD = 2(2x - 5)$ and $m\angle WOZ = 3(x + 6)$, find $m\angle BRC$. 78

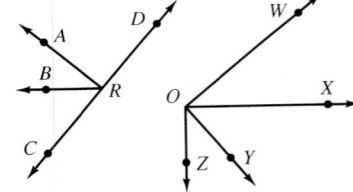

14. **Given:** $\angle AOC \cong \angle COE$; $\overrightarrow{OB}$ bisects $\angle AOC$; $\overrightarrow{OD}$ bisects $\angle COE$.
    Prove: $\angle AOB \cong \angle DOE$ See page 705.

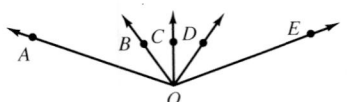

Challenge

If $\overrightarrow{PA} \perp \overrightarrow{PC}$, $\overrightarrow{PB} \perp \overleftrightarrow{ED}$, $\angle 3 \cong \angle 4$, $m\angle 1 = x^2 - 4x$, and $m\angle 2 = 10x - 49$, find the measures of angles 1, 2, 3 and 4. $m\angle 1 = m\angle 2 = 21$; $m\angle 3 = m\angle 4 = 69$

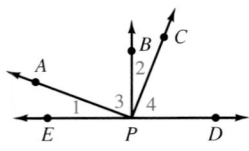

Alternative Assessment   Have students explain how to change a statement into a conditional and describe its inverse, converse, and contrapositive. Have students outline the proof for Exercise 14 on p. 76.

Directions: In each item, compare a quantity in Column 1 with a quantity in Column 2. Write the letter of the correct answer from these choices:

A. The quantity in Column 1 is greater than the quantity in Column 2.
B. The quantity in Column 2 is greater than the quantity in Column 1.
C. The quantity in Column 1 is equal to the quantity in Column 2.
D. The relationship cannot be determined from the given information.

Notes: A symbol that appears in both columns has the same meaning in each column. All variables represent real numbers. Most figures are not drawn to scale.

Column 1	Column 2
1. $\frac{3}{4} + \frac{2}{3}$ A	$\frac{4}{3}$
2. 60% of 45 C	27
3. supplement of B a 168° angle	complement of a 68° angle

$$2x + y = 5$$
$$x + y = 4$$

Column 1	Column 2
4. x B	y
5. $|(-3)^2 - (-4)^2|$ A	5
6. $m\angle A$ D	measure of complement of $\angle A$

Use this number line for 7–8.

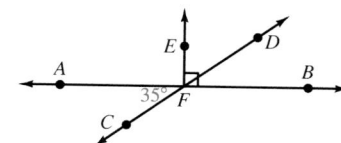

Column 1	Column 2
7. AC A	BD
8. coordinate of B midpoint of $\overline{AD}$	coordinate of midpoint of $\overline{BC}$

Column 1	Column 2
9. $\frac{2}{3}$ of 171 A	24% of 470

$$3(x - 2) + 6 = 19 - 2(5x + 3)$$

Column 1	Column 2
10. x B	2
11. $\sqrt{x^2 + 9}$ D	$x + 3$

$$x = 0 \text{ and } y = -1$$

Column 1	Column 2
12. $x^2y^3 + x^3y^2$ B	$x^4 + y^4$

Use this diagram for 13–15.

$\overrightarrow{EF} \perp \overleftrightarrow{AB}$, $\overleftrightarrow{CD}$ intersects $\overleftrightarrow{AB}$ at F.

Column 1	Column 2
13. $m\angle EFB$ C	90
14. $m\angle DFE$ A	35
15. $m\angle AFD$ C	145

6. If 2 adj. ∠s have noncommon sides that are ⊥, then the ∠s are comp. False
7. If 2 adj. ∠s are comp., then their noncommon sides are ⊥. True
8. If 2 adj. ∠s have noncommon sides that are not ⊥, then the ∠s are not comp. False
9. If 2 adj. ∠s are not comp. then their noncommon sides are not ⊥. True

The individual comments provided for certain problems can help guide student in solving them.

1. Using the decimal form of the numbers would provide an alternate solution to this problem. Since $\frac{3}{4} + \frac{2}{3} = 0.75 + 0.\overline{666} = 1.41\overline{6}$, while $\frac{4}{3} = 1.\overline{333}$.

7–8. Students should be encouraged to calculate these using formulas and then counting as a check, or vice versa.

11. This problem provides an opportunity for students to substitute different kinds of values for x, using positive and negative values as well as zero.

See *Teacher's Resource* Book for *Preparing for College Entrance Exams.*

See *Teacher's Resource Book*, Chapter 2, *Tests*, pp. 21–24.

$\overleftrightarrow{AD}$ and $\overleftrightarrow{BE}$ intersect at *F*. Complete.

1. Points *A*, *F*, and $\underline{\ ?\ }$ are collinear. D   1.1

2. $\overrightarrow{FC}$ is perpendicular to $\underline{\ ?\ }$. $\overleftrightarrow{AD}$ 1.6

3. ∠*CFD* is a $\underline{\ ?\ }$ angle. rt.   1.6

4. The intersection of $\overleftrightarrow{AD}$ and $\overleftrightarrow{BE}$ is $\underline{\ ?\ }$. F   1.1

5. If *F* is the midpoint of $\overline{AD}$, then $\overline{AF} \cong \underline{\ ?\ }$. $\overline{FD}$ 1.3

6. ∠*AFB* and $\underline{\ ?\ }$ are vertical angles. ∠EFD   1.5, 1.4

7. The vertex of ∠*BFH* is $\underline{\ ?\ }$. F

8. The sides of ∠*CFH* are $\underline{\ ?\ }$ and $\underline{\ ?\ }$. $\overrightarrow{FC}$; $\overrightarrow{FH}$ 1.4, 1.5

9. ∠*AFE* ≅ ∠*BFD* because $\underline{\ ?\ }$. vert. ∠s are ≅.

10. What is the complement of a 49° angle? the supplement? a 41°∠; a 131°∠   1.5

11. Write the negation of the statement *All right angles are congruent*. Is the statement true? Is the negation true? All rt. ∠s are not ≅; yes; no   2.1

12. Given: *Vertical angles are congruent*. Write the conditional, converse, inverse, and contrapositive. State the truth value of each.   2.1, 2.2
See Additional Answers, p. 702.

Support each statement with a reason.   2.3

13. $2\left(x + \frac{5}{2}\right) = 11$ Given
    $2x + 5 = 11$ $\underline{\ ?\ }$ Dist. prop.
    $2x = 6$ $\underline{\ ?\ }$ Subtr. prop.
    $x = 3$ $\underline{\ ?\ }$ Div. prop.

14. $m\angle A - m\angle B = 70$ Given
    $m\angle B = 40$ Given
    $m\angle A - 40 = 70$ $\underline{\ ?\ }$ Subst. prop.
    $m\angle A = 110$ $\underline{\ ?\ }$ Add. prop.

15. Supply the missing information.   2.5

Given: $\overline{BD} \perp \overline{AC}$, ∠1 ≅ ∠4
Prove: ∠2 ≅ ∠3

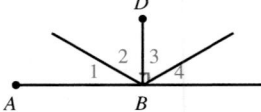

Plan: Use the *Given* to show that angle pairs ∠1 and ∠2, and ∠3 and ∠4 are complementary. Conclusion follows by Theorem 2.4.

Statements	Reasons	
1. $\overline{BD} \perp \overline{AC}$, ∠1 ≅ ∠4	1. $\underline{\ ?\ }$ Given	1.5
2. ∠1 is complementary to ∠2; ∠3 is complementary to ∠4.	2. $\underline{\ ?\ }$ Th. 1.13	
3. $\underline{\ ?\ }$ ∠2 ≅ ∠3	3. $\underline{\ ?\ }$ Comps. of ≅ ∠s are ≅.	2.5

Conclusion: In the given figure, if $\overline{BD} \perp \overline{AC}$ and $\underline{\ ?\ }$, then ∠2 ≅ ∠3. ∠1 ≅ ∠4

OVERVIEW · Chapter 3

SUMMARY

In Chapter 3, students define parallel and skew lines. The concept of angles formed by the intersection of transversals and parallel lines is developed and students are introduced to the Parallel Postulate. Relationships of angles in triangles and other polygons are then explored. Students also learn to classify triangles and to identify polygons with up to 10 sides.

CHAPTER OBJECTIVES

- To identify parallel and skew lines, parallel planes, transversals, and the angles formed by them

- To prove and apply the theorem about the intersection of two parallel planes by a third plane

- To state the Parallel Postulate

- To prove and use theorems relating parallel lines and angles formed by a transversal of those lines

- To classify triangles by sides and angles

- To prove and apply theorems regarding angle measure and angle relationships in a triangle

- To recognize and name convex, concave, and regular polygons and find the measures of the interior and exterior angles of a convex polygon

- To recognize patterns and create generalizations by *inductive reasoning*

CHAPTER HIGHLIGHTS

DEVELOPING MATHEMATICAL POWER

Problem Solving

The four problem solving steps are used to introduce students to inductive reasoning, a strategy which they later use to draw conclusions about polygons.

Communication

A number of the lesson Investigations involve the use of manipulatives to meet alternative learning styles and to provide cooperative learning situations. One cooperative learning project is the building of a periscope. The *Teacher's Resource Book* offers a Chapter Summary and Review in Spanish. The side column provides topics for students' portfolios.

Reasoning

Students use patterns to write polygonal numbers. With the introduction of more postulates, theorems, and definitions, students are able to write more involved proofs. Students compare and contrast inductive and deductive reasoning.

Connections

The discussion of Euclid's best-selling book provides an example of the variety of cultural influences on mathematics. Real-world applications include such topics as navigation, architecture, and sports. The Integrating Geometry feature discusses longitude and latitude. The side column references two types of non-Euclidean geometry.

Technology

The use of a calculator is suggested for the more cumbersome calculations concerning polygons. Logo exercises are presented throughout the chapter.

STUDENT TEXT

Chapter Content	Basic	Average	Enriched	NCTM STANDARDS*
3.1 Lines, Planes, and Transversals	D: 83/9-23, 37	D: 83/9-29, 37, 38	D: 83/1-8, 14-29, 35-38	2, 3, 4, 7
3.2 Properties of Parallel Lines	D: 89/1-10 even, 33, MR R: 83/1-8	D: 89/1-19, 33, 49, MR R: 83/30-34	D: 89/1-20 odd, 26-34, 49, MR R: 83/30-34	2, 3, 7, 8
3.3 Proving Lines Parallel	D: 95/1-8, 23 R: 89/11-16	D: 95/1-7, 8-21 even, 24 R: 89/20-25	D: 95/5-12, 13-22 even, 23-35 R: 89/11-20 even	2, 4, 5, 7, 8
3.4 Parallel Lines and Triangles	D: 101/1-13, 32, 35 R: 95/9, 11, 13	D: 101/1-22, 23-28 odd, 32, 34 R: 95/8-21 odd	D: 101/6-22, 23-31 odd, 33, 36 R: 95/13-22 odd	1, 4, 5, 7
3.5 Polygons	D: 107/1-14, 15-22 odd, 31, 57, AR R: 101/14-16	D: 107/1-5, 15-20, 21, 23, 25, 26, 32, 57, AR R: 101/23-28 even	D: 107/15-20, 25-33, AR R: 101/23-31 even	1, 2, 3, 14
3.6 Strategy: Use Inductive Reasoning	D: 112/1-3, 5-7 R: 107/15-22 even	D: 112/1-4, 5-19 odd R: 107/11-14, 22, 24, 56	D: 112/1-4, 5-19 odd, 20 R: 107/21-24	1, 2, 12, 13
3.7 Angles of a Polygon	D: 117/1-16, 24, 37 R: 112/4, 9	D: 117/4-11, 12-30 even, 38 R: 112/5-19 even	D: 117/4-11, 12-30 odd, 31-39 R: 112/5-19 even	1, 2, 3, 8, 12

D = Daily   R = Review   MR = Mixed Review   AR = Algebra Review

*For a complete list of NCTM Standards, see p. T7.

STUDENT TEXT

Review/Assessment

Mixed Review 91
Algebra Review 109, 126
Summary and Review 122
College Ent. Exam Rev. 125

Extra Practice 645
Test Yourself 102, 119
Chapter Test 124
Chapter Project 79

Special Features

Constructions 96
Historical Note 84
Technology 84, 90, 96, 108, 119
Devel. Math. Power 91, 103, 109
Applications 84, 90, 96, 102-103, 109, 119, 120-121
Project 113

RESOURCES

Teacher's Resource Book

Ch. 3: Investigation/Practice/ Enrichment 1-22
Spanish Sum. and Rev. 5-6
Quizzes 25-28
Chapter Tests 29-32
Perf. Assessment Proj. Ch. 3
Critical Thinking 3

Reading and Writing in Geom. 3
Applications—Ch. 3, 23
Teaching Aid 3
Transparency 3

Teaching Transparencies 13-20
Computer Test Bank 133-192
PH Graph. Utility
Overhead Manip. Kit

3 Parallelism

Drawing a parallel!

Developing Mathematical Power

om the construction of a
kage made of hinged rods
ed for drawing a straight
e, came the construction of
linkage that could be used
guide the motion of a
am engine's piston. In the
e 1800s, steam locomotives
ed parallel linkages to
oduce straight-line motion
th a minimum of friction.

e pantograph, a mechanical
trument used to copy
wings, is a simple linkage

in the form of a parallelogram. It is made of four rods
held together by pins. By ad-
justing the pins, a pantograph
can be set to copy a drawing
in any scale. Parallel linkages
also can be constructed so
that motion is turned 180°.
This kind of inverted linkage

can be used to make an up-
side-down copy of a drawing.

Project

Build a parallel linkage that
will enlarge a drawing. Then
devise a parallel linkage that
will invert a drawing.

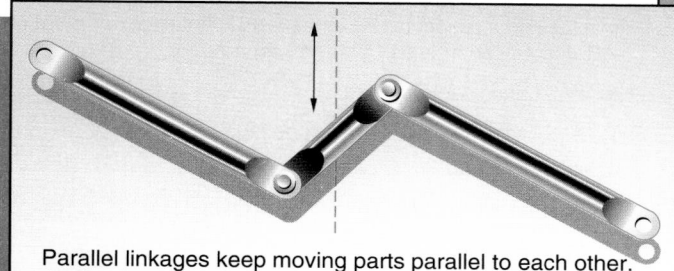

Parallel linkages keep moving parts parallel to each other.
As the center of the middle bar moves up and down,
the front and back bars remain parallel.

MODELING

Mathematics provides the power to
make everyday living easier. This
project involves building working models of parallel linkages. The models
are developed by analyzing samples
and using mathematical skills.

Cooperative Learning

This project is accomplished through
a succession of tasks, each of which is
well-suited to a cooperative learning
situation. These tasks include:

1. Analyzing and applying concepts of
   parallelism.
2. Designing models.
3. Constructing models.
4. Analyzing results for accuracy.

Alternative Assessment

See the *Teacher's Resource Book*,
Assessment, Chapter 3. This project
and the TRB page may be used as an
alternative form of assessment for selected topics in Chapter 3.

LESSON FOCUS

Review

Review *perpendicular lines.* Use part
of the classroom as a model. For example, the line formed by the intersection of two walls is perpendicular to the
line formed by a wall and the ceiling.

Alternative Learning Styles

• Providing a real-world model in the
  investigation of lines and planes
  that are parallel or intersecting and
  lines that are skew, helps students
  to visualize these concepts. Parts
  of the classroom can also be used
  as models for these terms. For example, the intersection of one wall
  with the ceiling and the intersection
  of an adjacent wall with the floor
  are skew.

• Ask a student to draw a model of
  the classroom on the chalkboard.
  Refer to the classroom and the
  model when discussing *parallel, intersecting,* and *skew.*

3.1

Lines, Planes, and Transversals

Objectives: To identify parallel and skew lines, parallel planes, transversals, and the angles formed by them
To prove and apply the theorem about the intersection of two parallel planes by a third plane

Our environment is a constant reminder of geometric concepts, with representations of lines and planes everywhere. Some lines are *intersecting*; some are not. Nonintersecting lines are either *parallel* or *skew*.

Investigation—*Visualizing the Concept*

In this skyscraper under construction, the girders shown as $\overline{BE}$ and $\overline{AB}$ lie in lines k and l, respectively. Lines k and l intersect at point B. Girders shown as $\overline{AB}$ and $\overline{CD}$ lie in lines l and m, respectively.

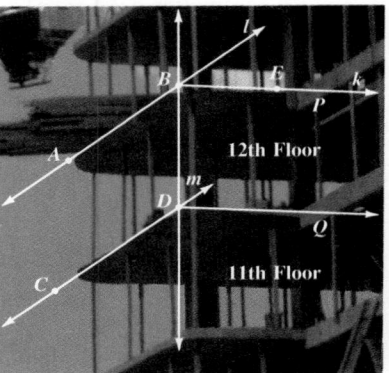

1. Will l and m intersect? no

2. Are l and m in the same plane? yes

> They are *parallel lines.*

> $\overline{BE}$ and $\overline{CD}$ lie in k and m, respectively.

3. Will k and m intersect? no

4. Are k and m in the same plane? no

> They are *skew lines.*

5. Do the planes Q and P, in which the 11th and 12th floors appear to lie, intersect? no

> They are *parallel planes.*

Definitions

Two **lines** are **parallel** if and only if they lie in the same plane and do not intersect. In symbols, if $\overleftrightarrow{AB}$ is parallel to $\overleftrightarrow{CD}$, $\overleftrightarrow{AB} \parallel \overleftrightarrow{CD}$.

Two **lines** are **skew** if and only if they do not lie in the same plane and do not intersect.

Two **planes** are **parallel** if and only if they do not intersect.

Segments or **rays** are **parallel** if and only if the lines that contain them are parallel.

The definitions above are helpful in proving the next theorem.

80   Chapter 3 Parallelism

Developing Mathematical Power

Keeping a Portfolio Have students write a paragraph or more in their math journals in which they compare and contrast parallel lines, skew lines, and parallel
planes. Ask them to describe how parallel and skew lines are related to intersecting
lines and how they would explain these concepts to an alien. Can they decode
$s \rightarrow \sim p \wedge \sim i$? $p \vee \sim i \rightarrow \sim s$?

Theorem 3.1 If two parallel planes are intersected by a third plane, then the lines of intersection are parallel.

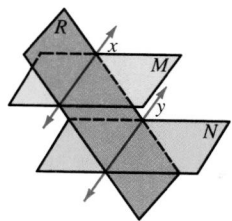

Given: Plane $M \parallel$ plane N;
plane R intersects M in line x;
plane R intersects N in line y.

Prove: $x \parallel y$

Plan: Show that x and y do not intersect since M and N are parallel planes. Show that x and y are coplanar since they both lie in plane R. Then use the definition of parallel lines. Proved in Class
Exercise 17

EXAMPLE 1 **Identify the suggested pairs of lines, rays, segments, or planes as parallel, intersecting, or skew.**

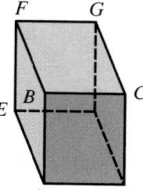

a. edges $\overline{AB}$ and $\overline{CD}$ **b.** $\overrightarrow{AE}$ and $\overrightarrow{BF}$ **c.** $\overleftrightarrow{BC}$ and $\overleftrightarrow{EF}$
d. front and back **e.** $\overleftrightarrow{AE}$ and $\overleftrightarrow{AD}$ **f.** top and left side

a. parallel segments **b.** parallel rays **c.** skew lines
d. parallel planes **e.** intersecting lines **f.** intersecting planes

Definition A line is a **transversal** if and only if it intersects two or more coplanar lines at different points.

Line t is the transversal in the figure below. Angles and pairs of angles take special names from their positions with respect to a transversal.

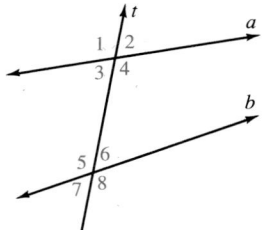
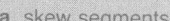

Interior angles $\angle 3, \angle 4, \angle 5, \angle 6$

Exterior angles $\angle 1, \angle 2, \angle 7, \angle 8$

Corresponding angles are a pair of nonadjacent angles—one interior, one exterior—both on the same side of the transversal.

$\angle 1$ and $\angle 5$
$\angle 2$ and $\angle 6$
$\angle 3$ and $\angle 7$
$\angle 4$ and $\angle 8$

Alternate interior angles are a pair of nonadjacent angles, both interior angles, on opposite sides of the transversal.

$\angle 3$ and $\angle 6$
$\angle 4$ and $\angle 5$

Alternate exterior angles are a pair of nonadjacent angles, both exterior angles, on opposite sides of the transversal.

$\angle 1$ and $\angle 8$
$\angle 2$ and $\angle 7$

3.1 Lines, Planes, and Transversals **81**

• **For Example 2**

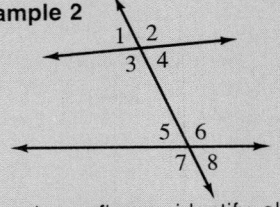

In the coplanar figure, identify all pairs of:

a. alternate interior angles
b. corresponding angles
c. alternate exterior angles
d. vertical angles

a. ∠3 and ∠6; ∠4 and ∠5
b. ∠1 and ∠5; ∠2 and ∠6;
   ∠3 and ∠7; ∠4 and ∠8
c. ∠1 and ∠8; ∠2 and ∠7
d. ∠1 and ∠4; ∠2 and ∠3;
   ∠5 and ∠8; ∠6 and ∠7

Common Errors

• Some students may confuse types of angles. A display chart with angle types marked in color can help students keep them straight.
• Some students may think that two lines having a transversal must be parallel in order to have corresponding angles, etc. It is important to do examples and exercises like Example 2 to prepare students for Lesson 3.3
• See *Teacher's Resource Book* for additional remediation.

LESSON FOLLOW-UP

Assignment Guide
See p. 78B for assignments.

EXAMPLE 2 $\overleftrightarrow{EJ}$ and $\overleftrightarrow{GL}$ have transversal $\overleftrightarrow{IK}$. Name the type of angle pair formed by the given angles.

a. ∠IFJ and ∠KHL   **b.** ∠EFH and ∠KHL
c. ∠JFH and ∠HFE   **d.** ∠LHF and ∠KHG
e. ∠GHF and ∠EFH   **f.** ∠GHF and ∠JFI

a. alternate exterior   **b.** corresponding   **c.** linear pair
d. vertical   **e.** alternate interior   **f.** corresponding

CLASS EXERCISES

Drawing in Geometry Check students' drawings. Answers may vary.

1. Copy the figure. Draw and label 2 skew lines that do not include the edges of the figure. $\overleftrightarrow{AF}$ and $\overleftrightarrow{ED}$.

2. On your copy trace and name 3 pairs of parallel lines.
   $\overline{FG} \| \overline{BC}$, $\overline{BF} \| \overline{GC}$, $\overline{EF} \| \overline{GH}$,

3. Trace 4 pairs of intersecting lines on your copy. Name them. See side column.

4. Now trace $\overleftrightarrow{AB}$ and $\overleftrightarrow{EF}$ and name 2 of their transversals.
   $\overleftrightarrow{AE}$, $\overleftrightarrow{BF}$,

Given that $\overleftrightarrow{AB} \| \overleftrightarrow{DE}$, justify each conclusion.

5. $\overline{AB} \| \overleftrightarrow{DF}$ 6. $\overline{AB} \| \overline{EF}$ 7. $\overrightarrow{BA} \| \overrightarrow{EF}$
                           See side column.

Identify the pairs of angles.

Line *t* is a transversal of lines *f* and *g*.
8. ∠1 and ∠7   **9.** ∠3 and ∠5   **10.** ∠4 and ∠8
   alt. ext.   alt. int.   corr.
11. ∠6 and ∠8   **12.** ∠2 and ∠3   **13.** ∠2 and ∠6
   vert.   linear pair   corr.
14. ∠4 and ∠6   **15.** ∠2 and ∠8   **16.** ∠1 and ∠5
   alt. int.   alt. ext.   corr.

17. Use the Figure, Given, Prove, and Plan for Theorem 3.1 to complete this proof.

Proof:

Statements	Reasons
1. $M \| N$; plane R intersects M in x, and N in y.	1. _?_ Given
2. x and y do not intersect.	2. _?_ Lines contained in ‖ planes do not intersect.
3. x and y both lie in _?_ plane R	3. Given
4. _?_ x and y are coplanar.	4. Definition of coplanar
5. _?_ $x \| y$	5. _?_ Def. of ‖ lines

Conclusion: _?_ When 2 ‖ planes are both intersected by a third plane, then the lines of intersection are ‖.

---

3. Answers will vary, at *F*, 3 pairs of intersecting lines: $\overleftrightarrow{FB}$, $\overleftrightarrow{FG}$; $\overleftrightarrow{EF}$, $\overleftrightarrow{FG}$; $\overleftrightarrow{EF}$, $\overleftrightarrow{FB}$; at *H*: $\overleftrightarrow{EH}$, $\overleftrightarrow{HG}$; etc
5. yes; a segment is ‖ to a line if the line containing it is ‖ to the line
6. yes; 2 segments are ‖ if they lie in ‖ lines
7. yes; 2 rays are ‖ if they lie in ‖ lines

Identify the given pairs of lines, rays, segments, or planes as parallel, intersecting, or skew as suggested in the figure.

A
1. edges $\overleftrightarrow{XW}$ and $\overleftrightarrow{ST}$ parallel segments
2. top and bottom parallel planes
3. $\overrightarrow{RS}$ and $\overrightarrow{RZ}$ intersecting rays
4. front and right side
5. $\overleftrightarrow{XY}$ and $\overleftrightarrow{ST}$ skew lines
6. $\overleftrightarrow{ZT}$ and $\overleftrightarrow{WV}$ parallel lines
7. edges $\overline{RZ}$ and $\overline{VW}$ skew segments
8. $\overrightarrow{VY}$ and $\overrightarrow{RZ}$ parallel rays
4. intersecting planes

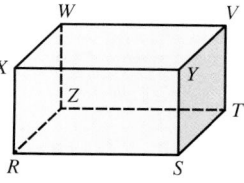

Use the stairway to indicate each answer.
Answers may vary. See side column.
9. Name 2 parallel planes.
10. Name 2 skew lines.
11. Name a plane parallel to plane ABN.
12. Name a line that intersects $\overleftrightarrow{IK}$.
13. Name 3 lines parallel to $\overleftrightarrow{FG}$.

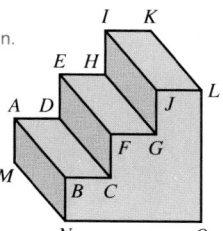

Use the figure at the right for Exercises 14–18.

14. Name 4 exterior angles.   15. Name 4 interior angles.
16. Name 4 pairs of corresponding angles.
17. Name 2 pairs of alternate interior angles.
18. Name 2 pairs of alternate exterior angles.
∠NEF, ∠ABG; ∠NED, ∠CBG

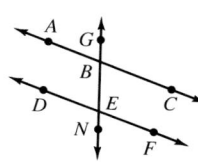

Each of the figures is coplanar. Sketch and label the lines and transversal that will form ∠1 and ∠2. Identify the type of angle pair that is formed.

19.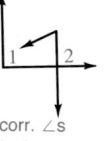
corr. ∠s

20.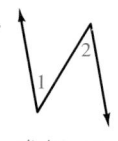
alt. int. ∠s

21.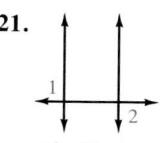
alt. ext. ∠s

22.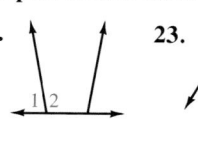
linear pair

23.
alt. int. ∠s

Use $\overleftrightarrow{AB}$ as a transversal of $\overleftrightarrow{BC}$ and $\overleftrightarrow{CA}$.
See side column for 26 and 28.
B
24. Name 4 interior angles. ∠1, ∠4, ∠5, ∠6
25. Name 4 exterior angles. ∠2, ∠3, ∠7, ∠8
26. Name 4 pairs of corresponding angles.
27. Name 2 pairs of alternate interior angles.
28. Name 2 pairs of alternate exterior angles.

29. If two lines are intersected by a transversal and the measures of a pair of corresponding angles are given, can you find the measures of all the angles formed by the transversal? Justify your answer. yes, by using the Vert. ∠ Th. and Linear Pair Post.

3.1 Lines, Planes, and Transversals   **83**

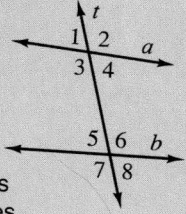

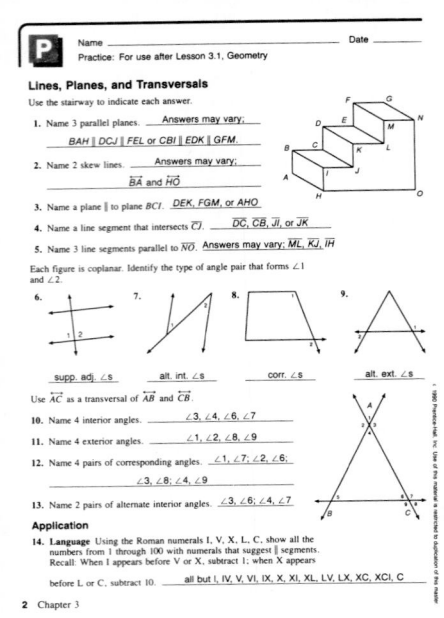

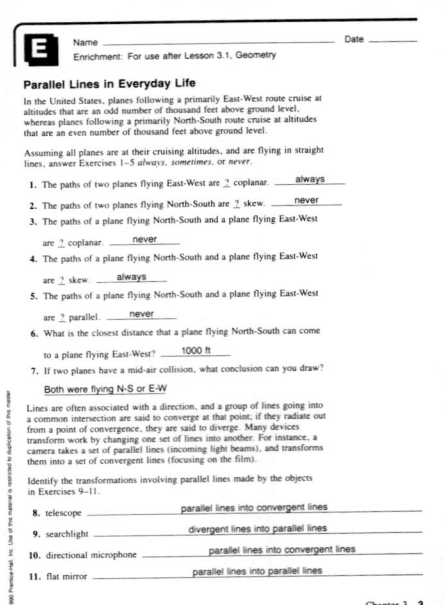

Name a transversal for each pair.

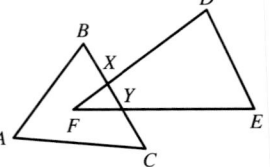

30. $\overleftrightarrow{AB}$ and $\overleftrightarrow{DF}$ $\overleftrightarrow{BC}$ **31.** $\overleftrightarrow{DE}$ and $\overleftrightarrow{AC}$ $\overleftrightarrow{DF}$

32. $\overleftrightarrow{FE}$ and $\overleftrightarrow{AC}$ $\overleftrightarrow{BC}, \overleftrightarrow{AB}$ **33.** $\overleftrightarrow{DE}$ and $\overleftrightarrow{AB}$ $\overleftrightarrow{DF}, \overleftrightarrow{EF}, \overleftrightarrow{AC}$

34. Using $\overleftrightarrow{BC}$ as a transversal of $\overleftrightarrow{FD}$ and $\overleftrightarrow{FE}$, name 4 pairs of corresponding angles.
∠BXF, ∠BYF; ∠BXD, ∠EYX; ∠FXY, ∠FYC; ∠DXY, ∠EYC

Decide whether the statement is true or false. Justify your conclusion.

C   **35.** All lines lying in the plane of the top of a cube are skew to all lines lying in the plane of the bottom of the cube. false; there are also infinitely many ∥ lines such as those determined by selected edges

36. All lines lying in the plane of the top of a cube intersect all lines lying in the plane of the front of the cube. false; some are skew and some are ∥

Applications See Solutions Manual.

37. Technology   The numerals in digital clocks appear to be formed from segments. Write Logo procedures to draw these digital clock numbers. In which of the digits can you identify just 1 pair of parallel segments? 2 pairs? 3 pairs? 4 pairs?

38. Technology   Use Logo or another computer program to create a working digital clock.

HISTORICAL NOTE

Have you ever thought of a math book as a "runaway best seller"? "Elements," written by a Greek mathematician, Euclid, is such a book. He wrote it nearly 2300 years ago, yet to this day it still forms part of every high school geometry text.

Euclid's genius lay not in inventing or discovering new mathematics, but in organizing mathematical knowledge. He developed a pattern of reasoning so clear and simple that it became the model for reasoning in geometry. He started with five assumptions (postulates), and five "common notions" (axioms). These were connected so directly with ordinary experience that they could readily be accepted by everyone. Euclid applied his patterns of reasoning to these postulates and axioms to develop the structure in mathematics known today as *Euclidean geometry*.

Properties of Parallel Lines

Objective: To prove and use theorems about angles formed by a transversal intersecting parallel lines

Through the centuries mathematicians have developed important theorems based on the ideas underlying parallelism. For example, if a transversal intersects parallel lines, certain deductions can be made about the pairs of angles formed. Many applications of these concepts can be observed in the world around you.

Investigation—*Visualizing the Concept*

The flight paths of two aircraft flying in the same direction at the same altitude can be thought of as two coplanar lines. Lines *l* and *m* represent the flight paths of the two aircraft.

1. What must remain constant about the flight paths to avoid a collision?
l and *m* must be ∥.

Locate a pair of corresponding angles formed by the flight paths and the line pointing north. Use a protractor to measure these angles. Answers may vary. $m\angle 2 = m\angle 6 = 70$

Now compare the measures of the other pairs of corresponding angles.

2. What seems to be true about each pair of corresponding angles? Their measures are =.

When parallel lines are intersected by a transversal, the pairs of angles formed have special relationships. These are stated in the following postulate and theorems.

Postulate 11 If parallel lines have a transversal, then corresponding angles are congruent.

Use Postulate 11 to prove that pairs of alternate interior angles are also congruent (Theorem 3.2).

Developing Mathematical Powers

Cooperative Learning Miras or mirrors can be used by small groups of students to demonstrate properties of parallel lines and a law of physics. Have each group complete Enrichment, p. 6, in the *Teacher's Resource Book* (see side column, p. 91) by actually doing the "experiment" for Questions 1 and 2 and by constructing a periscope.

Critical Thinking

Generalization Ask students to draw some conclusions about the angles formed by two parallel lines intersected by a transversal.

TEACHING SUGGESTIONS

- To reinforce the structure of geometry, emphasize that Postulate 11 is used to prove the theorems in this lesson.
- Discuss the *hypothesis* and *conclusion* of each postulate and theorem presented in this lesson.
- When you feel that students know and understand the meaning of Postulate 11 and the theorems of this lesson, you may wish to allow them to write abbreviated statements. For example: ∥ lines have ≅ corr. ∠s.
- Class Exercises 1–3 may be used orally. Students can work in pairs to complete Class Exercises 4–9.

CHALKBOARD EXAMPLES

- **For Example 1**

  $a \parallel b$ and $m\angle 6 = 35$. Find the measures of the other angles. Justify each solution.

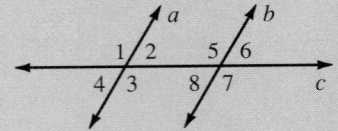

Angle Measures   Justifications
a. $m\angle 5 = 145$ ∠5 and ∠6 supp. ∠s
b. $m\angle 8 = 35$ ∠6 and ∠8 vert. ∠s
c. $m\angle 3 = 145$ ∠8 and ∠3 supp. ∠s
d. $m\angle 2 = 35$ ∠6 and ∠2 corr. ∠s
e. $m\angle 7 = 145$ ∠6 and ∠7 supp. ∠s
f. $m\angle 1 = 145$ ∠3 and ∠1 vert. ∠s
g. $m\angle 4 = 35$ ∠6 and ∠4 alt. ext. ∠s
Other justifications are possible.

> **Theorem 3.2**   If parallel lines have a transversal, then alternate interior angles are congruent.

Given: $h \parallel k$; t is a transversal of h and k.

Prove: $\angle 3 \cong \angle 2$

Plan: Since $h \parallel k$, corresponding angles, $\angle 3$ and $\angle 1$, are congruent. Vertical angles, $\angle 1$ and $\angle 2$, are also congruent. Use the transitive property to show that $\angle 3 \cong \angle 2$.

Proof:

Statements	*Reasons*
1. $h \parallel k$ with transversal t	1. Given
2. $\angle 3 \cong \angle 1$	2. If parallel lines have a transversal, then corresponding angles are congruent.
3. $\angle 1 \cong \angle 2$	3. Vertical angles are congruent.
4. $\angle 3 \cong \angle 2$	4. Transitive property of congruence

Conclusion: If $h \parallel k$, then the alternate interior angles, $\angle 3$ and $\angle 2$, are $\cong$.

> **Theorem 3.3**   If parallel lines have a transversal, then alternate exterior angles are congruent.

Given: $h \parallel k$; t is a transversal of h and k.

Prove: $\angle 1 \cong \angle 4$

Plan: Since $\angle 2 \cong \angle 1$ and $\angle 2 \cong \angle 4$, use the transitive property to show that $\angle 1 \cong \angle 4$.
Proved in Practice Exercise 17

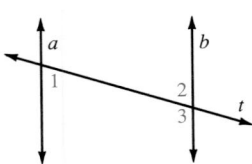

> **Theorem 3.4**   If parallel lines have a transversal, then interior angles on the same side of the transversal are supplementary.

Given: $a \parallel b$; t is a transversal of a and b.

Prove: $\angle 1$ is supplementary to $\angle 3$.

You will complete the proof in Class Exercise 7.

EXAMPLE 1 In this figure, lines *r* and *s* are intersected by transversal *t* and *r* ∥ *s*. If *m*∠3 = 95, find the measures of the other angles. Justify each solution by using Postulate 10 or Theorems 3.2–3.4.

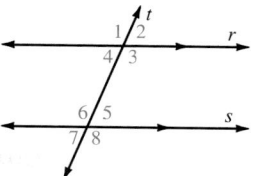

Angle Measures	Justifications
a. *m*∠8 = 95	**a.** ∠3 and ∠8 are corresponding angles.
b. *m*∠1 = 95	**b.** ∠8 and ∠1 are alternate exterior angles.
c. *m*∠6 = 95	**c.** ∠1 and ∠6 are corresponding angles.
d. *m*∠4 = 85	**d.** ∠6 is supplementary to ∠4.
e. *m*∠5 = 85	**e.** ∠4 and ∠5 are alternate interior angles.
f. *m*∠2 = 85	**f.** ∠5 and ∠2 are corresponding angles.
g. *m*∠7 = 85	**g.** ∠2 and ∠7 are alternate exterior angles.

> **Theorem 3.5** If a transversal intersecting two parallel lines is perpendicular to one of the lines, it is also perpendicular to the other line.
> Proved in Practice Exercise 18

In the figure in the following Example and throughout the text, pairs of matching arrowheads illustrate that the indicated lines are parallel.

EXAMPLE 2 Find *m*∠1, *m*∠2, and *m*∠3.

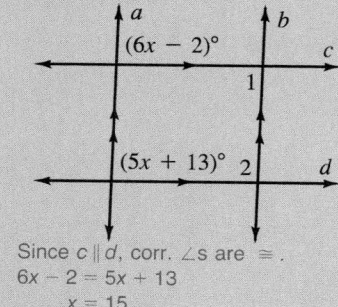

$m\angle 1 = 2x$	$a \parallel b$, thus alt. ext. ∠s are ≅.
$2x + (3x - 5) = 180$	Linear Pairs form supp. ∠s.
$5x = 185$	Properties of algebra
$x = 37$, $2x = 74$, and $3x - 5 = 106$	

$m\angle 1 = 74$	Transitive property of equality
$m\angle 2 = 106$	$z \parallel y$, thus corresponding ∠s are ≅.
$m\angle 3 = 106$	$a \parallel b$, thus alternate interior ∠s are ≅.

If you are given that lines are parallel and have a transversal, then you can draw these conclusions:
Corresponding angles are congruent.
Alternate interior angles are congruent.
Alternate exterior angles are congruent.
Interior angles on the same side of the transversal are supplementary.

3.2 Properties of Parallel Lines **87**

Assignment Guide

See p. 78B for assignments.

Lesson Quiz

Find the measure of each angle if $m \parallel n$ and if:

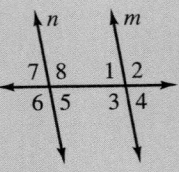

1. $m\angle 1 = 80$
2. $m\angle 3 = (3x + 2)$
   $m\angle 5 = (4x + 3)$

1. $m\angle 1 = m\angle 4 = m\angle 5 = m\angle 7 = 80$
   $m\angle 2 = m\angle 3 = m\angle 6 = m\angle 8 = 100$
2. $m\angle 3 + m\angle 5 = 180$, so $x = 25$.
   $m\angle 1 = m\angle 4 = m\angle 5 = m\angle 7 = 77$,
   $m\angle 2 = m\angle 3 = m\angle 6 = m\angle 8 = 103$

Enrichment

Find the values of x and y.

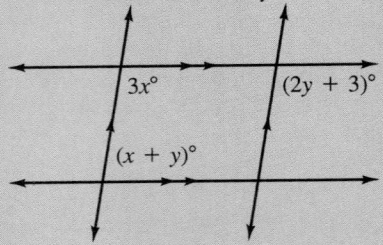

$3x = (2y + 3)$
$3x + (x + y) = 180$
Write the second equation as $y = 180 - 4x$ and substitute $180 - 4x$ for y in the first equation. $x = 33$, $y = 48$

CLASS EXERCISES

Give the theorem or postulate that justifies each conclusion. See side column.

1.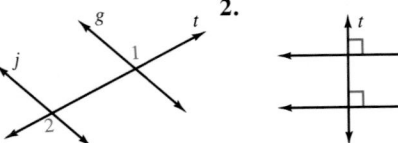

If $j \parallel g$, then $\angle 1 \cong \angle 2$.

2.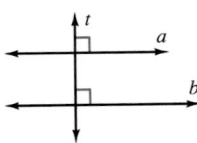

If $a \parallel b$, and $t \perp a$, then $t \perp b$.

3.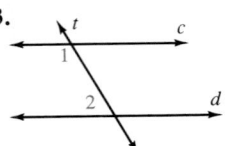

If $c \parallel d$, then $\angle 1$ is supplementary to $\angle 2$.

Justifications may vary.

4. If $m\angle 8 = 110$, find the measures of all the other angles and justify your answers.

5. If $m\angle 4 = 2x + 16$, and $m\angle 13 = x + 14$, find the measures of all the angles and justify your answers. Justifications may vary.

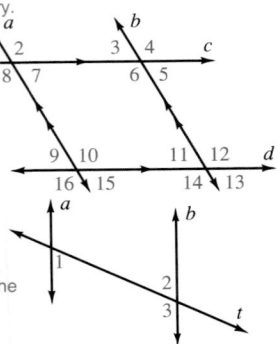

6. If some line GH is perpendicular to a, would it be perpendicular to b? Justify your answer. yes; Th. 3.5

7. Supply a Plan and complete this proof of Theorem 3.4.
In the figure, $\angle 2$ and $\angle 3$ form a linear pair. Use this information and the def. of supp. to prove $\angle 1$ and $\angle 3$ are supp.

Proof:

Statements	Reasons
1. __?__ $a \parallel b$; t is a transversal of a and b.	1. Given
2. $\angle 1 \cong \angle 2$	2. __?__ If 2 ∥ lines have a transv., alt. int. ∠s are ≅.
3. $m\angle 1 = m\angle 2$	3. __?__ Def. of ≅ ∠s
4. $\angle 2$ and $\angle 3$ are __?__ suppl.	4. Linear Pair Postulate
5. $m\angle 2 + m\angle 3 = 180$	5. __?__ Def. of supplementary
6. $m\angle 1 + m\angle 3 = 180$	6. __?__ Subst. prop.
7. $\angle 1$ is supplementary to $\angle 3$.	7. __?__ Def. of suppl.

Conclusion: If a is parallel to b, then the interior angles on the same side of the transversal, $\angle 1$ and $\angle 3$, are supplementary.

8. What is common to the hypotheses of the theorems of this lesson? Lines are parallel.

9. Thinking Critically Skew lines do not intersect. If two skew lines have a transversal, are corresponding angles congruent? How could you justify your answer? No; answers may vary. One possibility, use straws to illustrate.

88 Chapter 3 Parallelism

---

1. If 2 ∥ lines have a transv., then alt. ext. ∠s are ≅.
2. If a transv. to 2 ∥ lines is ⊥ to one of the lines, then it is ⊥ to the other.
3. If 2 ∥ lines have a transv., then int. ∠s on the same side of the transv., are supp.
4. Measure of each odd-numbered ∠ is 70; of each even-numbered ∠ is 110; use vert. ∠s, linear pairs, corr. ∠s and transitivity.
5. $x = 50$; $m\angle 4 = 116$; $m\angle 13 = 64$; use properties of Ex. 4 to show all odd-numbered ∠s have measures of 64 and all even-numbered ∠s have measures of 116.

PRACTICE EXERCISES 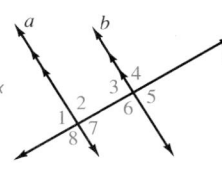 Use technology where appropriate.

1. $m\angle 1 = m\angle 3 = m\angle 5 = m\angle 7 = 89; m\angle 2 = m\angle 4 = m\angle 6 = m\angle 8 = 91$

A **Find the measures of all eight angles.**

2. $m\angle 1 = m\angle 3 = m\angle 5 = m\angle 7 = 75; m\angle 2 = m\angle 4 = m\angle 6 = m\angle 8 = 105$

1. If $m\angle 2 = 91$ 　　 **2.** If $m\angle 3 = 75$ 　　 **3.** If $m\angle 8 = x$

3. $m\angle 1 = m\angle 3 = m\angle 5 = m\angle 7 = 180 - x; m\angle 2 = m\angle 4 = m\angle 6 = m\angle 8 = x$

4. If $m\angle 1 = 2x$ and $m\angle 2 = 3x$　$x = 36; m\angle 1 = m\angle 3 = m\angle 5 =$
$m\angle 7 = 72; m\angle 2 = m\angle 4 = m\angle 6 = m\angle 8 = 108$

5. If $m\angle 1 = 5x - 10$ and $m\angle 2 = 8x + 34$　$x = 12; m\angle 1 = m\angle 3 =$
$m\angle 5 = m\angle 7 = 50; m\angle 2 = m\angle 4 = m\angle 6 = m\angle 8 = 130$

6. If $m\angle A = 52$, find the $m\angle B$, $m\angle C$, and $m\angle D$.
$m\angle B = m\angle D = 128; m\angle C = 52$

7. If $m\angle D = 2m\angle C$, find the $m\angle A$, $m\angle B$, $m\angle C$,
and $m\angle D$. $m\angle A = m\angle C = 60; m\angle B = m\angle D = 120$

Write a plan, then complete the statements and reasons in the proof.

8. **Given:** $v \parallel w; \angle 2 \cong \angle 3$
   Prove: $\angle 1 \cong \angle 3$
   Plan: ___?___ Since $v \parallel w$, $\angle 1 \cong \angle 2$ by Th. 3.3.
   By transitivity, $\angle 1 \cong \angle 3$.

   Proof:

Statements	Reasons
1. ___?___ $v \parallel w; \angle 2 \cong \angle 3$	1. Given
2. $\angle 1 \cong \angle 2$	2. ___?___ If 2 ∥ lines have a transv., alt. ext. ∠s are ≅.
3. ___?___ $\angle 1 \cong \angle 3$	3. ___?___ Trans. prop.

Write a proof. See Additional Answers, p. 702.

9. **Given:** $k \parallel l$
   Prove: $\angle 3$ is supplementary to $\angle 4$.

10. State the theorem that you proved in Exercise 9.
    If 2 ∥ lines have a transversal, then ext. ∠s on the same side
    of the transversal are supplementary.

Find the angle measures. Justify your answers.

See side column.

B **11.** $\angle 1$ 　 **12.** $\angle 2$ 　 **13.** $\angle 5$

14. $\angle 3$ 　 **15.** $\angle 4$ 　 **16.** $\angle 6$

17. Complete the proof of Theorem 3.3.

18. Prove Theorem 3.5. See Additional Answers, p. 702.

19. **Given:** $\overleftrightarrow{AO} \parallel \overleftrightarrow{BQ}$; $\overrightarrow{OP}$ and $\overrightarrow{QR}$ bisect
    $\angle AOQ$ and $\angle OQB$, respectively.
    Prove: $\angle 2 \cong \angle 4$

20. **Given:** $\overleftrightarrow{AO} \parallel \overleftrightarrow{BQ}$; $\overrightarrow{OP} \parallel \overrightarrow{QR}$
    Prove: $\angle 1 \cong \angle 4$

3.2 Properties of Parallel Lines 　 **89**

11. 100; vert. ∠s are ≅
13. 80; Linear Pair Post. and def. of suppl.
15. 80; ∠4 is supp. to an ∠ that is ≅ ∠3.
12. 100; if lines are ∥, corr. ∠s are ≅.
14. 100; if lines are ∥, alt. ext. ∠s are ≅.
16. 80; if lines are ∥, corr. ∠s are ≅.

Given $\overleftrightarrow{AB} \parallel \overleftrightarrow{CD}$; $\overleftrightarrow{AC} \parallel \overleftrightarrow{BD}$.

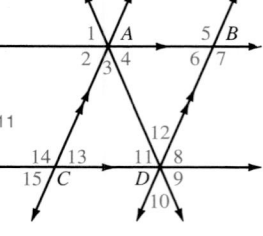

21. Name all angles congruent to $\angle 2$.
$\angle 6$; $\angle 8$; $\angle 13$; $\angle 15$

22. Name all angles congruent to $\angle 7$. $\angle 5$; $\angle 14$

23. Name all angles congruent to $\angle 4$. $\angle 1$; $\angle 9$; $\angle 11$

24. Name all angles supplementary to $\angle 13$.
$\angle 5$; $\angle 7$; $\angle 14$

25. Name all angles supplementary to $\angle 14$.
$\angle 2$; $\angle 6$; $\angle 8$; $\angle 13$; $\angle 15$

Use the figure and the given; justify your conclusions.

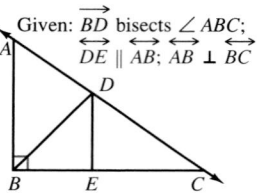

Given: $\overrightarrow{BD}$ bisects $\angle ABC$; $\overleftrightarrow{DE} \parallel \overleftrightarrow{AB}$; $\overleftrightarrow{AB} \perp \overleftrightarrow{BC}$

26. Find $m\angle DEB$. 90; **27.** Find $m\angle DBE$.
Th. 3.5 means $\overline{DE} \perp \overline{BC}$.   45; def. of $\angle$ bis.

28. Find $m\angle EDB$.   **29.** Find $m\angle ABD$.
45°; alt. int. $\angle$s $\cong$ 45; def. of $\angle$ bis.

30. Find an angle congruent to $\angle BAD$.
$\angle EDC$, if lines are $\parallel$, corr $\angle$s are $\cong$

C   **Given:** $\overleftrightarrow{BA} \parallel \overleftrightarrow{ED}$; $\overleftrightarrow{BC} \parallel \overleftrightarrow{EF}$

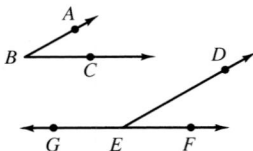

31. Prove: $\angle B \cong \angle DEF$
See Additional Answers, p. 702.

32. Prove: $\angle B$ is supplementary to $\angle DEG$.
See side column.

Applications

33. Navigation   Suppose an airport has two parallel runways as shown. What must be true about $\angle 1$ and $\angle 2$? Write an argument to justify your answer.
$\angle 1 \cong \angle 2$; $\angle$s 1 and 2 are $\cong$ because they are corr. $\angle$s.

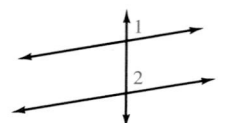

34. Technology   Logo procedures often involve variable inputs. A variable name is always preceded by dots (:) and is found in the title line and everywhere that the variable is used in the procedure. To use the procedure, type the name of the procedure followed by the input. For example:

```
to triangle :length
repeat 3 [forward :length right 120]
end
```
Defines a procedure for drawing a triangle of variable side length

```
triangle 30
```
Draws a triangle with side length 30

Write a procedure to draw this figure. Find the pairs of parallel lines. See Solutions Manual.

32. Extend $\overleftrightarrow{BC}$ and $\overleftrightarrow{ED}$ so that they intersect at X (as in the figure used for Exercise 31). By Exercise 31 $\angle B \cong \angle DEF$. Since $\angle DEG$ is supp. to $\angle DEF$, it follows that $\angle DEG$ is supp. to $\angle B$.

Mixed Review

Supply the missing information to make each statement always true.

35. All right angles are _?_. congruent

36. A conditional and its _?_ have the same truth value. contrapositive

37. _?_ distinct points determine a unique line. two

38. If $AB = DF$ and _?_, then $AB = KL$. DF = KL

39. If two lines intersect to form a pair of congruent adjacent angles, then the lines are _?_. perpendicular

Refer to this number line for Exercises 40–45.

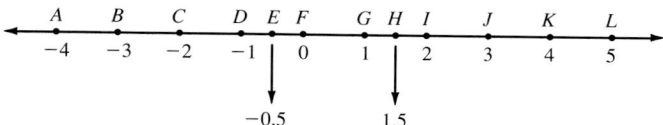

Find each length.

40. GH 0.5   **41.** AD 3   **42.** $GL - IL$ 1   **43.** $BE - DE$ 2

44. What is the coordinate of the midpoint of CG? −0.5

45. What is the coordinate of the point that is three fourths of the way from A to K? 1

46. Find $m\angle BFE$ if $m\angle DFE = 2x + 35$ and $m\angle DFB = 12x - 10$. 165

47. Find $m\angle AFB$ if $m\angle CFD = 4x + 6$ and $m\angle DFE = 5x - 3$. 54

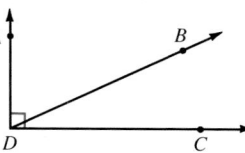

48. Write a plan to prove Theorem 1.13: If the exterior sides of two adjacent acute angles are perpendicular, then the angles are complementary.

Given: $\overrightarrow{DA} \perp \overrightarrow{DC}$

Prove: $\angle ADB$ and $\angle BDC$ are complementary.

Plan: _?_ Show that $\angle ADC$ is a right angle. Show that $m\angle ADB + m\angle BDC = 90$. Then use the definition of complementary angles.

Developing Mathematical Power

49. Writing in Mathematics   Parallel lines are used to bend light in a process called *diffraction grating*. Report on how this process separates visible light into component parts of the spectrum and provides information about stars. Answers may vary.

Developing Mathematical Power

Keeping a Portfolio   Have students respond to Exercise 49 in their math journals. Illustrated diagrams should be used wherever possible. Ask students to compare diffraction and refraction of light and use these terms to explain rainbows and sunsets.

Teacher's Resource Book
Follow-Up Investigation, Chapter 3, p. 4

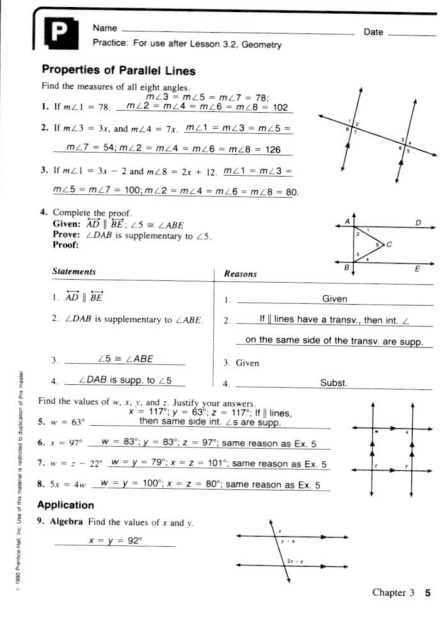

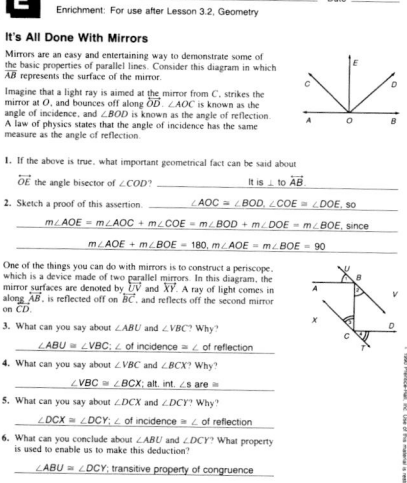

Materials/Manipulatives
Colored sticks or straws
Lined paper and tape
Protractors
Teaching Transparency 15

Technology
*Computer Test Bank, pp.
155–167*

LESSON FOCUS

Review
Draw this figure
on the chalk-
board. Ask stu-
dents what they
can conclude
from the given in-
formation. They
should justify their
answers.

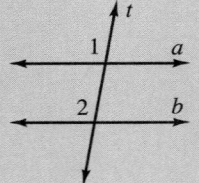

Given: $a \parallel b$
Conclusion: __?__ $\angle 1 \cong \angle 2$ Post. 11
Given: $\angle 1 \cong \angle 2$
What do you *think* is true of lines a and
b? Can you justify your answer?
It appears that if $\angle 1 \cong \angle 2$, then $a \parallel b$, but
this cannot be justified by any definition,
postulate, or theorem introduced thus far.

Alternative Learning Styles
• Using manipulatives can help con-
cretize a concept for students. The
Investigation provides an excellent
opportunity for students to "prove"
Euclid's fifth postulate. Suggest to
students that they tape the straws
to the paper to avoid having them
shift.
• Shading the region between the
parallel lines clearly delineates interior angles (shaded) and exterior
angles (not shaded) for the visual
learner.

3.3

Proving Lines Parallel

Objectives: To state the Parallel Postulate
To prove and use theorems that establish that two lines
are parallel

The following statement is the logical equivalent of Euclid's fifth postulate,
which is often called the *Parallel Postulate*.

> **Postulate 12** Through a point not on a line, there is exactly one line
> parallel to the given line.

Investigation—*Using Manipulatives*

In his famous work, *Elements,* Euclid stated his fifth postulate as:

If a transversal falls on two lines in such a way that the interior angles on one
side of the transversal are less than two right angles, then the lines meet on the
side on which the angles are less than two right angles.

For this investigation you will need colored sticks, straws, or pencils; a
protractor; and lined loose-leaf paper.

1. Line up two sticks with two lines on a sheet of
   loose-leaf paper. Let them represent $l \parallel m$. Place
   another stick on the model to intersect the other
   two. Let it represent transversal t.

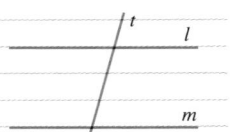

2. Use a protractor to measure the interior angles on
   one side of the transversal. Add the measures.
   Now do the same for the interior angles on the other
   side of the transversal. In each case, is the sum of
   the measures of the interior angles equal to the
   sum of the measures of two right angles? yes

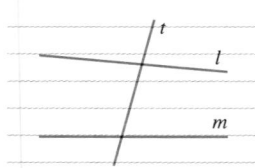

3. Rearrange the model above by moving the left end
   of the stick representing line l up a bit. Now $l \nparallel m$.
   Repeat step 2.

4. Use additional sticks to extend the model to show that l and m intersect. On
   which side of t do they intersect? Is this the side where the sum of the
   measures of the interior angles is less than the sum of the measures of the
   two right angles? the right; yes

5. Continue to rearrange the model and measure the angles. Can you model
   a situation that contradicts Euclid's statement? no

92 Chapter 3 Parallelism

Developing Mathematical Power
Keeping a Portfolio Have students summarize the concepts in this lesson by
listing in their math journals the ways in which lines can be proved parallel. Ask
them to write a paragraph comparing and contrasting the different methods.

The following postulate is the converse of Postulate 11.

> **Postulate 13** If two lines have a transversal and a pair of congruent corresponding angles, then the lines are parallel.

The following theorems are converses of Theorems 3.2 to 3.4. Postulate 13 can be used to prove these theorems.

> **Theorem 3.6** If two lines have a transversal and a pair of congruent alternate interior angles, then the lines are parallel. Proved in Class Exercise 6
>
> **Theorem 3.7** If two lines have a transversal and a pair of congruent alternate exterior angles, then the lines are parallel. Proved in Practice Exercise 4
>
> **Theorem 3.8** If two lines have interior angles on the same side of the transversal that are supplementary, then the lines are parallel. Proved in Practice Exercise 11

EXAMPLE Are lines *x* and *y* parallel? Give a reason for your conclusion.

a.
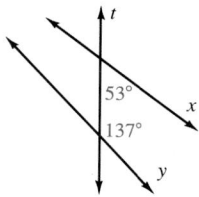

b.
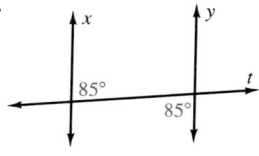

c.
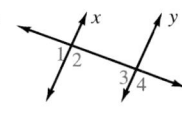

$m\angle 1 = 87°$
$m\angle 4 = 93°$

a. $x \nparallel y$;
   $53 + 137 \neq 180$

b. $x \parallel y$; alternate interior angles are $\cong$.

c. $x \parallel y$; corresponding angles are $\cong$.

> **Theorem 3.9** If two coplanar lines are perpendicular to the same line, then they are parallel.

Given: *l* and *k* are coplanar;
    $l \perp t$, and $k \perp t$.
Prove: $l \parallel k$
Plan: Since $l \perp t$ and $k \perp t$, $\angle 1$ and $\angle 2$ are right angles, and thus $\angle 1 \cong \angle 2$. $\angle 1$ and $\angle 2$ are congruent corresponding angles; therefore, $l \parallel k$ by Postulate 13.
Proved in Class Exercise 7

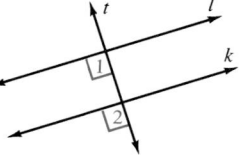

3.3 Proving Lines Parallel **93**

Developing Mathematical Power

Cooperative Learning Have each group choose a theme such as architecture, transportation, nature, etc., and design a collage that shows examples of parallel lines in that theme. Display completed work on a bulletin board.

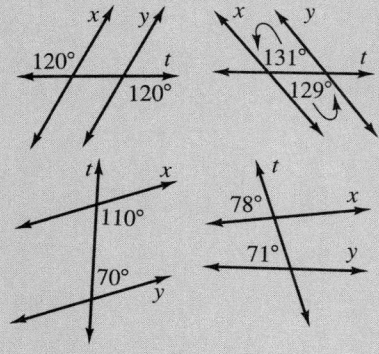

Common Error

- Students may confuse the theorems of this lesson with those of the previous lesson. Ask them to write the converse and contrapositive of each theorem, then draw a suitable figure for each.
- See *Teacher's Resource Book* for additional remediation.

LESSON FOLLOW-UP

Discussion

For each postulate or theorem in Lesson 3.2 whose converse is now known to be true, have students form the biconditional. Also have them give the contrapositive of each conditional. You may wish to refer students to the featured construction on page 27 or Construction 3 on page 398.

Assignment Guide

See p. 78B for assignments.

Additional Answers

7. Proof:

Statements	Reasons
1. *l* and *k* are coplanar, *l* ⊥ *t* and *k* ⊥ *t*	1. Given
2. ∠1 and ∠2 are rt. ∠s.	2. Def. of ⊥ lines
3. ∠1 ≅ ∠2	3. All rt. ∠s are ≅.
4. *l* ∥ *k*	4. Post. 13
Conclusion:	If lines *t, l* and *k* are coplanar and *t* ⊥ *l* and *t* ⊥ *k*, then *l* ∥ *k*.

> **Theorem 3.10** If two lines are parallel to a third line, then they are parallel to each other. Proved in Practice Exercise 12

Two lines intersected by a transversal are parallel if:
Corresponding angles are congruent.   Alternate interior angles are congruent.
Alternate exterior angles are congruent.   Interior angles on the same side of the transversal are supplementary.

CLASS EXERCISES

1. If 2 int. ∠s on the same side of the transv. are supp., the lines are ∥.
2. If 2 lines have a transv. and a pair of ≅ alt. ext. ∠s, the lines are ∥.

Give the postulate or theorem that proves *x* ∥ *y*.

1.
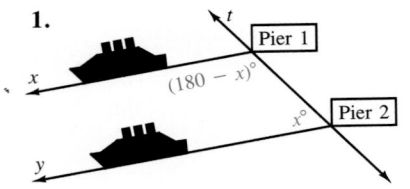

2.
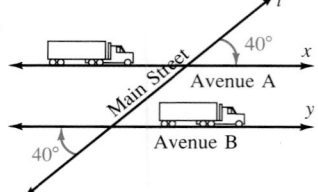

Are lines *x* and *y* parallel? Give a reason for your conclusion.

3.
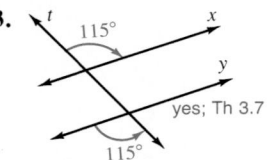
yes; Th 3.7

4.
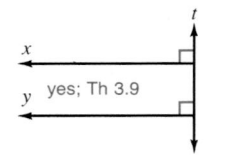
yes; Th 3.9

5.
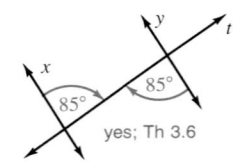
yes; Th 3.6

6. Write a plan, then fill in the reasons to prove Theorem 3.6.

Given: ∠2 ≅ ∠3; *t* is a transversal of *m* and *n*.
Prove: *m* ∥ *n*
Plan: _?_

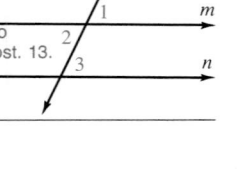

Vert. ∠s 1 and 2 are ≅.
Use the Given and the trans. prop. to show ∠1 ≅ ∠3. Concl. follows by Post. 13.

Proof:

Statements	Reasons
1. ∠2 ≅ ∠3	1. _?_ Given
2. _?_ ∠1 ≅ ∠2	2. Vertical angles are congruent.
3. ∠1 ≅ ∠3	3. _?_ Trans. prop.
4. _?_ *m* ∥ *n*	4. _?_ If 2 lines have a transv. and a pair of ≅ corr. ∠s, the lines are ∥.

Conclusion: Whenever alternate interior angles ∠2 and ∠3 are congruent, then the lines *m* and *n* are parallel.

7. Refer to the plan for Theorem 3.9 to write a formal proof of the theorem.
See side column.

94 Chapter 3 Parallelism

PRACTICE EXERCISES ⊕ Use technology where appropriate.

State the theorem that proves that the vehicles must be on parallel paths.

A

1.

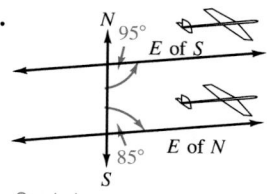

See below.

2.

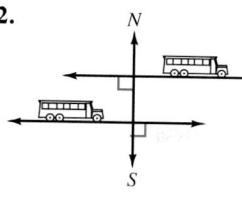

3.

4. Use the information to prove Theorem 3.7.

Given: $\angle 1 \cong \angle 3$; t is a transversal of a and b.
Prove: $a \parallel b$

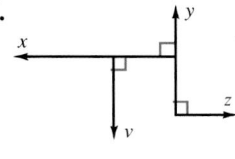

Determine which lines are parallel. Justify each conclusion.

5.

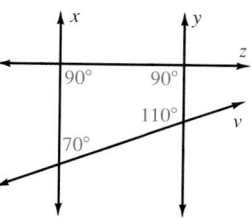

6.

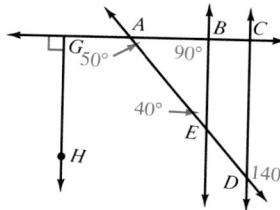

7.

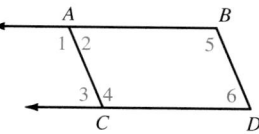

See Additional Answers, p. 702.

B

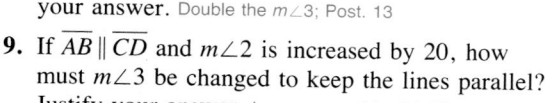

8. If $\overline{AC} \parallel \overline{BD}$ and $m\angle 6$ is doubled, how must $m\angle 3$ be changed to keep the lines parallel? Justify your answer. Double the $m\angle 3$; Post. 13

9. If $\overline{AB} \parallel \overline{CD}$ and $m\angle 2$ is increased by 20, how must $m\angle 3$ be changed to keep the lines parallel? Justify your answer. Increase $m\angle 3$ by 20; Th. 3.6

10. If $\overline{AC} \parallel \overline{BD}$ and $m\angle 5$ is decreased by 30, how must $m\angle 2$ be changed to keep the lines parallel? Justify your answer. Increase $m\angle 2$ by 30; Th. 3.8

11. Prove Theorem 3.8. **12.** Prove Theorem 3.10.
See Additional Answers, p. 702.

Use the given information to determine which lines are parallel. Justify your answers.

13. $\angle 1 \cong \angle 7$ $l \parallel m$; Post. 13 **14.** $\angle 11 \cong \angle 6$ no $\parallel$ lines

15. $\angle 8 \cong \angle 11$ $s \parallel t$; Th. 3.6 **16.** $\angle 1 \cong \angle 18$ $l \parallel n$; Th. 3.7

17. $m\angle 4 = 112$, $m\angle 16 = 58$ no $\parallel$ lines

18. $m\angle 8 = 79$, $m\angle 4 = 101$ $l \parallel m$; Th. 3.8

19. $m\angle 6 = 72$, $m\angle 14 = 72$ $m \parallel n$; Post. 13

1. If 2 lines have supp. int. ∠s on the same side of a transv., the lines are ∥.
2. If 2 coplanar lines are ⊥ to the same line, the lines are ∥.
3. If 2 lines have a transv. and a pair of ≅ alt. int. ∠s, the lines are ∥.

3.3 Proving Lines Parallel **95**

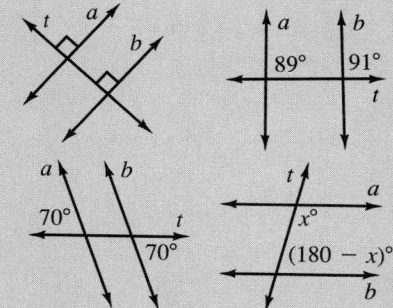
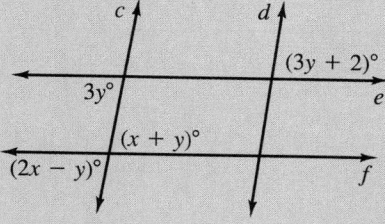
4. Plan: Vert. ∠s 1 and 2 are ≅. Use the given information and the transitive prop. to show $\angle 2 \cong \angle 3$. Concl. follows by Post. 13.

Proof:

Statements	Reasons
1. $\angle 1 \cong \angle 3$; t	1. Given.
2. $\angle 2 \cong \angle 1$	2. Vert. ∠s are ≅.
3. $\angle 2 \cong \angle 3$	3. Trans. prop.
4. $a \parallel b$	4. Post. 13

Conclusion: In the given figure, if alt. ext ∠s 1 and 3 are ≅, then $a \parallel b$.

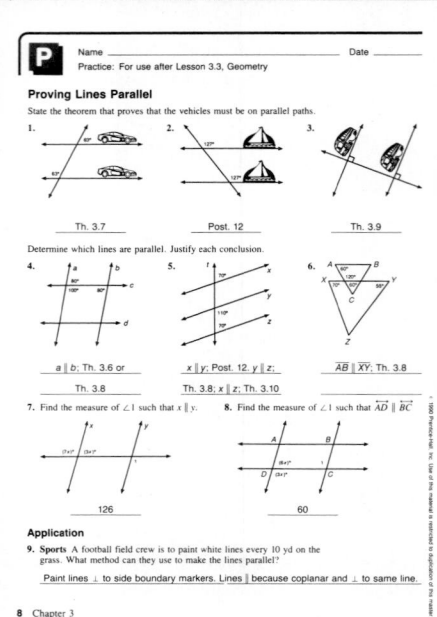

P Name _____ Date _____
Practice: For use after Lesson 3.3, Geometry

Proving Lines Parallel

State the theorem that proves that the vehicles must be on parallel paths.

1. _____ 2. _____ 3. _____

Th. 3.7   Post. 12   Th. 3.9

Determine which lines are parallel. Justify each conclusion.

4. _____ 5. _____ 6. _____

a ∥ b; Th. 3.6 or   x ∥ y; Post. 12. y ∥ z;   AB ∥ XY; Th. 3.8
Th. 3.8   Th. 3.8; x ∥ z; Th. 3.10

7. Find the measure of ∠1 such that x ∥ y.   8. Find the measure of ∠1 such that AD ∥ BC

126   60

Application

9. **Sports** A football field crew is to paint white lines every 10 yd on the grass. What method can they use to make the lines parallel?

Paint lines ⊥ to side boundary markers. Lines ∥ because coplanar and ⊥ to same line.

8 Chapter 3

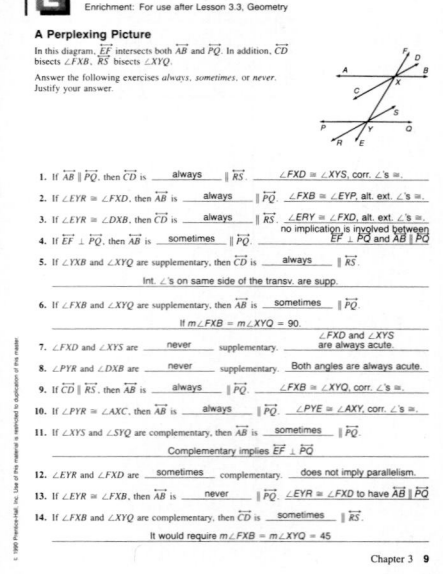

E Name _____ Date _____
Enrichment: For use after Lesson 3.3, Geometry

A Perplexing Picture

In this diagram, EF intersects both AB and PQ. In addition, CD bisects ∠FXB. RS bisects ∠XYQ.

Answer the following exercises *always, sometimes,* or *never.* Justify your answer.

1. If AB ∥ PQ, then CD is __always__ ∥ RS. ∠FXD ≅ ∠XYS, corr. ∠'s ≅.

2. If ∠EYR ≅ ∠FXD, then AB is __always__ ∥ PQ. ∠FXB ≅ ∠EYP, alt. ext. ∠'s ≅.

3. If ∠EYR ≅ ∠DXB, then CD is __always__ ∥ RS. ∠ERY ≅ ∠FXD, alt. ext. ∠'s ≅.

4. If EF ⊥ PQ, then AB is __sometimes__ ∥ PQ. no implication is involved between EF ⊥ PQ and AB ∥ PQ

5. If ∠YXB and ∠XYQ are supplementary, then CD is __always__ ∥ RS. Int. ∠'s on same side of the transv. are supp.

6. If ∠FXB and ∠XYQ are supplementary, then AB is __sometimes__ ∥ PQ.

If m∠FXB = m∠XYQ = 90.

7. ∠FXD and ∠XYS are __never__ supplementary. ∠FXD and ∠XYS are always acute.

8. ∠PYR and ∠DXB are __never__ supplementary. Both angles are always acute.

9. If CD ∥ RS, then AB is __always__ ∥ PQ. ∠FXB ≅ ∠XYQ, corr. ∠'s ≅.

10. If ∠PYR ≅ ∠AXC, then AB is __always__ ∥ PQ. ∠PYE ≅ ∠AXY, corr. ∠'s ≅.

11. If ∠XYS and ∠SYQ are complementary, then AB is __sometimes__ ∥ PQ. Complementary implies EF ⊥ PQ

12. ∠EYR and ∠FXD are __sometimes__ complementary. does not imply parallelism.

13. If ∠EYR ≅ ∠FXB, then AB is __never__ ∥ PQ. ∠EYR ≅ ∠FXD to have AB ∥ PQ

14. If ∠FXB and ∠XYQ are complementary, then CD is __sometimes__ ∥ RS.

It would require m∠FXB = m∠XYQ = 45

Chapter 3 **9**

---

20. Find the measure of ∠1 such that $\overleftrightarrow{AC} \parallel \overleftrightarrow{DF}$. $m\angle 1 = 72$

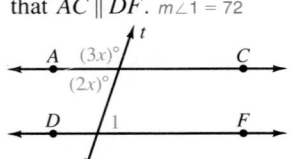

21. Prove that $k \parallel l$.

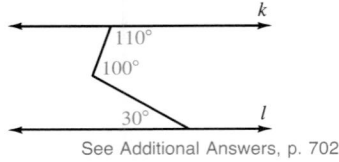

See Additional Answers, p. 702.

C **22.** Prove: If two parallel lines are intersected by a transversal, the bisectors of a pair of corresponding angles are parallel. See Additional Answers, p. 702.

Applications **23.** Paint the first parking line in a satisfactory place. Use another line (such as a curb) as a transv. Get other lines ∥ by constructing ≅ corr. ∠s.

23. Maintainence A crew is sent to a new parking lot to paint the parking lines. What method can they use to be sure the lines are parallel?

24. Architecture The floors of a skyscraper are perpendicular to each of the walls. What theorem justifies the fact that the floors are therefore parallel? Answers may vary.

25. Technology Using Logo, create a grid with parallel and perpendicular lines. Turn your grid into a maze and try moving the turtle through the maze. Answers may vary.

CONSTRUCTION

Given: Line *l* and point *P*, not on *l*.
Construct: Line *m* through *P* parallel to *l*.

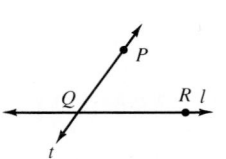

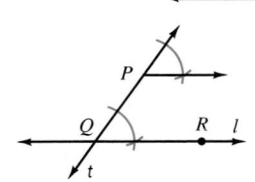

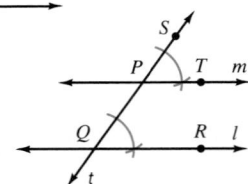

1. Through *P* draw line *t*, intersecting *l*. Label the point of intersection *Q*.

2. Select a point on line *l*, and label it *R* (making *R* distinct from point *Q*).

3. On the same side of line *t* as ∠PQR, copy ∠PQR with point *P* as the vertex.

4. Label point *S* on *t*, with *P* between *Q* and *S*. Label point *T* on the other ray of the new angle.

5. Draw $\overleftrightarrow{PT}$ and label it *m*. Now *m* ∥ *l*.

EXERCISE Copy line *f* and point *R*. Then construct line *g* through *R* so that *g* ∥ *f*.
Check students' constructions.

Parallel Lines and Triangles

3.4

Objectives: To classify triangles by sides and angles
To prove and apply theorems regarding angle measure and angle relationships in a triangle

Much of your work in geometry will be related to or based on triangles. Triangles have many special properties.

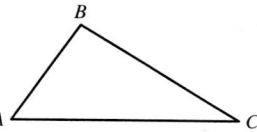

Investigation—*Using Manipulatives*

Draw a triangle similar in shape to the above △*ABC* but larger in size. Cut it out. Now try this paper-folding exercise.

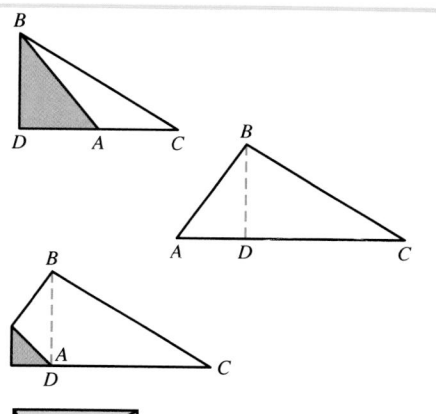

a. Slide point *A* along $\overline{AC}$ toward point *C* until the fold passes through point *B*. The crease intersects $\overline{AC}$ at point *D*. Unfold the triangle.

b. Bring point *A* to point *D* and crease.

c. Bring points *B* and *C* to point *D* and crease.

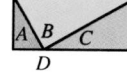

1. What appears to be true about the sum of the measures of these three angles?
It appears to be 180.
2. What conclusion can you come to about the three angles of △*ABC*? Why?
The sum of their measures = 180. The 3 ∠s formed are adj. The noncommon sides of ∠*A* and ∠*C* form opp. rays.

Definition A set of points is a **triangle** if and only if it consists of the figure formed by three segments connecting three noncollinear points.

Each of the three noncollinear points is called a *vertex*. The segments are called *sides*. The three vertices are used to name the triangle. The triangle at the right is triangle *RST*, △*RST*, with angles: ∠*R*, ∠*S*, and ∠*T*, and sides: $\overline{RS}$, $\overline{ST}$, $\overline{TR}$. Lowercase letters, such as *r*, *s*, and *t*, can also be used to name sides.

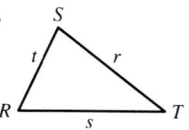

Developing Mathematical Power

Cooperative Learning   Provide each group with *Connections, p. 6*. Have them state the reasons for their rankings before they test their answers with models. If they rerank any, have them explain why. Each group should summarize their thoughts on rigidity and design a rigid figure. Test each group's design.

LESSON PLAN

Vocabulary
Acute triangle
Equiangular triangle
Equilateral triangle
Exterior angle
Interior angle
Isosceles triangle
Obtuse triangle
Remote interior angles
Right triangle
Scalene triangle
Triangle
Vertex (vertices)

Materials/Manipulatives
Paper and scissors
Straightedges
Computer
Teaching Transparency 16
Connections, pp. 6 and 8

Technology
Computer Test Bank, pp. 168–174
The Geometric Supposer: Triangles
Geometry Problems and Projects: Triangles, Worksheets T1–T4

LESSON FOCUS

Review
Review classifications of angles. Draw angles on the chalkboard and have students measure and classify them.

Alternative Learning Styles
• Manipulatives provide a concrete approach to help students grasp a concept. In the Investigation, the use of manipulatives helps students discover that the sum of the angle measures of a triangle is 180.

• Another approach is to have students draw a triangle, cut it out, tear off the angles to make 3 triangles, and then put them together to form a straight line.

- Some students will recall from earlier courses that the sum of the measures of the angles of a triangle is 180, and not see the need to *prove* the statement. Remind them that our geometric structure is based on definitions, postulates, and theorems.
- When you discuss the proof of Theorem 3.11, point out how $\overleftrightarrow{DE}$ was added to the figure to aid in the proof. Tell students that they can add an *auxiliary* line, segment, or ray to a figure to aid in a proof or solution to a problem.
- Help students plan proofs of the corollaries.
- You can use Practice Exercise 1 to make sure that students can identify the six exterior angles of a triangle.
- You may wish to tell students that in Lesson 5.1 it will be proved that congruent sides imply congruent opposite angles and vice versa (and hence a triangle is equilateral if it is equiangular).

A triangle can be classified by its sides or by its angles.

Scalene	**Isosceles**	**Equilateral**
No sides congruent	At least 2 sides congruent	All sides congruent

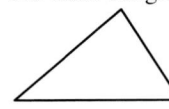 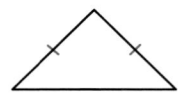 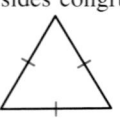

Acute	**Obtuse**	**Right**	**Equiangular**
3 acute angles	1 obtuse angle	1 right angle	3 congruent angles

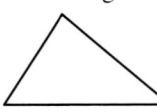 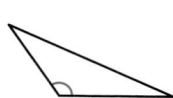

Theorem 3.11 The sum of the measures of the angles of a triangle is 180.

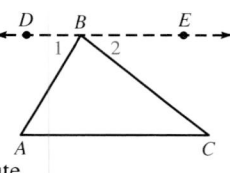

Given: $\triangle ABC$

Prove: $m\angle A + m\angle B + m\angle C = 180$

Plan: Through B construct $\overleftrightarrow{DE} \parallel \overleftrightarrow{AC}$. Thus, $m\angle A = m\angle 1$ and $m\angle C = m\angle 2$. Show $m\angle 1 + m\angle ABC + m\angle 2 = 180$; then substitute.

Proof:

Statements	*Reasons*
1. Through B, construct $\overleftrightarrow{DE}$ parallel to $\overleftrightarrow{AC}$.	1. Through a point not on a line, there is exactly one line parallel to the given line.
2. $\angle DBC$ and $\angle 2$ form a linear pair.	2. Definition of linear pair
3. $\angle DBC$ and $\angle 2$ are supplementary angles.	3. Linear Pair Postulate
4. $m\angle DBC + m\angle 2 = 180$	4. Definition of supplementary angles
5. $m\angle DBC = m\angle 1 + m\angle ABC$	5. Definition of betweenness of rays
6. $m\angle 1 + m\angle ABC + m\angle 2 = 180$	6. Substitution property
7. $\angle 1 \cong \angle A; \angle 2 \cong \angle C$	7. If $\parallel$ lines have a transv., then alt. int. $\angle$s are $\cong$.
8. $m\angle 1 = m\angle A; m\angle 2 = m\angle C$	8. Definition of congruent angles
9. $m\angle A + m\angle B + m\angle C = 180$	9. Substitution property

Conclusion: If figure ABC is a triangle, then $m\angle A + m\angle B + m\angle C = 180$.

In the proof of Theorem 3.11, $\overleftrightarrow{DE}$ is an added line. Such an addition is called an *auxiliary line* because it helps to prove a theorem.

EXAMPLE 1   **Find the measure of the third angle. Then classify each triangle.**

a. 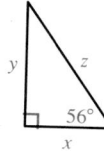   b. 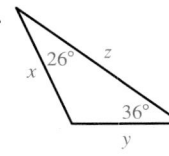   c. 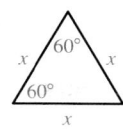   d.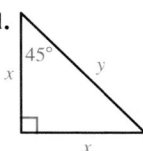

a. 34; right; scalene   **b.** 118; obtuse; scalene

c. 60; acute; equiangular; equilateral   **d.** 45; right; isosceles

These four theorems are corollaries of Theorem 3.11.

Corollary 1   If two angles of one triangle are congruent to two angles of a second triangle, then the third angles are congruent.
Proved in Practice Exercise 13

Corollary 2   Each angle of an equiangular triangle measures 60°.
Proved in Practice Exercise 28

Corollary 3   In a triangle, there can be at most one right angle, or at most one obtuse angle. Proved in Practice Exercise 31

Corollary 4   The acute angles of a right triangle are complementary.
Proved in Class Exercise 11

In this figure, each side of $\triangle ABC$ has been extended to form *exterior angles*: $\angle 1$, $\angle 2$, and $\angle 3$. Each exterior angle has an *adjacent interior angle* and two *remote interior angles*. Exterior angle 2 is adjacent to interior angle ABC. Its two remote interior angles are $\angle BAC$ and $\angle ACB$. Which are the remote interior angles of exterior angle 3?
$\angle BAC$ and $\angle ABC$

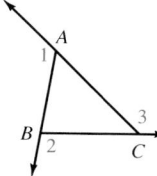

Theorem 3.12   The measure of an exterior angle of a triangle is equal to the sum of the measures of the two remote interior angles.

Given: $\angle 1$ is an exterior angle of $\triangle ABC$.

Prove: $m\angle 1 = m\angle B + m\angle C$

Plan: $m\angle CAB + m\angle 1 = 180$. Also, $m\angle CAB + m\angle B + m\angle C = 180$.
By the transitive property, $m\angle CAB + m\angle 1 = m\angle CAB + m\angle B + m\angle C$.
Use the subtraction property to show $m\angle 1 = m\angle B + m\angle C$.
Proved in Practice Exercise 27

 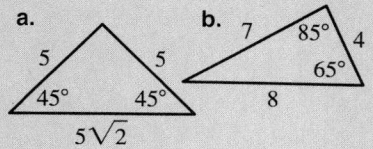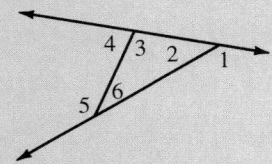

Class Exercises

11. Proof:

Statements	Reasons
1. Rt. $\triangle ABC$ with rt. $\angle C$	1. Given
2. $m\angle C = 90$	2. Def. of rt. $\angle$
3. $m\angle A + m\angle B + m\angle C = 180$	3. the sum of the measures of $\angle$s of a $\triangle$ is 180.
4. $m\angle A + m\angle B + 90 = 180$	4. Subs. prop.
5. $m\angle A + m\angle B = 90$	5. Subtr. prop.
6. $\angle A$ and $\angle B$ are comp. $\angle$s.	6. Def. of compl.

Conclusion: In rt. $\angle ABC$ with rt. $\angle C$, $\angle A$ and $\angle B$ are compl. $\angle$s.

Developing Mathematical Power

- *Modeling* Students provide an algebraic model for a geometric concept.
- *Writing in Mathematics* Students provide real-world examples of triangular objects.
- *Investigation* Students draw conclusions resulting from the piecing together of equilateral triangles.

EXAMPLE 2 Find the measure of the indicated angle.

a. $m\angle 2$ if $m\angle 6 = 118$ and $m\angle 3 = 83$

b. $m\angle 5$ if $m\angle 3 = 79$ and $m\angle 1 = 158$

c. $m\angle 3$ if $m\angle 1 = 152$ and $\angle 3 \cong \angle 5$

d. $m\angle 4$ if $\angle 3 \cong \angle 5$ and $m\angle 2 = 34$

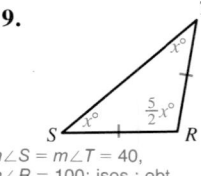

a. 35   b. 79   c. 76   d. 107

CLASS EXERCISES

Drawing in Geometry Sketch the triangle, if it exists. See Additional Answers, p. 702.

1. equilateral, obtuse triangle does not exist
2. right, isosceles triangle
3. right, obtuse triangle does not exist
4. right, scalene triangle
5. scalene, acute triangle
6. scalene, obtuse triangle

Find the angle measures in each triangle. Then classify each triangle.

7.

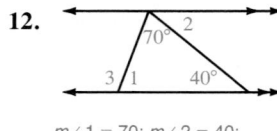

$m\angle 1 = m\angle 2 = 45$; isos.; rt.

8.

$m\angle D = 60$, $m\angle E = 60$; equiangular; equilateral

9.

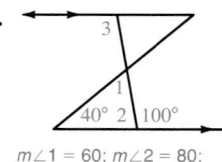

$m\angle S = m\angle T = 40$, $m\angle R = 100$; isos.; obt.

10.

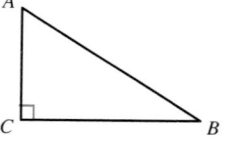

$m\angle M = 69$, $m\angle P = 85$, $m\angle N = 26$; acute; scalene

11. Complete this proof of Corollary 4 to Theorem 3.11.

Given: $\triangle ABC$ is a right triangle with right $\angle C$.

Prove: $\angle A$ and $\angle B$ are complementary angles.

Plan: Form an equation in which $m\angle A + m\angle B = 90$. Conclusion follows by the definition of complementary angles. See side column.

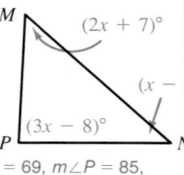

Find the measures of the numbered angles.

12.

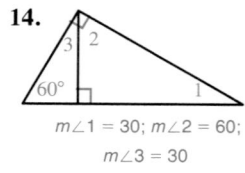

$m\angle 1 = 70$; $m\angle 2 = 40$; $m\angle 3 = 110$

13.

$m\angle 1 = 60$; $m\angle 2 = 80$; $m\angle 3 = 100$

14.

$m\angle 1 = 30$; $m\angle 2 = 60$; $m\angle 3 = 30$

True or false? Justify your answers.

15. All equiangular triangles are acute triangles. true; each $\angle$ measures 60°.

16. An equilateral triangle is an isosceles triangle. true; def. of isos. $\triangle$

PRACTICE EXERCISES

A
1. **Drawing in Geometry** Copy △*ABC*.
Extend $\overrightarrow{BA}$, $\overrightarrow{AC}$, and $\overrightarrow{CB}$. Use 1, 2, and 3 to
label the exterior angles formed. Are there
any other exterior angles of △*ABC*? If so,
how are they formed? Yes; 3 more. They
are formed by extending $\overrightarrow{AB}$, $\overrightarrow{CA}$, and $\overrightarrow{BC}$.
2. How many exterior angles can be formed at
each vertex of any triangle? two

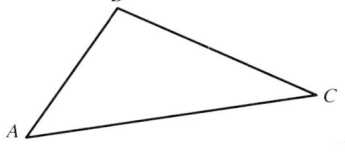

Find the missing angle measures for △*ABC*.

3. ∠*C* is a right angle.
$m\angle A = 25$ $m\angle B = 65$

4. $m\angle A = 110$
$m\angle C = m\angle B$
$m\angle C = m\angle B = 35$

5. $m\angle A = 30$
$m\angle C = 4(m\angle B)$
$m\angle B = 30$ $m\angle C = 120$

Find the measures of the numbered angles. Classify each triangle.

6.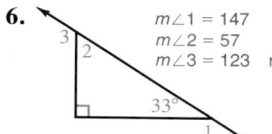
$m\angle 1 = 147$
$m\angle 2 = 57$
$m\angle 3 = 123$ rt. △

7.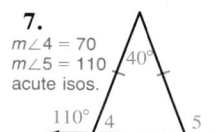
$m\angle 4 = 70$
$m\angle 5 = 110$
acute isos.

8.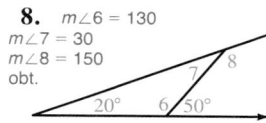
$m\angle 6 = 130$
$m\angle 7 = 30$
$m\angle 8 = 150$
obt.

True or false? Justify your answers.

9. Equilateral triangles are isosceles.
true; def. of isos. △
10. All isosceles triangles are equilateral.
false; they may have only 2 ≅ sides
11. Some right triangles are scalene.
true; sides of a rt. △ may or may not be ≅
12. All obtuse triangles are scalene.
false; they may be isos.
13. Complete this proof of Corollary 1
of Theorem 3.11. See Additional Answers, p. 702.

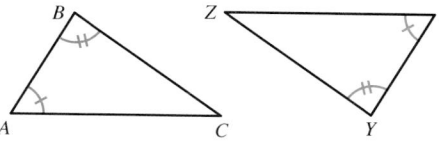

Given: △*ABC* and △*XYZ*;
∠*A* ≅ ∠*X*; ∠*B* ≅ ∠*Y*

Prove: ∠*C* ≅ ∠*Z*

Plan: The sum of the measures of the angles in each triangle is 180.
The measures of angles *A* and *B* of △*ABC* are equal respectively
to the measures of angles *X* and *Y* of △*XYZ*. Using the
subtraction property, $m\angle C = m\angle Z$, and ∠*C* ≅ ∠*Z*.

Find the measures of the numbered angles.

14.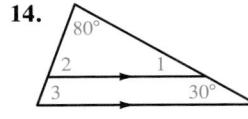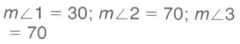

$m\angle 1 = 30; m\angle 2 = 70; m\angle 3 = 70$

15.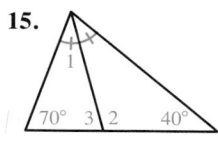

$m\angle 1 = 35; m\angle 2 = 105; m\angle 3 = 75$

16.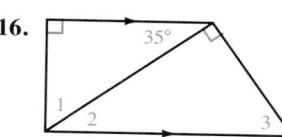

$m\angle 1 = 55; m\angle 2 = 35; m\angle 3 = 55$

3.4 Parallel Lines and Triangles **101**

Find the measures of the angles of △ABC, using the information given.

B   **17.** $\angle A \cong \angle B \cong \angle C$ $m\angle A = m\angle B =$
      $m\angle C = 60$

18. $m\angle A : m\angle B : m\angle C$ as $1:3:5$
    $m\angle A = 20, m\angle B = 60, m\angle C = 100$

19. $m\angle A : m\angle B : m\angle C$ as $2:3:5$
    $m\angle A = 36; m\angle B = 54; m\angle C = 90$

20. $m\angle B : m\angle C : m\angle A$ as $4:5:6$
    $m\angle B = 48; m\angle C = 60; m\angle A = 72$

21. $m\angle A + m\angle B = 90$; $\angle A \cong \angle B$
    $m\angle A = m\angle B = 45; m\angle C = 90$

22. $m\angle A = 3m\angle B$; $m\angle C$ is 20 greater
    than $m\angle B$. $m\angle A = 96, m\angle B = 32,$
    $m\angle C = 52$

23. Find $m\angle R$, $m\angle S$, and $m\angle T$.
    $m\angle R = 60, m\angle S = 96, m\angle T = 24$

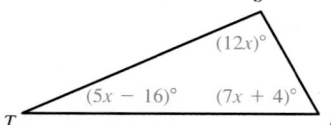

24. Find $m\angle J$, $m\angle K$, and $m\angle JLM$.
    $m\angle J = 40, m\angle K = 110, m\angle JLM = 150$

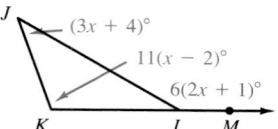

25. An exterior angle of a triangle has a measure of 60. If one of its remote interior angles has twice the measure of the other, find their measures.
20, 40

26. One of the acute angles of a right triangle has a measure that is 5 less than four times the measure of the other. Find the measures. 19, 71

27. Complete the proof of Theorem 3.12. See Additional Answers, p. 702.

28. Write a proof of Corollary 2 of Theorem 3.11.

C   **29.** The measure of an exterior angle of a triangle is 3 less than twice the measure of the adjacent interior angle. If the measures of the remote interior angles differ by 1, find the measure of each. 59, 60

30. Given: △ABC with exterior angles, ∠1, ∠2, and ∠3. See Additional Answers, p. 702.
      Prove: $m\angle 1 + m\angle 2 + m\angle 3 = 360$.

31. Write a justification of Corollary 3 of Theorem 3.11.
See below.

Applications

32. Band Routine This diagram shows a marching band routine that starts and ends at Point X. Describe the routine and give the measure of each interior and exterior angle.
See side column.

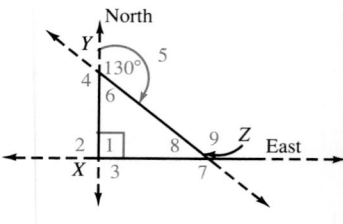

33. Surveying The surveyors at the Garden of Triangles must measure the angles of each triangular flower bed. What is the fewest number of angles they can measure if the bed is an acute scalene triangle? a right scalene triangle? an obtuse scalene triangle? an equilangular triangle? 2; 1; 2; 0

31. If a △ has 2 or more rt. ∠s, or 2 or more obtuse ∠s, the sum of the ∠ measures of the △ is greater than 180. This contradicts the angle sum theorem, so a △ may have at most 1 rt. ∠ or at most 1 obtuse ∠.

32. Go North from X to Y; turn 130° E of N; go to Z; turn West and go to X. $m\angle 1 = m\angle 2 = m\angle 3 = 90$; $m\angle 4 = 130$; $m\angle 5 = 130, m\angle 6 = 50, m\angle 7 = 140, m\angle 8 = 40, m\angle 9 = 140$

Developing Mathematical Power

34. Modeling In a triangle, if the sum of the measures of two of the angles is equal to the measure of the third angle, then the triangle is a right triangle. Justify this statement using an algebraic model. $a + b = c$; $(a + b) + c = 180$; $c + c = 180$; $2c = 180$; $c = 90$

35. Writing in Mathematics Think of two real-world objects that are triangular in shape. Write an essay in which you identify the objects, speculate why they are triangular in shape, and tell what types of triangles they illustrate. Answers may vary.

36. Investigation How many nonoverlapping coplanar equiangular triangles can share a single vertex? Sketch the figure and describe it in terms of its sides and in terms of its angles. Six; the figure has six sides equal in length (equilateral) and six angles of equal measure (equiangular).

TEST YOURSELF

In Exercises 1–6, use this photo of an escalator.

1. Name one pair of parallel planes.
   ABC, GDE   3.1
2. Name four pairs of parallel lines.
   Answers may vary. $\overrightarrow{AH} \parallel \overrightarrow{BC}$, $\overrightarrow{AB} \parallel \overrightarrow{HC}$, $\overrightarrow{HC} \parallel \overrightarrow{GD}$, $\overrightarrow{GD} \parallel \overrightarrow{FE}$
3. Name a point where three lines intersect.
   H, C, G, or D
4. Name two lines skew to $\overleftrightarrow{FG}$.
   Answers may vary. $\overleftrightarrow{HC}$, $\overleftrightarrow{AB}$
5. Name the intersection of ABC and HGD.
   $\overleftrightarrow{HC}$
6. Name a transversal of $\overleftrightarrow{HG}$ and $\overleftrightarrow{CD}$.
   $\overleftrightarrow{HC}$ or $\overleftrightarrow{GD}$
7. If $k \parallel m$, name four pairs of alternate exterior angles.
   $\angle 3$ and $\angle 16$, $\angle 4$ and $\angle 15$, $\angle 1$ and $\angle 14$, $\angle 2$ and $\angle 13$ 3.2, 3.3
8. Using angles 1, 6, and 9, write two congruence statements that would prove $k \parallel m$. Justify.
   $\angle 6 \cong \angle 9$ (alt. int. $\angle$s); $\angle 1 \cong \angle 9$ (corr. $\angle$s)
9. If $k \parallel m$ and $m\angle 7 = 2m\angle 11$, find the measures of angles 3, 4, 7, 8, 11, 12, 15, and 16. 60, 120, 120, 60, 60, 120, 120, 60   3.4
10. If $k \parallel m$, and $m\angle 15 = \frac{3}{2}m\angle 14$, and $\angle 14$ is a right angle, find the measures of all the numbered angles. $m\angle 1 = m\angle 2 = m\angle 5 = m\angle 6 = m\angle 9 = m\angle 10 = m\angle 13 = m\angle 14 = 90$; $m\angle 4 = m\angle 7 = m\angle 12 = m\angle 15 = 135$; $m\angle 3 = m\angle 8 = m\angle 11 = m\angle 16 = 45$

If $\triangle ABC$ exists with the following conditions, find the missing angle measures.

11. $m\angle A = 96$; $\angle B \cong \angle C$ 12. $\angle B$ is a right angle; $m\angle A = 2m\angle C$
    $m\angle B = m\angle C = 42$ $m\angle A = 60$
                                                      $m\angle B = 90$
                                                      $m\angle C = 30$

If possible, draw a sketch of each type of triangle listed.

13. Right scalene   14. Obtuse scalene   15. Isosceles scalene
    See side column.   not possible by def. of
                                                      isos.

3.4 Parallel Lines and Triangles   **103**

13.   14.

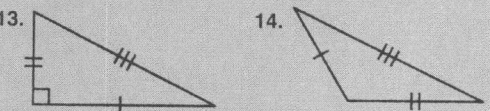

Teacher's Resource Book
Follow-Up Investigation, Chapter 3, p. 10

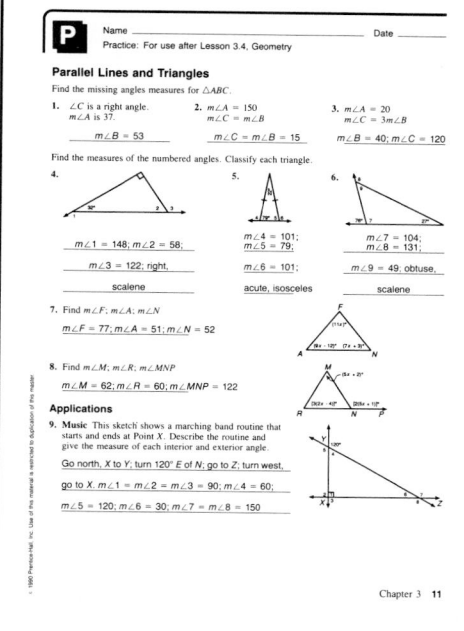

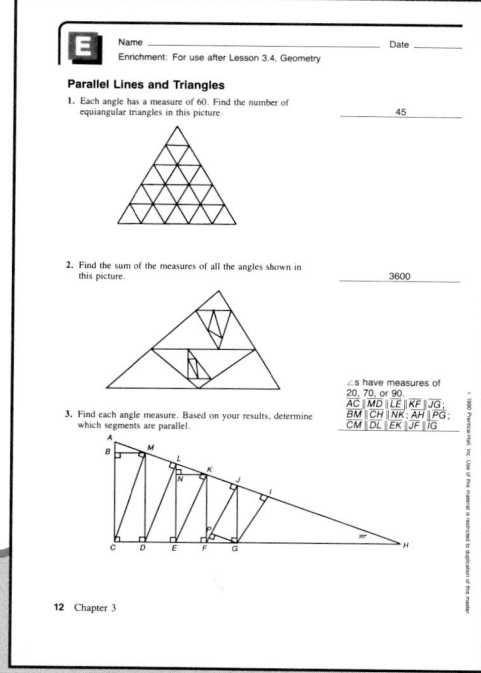

LESSON PLAN

Vocabulary

Concave polygon	n-gon
Convex polygon	Nonagon
	Octagon
Decagon	Pentagon
Diagonal	Perimeter
Heptagon	Quadrilateral
Hexagon	Regular polygon

Materials/Manipulatives

Rulers and protractors
Tracing paper
Computer
Teacher's Resource Book, Teaching Aid 3
Teaching Transparency 18
Connections, p. 7

Technology

Computer Test Bank, pp. 179–185
The Geometric Supposer: Triangles, p. 89

LESSON FOCUS

Review

- Draw several different types of triangles on the chalkboard. Have the students classify them by sides and by angles.
- Exercises 34–54 provide an Algebra Review.

Alternative Learning Styles

- In the Investigation, students have an opportunity to visualize and to differentiate among the various polygons in a complex diagram.
- Tracing the shapes in the lesson will help to familiarize students with the characteristics of a polygon.

3.5

Polygons

Objective: To recognize and name convex, concave, and regular polygons

The word *polygon* is from two ancient Greek words: *poly*, meaning many, and *gon*, meaning angles. This lesson extends the study of three-sided polygons, triangles, to those with more than three sides.

Investigation—*Visualizing the Concept*

This figure contains many polygons.

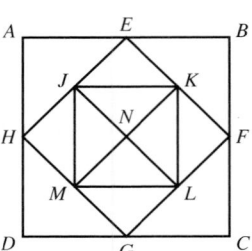

1. How many triangles are there? 16
2. Name four 4-sided figures. Answers may vary.
   ABCD; EFGH; JKLM; JEKN
3. Name five 5-sided figures. Answers may vary.
   AEFGH; CGMKF; BFGHE; DHJLG; HJKLM
4. Name four 6-sided figures. Answers may vary.
   AEFCGH; BFGDHE; HJKFLM; EKLGMJ

Definition A **polygon** consists of three or more coplanar segments; the segments, **sides,** intersect only at endpoints; each endpoint, **vertex,** belongs to exactly two segments; no two segments with a common endpoint are collinear.

Use the definition to tell why the last two figures below are not polygons.
3rd figure: vertex Q has 4 segments;
4th figure: endpoint W belongs to only one segment.

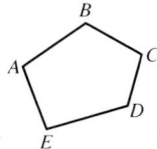 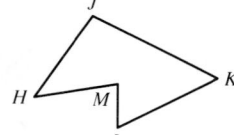 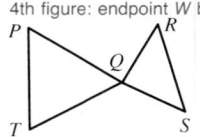 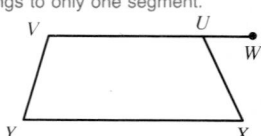

Polygons are named by writing their consecutive vertices in order, such as *ABCDE* or *CBAED* for the first polygon above. Some *consecutive vertices* for the first polygon are *A* and *B*, *B* and *C*. Some *consecutive sides* are $\overline{AB}$ and $\overline{BC}$, $\overline{BC}$ and $\overline{CD}$. Some *consecutive angles* are $\angle C$ and $\angle D$, $\angle D$ and $\angle E$.

A polygon separates a plane into three sets of points: the polygon itself, points in the interior of the polygon, and points in the exterior of the polygon. Compare the differences in the two polygons that follow.

Developing Mathematical Power

Keeping a Portfolio Have students write the definitions of the prefixes *tri, quad, septa, octa,* and *deca.* Encourage them to write as many words as they can that begin with each prefix. Have them compare the polygon prefixes to those used in naming months. Why aren't September through December the seventh through tenth months?

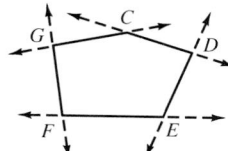

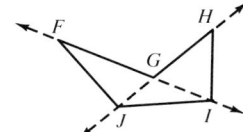

None of the lines contain points in
the polygon's interior.

$\overleftrightarrow{FG}$ and $\overleftrightarrow{GH}$ contain points in
the polygon's interior.

A polygon is called **convex** if and only if the lines containing the sides do not
contain points in the polygon's interior. If any of the lines do contain interior
points, the polygon is called **concave.** Thus, polygon *CDEFG* is convex, and
polygon *FGHIJ* is concave. Unless otherwise noted, in this course the word
polygon will mean *convex polygon*.

A **diagonal** of a polygon is a segment that joins
two nonconsecutive vertices of the polygon. Note
that polygon *RSTU* has two diagonals, $\overline{RT}$ and $\overline{SU}$.

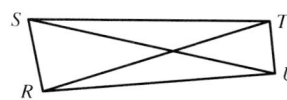

EXAMPLE 1   **Use polygon *HJKLMN* to answer the following.**

  a. Name *HJKLMN* another way.

  b. Is it convex or concave? Explain.

  c. Name a pair of consecutive sides.

  d. Name a pair of consecutive angles.

  e. Name the diagonals from vertex *J*.

  f. How many diagonals are there in all?

  a. *JKLMNH*   **b.** Convex; lines containing sides contain no interior points.
  c. $\overline{JK}$ and $\overline{KL}$ **d.** $\angle L$ and $\angle M$ **e.** $\overline{JN}$, $\overline{JM}$, $\overline{JL}$ **f.** 9

A polygon is classified by the number of its sides.

Number of Sides	Name of Polygon	Number of Sides	Name of Polygon
3	triangle	7	heptagon
4	quadrilateral	8	octagon
5	pentagon	9	nonagon
6	hexagon	10	decagon

Although names exist for some polygons with more than ten sides, you will
often see them referred to simply as 11-gon, 12-gon, and so on. When the
number of sides of a polygon is not given, the number of sides is assigned the
variable *n*, and the polygon is called an *n-gon*.

CHALKBOARD EXAMPLES

- **For Example 1**

  Use polygon *ABCDEF* to answer
  the following.

  a. Name *ABCDEF* another way.
  b. Is it convex or concave? Explain.
  c. Name a pair of consecutive
  sides.
  d. Name a pair of consecutive angles.
  e. Name the diagonals from vertex
  E.

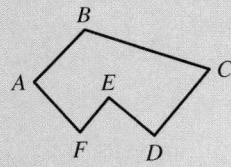

  a. $\overleftrightarrow{BCDEFA}$ **b.** concave: both $\overleftrightarrow{EF}$ and
  $\overleftrightarrow{ED}$ contain interior points. **c.** $\overline{AB}$ and
  $\overline{BC}$ **d.** $\angle A$ and $\angle B$ **e.** $\overline{AE}$, $\overline{BE}$, and
  $\overline{CE}$

- **For Example 2**

  Classify each polygon.
  a. polygon *ABCDE*
  b. polygon *ABCE*
  c. polygon *CDE*

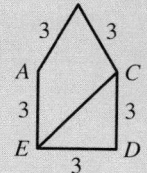

  Which polygon(s) are
  d. equilateral?
  e. equiangular?
  f. Find the perimeter of *ABCDE*.
  a. pentagon **b.** quadrilateral **c.** triangle **d.** *ABCDE* **e.** none **f.** 15

105

106

Critical Thinking

1. *Classification* Ask students to research the meanings and origins of certain prefixes and suffixes.
2. *Creative Thinking* Ask students to examine a regular hexagon and discover how to modify it to form hexagons that are equilateral but not equiangular, and equiangular but not equilateral.

Common Error

- If some students have trouble recalling the name of a particular polygon, ask them to make a list of objects sharing the same prefix. (See the list in the dictionary for that prefix.)
- See *Teacher's Resource Book* for additional remediation.

LESSON FOLLOW-UP

Discussion

Ask students what they have observed must be true of the angles of an equiangular quadrilateral. What must be true of the angles of an equiangular hexagon?

Each angle measures 90; each angle measures 120.

Ask students if they can formulate any conjectures about the angles of *any* quadrilateral and *any* hexagon.

The sum of the measures of the angles of a quadrilateral is 4(90), or 360; the sum of the measures of the angles of a hexagon is 6(120), or 720.

Critical Thinking

Generalization Ask students to make general statements about polygons.

Assignment Guide

See p. 78B for assignments.

Recall the meanings of equilateral triangle and equiangular triangle. The same terminology can be applied to other polygons. Study these examples.

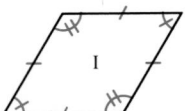 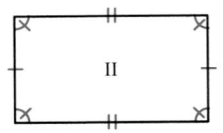 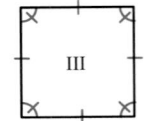 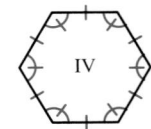

equilateral but not equiangular   equiangular but not equilateral   equilateral and equiangular   equilateral and equiangular

A polygon is a **regular polygon** if and only if it is both equilateral and equiangular. (III is a regular quadrilateral, and IV is a regular hexagon.) The **perimeter** of a polygon is the sum of the lengths of its sides.

EXAMPLE 2   **Classify each polygon according to the number of sides; identify each as *only equilateral, only equiangular, neither equilateral nor equiangular*, or *regular*; find the perimeter of each.**

a. 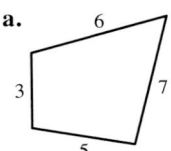   b. 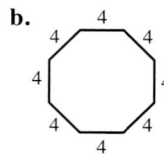   c.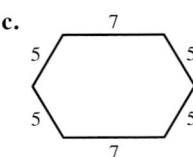

a. quadrilateral; neither equilateral nor equiangular; 21

b. octagon; regular; 32   c. hexagon; only equiangular; 34

CLASS EXERCISES

Check students' drawings for Ex. 1–4.

Drawing in Geometry   Use a straightedge to draw the following.

1. A convex quadrilateral; draw and label an interior point *I* and an exterior point *E*.

2. A concave pentagon

3. A closed figure that is not a polygon

4. A convex heptagon and all its diagonals. How many are there? 14

Use hexagon *PQRSTU* to name the following.

Answers may vary.

5. A pair of consecutive angles ∠Q and ∠R

6. A pair of nonconsecutive sides $\overline{QP}$ and $\overline{VT}$

7. All the diagonals from *R* $\overline{RP}$; $\overline{RV}$; $\overline{RT}$

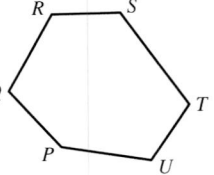

8. A regular pentagon has a perimeter of 30 cm. What is the length of each side? 6 cm

9. The side of a regular octagon is 24 mm. What is the perimeter? 192 mm

10. A regular hexagon has an angle whose measure is 120. What is the sum of the measures of all the angles? 720

11. The sum of the measures of the angles of a regular decagon is 1440. What is the measure of each angle? 144

PRACTICE EXERCISES   Use technology where appropriate.

Classify each figure as a convex polygon, a concave polygon, or not a polygon. Justify your answers. See side column.

A   **1.** 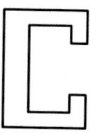   **2.** 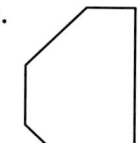   **3.** 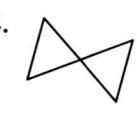   **4.**    **5.**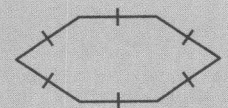

Use heptagon *MNOPQRS* to name the following. Answers may vary.

6. Two other names of *MNOPQRS*
PQRSMNO; NMSRQPO

7. A pair of consecutive sides $\overline{SR}$ and $\overline{RQ}$

8. A pair of nonconsecutive sides $\overline{SM}$ and $\overline{OP}$

9. A pair of consecutive angles ∠N and ∠O

10. A pair of nonconsecutive angles ∠P and ∠R

11. The diagonals that can be drawn from vertex *S* $\overline{SQ}$; $\overline{SP}$; $\overline{SO}$; $\overline{SN}$

12. The number of diagonals that can be drawn from *M* 4

13. The total number of diagonals from all vertices 14

14. The number of triangles formed when all diagonals from *P* are drawn 5

True or false? Justify each answer.

15. A triangle has three diagonals. false; a △ has no diagonals

16. An equiangular quadrilateral is always equilateral. false

17. An equilateral hexagon is always equiangular. false; See side column.

18. To find the side length of a regular nonagon, divide the perimeter by 9.
true; a reg. nonagon has 9 = side lengths

19. To find the perimeter of a regular decagon, divide the side length by 10.
false; multiply the length of a side by 10

B   **20.** If each side of a regular *n*-gon has length *k*, an expression for the perimeter would be *nk*. true; multiply a side length by the no. of sides in the reg. polygon

3.5 Polygons   **107**

17.
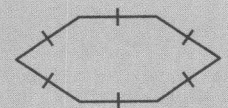

Lesson Quiz

Use this figure for Exercises 1–6.

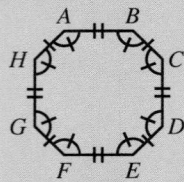

1. Classify the polygon according to the number of its sides. Octagon
2. How many diagonals can be drawn from vertex *A*? 5
3. How many diagonals does the polygon have? 20
4. If *AB* = 10 and *BC* = 5, what is the perimeter? 60 units
5. Is the polygon regular? Justify your answer.
   No; it is equiangular, but not equilateral.
6. If *AB* = 3*x*, *BC* = *x* + 2, and the perimeter of *ABCDEFGH* is 88 cm, find the length of each side.
   AB = *CD* = *DF* = *GH* = 15 cm;
   BC = *DE* = *FG* = *HA* = 7 cm

21. A regular triangle and a regular hexagon have the same perimeter length. If the length of a side of the hexagon is 14 cm, how long is each side of the triangle? 28 cm

22. The length of a side of an equilateral triangle is the same as the perimeter of a regular octagon. If the length of the side of the octagon is 3 cm, find the perimeter of the triangle. 72 cm

23. A quadrilateral has sides 3*x*, 2*x*, 4*x* − 5, and *x* + 10. If the perimeter is 45, find the length of each side. *x* = 4; 12, 8, 11, 14

24. A pentagon has sides 7*t*, 5*t* − 6, 2*t* + 7, 3*t* + 2, and 6. If the perimeter is 60, find the length of each side. *t* = 3; 21, 9, 13, 11, 6

Complete the table for convex polygons.

25.
Number of sides	3	4	5	6	7	8	9	10
Number of diagonals	0	2	5	9	14	20	27	35

26.
Number of sides	3	4	5	6	7	8	9	10
Number of diagonals from one vertex	0	1	2	3	4	5	6	7
Number of triangles	1	2	3	4	5	6	7	8

27. Draw a 12-sided polygon, called a *dodecagon*. Draw all the diagonals from one vertex. How many are there? How many triangles are formed?
9 diagonals from 1 vertex; 10 ⚠

C 28. Write an expression for the number of diagonals from one vertex of an *n*-gon. Write an expression for the number of triangles formed. *n* − 3; *n* − 2

29. Write an expression for the total number of diagonals in an *n*-gon. $\frac{n(n-3)}{2}$

30. **Given:** quadrilateral *RSTV* with diagonal $\overline{RT}$
    Prove: $m\angle SRV + m\angle S + m\angle STV + m\angle V = 360$
    See Additional Answers, p. 702.

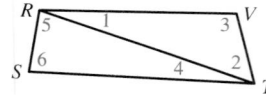

Applications

31. **Technology** This Logo procedure can be used to define a regular polygon of side 50. See Solutions Manual.

```
to polygon :n :angle
    repeat :n [forward :50 right :angle]
end
```

Polygon 4 90 draws a square. The variable :angle represents the measure of the exterior angle through which the turtle must turn. Experiment with various values for :n and :angle and chart your results. Give values for :n and :angle to draw a regular hexagon; a regular octagon.

108   Chapter 3 Parallelism

32. Technology Logo has a RANDOM command which generates a positive integer from 0 to the chosen number. For example, RANDOM 20 will generate an integer from 0 through 19. Use the RANDOM command in the polygon procedure to generate polygons with sides of random length.

33. Technology Use Logo to generate a graphic that places polygons randomly on the screen.

Algebra Review

Solve and check.

34. $\dfrac{13x}{4} = \dfrac{39}{8}$ $\dfrac{3}{2}$

35. $\dfrac{6}{x} = \dfrac{4}{x-1}$ 3

36. $\dfrac{x+3}{x-2} = \dfrac{8}{3}$ 5

37. $\dfrac{2x+4}{x-3} = \dfrac{3x}{x-3}$ 4

38. $\dfrac{1}{3} + \dfrac{5z}{6} = 2$ 2

39. $\dfrac{1}{3} + \dfrac{1}{x} = \dfrac{5}{6}$ 2

40. $\dfrac{y-2}{y} - \dfrac{y-3}{y-6} = \dfrac{1}{y}$ 3

41. $\dfrac{a}{2a+4} - \dfrac{1}{a+2} = 1$ -6

42. What is 13% of 650? 84.5

43. 63 is what percent of 420? 15%

44. What percent of 450 is 9? 2%

45. What percent of 36 is 54? 150%

Solve.

46. $2t + 3 < 17$ $t < 7$

47. $2x - 3 \geq 23$ $x \geq 13$

48. $4 - 3x \geq 16$ $x \leq -4$

49. $4y < 2y + 8$ $y < 4$

50. $6 - 2p \geq 3 - p$ $p \leq 3$

51. $2(k - 6) < 3(k - 2)$ $k > -6$

Solve each literal equation for the underlined variable.

52. $\underline{x} + 10 = y$
$x = y - 10$

53. $P = 2\underline{l} + 2w$
$l = \dfrac{P - 2w}{2}$

54. $A = \underline{P} + Prt$
$P = \dfrac{A}{1 + rt}$

Developing Mathematical Power

Drawing in Geometry Use a straightedge to draw the following.

55. An equilateral pentagon that is not equiangular Check students' drawings.

56. An equiangular pentagon that is not equilateral Check students' drawings.

57. Each of these arrays represents a *triangular number*. Study how they are formed. Then draw figures for the first four hexagonal numbers. Use the pattern to draw the fifth.

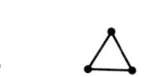 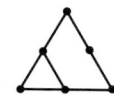 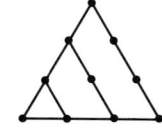

| 1 | 1 + 2 = 3 | 1 + 2 + 3 = 3 + 3 = 6 | 1 + 2 + 3 + 4 = 6 + 4 = 10 |

See Additional Answers, p. 702.

1 1 + 5 = 6 (1 + 5) + 9 = 15 (1 + 5 + 9) + 13 = 28 (1 + 5 + 9 + 13) + 17 = 45

3.5 Polygons **109**

Teacher's Resource Book
Follow-Up Investigation, Chapter 3, p. 15

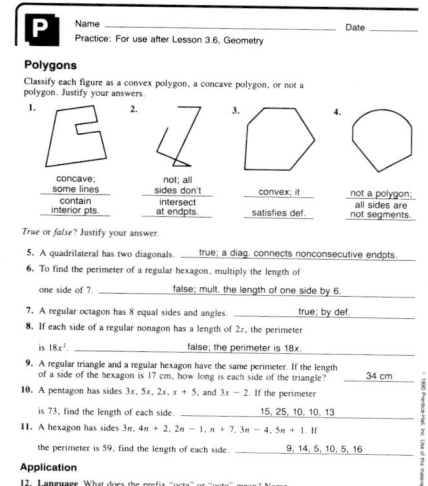

P Name _____ Date _____
Practice: For use after Lesson 3.6, Geometry

Polygons

Classify each figure as a convex polygon, a concave polygon, or not a polygon. Justify your answers.

1. concave; some lines contain interior pts.
2. not; all sides don't intersect at endpts.
3. convex; it satisfies def.
4. not a polygon; all sides are not segments.

True or false? Justify your answers.

5. A quadrilateral has two diagonals. _____ true; a diag. connects nonconsecutive endpts.

6. To find the perimeter of a regular hexagon, multiply the length of one side of 7. _____ false; mult. the length of one side by 6.

7. A regular octagon has 8 equal sides and angles. _____ true; by def.

8. If each side of a regular nonagon has a length of $2x$, the perimeter is $18x^2$. _____ false; the perimeter is 18x.

9. A regular triangle and a regular hexagon have the same perimeter. If the length of a side of the hexagon is 17 cm, how long is each side of the triangle? _____ 34 cm

10. A pentagon has sides $3x$, $5x$, $2x$, $x + 5$, and $3x - 2$. If the perimeter is 73, find the length of each side. _____ 15, 25, 10, 10, 13

11. A hexagon has sides $3n$, $4n + 2$, $2n - 1$, $n + 7$, $3n - 4$, $5n + 1$. If the perimeter is 59, find the length of each side. _____ 9, 14, 5, 10, 5, 16

Application

12. **Language** What does the prefix "octa" or "octo" mean? Name some words that use this prefix. Can you see why it is used as part of the word?

Eight. Answers may vary. Octopod (8 arms); octave (8 notes); octad (a series of 8); octan (occurring every eight days); octant (an eighth of a circle)

16 Chapter 3

E Name _____ Date _____
Enrichment: For use after Lesson 3.6, Geometry

Informal Arguments

The two-column proof constitutes what is known as a formal proof. However, mathematicians and scientists, when communicating among themselves, often resort to informal proofs. These arguments are not always based precisely on the postulates and theorems, but or an appeal to common sense.

In the final analysis, an informal argument is not completely acceptable. However, informal arguments often lead to formal proofs and new insights. In a sense, drawing a picture constitutes an informal proof, and pictures can help suggest proofs and theorems.

1. Suppose that P is a convex n-gon. Construct a new polygon P^* from P by using the midpoints of the sides of P as the vertices of P^*. How many sides does P^* have? _____ n

2. Draw a square S in the space at the right and construct the polygon S^* described in Exercise 1.

3. From the picture, make a conjecture about the nature of polygon S^*. _____ It is a square.

4. What would you have to do in order to establish this conjecture? _____ Show all sides of S^* have equal length and are $\perp$.

The theorems that have been proved so far do not enable us to prove this theorem *formally*. We would need to know more about the length of segments, or sides of triangles, (these will be proved in a later chapter). However, there is a very simple *informal* argument that will establish this result. Imagine that a pin is stuck through the center of the square, then rotate the square 90°.

5. What is the result? _____ The rotated square lies on top of the original square.

6. Suppose that a segment connecting two adjacent midpoints is drawn. What would happen to it after the 90° rotation? _____ It would lie on top of an adj. edge of S^*.

7. What happens to this segment if four consecutive 90° rotations are performed? _____ It will lie on top of all 4 sides of S^*.

8. What conclusions can you draw? _____ S^* is a square.

Chapter 3 17

Developing Mathematical Power

Cooperative Learning Have each group work on Exercises 31–33 and *Connections* p. 7. Instruct students to summarize what they have learned about regular polygons as a result of their computer work. If the side length of each polygon in "NEST" is the same, why do the figures get bigger? Have them extend "NEST" and share results and insights.

Vocabulary
Inductive reasoning

Materials/Manipulatives
8 × 8 checkerboard
Handout sheets with circles
Centimeter rulers
Calculators
Teaching Transparency 19

Technology
Computer Test Bank, pp.
185–187

LESSON FOCUS

Review
Discuss the problem solving strategies with which the students are familiar: drawing a picture, making a list, looking for a pattern, generalizing.

Alternative Learning Style
A real-world experience can help students understand inductive reasoning based on experimentation. Show the students two boxes. Tell them that one box contains a prize and the other box is empty. When they choose a box and open it, they find the prize. *Without opening the other box,* what can they conclude about its contents? They can conclude that it is empty by *inductive reasoning.*

Critical Thinking
Comparing—Contrasting Ask students to distinguish between inductive and deductive reasoning and the roles played by each type of reasoning in mathematics.

3.6 Strategy: Use Inductive Reasoning

When you use deductive reasoning, your conclusions are true because they are based on definitions, postulates, and previously proven theorems. Mathematicians sometimes draw conclusions by means of *inductive reasoning.* In inductive reasoning, conclusions are based upon experimentation and observation of patterns. Since inductive reasoning can sometimes lead to an invalid conclusion, mathematicians try to confirm their inductive conclusions with deductive reasoning. However, good inductive reasoning can help to simplify and solve a long or complicated problem.

EXAMPLE 1 How many segments are determined by using 10 collinear points as endpoints?

⬜ **Understand the Problem**

Do you understand the situation?

What are the facts?
Ten points lie on a line.

Draw and label a figure.

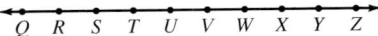

$Q \quad R \quad S \quad T \quad U \quad V \quad W \quad X \quad Y \quad Z$

What is the question?
How many segments can be formed using the 10 points as endpoints?

⬜ **Plan Your Approach**

Choose a method to organize the given information. Since the 10 endpoints form many segments, simplify the problem by trying to solve the problem for 1 point, then 2 points, then 3 points, until you see a pattern that might help you to solve the problem using inductive reasoning.

Develop a table.
Use a table to list the results and find a pattern, if possible.

Developing Mathematical Power
Keeping a Portfolio   Have students write an explanation of inductive reasoning in their own words. They should include a definition, how it differs from deductive reasoning, when it would be used, how to check for faulty conclusions, etc. Examples should be included.

Implement the Plan	Number of points	Figure	Segments	Number of segments
	1	Q	none	0
	2	Q R	$\overline{QR}$	1
	3	Q R S	$\overline{QR}, \overline{QS}, \overline{RS}$	3
	4	Q R S T	$\overline{QR}, \overline{QS}, \overline{QT}$ $\overline{RS}, \overline{RT}, \overline{ST}$	6

Study how the numbers of segments formed are related.

0   1   3   6

+1   +2   +3

Continue the pattern.

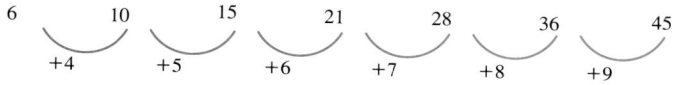

6   10   15   21   28   36   45

+4   +5   +6   +7   +8   +9

Interpret the Results   Thus by inductive reasoning, the number of segments determined by 10 collinear points is 45.

Sometimes a generalization in the form of a formula can be found. Study the numbers of segments again.

Points: 1   2   3   4   5   6

Segments: 0   1   3   6   10   15

+1   +2   +3   +4   +5

$\frac{1 \cdot 2}{2}$ $\frac{2 \cdot 3}{2}$ $\frac{3 \cdot 4}{2}$ $\frac{4 \cdot 5}{2}$

1   3   6   10

If the second factor in each numerator stands for the number of points, n, then each fraction is $\frac{(n-1)n}{2}$.

Check the answer for $n = 10$: $\frac{(10-1)10}{2} = \frac{(9)10}{2} = 45$

3.6 Strategy: Use Inductive Reasoning   **111**

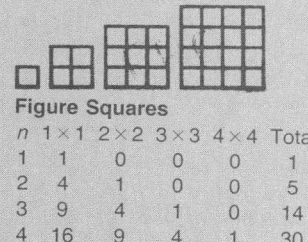
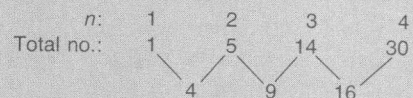
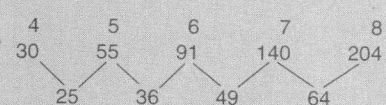

Results: An 8×8 checkerboard has 204 squares.
Generalization: An $n \times n$ checkerboard has $1 + 2^2 + 3^2 + \ldots + (n-1)^2 + n^2$ squares.

- **For Example 2**
  Use inductive reasoning to state a theorem relating lengths of segments formed when two segments with endpoints on a circle intersect.

  Draw and measure many examples. In terms of the circle shown, $AE \cdot EB = CE \cdot ED$.

Common Errors

- Some students will have difficulty generalizing a pattern once it is obtained. Use simple patterns until students gain some experience.
- Some students will attempt to generalize from too few examples. Make certain that they understand that generalizations obtained from inductive reasoning may be faulty.
- See *Teacher's Resource Book* for additional remediation.

LESSON FOLLOW-UP

Assignment Guide

- See p. 78B for assignments.
- See *Teacher's Resource Book*, Critical Thinking, p. 3.
- See *Teacher's Resource Book*, Reading and Writing in Geometry, p. 3.

Project

Students who enjoy doing sequences could be asked to research books for additional sequence-type puzzles.

Lesson Quiz

How many lines are determined by 8 coplanar points, no 3 of which are collinear? Generalize your result. 28; for n points, there are $\frac{n(n-1)}{2}$ lines.

> **Problem Solving Reminders**
>
> - By recognizing patterns, you can sometimes use inductive reasoning to arrive at a solution.
> - Check your inductive conclusion by experimenting with more numbers.

You have already proved the next theorem deductively. If you had had no theorems to use, you might have tried an inductive approach.

EXAMPLE 2 Prove that the sum of the measures of the angles of any triangle is 180.

▢ **Understand the Problem** The problem involves the measurement of the angles of any triangle. You will need an example of each type of triangle (acute, right, obtuse, equilateral, isosceles, and scalene). Carefully draw an example of each.

▢ **Plan Your Approach** **Use a protractor to measure the angles.**

▢ **Implement the Plan** **Find the sum of the angle measures for each triangle.** Compare the sums.

▢ **Interpret the Results** In each case, the sum should be equal to or very nearly equal to 180. Since measurement is never totally accurate, it would seem reasonable to make the induction that the sum of the measures of any triangle is 180. The deductive proof you studied confirms this result.

CLASS EXERCISES

Explain how inductive reasoning can be used to check each conclusion.

1. The side opposite the right angle of a right triangle is the longest side. Draw several different rt. $\triangle$s. Meas. the sides of each $\triangle$ and compare the 3 lengths.
2. The sum of the lengths of two sides of a triangle is greater than the length of the third side. Draw an example of each type of $\triangle$. Meas. the sides of each $\triangle$ and write all inequalities that compare the sum of 2 side lengths to the third side length.
3. The 9th number in this pattern is 72: 0, 9, 18, 27, ... Determine the pattern (adding 9) and continue through the 9th term.

PRACTICE EXERCISES Use technology where appropriate.

A **Use inductive reasoning to check these conjectures.**

1. The measure of any exterior angle of a triangle is equal to the sum of the measures of the two remote interior angles. Draw examples of each type of $\triangle$ and check by measuring. This ex. is a statement of Th. 3.12.

Developing Mathematical Power

Cooperative Learning Have each group draw arrays that show patterns for figurate or polygonal numbers (triangular numbers are on p. 109 and in Example 1) through pentagonal numbers. Using the patterns, have them write a general formula for each and check it.

2. A triangle with two congruent angles is isosceles. Draw several examples of ⚠ with 2 ≅ ∠s and check by measuring. This th. has not yet been proven.
3. The bisectors of a linear pair of angles are perpendicular. Draw several examples of linear pairs and const. ∠ bisectors. Check with a protractor. This th. was an ex. in Lesson 2.5.
4. When two lines intersect, the bisectors of both pairs of vertical angles formed are perpendicular. Draw several examples and use a protractor to measure the angle formed by the bisectors.

Find the 6th–9th numbers and the 13th.

5. 0, 11, 22, 33, 44, . . . , 99, . . .
   55, 66, 77, 88; 132

6. 1, 3, 9, 27, 81, . . . , 19,683, . . .
   243, 729, 2187, 6561; 531,441

7. 113, 104, 95, 86, 77, . . . , 32, . . .
   68, 59, 50, 41; 5

8. 32, 16, 8, 4, 2, . . . , $\frac{1}{16}$, . . .
   1, $\frac{1}{2}$, $\frac{1}{4}$, $\frac{1}{8}$; $\frac{1}{128}$

9. 1, 8, 6, 13, 11 . . . , 28, . . .
   18, 16, 23, 21; 31

10. 1, 6, 2, 12, 4, . . . , 96, . . .
    24, 8, 48, 16; 64

11. 1, 1, 2, 3, 5, 8, . . . , 55, . . .
    8, 13, 21, 34; 233

12. 2, 20, 10, 100, 50, . . . , 12,500, . . .
    500, 250, 2500, 1250; 31,250

13. 128, −64, 32, −16, 8, . . . , $\frac{1}{8}$, . . .
    −4, 2, −1, $\frac{1}{2}$; $\frac{1}{32}$

14. 1, 4, 9, 16, . . . , 100, . . .
    36, 49, 64, 81; 169

15. 0, 3, 8, 15, 24, . . . , 120, . . .
    35, 48, 63, 80; 168

16. 2, 3, 5, 8, 12, . . . , 57, . . .
    17, 23, 30, 38; 80

Use inductive reasoning to show whether or not these formulas generate sets of prime numbers. (*n* is a positive integer.)

17. $n^2 + n + 5$ no; if $n = 4$, $n^2 + n + 5 = 25$

18. $n^2 + n + 11$ no; if $n = 11$, $n^2 + n + 11 = 143$

19. $n^2 + n + 17$ no; if $n = 17$, $n^2 + n + 17 = 323$

20. In the table are four numbers divisible by 11, followed by four numbers NOT divisible by 11. Use the table to state when a number is divisible by 11.

A number is divisible by 11 when the diff. of the sum of the digits in 1's and 100's places and the sum of the digits in 10's and 1000's places is divisible by 11.

Number	Sum of Digits in:	
	1's and 100's places	10's and 1000's places
2211	3	3
4939	18	7
121	? 2	? 2
2827	? 15	? 4
2201	? 3	? 2
4938	? 17	? 7
125	? 6	? 2
2829	? 17	? 4

PROJECT

Find the next two terms in the sequence. 16, 22

| *n* = 1 | *n* = 2 | *n* = 3 | *n* = 4 |

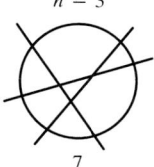
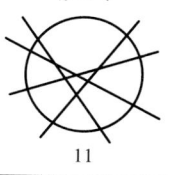

2 (parts)   4 (parts)   7   11

3.6 Strategy: Use Inductive Reasoning   **113**

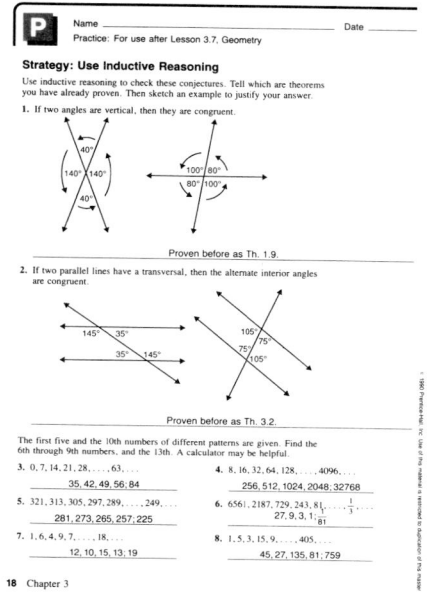

Materials/Manipulatives
Tracing paper
Rulers and protractors
Teaching Transparency 20

Technology
Computer Test Bank, pp. 188–192

LESSON FOCUS

Review
- Discuss the names and shapes of convex polygons and how each polygon can be divided into triangles.
- The Chapter Summary and Review, pp. 122 and 123, gives vocabulary and concepts and review exercises by lesson.
- The end of the chapter features an Algebra Review on p. 126.

Alternative Learning Styles
- Manipulatives enable students to work with concrete objects as an alternate means of grasping the lesson concepts. Manipulatives are used in the Investigation to show that the sum of the interior angles of a hexagon is 720. This approach puts pieces together to form a whole.
- Taking something apart is another approach to aid understanding. Have students trace one of the pentagons on p. 104, draw all the diagonals from one vertex, and then cut out the triangles formed by the diagonals. They can then use a calculator to multiply the number of triangles by 180 to determine the sum of the measures of the interior angles of a pentagon.

114

3.7

Angles of a Polygon

Objective: To find the measures of the interior and exterior angles of a convex polygon

Theorems concerning the angles of a polygon are based on the fact that the sum of the measures of the angles of a triangle is 180.

Investigation—*Using Manipulatives*

Trace and cut out the triangular puzzle pieces. Use them to form a convex polygon.

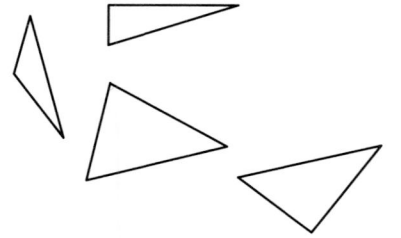

1. What kind of polygon can be formed? hexagon

2. Use the puzzle pieces to find the sum of the measures of the angles of the convex polygon. Explain your method. Use the ∠ measures of the 4 △: 4 · 180 = 720.

In the first column of the following table, all the diagonals from one vertex of each polygon are drawn. Study the table. Note that many terms that apply to triangles also apply to all polygons.

Polygon	Number of Sides	Number of Triangles Formed	Sum of the Measures of the Interior Angles
	3	(3 − 2), or 1	(3 − 2) · 180 = 1 · 180 = 180
	4	(4 − 2), or 2	(4 − 2) · 180 = 2 · 180 = 360
	5	(5 − 2), or 3	(5 − 2) · 180 = 3 · 180 = 540
	8	(8 − 2), or 6	(8 − 2) · 180 = 6 · 180 = 1080

Compare the number of sides of each polygon in the table to the number of triangles formed. The number of triangles is always two less than the number of sides, or $n - 2$. This suggests the following theorem.

114 Chapter 3 Parallelism

Developing Mathematical Power
Cooperative Learning   Have each student in each group choose a different polygon (with at least 7 sides) and compile the following information about it: name, sum of measures of interior angles and of exterior angles, number of diagonals from one vertex, and number of triangles formed. Share group results and generalize formulas to share with the class.

> **Theorem 3.13** The sum of the measures of the interior angles of a convex polygon with n sides is $(n - 2)180$.

The formal proofs of the theorems of this lesson involve a technique called *mathematical induction*. You should be able to see why the theorems are true by studying the patterns that are established for several polygons.

EXAMPLE 1 **Find the sum of the measures of the interior angles of**
   a. a hexagon   **b.** a 14-gon

Figure	Hexagon	14-gon
Number of sides, n	6	14
Number of triangles, $n - 2$	$6 - 2 = 4$	$14 - 2 = 12$
Sum of the measures of the interior angles, $(n - 2)180$	$(4)180 = 720$	$(12)180 = 2160$

Since the angles in a regular polygon are congruent, you can find the measure of one interior angle of a regular polygon by dividing $(n - 2)180$ by the number of angles, n. The formula for this is $\dfrac{(n - 2)180}{n}$.

EXAMPLE 2 **Find the measure of one interior angle for**
   a. a regular pentagon   **b.** a regular octagon

   a. $\dfrac{(5 - 2)180}{5} = \dfrac{540}{5}$ or 108   **b.** $\dfrac{(8 - 2)180}{8} = \dfrac{1080}{8}$ or 135

In any convex polygon, exterior angles are formed by extending the sides. Study $\triangle ABC$. What do you notice about $\angle 1$ and $\angle A$? $\angle 2$ and $\angle B$? $\angle 3$ and $\angle C$? Since three linear pairs are formed: They form linear pairs and are suppl.

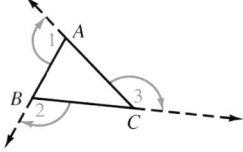

$$
\begin{array}{ccccl}
m\angle 1 & + & m\angle A & = & 180 \\
m\angle 2 & + & m\angle B & = & 180 \\
m\angle 3 & + & m\angle C & = & 180 \\
\hline
m\angle 1 + m\angle 2 + m\angle 3 & + & 180 & = & 540 \\
& m\angle 1 + m\angle 2 + m\angle 3 & = & 360 &
\end{array}
$$

Why does $m\angle A + m\angle B + m\angle C$ equal 180? What conclusion can you state about the sum of the measures of the exterior angles of a triangle, one at each vertex? sum = 360; Sum of the meas. of $\angle$s of a $\triangle$ = 180.

TEACHING SUGGESTIONS

Point out that if a student needs to find the measure of an interior angle of a regular polygon (or the sum of the interior angles) and can't recall the formula, the answer can be calculated if the student recalls that the sum of the measures of the exterior angles, one at each vertex, is always 360. For example, the measure of each exterior angle of a regular polygon with 20 sides is $\dfrac{360}{20}$, or 18. So the measure of each interior angle is $180 - 18$, or 162. The sum of the measures of the interior angles of a polygon with 20 sides (whether or not it is regular) is $20(162)$, or 3240.

CHALKBOARD EXAMPLES

- **For Example 1**
   Find the sum of the measures of the interior angles of a:

   a. 15-gon   **b.** 36-gon

   a. (13)180, or 2340
   b. (34)180, or 6120

- **For Example 2**
   Find the measure of one interior angle of:

   a. regular 15-gon
   b. regular 36-gon

   a. $\dfrac{(15 - 2)180}{15} = 156$
   b. $\dfrac{(36 - 2)180}{36} = 170$

116

For Example 3

Find the sum of the measures of the exterior angles of a 15-gon. 360

For Example 4

Find the measure of an exterior angle of:

a. regular octagon
b. regular 15-gon

a. $\frac{360}{8} = 45$ b. $\frac{360}{15} = 24$

For Example 5

Find the number of sides in a regular polygon if each interior angle measures 144.

Each exterior angle measures 36°. $\frac{360}{36} = 10$, so the polygon has 10 sides and is a regular decagon.

Common Error

- Some students will mix up or forget the formulas. If they forget the formulas, students can reconstruct them rather easily if they understand the reasoning involved in developing them.
- See *Teacher's Resource Book* for additional remediation.

The figure shows a portion of a convex n-gon with exterior angles $1e$, $2e$, and $3e$, and interior angles 1, 2, and 3 as shown.

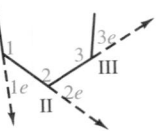

Vertex	Measure of an Exterior Angle	Measure of an Interior Angle	Sums of the Measures
I	$m\angle 1e$	$m\angle 1$	$m\angle 1e + m\angle 1 = 180$
II	$m\angle 2e$	$m\angle 2$	$m\angle 2e + m\angle 2 = 180$
III	$m\angle 3e$	$m\angle 3$	$m\angle 3e + m\angle 3 = 180$
N	$m\angle ne$	$m\angle n$	$m\angle ne + m\angle n = 180$

$$m\angle 1e + m\angle 2e + m\angle 3e + \cdots + m\angle ne + (n-2)180 = n \cdot 180$$
$$m\angle 1e + m\angle 2e + m\angle 3e + \cdots + m\angle ne = n \cdot 180 - (n-2)180$$
$$= 180[n - (n-2)]$$
$$= 180(2) \text{ or } 360$$

> **Theorem 3.14**   The sum of the measures of the exterior angles of any convex polygon, one angle at each vertex, is 360.

EXAMPLE 3   **For each, find the sum of the measures of the exterior angles.**
   a. quadrilateral   **b.** pentagon   **c.** decagon   **d.** n-gon

   a. 360   **b.** 360   **c.** 360   **d.** 360

EXAMPLE 4   **For each regular figure find the measure of an exterior angle.**
   a. quadrilateral   **b.** pentagon   **c.** decagon   **d.** n-gon

   a. $360 \div 4 = 90$ **b.** $360 \div 5 = 72$ **c.** $360 \div 10 = 36$ **d.** $360 \div n = \frac{360}{n}$

EXAMPLE 5   **Find the number of sides in a regular polygon if each interior angle measures 120.**

Extend a side using an auxiliary ray. Each exterior angle measures 60. Their sum is 360. Hence, there must be 6 angles: $\frac{360}{60} = 6$. Thus, the figure has 6 sides and is a *regular hexagon*.

The sum of the measures of the interior angles of an n-gon is $(n-2)180$. The sum of its exterior angles, one at each vertex, is 360.

CLASS EXERCISES

True or false? Justify your answers.

1. The larger the number of sides of a polygon, the greater the sum of its interior angle measures. true; as n increases, $(n-2)180$ increases

2. The larger the number of sides of a polygon, the greater the sum of its exterior angle measures. false; the sum is always 360

3. The larger the number of sides of a regular polygon, the smaller the measure of each interior angle. false; as n increases, $\frac{(n-2)180}{n}$ increases

4. The larger the number of sides of a regular polygon, the smaller the measure of each exterior angle. true; as n increases, $\frac{360}{n}$ decreases

5. The sum of the measures of the interior angles of a polygon is always a multiple of 180. true; the formula is $(n-2) \cdot 180$

6. There is a polygon, the sum of whose interior angle measures is 300. false, 300 is not a multiple of 180

7. Each exterior angle of a regular pentagon is acute. true; $\frac{360}{5} = 72$

8. An interior angle of a polygon and its adjacent exterior angle are complementary. false; they are supplementary

Find the sum of the measures of the interior angles and the sum of the measures of the exterior angles.

9. nonagon
1260; 360

10. heptagon
900; 360

11. 11-gon
1620; 360

12. decagon
1440; 360

PRACTICE EXERCISES   Use technology where appropriate.

Drawing in Geometry   Draw and cut out a polygon. Count the sides, and call that number n. Draw all the diagonals from one vertex and then cut along each diagonal.

A

1. What kind of figure(s) do you now have? triangles

2. How many figures do you now have? 2 fewer than the no. of sides of the polygon

3. How does the number of figures compare to n? $n - 2$

Copy and complete.

	Figure	Sum of the Interior Angle Measures	Sum of the Exterior Angle Measures
4.	Hexagon	_?_ 720	_?_ 360
5.	Heptagon	_?_ 900	_?_ 360
6.	12-gon	_?_ 1800	_?_ 360
7.	20-gon	_?_ 3240	_?_ 360

3.7 Angles of a Polygon   **117**

LESSON FOLLOW-UP

Discussion
Polygons have long been a favorite of artists and architects. Have students investigate some interesting polygonal shapes used by artists and architects.

Critical Thinking
Synthesis   Ask students to research the use of polygons by artists and architects and to combine their information in a report.

Assignment Guide
See p. 78B for assignments.

Test Yourself

See *Teacher's Resource Book, Tests,*
pp. 27–28.

Lesson Quiz

Find the measure of each interior angle, and of each exterior angle for the following.

1. a regular octagon
2. a regular 18-gon
3. Find the sum of the angle measures of a pentagon.
4. How many sides are there in a regular polygon if the measure of each interior angle is 150?

   1. 135; 45   2. 160; 20
   3. 540   4. 12 sides

Copy and complete.

	Figure	Each Interior Angle Measure	Each Exterior Angle Measure
8.	Regular hexagon	$\underline{\quad?\quad}$ 120	$\underline{\quad?\quad}$ 60
9.	Regular heptagon	$\underline{\quad?\quad}$ $128\frac{4}{7}$	$\underline{\quad?\quad}$ $51\frac{3}{7}$
10.	Regular 12-gon	$\underline{\quad?\quad}$ 150	$\underline{\quad?\quad}$ 30
11.	Regular 20-gon	$\underline{\quad?\quad}$ 162	$\underline{\quad?\quad}$ 18

Find the number of sides of the regular polygon having the given measure for each interior angle.

12. 140 9   13. 60 3   14. 108 5   15. 150 12

16. If four angles of a pentagon have measures of 100, 96, 87, and 97, find the measure of the fifth angle. 160

17. If four angles of a hexagon have measures of 100, 90, 105, and 75, and if the other two angles are congruent, find the measure of each. 175

18. If the sum of the measures of two exterior angles of a triangle is 230, find the measure of the third exterior angle and its adjacent interior angle.
130, 50

19. The sum of the measures of two exterior angles of a quadrilateral is 300, and the other two exterior angles are congruent. Find the measure of each. 30

Find the number of sides of the regular polygon having the given measure for each interior angle.

B 20. 160 18   21. 120 6   22. $147\frac{3}{11}$ 11   23. 157.5 16

Find the number of sides of a polygon whose interior angle measures have the given sum.

24. 1260 9   25. 2880 18   26. 1980 13   27. 540 5

28. One polygon has three more sides than another. How many more degrees are in the sum of the interior angle measures of the first polygon? 540

29. The sum of the measures of the interior angles of a polygon is between 2100 and 2400. How many sides does the polygon have? 14 or 15

30. The measure of each interior angle of a regular polygon is 36 more than its adjacent exterior angle. How many sides has the polygon? 5

31. The measure of each exterior angle of a regular polygon is one-third the measure of its adjacent interior angle. How many sides has the polygon? 8

32. Octagon *PQRSTUVW* is equilateral and equiangular. If $\overline{TU}$ and $\overline{WV}$ are extended until they intersect, find the measure of the angle formed. 90

118   Chapter 3 Parallelism

33. Two lines bisect consecutive angles of a regular pentagon and intersect in the pentagon's interior. Find the measure of the angle formed by the intersecting lines. 72

C **34.** Give a formula for finding the measure of an interior angle of a regular polygon. $\frac{(n-2)180}{n}$

35. Give the formula for finding the measure of an exterior angle of a regular polygon. $\frac{360}{n}$

36. In a decagon, the sum of the measures of the first six interior angles totals 1000. If the remaining four angles have equal measures, find each of the remaining angles. 110 each

Applications

37. Sports Home plate on a baseball field is a pentagon with three right angles. The remaining two angles are congruent. Sketch home plate and give the measure of each interior and exterior angle. See side column.

38. Art In many ornamental windows, a regular octagon is placed in a circle. Give the measure of each interior angle. 135

39. Technology What general algebraic expression can be used for :angle in the Logo procedure on p. 108? See Solutions Manual.

TEST YOURSELF

3.5

1. The measures of the angles of a four-sided figure can be represented by x, x, $5x$, and $4x - 3$. Find the measure of each angle.
33, 33, 165, 129
2. Find the perimeter of a regular hexagon with side length 4.5 cm. 27 cm

Predict the next two numbers of each pattern.

3.6

3. 2, 4, 16, 256, . . .   **4.** 15, 20, 10, 15, 5, . . .
65536, 4294967296   10, 0

3.7

5. Find the sum of the interior angle measures and the sum of the exterior angle measures of a decagon. 1440, 360

6. What is the measure of each interior angle of a 7-sided regular polygon?
$128\frac{4}{7}$
7. Find the number of sides of a regular polygon if each interior angle has a measure of 160. 18

8. A scout troop is planning a hike in the desert. The leader claims that they will end up at their starting point if they hike 1 km to the east, then hike 1 km in a direction 60° counterclockwise from the east, then continue to turn 60° counterclockwise after each km hiked. Is the leader correct? Explain.
yes; the path is a regular hexagon in which each side measures 1 km and each exterior angle measures 60°

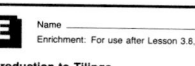

3.7 Angles of a Polygon **119**

37.

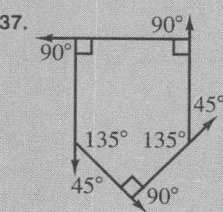

Teacher's Resource Book
Follow-Up Investigation, Chapter 3, p. 20

See *Teacher's Resource Book*, Chapter 3, Follow-up Application, p. 23.

INTEGRATING GEOMETRY
Longitude and Latitude

Parallel planes and parallel circles help locate places on the Earth's surface. Since the intersection of a plane with a sphere is a circle, reference circles have been chosen to form a grid system for the Earth. The reference circles have been chosen using three points. Every 24 hours, the Earth turns about its axis of rotation, which contains two of these points—the North Pole and the South Pole.

Planes that contain the center point of a sphere produce *great circles*. You can think of many planes passing through the Earth's axis of rotation, each of which intersects the Earth in a great circle. The *semicircles* formed by these intersections are called *meridians*. The third reference point in the grid is the observatory in Greenwich, England. The meridian that passes through Greenwich is called the *prime meridian*. The measure of the *longitude* of a point on the Earth is the angle ($\leq 180°$ east or west) between the plane of the prime meridian and the plane of the meridian passing through the point.

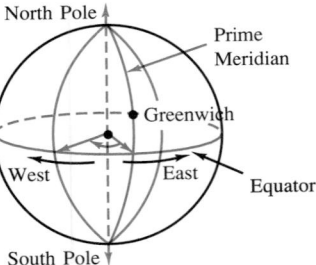

The plane perpendicular to the axis of rotation and containing the center of the Earth intersects the surface in a great circle called the *equator*. The equator is a reference circle.

A series of planes parallel to the equatorial plane intersect the Earth in small circles called *latitudes*. The measure of a latitude is the angle formed by two rays from the center of the Earth in the plane of a meridian, one ray passing through the equator and the other passing through the point to be located.

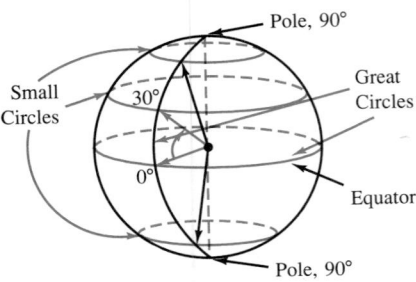

120 Chapter 3 Parallelism

A meridian is marked off in degrees that correspond to the angles, which range from 0° to 90° north or south of the equator.

Thus, the two reference numbers, longitude and latitude, locate any point on the Earth. The specific angles of a point are measured in degrees, minutes, and seconds. One degree = 60 minutes (60'), and 1' = 60 seconds (or 60"). Using these units, the location of Athens, Greece is 23°46'E and 37°58'N, to the nearest minute.

This map shows markings for longitudes and latitudes every 5 degrees.

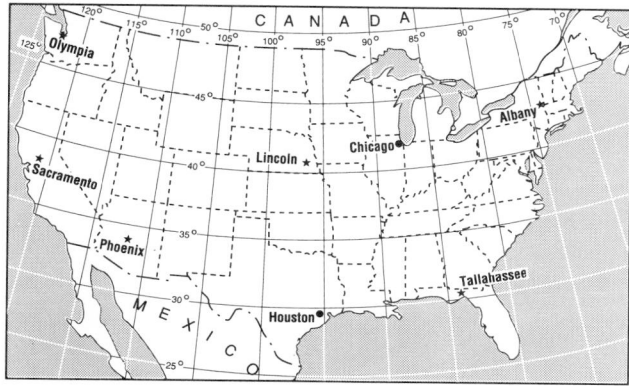

EXAMPLE **Find the longitude and latitude of each city to the nearest 5°.**
  a. Houston **b.** Chicago **c.** Sacramento

  a. Houston: 95°W, 30°N **b.** Chicago: 85°W, 40°N

  c. Sacramento: 120°W, 40°N

EXERCISES

Find the longitude and latitude of each city to the nearest 5°.

1. Albany **2.** Olympia **3.** Tallahassee **4.** Phoenix **5.** Lincoln
   75°W, 45°N   125°W, 50°N   85°W, 30°N   110°W, 35°N   95°W, 40°N
6. What happens to the latitude as you look farther north? The latitude gets larger.

7. Approximate the longitude and the latitude of your town or city.
   Answers may vary.
8. Are the lines indicating longitude on a sphere parallel? Explain. Not in the
   Euclidean sense, since they intersect at the North and South Poles.

- See *Teacher's Resource Book, Spanish Chapter Summary and Review*, pp. 5–6.
- See Extra Practice, p. 645.

Vocabulary

acute triangle (98)	exterior angle of a polygon (116)	parallel (80)
alternate exterior angles (81)	heptagon (105)	pentagon (105)
alternate interior angles (81)	hexagon (105)	perimeter (106)
auxiliary line (98)	inductive reasoning (110)	polygon (104)
concave polygon (105)	interior angle of a polygon (115)	quadrilateral (105)
convex polygon (105)		regular polygon (106)
corresponding angles (81)	isosceles triangle (98)	right triangle (98)
decagon (105)	n-gon (105)	same-side interior angles (86)
diagonal (105)	nonagon (105)	scalene triangle (98)
equiangular triangle (98)	obtuse triangle (98)	skew (80)
equilateral triangle (98)	octagon (105)	transversal (81)
		triangle (97)

Lines, Planes, and Transversals   Nonintersecting coplanar lines are parallel. Coplanar lines intersected by a transversal form special angle pairs. Two planes either intersect in a line or are parallel. Check students' drawings.   **3.1**

Use this figure to name the following.

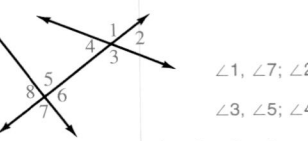

1. Two pairs of alternate exterior angles   ∠1, ∠7; ∠2, ∠8
2. Two pairs of alternate interior angles   ∠3, ∠5; ∠4, ∠6
3. Four pairs of corresponding angles   ∠1, ∠5; ∠2, ∠6; ∠3, ∠7; ∠4, ∠8

Properties of Parallel Lines   If two parallel lines have a transversal, then the following angle pairs formed are congruent: corresponding angles; alternate interior angles; alternate exterior angles. If two lines are parallel, then the interior angles on the same side of a transversal are supplementary.   **3.2**

In this figure, $p \parallel q$. State the relationship between each pair of angles. Justify each answer.

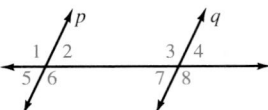

4. ∠1 and ∠3   ≅; corr ∠s
5. ∠4 and ∠5   ≅; alt. ext. ∠s
6. ∠7 and ∠2   ≅; alt. int. ∠s
7. ∠6 and ∠7   supp.; int. ∠s on same side of transv.
8. ∠3 and ∠8   ≅; vert. ∠s
9. ∠2 and ∠8   supp.; ∠2 is supp. to ∠3, and ∠3 ≅ ∠8
10. If $4 \cdot m\angle 2 = 5 \cdot m\angle 3$, find the measures of all eight angles.
    $m\angle 2 = m\angle 4 = m\angle 5 = m\angle 7 = 100$; $m\angle 1 = m\angle 3 = m\angle 6 = m\angle 8 = 80$

Proving Lines Parallel If two lines have a transversal and certain angle pairs are congruent or supplementary, then the two lines are parallel.   3.3

State the relationship between each pair of angles that would lead to the conclusion $m \parallel k$. Justify each answer.
See side column for 11, 12, and 16.

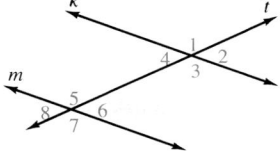

11. $\angle 5$ and $\angle 3$
12. $\angle 6$ and $\angle 3$
13. $\angle 2$ and $\angle 8$ ≅; if alt. ext. ∠s ≅, lines are ∥
14. $\angle 7$ and $\angle 3$ ≅; if corr. ∠s ≅, lines are ∥
15. $\angle 1$ and $\angle 7$ ≅; if alt. ext. ∠s ≅, lines are ∥
16. $\angle 3$ and $\angle 8$
17. If $m\angle 4 = 3x + 32$ and $m\angle 5 = 4x - 13$, find the measures of $\angle 4$ and $\angle 5$ that would make k and m parallel. $m\angle 4 = 101; m\angle 5 = 79$

Parallel Lines and Triangles The sum of the measures of the angles of a triangle is 180. The measure of an exterior angle of a triangle equals the sum of the measures of the remote interior angles.   3.4

18. Explain why a right obtuse triangle cannot exist. If a △ had both an obt. ∠ and a rt. ∠, the sum of the measures of the ∠s would be greater than 180.
19. If $\angle A$ is a right angle and $m\angle C = 3x$ and $m\angle ABC = 2x$, find the measure of each interior angle and $m\angle ABX$. $m\angle A = 90; m\angle ABC = 36; m\angle C = 54; m\angle ABX = 144$
20. If $m\angle A = 2m\angle C$ and $m\angle ABX = 132$, find $m\angle A$ and $m\angle C$. $m\angle A = 88; m\angle C = 44$
21. Using the given $\triangle ABC$, the theorem about the measure of exterior $\angle ABX$ can be proven by drawing an auxiliary line through B. Explain. Through B, draw a line ∥ $\overleftrightarrow{AC}$. Then use the corr. ∠s formed and the alt. int. ∠s formed to relate $m\angle C$ and $m\angle A$ to $m\angle ABX$.   3.5
22. What inductive approach could be used to verify the theorem about the measure of an exterior angle of a triangle? Draw several △ and extend the sides. Measure the ext. ∠s and their corresp. remote int. ∠s. Record the data and draw a concl.   3.6

Polygons A regular polygon is equilateral and equiangular. The sum of the measures of the interior angles of a convex polygon with n sides is $(n - 2)180$. The sum of the measures of the exterior angles of any convex polygon, one angle at each vertex, is 360.   3.5, 3.7

23. Find the sum of the interior angle measures of a decagon. If the polygon is regular, give the measure of each interior angle. 1440; 144
24. Find the number of sides of a regular polygon in which each interior angle measures 168. 30
25. A tile company produces a tile in the shape of a regular polygon. If each interior angle has a measure that is three times an exterior angle measure, identify the regular polygon. If one side of a tile has a length of 2.3 cm, find the perimeter of a tile. octagon; 18.4 cm

Additional Answers

11. ≅; if alt. int. ∠s are ≅, lines are ∥

12. supp.; if int. ∠s on same side of transv. are supp., lines are ∥

16. supp.; ∠8 ≅ ∠6; if int. ∠s on same side of transv. are supp., then lines are ∥

Additional Answers for Chapter 3 Test, p. 124

3. $m\angle 2 = 70$, $m\angle 3 = 110$, $m\angle 4 = 70$, $m\angle 5 = 70$, $m\angle 6 = 110$, $m\angle 7 = 70$, $m\angle 8 = 110$, $m\angle 9 = 110$, $m\angle 10 = 70$, $m\angle 11 = 110$, $m\angle 12 = 70$, $m\angle 13 = 70$, $m\angle 14 = 110$, $m\angle 15 = 70$, $m\angle 16 = 110$

7. $a \parallel b$; int. ∠s on same side of transv. are supp.

11. A △ can have 3 acute ∠s and no 2 sides ≅.

See *Teacher's Resource Book*, Tests, pp. 29–32.

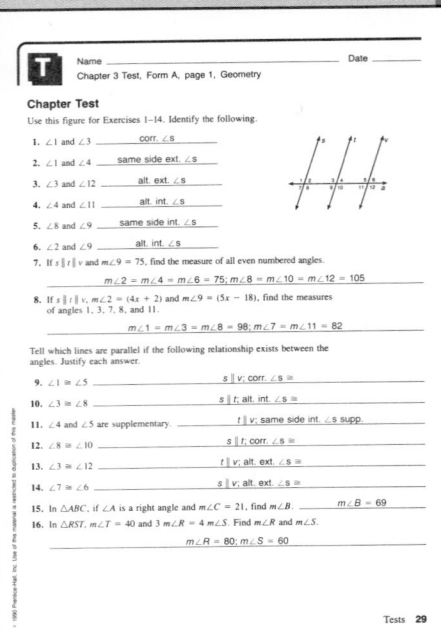

(Reduced test pages shown in left margin — Chapter 3 Test, Form A, pages 1 and 2, Geometry)

See p. 123 for Exercises 3, 7, and 11.

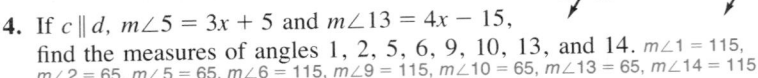

Use the figure for Exercises 1–7. Identify:

1. ∠14 and ∠15   int. ∠s same side of trans.

2. ∠14 and ∠16   corr. ∠s

3. If $a \parallel b$ and $c \parallel d$ and $m\angle 1 = 110$, find the measures of all numbered angles.

4. If $c \parallel d$, $m\angle 5 = 3x + 5$ and $m\angle 13 = 4x - 15$, find the measures of angles 1, 2, 5, 6, 9, 10, 13, and 14. $m\angle 1 = 115$, $m\angle 2 = 65$, $m\angle 5 = 65$, $m\angle 6 = 115$, $m\angle 9 = 115$, $m\angle 10 = 65$, $m\angle 13 = 65$, $m\angle 14 = 115$

Tell which lines are parallel. Justify each answer.

5. ∠3 ≅ ∠11 $c \parallel d$; corr. ∠s ≅

6. ∠1 ≅ ∠8 $a \parallel b$; alt. ext. ∠s ≅

7. ∠6 and ∠7 are supplementary.

8. In △ABC, if ∠B is a right angle and $m\angle A = 49$, find $m\angle C$.   41

9. In △DEF, $m\angle D = 100$ and $2 \cdot m\angle E = 3 \cdot m\angle F$. Find $m\angle E$ and $m\angle F$. $m\angle E = 48$, $m\angle F = 32$

Explain why each kind of triangle exists. Sketch an example of each.

10. right isosceles   A rt. △ may have ≅ legs.

11. acute scalene

12. In △RST, an exterior angle at T has a measure of 75. If $m\angle R = 2 \cdot m\angle S$, find the measure of each interior angle of △RST. $m\angle S = 25$, $m\angle R = 50$, $m\angle T = 105$

Polygon ABCDEF is regular.

13. Name it according to the number of its sides. hexagon

14. If $EF = 4.5$ cm, find the perimeter.   27 cm

15. Find the measure of angles 1, 2, and 3. $m\angle 1 = 120$, $m\angle 2 = 90$, $m\angle 3 = 60$

16. Find the sum of the measures of the interior angles of BCDEF.   540

17. How do the sums of the measures of the exterior angles of polygon ABCDEF and BCDEF compare? Explain your answer. They are =; the sum of the measures of the ext ∠s of any polygon is 360.

18. Find the number of sides of a regular polygon if each interior angle measures four times the measure of each exterior angle.   10

Challenge

Given two congruent isosceles triangles, what is the only type of regular polygon that can be drawn using only one auxiliary line segment? pentagon

Alternative Assessment   Have students identify all pairs of congruent angles in the drawing at the top of the page and justify why they are congruent. Ask them to describe different ways the lines can be proved parallel and illustrate with specific angles. Have the students draw a regular polygon, *RSTUVW*, and tell all that they know about it.

Select the best choice for each question.

1. An angle has a measure that is 42°
E   less than its complement. Its
measure in degrees is:

   A. 66   **B.** 60   **C.** 48
   D. 36   **E.** 24

2. The measures of the sides of a
C   regular polygon are integers and its
perimeter is 54. This polygon could
be a(n):

   A. square   **B.** pentagon
   C. hexagon   **D.** octagon
   E. decagon

3. Find k when x is 15% of y, y is 40%
B   of z, and x is k% of z.

   A. 3.75   **B.** 6   **C.** 37.5
   D. 55   **E.** 60

4. If C is the midpoint of $\overline{AB}$, D is the
D   midpoint of $\overline{CB}$, and E is the
midpoint of $\overline{DB}$, find the value of AB
when $CE = 12$.

   A. 24   **B.** 28   **C.** 30
   D. 32   **E.** 36

5. If $p \parallel q$, then x must equal:
B

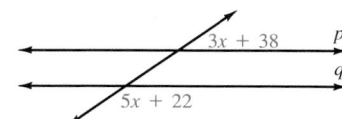

   A. 8   **B.** 15   **C.** 16
   D. 30   **E.** 62

6. Solve for x:
A $2(3x - 7) + 1 \le 5(x + 1) - 9$

   A. $x \le 9$ **B.** $x \le -17$
   C. $x \ge 17$ **D.** $x \le 17$
   E. $x \le -9$

7. If $\angle PQR$ is drawn using $P(4, 3)$,
   $Q(0, -5)$, and $R(-1, -2)$, which
C   point is in the interior of the angle?

   A. $(-4, 0)$ **B.** $(-2, -1)$
   C. $(-1, 4)$ **D.** $(2, -4)$
   E. $(3, 1)$

8. $\sqrt{9^2 + 12^2 + 8^2} =$
C

   A. 13   **B.** 15   **C.** 17
   D. $12\sqrt{3}$ **E.** 29

9. Ann bought a pair of ski boots on
sale at a 25% discount. If she paid
$135 for them, what was the
D   original price of the boots?

   A. $540   **B.** $270   **C.** $245
   D. $180   **E.** $160

10. The angles of a triangle are in the
ratio 2:5:8. What is the measure of
D   the largest angle?

   A. 60   **B.** 72   **C.** 84
   D. 96   **E.** 108

**For Questions 11 and 12, the operation
* is defined by $a * b = 3a - 2b$.**

11. Find $2 * (4 * 3)$.
A
   A. -6 **B.** 0   **C.** 6
   D. 9   **E.** 12

12. If $x * 7 = 1$, then x equals:
B
   A. 6   **B.** 5   **C.** 4
   D. 3   **E.** 2

The individual comments provided for certain problems can assist the students in solving them.

2. This type of problem requires that a student think about integers, an introductory topic in number theory. This topic is vital for good problem solving.

3. The generalization of this problem is a good extension of it.

5. An alternate solution involves using the alternate interior angles.
$$3x + 38 = 180 - (5x + 22)$$
$$3x + 38 = 158 - 5x$$
$$8x = 120$$
$$x = 15$$

8. For any student who is aware of the special Pythagorean Triples, 3-4-5, 5-12-13, etc., this problem offers an opportunity to use them. Thus, $\sqrt{9^2 + 12^2 + 8^2}$ becomes $\sqrt{15^2 + 8^2} = \sqrt{17^2} = 17$, where 9-12-15 and 8-15-17 are the triples used.

See *Teacher's Resource Book,* for Preparing for College Entrance Exams.

The following skills and concepts are reviewed:
Simplifying expressions
Solving inequalities
Squaring binomials
Factoring

Simplify.

1. $6 - 3(x - 5)$ $-3x + 21$

2. $4(x + 6) + x(x + 6)$
$x^2 + 10x + 24$

3. $|7 - 10|$ 3

4. $\sqrt{121}$ 11

5. $(x - 2)(x + 3)$ $x^2 + x - 6$

6. $3\sqrt{98}$ $21\sqrt{2}$

Solve.

Example
$$2x - 7 \le 3(4x + 1)$$
$$2x - 7 \le 12x + 3 \qquad \text{Distributive property}$$
$$2x - 2x - 7 \le 12x - 2x + 3 \qquad \text{Subtraction property}$$
$$-7 \le 10x + 3 \qquad \text{Combine like terms.}$$
$$-7 - 3 \le 10x + 3 - 3 \qquad \text{Subtraction property}$$
$$-10 \le 10x \qquad \text{Combine like terms.}$$
$$-1 \le x \qquad \text{Division property}$$

7. $x - 7 < 2$ $x < 9$

8. $9 - 12x = 45$ $x = -3$

9. $-4x \ge 40$ $x \le -10$

10. $\frac{2}{5}x + 1 = -19$ $x = -50$

11. $3x + 1 > -5$ $x > -2$

12. $6x - 7 < 4x + 11$
$x < 9$

13. $4(x - 3) = 7(x + 6)$
$x = -18$

14. $-12x + 2 \ge 2(11 - x)$
$x \le -2$

15. $|x - 6| = 10$ $x = -4, 16$

To square a binomial, rewrite as the product of two binomials and apply the distributive property.

Square the binomial.

Example
$$(x + y)^2 = (x + y)(x + y) \qquad \text{Factor.}$$
$$= x(x + y) + y(x + y) \qquad \text{Distributive property}$$
$$= x^2 + xy + xy + y^2 \qquad \text{Distributive property}$$
$$= x^2 + 2xy + y^2 \qquad \text{Combine like terms.}$$

16. $(x - 3)^2$ $x^2 - 6x + 9$

17. $(2x + 1)^2$ $4x^2 + 4x + 1$

18. $(3x - 2)^2$ $9x^2 - 12x + 4$

19. $(2x - y)^2$ $4x^2 - 4xy + y^2$

20. $(5x + 2y)^2$
$25x^2 + 20xy + 4y^2$

21. $(-x + 2)^2$ $x^2 - 4x + 4$

Factor.

Example $x^2 - 5x - 6$

$$x^2 - 5x - 6 = (x - \underline{?})(x + \underline{?}) \qquad \text{Try 2, 3 or 6, 1.}$$
$$= (x - 6)(x + 1)$$

22. $x^2 - 10x + 24$
$(x - 6)(x - 4)$

23. $x^2 - 10x - 24$
$(x - 12)(x + 2)$

24. $2x^2 + 5x + 2$
$(2x + 1)(x + 2)$

25. $x^2 - 9x + 14$
$(x - 7)(x - 2)$

26. $3t^2 - 48$ $3(t + 4)(t - 4)$

27. $x^3 - x$ $x(x + 1)(x - 1)$

OVERVIEW • Chapter 4

SUMMARY

In Chapter 4, students learn about corresponding parts and finding measures in congruent triangles. They are introduced to the SSS, SAS, and ASA Postulates, and they prove the AAS, LL, HL, LA, and HA Theorems. Students use these postulates and theorems to solve increasingly complex proofs and to develop related theorems concerning medians and altitudes of a triangle and perpendicular bisectors of segments.

CHAPTER OBJECTIVES

- To identify the corresponding parts of congruent triangles

- To find measures in congruent triangles

- To identify right triangles and their parts

- To prove two triangles congruent by using the SSS, SAS, and ASA Postulates and the AAS, LL, HL, LA, and HA Theorems

- To prove segments or angles congruent by first proving two triangles congruent

- To prove two triangles congruent by first proving two other triangles congruent

- To apply definitions of median and altitude of a triangle and perpendicular bisector of a segment

- To apply the theorems about points on perpendicular bisectors of segments and on bisectors of angles

- To structure complex proofs by *identifying intermediate goals*

- To decide if a figure exists or can be uniquely represented by *underdetermining or overdetermining a figure*

CHAPTER HIGHLIGHTS

DEVELOPING MATHEMATICAL POWER

Problem Solving

Students use the four problem solving steps to identify intermediate goals in proofs in Lesson 4.4. In Lesson 4.6, students learn how a description can underdetermine or overdetermine a figure.

Communication

This chapter provides opportunities for the use of manipulatives for alternative learning styles and for cooperative learning situations. The *Teacher's Resource Book* offers a Chapter Summary and Review in Spanish. One of the journal-writing topics for students' portfolios is to compare a triangle's median, bisector, and altitude.

Reasoning

Students continue to apply deductive reasoning to write proofs about triangle congruence. A thinking critically topic involves analyzing a figure consisting of overlapping triangles and finding the total number of triangles.

Connections

Real-world applications include such topics as probability, architecture, and carpentry. The Integrating Geometry feature discusses precision and accuracy in manufacturing.

Technology

Logo topics and exercises are presented throughout the chapter.

STUDENT TEXT

Chapter Content	Basic	Average	Enriched	NCTM STANDARDS*
4.1 Correspondence and Congruence	D: 131/1-15, 19, 37, 39	D: 131/1-21, 28, 29, 37-39	D: 131/6-21, 28-39	2, 3, 4, 7, 11
4.2 Proving Triangles Congruent	D: 136/1-4, 9-14, 21, 35, MR R: 131/16-18, 20	D: 136/5-14, 21-27, 29, 35, 36, 42, MR R: 131/21-27, 29	D: 136/15-21, 28, 29, 31-36, 42-44, MR R: 131/22-27	2, 3, 5, 7
4.3 Using Congruent Triangles	D: 141/1-5, 6-11 even, 13, 29 R: 136/5-8, 15-20	D: 141/1-5, 12-15, 17-25 odd R: 136/15-20, 28, 30	D: 141/1-5, 14-25 even, 26-30 R: 136/22-27, 30	4, 7
4.4 Strategy: Identify Intermediate Goals	D: 148/1-5 R: 141/6-11 odd, 16	D: 148/1-6 R: 141/17-25 even, 39	D: 148/1-6 R: 141/14-25 odd	1, 2, 3, 12
4.5 Medians, Altitudes, and Bisectors	D: 152/1-8, 9-17 odd, 26-29 R: 145/6	D: 152/7-14, 15-23 odd, 26-29 R: 145/7	D: 152/9-21, 24-29 R: 145/7, 8	2, 3, 4, 7
4.6 Strategy: Recognize Underdetermined and Overdetermined Figures	D: 157/1-10 R: 152/9-17 even	D: 157/1-10, 14 R: 152/15-23 even	D: 157/1-10, 11-17 odd R: 152/22, 23	1, 3, 7, 14
4.7 Proving Right Triangles Congruent	D: 161/1-18, 26-28, AR R: 157/11-13	D: 161/1-22, 26-28, AR R: 157/11-13, 15	D: 161/9-28, AR R: 157/11-17 even	2, 3, 4, 7

D = Daily   R = Review   MR = Mixed Review   AR = Algebra Review

*For a complete list of NCTM Standards, see p. T7.

STUDENT TEXT

Review/Assessment

Mixed Review 138

Algebra Review 163

Summary and Review 166

College Ent. Exam Rev. 169

Cumulative Review 170

Extra Practice 646

Test Yourself 144, 163

Chapter Test 168

Chapter Project 127

Special Features

Construction 154

Technology 132, 138, 154, 162

Devel. Math. Power 138, 154

Applications 132, 138, 144, 154, 162, 164-165

Project 148, 158

Reading in Geometry 132

RESOURCES

Teacher's Resource Book

Ch. 4: Investigation/Practice/ Enrichment 1-19

Spanish Sum. and Rev. 7-8

Quizzes 33-6

Chapter Tests 37-40

Cumulative Tests 41-48

Perf. Assessment Proj. Ch. 4

Critical Thinking 4

Reading and Writing in Geom. 4

Applications—Ch. 4, 20

Teaching Aid 4

Transparencies 4-5

Teaching Transparencies 21-27

Computer Test Bank 193-248

Connections 1-8

PH Graph. Utility

Overhead Manip. Kit

Congruent Triangles

Precisely your size?

Developing Mathematical Power

...thing manufacturers can ...duce thousands of items ...e same size. But in reality, ...s that are sized the same ...never *exactly* congruent.

...manufacturers must ...de how much error is ...wable in the desired ...surements.

Project

Suppose you own the Precision T-shirt Company. Design a new T-shirt and draw a full-scale pattern, indicating the desired measurements. Then, using the information on pages 164–165, specify the precision, tolerance, and accuracy you require for each measurement.

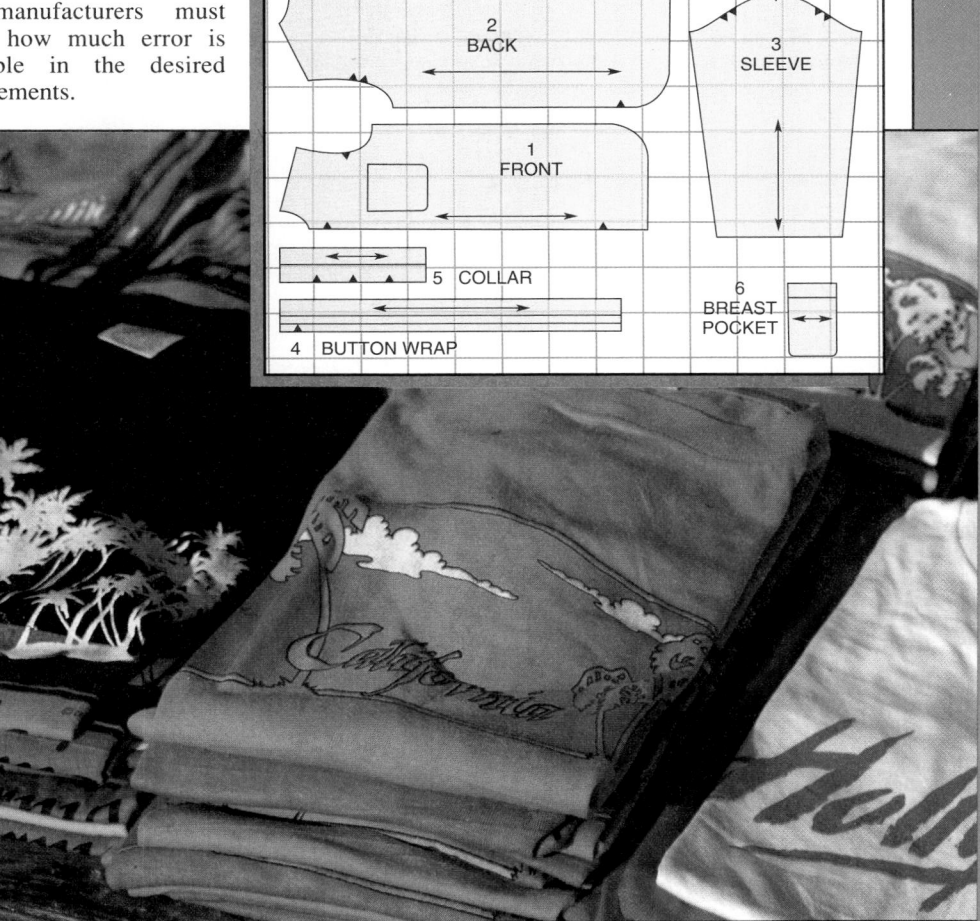

Vocabulary
Congruent triangles
Correspondence
Corresponding angles
Corresponding sides
Equivalent correspondences
One-to-one correspondence

Materials/Manipulatives
Triangles and rectangles cut from
  construction paper
Teacher's Resource Book,
  Transparency 4
Teaching Transparency 21

Technology
Computer Test Bank, pp.
  193–199

LESSON FOCUS

Review
Display these noncongruent figures.

a.

b.
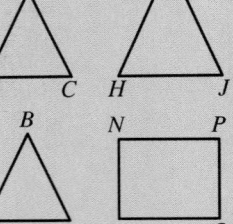

Have students compare the number of
vertices and sides in each pair of figures and decide which pair may be
more readily compared and why.

Alternative Learning Styles
Helping students visualize a concept
may facilitate their understanding of
the concept. For example, in the Investigation, the replacement glass
must be cut to fit the template as precisely as possible. Discuss real-life situations in which molds are used to
produce identical products.

128

4.1

Correspondence and Congruence

Objectives: To identify the corresponding parts of congruent triangles
To find measures in congruent triangles

Congruence is a basic geometric
relationship. Congruent figures have
the same shape and size.

Investigation—*Visualizing the Concept*

A piece of stained glass must be replaced
in a transom window over a doorway. A
glazier (glass cutter) makes a template
from the missing space and then uses the
template to cut the replacement glass.

1. How must the glazier cut the glass to
   ensure a proper fit? The sides and angles
of the glass must correspond in size to those of the space.
2. What elements of this picture have
   the same shape and size? the doors,
the panes of glass, the molding

It is often necessary to associate members of one set with members of another,
as, for example, with student locker assignments:

Students: {Art, Beth, Cory}   **Locker Numbers:** {1, 2, 3}

One possible association or *pairing* is:

Student	Locker Number	Pairing
Art	1	$A \leftrightarrow 1$
Beth	2	$B \leftrightarrow 2$
Cory	3	$C \leftrightarrow 3$

Such a pairing is called a *one-to-one correspondence*, because *exactly one*
student is paired with *exactly one* locker and vice versa. It can be
written as $ABC \leftrightarrow 123$, and visualized as

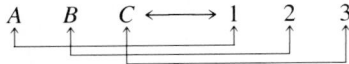

to show that A pairs with 1, B pairs with 2, and C pairs with 3.

The *order* in which the objects are paired is important. Why are the
correspondences $ABC \leftrightarrow 123$ and $ABC \leftrightarrow 231$ different? Answers may vary. In the
first corresp. $A \leftrightarrow 1$, and in the second $A \leftrightarrow 2$.

128   Chapter 4 Congruent Triangles

Developing Mathematical Power
Cooperative Learning   Congruence is aesthetically pleasing. Have small groups
find or create examples of the use of congruence in art, architecture, advertising,
and so on, to create an aesthetically pleasing picture, building, or logo. They can
create a bulletin board display with their findings.

When two polygons have the same number of vertices, a one-to-one correspondence can be established between their vertices. There are six different correspondences between the vertices of $\triangle BIG$ and $\triangle SML$:

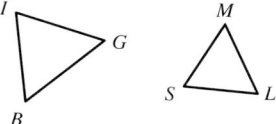

$$BIG \leftrightarrow SML \qquad BIG \leftrightarrow SLM \qquad BIG \leftrightarrow MSL$$
$$BIG \leftrightarrow MLS \qquad BIG \leftrightarrow LMS \qquad BIG \leftrightarrow LSM$$

Visualize $BIG \leftrightarrow SML$ as

B   I   G ⟷ S   M   L.

The arrows indicate corresponding vertices.

The correspondence $BIG \leftrightarrow SML$ identifies three pairs of *corresponding angles* and three pairs of *corresponding sides*.

$\angle B \leftrightarrow \angle S \qquad \overline{BI} \leftrightarrow \overline{SM}$
$\angle I \leftrightarrow \angle M \qquad \overline{BG} \leftrightarrow \overline{SL}$
$\angle G \leftrightarrow \angle L \qquad \overline{IG} \leftrightarrow \overline{ML}$

EXAMPLE 1 Consider $\triangle ABC$ and $\triangle XYZ$ and the correspondence $ABC \leftrightarrow ZXY$. List the three pairs of corresponding angles and the three pairs of corresponding sides.

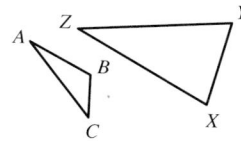

$\angle A \leftrightarrow \angle Z, \angle B \leftrightarrow \angle X, \angle C \leftrightarrow \angle Y,$
$\overline{AB} \leftrightarrow \overline{ZX}, \overline{AC} \leftrightarrow \overline{ZY}, \overline{BC} \leftrightarrow \overline{XY}$

Some correspondences appear different, yet represent the same pairing of vertices. The correspondence $HAL \leftrightarrow TOM$ is the same as, or is *equivalent to*, the correspondence $AHL \leftrightarrow OTM$, because in both correspondences $A \leftrightarrow O$, $H \leftrightarrow T$, and $L \leftrightarrow M$. Why is $HAL \leftrightarrow TMO$ not equivalent to $HAL \leftrightarrow TOM$?
In $HAL \leftrightarrow TMO$, $A \leftrightarrow M$ and $L \leftrightarrow O$.

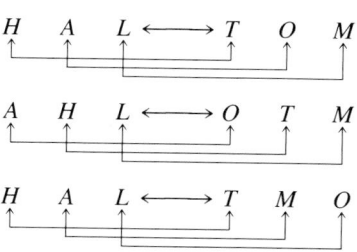

EXAMPLE 2 **Which correspondences are equivalent to $ABC \leftrightarrow MNO$? Explain.**

a. $CBA \leftrightarrow ONM$ **b.** $BAC \leftrightarrow NMO$ **c.** $ACB \leftrightarrow MNO$

$CBA \leftrightarrow ONM$ and $BAC \leftrightarrow NMO$ are equivalent to $ABC \leftrightarrow MNO$; each pairs C with O, B with N, and A with M.

Sometimes a correspondence between polygons is also a *congruence*. Two **triangles** are **congruent** if and only if there is a correspondence between the vertices of the triangles such that the corresponding angles are congruent and the corresponding sides are congruent.

4.1 Correspondence and Congruence   **129**

TEACHING SUGGESTIONS

- The concept of correspondence is prerequisite to the study of congruence. Use real-life examples of sets in one-to-one correspondence to help students understand correspondence. For example, every person has a unique social security number.
- Using cut-out figures, show that figures with the same number of vertices can be put into correspondence in several ways. Use noncongruent and congruent pairs.
- To illustrate the necessity of writing a correspondence correctly, create a correspondence between a pair of congruent figures that does not pair congruent parts.
- You may want to allow students to combine the step that proves congruency of angles and segments with the step that proves equality of measure, to simplify proofs.

Critical Thinking

1. *Classifying* Have students identify situations in which correspondences between sets cannot be created.
2. *Causal Explanation* Have students analyze and explain when a correspondence is or is not a congruence.

CHALKBOARD EXAMPLES

- **For Example 1**

Given the correspondence $DEF \leftrightarrow TPS$, identify the three pairs of corresponding angles and the three pairs of corresponding sides.
$\angle D \leftrightarrow \angle T$; $\angle E \leftrightarrow \angle P$; $\angle F \leftrightarrow \angle S$; $\overline{DE} \leftrightarrow \overline{TP}$; $\overline{DF} \leftrightarrow \overline{TS}$; $\overline{EF} \leftrightarrow \overline{PS}$

For Example 2

Which correspondences are equivalent to $XYZ \leftrightarrow DAR$? Explain.

a. $XZY \leftrightarrow DRA$ yes
b. $XYZ \leftrightarrow ARD$ no
c. $ZYX \leftrightarrow RAD$ yes
d. $YXZ \leftrightarrow ADR$ yes
e. $YZX \leftrightarrow ADR$ no
f. $ZXY \leftrightarrow RDA$ yes

Each of (a), (c), (d), and (f) pairs X with D, Y with A, and Z with R. (b) pairs X with A, and (e) pairs X with R.

For Example 3

If $\triangle JKL \cong \triangle GAR$, with $JK = 3$, $LK = 4$, $LJ = 5$, $m\angle K = 90$, and $m\angle R = 37$, find each indicated measure.

a. $RA = \underline{\ ?\ }$ 4
b. $RG = \underline{\ ?\ }$ 5
c. $AG = \underline{\ ?\ }$ 3
d. $m\angle A =$
       $\underline{\ ?\ }$ 90
e. $m\angle L =$
       $\underline{\ ?\ }$ 37
f. $m\angle J =$
       $\underline{\ ?\ }$ 53

Common Error

- Some students, given a statement such as $\triangle ABC \cong \triangle DEF$, will not recognize corresponding sides and angles identified in the statement, nor will they be able to identify an equivalent form of the statement. Have these students draw a sketch of the given triangles and try to mark the congruent parts.
- See *Teacher's Resource Book* for additional remediation.

LESSON FOLLOW-UP

Assignment Guide

See p. 126B for assignments.

Consider $\triangle HOP$ and $\triangle SKI$. Correspondence $HOP \leftrightarrow IKS$ is a congruence between $\triangle HOP$ and $\triangle IKS$, because all pairs of corresponding parts are congruent. Thus, $\triangle HOP \cong \triangle IKS$. Recall that since $OH = HO$ and $IK = KI$, $\overline{OH} \cong \overline{HO}$ and $\overline{IK} \cong \overline{KI}$. Therefore, $\overline{HO} \cong \overline{IK}$ can be written as $\overline{HO} \cong \overline{KI}$, $\overline{OH} \cong \overline{IK}$, or $\overline{OH} \cong \overline{KI}$. Throughout this text it will be understood that such congruence statements are interchangeable.

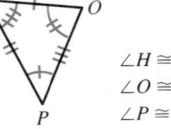
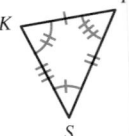

$\angle H \cong \angle I$ $\overline{HO} \cong \overline{IK}$
$\angle O \cong \angle K$ $\overline{HP} \cong \overline{IS}$
$\angle P \cong \angle S$ $\overline{OP} \cong \overline{KS}$

EXAMPLE 3   If $\triangle RED \cong \triangle BLU$, complete the congruence statement or find the indicated measure.

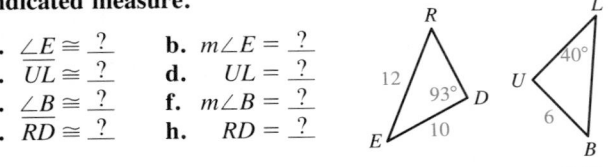

a. $\angle E \cong \underline{\ ?\ }$ b. $m\angle E = \underline{\ ?\ }$
c. $\overline{UL} \cong \underline{\ ?\ }$ d. $UL = \underline{\ ?\ }$
e. $\angle B \cong \underline{\ ?\ }$ f. $m\angle B = \underline{\ ?\ }$
g. $\overline{RD} \cong \underline{\ ?\ }$ h. $RD = \underline{\ ?\ }$

a. $\angle L$ b. 40   c. $\overline{DE}$ d. 10   e. $\angle R$ f. 47   g. $\overline{BU}$ h. 6

Since every definition is a *biconditional*, these two statements are justified by the definition of congruent triangles:

1. If the six pairs of corresponding parts are congruent, then the two triangles are congruent.

2. If two triangles are congruent, then the six pairs of corresponding parts are congruent.

CLASS EXERCISES

Decide which figures could be congruent. Explain.

1.

2.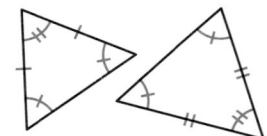

3.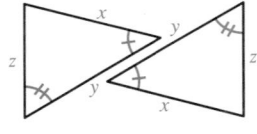

yes; all corr. parts are $\cong$ no; corr. sides are not $\cong$ yes; the unmarked $\angle$s are $\cong$, because the other 2 pairs are; therefore all corr. parts are $\cong$

True or false? If false, give a counterexample.

4. Every polygon is congruent to itself.
true

5. All right triangles are congruent.
false; the sides need not be $\cong$; see below

6. The correspondence $ABC \leftrightarrow DEF$ is equivalent to $BCA \leftrightarrow EDF$.
false; $BCA \leftrightarrow EFD$

7. Congruence of triangles is reflexive, symmetric, and transitive. true

Given $\triangle CUB$, $\triangle DOL$, and $CUB \leftrightarrow DOL$, find each corresponding part.

8. $\angle U$ $\angle O$ 9. $\overline{DL}$ $\overline{CB}$ 10. $\overline{UB}$ $\overline{OL}$ 11. $\angle D$ $\angle C$

PRACTICE EXERCISES ~~ Use technology where appropriate.

A 1. **Using Manipulatives** One way to check for congruence between two triangles is to *superimpose* one on the other so that they match exactly. Which triangles appear to be congruent? Check your answer by tracing the triangles and superimposing each one over the others.
I and IV

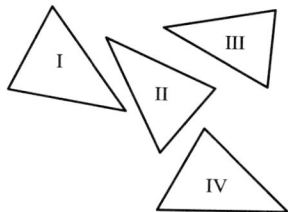

Which correspondences are equivalent to $XYZ \leftrightarrow MNQ$? Explain.

2. $YZX \leftrightarrow NQM$ 3. $ZXY \leftrightarrow QMN$ 4. $XZY \leftrightarrow MNQ$ 5. $YZX \leftrightarrow NMQ$

$YZX \leftrightarrow NQM$ and $ZXY \leftrightarrow QMN$, because each pairs X with M, Y with N, and Z with Q.

Given: $\triangle AMY \cong \triangle LIN$. Complete the congruence statements.

6. $\angle A \cong \underline{\ ?\ }$ 7. $\underline{\ ?\ } \cong \overline{LI}$ 8. $\underline{\ ?\ } \cong \angle N$ 9. $\overline{MY} \cong \underline{\ ?\ }$
   $\angle L$ $\overline{AM}$ $\angle Y$ $\overline{IN}$

If $\triangle MNP \cong \triangle ORS$, $m\angle P = 36$, and $m\angle O = 120$, find the indicated measures.

10. $m\angle S = \underline{\ ?\ }$ 36   11. $MN = \underline{\ ?\ }$ 8
12. $RS = \underline{\ ?\ }$ 12   13. $m\angle R = \underline{\ ?\ }$ 24
14. $m\angle M = \underline{\ ?\ }$ 120   15. $m\angle N = \underline{\ ?\ }$ 24

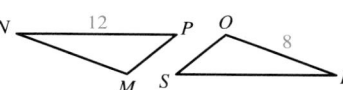

Write a statement of congruence between the triangles in each figure.

16. 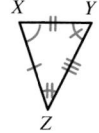   17. 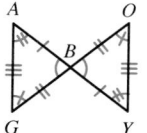   18.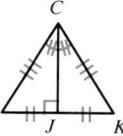

$\triangle XYZ \cong \triangle KML$ (or equiv.) $\triangle ABG \cong \triangle YBO$ (or equiv.) $\triangle AJC \cong \triangle KJC$ (or equiv.)

Complete the congruence statements.

19. 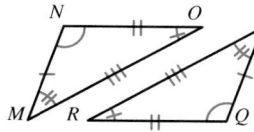   20.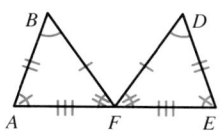

19.
a. $\overline{MN} \cong \underline{\ ?\ }$ $\overline{PQ}$ b. $\underline{\ ?\ } \cong \overline{MO}$ $\overline{PR}$
c. $\overline{NO} \cong \underline{\ ?\ }$ $\overline{QR}$ d. $\underline{\ ?\ } \cong \angle Q$ $\angle N$
e. $\angle O \cong \underline{\ ?\ }$ $\angle R$ f. $\angle M \cong \underline{\ ?\ }$ $\angle P$
g. $\triangle \underline{\ ?\ } \cong \triangle \underline{\ ?\ }$
   MON PRQ (or equiv.)

20.
a. $\underline{\ ?\ } \cong \overline{FE}$ $\overline{FA}$ b. $\angle B \cong \underline{\ ?\ }$ $\angle D$
c. $\overline{AB} \cong \underline{\ ?\ }$ $\overline{ED}$ d. $\underline{\ ?\ } \cong \angle DFE$ $\angle BFA$
e. $\overline{BF} \cong \underline{\ ?\ }$ $\overline{DF}$ f. $\underline{\ ?\ } \cong \angle E$ $\angle A$
g. $\triangle \underline{\ ?\ } \cong \triangle \underline{\ ?\ }$
   AFB EFD (or equiv.)

4.1 Correspondence and Congruence **131**

Lesson Quiz
Given $\triangle ABC \cong \triangle XYZ$, complete the following.

1. $\overline{BC} \cong \underline{\ ?\ }$ $\overline{YZ}$
2. $\angle A \cong \underline{\ ?\ }$ $\angle X$
3. $\underline{\ ?\ } \cong \angle Y$ $\angle B$
4. $\underline{\ ?\ } \cong \overline{XZ}$ $\overline{AC}$
5. $\angle C \cong \underline{\ ?\ }$ $\angle Z$
6. $\underline{\ ?\ } \cong \triangle YXZ$ $\triangle BAC$
7. Write a statement of congruence for the two triangles.

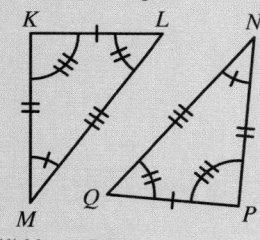

$\triangle KLM \cong \triangle PQN$
(or equivalent congruence)

Enrichment
Describe how to set up a one-to-one correspondence between members of the set of all integers and the members of the set of positive integers.

If n is a positive integer, $n \leftrightarrow 2n$.
If n is not positive, $n \leftrightarrow -2n + 1$.

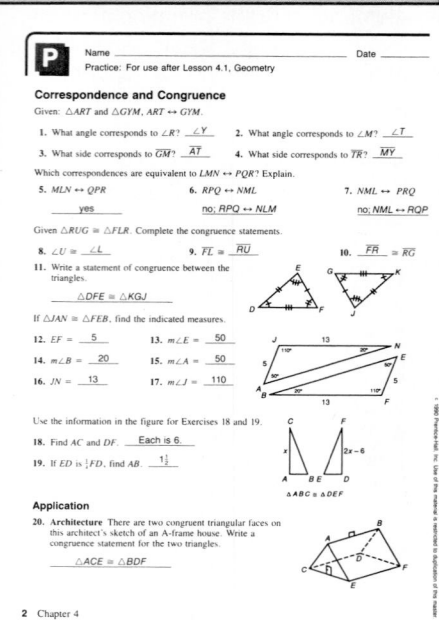

B 21. **Given:** $\triangle XYZ \cong \triangle RST$. Write six congruence statements involving the angles and the sides of the two triangles. $\angle X \cong \angle R, \angle Y \cong \angle S, \angle Z \cong \angle T, \overline{XY} \cong \overline{RS}, \overline{XZ} \cong \overline{RT}, \overline{YZ} \cong \overline{ST}$

If $\triangle DEF \cong \triangle IGH$, find the indicated measures.

22. $m\angle E = \underline{\ ?\ }$ 80   23. $m\angle I = \underline{\ ?\ }$ 55

24. $m\angle F = \underline{\ ?\ }$ 45   25. $EF = \underline{\ ?\ }$ 8

26. $DE = \underline{\ ?\ }$ 6   27. $HI = \underline{\ ?\ }$ 9

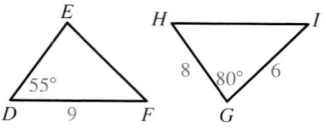

28. Find JL and NM. $JL = NM = 14$

29. If MO is 35 less than $3NM$, find KL. 7

List each valid triangle congruence statement for:

C 30. Scalene $\triangle ABC$
$\triangle ABC \cong \triangle ABC$ (or equivalent)

31. Equilateral $\triangle ABC$
$\triangle ABC \cong \triangle ABC, \triangle ABC \cong \triangle ACB,$
$\triangle ABC \cong \triangle BAC, \triangle ABC \cong \triangle BCA,$
$\triangle ABC \cong \triangle CAB, \triangle ABC \cong \triangle CBA$

32. Isosceles $\triangle ABC$
with $\overline{AB} \cong \overline{AC}$
$\triangle ABC \cong \triangle ABC$ (or equiv.)
$\triangle ABC \cong \triangle ACB$(or equiv.)

Draw triangles ATC and OGD with the given conditions.
Is $\triangle ATC \cong \triangle OGD$? How can you verify your answers? In Exercises 33–36, verify by the trace-and-superimpose technique found on p. 131.

33. $\angle C \cong \angle D; \angle A \cong \angle O; \angle T \cong \angle G$ no   34. $\angle C \cong \angle D; \angle A \cong \angle O; \overline{CA} \cong \overline{DO}$ yes

35. $\overline{CA} \cong \overline{DO}; \overline{CT} \cong \overline{DG}; \overline{AT} \cong \overline{OG}$ yes   36. $\angle C \cong \angle D; \angle A \cong \angle O; \overline{CT} \cong \overline{DG}$ yes

Applications

37. **Architecture** There are four congruent triangular faces in this square pyramid. Write a congruence statement involving the four triangles.
$\triangle RST \cong \triangle RSW \cong \triangle RVW \cong \triangle RVT$

38. **Probability** List the possible pairing of candidates A, B, and C with positions of President, Vice President, and Secretary.
A-P, B-VP, C-S; A-P, B-S, C-VP; A-VP, B-P, C-S; A-VP, B-S, C-P; A-S, B-P, C-VP; A-S, B-VP, C-P

39. **Technology** Use Logo to draw two congruent equilateral triangles. Try drawing congruent nonregular triangles. See Solutions Manual.

READING IN GEOMETRY

Euclidean geometry does not employ the concept of measure. Two segments or triangles are said to be congruent if they match exactly when one is *superimposed* on the other. This concept involving motion disturbs some mathematicians, since there are no postulates concerning motion in Euclidean mathematics. The solution is to incorporate concepts from two branches of geometry that have developed in more recent times: the *concept of correspondence* from *transformational geometry,* and the *concept of the number line* from *analytic geometry.* Research these two types of geometry.

132   Chapter 4 Congruent Triangles

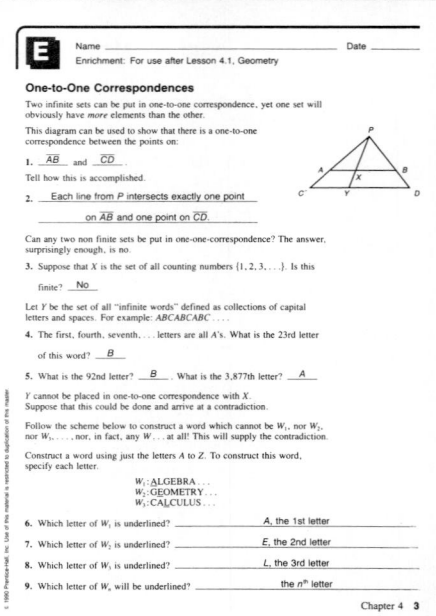

<table>
<tr><td>

4.2

</td><td>

Proving Triangles Congruent

Objective: To prove two triangles congruent by using the SSS, SAS, and ASA Postulates and the AAS Theorem

</td></tr>
</table>

It is usually not necessary to use the *definition of congruent triangles* to prove two triangles congruent. There are more concise methods.

Investigation—*Coordinate Geometry*

A new park site will contain four small triangular gardens. The design for the first three is shown on the graph paper.

1. Which gardens appear to have the same size and shape?
   1 and 2
2. Where could you locate point *L* so that △*GHI* and △*JKL* would have the same size and shape? 6 units above point *J*

3. How much fencing do you think is needed for garden *JKL*? 120′

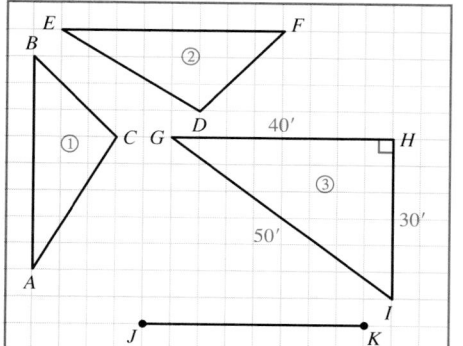

The three postulates and the theorem that follow are instrumental in proving triangles congruent.

> **Postulate 14** **SSS Postulate** If three sides of one triangle are congruent to three sides of another triangle, then the two triangles are congruent.

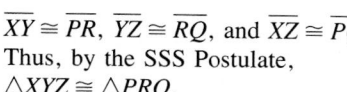

$\overline{XY} \cong \overline{PR}$, $\overline{YZ} \cong \overline{RQ}$, and $\overline{XZ} \cong \overline{PQ}$.
Thus, by the SSS Postulate,
△*XYZ* ≅ △*PRQ*.

Study the next two cases and compare the conclusions.

Case I

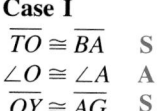

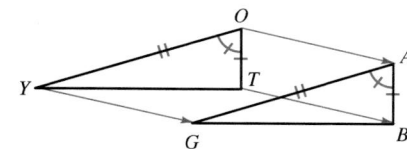

Conclusion: △*TOY* ≅ △*BAG*

4.2 Proving Triangles Congruent **133**

Developing Mathematical Power

Keeping a Portfolio Have students write a paragraph about congruence. In it they should give a general definition of *congruence* in their own words and explain how it is used in mathematics and for triangles in particular. They should analyze conditions that guarantee congruence of triangles and also determine minimal sets of conditions for it.

LESSON PLAN

Vocabulary
Included angle
Included side
Opposite angle
Opposite side

Materials/Manipulatives
Protractors and rulers
Sticks for sides of a triangle
*Teacher's Resource Book,
 Teaching Aid 4
 Transparency 4
 Teaching Transparency 22*

Technology
*Computer Test Bank, pp.
200–211*

LESSON FOCUS

Review
- Draw congruent triangles on the chalkboard. Have students identify the congruent parts and then write congruence statements about the triangles.
- The Mixed Review, Exercises 37–41, involves finding measures of angles of triangles and regular polygons.

Alternative Learning Styles
Some students will benefit by experimenting with the four congruence statements by using coordinate geometry to explore and visualize relationships. For example, in the Investigation, if they draw a triangle and then create another triangle by copying the three sides, they should see that the triangles are congruent because all the corresponding parts are congruent.

133

TEACHING SUGGESTIONS

- Use a set of three sticks that could be sides of a triangle (that is, such that the sum of the lengths of any two is greater than the length of the third) to motivate SSS. Show that the lengths of the three sides completely determine the size and shape of the triangle.
- Point out the relationship between the names of two angles of a triangle and their included side (i.e., ∠*A* and ∠*B* include $\overline{AB}$) and between the names of two sides of a triangle and their included angle (i.e., $\overline{CD}$ and $\overline{DE}$ include ∠*D*).
- Help students identify situations in which information about congruent segments or angles must be deduced, as for example when vertical angles are involved or when two triangles share a side.

Critical Thinking

1. *Making Decisions* Have students decide whether sufficient information is given to determine the congruence of two triangles.
2. *Translation* Have students translate pictorial information to verbal information in order to determine given information and draw conclusions.

CHALKBOARD EXAMPLES

- **For Example 1**

  Use △*CAT* to find each answer.

  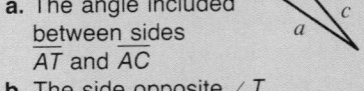

  a. The angle included between sides $\overline{AT}$ and $\overline{AC}$
  b. The side opposite ∠*T* (Name two ways.)
  c. The side included between ∠*C* and ∠*T* (Name two ways.)
  d. The angle included between *a* and *t*

  a. ∠*A* b. $\overline{AC}$ or *t* c. $\overline{CT}$ or *a* d. ∠*C*

Case II

$$\overline{XY} \cong \overline{MN} \quad \text{S}$$
$$\overline{YZ} \cong \overline{NO} \quad \text{S}$$
$$\angle X \cong \angle M \quad \text{A}$$

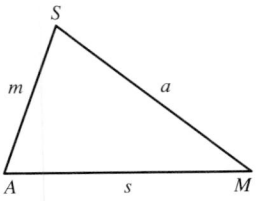

Conclusion: △*XYZ* ≇ △*MNO*

Both cases involve the congruence of two sides and an angle, but only in Case I, where the angle is *included between* the two sides, does the information lead to a triangle congruence, as stated in Postulate 15.

> **Postulate 15 SAS Postulate** If two sides and the *included angle* of one triangle are congruent to two sides and the *included angle* of another triangle, then the two triangles are congruent.

EXAMPLE 1 Use △*SAM* to find each answer.

a. The angle included between sides $\overline{SA}$ and $\overline{AM}$
b. The side opposite ∠*A* (Name two ways.)
c. The side included between ∠*S* and ∠*A* (Name two ways.)
d. The angle included between sides *a* and *m*

a. ∠*A*   b. $\overline{SM}$ or *a*   c. $\overline{SA}$ or *m*   d. ∠*S*

Note the position of the congruent sides in the following postulate and theorem.

> **Postulate 16 ASA Postulate** If two angles and the *included side* of one triangle are congruent to two angles and the *included side* of another triangle, then the two triangles are congruent.

> **Theorem 4.1 AAS Theorem** If two angles and the *nonincluded side* of one triangle are congruent, respectively, to the corresponding angles and *nonincluded side* of another triangle, then the two triangles are congruent.

Given: ∠*A* ≅ ∠*D*; ∠*B* ≅ ∠*E*; $\overline{BC} \cong \overline{EF}$

Prove: △*ABC* ≅ △*DEF*

Plan: Show ∠*C* ≅ ∠*F* so that $\overline{BC}$ and $\overline{EF}$ are included sides. Then use ASA.
Proved in Practice Exercise 34

134   Chapter 4 Congruent Triangles

EXAMPLE 2 Write the information that is given in each pair of triangles. Then state and verify the triangle congruence.

a.
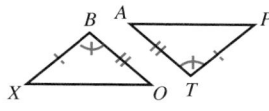

b.
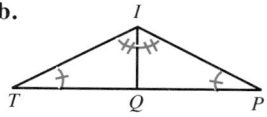

a. Given: $\overline{BX} \cong \overline{TP}$; $\angle B \cong \angle T$; $\overline{BO} \cong \overline{TA}$
  Conclusion: $\triangle BOX \cong \triangle TAP$ by SAS

b. Given: $\angle T \cong \angle P$; $\angle TIQ \cong \angle PIQ$; $\overline{IQ} \cong \overline{IQ}$
  Conclusion: $\triangle IQT \cong \triangle IQP$ by AAS

EXAMPLE 3 Supply the missing statements and reasons.

Given: $\overline{RE} \perp \overline{RO}$; $\overline{OS} \perp \overline{ES}$; $\overline{RE} \parallel \overline{OS}$

Prove: $\triangle RES \cong \triangle SOR$

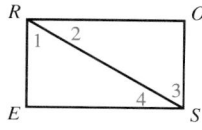

Proof:

Statements	Reasons
1. $\overline{RE} \parallel \overline{OS}$	1. ?
2. $\angle\ ? \cong \angle\ ?$	2. If $\parallel$ lines have a transversal, the alternate interior angles are $\cong$.
3. $\overline{RE} \perp \overline{RO}$; $\overline{OS} \perp \overline{ES}$	3. ?
4. $\angle 1$ and $\angle 2$ are complementary; $\angle 3$ and $\angle 4$ are complementary.	4. ?
5. $\angle\ ? \cong \angle\ ?$	5. ?
6. $\overline{RS} \cong$?	6. ?
7. ?	7. ?

1. Given
2. 1, 3
3. Given
4. If the exterior sides of two adjacent angles are perpendicular, then the angles are complementary.
5. 2, 4; Complements of congruent angles are congruent.
6. $\overline{SR}$; Reflexive property of congruence
7. $\triangle RES \cong \triangle SOR$; ASA Postulate

These methods are used to show that two triangles are congruent.

SSS Postulate (**S**ide—**S**ide—**S**ide)
SAS Postulate (**S**ide—Included **A**ngle—**S**ide)
ASA Postulate (**A**ngle—Included **S**ide—**A**ngle)
AAS Theorem (**A**ngle—**A**ngle—**N**onincluded **S**ide)

Developing Mathematical Power

Cooperative Learning Exercises 36 and 43 provide opportunities for students to work in cooperative groups. They should share their experiments and explorations as well as their finished products. They may want to create a math publication for their own class.

• **For Example 2**
State the given information and any additional congruence you can deduce.

a.
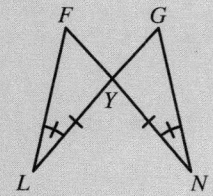

Given: $\angle L \cong \angle N$; $\overline{LY} \cong \overline{NY}$
Conclusion: $\angle FYL \cong \angle GYN$; $\triangle FYL \cong \triangle GYN$ by ASA

b.
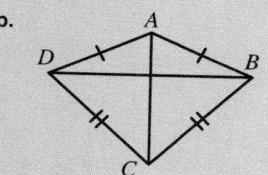

Given: $\overline{AD} \cong \overline{AB}$; $\overline{DC} \cong \overline{BC}$
Conclusion: $\overline{AC} \cong \overline{CA}$; $\triangle ADC \cong \triangle ABC$ by SSS

• **For Example 3**
Supply the missing statements and give the reasons.
Given: $\overline{AB} \parallel \overline{DC}$; $\angle B \cong \angle D$
Prove: $\triangle ABC \cong \triangle CDA$
Proof:

Statements	Reasons
1. $\overline{AB} \parallel \overline{DC}$	1. Given
2. $\angle BAC \cong \angle\ ?\ DCA$	2. If $\parallel$ lines have a trans., then alt. int. $\angle$s are $\cong$.
3. $\angle B \cong \angle\ ?$	3. Given
4. $\overline{AC} \cong\ ?\ \overline{CA}$	4. Refl. prop. of congruence
5. ? $\triangle ABC \cong \triangle CDA$	5. AAS Theorem

135

LESSON FOLLOW-UP

Discussion

Draw these triangles on the board.

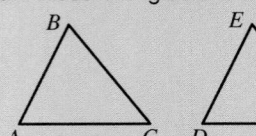

For the given information below, identify any additional conditions necessary to guarantee congruence of the triangles.

a. $\angle A \cong \angle D; \angle B \cong \angle E$ $\overline{AB} \cong \overline{DE}$ (ASA)

b. $\angle A \cong \angle D; \overline{AB} \cong \overline{DE}$ $\overline{AC} \cong \overline{DF}$
   (SAS) or $\angle B \cong \angle E$ (ASA)

c. $\angle C \cong \angle F; \overline{AB} \cong \overline{DE}$ $\angle A \cong \angle D$
   (AAS) or $\angle B \cong \angle E$ (AAS)

d. $\overline{AB} \cong \overline{DE}; \overline{BC} \cong \overline{EF}$ $\overline{AC} \cong \overline{DF}$ (SSS)
   or $\angle B \cong \angle E$ (SAS)

1.

2.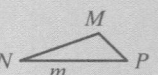

3.

CLASS EXERCISES

Sketch and label a triangle for each condition. See below.

1. $\angle R$ is included between sides $\overline{PR}$ and $\overline{RQ}$.

2. Side m is between $\angle N$ and $\angle P$.

3. Side a is opposite the angle between sides b and c.

Verify the congruence of the following triangles.

4. 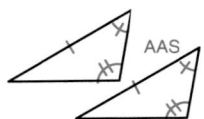 AAS

5. 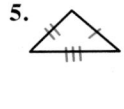 SSS

6. 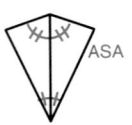 ASA

PRACTICE EXERCISES

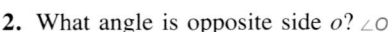 Use technology where appropriate.

Use △YTO for Exercises 1–4.

A **1.** Name the side included between $\angle Y$ and $\angle T$ in two ways. $\overline{TY}$, o

2. What angle is opposite side o? $\angle O$

3. What angle is included between sides $\overline{TY}$ and $\overline{YO}$? $\angle Y$

4. Name the sides that make $\angle T$ an included angle. $\overline{YT}$ and $\overline{TO}$ or o and y

In Exercises 5–8, use any △ABC.

5. What angle is included between sides $\overline{AB}$ and $\overline{BC}$? $\angle B$

6. What angle is opposite side c? $\angle C$

7. Name the side opposite $\angle B$ in two ways. $\overline{AC}$, b

8. What side is included between $\angle A$ and $\angle C$? $\overline{AC}$ or b

If enough information is given, state the postulate or theorem that verifies the congruence of the triangles.

9.  SSS

10. 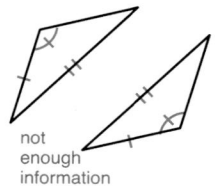 not enough information

11. 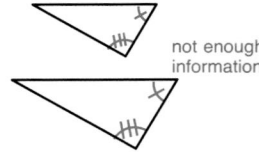 not enough information

12. 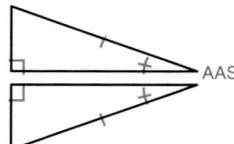 AAS

13. 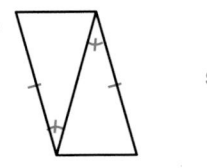 SAS

14. 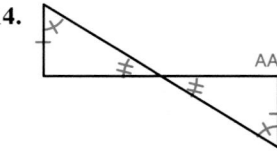 AAS

27. Plan: Use the Given and the def. of ∠bis. to show $\angle KQB \cong \angle AQB$. Then use the reflex. prop. to show $\triangle \cong$.

Statements	Reasons
1. $\overline{QK} \cong \overline{QA}$; $\overline{QB}$ bisects $\angle KQA$.	1. Given
2. $\angle KQB \cong \angle AQB$	2. Def. of ∠ bis.
3. $\overline{BQ} \cong \overline{BQ}$	3. Reflex. prop.
4. $\triangle BQK \cong \triangle BQA$	4. SAS

Conclusion: In the given figure, if $\overline{QK} \cong \overline{QA}$ and $\overrightarrow{QB}$ bisects $\angle KQA$, then $\triangle BQK \cong BQA$.

Write the given information. Verify the triangle congruence. $\overline{TO} \cong \overline{BZ}$; $\angle O \cong \angle Z$, $\overline{OY} \cong \overline{ZI}$, $\triangle TOY \cong \triangle BZI$; SAS

15.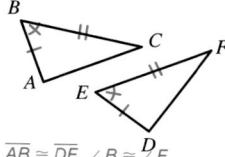

$\overline{AB} \cong \overline{DE}$, $\angle B \cong \angle E$,
$\overline{BC} \cong \overline{EF}$; $\triangle ABC \cong \triangle DEF$;
SAS

16.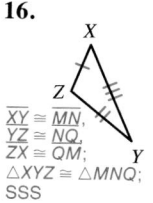

$\overline{XY} \cong \overline{MN}$,
$\overline{YZ} \cong \overline{NQ}$,
$\overline{ZX} \cong \overline{QM}$;
$\triangle XYZ \cong \triangle MNQ$;
SSS

17.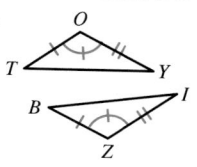

18.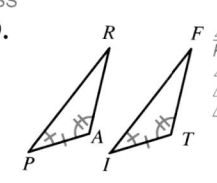

$\angle M \cong \angle S$, $\angle MAN \cong \angle SAW$,
$\overline{MN} \cong \overline{SW}$; $\triangle MNA \cong \triangle SWA$; AAS

19.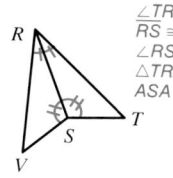

$\angle P \cong \angle I$,
$\overline{PA} \cong \overline{IT}$,
$\angle A \cong \angle T$,
$\triangle PAR \cong$
$\triangle ITF$; ASA

20.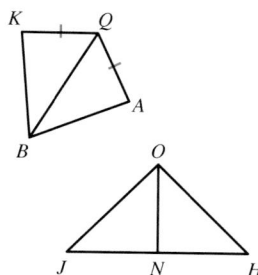

$\angle TRS \cong \angle VRS$,
$\overline{RS} \cong \overline{RS}$,
$\angle RST \cong \angle RSV$,
$\triangle TRS \cong \triangle VRS$;
ASA

21. Supply the missing statements and reasons.

Given: $\overline{KJ} \parallel \overline{NM}$; $\overline{KJ} \cong \overline{NM}$
Prove: $\triangle KJL \cong \triangle NML$
Proof:

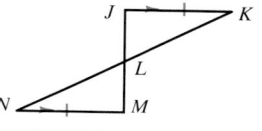

Statements	Reasons
1. $\underline{\ ?\ }$ $\overline{KJ} \cong \overline{NM}$; $\overline{KJ} \parallel \overline{NM}$	1. Given
2. $\angle LJK \cong \angle \underline{\ ?\ }$ LMN	2. $\underline{\ ?\ }$ If $\parallel$ lines have a transv., then alt. int. $\angle$s are $\cong$.
3. $\angle JLK \cong \angle \underline{\ ?\ }$ MLN	3. $\underline{\ ?\ }$ Vert. $\angle$s are $\cong$.
4. $\underline{\ ?\ }$ $\triangle KJL \cong \triangle NML$	4. $\underline{\ ?\ }$ AAS

Find the missing congruence necessary to prove $\triangle ABC \cong \triangle DEF$.

Given	Method to Be Used	Missing Congruence
22. $\overline{AB} \cong \overline{DE}$; $\angle A \cong \angle D$	SAS	$\underline{\ ?\ }$ $\overline{AC} \cong \overline{DF}$
23. $\angle C \cong \angle F$; $\overline{AB} \cong \overline{DE}$	AAS	$\angle A \cong \angle D$ or $\underline{\ ?\ }$ $\angle B \cong \angle E$
24. $\angle C \cong \angle F$; $\overline{AC} \cong \overline{DF}$	ASA	$\underline{\ ?\ }$ $\angle A \cong \angle D$
25. $\overline{AB} \cong \overline{DE}$; $\overline{BC} \cong \overline{EF}$	SSS	$\underline{\ ?\ }$ $\overline{AC} \cong \overline{DF}$
26. $\overline{BC} \cong \overline{EF}$; $\overline{CA} \cong \overline{FD}$	SAS	$\underline{\ ?\ }$ $\angle C \cong \angle F$

See Additional Answers, p. 702.

27. Given: $\overline{QK} \cong \overline{QA}$; $\overrightarrow{QB}$ bisects $\angle KQA$
Prove: $\triangle BQK \cong \triangle BQA$

28. Given: $\overline{QK} \cong \overline{QA}$; $\overline{KB} \cong \overline{BA}$
Prove: $\triangle BQK \cong \triangle BQA$

29. Given: $\overline{ON}$ is the perpendicular bisector of $\overline{JH}$.
Prove: $\triangle JON \cong \triangle HON$

30. Given: $\overline{ON}$ bisects $\angle JOH$; $m\angle J = x$; $m\angle H = x$
Prove: $\triangle NOJ \cong \triangle NOH$

4.2 Proving Triangles Congruent **137**

28. Plan: Use the Given and the reflex. prop. to show $\triangle \cong$ by SSS.

Statements	Reasons
1. $\overline{QK} \cong \overline{QA}$; $\overline{KB} \cong \overline{BA}$	1. Given
2. $\overline{BQ} \cong \overline{BQ}$	2. Reflex. prop.
3. $\triangle BQK \cong \triangle BQA$	3. SSS

Concl. In the given figure, if $\overline{QK} \cong \overline{QA}$ and $\overline{KB} \cong \overline{BA}$, then $\triangle BQK \cong \triangle BQA$.

 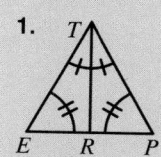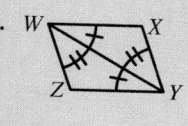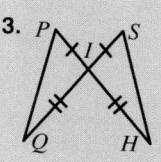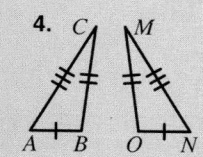
B

137

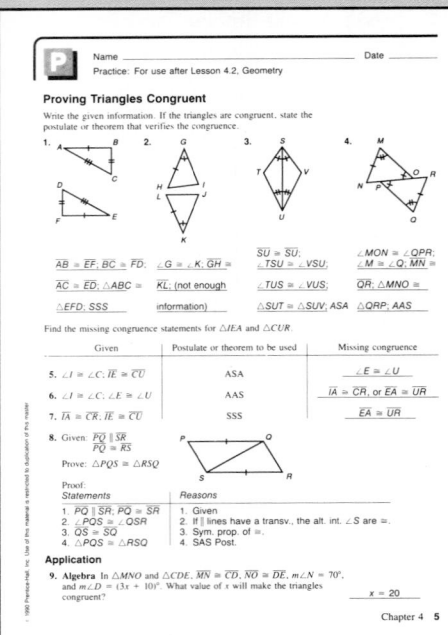

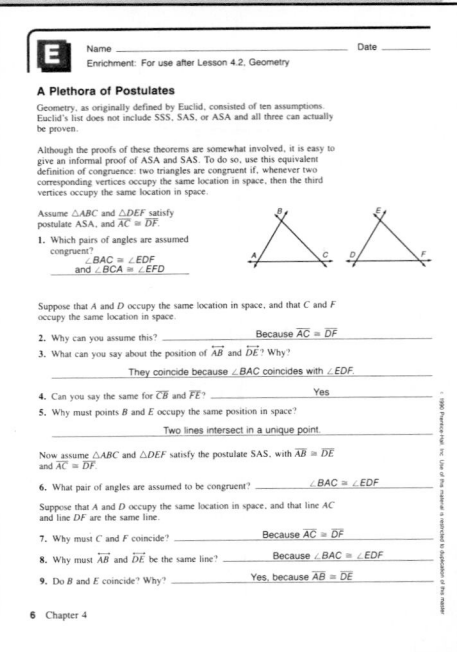

Write a statement in "if-then" form that identifies what is given and what triangles could be proven congruent.

C 31.

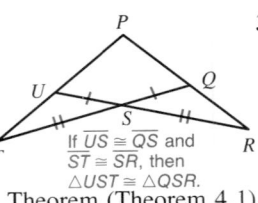

If ∠BET ≅ ∠RTE
and ∠BTE ≅ ∠RET,
then △BET ≅ △RTE.

32.

If $\overline{US} ≅ \overline{QS}$ and
$\overline{ST} ≅ \overline{SR}$, then
△UST ≅ △QSR.

33.

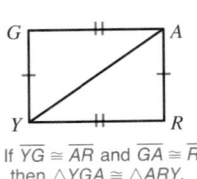

If $\overline{YG} ≅ \overline{AR}$ and $\overline{GA} ≅ \overline{RY}$,
then △YGA ≅ △ARY.

34. Complete the proof of the AAS Theorem (Theorem 4.1).
See side column.

Applications

35. Carpentry A triangular peak of one house is trimmed with three 6-ft pieces of molding. 18 ft of molding are used to trim a second triangular peak. Are the two triangles formed congruent? Explain. Not necessarily—the second peak could have sides: 5 ft, 6 ft, 7 ft.

36. Technology To define a variable within a procedure, use the MAKE command, such as MAKE "LENGTH RANDOM 50. After defining the variable with the MAKE command, the variable can be used, such as FD :LENGTH. Use Logo and the ASA congruence postulate to draw congruent triangles with random orientations. See Solutions Manual.

Mixed Review

Find the missing angle measures for △ABC.

37. $m\angle B = 120$
$m\angle A = m\angle C$
$m\angle A = m\angle C = 30$

38. $m\angle A = 50$
$m\angle B = 2(m\angle A)$
$m\angle B = 100; m\angle C = 30$

39. ∠C is a right angle.
$m\angle A = 20$
$m\angle B = 70$

40. What is the measure of each interior angle of a regular octagon? 35

41. What is the measure of each exterior angle of a regular hexagon? 60

Developing Mathematical Power

42. Thinking Critically How could you prove Exercise 21, using a postulate?
Use both pairs of ≅ alt. int. ∠s to prove △KJL ≅ △NML by ASA Post.

43. Investigation The triangle is a rigid figure. Its shape will not change until the pressure on the sides of the figure causes them to break. A quadrilateral is not a rigid figure. Under pressure, the angles of the figure will change. The property of rigidity is extremely important to engineers and architects. Thus, they use triangles extensively in roof supports, bridges, transmission towers, and geodesic domes. A *solid* triangle is not required in any of these cases. Why is this an advantage? It is economical, because the interior does not have to be filled in; also, the structure is lighter.

34.

Statements	Reasons
1. ∠A ≅ ∠D; ∠B ≅ ∠E; $\overline{BC} ≅ \overline{EF}$	1. Given
2. ∠C ≅ ∠F	2. If 2 ∠s of one △ are ≅ to 2 ∠s of another △, then the third ∠s are ≅.
3. △ABC ≅ △DEF	3. ASA

Conclusion: If 2 ∠s and a nonincluded side of one △ are ≅ to the corr. parts of another △, then the △ are ≅.

Using Congruent Triangles

Objectives: To prove segments or angles congruent by first proving two triangles congruent
To prove two triangles congruent by first proving two other triangles congruent

The *corresponding parts of congruent triangles* are often used to prove statements about overlapping triangles and sequences of congruence.

Investigation—*Using Manipulatives*

Use a geoboard and elastic bands to form two different triangles whose sides measure 3, 4, and 5 units.

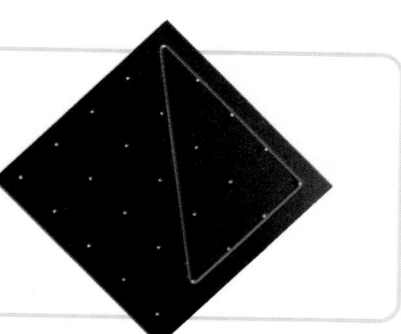

1. Are the triangles congruent? Explain. yes; SSS Post.
2. Sketch the triangles and label the vertices. Are the corresponding angles congruent? How can you justify your answer? yes; the definition of congruent triangles

CPCTC is the abbreviation for *corresponding parts of congruent triangles are congruent.* Which sides and angles are congruent by CPCTC if $\triangle QRB \cong \triangle AGT$?
$QB \cong AT$, $QR \cong AG$, $RB \cong GT$; $\angle B \cong \angle T$, $\angle R \cong \angle G$, $\angle Q \cong \angle A$

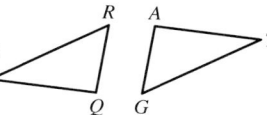

EXAMPLE 1   **Given:** $\overline{RT} \cong \overline{RY}$; $\overline{RS} \cong \overline{RO}$

Prove: $\overline{TS} \cong \overline{YO}$

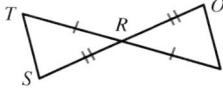

Plan: Use the given and the vertical angles to prove $\triangle RTS \cong \triangle RYO$. Thus, $\overline{TS} \cong \overline{YO}$ by CPCTC.

Proof:

Statements	Reasons
1. $\overline{RT} \cong \overline{RY}$; $\overline{RS} \cong \overline{RO}$	1. Given
2. $\angle TRS \cong \angle YRO$	2. Vertical angles are congruent.
3. $\triangle RTS \cong \triangle RYO$	3. SAS Postulate
4. $\overline{TS} \cong \overline{YO}$	4. CPCTC

Conclusion: Since $\triangle RST \cong \triangle RYO$, $\overline{TS} \cong \overline{YO}$ by CPCTC.

4.3 Using Congruent Triangles   **139**

Developing Mathematical Power

Cooperative Learning Working in groups, students may work to create complex figures involving overlapping triangles. Each student in the group draws a triangle and then the group works to incorporate the triangles into a complex figure. Have each group describe how the complex figure was constructed.

LESSON PLAN

Vocabulary
CPCTC
Overlapping triangles

Materials/Manipulatives
Teacher's Resource Book, Transparency 5
Teaching Transparencies 23 and 23A

Technology
Computer
Computer Test Bank, pp. 211–220
The Geometric Supposer: Triangles
Geometry Problems and Projects: Triangles, Worksheet T22

LESSON FOCUS

Review
Draw this diagram on the board.

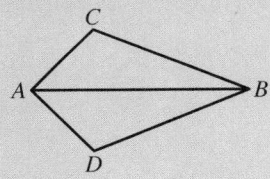

Given: $\triangle ABC \cong \triangle ABD$.
Must $\angle C$ be congruent to $\angle D$?
Yes. Since $\angle C$ and $\angle D$ are corr. $\angle$s of $\cong$ $\triangle$s, they must be congruent.

Alternative Learning Styles
• In the Investigation, students use manipulatives (a geoboard and elastic bands) to make congruent triangles by SSS.
• Students can visualize discrete triangles in a complex figure by using tracing paper. For overlapping triangles, students can trace individual triangles on separate sheets of different colored paper, then reconstruct the complex figure.

- Use an overhead projector and transparencies with overlays to show how overlapping figures can be analyzed.
- Emphasize the planning of proofs.
- Help students evaluate their proofs. They should be able to explain their logic and identify key steps.

CHALKBOARD EXAMPLES

- **For Example 1**

Give a plan for proof.

Given: $\overline{KJ} \cong \overline{AJ}$;
$\angle KJC \cong \angle AJC$

Prove: $\angle K \cong \angle A$

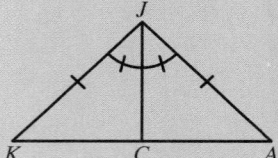

Plan: Use the given information and the reflexive property of congruence to prove $\triangle KJC \cong \triangle AJC$ by SAS. Then $\angle K \cong \angle A$ by CPCTC.

- **For Example 2**

Use the figure below.

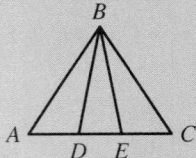

a. Identify all triangles that have D as a vertex.
b. Identify all triangles that have BE as a side.
c. Identify all triangles in the figure.
a. Triangles *BDC, BDE, BDA*
b. Triangles *ABE, DBE, CBE*
c. Triangles *ABC, ABE, DBC, ABD, DBE, EBC*

Sometimes figures are made up of triangles that *overlap* and share a common vertex, side, or even a portion of a side. Separating the figures makes it easier to visualize them.

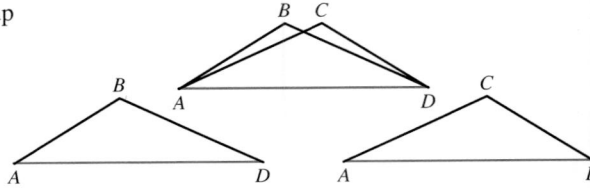

EXAMPLE 2   Use the figure to the right.

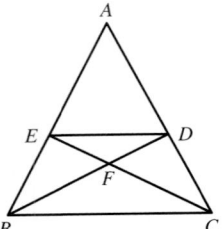

a. Identify all triangles that have A as a vertex.
b. Identify all triangles that have $\overline{BC}$ as a side.
c. Identify all triangles in this figure.

a. Triangles *ABC, AED, ABD, ACE*
b. Triangles *ABC, FBC, DBC, EBC*
c. Triangles *ABC, AED, ABD, ACE, BED, CDE, BCE, CBD, BCF, EDF, BFE, CFD*

EXAMPLE 3   Write a proof for the following plan.

Given: $\overline{HL} \cong \overline{HR}$; $\overline{HA} \cong \overline{HD}$

Prove: $\angle L \cong \angle R$

Plan: Separate the triangles that use the given information. Show that they are congruent and thus $\angle L \cong \angle R$.

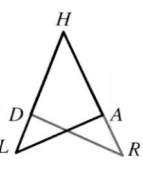 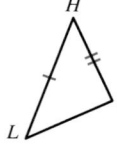 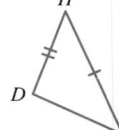

Proof:

Statements	Reasons
1. $\overline{HL} \cong \overline{HR}$; $\overline{HA} \cong \overline{HD}$	1. Given
2. $\angle H \cong \angle H$	2. Reflexive prop. of $\cong$
3. $\triangle HLA \cong \triangle HRD$	3. SAS Postulate
4. $\angle L \cong \angle R$	4. CPCTC

Conclusion: Since $\triangle HLA \cong \triangle HRD$, $\angle L \cong \angle R$ by CPCTC.

EXAMPLE 4   Plan a proof for the following statement.

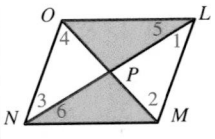

Given: $\overline{LM} \cong \overline{NO}$; $\angle 1 \cong \angle 3$; $\angle 2 \cong \angle 4$; $\angle 5 \cong \angle 6$

Prove: $\triangle LPO \cong \triangle NPM$

Plan: By ASA, $\triangle LMP \cong \triangle NOP$ and $\overline{LP} \cong \overline{NP}$ by CPCTC. $\angle LPO \cong \angle NPM$ since vertical angles are congruent; thus, by ASA, $\triangle LPO \cong \triangle NPM$.

140   Chapter 4 Congruent Triangles

6. Use the given def. of $\angle$bisector and refl. prop. to prove $\triangle TIN \cong \triangle TGN$ by AAS. Concl. follows by CPCTC.

7. Use the *Given* and the refl. prop. to prove $\triangle TIN \cong \triangle TGN$ by SAS. Concl. follows by CPCTC.

CLASS EXERCISES

Visualizing in Geometry

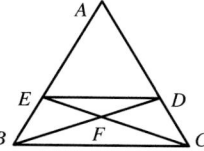

1. How many triangles can you find? 12

2. Which triangles appear to be congruent?
△EFB and △DFC; △EDC and △DEB; △EBC and
△DCB; △AEC and △ADB

Which triangles must be congruent in order to arrive at each conclusion?

3. a. $\overline{ST} \cong \overline{SR}$
   PST and QSR
   b. $\overline{PT} \cong \overline{QR}$
   PST and QSR or PQT
   c. $\overline{TU} \cong \overline{RU}$ and QPR
   TQU and RPU
   d. $\angle TPQ \cong \angle RQP$
   TPQ and RQP
   e. $\overline{UQ} \cong \overline{UP}$
   TUQ and RUP

4. a. $\overline{AF} \cong \overline{CD}$
   AFG and CDH
   or AFE and CDE
   b. $\angle 7 \cong \angle 10$
   GFE and HDE
   c. $\overline{CH} \cong \overline{AG}$
   CHD and AGF
   d. $\angle 1 \cong \angle 5$
   AFG and CDH
   e. $\angle 3 \cong \angle 6$
   GFE and HDE

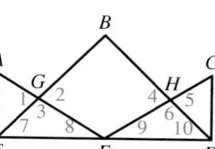

PRACTICE EXERCISES

Use the figure and the given information to complete the chart.

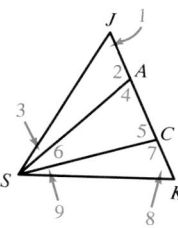

	Given	Congruent Triangles	Justification	Further Conclusion
A	1. $\overline{JA} \cong \overline{KC}$ $\angle 2 \cong \angle 7$ $\overline{AS} \cong \overline{CS}$	△JAS ≅ △KCS ?	SAS ?	$\overline{JS} \cong \underline{?}$ $\overline{KS}$
	2. $\overline{JS} \cong \overline{KS}$ $\angle 1 \cong \angle 8$ $\angle 2 \cong \angle 7$	△JAS ≅ △KCS ?	AAS ?	$\underline{?} \cong \overline{CS}$ $\overline{AS}$
	3. $\angle 1 \cong \angle 5$ $\overline{JA} \cong \overline{CA}$ $\angle 2 \cong \angle 4$	△AJS ≅ △ACS ?	ASA ?	$\overline{JS} \cong \underline{?}$ $\overline{CS}$
	4. $\overline{AS} \cong \overline{KS}$ $\angle 6 \cong \angle 9$	△ASC ≅ △KSC ?	SAS ?	$\angle 8 \cong \underline{?}$ $\angle 4$
	5. $\overline{AC} \cong \overline{KC}$ $\overline{AS} \cong \overline{SK}$	△ACS ≅ △KCS ?	SSS ?	$\underline{?} \cong \angle 7$ $\angle 5$

4.3 Using Congruent Triangles **141**

Additional Answers for p. 142

8. Use def. of ∠ bisector and the refl. prop. to prove △TIN ≅ △TGN by ASA. Concl. follows by CPCTC.

9. Use def. of seg. bisector and vertical ∠s to prove △RNP ≅ △LNM by SAS. ∠MLN ≅ ∠RPN by CPCTC. Concl. follows by alt. int. ∠s.

• **For Example 3**
   Given: $\overline{MY} \cong \overline{ON}$; $\overline{OY} \cong \overline{MN}$
   Prove: $\angle MYO \cong \angle ONM$

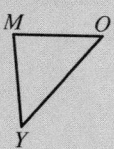

Plan: Redraw the figure as shown. Show that △MOY ≅ △OMN by SSS. Then ∠MYO ≅ ∠ONM by CPCTC.

Statements	Reasons
1. $\overline{MY} \cong \overline{ON}$; $\overline{OY} \cong \overline{MN}$	1. Given
2. $\overline{MO} \cong \overline{OM}$	2. Refl. prop. of congruence
3. △MOY ≅ △OMN	3. SSS Post.
4. ∠MYO ≅ ∠ONM	4. CPCTC

Conclusion: If $\overline{MY} \cong \overline{ON}$ and $\overline{OY} \cong \overline{MN}$, then ∠MYO ≅ ∠ONM.

• **For Example 4**
   Give a plan for the proof.
   Given: $\angle 1 \cong \angle 2$; $\overline{MP} \cong \overline{OP}$
   Prove: $\overline{LO} \cong \overline{NM}$

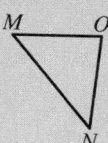

Plan: Use the given information and vertical angles MPL and OPN to prove △MPL ≅ △OPN by ASA. Then $\overline{PL} \cong \overline{PN}$ by CPCTC. Using vertical angles LPO and NPM, △LPO ≅ △NPM by SAS, $\overline{LO} \cong \overline{NM}$ by CPCTC.
(Alternatively, after △MPL is shown to be congruent to △OPN, you could use congruent corresponding parts $\overline{LM}$ and $\overline{NO}$, and $\overline{MO} \cong \overline{OM}$ to show that △LMO ≅ △NOM by SAS, and thus $\overline{LO} \cong \overline{NM}$).

Common Errors
• Students may have difficulty writing proofs if they do not think through a plan. Help them understand that planning is essential.
• Students may have trouble working with overlapping triangles. See the suggestion in Alternative Learning Styles.
• See *Teacher's Resource Book* for additional remediation.

141

Discussion

Put this figure on the board.

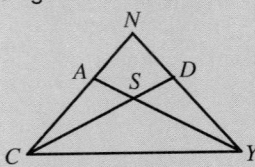

Ask students to pick out all pairs of overlapping triangles that appear to be congruent. △CDN and △YAN; △ACY and △DYC.

Critical Thinking

1. *Analysis* Ask students to analyze figures for congruence.
2. *Creative Thinking* Have students identify subgoals that can facilitate a proof involving CPCTC.

Assignment Guide

See p. 126B for assignments.

17. Plan: Show alt. int ∠s *BUS* and *GSU* ≅. Then use the given and the reflex. prop. to prove △*BUS* ≅ △*GSU*. *BS* and *UG* are ≅ corr. parts.

Proof:

Statements	Reasons
1. $\overline{BU} \parallel \overline{SG}$; $\overline{BU} \cong \overline{SG}$	1. Given
2. ∠*BUS* ≅ ∠*GSU*	2. If lines are ∥, alt. int. ∠s are ≅.
3. $\overline{US} \cong \overline{SU}$	3. Refl. prop.
4. △*BUS* ≅ △*GSU*	4. SAS
5. $\overline{BS} \cong \overline{GU}$	5. CPCTC

Conclusion: If △ *BUS* and *GSU* can be shown ≅, then corr. sides $\overline{BS}$ and $\overline{GU}$ are ≅.

18. Plan: Use the Given and refl. prop. of ≅ to show △ ≅. Concl. follows by CPCTC.

Proof:

Statements	Reasons
1. ∠*B* ≅ ∠*G*; ∠*BUS* ≅ ∠*GSU*	1. Given
2. $\overline{US} \cong \overline{SU}$	2. Refl. prop. of ≅
3. △*BUS* ≅ △*GSU*	3. AAS
4. $\overline{BS} \cong \overline{GU}$	4. CPCTC

Conclusion: If △ *BUS* and *GSU* can be shown ≅, then corr. sides $\overline{BS}$ and $\overline{GU}$ are ≅.

Write a detailed plan for each proof.

See side column, p. 140.

6. Given: $\overline{TN}$ bisects ∠*ITG*; ∠*TIN* ≅ ∠*TGN*

   Prove: $\overline{IN} \cong \overline{GN}$

7. Given: $\overline{TI} \cong \overline{TG}$; ∠*ITN* ≅ ∠*GTN*

   Prove: ∠*INT* ≅ ∠*GNT*

8. Given: $\overline{TN}$ bisects ∠*ITG* and ∠*ING*.

   Prove: $\overline{TI} \cong \overline{TG}$ For Exercises 8–9 see side column, p. 141.

9. Given: $\overline{LP}$ and $\overline{RM}$ bisect each other.

   Prove: $\overline{LM} \parallel \overline{RP}$

10. Given: $\overline{LM} \parallel \overline{RP}$; $\overline{LM} \cong \overline{RP}$ See below.

   Prove: $\overline{PL}$ bisects $\overline{RM}$.

11. Given: ∠1 ≅ ∠2; $\overline{LP}$ bisects $\overline{MR}$ at *N*.

   Prove: $\overline{LN} \cong \overline{PN}$

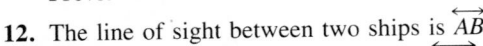

12. The line of sight between two ships is $\overleftrightarrow{AB}$.
   After 10 minutes the line of sight is $\overleftrightarrow{A'B'}$.
   Are the ships on parallel courses? Explain. Yes, the △s are ≅ by SAS. The ∠s at *A* and *B* are ≅ alt. int. ∠s.

Complete the missing statements and reasons.

13. Given: △*ABC* ≅ △*AED*

   Prove: ∠*BAD* ≅ ∠*EAC*

Proof:

Statements	Reasons
1. _?_ △*ABC* ≅ △*AED*	1. Given
2. ∠_?_ ≅ ∠*EAD* BAC	2. _?_ CPCTC
3. $m\angle$ _?_ = $m\angle$ _?_ BAC, EAD	3. _?_ Def. of ≅ ∠s
4. $m\angle$ _?_ + $m\angle CAD$ = $m\angle$ _?_ + $m\angle CAD$ BAC EAD	4. _?_ Add. prop.
5. $m\angle BAD$ = _?_ ; $m\angle EAC$ = _?_ $m\angle BAC$ + $m\angle CAD$	5. _?_ Def. of betweenness
6. _?_ = _?_ $m\angle BAD$, $m\angle EAC$ $m\angle EAD$ + $m\angle CAD$	6. _?_ Subst. prop.
7. _?_ ≅ _?_ ∠*BAD*, ∠*EAC*	7. _?_ Def. of ≅ ∠s

In Exercises 14–15 write a detailed plan for each proof. For Exercises 14–15, see Additional Answers, p. 702.

14. Given: $\overline{AD} \cong \overline{AE}$; $\overline{AB} \cong \overline{AC}$

   Prove: $\overline{DC} \cong \overline{BE}$

15. Given: $\overline{DB} \cong \overline{EC}$; $\overline{BE} \cong \overline{DC}$

   Prove: ∠1 ≅ ∠2

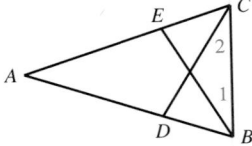

10. Use alt. int. ∠s and the *Given* to show that △*RNP* ≅ △*LNM* by ASA. Use CPCTC to show that $MN \cong NR$ and $LN \cong NP$. Concl. follows by def. of bisector.

11. Use suppl. of ≅ ∠s, def. of bisector, and vertical ∠s to prove ∠*RNP* ≅ △*LNM* by ASA. Concl. follows by CPCTC.

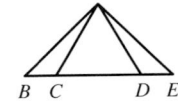

16. Given: $\overline{LI} \cong \overline{ID} \cong \overline{AI} \cong \overline{IN}$

Prove: $\angle 1 \cong \angle 2$

Proof:

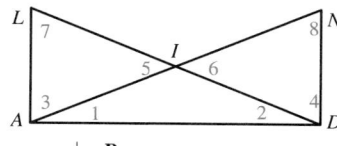

Statements	Reasons
1. $\overline{LI} \cong \overline{ID} \cong \overline{AI} \cong \overline{IN}$	1. Given
2. $\angle 5 \cong \angle 6$	2. _?_ Vert. $\angle$s are $\cong$.
3. $\triangle$_?_ $\cong \triangle$_?_ LIA, NID	3. SAS Postulate
4. $\overline{LA} \cong$ _?_ ; $\angle 7 \cong \angle$ _?_ $\overline{ND}$, 8	4. _?_ CPCTC
5. $LI = ID = AI = IN$	5. _?_ Def. of $\cong$ segments
6. $LI + ID = AI + IN$	6. _?_ Add. prop.
7. $LI + ID =$ _?_ ; $AI + IN =$ _?_	7. _?_ Def. of betweenness
8. _?_ = _?_ LD, AN	8. _?_ Subst. prop.
9. _?_ $\cong$ _?_ $\overline{LD}$, $\overline{AN}$	9. _?_ Def. of $\cong$ segments
10. $\triangle$_?_ $\cong \triangle$_?_ ALD, DNA	10. _?_ SAS
11. _?_ $\angle 1 \cong \angle 2$	11. _?_ CPCTC

B

17. Given: $\overline{BU} \parallel \overline{GS}$; $\overline{BU} \cong \overline{GS}$

Prove: $\overline{BS} \cong \overline{UG}$

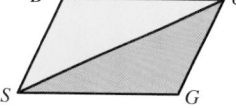

See side column, page 142.

18. Given: $\angle B \cong \angle G$; $\angle BUS \cong \angle GSU$

Prove: $\overline{BS} \cong \overline{GU}$

19. Given: $\overline{TY}$ and $\overline{MR}$ bisect each other at A.

Prove: $\overline{TR} \cong \overline{YM}$ See side column.

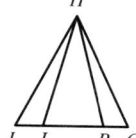

20. Given: $\angle R \cong \angle Y$; $\overline{TR} \cong \overline{MY}$

Prove: $\angle T \cong \angle M$

21. Given: $\overline{HI} \cong \overline{HO}$; $\angle I \cong \angle O$; $\overline{IJ} \cong \overline{OP}$

Prove: $\overline{HJ} \cong \overline{HP}$

22. Given: $\overline{HI} \cong \overline{HO}$; $\overline{IJ} \cong \overline{PO}$; $\angle I \cong \angle O$

Prove: $\angle IHP \cong \angle OHJ$

For Exercises 22–25 see Additional Answers, p. 702.

23. Given: $JKLMNO$ is a regular hexagon; $\overline{KN}$ and $\overline{OL}$ bisect each other

Prove: $\overline{KL} \parallel \overline{NO}$

24. M and N lie on opposite sides of $\overleftrightarrow{PQ}$ such that $\overline{MP} \cong \overline{NP}$ and $\overline{MQ} \cong \overline{NQ}$. Prove that $\angle M \cong \angle N$.

25. M and N lie on opposite sides of $\overleftrightarrow{PQ}$ such that $\overline{MP} \cong \overline{NQ}$ and $\overleftrightarrow{MP} \parallel \overleftrightarrow{NQ}$. Prove that $\overline{MQ} \cong \overline{NP}$.

4.3 Using Congruent Triangles **143**

Lesson Quiz

Using the figure and the given information, complete the statements.

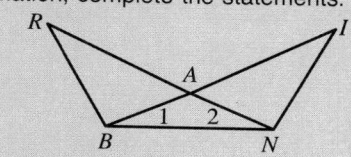

1. Given: $\angle 2 \cong \angle 1$; $\angle R \cong \angle I$

$\triangle$ _?_ $\cong \triangle$ _?_ by _?_. RBN; INB; AAS

Then $\overline{RB} \cong$ _?_ by _?_. $\overline{IN}$; CPCTC

2. Given: $\overline{AB} \cong \overline{AN}$; $\overline{AR} \cong \overline{AI}$

Prove: $\angle 2 \cong \angle 1$

$\triangle$ _?_ $\cong \triangle$ _?_ by _?_. RAB; IAN; SAS

Then _?_ $\cong \overline{IN}$. $\overline{RB}$

$\triangle$ _?_ $\cong \triangle$ _?_ by _?_. RBN; INB; SSS

Then _?_ $\cong$ _?_. $\angle 2$; $\angle 1$

19. Plan: Use the def. of bisector and vertical $\angle$s to prove $\triangle TAR \cong \triangle YAM$. Then $\overline{TR}$ and $\overline{MY}$ are $\cong$ corr. parts.

Proof:

Statements	Reasons
1. $\overline{TY}$ and $\overline{MR}$ bisect each other.	1. Given
2. $\overline{AT} \cong \overline{AY}$; $\overline{AM} \cong \overline{AR}$	2. Def. of bisector
3. $\angle TAR \cong \angle YAM$	3. Vert. $\angle$s are $\cong$.
4. $\triangle TAR \cong \triangle YAM$	4. SAS
5. $\overline{TR} \cong \overline{YM}$	5. CPCTC

Conclusion: If $\triangle$ *TAR* and *MAY* $\cong$, then corr. sides $\overline{TR}$ and $\overline{MY}$ are $\cong$.

20. Plan: Use the Given and vert. $\angle$s to show $\triangle$ $\cong$. Concl. follows by CPCTC.

Proof:

Statements	Reasons
1. $\angle R \cong \angle Y$; $\overline{TR} \cong \overline{MY}$	1. Given
2. $\angle TAR \cong \angle MAY$	2. Vert. $\angle$s are $\cong$.
3. $\triangle TAR \cong \triangle MAY$	3. AAS
4. $\angle T \cong \angle M$	4. CPCTC

Conclusion: If $\triangle$ *TAR* and *MAY* can be shown $\cong$, then corr. $\angle$s T and M are $\cong$.

21. Plan: Use the Given to prove $\triangle HIJ \cong \triangle HOP$. Concl. follows by CPCTC.

Proof:

Statements	Reasons
1. $\overline{HI} \cong \overline{HO}$; $\angle I \cong \angle O$; $\overline{IJ} \cong \overline{OP}$	1. Given
2. $\triangle HIJ \cong \triangle HOP$	2. SAS
3. $\overline{HJ} \cong \overline{HP}$	3. CPCTC

Conclusion: If $\triangle$ *HIJ* and *HOP* can be shown $\cong$, then corr. sides $\overline{HJ}$ and $\overline{HP}$ are $\cong$.

Teacher's Resource Book
Follow-Up Investigation, Chapter 4,
p. 7

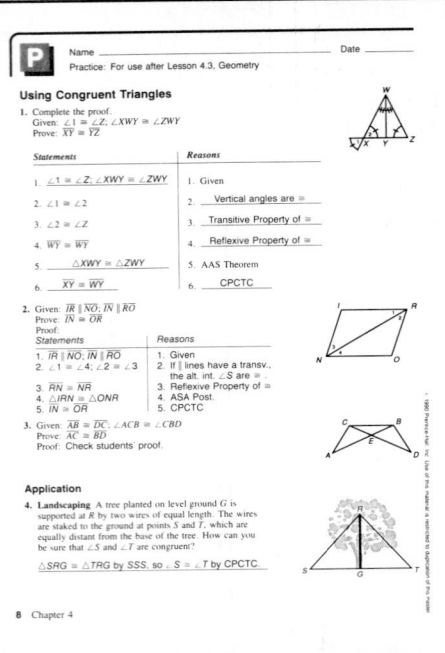

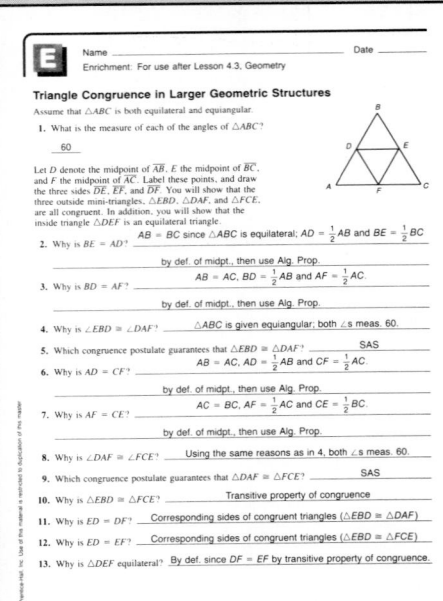

C **26. Given:** $\overleftrightarrow{KL} \parallel \overrightarrow{NO}$;
$\overrightarrow{OK} \parallel \overrightarrow{LN}$

Prove: $\overline{OK} \cong \overline{LN}$

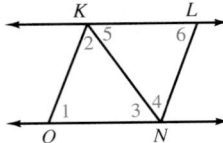

27. Given: $\overline{AM} \cong \overline{MB}$;
$\angle A \cong \angle B$; $\angle 1 \cong$
$\angle 4$; $\angle 2 \cong \angle 3$

Prove: $\overline{FC} \cong \overline{GC}$

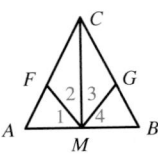

28. Given: $\angle 1 \cong \angle 2$;
$\overline{BT} \cong \overline{BU}$;
$\angle 3 \cong \angle 4$

Prove: $\overline{KC} \cong \overline{KE}$

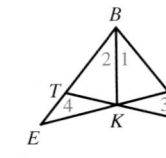

Applications

29. Maps As shown on the map, the paths of two motorists formed congruent triangles. Why are you sure that they covered the same amount of mileage? Since the △ are ≅, the corr. sides have = measures. By add. prop., the sums are =.

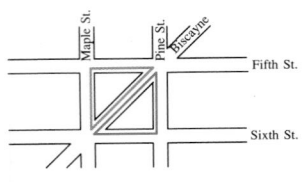

30. Design This is a side view of an adjustable-height table that has legs hinged in the center C as shown. Explain why the top of the table is always parallel to the floor. Congruent triangles assure that alt. int. ∠s are ≅ so the table remains ∥ to the floor.

TEST YOURSELF

1. Which of the correspondences are equivalent to $\triangle PQR \leftrightarrow \triangle STU$?   4.1

   a. $\triangle RQP \leftrightarrow \triangle UTS$ **b.** $\triangle PRQ \leftrightarrow \triangle SUT$ **c.** $\triangle QPR \leftrightarrow \triangle TSU$ a, b, c

Given $\triangle EJO \cong \triangle AMS$, **complete.**

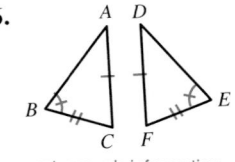

2. $\angle J \cong \underline{\ ?\ } \angle M$ **3.** $\overline{JE} \cong \underline{\ ?\ } \overline{MA}$
4. $\angle E \cong \underline{\ ?\ } \angle A$ **5.** $\underline{\ ?\ } \cong \overline{AS}$ $\overline{EO}$

If the two triangles are congruent, state and verify the congruence.

6.

7.

8.   4.2

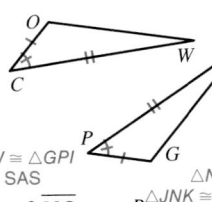

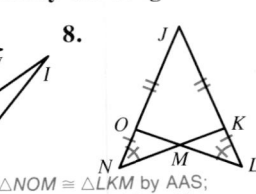

$\triangle OCW \cong \triangle GPI$
by SAS

not enough information

$\triangle NOM \cong \triangle LKM$ by AAS;
$\triangle JNK \cong \triangle JLO$ by SAS or ASA   4.3

9. Given: M is the midpoint of $\overline{NO}$;
$\angle N \cong \angle O$; $\overline{NP} \cong \overline{OS}$

Prove: $\angle P \cong \angle S$ See below.

144 Chapter 4 Congruent Triangles

9. Plan: Show △ ≅ by SAS. Concl. follows by CPCTC.

Proof:

Statements	Reasons
1. M is the midpt. of $\overline{NO}$.	1. Given
2. $\overline{NM} \cong \overline{OM}$	2. Def. of midpt.
3. $\angle N \cong \angle O$; $\overline{NP} \cong \overline{OS}$	3. Given
4. $\triangle PNM \cong \triangle SOM$	4. SAS
5. $\angle P \cong \angle S$	5. CPCTC

Conclusion: In the given figure, if M is the midpoint of $\overline{NO}$, $\angle N \cong \angle O$, and $\overline{NP} \cong \overline{OS}$, then $\angle P \cong \angle S$.

Strategy: Identify Intermediate Goals

LESSON PLAN

Vocabulary
Intermediate goals

Materials/Manipulatives
*Teacher's Resource Book,
Transparency 5
Teaching Transparency 24*

Technology
*Computer Test Bank, pp.
220–227*

In planning the solution to a problem, you might think to yourself, "If I knew *A*, I could get *B*, which leads me to *C*, which is what I want." *A* and *B* are called **intermediate goals.** Learning how to identify intermediate goals is an important part of the problem-solving process. When doing geometric proofs, the *Look back* and *Look ahead* techniques can often help you determine intermediate goals.

EXAMPLE 1   **Given:** $\overline{CD}$ is the perpendicular bisector of $\overline{AB}$; $\overline{CD}$ bisects $\angle EDF$.

   Prove: $\overline{DE} \cong \overline{DF}$

Understand the Problem

What is given?
$\overline{CD}$ is the $\perp$ bisector of $\overline{AB}$, and $\overline{CD}$ bisects $\angle EDF$.

What is to be proven?
$\overline{DE} \cong \overline{DF}$

Plan Your Approach

Look back.
$\overline{DE}$ would be congruent to $\overline{DF}$ if they were corresponding parts of congruent triangles. Since $\overline{DE}$ and $\overline{DF}$ are sides of two pairs of triangles, $\triangle ADE$ and $\triangle BDF$ and $\triangle DCE$ and $\triangle DCF$, establishing triangle congruences for these pairs of triangles might be helpful.

Look ahead.
Since $\overline{CD}$ is the perpendicular bisector of $\overline{AB}$, you can show that $\triangle ADC \cong \triangle BDC$. It is also given that $\overline{CD}$ bisects $\angle EDF$. Thus, $\angle EDC \cong \angle FDC$. These angles are parts of $\triangle DCE$ and $\triangle DCF$.

Showing $\triangle ADC \cong \triangle BDC$ and $\triangle DCE \cong \triangle DCF$ seem to be the appropriate intermediate goals.

Plan:
Show $\triangle ADC \cong \triangle BDC$ by SAS to get $\angle DCA \cong \angle DCB$ by CPCTC. Then $\triangle DCE \cong \triangle DCF$ by ASA and the conclusion follows.

4.4 Strategy: Identify Intermediate Goals   **145**

LESSON FOCUS

Review
Review the four basic steps to problem solving: Understand the problem, plan your approach, implement the plan, and interpret the results.

Alternative Learning Styles
Many students need experience in learning how to identify appropriate intermediate goals. Planning a trip can help students organize their thinking. Discuss a trip from the school to a place of interest. Emphasize that you cannot reach your final destination or goal without passing intermediate destinations or goals. Students can draw a map to help them identify the intermediate destinations.

Developing Mathematical Power
Cooperative Learning   Planning a trip provides an opportunity for students to identify intermediate goals. Have students work in groups on the Enrichment activity, p. 11, in the *Teacher's Resource Book* (see side column, p. 148). Encourage students to share results and insights.

- Students require constant reminders of the need for careful planning of proofs before they try to write the proofs. Use many examples of situations in which intermediate goals can be identified and have students explain why these intermediate steps are important.
- Give students an opportunity to verbalize their plans for proofs. This helps to identify appropriate intermediate goals.
- In addition to asking students to write proofs that require intermediate goals, have them concentrate on the plans for such proofs.

- **For Example 1**

  Write a plan and identify *intermediate goals.*

  Given:

  $\overline{MP} \cong \overline{KN}$;

  $\overline{JN} \cong \overline{LP}$;

  $\overline{JM} \cong \overline{LK}$

  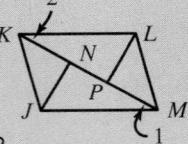

  Prove: $\angle 1 \cong \angle 2$

  Look back: $\angle 1$ and $\angle 2$ are $\cong$ if they are corr. parts of $\cong$ $\triangle$s, either $\triangle JMN$ and $\triangle LKP$ or $\triangle JMK$ and $\triangle LKM$.

  Look ahead: Since $\overline{MP} \cong \overline{KN}$, it can be shown that $\overline{MN} \cong \overline{KP}$. Thus, it can be shown that $\triangle JMN \cong \triangle LKP$.

  Plan: Use the add. prop. to show that $\overline{MN} \cong \overline{KP}$. Then $\triangle JMN \cong \triangle LKP$ by SSS, and $\angle 1 \cong \angle 2$ by CPCTC.

  Intermediate Goals: $\overline{MN} \cong \overline{KP}$; $\triangle JMN \cong \triangle LKP$

- **For Example 2**

  Write a plan and identify *intermediate goals.*

  Given: $\overline{DF} \cong \overline{EF}$; $\overline{AD} \cong \overline{DB} \cong \overline{BE} \cong \overline{EC}$

  Prove: $\overline{BF}$ is the $\perp$ bisector of $\overline{AC}$.

  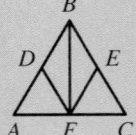

☐ **Implement the Plan**

Proof:

Statements	Reasons
1. $\overline{CD}$ is the $\perp$ bisector of $\overline{AB}$; $\overline{CD}$ bisects $\angle EDF$.	1. Given
2. D is the midpoint of $\overline{AB}$.	2. Def. of bisect
3. $\overline{AD} \cong \overline{BD}$	3. Def. of midpoint
4. $\angle ADC$ and $\angle BDC$ are rt. $\angle$s.	4. Def. of $\perp$
5. $\angle ADC \cong \angle BDC$	5. All right $\angle$s are $\cong$.
6. $\overline{DC} \cong \overline{DC}$	6. Reflexive prop.
7. $\triangle ADC \cong \triangle BDC$	7. SAS Post.
8. $\angle DCA \cong \angle DCB$	8. CPCTC
9. $\angle EDC \cong \angle FDC$	9. Def. of $\angle$ bis.
10. $\triangle DCE \cong \triangle DCF$	10. ASA Th.
11. $\overline{DE} \cong \overline{DF}$	11. CPCTC

☐ **Interpret the Results**

Conclusion: In the given figure, if $\overline{CD}$ is the perpendicular bisector of $\overline{AB}$ and if $\overline{CD}$ bisects $\angle EDF$, then $\overline{DE} \cong \overline{DF}$.

EXAMPLE 2 **Given:** $\overline{JK} \parallel \overline{ML}$; $\overline{JK} \cong \overline{ML}$

Prove: $\overleftrightarrow{JM} \parallel \overleftrightarrow{KL}$

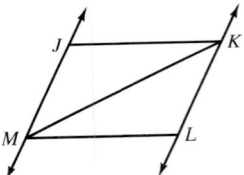

☐ **Understand the Problem**

Given: $\overline{JK}$ and $\overline{ML}$ are parallel and congruent.

Prove: $\overleftrightarrow{JM}$ and $\overleftrightarrow{KL}$ are parallel.

☐ **Plan Your Approach**

Look back.

$\overleftrightarrow{JM}$ would be parallel to $\overleftrightarrow{KL}$ if alternate interior angles JMK and LKM were congruent. These angles are parts of $\triangle JMK$ and $\triangle LKM$.

Look ahead.

Since $\overline{JK} \parallel \overline{ML}$, $\angle JKM \cong \angle LMK$ and it can be shown that $\triangle JMK \cong \triangle LKM$.

Thus, an intermediate goal is to show $\triangle JMK \cong \triangle LKM$.

Plan:

Use the given to show $\triangle JKM \cong \triangle LMK$. Then $\angle JMK \cong \angle LKM$ by CPCTC, and $\overleftrightarrow{JM} \parallel \overleftrightarrow{KL}$.

Implement the Plan

Proof:

Statements	Reasons
1. $\overline{JK} \parallel \overline{ML}$; $\overline{JK} \cong \overline{ML}$	1. Given
2. $\angle JKM \cong \angle LMK$	2. If $\parallel$ lines have a transv., alt. int. $\angle$s are $\cong$.
3. $\overline{KM} \cong \overline{MK}$	3. Reflexive prop.
4. $\triangle JKM \cong \triangle LMK$	4. SAS Post.
5. $\angle JMK \cong \angle LKM$	5. CPCTC
6. $\overleftrightarrow{JM} \parallel \overleftrightarrow{KL}$	6. If two lines have a transv. with alt. int. $\angle$s $\cong$, the lines are $\parallel$.

Interpret the Results

Conclusion: Lines that join the endpoints of two segments that are parallel and congruent are themselves parallel.

Problem Solving Reminders

- It is sometimes necessary to establish and prove intermediate steps (goals) in order to reach a desired conclusion.
- The *Look back* and *Look ahead* techniques can help you find the necessary intermediate goals in a proof.

CLASS EXERCISES

Identify all required intermediate steps to demonstrate the conclusion.

1.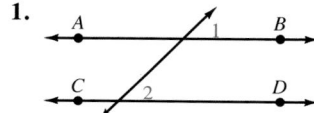

Conclusion: $\angle 1 \cong \angle 2$
Prove $\overline{AB} \parallel \overline{CD}$.

2.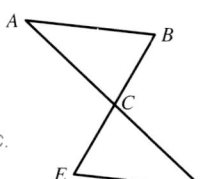

Conclusion: $\overline{MN} \cong \overline{PN}$
Prove $\triangle MNO \cong \triangle PNO$.

Identify the intermediate goal(s) given in each plan.

3. **Given:** $\overline{AB} \parallel \overline{DE}$; C is the midpoint of $\overline{EB}$.
   Prove: C is the midpoint of $\overline{AD}$.
   Plan: Use the Given and vertical angles to get $\triangle ABC \cong \triangle DEC$. Then $\overline{AC} \cong \overline{DC}$ by CPCTC.
   Prove $\triangle ABC \cong \triangle DEC$.

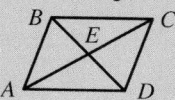

4. **Given:** $\overline{AD}$ and $\overline{BE}$ bisect each other.
   Prove: $\overline{AB} \parallel \overline{DE}$
   Plan: Use the Given and vertical angles to get $\triangle ABC \cong \triangle DEC$. Then $\angle ABC \cong \angle DEC$ by CPCTC.
   Prove $\triangle ABC \cong \triangle DEC$.

4.4 Strategy: Identify Intermediate Goals **147**

Look back: We need to prove that $\overline{AF} \cong \overline{FC}$ and $\overline{BF} \perp \overline{AC}$ (or $\angle AFB \cong \angle CFB$). Both will follow from $\triangle ABF$ being $\cong$ to $\triangle CBF$.

Look ahead: The given information can be used to prove $\triangle BDF \cong \triangle BEF$. Then $\angle DBF \cong \angle EBF$. The given leads to $\overline{AB} \cong \overline{CB}$, so $\triangle ABF \cong \triangle CBF$.

Plan: Prove $\triangle BDF \cong \triangle BEF$ by SSS. Then $\angle DBF \cong \angle EBF$. Show that $\overline{AB} \cong \overline{CB}$, so $\triangle ABF \cong \triangle CBF$. Now $\overline{AF} \cong \overline{CF}$ and $\angle AFB \cong \angle CFB$ and the conclusion follows.

Intermediate goals: $\triangle BDF \cong \triangle BEF$; $\triangle ABF \cong \triangle CBF$;

Common Error

- Some students have difficulty in determining intermediate goals. Encourage them to find intermediate goals in real-life situations to reinforce the concept.
- See *Teacher's Resource Book* for additional remediation.

LESSON FOLLOW-UP

Assignment Guide
See p. 126B for assignments.

Project
On a road map, find a direct route from one city to another. Identify intermediate destinations.

Lesson Quiz
Write a plan. List intermediate goals.

Given: $\overline{BE} \cong \overline{ED}$; $\overline{CE} \cong \overline{EA}$

Prove: $\overline{BC} \parallel \overline{AD}$

Plan: Prove $\triangle BEC \cong \triangle DEA$. Then $\angle CBE \cong \angle ADE$ and $\overline{BC} \parallel \overline{AD}$.

Intermediate goals: $\triangle BEC \cong \triangle DEA$; $\angle CBE \cong \angle ADE$

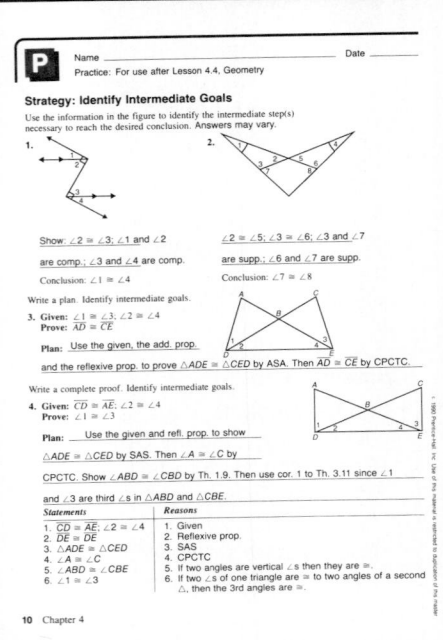

PRACTICE EXERCISES

Use the information given in the figure to identify the intermediate step(s) necessary to reach the desired conclusion.

A 1.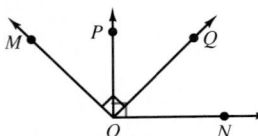

Conclusion: ∠MOP ≅ ∠NOQ
Show: ∠MOQ ≅ ∠PON; ∠POQ ≅ ∠POQ;
m∠MOQ − m∠POQ = m∠PON − m∠POQ

2.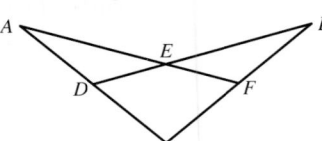

Conclusion: CD ∥ AB
Show alt. int. ∠s 2 and 4 ≅.

Write a plan for each. Identify intermediate goals.
See Additional Answers, p. 702.

B 3. **Given:** CD ≅ CF; DA ≅ FB
   Prove: ∠A ≅ ∠B

4. **Given:** DE ≅ FE; FA ≅ DB
   Prove: ∠EDC ≅ ∠EFC

Write a complete proof for each. Identify intermediate goals.

C 5. **Given:** M and N are midpoints;
      ∠1 ≅ ∠2; NO ≅ KM.
   Prove: ∠3 ≅ ∠4

6. **Given:** CD ⊥ AB;
      ∠1 ≅ ∠2; DE ≅ DF.
   Prove: EC ≅ FC

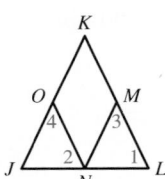

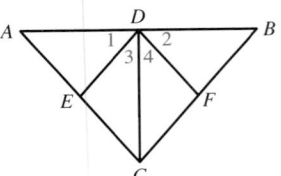

7. **Given:** In △JKL, KM is the perpendicular bisector of JL.
   Prove: △JKL is isosceles.

8. **Given:** In isosceles △JKL, KM bisects JL.
   Prove: KM ⊥ JL

PROJECT

Find a map showing commercial air routes in the United States. Choose a starting city and a destination city. Give several possible routes that involve different sets of stopovers (intermediate goals).

Developing Mathematical Power

Keeping a Portfolio   Have students write their reactions to proofs. They should include what they like most and least and what they find hardest and easiest about them. They should explain what they think is the most important part of doing a proof.

4.5 Medians, Altitudes, and Bisectors

Objectives: To apply the definitions of median and altitude of a triangle, and perpendicular bisector of a segment
To apply the theorems about points on perpendicular bisectors of segments and on bisectors of angles

Median, altitude, and bisector are three types of segments associated with triangles. They can provide additional information in a problem.

Investigation—*Visualizing the Concept*

A ship heads directly south through a channel. From S_1, the navigator sights two buoys, A and B. The buoys are 0.24 miles apart, and the ship is 0.13 miles from each buoy. On its course the ship always stays the same distance from each buoy. The final sighting of the buoys is at S_2, which is 0.13 miles from each buoy.

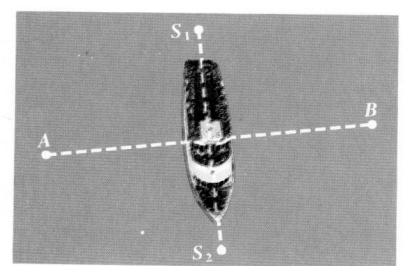

1. Relate the ship's course to the line of sight between the buoys. It appears to be the ⊥ bisector.
2. When does it appear that the ship was closest to the buoys? when its course intersected the line of sight between the buoys

Every triangle has three *medians* and three *angle bisectors*.

Definition A segment is a **median** of a triangle if and only if it extends from a vertex of the triangle to the midpoint of the opposite side.

A segment is an **angle bisector** of a triangle if and only if it bisects an angle of the triangle and has one endpoint on the opposite side.

Medians of △QPR

$\overline{PA}$
$\overline{QB}$
$\overline{RC}$

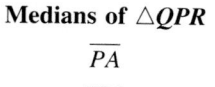

Angle Bisectors of △QPR

$\overline{PD}$
$\overline{QE}$
$\overline{RF}$

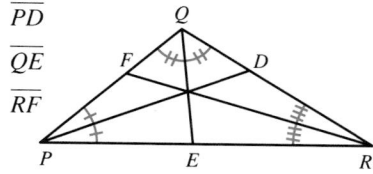

4.5 Medians, Altitudes, and Bisectors   **149**

Developing Mathematical Power

Keeping a Portfolio   Have students use their own words to compare the special segments of a triangle: median, altitude, and bisector. Have them describe the special characteristics of each, and if and when a segment can be classified as more than one of the three.

LESSON PLAN

Vocabulary
Altitude of a triangle
Angle bisector of a triangle
Distance from a point to a line
Equidistant
Median of a triangle

Materials/Manipulatives
Waxed paper for paper-folding
  activity
Teacher's Resource Book,
  Teaching Aid 4
Teaching Transparency 25

Technology
Computer
Computer Test Bank, pp.
  227–236
The Geometric Supposer:
  Triangles
Geometry Problems and
  Projects: Triangles, Worksheets
  T15–T17

LESSON FOCUS

Review
Ask students to characterize $\overline{MN}$ in each triangle.

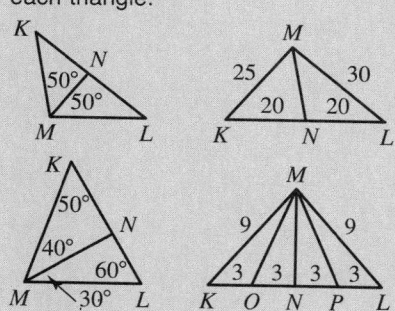

angle bisector; median; altitude; bisector of $\overline{KL}$ and $\overline{OP}$

See next page for Alternative Learning Styles.

149

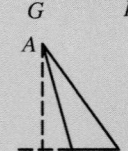
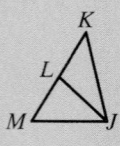
Every triangle also has three *altitudes*. However, while medians and angle
bisectors lie in the interior of the triangle, the position of the altitudes depends
on the type of triangle.

Definition   A segment is an **altitude** of a triangle if and only if it is
perpendicular from a vertex of the triangle to the line containing the opposite
side of the triangle.

Altitudes of Acute △*AMN*	Altitudes of Right △*CDE*	Altitudes of Obtuse △*EHI*
$\overline{AB}$ $\overline{MC}$ $\overline{ND}$	$\overline{CD}$ $\overline{ED}$ $\overline{DR}$	$\overline{EF}$ $\overline{HG}$ $\overline{IQ}$
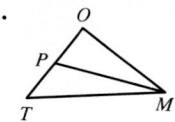	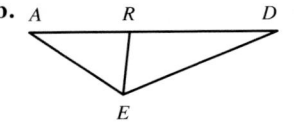	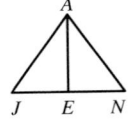

EXAMPLE   **Determine any conclusion(s) that follow.**

a.

Given: $\overline{MP}$ is a median
of △*TOM*.

Conclusions: ?

a. *P* is the midpoint
of $\overline{OT}$; $\overline{TP} ≅ \overline{PO}$.

b.

Given: $\overline{ER}$ bisects ∠*E*.

Conclusion: ?

b. ∠*AER* ≅ ∠*RED*

c.

Given: $\overline{AE}$ is the ⊥
bisector of $\overline{JN}$.

Conclusions: ?

c. $\overline{AE} ⊥ \overline{JN}$; $\overline{JE} ≅ \overline{EN}$;
△*AEJ* ≅ △*AEN*
by SAS.

Part c of the Example leads to the following theorem.

> **Theorem 4.2**   If a point lies on the perpendicular bisector of a segment,
> then the point is equidistant from the endpoints of the segment. Proved in Practice
> Exercise 17

Theorem 4.3 is the converse of Theorem 4.2.

Theorem 4.3 If a point is equidistant from the endpoints of a segment, then it lies on the perpendicular bisector of the segment.

Given: $\overline{MQ} \cong \overline{NQ}$

Prove: Q lies on the perpendicular bisector of $\overline{MN}$.

Plan: Draw the median from Q. By SSS, $\triangle MTQ \cong \triangle NTQ$, and $\angle MTQ \cong \angle NTQ$ by CPCTC. $\angle MTQ$ and $\angle NTQ$ are $\cong$ adjacent $\angle$s, so $\overline{QT} \perp \overline{MN}$.
Proved in Practice Exercise 20

Corollary If two points are each equidistant from the endpoints of a segment, then the line joining the points is the perpendicular bisector of the segment.
Proved in Practice Exercise 21

The **distance from a point to a line** is defined as the length of the perpendicular segment from the point to the line. Here the distance from P to q is PO.

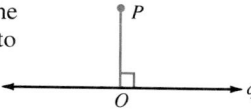

Theorem 4.4 If a point lies on the bisector of an angle, then the point is equidistant from the sides of the angle.

Given: $\overrightarrow{AR}$ bisects $\angle CAT$; P is on $\overrightarrow{AR}$.

Prove: $\overline{PQ} \cong \overline{PS}$

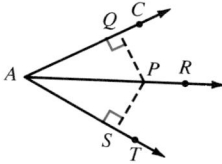

Plan: $\overline{PQ}$ and $\overline{PS}$ may be corresponding parts of congruent triangles. Thus, try to prove $\triangle PQA \cong \triangle PSA$.
Proved in Practice Exercise 22

Theorem 4.5 If a point is equidistant from the sides of an angle, then the point lies on the bisector of the angle. Proved in Practice Exercise 23

The pairs of converse theorems of this lesson lead to these *biconditionals*:

A point lies on the perpendicular bisector of a segment if and only if it is equidistant from the endpoints of the segment.
A point lies on the bisector of an angle if and only if it is equidistant from the sides of an angle.

4.5 Medians, Altitudes, and Bisectors   **151**

152

LESSON FOLLOW-UP

Discussion

Hand out waxed paper. Have each student cut out three triangles. If they fold the medians of one of the triangles, what happens? Ask them to use the remaining triangles to fold the angle bisectors and the altitudes. Have students compare results. *The segments intersect in one point.*

Critical Thinking

Generalization Have students generalize about the intersection of the medians, of the angle bisectors, and of the altitudes of a triangle.

Assignment Guide

See p. 126B for assignments.

Developing Mathematical Power

Manipulatives These exercises provide a cooperative learning opportunity. Students use manipulatives to discover properties of the medians of a triangle.

CLASS EXERCISES

True or false? If false, tell why.

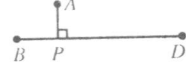

1. If $\overline{AP} \perp \overline{BD}$, then $\overline{BP} \cong \overline{PD}$. false;
2. If $\overline{PM}$ is a median of $\triangle PAT$, then $\overline{AM} \cong \overline{MT}$. true
3. If $\overline{PM}$ bisects $\angle P$ of $\triangle PAT$, then $\angle PMA \cong \angle PMT$. false; $\angle MPA \cong \angle MPT$
4. A median of a triangle bisects the side to which it is drawn. true
5. If $\overrightarrow{IT}$ is an altitude of $\triangle HIP$, then $\overline{IT}$ bisects $\angle I$. false;

6. If $\triangle PQR$ is equilateral, its medians are congruent. true
7. If $\triangle ABC$ is a right triangle with right angle B, $\overline{CB}$ is an altitude. true
8. If $\overline{TU}$ is the perpendicular bisector of $\overline{VW}$, $\overline{UV} \cong \overline{UW}$. true
9. If $\overrightarrow{OC}$ bisects $\angle AOB$, then $\angle AOC \cong \angle COB$. true
10. If $\overrightarrow{OC}$ bisects $\angle AOB$, then $\overline{CA} \perp \overline{OA}$. false;

PRACTICE EXERCISES    Use technology where appropriate.

Determine any conclusion(s) that follow.

A 1. **Given:** $\overleftrightarrow{PQ}$ is the $\perp$ bisector of $\overline{RS}$. $\overline{OR} \cong \overline{OS}$;
   Conclusion(s): ___?___
   $\overline{PR} \cong \overline{PS}$; $\overline{QR} \cong \overline{QS}$; $\angle sROP$, ROQ, SOP, and QOS are rt. $\angle$s.

2. **Given:** $\overline{AE}$ is a median of $\triangle JAN$.
   Conclusion(s): ___?___
   E is the midpt. of $\overline{JN}$; $\overline{JE} \cong \overline{NE}$

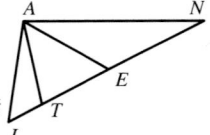

Complete each statement in as many ways as possible.

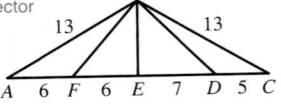

3. $\overline{BF}$ is ___?___ of $\triangle ABE$. median
4. $\overline{BE}$ is ___?___ of $\triangle ABC$. median; altitutde; $\perp$ bisector; $\angle$ bisector
5. $\overline{BE}$ is ___?___ of $\triangle FBC$. altitude
6. $\overline{BE}$ is ___?___ of $\triangle FBD$. altitude

In Exercises 7 and 8, complete the plan.

7. **Given:** $l_1 \perp l_2$; $\angle BSQ \cong \angle ASQ$
   Prove: $\overline{AQ} \cong \overline{BQ}$
   Plan: Show $\triangle \underset{AQS}{?} \cong \triangle \underset{BQS}{?}$ by $\underset{ASA}{?}$.
   Then $\overline{AQ} \cong \overline{BQ}$ by ___?___. CPCTC

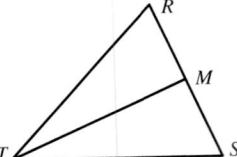

8. **Given:** $\triangle RST$ with median $\overline{TM}$; $\overline{TS} \cong \overline{TR}$
   Prove: $\angle S \cong \angle R$
   Plan: Show $\triangle \underset{RMT}{?} \cong \triangle \underset{SMT}{?}$ by $\underset{SSS}{?}$.
   Then $\angle S \cong \angle R$ by ___?___. CPCTC

Determine the conclusion(s) that follow.

9. $\overline{SP}$ is an altitude of $\triangle RST$. $\overline{SP} \perp \overline{RT}$

10. $\overline{RT}$ is the $\perp$ bisector of $\overline{SQ}$.
    $\overline{SP} \cong \overline{PQ}; \overline{RT} \perp \overline{SQ}$

11. $\overline{TP}$ is a median of $\triangle STQ$. $\overline{SP} \cong \overline{PQ}$

12. $\overline{RP}$ is the bisector of $\angle SRQ$.
    $\angle SRP \cong \angle PRQ$

13. $\overline{TP}$ is an altitude of $\triangle STQ$. $\overline{TP} \perp \overline{SQ}$

14. $\overline{PR}$ is a median of $\triangle RSQ$. $\overline{SP} \cong \overline{PQ}$

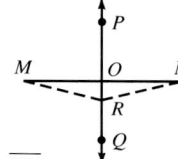

15. **Given:** $\triangle RST$ with median $\overline{TM}$; $\overline{TS} \cong \overline{TR}$

    Prove: $\angle S \cong \angle R$. See Additional Answers, p. 702.

16. **Given:** $\overline{TM}$ bisects $\angle RTS$: $\angle R \cong \angle S$

    Prove: $\overline{TM}$ is an altitude of $\triangle RTS$.

17. Complete this proof of Theorem 4.2.

    Given: $\overleftrightarrow{PQ}$ is the perpendicular bisector
    of $\overline{MN}$; R is any point on $\overleftrightarrow{PQ}$.

    Prove: $\overline{RM} \cong \overline{RN}$

    Plan: Prove $\triangle ORM \cong \triangle ORN$. Thus, $\overline{RM} \cong \overline{RN}$.

For Exercises 18 and 19, draw a figure, state the Given, Prove, and Plan.
See Additional Answers, p. 702.

18. If the bisector of one angle of a triangle is perpendicular to the opposite side, the triangle is isosceles.

19. Altitudes drawn to the congruent sides of an isosceles triangle are congruent.

20. Supply the missing statements and reasons in this proof for Theorem 4.3.

Statements	Reasons
1. $\underline{?}$ $\overline{MQ} \cong \overline{NQ}$	1. Given
2. Draw median $\overline{QT}$ of $\triangle MQN$.	2. $\underline{?}$ Two points determine one line.
3. $\underline{?}$ T is the midpt. of $\overline{MN}$.	3. Definition of a median
4. $\overline{MT} \cong \underline{?}$ $\overline{NT}$	4. $\underline{?}$ Def. of midpt.
5. $\underline{?}$ $\overline{TQ} \cong \overline{TQ}$	5. Reflexive property
6. $\underline{?}$ $\triangle MTQ \cong \triangle NTQ$	6. SSS Postulate
7. $\angle MTQ \cong \underline{?}$ $\angle NTQ$	7. $\underline{?}$ CPCTC
8. $\overline{QT} \underline{?} \overline{MN} \perp$	8. $\underline{?}$ If two lines intersect to form $\cong$ adj. $\angle$s, then the lines are $\perp$.
9. $\underline{?}$ Q lies on $\perp$ bisector of $\overline{MN}$.	9. $\underline{?}$ Def. of $\perp$ bisector

Prove. See Additional Answers, p. 702.

21. Corollary (Th. 4.3)   22. Theorem 4.4   23. Theorem 4.5

153

Construction

Show students a line *l* and a point *P* not on the line. Challenge them to describe a way to construct the line perpendicular to the given line through the given point.

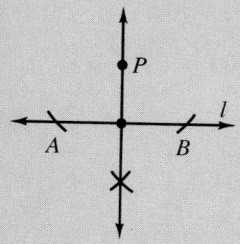

Using a compass opening greater than the distance from *P* to *l*, make arcs with *P* as center. Let *A* and *B* be the points where the arcs intersect *l*. Construct $\perp$ bis. of $\overline{AB}$.

Lesson Quiz

1. Draw a figure, state the Given, Prove, and Plan: If two angles of a triangle are congruent, then the bisectors of those angles are congruent.

2. **Given:** $\overline{LM} \cong \overline{LN}$;
   $\angle MLK \cong \angle NLK$

   Prove: $\overline{LK}$ is a median of $\triangle MNL$.

1. **Given:** $\triangle ABC$ with
   $\angle BAC \cong \angle BCA$; $\overline{AD}$
   and $\overline{CE}$ are $\angle$ bis.
   Prove: $\overline{CE} \cong \overline{AD}$

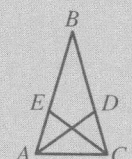

Plan: Since $\overline{AD}$ and $\overline{CE}$ are $\angle$ bis., it follows that $\angle ECA \cong \angle DAC$; $\overline{AC} \cong \overline{CA}$, so $\triangle EAC \cong \triangle DCA$ by ASA. $\overline{AD} \cong \overline{CE}$ by CPCTC.

2. **Proof:**

Statements	Reasons
1. $\overline{LM} \cong \overline{LN}$; $\angle MLK \cong \angle NLK$	1. Given
2. $\overline{LK} \cong \overline{LK}$	2. Refl. prop.
3. $\triangle MLK \cong \triangle NLK$	3. SAS
4. $\overline{MK} \cong \overline{NK}$	4. CPCTC
5. K is the midpt. of $\overline{MN}$.	5. Def. of midpt.
6. $\overline{LK}$ is median of $\triangle MNL$.	6. Def. of median

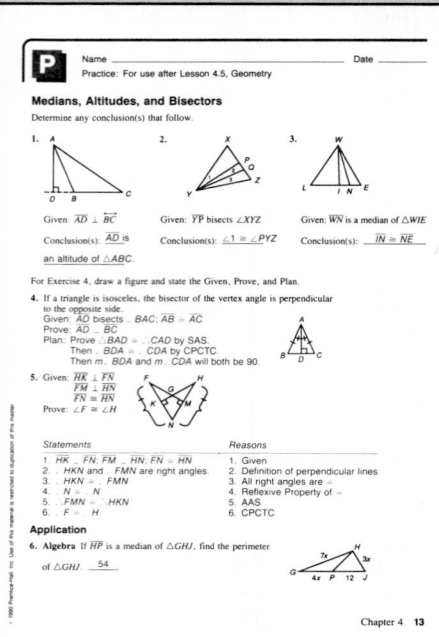

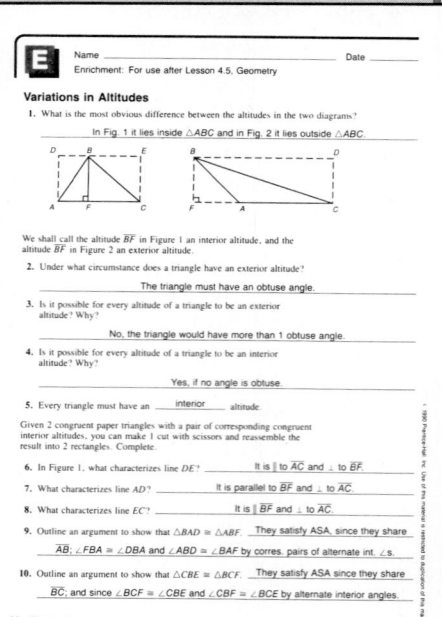

See Additional Answers, p. 702.

C **24. Given:** $\angle 1 \cong \angle 2$; $\overline{OM}$ is an altitude of $\triangle JOH$; $\overline{NP}$ is an altitude of $\triangle HNJ$; $\overline{JM} \cong \overline{HP}$.

Prove: $\overline{OM} \cong \overline{NP}$

25. Given: $\overline{OH} \parallel \overline{JN}$; $\overline{OM}$ is an altitude of $\triangle JOH$; $\overline{NP}$ is an altitude of $\triangle HNJ$; $\overline{OM} \cong \overline{NP}$

Prove: $\overline{OJ} \cong \overline{NH}$

Applications   See Solutions Manual.

26. Technology Use Logo to draw several types of triangles and their angle bisectors. What is the difference between the two procedures?

27. Technology Use Logo to create a starburst with rays of random lengths.

Developing Mathematical Power

Manipulatives Cut out an acute scalene triangle and make a fold along each median.

28. Describe the intersection of the medians.
a point in the interior of the △

29. The intersection separates each median into two segments. Measure each pair of segments and describe the pattern. Each median is separated into 2 segments whose lengths are in the ratio 2:1. The longer segment is from the vertex to the intersection point.

CONSTRUCTION

Using only a compass and a straightedge, you can construct a line that bisects a given segment and is perpendicular to that segment.

Given: $\overline{AB}$ *Construct:* $\overleftrightarrow{CD}$ that bisects and is perpendicular to $\overline{AB}$.

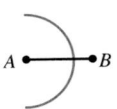 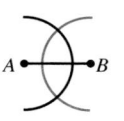 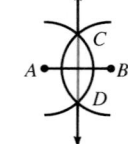

1. *Using a compass opening greater than $\frac{1}{2}AB$, make an arc with point A as the center.*

2. *Using the same opening, make an arc with point B as the center. Intersect the arcs above and below $\overline{AB}$.*

3. *Label the intersection points of the arcs C and D. Draw $\overleftrightarrow{CD}$. $\overleftrightarrow{CD}$ bisects $\overline{AB}$. $CD \perp \overline{AB}$.*

EXERCISE *Given:* $\overline{XY}$ X •———• Y *Construct:* $\overleftrightarrow{RS}$ that bisects and is perpendicular to $\overline{XY}$ at T. Compare $\overline{XT}$ and $\overline{YT}$. Measure the angles at T. Check students' constructions.

Strategy: Recognize Underdetermined and Overdetermined Figures

Lines, segments, and points are often drawn so that they meet certain requirements, or conditions. When one and only one figure can be drawn that meets stated conditions, the figure is said to be *determined* by those conditions. For example, claiming that B is the midpoint of $\overline{AC}$ puts a condition on B. Similarly, drawing a line so that it passes through a particular point or drawing a segment so that it bisects an angle places conditions on the line or segment.

Some common errors in using auxiliary figures are:
1. To *overdetermine* the figure (put too many conditions on it)

2. To *underdetermine* the figure (put too few conditions on it) so that it is not uniquely determined

3. To determine a figure such that it *contradicts* a known fact

EXAMPLE 1   Do the following conditions determine, overdetermine, or underdetermine the auxiliary figure?

In $\triangle XYZ$, draw an auxiliary segment from Y through A on $\overline{XZ}$ such that two congruent right triangles are formed.

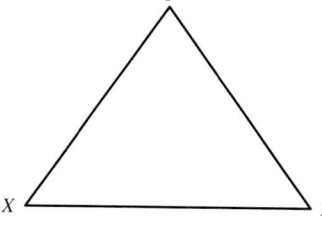

Understand the Problem

What is given?
A triangle with vertices X, Y, and Z.

What are you asked to find?
Is $\overline{YA}$ determined, overdetermined, or underdetermined by the following conditions?

1. Point A is on $\overline{XZ}$.

2. $\angle XAY$ and $\angle ZAY$ are right angles.

3. $\triangle XAY \cong \triangle ZAY$

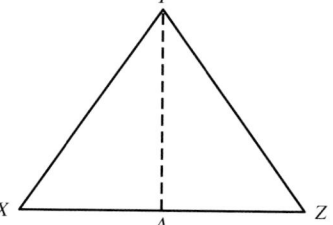

4.6 Strategy: Recognize Overdetermined and Underdetermined Figures   **155**

Students need to understand that they must be able to justify any auxiliary line that they introduce in a proof. It is important that the auxiliary line be described in terms of the minimal conditions necessary to determine it. For example, in an isosceles triangle, the bisector of the angle included by the congruent sides is also the perpendicular bisector of the opposite side. The auxiliary segment should be described in terms of one condition. The other conditions that follow would need to be *proven*.

CHALKBOARD EXAMPLES

For Examples 1 and 2, do the following conditions determine, overdetermine, or underdetermine the auxiliary figure?

- **For Example 1**

  Through point P, construct the perpendicular bisector of $\overline{AB}$. There is one and only one $\perp$ to $\overline{AB}$ through P. $\overline{AB}$ has one and only one $\perp$ bis. These lines may or may not coincide. (They will coincide only if the $\perp$ through P goes through the midpt. of $\overline{AB}$.) Thus, the conditions *overdetermine* the figure.

- **For Example 2**

  Draw the points that are equidistant from the sides of $\angle PQR$.

  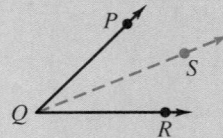

  Since an $\angle$ has a unique bis., and since a pt. is on the bis. iff it is equidistant from the sides of the $\angle$, the conditions *determine* $\angle$ bis. $\overrightarrow{QS}$.

☐ **Plan Your Approach** — **Decide how definitions, postulates, and theorems will affect the choice of the auxiliary segment.**
A must lie on $\overline{XZ}$; thus, A is any point between X and Z.

The segments that meet to form right angles $\angle XAY$ and $\angle ZAY$ must be perpendicular.

Corresponding parts of the congruent triangles $\triangle XAY$ and $\triangle ZAY$ must be congruent.

☐ **Implement the Plan** — **Draw the appropriate auxiliary segment.**
By satisfying the given conditions, this figure is obtained.

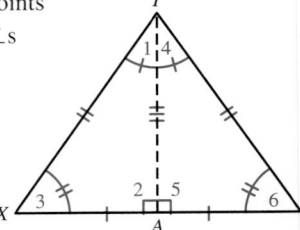

$XA + AZ = XZ$	Betweenness of points
$\overline{YA} \perp \overline{XZ}$	$\perp$ lines form rt. $\angle$s
$\overline{XA} \cong \overline{ZA}$; $\angle 1 \cong \angle 4$	CPCTC
$\overline{XY} \cong \overline{ZY}$; $\angle 2 \cong \angle 5$	
$\overline{YA} \cong \overline{YA}$; $\angle 3 \cong \angle 6$	

☐ **Interpret the Results** — **Check the figure.**
$\overline{YA}$ bisects $\angle Y$, is the *median* from vertex Y and is an *altitude* to $\overline{XZ}$.

These conditions necessitate that $\triangle XYZ$ is an isosceles triangle. $\triangle XYZ$ was *not given* as an isosceles triangle; therefore, the given conditions *overdetermined* $\overline{YA}$.

Note in Example 1 that if $\triangle XYZ$ only had to be separated into *right* triangles, then $\overline{YA}$ could have been determined.

Problem Solving Reminders

- It is often necessary to solve a problem by using an auxiliary figure.
- In determining an auxiliary figure be careful not to contradict a known fact or to assume information that is not given.
- Do not place too many (overdetermine) or too few (underdetermine) conditions on a figure.

In the next example, you are given conditions for drawing an angle. In this case, the drawing itself is the auxiliary figure.

EXAMPLE 2   Do the following conditions determine, overdetermine, or underdetermine a figure?

Draw ∠AOB having vertex O and classify it.

☐ **Understand the Problem**   In a half-plane, an angle is formed by the union of two noncollinear rays with a common endpoint and can be classified as acute, obtuse, or right.

☐ **Plan Your Approach**   **Draw an angle with vertex O.**
Use the definitions of acute, obtuse, and right angles to classify ∠AOB.

☐ **Implement the Plan**   **From vertex O draw $\overrightarrow{OA}$ and $\overrightarrow{OB}$ to form ∠AOB.**
Here are three possibilities that satisfy the given condition.

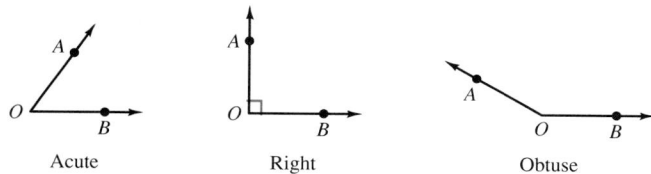

Acute   Right   Obtuse

☐ **Interpret the Results**   Since each angle satisfies the given condition, ∠AOB is not uniquely determined. Thus, the angle is *underdetermined*.

CLASS EXERCISES

Is each auxiliary figure determined, overdetermined, or underdetermined by the given conditions?

1. In △ABC draw $\overline{BD}$ so that ∠ABD ≅ ∠CBD and D is the midpoint of $\overline{AC}$.
   overdetermined; not given that $\overline{AB} \cong \overline{BC}$

2. In right triangle DEF with right angle D, draw $\overline{DA}$ so that A is between E and F and $\overline{DA} \perp \overline{EF}$. determined

3. In △BQE draw point F so that F is in the interior of the triangle.
   underdetermined; infinitely many possibilities

PRACTICE EXERCISES

Is each auxiliary figure determined, overdetermined, or underdetermined?

1. In △AEI draw point R on $\overleftrightarrow{EI}$ so that $\overline{AR} \perp \overleftrightarrow{EI}$. determined

2. In △CRX draw $\overline{XA}$ so that A is between C and R, and ∠CAX and ∠XAR form a linear pair. underdetermined; A could be any pt. between C and R

- Students have difficulty distinguishing between underdetermined and overdetermined figures. Explain that too few conditions underdetermine a figure, while too many conditions overdetermine a figure.
- See *Teacher's Resource Book* for additional remediation.

LESSON FOLLOW-UP

Assignment Guide
See p. 126B for assignments.

Project
This project provides excellent practice in comparing underdetermined and overdetermined figures, provided that descriptions progress from simple to complex.

Lesson Quiz
Do the following conditions determine, overdetermine, or underdetermine the auxiliary figure?

1. Draw the line through point P that is parallel to $\overleftrightarrow{MN}$, where P is between M and N.
2. For △ABC, draw altitude $\overline{BD}$.
3. Draw the right angle having $\overrightarrow{OC}$ as a side.

1. Overdetermined—there is no such figure.
2. Determined
3. Underdetermined—there are two such angles.

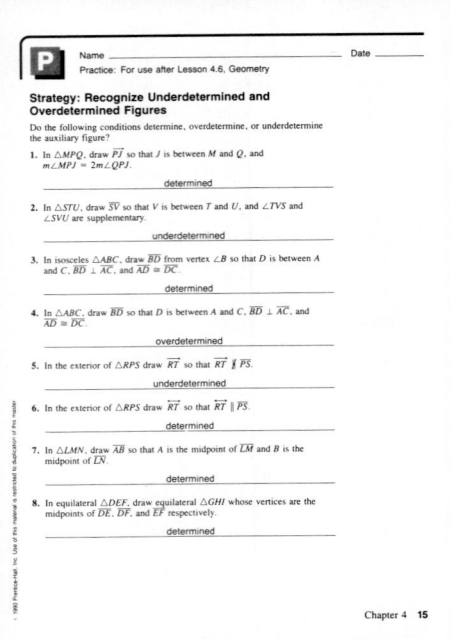

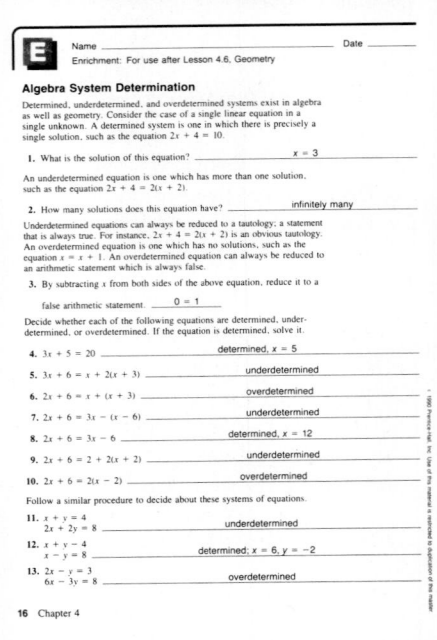

3. Draw a line through points M and N. determined

4. Find the midpoint of $\overline{RT}$. determined

5. In $\triangle ABC$, draw median $\overline{BD}$. determined

6. Draw a line through point P. underdetermined; infinitely many such lines

7. In $\triangle PQR$, draw the bisector of $\angle P$ that bisects $\overline{QR}$. overdetermined; unless $\triangle PQR$ is isos.

8. Draw a line perpendicular to $\overline{EF}$. underdetermined; infinitely many such lines unless restricted to one plane

9. In $\triangle LEB$, extend $\overline{EB}$ to point R so that E is a between point and $\angle EBL \cong \angle RBL$. underdetermined; infinitely many such pts.

10. In $\triangle LEB$, draw $\overrightarrow{ER}$ so that R is in the exterior of the triangle and $\angle LER$ is acute. underdetermined; infinitely many such rays

11. In $\triangle LEB$, draw $\overrightarrow{ER}$ so that R is in the exterior of the triangle and $\angle LER$ is obtuse. underdetermined; infinitely many such rays

12. On $\overleftrightarrow{AT}$, draw $\overleftrightarrow{RT}$ so that $\overleftrightarrow{RT} \perp \overleftrightarrow{AT}$. determined

13. In $\triangle RST$, draw $\overrightarrow{TU}$ so that $\overrightarrow{TS}$ bisects $\angle RTU$. determined

B 14. In $\triangle RST$, draw $\overrightarrow{TU}$ so that $m\angle STU = m\angle RST + m\angle SRT$. underdetermined; 2 poss. such rays.

15. In equilateral triangle EQT, draw $\overline{EA}$ so that A is on $\overline{QT}$ and $\overline{EA} \perp \overline{QT}$, and draw $\overline{EB}$ so that B is on $\overline{QT}$ and $\overline{QB} \cong \overline{TB}$. A and B are each determined. However, they are the same point and $\overline{EA}$ and $\overline{EB}$ are the same segment.

C 16. In $\triangle QXR$, draw interior point E so that $\overrightarrow{QE}$ bisects $\angle Q$, $\overrightarrow{XE}$ bisects $\angle X$ and $\overrightarrow{RE}$ bisects $\angle R$. determined

17. In $\triangle QXR$, draw interior point L so that $\overline{QL} \perp \overline{XR}$, $\overline{RL} \perp \overline{QX}$ and $\overline{XL} \perp \overline{QR}$. overdetermined; not given that $\triangle QXR$ is acute

PROJECT

Most problems in geometry books have an accompanying drawing to help make the relationships between geometric figures clear. When only a word description for a geometric figure is given, it is helpful to make your own drawing.

Write a description of a geometric figure. Ask the rest of the class to draw the figure. Did your description *determine* the figure?

4.7 Proving Right Triangles Congruent

Objectives: To identify right triangles and their parts
To prove and apply the LL, HL, LA, and HA Theorems, which show congruence for right triangles

There are four special theorems that can be used to prove that pairs of right triangles are congruent.

Investigation—*Visualizing the Concept*

When this envelope was sealed, three triangular regions were formed. Study the figure.

1. Classify the triangles. △ *DAE* and *CBE* are rt △; △*DEC* is isosceles.
2. Which triangles appear congruent? △*DAE* and △*CBE*
3. Is there a method that can be used to verify that the triangles are congruent? None of the shortcuts apply. However, if one △ is traced and then superimposed on the other, the congruence can be verified.

In a right triangle, the nonright angles must be acute. Why? The side of a right triangle that is opposite the right angle is the **hypotenuse.** The sides that are opposite the acute angles are **legs.** The sum of meas. of int. ∠s = 180. Since the rt. ∠ measures 90, the other two ∠s have a sum measure of 90.

Since the right angles of right triangles are always congruent, the next four theorems each require finding only *two* other congruent corresponding parts. To prove the first three right triangle theorems, show that the given information correlates with one of the general methods of proving triangles congruent.

Theorem 4.6   LA Theorem   If a leg and an acute angle of one right triangle are congruent to the corresponding parts of another right triangle, then the triangles are congruent. Proved in Class Exercise 6

Theorem 4.7   HA Theorem   If the hypotenuse and an acute angle of one right triangle are congruent to the corresponding parts of another right triangle, then the triangles are congruent. Proved in Practice Exercise 23

Theorem 4.8   LL Theorem   If the two legs of one right triangle are congruent to the two legs of another right triangle, then the triangles are congruent. Proved in Practice Exercise 9

Since there is *no* SSA method, the proof of Theorem 4.9 is more involved.

4.7 Proving Right Triangles Congruent   **159**

Developing Mathematical Power

Keeping a Portfolio   Have students complete the Reading and Writing in Geometry activity, p. 4, in the *Teacher's Resource Book.* Instruct them to illustrate each of the terms and label them appropriately.

LESSON PLAN

Vocabulary
Hypotenuse of a right triangle
Legs of a right triangle
Right triangle

Materials/Manipulatives
Teacher's Resource Book,
Teaching Aid 4
Transparency 5
Teaching Transparency 27

Technology
Computer Test Bank, pp.
238–247

LESSON FOCUS

Review

- Have students tell which triangles are congruent and why.
  first, third, fourth (SAS)

  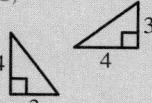

- The Algebra Review, Exercises 29–40, involves inequalities.
- The Chapter Summary and Review, pp. 166–167, gives vocabulary and concepts and review exercises by lesson.
- The end of the chapter features a Cumulative Review on pp. 170–172.

Alternative Learning Styles

Cutting out the triangles formed by a sealed envelope as in the Investigation can help students identify right triangles. The Investigation prepares students for a more formal development of HL, which is not related to any general congruence method.

Critical Thinking

Generalization   Ask students to generalize about circumstances under which right triangles are congruent.

159

TEACHING SUGGESTIONS

- Emphasize that LL, HL, LA, and HA are applied only to right triangles.
- Insist that students include as part of their proofs statements such as "△*ABC* is a right triangle" when they use any of the right triangle congruence theorems.
- The proof of the HL Theorem is a good example of a complicated proof that requires many intermediate goals, so you may want to do Exercise 16 as a class.

CHALKBOARD EXAMPLES

- **For Example 1**

  What right triangle theorem verifies the triangle congruency?

  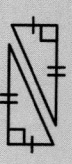

  HA   HL   LL

- **For Example 2**

  Use the figure and given information to complete each question.

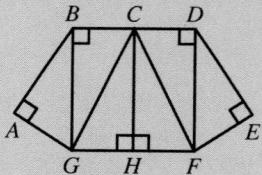

  a. Given: $\overline{BG} \cong \overline{DF}$; ∠*BGC* ≅ ∠*DFC*

  Conclusion: △ _?_ ≅ △ _?_
                 BGC   *DFC*

  Reason: _?_   LA

  b. Given: $\overline{BG} \cong \overline{DF}$; ∠*BGA* ≅ ∠*DFE*

  Conclusion: △ _?_ ≅ △ _?_
                 BGA   *DFE*

  Reason: _?_   HA

- **c. Given:** $\overline{GC} \cong \overline{FC}$

  Conclusion: △ _?_ ≅ △ _?_
                 GCH   *FCH*

  Reason: _?_   HL

Theorem 4.9   HL Theorem   If the hypotenuse and a leg of one right triangle are congruent to the corresponding parts of another right triangle, then the triangles are congruent.

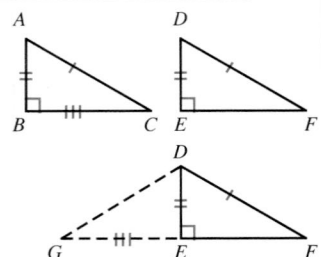

Given: Right △s *ABC* and *DEF*; $\overline{AC} \cong \overline{DF}$; $\overline{AB} \cong \overline{DE}$

Prove: △*ABC* ≅ △*DEF*

Plan: Extend $\overrightarrow{FE}$ so that $\overline{EG} \cong \overline{BC}$. Prove △*ABC* ≅ △*DEG*. Use CPCTC and the fact that $\overline{DE}$ is a perpendicular bisector to prove △*ABC* ≅ △*DEF*.
      Proved in Practice Exercise 16

EXAMPLE 1   **Which right triangle theorem verifies the triangle congruence?**

a. 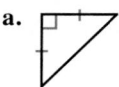   b.   c.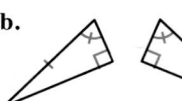

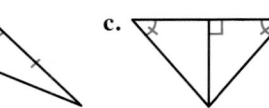

     a. LL Theorem   **b. HA Theorem**   **c. LA Theorem**

EXAMPLE 2   **Complete and verify each conclusion.**

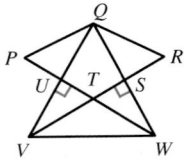

     a. Given: $\overline{VU} \cong \overline{WS}$;   **b. Given:** $\overline{PQ} \cong \overline{RQ}$;
                $\overline{VT} \cong \overline{WT}$ ∠*PQU* ≅ ∠*RQS*

        Conclusion: △ _?_ ≅ △ _?_   **Conclusion:** △ _?_ ≅ △ _?_

     a. △*VTU* ≅ △*WTS* **by HL**   **b.** △*PQU* ≅ △*RQS* **by HA**

These four methods are *only* used to prove that *right* triangles are congruent:
LA Theorem   (**L**eg-**A**cute Angle)   HA Theorem   (**H**ypotenuse-**A**cute Angle)
LL Theorem   (**L**eg-**L**eg)   HL Theorem   (**H**ypotenuse-**L**eg)

CLASS EXERCISES

If possible, verify that △*TAR* ≅ △*TOH*.

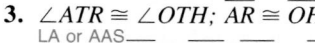

1. $\overline{RA} \cong \overline{HO}$; $\overline{TA} \cong \overline{TO}$ HL   2. ∠*R* ≅ ∠*H*; $\overline{RT} \cong \overline{HT}$
                                         not enough information
3. ∠*ATR* ≅ ∠*OTH*; $\overline{AR} \cong \overline{OH}$ 4. $\overline{TA} \cong \overline{TO}$; ∠*TAR* ≅ ∠*TOH*
   LA or AAS   HA or AAS
5. **Given:** $\overline{YA} \perp \overline{MR}$; $\overline{MT} \perp \overline{YR}$; $\overline{SM} \cong \overline{SY}$

     Prove: △*SAM* ≅ △*STY* See Additional Answers, p. 702.

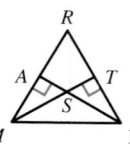

6. Using the following information, complete the proof of Theorem 4.6: △*YAM* and △*MTY* are rt. △s; $\overline{AM} \cong \overline{TY}$; ∠*AYM* ≅ ∠*TMY*.

PRACTICE EXERCISES Use technology where appropriate.

If there is enough information, state and verify the triangle congruence.

A

1.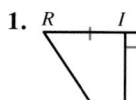

$\triangle RIE \cong \triangle TIE$
by LL or SAS

2.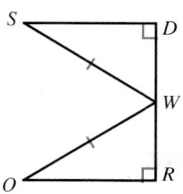

not enough
information

3.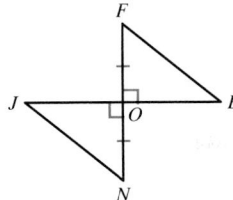

not enough
information

4.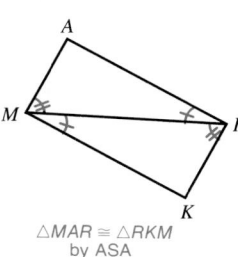

$\triangle MAR \cong \triangle RKM$
by ASA

5.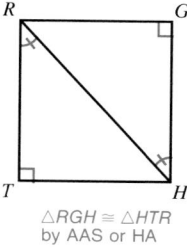

$\triangle RGH \cong \triangle HTR$
by AAS or HA

6.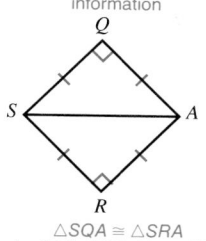

$\triangle SQA \cong \triangle SRA$
by SAS, SSS, LL, or HL

7. In $\triangle RET$ above, if $RI = 9x$ and $IT = x + 4$, find RT. 9

8. In $\triangle RET$ above, if $m\angle R = 10x$ and $m\angle T = 30x - 80$, find $m\angle REI$. 50

9. Complete this proof of Theorem 4.8.
   Given: $\triangle TAG$ and $\triangle HOP$ are right
   triangles; $\overline{AG} \cong \overline{OP}$; $\overline{TA} \cong \overline{HO}$
   Prove: $\triangle TAG \cong \triangle HOP$
   See Additional Answers, p. 702.

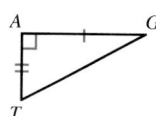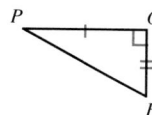

10. In $\triangle TAG$ above, if $m\angle T = x$, and $m\angle G = 2x - 30$, then $x = \underline{\ ?\ }$. 40

11. In $\triangle TAG$ above, if $m\angle T = 2m\angle G$, find $m\angle T$ and $m\angle G$.
   $m\angle T = 60$, $m\angle G = 30$

Find the indicated value, if possible.

12. If $AB = 3x$ and $AC = 2x + 5$, then $x = \underline{\ ?\ }$. 5

13. If $m\angle R = 4x - 7$ and $m\angle CAT = 2x + 31$,
   then $x = \underline{\ ?\ }$. 19

14. If $AT = 4x$ and $MC = 3x + 8$,
   then $x = \underline{\ ?\ }$. not enough information

15. If $m\angle BAT = 10x + 2$ and $m\angle RCM = 12x$,
   then $x = \underline{\ ?\ }$. 4

16. Complete the proof of the Hypotenuse-Leg Theorem (Theorem 4.9). See
   Additional Answers, p. 702.

Common Error

• Some students will attempt to apply the right triangle congruence theorems to nonright triangles. Emphasize the phrase "in a right triangle" in order to eliminate this error.

• See *Teacher's Resource Book* for additional remediation.

LESSON FOLLOW-UP

Discussion

Draw these right triangles on the board. Give students one congruence at a time (for example, $\overline{BC} \cong \overline{EF}$) and ask what additional congruence would enable them to prove the triangles congruent. Given $\overline{BC} \cong \overline{EF}$, either $\overline{CA} \cong \overline{FD}$ (HL), $\overline{BA} \cong \overline{ED}$ (HL), $\angle C \cong \angle F$ (HA), or $\angle B \cong \angle E$ (HA).

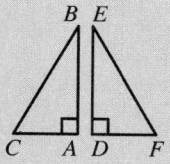

Critical Thinking

Making Decisions Have students analyze given information and make decisions about what additional information is needed to verify congruence.

Assignment Guide

See p. 126B for assignments.

Test Yourself

See *Teacher's Resource Book, Tests,* pp. 35–36.

Lesson Quiz

If there is enough information to conclude that the triangles are congruent, verify the congruence.

1.
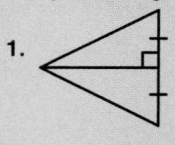

2.
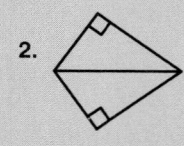

LL (or SAS)   not enough information

3.
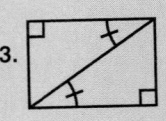

4.
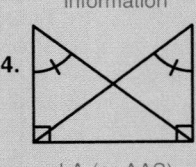

HA (or AAS)   LA (or AAS)

Enrichment

Describe as many plans for proof as you can that involve drawing an auxiliary line.

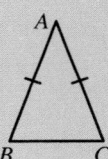

Given: $\overline{AB} \cong \overline{AC}$
Prove: $\angle B \cong \angle C$

For each plan, it follows that $\angle B \cong \angle C$ by CPCTC.

1. Draw median $\overline{AM}$. Show $\triangle ABM \cong \triangle ACM$ by SSS.

2. Draw angle bisector $\overline{AD}$, with D on $\overline{BC}$. Show $\triangle ABD \cong \triangle ACD$ by SAS.

3. Draw altitude $\overline{AE}$. Show $\triangle ABE \cong \triangle ACE$ by HL.

B **17. Given:** $\overline{BE} \perp \overline{AC}$; $\angle A \cong \angle C$
Prove: $\angle ABE \cong \angle CBE$

18. Given: $\overline{BE} \perp \overline{AC}$; $\overline{AE} \cong \overline{CE}$
Prove: $\triangle ABC$ is isosceles.

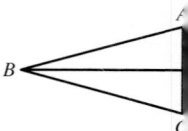

B **19. Given:** $\overline{YX} \cong \overline{YZ}$; $\overline{TY} \perp \overline{YX}$; $\overline{WY} \perp \overline{YZ}$; Y is on the $\perp$ bisector of $\overline{TW}$
Prove: $\angle X \cong \angle Z$

20. Given: $\triangle XYT$ and $\triangle ZYW$ are rt. $\triangle s$; $\angle X \cong \angle Z$; $\overline{XY} \cong \overline{ZY}$
Prove: $\angle YTW \cong \angle YWT$

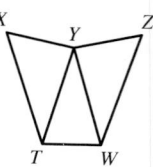

21. Given: $\overline{DT} \cong \overline{OA}$; $\overline{TO} \cong \overline{AD}$; $\overline{DF}$ is an altitude of $\triangle DTO$ and $\overline{OE}$ is an altitude of $\triangle ODA$.
Prove: $\overline{OE} \cong \overline{DF}$

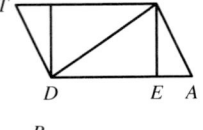

22. Given: $\overline{RH} \parallel \overline{NO}$; $\overline{RH} \cong \overline{ON}$; $\overline{RD} \perp \overline{NH}$; $\overline{OA} \perp \overline{NH}$
Prove: $\overline{ND} \cong \overline{HA}$

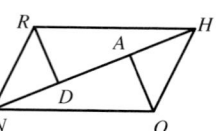

C **23.** Prove the Hypotenuse-Acute Angle Theorem (Theorem 4.7).

24. Prove that the acute angles of an isosceles right triangle are congruent.

25. Prove: If two right triangles are congruent, then altitudes from the right angles are congruent.

Applications

26. Construction A utility pole is supported by two guy wires of equal length. How do you know that the points where the wires are fastened to the ground are the same distance from the base of the pole? The $\triangle s$ formed are $\cong$ by HL. The distances are the same by CPCTC.

27. Technology Use Logo to generate congruent right triangles at different orientations. Do all of your triangles appear to be congruent? Explain. Answers may vary. See Solutions Manual.

28. Geometry A square is folded to form two congruent right triangles. What type of right triangles are they? Justify their congruence. isos.; LL or HL

162 Chapter 4 Congruent Triangles

Algebra Review

Fill in the blank with <, >, or = to make the statement true.

29. $120 \underline{\;?\;} 210$ $<$

30. $560 \underline{\;?\;} 560$ $=$

31. $68 + 42 \underline{\;?\;} 100$ $>$

32. $80 + 30 \underline{\;?\;} 30 - 80$ $>$

33. $2\sqrt{9} \underline{\;?\;} 3\sqrt{4}$ $=$

34. $\sqrt{16} + \sqrt{25} \underline{\;?\;} \sqrt{41}$ $>$

Solve.

35. $x + 12 < 34$ $x < 22$

36. $5x \le 120$ $x \le 24$

37. $4x - 11 > 25$ $x > 9$

For what value of x will each statement be true?

38. $2x < x + 1$
{all real numbers less than 1}

39. $2x > x + 1$
{all real numbers greater than 1}

40. $2x = x + 1$ 1

TEST YOURSELF

What conclusion follows from the given information?

1.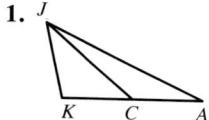

Given: $\overline{JC}$ is a median of $\triangle JAK$.

Conclusion: $\underline{\;?\;}$
C is midpt. of $\overline{KA}$.

2.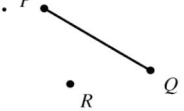

Given: R is equidistant from P and Q.

Conclusion: $\underline{\;?\;}$
R lies on ⊥ bisector of $\overline{PQ}$.

3. 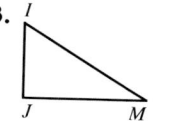 4.5

Given: $\overline{IJ}$ is an altitude of $\triangle JIM$.

Conclusion: $\underline{\;?\;}$ $\overline{IJ} \perp \overline{JM}$
$\triangle JIM$ is a rt. $\triangle$.

4. Given: C is equidistant from $\overrightarrow{OA}$ and $\overrightarrow{OB}$.

Conclusion: $\underline{\;?\;}$ $\overrightarrow{OC}$ bisects $\angle AOB$.

4.4–4.6

5. Given: $\overline{AE} \cong \overline{DC}$; $\overline{EC} \perp \overline{CD}$; $\overline{CE} \perp \overline{AE}$

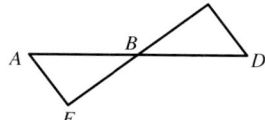

Prove: $\angle A \cong \angle D$
See Additional Answers, p. 702.

If there is enough information to conclude that the given triangles are congruent, verify the congruence. 4.7

6.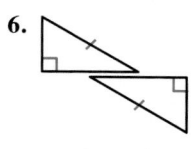
not enough information

7.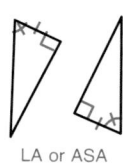
LA or ASA

8.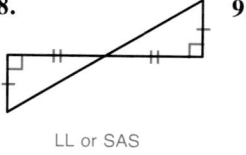
LL or SAS

9.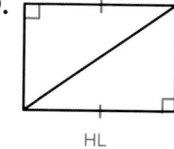
HL

4.7 Proving Right Triangles Congruent **163**

Teacher's Resource Book
Follow-Up Investigation, Chapter 4, p. 17

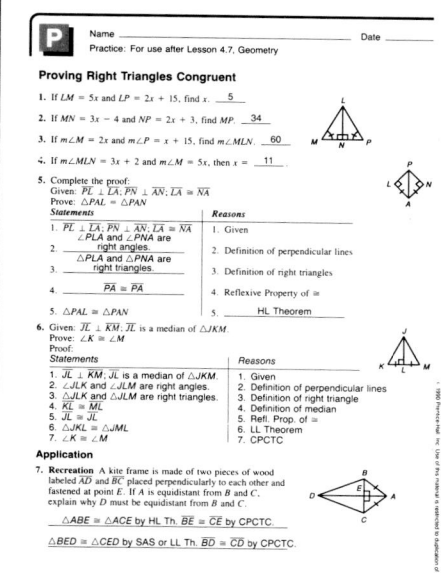

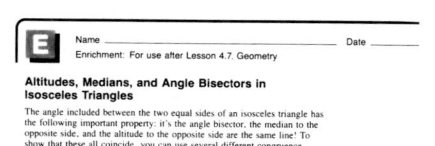

See *Teacher's Resource Book, Fol-low-Up Application,* Chapter 4, p. 20.

INTEGRATING GEOMETRY
Precision and Accuracy

Did you know that no two real-world objects are actually congruent? Euclidean geometry deals with "ideal" objects. If a degree measure of 30 is assigned to each of two angles, the measure of each is *precisely* 30, and those angles are congruent.

However, real-world objects cannot be measured exactly, so a method is needed to specify how "close" a measurement is. For example, in manufacturing it cannot be guaranteed that a measurement is *exactly* 6 cm, but the measurement can be made as "close" as necessary with the use of refined measuring instruments and careful manufacturing processes.

To specify mathematically the quality or closeness of a measurement, the concept of *precision* is used. **Precision** indicates by how much a measurement may be in error.

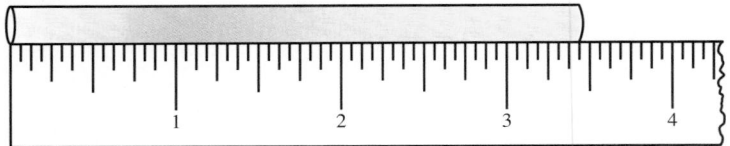

In this diagram, the measurement being made is $3\frac{7}{16}$ in. The precision is $\frac{1}{16}$ in., the smallest unit that can be measured on the scale shown. The true measurement lies between $3\frac{13}{32}$ in. and $3\frac{15}{32}$ in., since

$$3\frac{15}{32} - 3\frac{13}{32} = \frac{2}{32} = \frac{1}{16}$$

The *greatest possible error* between the desired measurement and the true measurement is $\frac{1}{32}$ in., one-half the smallest unit of measure. Designers often write a required measurement in the form $3\frac{13}{32}'' \pm \frac{1}{32}''$. The allowable error $\frac{1}{32}$ in. above and below the measurement is called the *tolerance*. It is very important for designers and engineers to specify tolerances so that the manufacturer knows how close to the desired measurement the true measurements must be held.

Some work requires high precision. For example, a piston must fit very well into a cylinder of a car's engine. If the diameter of the piston is too large, it will not fit into the cylinder at all. If the diameter is too small, there will be leakage around the piston. The designer has to carefully specify the measurements and the precision required, and the manufacturer of the parts has to provide quality control to assure that the specifications are met.

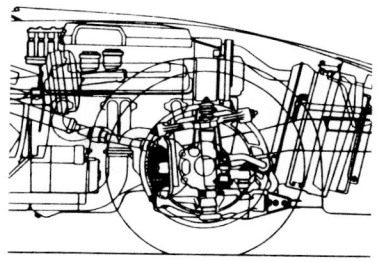

Another way to express the quality of a measurement is to indicate the ratio between the greatest possible error and the measurement. This ratio provides the *accuracy* of the measurement and is usually expressed as a percent. Thus, the accuracy of the $3\frac{7}{16}$ (or $\frac{55}{16}$) measurement is

$$\frac{1}{32} \div \frac{55}{16} = \frac{1}{110} \approx 0.9\%$$

EXERCISES

Give the precision, greatest possible error, and accuracy for each measurement. See side column.

1. $7\frac{7}{8}''$ **2.** $\frac{15''}{16}$ **3.** 3.7 cm **4.** $\frac{14}{16}$ in. **5.** 4.30 cm

6. Measure floor tiles in your school or home. Compare their widths. Answers may vary.

7. Measure the waistband of four pairs of pants that are the same size. How do they compare? Consult a clothing catalog for the waist measurement for that size. Answers may vary.

8. Measure the lengths of both sleeves of the same shirt. How do they compare? Answers may vary.

9. Compare several clocks in your school. Are they precisely synchronized? Answers may vary.

10. Measure the height of several matching chairs in your home or school. Are they the same height? What is the difference between the least and greatest heights? Answers may vary.

1. $\frac{1}{8}$; $\frac{1}{16}$; 0.8%
2. $\frac{1}{16}$; $\frac{1}{32}$; 3.$\overline{3}$%
3. $\frac{1}{10}$; 0.05; 1.4%
4. $\frac{1}{16}$; $\frac{1}{32}$; 3.6%
5. $\frac{1}{100}$; 0.005; 0.12%

Additional Answers

10. Plan: Show overlapping △s *TUW* and *ZWU* ≅. Then ∠*T* and ∠*Z* are ≅ corr. parts.

Proof:

Statements	Reasons
1. $\overline{TU} \cong \overline{ZW}$; ∠*TUW* ≅ ∠*ZWU*	1. Given
2. $\overline{UW} \cong \overline{WU}$	2. Refl. prop. of ≅
3. △*TUW* ≅ △*ZWU*	3. SAS
4. ∠*T* ≅ ∠*Z*	4. CPCTC

Conclusion: In the given figure, if $\overline{TU} \cong \overline{ZW}$ and ∠*TUW* ≅ ∠*ZWU*, then ∠*T* ≅ ∠*Z*.

11. Plan: Use the ≅ corresp. parts of △s *TUW* and *ZWU* to prove △*TVU* ≅ △*ZVW*. Then *UV* and *WV* are ≅ corr. parts.

Proof:

Statements	Reasons
1. △*TUW* ≅ △*ZWU*	1. Given
2. $\overline{TU} \cong \overline{ZW}$; ∠*T* ≅ ∠*Z*	2. CPCTC
3. ∠*TVU* ≅ ∠*ZVW*	3. Vert. △s are ≅.
4. △*TVU* ≅ △*ZVW*	4. AAS
5. $\overline{UV} \cong \overline{WV}$	5. CPCTC

Conclusion: In the given figure, if △*TUW* ≅ △*ZWU*; then $\overline{UV} \cong \overline{WV}$.

Vocabulary

altitude of a triangle (150)	included angle (134)
angle bisector of a triangle (149)	included side (134)
CPCTC (139)	legs of a right triangle (159)
congruent triangles (129)	median of a triangle (149)
correspondence (128)	one-to-one correspondence (128)
corresponding angles (129)	opposite angle (159)
corresponding sides (129)	opposite side (159)
distance from a point to a line (151)	overlapping triangles (140)
equivalent correspondences (129)	perpendicular bisector (150)
hypotenuse (159)	right triangle (159)

Correspondence and Congruence   Two triangles are congruent if and only if the six pairs of corresponding parts are congruent.   **4.1**

1. List the correspondences if △*EFG* ↔ △*HIJ*. $\overline{EF} \leftrightarrow \overline{HI}$, $\overline{EG} \leftrightarrow \overline{HJ}$, $\overline{FG} \leftrightarrow \overline{IJ}$, ∠*E* ↔ ∠*H*, ∠*F* ↔ ∠*I*, ∠*G* ↔ ∠*J*

Proving Triangles Congruent   Triangles can be proven congruent by the SSS, SAS, or ASA Postulates, or by the AAS Theorem.   **4.2**

If enough information is given, verify that △*MAY* ≅ △*RAY*.

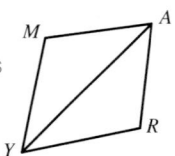

2. $\overline{MA} \cong \overline{RA}$; ∠*MAY* ≅ ∠*RAY* SAS

3. *m*∠*M* = 80; *m*∠*MAY* = 40; *m*∠*RYA* = 60; $\overline{MY} \cong \overline{RY}$ SAS

4. $\overline{AY}$ bisects ∠*MAR* and ∠*RYM*. ASA

5. $\overline{YM} \cong \overline{YR}$; ∠*M* ≅ ∠*R* not enough information

Using Congruent Triangles   Segments or angles can be proven congruent by showing that they are corresponding parts of congruent triangles (CPCTC).   **4.3**

Name the triangles that would have to be congruent to verify that each statement is true by CPCTC.

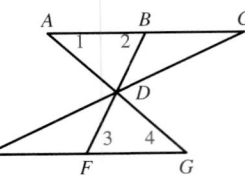

6. ∠1 ≅ ∠4 *ABD* and *GFD* or *ACD* and *GED*

7. $\overline{BC} \cong \overline{FE}$ *BCD* and *FED*

8. ∠3 ≅ ∠2 *DAB* and *DGF*

9. $\overline{DG} \cong \overline{DA}$ *DGE* and *DAC* or *DFG* and *DBA*

10. Given: $\overline{TU} \cong \overline{ZW}$;
$\angle TUW \cong \angle ZWU$

Prove:
$\angle T \cong \angle Z$
See side column, page 166.

11. Given: $\triangle TUW \cong \triangle ZWU$

Prove:
$\overline{UV} \cong \overline{WV}$

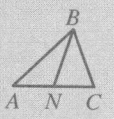

Medians, Altitudes, and Bisectors
The definitions of median, altitude, and angle bisector provide useful information in proofs.

4.4, 4.5

Copy △ABC. Draw in the necessary segments.

D is the midpt. of $\overline{BC}$.

12. If $\overline{AD}$ is a median of $\triangle ABC$, then __?__.

13. If $\overline{BE}$ bisects $\angle B$, then __?__. $\angle ABE \cong \angle CBE$

14. If $\overline{CF}$ is an altitude of $\triangle ABC$, then __?__. $CF \perp AB$

15. If $\overline{CG}$ bisects $\overline{AB}$, then __?__ $\overline{CG}$ is a median, and $\overline{AG} \cong \overline{BG}$.

Complete a figure, Given, Prove, and the proof.

16. If two triangles are congruent, their corresponding medians are congruent. See side column.

17. If P is a point on the perpendicular bisector of $\overline{AB}$ such that P is not on $\overline{AB}$, then $\triangle PAB$ is isosceles. See Additional Answers, p. 702.

18. Explain why the auxiliary figure is underdetermined or overdetermined: In $\triangle JKL$, draw $\overline{KM}$ such that M is the midpoint of $\overline{JL}$ and $\angle JKM \cong \angle LKM$.
overdetermined; M is the midpt. of $\overline{JL}$ and $\angle JKM \cong \angle LKM$ only when $\overline{JK} \cong \overline{KL}$, which was not given.

4.6

Proving Right Triangles Congruent
Right triangles can be proven congruent by the LL, HL, HA, and LA Theorems.

4.7

Name the theorem that verifies the congruence of each pair of triangles.

19.

LA or AAS

20.

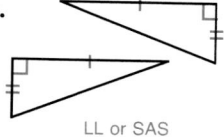
LL or SAS

21.

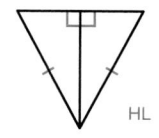
HL

22. Given: $\overline{AO}$ is the perpendicular bisector of $\overline{PM}$; $\overline{PM}$ is the perpendicular bisector of $\overline{AO}$.

Prove: $\overline{AP} \cong \overline{OM}$
See Additional Answers, p. 702.

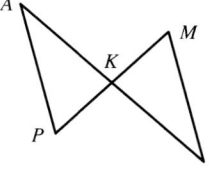

---

16. Given: $\triangle ABC \cong \triangle DEF$; $\overline{BN}$ is a median of $\triangle ABC$; $\overline{EM}$ is a median of $\triangle DEF$.

Prove: $\overline{BN} \cong \overline{EM}$

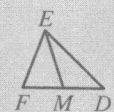

Plan: Use the corr. ≅ parts of △s ABC and DEF along with the def. of median to prove $\triangle ABN \cong \triangle DEM$. Then BN and EM are ≅ corr. parts.

Proof:

Statements	Reasons
1. $\triangle ABC \cong \triangle DEF$	1. Given
2. $\overline{AB} \cong \overline{DE}$; $\angle A \cong \angle D$	2. CPCTC
3. $\overline{AC} \cong \overline{DF}$	3. CPCTC
4. $AC = DF$	4. Def. of ≅ segments
5. $\frac{1}{2}AC = \frac{1}{2}DF$	5. Mult. prop.
6. $\overline{BN}$ and $\overline{EM}$ are medians of △s ABC and DEF, respectively	6. Given
7. N and M are the midpoints of $\overline{AC}$ and $\overline{DF}$, respectively	7. Def. of median
8. $AN = (\frac{1}{2})AC$; $DM = (\frac{1}{2})DF$	8. Midpt. theorem
9. $AN = DM$	9. Subst. prop.
10. $\overline{AN} \cong \overline{DM}$	10. Def. of ≅ segments
11. $\triangle ABN \cong \triangle DEM$	11. SAS
12. $\overline{BN} \cong \overline{EM}$	12. CPCTC

Conclusion: If two △s are ≅, their corr. medians are ≅.

True or false? If false, tell why.

1. If △ABC ↔ △EDF, then $\overline{BC}$ ↔ $\overline{ED}$. false; $\overline{BC}$ ↔ $\overline{DF}$

2. If point *P* is equidistant from points *Q* and *R*, then *P* is on the
perpendicular bisector of $\overline{QR}$. true

3. If in triangles *ABC* and *JKL*, ∠A ≅ ∠J, ∠B ≅ ∠L, and $\overline{AB}$ ≅ $\overline{JL}$, then
△ABC ≅ △JKL. false; △ABC ≅ △JLK

4. In any triangle, a median is a segment determined by a vertex and the
midpoint of the opposite side. true

5. If $\overline{XY}$ is an altitude of △XYZ, then ∠Z is a right angle. false; either ∠Y or ∠X
is a rt. ∠

6. If *Q* lies on the bisector of ∠LMN, then $\overline{LQ}$ ≅ $\overline{NQ}$. false; true if $\overline{LQ}$ ⊥ $\overline{ML}$ and
$\overline{NQ}$ ⊥ $\overline{MN}$

If the triangles are congruent, write and verify the congruence statement.

7.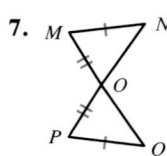

not enough information

8.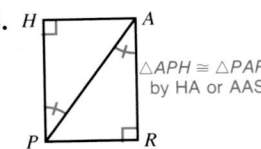

△APH ≅ △PAR by HA or AAS

9. △TAP ≅ ∠
by S

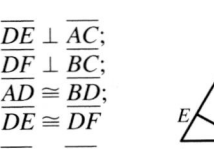

10. **Given:** $\overline{ES}$ is a median
of △EPA;

$\overline{AS}$ is a median
of △AER

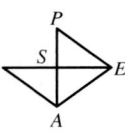

Prove: $\overline{EP}$ ≅ $\overline{RA}$
See Additional Answers, p. 702.

11. **Given:** $\overline{DE}$ ⊥ $\overline{AC}$;
$\overline{DF}$ ⊥ $\overline{BC}$;
$\overline{AD}$ ≅ $\overline{BD}$;
$\overline{DE}$ ≅ $\overline{DF}$

Prove: $\overline{AC}$ ≅ $\overline{BC}$

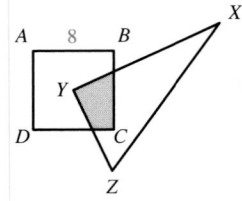

12. Prove that if two triangles are congruent, their corresponding altitudes are
congruent.

Challenge

A square *ABCD* and a right triangle *XYZ* overlap as
shown. The side of the square is 8 cm. The vertex of
the right angle of △XYZ is at the center of square
ABCD. Find the area of the shaded portion. See side
column page 167.

Alternative Assessment   Draw two triangles. Ask students what it means
when two triangles are "congruent." Then have them describe at least four
ways in which two triangles can be proved congruent. Have them draw a
median, an altitude, and a bisector for one of the triangles.

Solve. Grid in your response on the answer sheet.

1. Find $\frac{2}{7}$ of 40% of 665. 76

2. Find the positive value of x:
   $(x - 2)(3x + 4) = (2x + 1)(x - 1) + 5$ 4

3. Mrs. Wander traveled at 65 km/h for 3 h and then at 72 km/h for 1 h 30 min. Find her average speed in km/h for the entire $4\frac{1}{2}$-h trip. $67\frac{1}{3}$

4. What is the least number of distinct lines in a plane that can be drawn so that the total number of points of intersection is 6? 4

5. Consider any positive integer $\textcircled{a}$, defined by $\textcircled{a} = a + (a - 1) + (a - 2) + \ldots + 2 + 1$. For example, $\textcircled{5} = 5 + 4 + 3 + 2 + 1$.

   What is the value of $\textcircled{32} - \textcircled{30}$? 63

6. In $\triangle ABC$, $\overline{XY} \parallel \overline{AB}$ and $\overline{AY}$ bisects $\angle CAB$. If $m\angle C = 50$ and $m\angle AYB = 80$, then what is $m\angle B$? 70

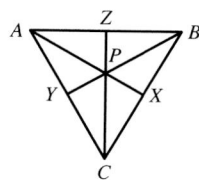

7. What is the measure of an acute angle if twice the measure of its supplement is 27 more than five times the measure of its complement? 39

8. The exterior angle at vertex F of $\triangle DEF$ has a measure of 105. If $m\angle D = 60$, find the $m\angle E$. 45

Use this diagram for 9.

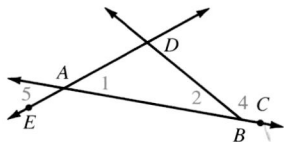

9. If $\overrightarrow{AD}$ and $\overrightarrow{AE}$ are opposite rays, $\overrightarrow{BA}$ and $\overrightarrow{BC}$ are opposite rays, and $m\angle 1 = m\angle 2$, then find $m\angle 5 + m\angle 4$. 180

10. Find the larger of two consecutive positive integers whose product is 272. 17

11. The ratio of the lengths of the sides of two squares is 1:4. Write the ratio of their areas as a fraction. $\frac{1}{16}$

12. The original price of a CD player is $146. Crazy Al's is offering a closeout price of 25.5% off the original price. To the nearest cent, what is the discount? $37.23

13. If $\triangle ABC \cong \triangle EDC$, $\triangle CDE \cong \triangle CDF$, and $m\angle 4 = 35$, then what is $m\angle F$? 35

14. If P and Q are each equidistant from $A(5, 4)$ and $B(3, 6)$, then what is the slope of the equation of $\overleftrightarrow{PQ}$? 1

College Entrance Exam Review **169**

According to the College Entrance Examination Board and the Educational Testing Service, the 1994 revision of the SAT will include a section of problems that require students to produce and grid in their own answers.

See *Teacher's Resource Book*, Preparing for College Entrance Exams, for grids.

See *Teacher's Resource Book, Tests,* 41–48.
See *Connections,* pp. 1 and 2.

Additional Answers

48. Plan: Prove rt. $\triangle$s ABD and $FEC \cong$ by LL. Concl. follows by CPCTC.

Proof:

Statements	*Reasons*
1. $\overline{AB} \perp \overline{BD}$; $\overline{FE} \perp \overline{CE}$; $\overline{AB} \cong \overline{EF}$	1. Given
2. $\angle B$ and $\angle E$ are rt. $\angle$s.	2. Def. of $\perp$
3. $\triangle ABD$ and $\triangle FEC$ are rt. $\triangle$s.	3. Def. of rt. $\triangle$
4. $\overline{BC} \cong \overline{DE}$	4. Given
5. $BC = DE$	5. Def. of $\cong$ seg.
6. $BC + CD = DE + CD$	6. Add. prop.
7. $BC + CD = BD$; $DE + CD = EC$	7. Def. of betw.
8. $BD = EC$	8. Subst. prop.
9. $\overline{BD} \cong \overline{EC}$	9. Def. of $\cong$ seg.
10. $\triangle ABD \cong \triangle FEC$	10. LL Th.
11. $\overline{AD} \cong \overline{CF}$	11. CPCTC

Concl.: In the given figure, when $\overline{AB} \perp \overline{BD}$, $\overline{FE} \perp \overline{CE}$, $\overline{BC} \cong \overline{DE}$ and $\overline{AB} \cong \overline{EF}$, then $\overline{AD} \cong \overline{CF}$.

50. Plan: Show $\triangle FGJ \cong \triangle IGH$ by SAS. Then $\angle J \cong \angle H$ by CPCTC.

Proof:

Statements	*Reasons*
1. $\overline{FI}$ and $\overline{HJ}$ have midpt. G.	1. Given
2. $\overline{FG} \cong \overline{IG}$; $\overline{HG} \cong \overline{JG}$	2. Def. of midpt.
3. $\angle FGJ \cong \angle IGH$	3. Vert. $\angle$s are $\cong$.
4. $\triangle FGJ \cong \triangle IGH$	4. SAS
5. $\angle J \cong \angle H$	5. CPCTC

Concl.: In the given figure, if $\overline{FI}$ and $\overline{HJ}$ have midpt. G, then $\angle J \cong \angle H$.

CUMULATIVE REVIEW (CHAPTERS 1–4)

Complete.

1. Three undefined terms in Geometry are __?__, __?__, __?__. pt. line plane — 1.1

2. Two angles are __?__ if the sum of their measures is 180. supp. — 1.5

3. If B is in the interior of $\angle ADQ$ and $m\angle ADB = m\angle BDQ$, then $\overrightarrow{DB}$ is called the __?__ of $\angle ADQ$. bis. — 1.4

4. If D, E, and F are collinear points, then __?__. they lie on the same line — 1.1

5. Coplanar angles with a common side, a common vertex, and no common interior points are called __?__. adj. $\angle$s — 1.4

6. The complement of a 51° angle measures __?__. 39° — 1.5

7. If two lines intersect at a 90° angle, they are __?__. $\perp$ — 1.6

8. Two lines that are not coplanar are called __?__. skew — 3.1

9. Three noncollinear points determine a __?__. plane — 1.2

10. If two distinct planes are not parallel, their intersection is __?__. a line — 1.2

Express each of the following in if-then form. Underline each hypothesis once and each conclusion twice. — 2.1

11. Vertical angles are congruent. If 2 $\angle$s are vertical, then they are $\cong$.

12. Babies cry often. If a person is a baby, then the person cries often.

13. Alternate interior angles formed by parallel lines are congruent. If lines are $\parallel$, then the alt. int. $\angle$s formed are $\cong$.

14. Two lines perpendicular to the same line are parallel to each other. If 2 lines are $\perp$ to the same line, then they are $\parallel$ to each other.

State the converse, inverse, and contrapositive for Exercises 15–17. — 2.2
See side column.

15. If an exterior angle of a triangle has a measure of 80, then the triangle is obtuse.

16. If two triangles are congruent, then they have at least 2 pairs of congruent sides.

17. If a polygon has n sides, then the sum of the measures of its interior angles is $180(n - 2)$. See side column, page 171.

18. State the truth values for Exercises 15 and 16. true; true — 3.4, 4.2

19. State the truth values for the converses of Exercises 15 and 16. false; false

20. State the biconditionals for Exercises 15 and 16. Explain why they are true or false.

15. Conv.: If a $\triangle$ is obt., then an ext. $\angle$ of the $\triangle$ has a meas. of 80.
Inv.: If an ext. $\angle$ of a $\triangle$ does not have a meas. of 80, then the $\triangle$ is not obt.
Ctpos: If a $\triangle$ is not obt., then an ext. $\angle$ of the $\triangle$ does not have a meas. of 80.

16. Conv.: If 2 $\triangle$s have at least 2 pairs of $\cong$ sides, then the $\triangle$s are $\cong$.
Inv.: If 2 $\triangle$s are not $\cong$, then they do not have at least 2 pairs of $\cong$ sides.
Ctpos.: If 2 $\triangle$s do not have at least 2 pairs of $\cong$ sides, then the $\triangle$s are not $\cong$.

Name the relationship between the given angles.

3.2

21. ∠3 and ∠6 alt. int. ∠s   **22.** ∠10 and ∠11 vert. ∠s

23. ∠9 and ∠16 alt. ext. ∠s   **24.** ∠8 and ∠15 int. ∠s on same side of transv.

25. If $l \parallel m$, $p \parallel q$, and $m\angle 3 = 72$, find the measures of all numbered angles. $m\angle 1 = m\angle 4 = m\angle 5 = m\angle 8 = m\angle 9 = m\angle 12 = m\angle 13 = m\angle 16 = 108$; $m\angle 2 = m\angle 3 = m\angle 6 = m\angle 7 = m\angle 10 = m\angle 11 = m\angle 14 = m\angle 15 = 72$

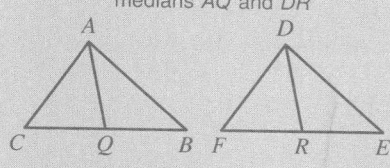

Tell which lines are parallel. Justify each answer.

3.3

26. ∠4 ≅ ∠8 $p \parallel q$; if corr. ∠s are ≅, then lines are ∥.   **27.** ∠7 ≅ ∠14 $l \parallel m$; if alt. ext. ∠s are ≅, then lines are ∥.

28. ∠4 and ∠11 are supplementary. $l \parallel m$; if int. ∠s on the same side of transv. are supp., then lines are ∥.

29. State three conclusions to the hypothesis *If parallel lines have a transversal,* __?__. Answers may vary. alt. int. ∠s are ≅; corr. ∠s are ≅; alt. ext. ∠s are ≅; int. ∠s on the same side of transv. are supp.

30. State three theorems ending with *then the lines are parallel.* See Th. 3.6, 3.7, 3.8

31. In △BQE, if ∠E is a right angle and $m\angle Q = 21$, find $m\angle B$. 69

3.4

32. In △WHY, if $m\angle W = 52$ and an exterior angle at Y has a measure of 97, find $m\angle H$. 45

Complete the table.

3.6

Number of Sides		Name of Polygon	Sum of Measures of Interior Angles	
33. 3		__?__ triangle	__?__	180
34. __?__	5	pentagon	__?__	540
35. __?__	4	__?__ quadrilateral	360	
36. 6		__?__ hexagon	__?__	720
37. __?__	8	octagon	__?__	1080

True or false? Justify each answer.

38. A regular polygon is always equiangular. true; def. of regular polygon

39. Corresponding angles are always congruent. false; only true when lines are ∥

3.2

40. In a right triangle, one of the exterior angles has a measure of 90. true; the ext. ∠ adj. to the rt. ∠ must meas. 90

3.4

41. A pentagon has 5 diagonals. true; an n-gon has $\frac{n(n-3)}{2}$ diagonals

3.6

42. If △RUN ≅ △MET, then $\overline{UN} \cong \overline{EM}$. false; $\overline{UN} \cong \overline{ET}$

4.1

43. In △XYZ, if M is the midpoint of $\overline{YZ}$, then $\overline{XM} \perp \overline{YZ}$. false; only true if △XYZ is equilateral or isos. with $\overline{XY} \cong \overline{XZ}$

44. In △JKL and △TWR, if $\overline{JK} \cong \overline{TW}$, $\overline{KL} \cong \overline{WR}$, and ∠L ≅ ∠R, then △JKL ≅ △TWR. false; there is no SSA congruence

4.2

49. Given: △ABC ≅ △DEF; medians $\overline{AQ}$ and $\overline{DR}$

Prove: $\overline{AQ} \cong \overline{DR}$

Plan: Use the given ≅ △s and the def. of median to prove △ACQ ≅ △DFR by SAS. The concl. follows by CPCTC.

Proof:

Statements	Reasons
1. △ABC ≅ △DEF; medians $\overline{AQ}$ and $\overline{DR}$	1. Given
2. $\overline{CB} \cong \overline{FE}$	2. CPCTC
3. $CB = FE$	3. Def. of ≅ seg.
4. $\frac{1}{2}CB = \frac{1}{2}FE$	4. Mult. prop.
5. Q is the midpt. of CB; R is the midpt. of FE	5. Def. of median
6. $CQ = \frac{1}{2}CB$; $FR = \frac{1}{2}FE$	6. Midpt. Th.
7. $CQ = FR$	7. Subst. Prop.
8. $\overline{CQ} \cong \overline{FR}$	8. Def. of ≅ seg.
9. $\overline{AC} \cong \overline{DF}$; ∠C ≅ ∠F	9. CPCTC
10. △ACQ ≅ △DFR	10. SAS
11. $\overline{AQ} \cong \overline{DR}$	11. CPCTC

Concl.: If △ABC ≅ △DEF, then their corr. medians are ≅.

51. Plan: Show rt. △s ABD and CBD ≅ by the HL Th. Then ∠A ≅ ∠C by CPCTC.

Proof:

Statements	Reasons
1. $\overline{BD} \perp \overline{AC}$; $\overline{AB} \cong \overline{BC}$	1. Given
2. ∠ADB and ∠CDB are rt. ∠s.	2. Def. of ⊥
3. △ABD and △CBD are rt. △s.	3. Def. of rt. △
4. $\overline{BD} \cong \overline{BD}$	4. Refl. prop.
5. △ABD ≅ △CBD	5. HL Th.
6. ∠A ≅ ∠C	6. CPCTC

Concl.: In △ABC, if $\overline{BD} \perp \overline{AC}$ and $\overline{AB} \cong \overline{BC}$, then ∠A ≅ ∠C.

17. Conv.: If the sum of the meas. of the int. ∠s of a polygon is $180(n-2)$, then the polygon has n sides.
Inv.: If a polygon does not have n sides, then the sum of the meas. of its int. ∠s is not $180(n-2)$.
Ctpos.: If the sum of the meas. of the int. ∠s of a polygon is not $180(n-2)$, then the polygon does not have n sides.

20. An ext. ∠ of a △ has a meas. of 80 iff the △ is obtuse; false; the conv. is false.
Two △s are ≅ iff they have at least 2 pairs of ≅ sides; false; the conv. is false.

52. Plan: Use the Given to prove rt. △s *LMP* and *NPM* ≅. Then ∠*L* ≅ ∠*N* by CPCTC.

Proof:

Statements	Reasons
1. $\overline{LP} \parallel \overline{MN}$	1. Given
2. ∠*LPM* ≅ ∠*NMP*	2. If lines are ∥, alt. int. ∠s are ≅.
3. $\overline{MP} \perp \overline{LM}$; $\overline{MP} \perp \overline{PN}$	3. Given
4. ∠*LMP* and ∠*NPM* are rt. ∠s.	4. Def. of ⊥
5. △*LMP* and △*NPM* are rt. △s.	5. Def. of rt. △
6. $\overline{MP} \cong \overline{PM}$	6. Refl. prop.
7. △*LMP* ≅ △*NPM*	7. LA Th.
8. ∠*L* ≅ ∠*N*	8. CPCTC

Concl.: In the given figure, if $\overline{LP} \parallel \overline{MN}$, $\overline{MP} \perp \overline{LM}$ and $\overline{MP} \perp \overline{PN}$, then ∠*L* ≅ ∠*N*.

53. Plan: Use the Given and corr. parts $\overline{WX}$ and $\overline{VY}$ of the ≅ △s to show the △s ≅ by SAS.

Proof:

Statements	Reasons
1. *V* is the midpt. of $\overline{UW}$.	1. Given
2. $\overline{WV} \cong \overline{UV}$	2. Def. of midpt.
3. △*VWX* ≅ △*XYV*	3. Given
4. $\overline{WX} \cong \overline{YV}$	4. CPCTC
5. $\overline{VY} \parallel \overline{WX}$	5. Given
6. ∠*W* ≅ ∠*UVY*	6. If lines are ∥, corr. ∠s are ≅.
7. △*UVY* ≅ △*VWX*	7. SAS

Concl.: In the given figure, if *V* is the midpt. of $\overline{UW}$, △*VWX* ≅ △*XYV* and $\overline{VY} \parallel \overline{WX}$, then △*UVY* ≅ △*VWX*.

If the triangles are congruent, write and verify the congruence statement.

45.
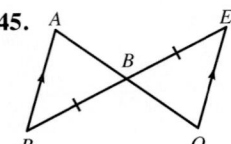
△*ABP* ≅ △*QBE*; AAS or ASA

46.
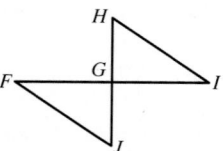
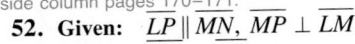
no △ congruence

47.
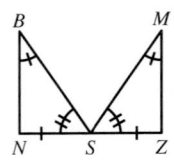
△*BNS* ≅ △*MZS*; AAS

48. Given: $\overline{AB} \perp \overline{BD}$; $\overline{FE} \perp \overline{CE}$; $\overline{BC} \cong \overline{DE}$; $\overline{AB} \cong \overline{EF}$
Prove: $\overline{AD} \cong \overline{CF}$
See side column page 170.

49. Prove: If two triangles are congruent, their corresponding medians are congruent.
See side column page 171.

50. Given: $\overline{FI}$ and $\overline{HJ}$ with midpoint *G*
Prove: ∠*J* ≅ ∠*H*

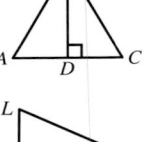

See side column pages 170–171.

51. Given: $\overline{BD} \perp \overline{AC}$; $\overline{AB} \cong \overline{BC}$
Prove: ∠*A* ≅ ∠*C*

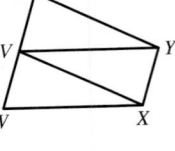

52. Given: $\overline{LP} \parallel \overline{MN}$, $\overline{MP} \perp \overline{LM}$, $\overline{MP} \perp \overline{PN}$
Prove: ∠*L* ≅ ∠*N*
See side column.

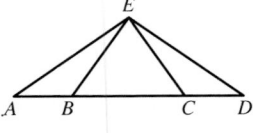

53. Given: *V* is the midpoint of $\overline{UW}$; △*VWX* ≅ △*XYV*; $\overline{VY} \parallel \overline{WX}$
Prove: △*UVY* ≅ △*VWX*

54. Given: △*UYV* ≅ △*VXW*; $XY = \frac{1}{2}UW$
Prove: $\overline{UY} \parallel \overline{VX}$ See page 715.

55. Given: △*AEC* ≅ △*DEB*
Prove: △*AEB* ≅ △*DEC*

56. Given: ∠*EBC* ≅ ∠*ECB*; ∠*AEC* ≅ ∠*DEB*; $\overline{AB} \cong \overline{CD}$
Prove: △*AEB* ≅ △*DEC*

4.5

OVERVIEW · Chapter 5

SUMMARY

In Chapter 5, students establish and use theorems about isosceles triangles. Algebraic properties of inequalities are reviewed and applied to the measures of segments and angles. Guidelines are established for inferring inequality from diagrams. Students write indirect proofs containing inequalities and make use of the Triangle Inequality Theorem as well as other inequality relations in one or two triangles. They then define dihedral angles and plane angles.

CHAPTER OBJECTIVES

- To prove and apply theorems and corollaries about isosceles triangles

- To state and apply properties of inequality to measures of segments and angles

- To prove statements involving inequalities

- To determine information using diagrams

- To write indirect proofs involving inequalities

- To state and apply inequality relations for one triangle and for two triangles

- To state and apply the Triangle Inequality Theorem

- To identify dihedral angles and their plane angles

- To prove theorems through the use of *indirect proof*

CHAPTER HIGHLIGHTS

DEVELOPING MATHEMATICAL POWER

Problem Solving

The four problem solving steps are used to introduce indirect reasoning for writing indirect proofs in Lesson 5.3.

Communication

This chapter suggests manipulatives for alternative learning styles and for cooperative learning situations to illustrate properties of isosceles triangles. Other cooperative learning suggestions are provided in the side column throughout the chapter. The *Teacher's Resource Book* offers a Chapter Summary and Review in Spanish. The side column mentions topics for students' portfolios such as writing a journal entry comparing equality and inequality in algebra and geometry.

Reasoning

Students apply indirect reasoning to proofs in Lessons 5.3–5.6. Thinking critically topics include the combining of two mathematical statements into one.

Connections

Real-world applications include such topics as navigation, architecture, and construction. Algebraic inequalities are integrated into the geometry. The Project at the end of Lesson 5.3 shows students another way to apply indirect reasoning.

Technology

The Technology feature discusses Logo recursion and tessellations. Other Logo topics are presented in exercises throughout the chapter.

STUDENT TEXT

Chapter Content	Basic	Average	Enriched	NCTM STANDARDS*
5.1 Congruence in a Single Triangle: Isosceles Triangle Theorem	D; 177/1-9, 10-20 even, 28, 36, MR	D: 177/1-9, 10-21 even, 28, 29, 36, 37, MR	D: 177/1-21, 22-27 even, 28, 29, 36, 37, MR	2, 3, 4, 7
5.2 Properties of Inequality	D: 182/1-14, 18, 19 R: 177/10-20 odd	D: 182/1-14, 18-22 R: 177/10-21 odd	D: 182/1-14, 18-23, 27-29 R: 177/22-27 odd	2, 3, 4, 5
5.3 Strategy: Use Indirect Proof	D: 187/1-5, 7 R: 182/15-17	D: 187/1-5, 7, 8 R: 182/15-17, 23	D: 187/1-5, 7, 8 R: 182/15-17, 24-26	1, 3, 7
5.4 Indirect Proof and Inequalities	D: 192/1-23 odd R: 187/6, 8	D: 192/1-6, 13-22, 28, 29 R: 187/6, 9, 10	D: 192/1-6, 13-22, 27-29 R: 187/6, 9-11	3, 4, 5, 7
5.5 Inequalities in One Triangle	D: 197/1-8, 13-15, 28, 32, AR R: 192/1-23 even	D: 197/18-23 even, 28, 32, AR R: 192/23-25	D: 197/1-17, 18-23 even, 24-28, 32, AR R: 192/23-26	2, 3, 4, 7
5.6 More on Inequalities	D: 202/1-11, 22-24 R: 197/9-12	D: 202/1-16, 22-24 R: 197/18-23 odd, 24	D: 202/1-16, 20, 22-24 R: 197/18-23 odd	2, 3, 7
5.7 Congruence in Space: Dihedral Angles	D: 207/1-14, 24-28 R: 202/12, 13	D: 207/1-21, 24-28 R: 202/17-19	D: 207/1-28 R: 202/17-19, 21	3, 4, 7

D = Daily   R = Review   MR = Mixed Review   AR = Algebra Review

*For a complete list of NCTM Standards, see p. T7.

STUDENT TEXT

Review/Assessment

Mixed Review 178

Algebra Review 198, 216

Summary and Review 212

College Ent. Exam Rev. 215

Extra Practice 647

Test Yourself 193, 209

Chapter Test 214

Chapter Project 173

Special Features

Construction 203

Technology 178, 183, 198, 203, 210-211

Devel. Math. Power 178, 183, 198, 203

Applications 178, 183, 193, 198, 203, 208

Project 188

RESOURCES

Teacher's Resource Book

Ch. 5: Investigation/Practice/ Enrichment 1-20

Spanish Sum. and Rev. 9-10

Quizzes 49-52

Chapter Tests 53-56

Perf. Assessment Proj. Ch. 5

Critical Thinking 5

Reading and Writing in Geom. 5

Technology 5-6

Teaching Aid 5

Transparency 6

Teaching Transparencies 28-34

Computer Test Bank 249-316

Connections 14, 17

PH Graph. Utility

Overhead Manip. Kit

Inequalities in Triangles

Going with the flow!

Developing Mathematical Power

hang gliders are ...hed off a hillside or a ...tainside. Once airborne, ...lot lies flat or sits in a ...ss attached to the wing. ...use thermals, the rising ...air produced when ...blows over a hill or ...tain, to stay aloft. The ...s movements can in-...e or decrease the speed, ...ll as turn the aircraft left ...t.

...s fly from thermal to ...al. The A-shaped wing ...ang glider produces a low lift, giving a low-speed flight. Cockpit gliders are not very fast, but the long straight wings produce high lift at low speeds.

Project

Prepare a presentation about gliders. Compare and contrast hang gliders and cockpit gliders. Research the advantages and disadvantages of flying each type of aircraft, what heights and speeds they attain, and how they are judged in professional competitions. Include a model of a glider in your presentation.

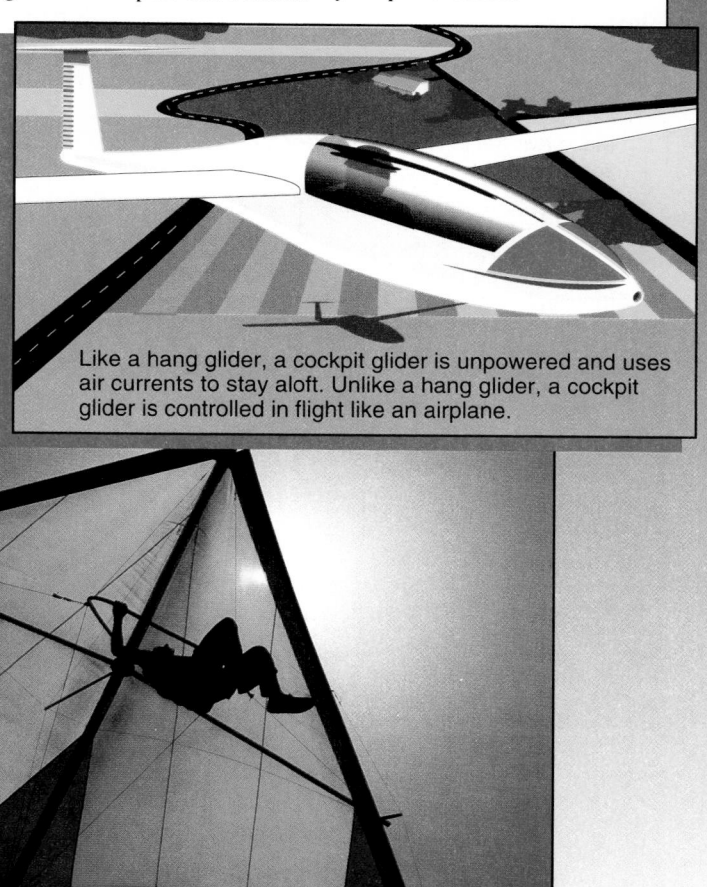

Like a hang glider, a cockpit glider is unpowered and uses air currents to stay aloft. Unlike a hang glider, a cockpit glider is controlled in flight like an airplane.

173

LESSON PLAN

Vocabulary

Base
Base angles
Identity
  congruence

Legs
Vertex angle

Materials/Manipulatives

Rulers and scissors
Teaching Transparency 28

Technology

Computer
Computer Test Bank, pp.
249–257
The Geometric Supposer:
Triangles
Geometry Problems and
Projects: Triangles, Worksheets
T38, T39

LESSON FOCUS

Review

• Draw the following triangles on the chalkboard. Ask students to classify the triangles by side.

1.
2.
3.

1. equilateral 2. scalene
3. isosceles

• The Mixed Review, Exercises 30–35, involves finding measures of sides and angles of a triangle.

Alternative Learning Styles

Manipulatives can help students discover properties. In the Investigation, students discover the identity congruence: every triangle is congruent to itself. Students can also cut out an isosceles triangle and fold it on the line of symmetry to generalize about the measure of the base angles.

5.1

Congruence in a Single Triangle: Isosceles Triangle Theorem

Objective: To prove and apply theorems and corollaries about isosceles triangles

Recall that scalene, isosceles, and equilateral triangles are defined with respect to the lengths of their sides. Deductions can be made regarding their angles.

Investigation—*Using Manipulatives*

Make two tracings of △ABC, each on a separate piece of paper. Rotate each tracing to show that △ABC ≅ △BCA and △ABC ≅ △CAB.

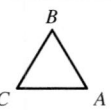
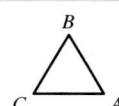

1. What type of triangle is △ABC? Justify.
   Equilateral; all 3 sides are ≅.
2. Name other possible triangle congruences.
   △ACB ≅ △BAC ≅ △CBA
   Make two tracings of △DEF, each on a separate piece of paper.

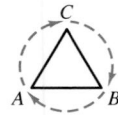
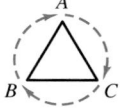

3. What type of triangle is △DEF? isosceles

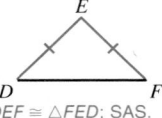

4. △DEF ≅ △DEF is the *identity congruence.*
   What can you do to show another congruence in the single triangle, △DEF? Justify this congruence.
   Turn over the tracing so that F falls on D, D on F, and E on itself; △DEF ≅ △FED; SAS.

In an isosceles triangle:

The two congruent sides are the **legs.**
The third side is the **base.**
The **vertex angle** is opposite the base.
The **base angles** include the base.

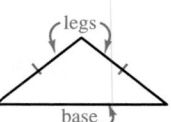
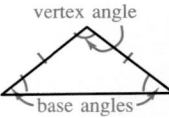

EXAMPLE 1 **Classify each triangle and write all the possible congruences between the given triangle and itself.**

a.
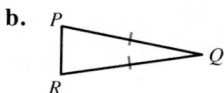

b.

c.

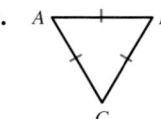

a. scalene; △XYZ ≅ △XYZ
b. isosceles; △PQR ≅ △PQR; △PQR ≅ △RQP
c. equilateral; △ABC ≅ △ABC ≅ △ACB ≅ △CAB ≅ △CBA ≅ △BAC ≅ △BCA

174   Chapter 5 Inequalities in Triangles

Developing Mathematical Power

Keeping a Portfolio Have the students organize the theorems and corollaries in this lesson according to the type of triangle to which they apply, isosceles or equilateral. They should draw a diagram to illustrate each theorem or corollary entered in their math journals.

Theorem 5.1   Isosceles Triangle Theorem   If two sides of a triangle are congruent, then the angles opposite those sides are congruent.

Given: $\overline{AB} \cong \overline{AC}$

Prove: $\angle B \cong \angle C$

Plan: Show that $\triangle ABC \cong \triangle ACB$. Then $\angle B$ and $\angle C$ are congruent corresponding parts.

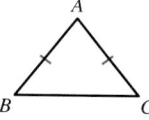

Proof:

Statements	*Reasons*
1. $\overline{AB} \cong \overline{AC}$	1. Given
2. $\angle A \cong \angle A$	2. Reflexive property of congruence
3. $\triangle ABC \cong \triangle ACB$	3. SAS Postulate
4. $\angle B \cong \angle C$	4. CPCTC

Conclusion: In $\triangle ABC$, whenever $\overline{AB} \cong \overline{AC}$, $\angle B \cong \angle C$.

Corollary 1   An equilateral triangle is also equiangular. Proved in Practice Exercise 22

Corollary 2   Each angle of an equilateral triangle has a measure of 60. Proved in Practice Exercise 23

Corollary 3   The bisector of the vertex angle of an isosceles triangle is perpendicular to the base at its midpoint. In other words, in an isosceles triangle, *the bisector of the vertex angle is also an altitude and a median of the triangle*. Proved in Class Exercise 12

EXAMPLE 2   Use the given information to draw conclusions. Justify your answer.

a.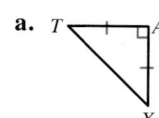

Given: $\overline{TA} \cong \overline{AX}$; $\overline{TA} \perp \overline{AX}$

Conclusion:

$\angle \underline{\ ?\ } \cong \angle \underline{\ ?\ }$	$\angle T \cong \angle X$ (Isos. $\triangle$ Th.)
$m\angle A = \underline{\ ?\ }$	$m\angle A = 90$ (Def. of rt. $\angle$)
$m\angle T = \underline{\ ?\ }$	$m\angle T = 45$ ($\cong$ comp. $\angle$s)

b.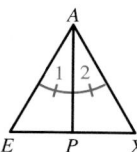

Given: $\triangle AXE$ is equilateral; $\angle 1 \cong \angle 2$.

Conclusion:

$\underline{\ ?\ } \perp \underline{\ ?\ }$	$\overline{AP} \perp \overline{EX}$ (Cor. 3 of Isos. $\triangle$ Th.)
$\overline{EP} \cong \underline{\ ?\ }$	$\overline{EP} \cong \overline{XP}$ (Cor. 3 of Isos. $\triangle$ Th.)
$m\angle 1 = \underline{\ ?\ }$	$m\angle 1 = 30$ (Cor. 2 of Isos. $\triangle$Th. and def. of $\angle$ bis.)

Theorem 5.2 is the converse of Theorem 5.1. It can be proven by the same method used in Theorem 5.1 or by adding an auxiliary segment.

 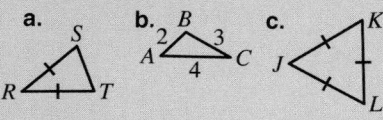

Common Errors

- Some students think that the side a triangle "sits on" is its base. Make sure students work with triangles in many different positions.
- Students may have trouble identifying opposite sides or angles. In addition to giving students practice with triangles in different positions, give them problems without diagrams, such as the following: In $\triangle RST$, $\angle R \cong \angle S$. If $RS = 6x$, $ST = 5x + 5$, and $RT = 7x - 1$, find the perimeter of $\triangle RST$. $ST = RT$; $x = 3$; perimeter $= 58$
- See *Teacher's Resource Book* for additional remediation.

LESSON FOLLOW-UP

Discussion

Ask students to suggest as many plans as possible for proving the Isosceles Triangle Theorem and its converse.

Isosceles Triangle Theorem:
1. Use the identity congruence.
2. Draw median $\overline{AM}$ and use SSS.
3. Draw altitude $\overline{AD}$ and use HL.
4. Draw $\angle$ bis. $\overline{AE}$ and use SAS.
Theorem 5.2:
1. Use the identity congruence.
2. Draw altitude $\overline{AD}$ and use LA or AAS.
3. Draw $\angle$ bis. $\overline{AE}$ and use AAS.

Critical Thinking

1. *Restructuring* Have students develop alternate plans for proof.
2. *Comparing-Contrasting* Ask students to evaluate different proofs.

Assignment Guide

See p. 172B for assignments.

> **Theorem 5.2** If two angles of a triangle are congruent, then the sides opposite those angles are congruent. Proved in Practice Exercise 24
>
> **Corollary** An equiangular triangle is also equilateral.
> Proved in Practice Exercise 25

CLASS EXERCISES

isosceles $\triangle$	equilateral $\triangle$
1. $\cong$ legs	1. $\cong$ sides
2. $\cong$ base $\angle$s	2. $\cong \angle$s; $60°$ $\angle$s
3. bis. of vertex $\angle$ is $\perp$ to base at midpt.	3. Median from a vertex is also the $\angle$ bis. and altitude of that vertex.

Thinking Critically

1. List the special properties of isosceles and equilateral triangles.

2. Discuss the various types of auxiliary line segments $\overline{AM}$ that could have been used in Theorem 5.1 to prove $\triangle AMB \cong \triangle AMC$. How would these proofs compare with the proof of Theorem 5.1? median, altitude, or $\angle$ bisector from the vertex $\angle$

True or false?

3. Every equilateral triangle is isosceles. true

4. Every isosceles triangle is equiangular. false

5. If two angles of one triangle are congruent to two angles of a second triangle, then the sides opposite those angles are congruent. false

6. If two isosceles triangles have a side of one congruent to the corresponding side of the other, then the triangles are congruent. false

Find the indicated measure when $\triangle RST$ is isosceles with base $\overline{RT}$ and $\triangle SUV$ is isosceles with base $\overline{UV}$.

7. If $m\angle S = 50$, $m\angle R = \underline{\ ?\ }$. 65

8. If $m\angle SUV = x$, $m\angle S = \underline{\ ?\ }$. $(180 - 2x)$

9. If $m\angle R = 5x + 10$ and $m\angle T = 3x + 30$, $m\angle S = \underline{\ ?\ }$. 60

10. If $m\angle R = 2x + 10$ and $m\angle S = x + 10$, $m\angle T = \underline{\ ?\ }$. 70

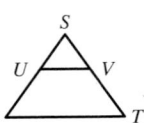

11. If isosceles $\triangle JKM$ has base $\overline{JM}$, name the congruent sides and the congruent angles. $\overline{KJ} \cong \overline{KM}$; $\angle J \cong \angle M$

12. Complete the proof of Corollary 3 of Theorem 5.1.
    Given: $\triangle NAS$ is isosceles with $\overline{NA} \cong \overline{NS}$; $\overline{NP}$ bisects $\angle N$. See side column, p. 177.
    Prove: $\overline{NP} \perp \overline{AS}$; $\overline{AP} \cong \overline{SP}$
    Plan: Show $\triangle NSP \cong \triangle NAP$. Use corresponding parts and the definition of a perpendicular bisector.

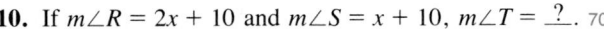
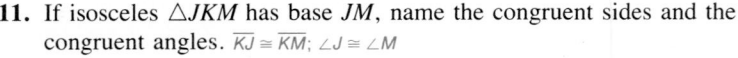

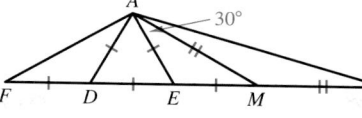
Find the indicated measures.

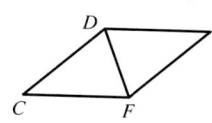

A
1. $m\angle ADF$ 2. $m\angle FAD$ 3. $m\angle AMR$
   120   30   150
4. $m\angle MAR$ 5. $m\angle AED$ 6. $m\angle DAR$
   15   60   105

7. Name two congruent triangles and verify the congruence. $\triangle FDA \cong \triangle MEA$ by SAS.

8. Classify $\triangle ADE$ in two ways. equilateral; equiangular

9. Write a plan and complete the proof.

Given: Isosceles $\triangle DCF$ with base $\overline{DF}$;
Isosceles $\triangle FED$ with base $\overline{FD}$; $\overline{CD} \cong \overline{EF}$
Prove: $\angle C \cong \angle E$
Plan: _?_ Since $\triangle DCF$ and $\triangle FED$ are isos., share a common base and have a ≅ pair of corr. sides, $\triangle DCF \cong \triangle FED$ by SSS. Thus $\angle C \cong \angle E$ by CPCTC.
Proof:

Statements	Reasons
1. $\triangle DCF$ is isosceles; $\triangle FED$ is isosceles; $\overline{CD} \cong \overline{EF}$.	1. Given
2. $\overline{CD} \cong \overline{CF}$; _?_ $\cong$ _?_ $\overline{ED}$ $\overline{EF}$	2. Definition of _?_ isos. $\triangle$
3. _?_ $\cong$ _?_ $\overline{CF}$ $\overline{ED}$	3. Substitution property
4. _?_ $\cong$ _?_ $\overline{DF}$ $\overline{FD}$	4. Reflexive property of congruence
5. $\triangle$ _?_ $\cong \triangle$ _?_ DCF; FED	5. SSS Postulate
6. $\angle$ _?_ $\cong \angle$ _?_ $\angle C \cong \angle E$	6. _?_ CPCTC

Conclusion: _?_ In the given figure, if isos. s DCF and FED share a common base and have $\overline{CD} \cong \overline{EF}$, then $\angle C \cong \angle E$.

Name the following.

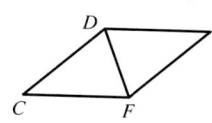

10. The vertex angle of $\triangle MNR$ $\angle MRN$

11. The legs of $\triangle MPR$ $\overline{MP}, \overline{RP}$

12. The base angles of $\triangle NPR$ $\angle NPR, \angle NRP$

13. The base of $\triangle MNR$ $\overline{MN}$ 14. The vertex angle of $\triangle MPR$ $\angle P$

15. The legs of $\triangle MNR$ $\overline{MR}, \overline{NR}$ 16. The base angles of $\triangle MRP$ $\angle M, \angle MRP$

Solve for x.

17. 65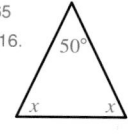
See page 716.

18. 40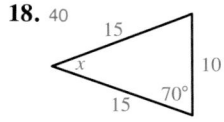

19. 5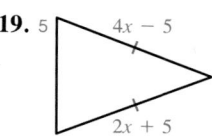

5.1 Congruence in a Single Triangle: Isosceles Triangle Theorem   **177**

Developing Mathematical Power

Thinking Critically Students are asked to draw a conclusion about line segments that form two sides of $\triangle PBJ$ and to write a biconditional.

Lesson Quiz

1. If $\overline{RS} \cong \overline{RT}$, name two congruent angles.
2. If $\angle R \cong \angle T$, name two congruent segments.

ABC is a triangle. Solve for x, then describe $\triangle ABC$.

3. $m\angle A = 3x$, $m\angle B = 2x + 20$, $m\angle C = 4x - 20$
4. $m\angle A = 55$, $m\angle B = 2x + 10$, $m\angle C = 2x - 5$

1. $\angle S \cong \angle T$ 2. $\overline{RS} \cong \overline{TS}$
3. Since $x = 20$, $\triangle ABC$ is equiangular, and hence also equilateral.
4. Since $x = 30$, $m\angle C = 55$. Hence $\triangle ABC$ is isos., with $\overline{BC} \cong \overline{AB}$.

Enrichment

$\triangle ABC$ is isosceles. If $m\angle A = 50$, find the measures of the other two angles.   Either 65 and 65 or 50 and 80.

Additional Answers

12. Proof:

Statements	Reasons
1. $\triangle NAS$ is isos.; $\overline{NA} \cong \overline{NS}$; $\overline{NP}$ bis. $\angle N$	1. Given
2. $\angle 1 \cong \angle 2$	2. Def. of $\angle$ bis.
3. $\angle A \cong \angle S$	3. Isos. $\triangle$ th.
4. $\triangle NAP \cong \triangle NSP$	4. ASA
5. $\angle 3 \cong \angle 4$; $\overline{AP} \cong \overline{SP}$	5. CPCTC
6. $\overline{NP} \perp \overline{AS}$	6. Two lines that int. to form ≅ adj. $\angle$s are $\perp$.

Conclusion: If $\triangle NAS$ is isos. $\overline{NA} \cong \overline{NS}$ and $\overline{NP}$ the bis. of $\angle N$, then $\overline{NP} \perp \overline{AS}$ and $\overline{AP} \cong \overline{SP}$.

Developing Mathematical Power

Cooperative Learning Assign students to work in cooperative groups to explore Triangle Tools (Technology, pp. 5 and 6 in the *Teacher's Resource Book*). The exercises on p. 6 should provide an excellent opportunity for students to visualize the concepts of this lesson.

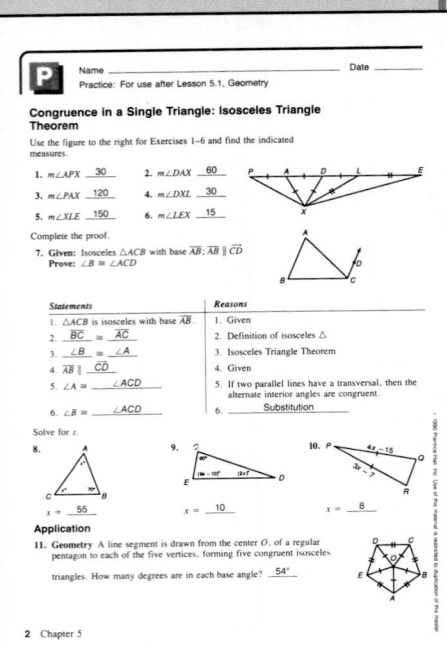

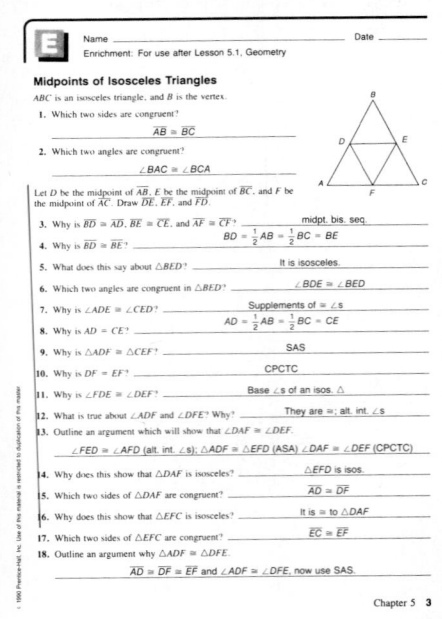

See Additional Answers, p. 702.

20. Given: $\overline{YA} \cong \overline{TA}$
    Prove: $\angle AYM \cong \angle ATR$

21. Given: $\angle AYM \cong \angle ATR$
    Prove: $\triangle AYT$ is isosceles.

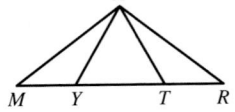

Draw and label a figure. Write the *Given* and *Prove* and then prove.

22. Corollary 1 of Theorem 5.1

23. Corollary 2 of Theorem 5.1

24. Theorem 5.2

25. Corollary of Theorem 5.2

C **26.** If the altitude to a side of a triangle is also a median, the triangle is isosceles.

27. The median from the vertex angle to the base of an isosceles triangle bisects the vertex angle.

Applications

28. Technology Use Logo to generate several isosceles triangles with the same vertex angle. See Solutions Manual.

29. Design A rectangular window is composed of four isosceles triangles. Name the isosceles triangles that are congruent. Justify your answers.
$\triangle BEC \cong \triangle AED$ (SAS); $\triangle BEA \cong \triangle CED$ (SAS)

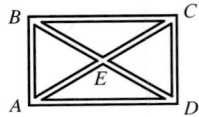

Mixed Review

$\triangle ABC \cong \triangle FGH$. $\overline{AD}$ is a median. $\overline{GJ}$ is an altitude. Find the indicated measures.

30. AB 6

31. $m\angle BCA$ 35

32. $m\angle JGH$ 55

33. BC 10

34. FH 12

35. $m\angle GFH$ 70

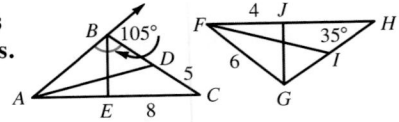

Developing Mathematical Power

36. Thinking Critically If you construct $\angle KJB$ congruent to $\angle PBJ$ as shown, and $\overrightarrow{BA}$ and $\overrightarrow{JK}$ intersect at P, what conclusion can you draw about $\overline{BP}$ and $\overline{JP}$? Why?
$\overline{BP} \cong \overline{JP}$. If 2 $\angle$s of a $\triangle$ are $\cong$, then the sides opp. those $\angle$s are $\cong$.

37. Thinking Critically Write the biconditional statement combining the Isosceles Triangle Theorem and its converse. Two sides of a triangle are congruent if and only if the angles opposite those sides are congruent.

178 Chapter 5 Inequalities in Triangles

5.2 Properties of Inequality

Objectives: To state and apply properties of inequality to measures of segments and angles
To prove statements involving inequalities
To determine information using diagrams

The algebraic inequalities *greater than* and *less than* are used to compare geometric figures containing segments or angles that are not congruent.

Investigation—*Visualizing the Concept*

Randy is using her computer to graph circles. After graphing points *A*, *B*, *C*, and *O* on the coordinate plane, she runs her program for a circle with center at *O* (0, 0) and radius 5. On a printout of the figure, Randy compares *OA*, *OB*, and *OC*.

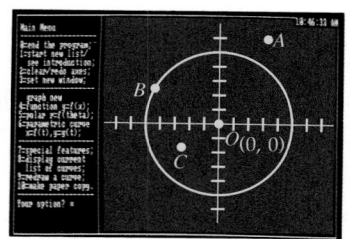

1. How would you compare these distances? *OA* > *OB* > *OC*
2. What algebraic statements can you write to show the comparisons?
OA > 5, *OB* = 5, *OC* < 5, so *OA* > *OB* > *OC*

Randy draws $\overrightarrow{AO}$ and labels the intersection points with the circle as *D* and *E*. Then she draws $\overrightarrow{OB}$ and $\overrightarrow{OC}$.

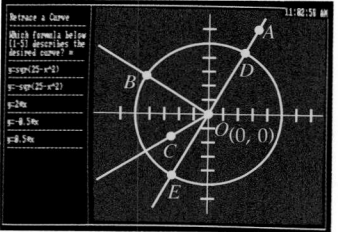

3. How does *m∠AOB* compare with *m∠AOC*? *m∠AOB* < *m∠AOC*

Two segments or two angles are not congruent when they have different measures. If *AB* is less than *CD*, (or *CD* is greater than *AB*), then *AB* ≠ *CD*. What could be said if ∠*E* and ∠*F* have different measures? *m∠E* > *m∠F* or *m∠E* < *m∠F*

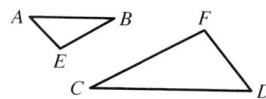

For real numbers *a* and *b*, *a* is **greater than** *b*, written *a* > *b*, if and only if there is a positive number *c* such that *a* = *b* + *c*. For segments, $\overline{AB}$ and $\overline{CD}$, *AB* > *CD* if and only if there exists some segment $\overline{EF}$ such that *AB* = *CD* + *EF*. For angles, ∠*A* and ∠*B*, *m∠A* > *m∠B* if and only if there exists some ∠*C* such that *m∠A* = *m∠B* + *m∠C*.

The next two theorems compare subsets of line segments and angles and are summarized by saying that *the whole is greater than any of its parts.*

LESSON PLAN

Vocabulary
Greater than
Less than

Materials/Manipulatives
Teacher's Resource Book,
Teaching Aid 5
Teaching Transparency 29

Technology
Computer Test Bank, pp.
257–266

LESSON FOCUS

Review
Draw this figure on the chalkboard. Ask students what they know about *m∠1*, *m∠A* and *m∠B*.
m∠1 = m∠A + m∠B

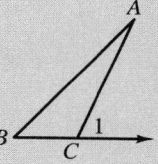

Alternative Learning Styles
• In the Investigation students use a real-life situation to visualize the relationship between segments that are not congruent.
• Manipulatives provide a kinesthetic approach to teaching the inequality properties of algebra. For example, working with two equal lengths and two unequal lengths of string, students can add one of the equal lengths to each of the unequal lengths. Comparing the results will illustrate the addition property of inequality.

Developing Mathematical Power
Cooperative Learning Select teams of students to create a presentation that demonstrates the addition or the subtraction property of inequality. Challenge students to be as creative as possible. The presentation can be audio, visual, theatrical, and so on. Invite outside judges to choose the most creative presentation.

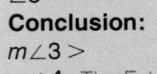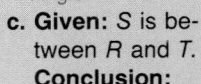
Theorem 5.3   If B is between A and C, then $AC > AB$ and $AC > BC$. Proved in Practice Exercise 19

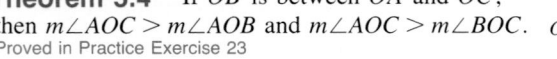

Theorem 5.4   If $\overrightarrow{OB}$ is between $\overrightarrow{OA}$ and $\overrightarrow{OC}$, then $m\angle AOC > m\angle AOB$ and $m\angle AOC > m\angle BOC$. Proved in Practice Exercise 23

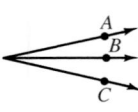

EXAMPLE 1   **Explain why the given inequality is valid.**

a. $5 > 2$ **b.** $-6 > -11$ **c.** $n < p$ where n is negative and p is positive.

a. $5 > 2$ because $5 = 2 + 3$.   **b.** $-6 > -11$ because $-6 = -11 + 5$.
c. $n < p$ because $p = n + (p - n)$. (Note that $p - n$ is positive.)

Theorem 5.5   **Exterior Angle Theorem**   The measure of an exterior angle of a triangle is greater than the measure of either remote interior angle.

Given: $\triangle XYZ$ with $\overrightarrow{XZ}$ extended
Prove: $m\angle 4 > m\angle 2$ and $m\angle 4 > m\angle 1$
Plan: $m\angle 4 = m\angle 1 + m\angle 2$. By the definition of greater than, $m\angle 4 > m\angle 2$ and $m\angle 4 > m\angle 1$.
Proved in Practice Exercise 20

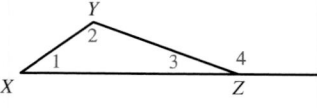

EXAMPLE 2   **Complete each statement by using $>$, $<$, or $=$.**

a. $m\angle 3\_\underline{?}\_ m\angle 1$ **b.** $m\angle 3\_\underline{?}\_ m\angle 5$
c. $m\angle 11\_\underline{?}\_ m\angle 4$ **d.** $m\angle 5\_\underline{?}\_ m\angle 7$
e. $m\angle 10\_\underline{?}\_ m\angle 6$ **f.** $m\angle 8\_\underline{?}\_ m\angle 4 + m\angle 10$

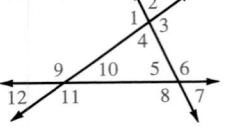

a. $=$ **b.** $>$ **c.** $>$ **d.** $=$ **e.** $<$ **f.** $=$

Properties of Inequality   (a, b, c, and d refer to real numbers.)
Proved in Practice Exercises 24–26

Addition	If $a > b$ and $c \geq d$, then $a + c > b + d$.
Subtraction	If $a > b$ and $c = d$, then $a - c > b - d$.
	If $a = b$ and $c > d$, then $a - c < b - d$.
Multiplication	If $a > b$ and $c > 0$, then $a \cdot c > b \cdot c$.
	If $a > b$ and $c < 0$, then $a \cdot c < b \cdot c$.
Division	If $a > b$ and $c > 0$, then $a \div c > b \div c$.
	If $a > b$ and $c < 0$, then $a \div c < b \div c$.
Transitive	If $a > b$ and $b > c$, then $a > c$.

The **trichotomy property** is stated as follows: If the numbers a and b are given, then $a > b$ or $a = b$ or $a < b$.

EXAMPLE 3 **Identify the property illustrated.**

a.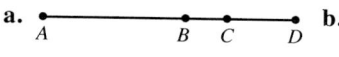

b.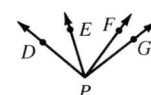

c.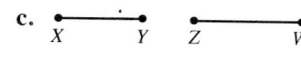

a.
Given: $AC > BD$

Conclusion:
$AC - BC > BD - BC$

b.
Given:
$m\angle EPF > m\angle DPE$;
$m\angle DPE > m\angle FPG$

Conclusion:
$m\angle EPF > m\angle FPG$

c.
Given: $XY \neq ZW$

Conclusion:
$XY > ZW$ or $XY < ZW$.

a. Subtraction property   **b.** Transitive property   **c.** Trichotomy property

EXAMPLE 4 **Use the *Given, Prove,* and *Figure* to write a *Plan* for a proof.**

Given: $\overline{AD}$ with $BD > AC$
Prove: $CD > AB$ Plan: ?

Plan: Use the definition of betweenness to write equations $BD = BC + CD$ and $AC = AB + BC$. Since $BD > AC$, then $BC + CD > AB + BC$. Apply the Subtraction property of inequality to show $CD > AB$.

CLASS EXERCISES

1. **Thinking Critically** Congruence of segments and congruence of angles have the reflexive, symmetric, and transitive properties. Do the relationships of noncongruence (either $>$ or $<$) of segments and angles have those three properties? Justify your answer. only the trans. prop.: if $a > b$ and $b > c$, then $a > c$; if $a < b$ and $b < c$, then $a < c$; not reflexive: $a \not< a$; not symmetric: if $a < b$, then $b \not< a$

Name the property of inequality suggested in Exercises 2–4.

2. If $AB = CD = 10$ cm, $XY = 4$ cm, and $PQ = 3$ cm, then $AB - XY < CD - PQ$.
    subtraction

3. If $MN > 8$ cm, then $2 \cdot MN > 16$ cm. multiplication

4. If $TR = 18$ cm, $PS = 24$ cm, and $HK = 15$ cm, then $TR + HK < PS + HK$. addition

$\triangle DGF$ **is isosceles with base** $\overline{GF}$. **Use** $>$, $<$, **or** $=$.
Justify your answers.

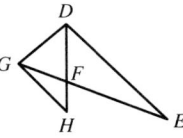

5. $m\angle DGF \underline{\ ?\ } m\angle DFG$
   =; base $\angle$s are $\cong$
6. $m\angle DGF \underline{\ ?\ } m\angle DEF$
   >; subst. prop. and Ext. $\angle$ Th.
7. $m\angle GDF \underline{\ ?\ } m\angle DFE$
   <; Ext. $\angle$ Th.
8. $m\angle HFG \underline{\ ?\ } m\angle FDG$
   >; Ext. $\angle$ Th.
9. $m\angle GFH \underline{\ ?\ } m\angle DFE$
   =; vert. $\angle$s are $\cong$.
10. $m\angle DGH \underline{\ ?\ } m\angle DEF$

10. $m\angle DGH > m\angle DGF$ because the whole is $>$ than any of its parts and $m\angle DGF > m\angle DEF$ by Ex. 6, so concl. follows by the trans. prop.

5.2 Properties of Inequality   **181**

Use the Given, Prove, and figure to write a Plan for a proof.
Given: $\overline{RW}$
with
$RS > TW$
Prove: $RT > SW$
Plan: By the add. prop. of inequality, $RS + ST > TW + ST$. By the def. of betweenness, $RS + ST = RT$ and $ST + TW = SW$. By substitution, $RT > SW$.

Common Error
• Some students may not apply the properties of inequality correctly. Ask these students to give their own examples illustrating each property.
• See *Teacher's Resource Book* for additional remediation.

LESSON FOLLOW-UP

Discussion
Put this figure and given information on the chalkboard.

Given: $AC > AB$

How do BD and DC compare?
How do $m\angle B$ and $m\angle C$ compare? It appears that $BD < DC$ and $m\angle B > m\angle C$.

Ask students if it is possible for BD to equal DC. What would then be true of AB and AC? (If necessary, help students work through the following reasoning step by step.) If $BD = DC$, then $\triangle ABD \cong \triangle ADC$ by SAS, so $\overline{AB} \cong \overline{AC}$. But that's not possible, since it is given that $AC > AB$.

Point out that students will learn more about this type of reasoning, called an *indirect proof,* in the next two lessons. Now that it has been shown that $BD \neq DC$, ask students what alternatives remain. $BD > DC$ or $BD < DC$

Tell students to assume that $BD < DC$ and ask them to suggest an auxiliary line that would help them *prove* that $m\angle B > m\angle C$.

On $\overrightarrow{DC}$ let E be the point such that $DE = BD$. Draw $\overline{AE}$. Show that $\overline{AB} \cong \overline{AE}$ and hence $\angle B \cong \angle AED$. Also, $m\angle AED > m\angle C$. Thus $m\angle B > m\angle C$.

Critical Thinking

1. *Differentiating* Have students distinguish between judging from the appearance of a figure and a proof.
2. *Application* Ask students to utilize auxiliary lines.
3. *Reasoning* Have students plan proofs.

Assignment Guide

See p. 172B for assignments.

Developing Mathematical Power

Drawing in Geometry Students are asked to draw a geometric figure from specific information.

Lesson Quiz

Write a *Plan* for a proof.

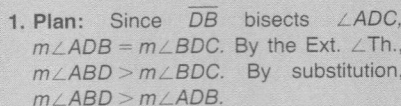

1. **Given:** $\overline{DB}$ bisects $\angle ADC$
   Prove: $m\angle ABD > m\angle ADB$
2. **Given:** $\angle RST \cong \angle RTS$
   Prove: $RW > RT$

1. **Plan:** Since $\overline{DB}$ bisects $\angle ADC$, $m\angle ADB = m\angle BDC$. By the Ext. $\angle$ Th., $m\angle ABD > m\angle BDC$. By substitution, $m\angle ABD > m\angle ADB$.
2. **Plan:** Since $\angle RST \cong \angle RTS$, $\overline{RS} \cong \overline{RT}$ and $RS = RT$. Since the whole is greater than any of its parts, $RW > RS$. By substitution, $RW > RT$.

PRACTICE EXERCISES Use technology where appropriate.

Name the property or theorem that justifies each statement.

A **1.** If $AB \neq CD$, then $AB > CD$ or $AB < CD$. trichotomy

2. If $a < b$, then $-2a > -2b$. multiplication

3. If $\overrightarrow{OB}$ is in the interior of $\angle AOC$, then $m\angle AOC > m\angle AOB$.
Whole is greater than any of its parts.

4. If $m\angle XYZ > m\angle PRS$ and if $m\angle PRS > m\angle JKL$, then $m\angle XYZ > m\angle JKL$. transitive

Identify the true statements. Justify each.

5.
P Q R S

a. $PS > RS$
true; Th 5.3

b. $PQ < PR$
true; Th. 5.3

c. $QS < RS$
false; $QS > RS$

d. $PR > QS$
cannot determine

6.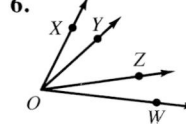

a. $m\angle XOY > m\angle YOZ$
cannot determine

b. $m\angle XOZ > m\angle YOZ$
true; Th 5.4

c. $m\angle ZOW < m\angle XOW$
true; Th 5.4

d. $m\angle YOZ < m\angle ZOW$
cannot determine

Refer to the figure and complete each statement.

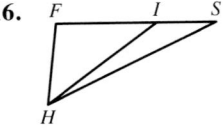

7. An exterior angle of $\triangle BAF$ is $\underline{?}$. $\angle BFG$ or $\angle AFE$

8. In $\triangle BGC$, the remote interior angles of $\angle HGC$ are $\underline{?}$ and $\underline{?}$.
$\angle GBC$ $\angle GCB$

9. Two angles with measures greater than $m\angle ACE$ are $\underline{?}$ and $\underline{?}$. $\angle DHC$ and $\angle BGC$ or $\angle BCH$ and $\angle GCD$

10. An angle congruent to $\angle AFB$ is $\underline{?}$. $\angle EFG$

11. If $FC > AG$, then $GC > \underline{?}$. AF

12. If $EH > CG$, and $CG > AF$, then $\underline{?} > \underline{?}$. $EH > AF$

13. Two angles with measures less than $m\angle CHD$ are $\underline{?}$ and $\underline{?}$. Answers may vary; $\angle CGH$ and $\angle GCH$

14. If $EB = BD$, then $\angle \underline{?} \cong \angle \underline{?}$. BED; BDE

Identify the property or theorem that justifies each conclusion.

15.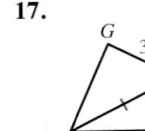

Conclusion:
$m\angle TMH > m\angle TMO$
Th. 5.4

16.
F I S
H

Conclusion: $FI < FS$
Th. 5.3

17.
G 3 A 5 R
N D

Conclusion: $RN > GD$
Add. prop. of inequal.

Developing Mathematical Power

Keeping a Portfolio Have students write a paragraph about inequalities. They should describe the relationship between $a = b + c$ and $a > b$, identify the properties of inequalities, and compare inequalities in algebra and in geometry.

B 18. Given $\triangle PQR$ with sides extended as shown, write six inequality statements that relate exterior and remote interior angles of $\triangle PQR$. See below.

19. Use the plan to complete a proof of Theorem 5.3.

Given: B is between A and C.
Prove: $AC > AB$; $AC > BC$ See Additional Answers, p. 702.
Plan: Since B is between A and C, $AB + BC = AC$, where AB, BC, and AC are all positive numbers. Then $AC > AB$ and $AC > BC$ by the definition of greater than.

20. Complete a proof of Theorem 5.5.

Write a two-column proof.

21. **Given:** I is the midpoint of $\overline{ME}$ and $\overline{XS}$.
    Prove: $m\angle MSR > m\angle XEI$

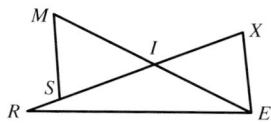

22. **Given:** $\triangle ABC$ with $\overrightarrow{BC}$ extended through D
    Prove: $m\angle A + m\angle ACB < 180$

    Generalize the result given by this theorem.

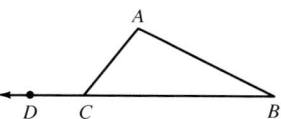

C 23. Prove Theorem 5.4.

Prove these properties of inequality. See Additional Answers, p. 702.

24. Addition   25. Transitive   26. Multiplication, when $c > 0$

Applications

27. **Technology** Use the Logo procedure from page 178, Exercise 28, to generate a windmill design. See Solutions Manual.

28. **Construction** Collinear points A, B, and C represent a segment of roadway that is less than 15 mi long. Solve for the possible values of x. Check your answers. $\frac{3}{2} < x < 3$

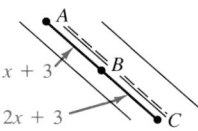

Developing Mathematical Power

29. **Drawing in Geometry** Draw a figure given this information: A, B, and C are collinear points; $\overrightarrow{OA}$, $\overrightarrow{OB}$, and $\overrightarrow{OC}$ have common endpoint O; $AB > AC$; and $m\angle AOC < m\angle AOB$. See below.

5.2 Properties of Inequality   **183**

29. Drawings may vary.

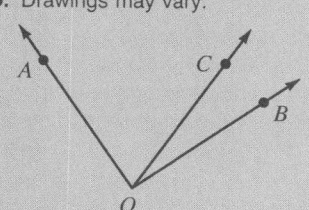

18. $m\angle 7 > m\angle 1$; $m\angle 7 > m\angle 2$;
$m\angle 6 > m\angle 1$; $m\angle 6 > m\angle 3$;
$m\angle 4 > m\angle 1$; $m\angle 4 > m\angle 3$

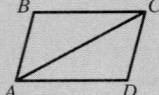
5.3 Strategy: Use Indirect Proof

The theorems you have studied so far have been proven *directly* by beginning with the given information and applying postulates, other theorems, and definitions to show that the conclusion must follow. Some theorems, however, are more easily proven by *indirect reasoning.*

Indirect reasoning is often used in everyday situations. Suppose you were taking a multiple choice test and each question had three possible responses. If you were not sure of the answer to a certain question but you could eliminate choices (a) and (b) because those choices contradicted other facts that you knew to be true, then you would feel confident that (c) is correct.

Indirect reasoning is the basis for *indirect proof* in which all conclusions except the desired one are eliminated as possibilities, with the result that the remaining conclusion must be true. The problem-solving steps can help you organize and write an indirect proof.

EXAMPLE 1   **Given:** $\triangle ABC$ with $\overline{AB} \not\cong \overline{BC}$
   Prove: $\angle C \not\cong \angle A$

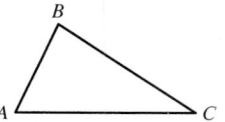

□ Understand   **What is given?**
   the Problem $\triangle ABC$ with $\overline{AB} \not\cong \overline{BC}$

               What is to be proven?
               $\angle C \not\cong \angle A$

□ Plan Your   **Look ahead.**
   Approach   No methods encountered so far apply to showing that two angles are *not* congruent.

               Look back.
               It is given that two segments are *not* congruent. This is unlike any problem encountered previously.

184   Chapter 5 Inequalities in Triangles

Think.
Since the desired conclusion is $\angle C \not\cong \angle A$, the only other possible conclusion is its *negation,* $\angle C \cong \angle A$. If this possibility is eliminated, the desired conclusion must be true.

Plan.
Start by assuming that $\angle C \cong \angle A$ is true. If this assumption leads to a contradiction of a known fact or of the hypothesis (the *Given*), then $\angle C \cong \angle A$ must be false. Hence, $\angle C \not\cong \angle A$ must be true.

Implement the Plan Indirect proofs can be written in *paragraph form* or in *two-column form*. In both methods, statements must be justified.

Proof:

Assume:	$\angle C \cong \angle A$	Negation of conclusion
	$\overline{AB} \cong \overline{BC}$	Converse of Isosceles Triangle Theorem
Contradiction:	$\overline{AB} \not\cong \overline{BC}$	

Interpret the Results **Conclusion:**
Since the assumption that $\angle C \cong \angle A$ leads to a contradiction of the *Given,* then $\angle C \cong \angle A$ must be false. Therefore, $\angle C \not\cong \angle A$.

The method of indirect proof is based on two important laws of logic: a statement in mathematics is either true or false and no other possibilities exist, and a statement cannot be both true and false at the same time.

Problem Solving Reminders

When writing an indirect proof:
- *Assume* that the negation of the conclusion is true.
- Show that the assumption leads to a *contradiction* of known facts or of the given information.
- *Conclude* that since the assumption is false, the original (desired) conclusion is true.

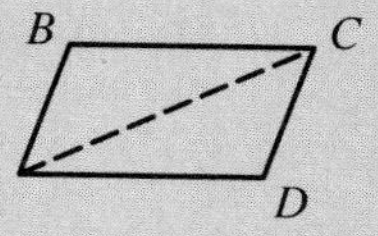

Indirect proof is often appropriate when you must show that two things are *not* related in some way.

TEACHING SUGGESTIONS

- Students often have difficulty with indirect proof, because the logic that underlies it is subtle. Emphasize the two laws of logic that are used in indirect proof: a statement is either true or false and it cannot be both at the same time. Make certain that students understand how these laws of logic are embodied in indirect proof.
- Part of students' difficulties with indirect proof can be alleviated by providing many examples and many opportunities in which they are asked to prove theorems indirectly. Mix direct and indirect proofs to give students experience in deciding when each proof form is appropriate.
- Point out that statements written in paragraph proofs must be justified, just as in proofs written in two-column form.

CHALKBOARD EXAMPLES

- **For Example 1**

Given: $\overline{AD} \nparallel \overline{BC}$; $\overline{DA} \cong \overline{BC}$

Prove: $\overline{CD} \not\cong \overline{AB}$

Proof:

Assume:	$\overline{CD} \cong \overline{AB}$	Neg. of concl.
	$\overline{DA} \cong \overline{BC}$	Given
	$\overline{CA} \cong \overline{AC}$	Refl. prop.
	$\triangle CDA \cong \triangle ABC$	SSS Post.
	$\angle DAC \cong \angle BCA$	CPCTC
	$\overline{AD} \parallel \overline{BC}$	If 2 lines have a trans. such that alt. int. $\angle$s are $\cong$, the lines are $\parallel$.

Contradiction: $\overline{AD} \nparallel \overline{BC}$
Conclusion: The assumption contradicted the given. Thus, it must be false; hence $\overline{CD} \not\cong \overline{AB}$.

- **For Example 2**
  Prove indirectly: If two coplanar lines are perpendicular to the same line, then they are parallel.

  Given: $k \perp j$;
  $l \perp j$

  Prove: $k \parallel l$
  Proof: Assume that $k \not\parallel l$. Then k and l intersect in some point P, since they are coplanar. Thus lines k and l, both of which contain P, are perpendicular to j. However, this contradicts the fact that through a point not on a line, there is one and only one line perpendicular to a given line. Therefore, the assumption that $k \not\parallel l$ must be false. Hence, $k \parallel l$.

Common Error

- Some students will have difficulty understanding the logic of indirect proofs and thus will have trouble writing them. Asking them to verbalize the process used, as well as asking them to complete sufficient examples, should help overcome these difficulties.
- See *Teacher's Resource Book* for additional remediation.

EXAMPLE 2 If a line intersects one side of a triangle and is parallel to the second side, then it must intersect the third side of the triangle.

☐ **Understand the Problem**

Draw a picture.

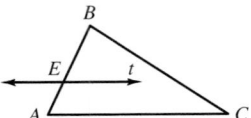

What is given?
$\triangle ABC$: t intersects $\overline{AB}$; $t \parallel \overline{AC}$

What is to be proven?
t intersects $\overline{BC}$.

☐ **Plan Your Approach**

Look ahead.
One way to show that t intersects $\overline{BC}$ is to show that t and $\overline{BC}$ are not parallel. This suggests an indirect approach.

Look back.
Recall that every pair of sides of a triangle intersects. In other words, a triangle cannot have a pair of parallel sides.

Plan.
Assume the negation of the conclusion, or $t \parallel \overline{BC}$. Show that this leads to a contradiction.

☐ **Implement the Plan**

Proof:
Assume that t does not intersect $\overline{BC}$. Since t and $\overline{BC}$ are coplanar, it must be true that $t \parallel \overline{BC}$. If $t \parallel \overline{BC}$ and $t \parallel \overline{AC}$, it follows that $\overline{BC} \parallel \overline{AC}$ since two lines parallel to the same line are parallel to each other. But this contradicts the fact that ABC is a triangle. Therefore, the assumption that t does not intersect $\overline{BC}$, or $t \parallel \overline{BC}$, must be false; hence, t intersects $\overline{BC}$.

☐ **Interpret the Results**

Conclusion:
Assuming the negation of the conclusion produced a contradiction of the given information that $\overline{AB}$, $\overline{BC}$, and $\overline{AC}$ must all intersect. Thus, the assumption must be false; consequently it is true that t intersects $\overline{BC}$.

The method of indirect proof is also useful in proving theorems about geometric inequalities which are considered in the next lesson.

CLASS EXERCISES

Thinking Critically

1. Describe the process to be followed in order for a theorem to be proven indirectly. Assume that the negation of the concl. is true; show that the assumption leads to a contradiction of known facts or of the given; conclude that since the assumption is false, the original (desired) concl. is true.

2. Why is the method of indirect proof sometimes called "proof by elimination"? All conclusions except the desired one are eliminated as possibilities with the result that the remaining concl. must be true.

3. In proving a theorem indirectly, why can't the hypothesis be assumed false instead of the conclusion? Assuming the hypothesis false will not necessarily lead to a single conclusion.

Explain how indirect reasoning is being used in each of the following situations.

4. An attorney argues that his client, Bob, could not be guilty because a witness saw Bob in a different place at the time the crime was committed. The statement of the witness contradicts the assumption that Bob was where the crime was committed.

5. The light goes out in your room as you turn on the switch. You decide that the problem must be the bulb, because lights are on in the rest of the house. All other explanations for the light going out were eliminated.

Suppose each theorem is to be proven indirectly. Write the first statement of the proof.

6. In $\triangle DEF$, if $\angle D \not\equiv \angle F$, then $\overline{EF} \not\equiv \overline{DE}$. Assume $\overline{EF} \cong \overline{DE}$.

7. If lines a and b are not parallel, then alternate interior angles 1 and 2 are not congruent. Assume alt. int. $\angle$s 1 and 2 are $\cong$.

8. If a and b are even numbers, then $a + b$ is an even number. Assume $a + b$ is not an even number.

9. If $a > b$ and $c = d$, then $a + c > b + d$. Assume $a + c \leq b + d$.

10. If $a \parallel b$ and $c \not\parallel b$, then $a \not\parallel c$. Assume $a \parallel c$.

PRACTICE EXERCISES

Write an indirect proof for each of the following. See Additional Answers, p. 702.

A
1. Given: $\overline{MP} \cong \overline{MN}$; $\overline{ON} \not\equiv \overline{OP}$
   Prove: $\overline{OM}$ does not bisect $\angle PMN$.

2. Given: $\overline{MP} \cong \overline{MN}$; $\overline{ON} \not\equiv \overline{OP}$
   Prove: $\overline{OM}$ not $\perp \overline{NP}$

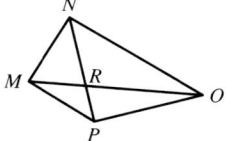

Assignment Guide
See p. 172B for assignments.

Project
This is an opportune time to assign students the College Entrance Exam Review page located at the end of any chapter. Ask them to solve each problem and determine the type of reasoning used for each.

Lesson Quiz
Given: $\triangle DEF$ with
        $\angle D \not\equiv \angle F$

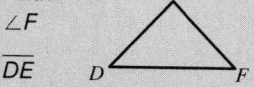

Prove: $\overline{EF} \not\equiv \overline{DE}$
Proof:
Assume: $\overline{EF} \cong \overline{DE}$ Negation of the conclusion
         $\angle D \cong \angle F$ Isos. $\triangle$ Th.

Contradiction: $\angle D \not\equiv \angle F$
Conclusion: Since the assumption that $\overline{EF} \cong \overline{DE}$ contradicts the given information, the assumption must be false. Thus $\overline{EF} \not\equiv \overline{DE}$.

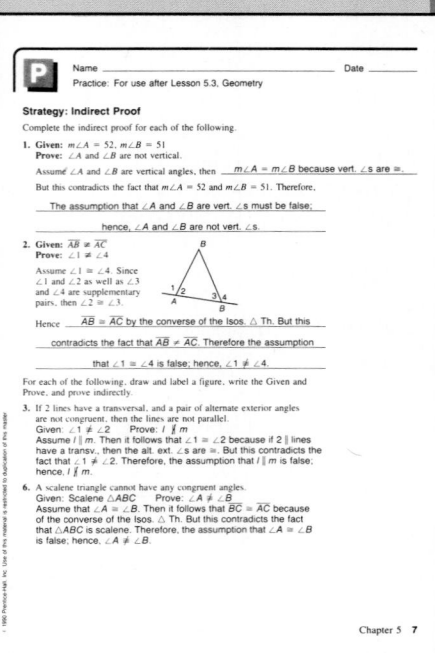

Chapter 5   **7**

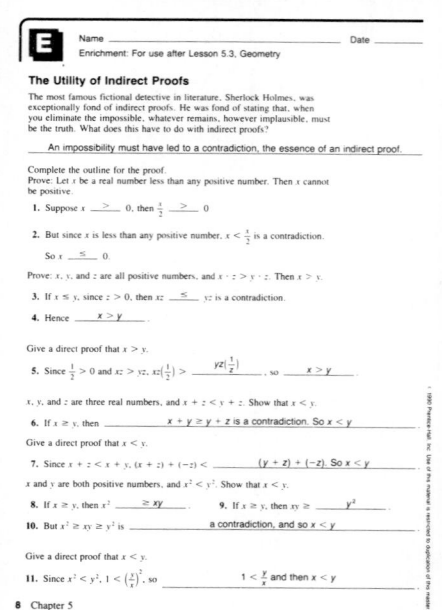

8   Chapter 5

See Additional Answers, p. 702.

Write an indirect proof for each of the following.

3. Given: $\angle 1 \not\cong \angle 3$
   Prove: $\angle 3$ and $\angle 4$ are not supplementary.

4. Given: $\angle 1$ and $\angle 5$ are not supplementary.
   Prove: $\angle 3$ and $\angle 4$ are not supplementary.

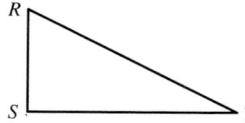

5. Given: $\angle 2 \not\cong \angle 3$ **6. Given:** $k \parallel l$
   Prove: $k \parallel l$ **Prove:** $\angle 1 \not\cong \angle 3$

7. Given: $\angle R$ and $\angle T$
   are not complements.
   Prove: $\angle S$ is not a right angle.

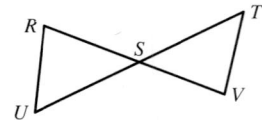

8. Given: $\overline{RU} \parallel \overline{TV}$; $\overline{US} \cong \overline{ST}$
   Prove: $\triangle RSU \not\cong \triangle VST$

9. Given: $\triangle RSU \not\cong \triangle VST$; $\overline{RU} \cong \overline{TV}$
   Prove: $\overline{RU} \parallel \overline{TV}$

B **For each of the following, draw and label a figure, write the *Given* and *Prove*, and prove indirectly.**

10. An obtuse triangle cannot contain a right angle.

11. In a scalene triangle, the altitude to a side of the triangle cannot also be a median of the triangle.

12. If a point is not equidistant from the endpoints of a segment, it does not lie on the perpendicular bisector of the segment.

C **13.** If a point is not equidistant from the sides of an angle, it does not lie on the bisector of the angle.

14. If two parallel lines have a transversal, alternate interior angles are congruent.

15. If two lines are parallel to the same line, they are parallel to each other.

PROJECT

Research the types of mathematics questions found on standardized tests such as the PSAT and SAT. Explain how indirect reasoning might be applied to answer each type of question.

5.4 Indirect Proof and Inequalities

Objective: To write indirect proofs involving inequalities

When you formulate a negation in an indirect proof, you may have to consider more than one alternative to the desired conclusion.

Investigation—*Coordinate Geometry*

Examine these statements.

Statement a: The graphs of $y = x + 1$ and $y = -x - 1$ are lines.
Statement b: The graphs of $y = x + 1$ and $y = -x - 1$ are not lines.
Statement b is the negation of Statement a.

Study this graph of the equations on the coordinate plane.

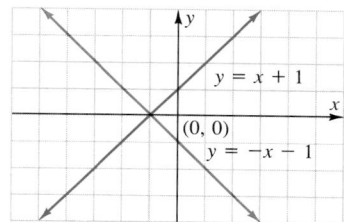

x	y = x + 1
1	2
0	1
−1	0

x	y = −x − 1
1	−2
0	−1
−1	0

1. Is Statement a true or false? true
2. Is Statement b true or false? false

Examine these statements.

Statement c: The graphs of $y = x + 1$ and $y = -x - 1$ are the same.
Statement d: The graphs of $y = x + 1$ and $y = -x - 1$ are not the same.

3. Is Statement d the negation of Statement c? yes
4. Which is false, Statement c or Statement d? Statement c
5. Compare your results for each pair of statements and make a generalization.
A statement and its negation have opposite truth values.

Recall the three steps to follow when writing an indirect proof.

1. Make an *assumption* that the negation of the conclusion is true.

2. Show that the assumption leads to a *contradiction* of known facts or of the given information.

3. Conclude that since the assumption has been shown to be false, the original conclusion must be true.

Developing Mathematical Power

Keeping a Portfolio   Have students record in their math journals each of the symbols that can be used to express a relation. Then have them write all the possible negations for each symbol. They should distinguish cases in which only one alternative results from a negation from those cases in which more than one alternative results.

- Continue to emphasize the logic of indirect proofs. This idea is often difficult for students.
- To help prepare students for the following two lessons, tell them that proofs involving inequalities are more likely to involve indirect reasoning than are proofs involving equations or congruences.

CHALKBOARD EXAMPLES

- **For Example 1**

  Give the negation of each statement. List all the alternatives that result.

  a. $XY < ZW$
  b. $m\angle A > m\angle B$
  c. $CD = DE$

  a. $XY \nless ZW$, so $XY = ZW$ or $XY > ZW$
  b. $m\angle A \ngtr m\angle B$, so $m\angle A = m\angle B$ or $m\angle A < m\angle B$
  c. $CD \neq DE$, so $CD < DE$ or $CD > DE$

- **For Examples 2 and 3**

  Suppose the given statement is to be proven indirectly. Write the first statement of the proof and identify all alternatives that must be considered.

  Given: $\triangle ABC$ and $\triangle DEF$ with $\overline{AB} \cong \overline{DE}$; $\overline{BC} \cong \overline{EF}$; $AC > DF$
  Prove: $m\angle B > m\angle E$
  Proof: Assume that $m\angle B \ngtr m\angle E$. Then $m\angle B = m\angle E$ or $m\angle B < m\angle E$.

Common Error

- Some students will fail to consider all the alternatives in forming a negation. Make sure they get lots of practice with exercises that involve the trichotomy property.
- See *Teacher's Resource Book* for additional remediation.

Indirect reasoning is often used in geometry proofs involving inequalities. Negating a theorem about inequalities may produce

one alternative   *or more than one alternative.*

↓   ↓

Conclusion: $\overline{AB} \cong \overline{CD}$ Conclusion: $AB = CD$
Negate the   Negate the
conclusion: $\overline{AB} \ncong \overline{CD}$ conclusion: $AB < CD$ or $AB > CD$

EXAMPLE 1   **Give the negation of each statement. List all the alternatives that result.**

     a. $m\angle D = m\angle E$ **b.** $AB > CD$ **c.** $m\angle A < m\angle B$

     a. $m\angle D \neq m\angle E$, so $m\angle D < m\angle E$ or $m\angle D > m\angle E$
     b. $AB \ngtr CD$, so $AB < CD$ or $AB = CD$
     c. $m\angle A \nless m\angle B$, so $m\angle A = m\angle B$ or $m\angle A > m\angle B$

If a statement is to be proven indirectly and the negation of the conclusion leads to more than one alternative, it is necessary to show that *each* alternative produces a contradiction.

EXAMPLE 2   **Write an indirect proof for this statement:**

In a scalene triangle, no two angles are congruent.

Given: Scalene $\triangle ABC$
Prove: $\angle A \not\cong \angle B$
Plan: Assume the negation of $\angle A \not\cong \angle B$. Show that this leads to a contradiction.

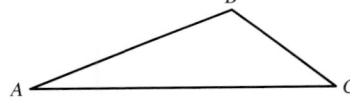

Proof:

Assume: $\angle A \cong \angle B$ Negation of the conclusion
         $\overline{BC} \cong \overline{AC}$ If two angles of $\triangle ABC$ are $\cong$, then the sides opposite those angles are $\cong$.

         $\triangle ABC$ is isosceles.   Definition of an isosceles triangle

Contradiction: $\triangle ABC$ is scalene.

Conclusion: Since the assumption that $\angle A \cong \angle B$ leads to a contradiction, then $\angle A \cong \angle B$ must be false. Therefore, $\angle A \not\cong \angle B$.

              Since $\angle A$ and $\angle B$ were chosen to be any two angles, the proof is complete.

Example 3 is an indirect proof of the Exterior Angle Theorem. It illustrates a situation in which two alternatives must be considered.

EXAMPLE 3   **Write an indirect proof for this statement:**

The measure of the exterior angle of a triangle is greater than the measure of either of its remote interior angles.

Given: △PQR with $\overrightarrow{PR}$ extended through S

Prove: $m\angle 4 > m\angle 1$

Plan: Since the negation of the conclusion leads to two alternatives, show that each one leads to a contradiction.

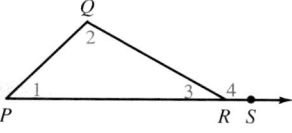

Proof:

(1) *Assume:* $m\angle 4 < m\angle 1$ Negation of the conclusion
  $m\angle 4 + m\angle 2 < m\angle 1 + m\angle 2$ Addition property of inequality
  $m\angle 1 + m\angle 2 = m\angle 4$ The measure of the exterior angle equals the sum of the measures of the two remote interior angles.
  $m\angle 4 + m\angle 2 < m\angle 4$ Substitution property

  Contradiction: The sum is greater than either positive addend.

(2) *Assume:* $m\angle 4 = m\angle 1$ Negation of the conclusion
  $m\angle 4 + m\angle 3 = m\angle 1 + m\angle 3$ Addition property of equality
  $m\angle 4 + m\angle 3 = 180$ Linear Pair Postulate and definition of supplementary angles
  $m\angle 1 + m\angle 3 = 180$ Substitution property

  Contradiction: In △PQR, $m\angle 1 + m\angle 2 + m\angle 3 = 180$.

Conclusion: Since both alternative assumptions produced contradictions, $m\angle 4 \nleq m\angle 1$. Therefore $m\angle 4 > m\angle 1$. The same argument can be used to show that $m\angle 4 > m\angle 2$.

When you are asked to prove a statement, analyze the possibilities before you decide which type of proof to use. If you choose to write an indirect proof, remember to show that *all* the alternative conclusions produce contradictions.

CLASS EXERCISES

Write a statement that contradicts each given statement.

1. $\overline{AB} \cong \overline{CD}$ $\overline{AB} \not\equiv \overline{CD}$

2. $AB > CD$ $AB \not> CD: AB < CD$ or $AB = CD$

3. $\overrightarrow{AD}$ bisects $\angle CAB$. $\overrightarrow{AD}$ does not bisect $\angle CAB$. 4. P is the midpoint of $\overline{OQ}$.   P is not the midpt. of $\overline{OQ}$.

5. $m\angle C < m\angle D$ $m\angle C \not< m\angle D$: $m\angle C > m\angle D$ or $m\angle C = m\angle D$

6. $\angle ABC$ is a right angle. $\angle ABC$ is not a rt. $\angle$: $\angle ABC$ is obtuse or $\angle ABC$ is acute.

LESSON FOLLOW-UP

Assignment Guide
• See p. 172B for assignments.

Lesson Quiz

Write the negation of each statement. List all the alternatives that result.

1. ∠E is obtuse.   **2.** AB > CD

3. Suppose the given statement is to be proven indirectly. Write the first statement of the proof and identify all alternatives that must be considered.

Prove: m∠A < m∠B

1. ∠E is not obt., so ∠E is acute or ∠E is a rt. ∠.
2. AB ≯ CD, so AB = CD or AB < CD.
3. Proof: Assume that m∠A ≮ m∠B. Then m∠A = m∠B or m∠A > m∠B.

Suppose the given statement is to be proven indirectly. Write the first statement of the proof and identify all alternatives to consider.

7. Given: △ABC and △DEF with
$\overline{AB} \cong \overline{DE}$;
$\overline{BC} \cong \overline{EF}$ and ∠B ≇ ∠E

   Prove: $\overline{AC} \not\cong \overline{DF}$ Assume $\overline{AC} \cong \overline{DF}$
   (only alternative)

8. Given: △ABC and △DEF with
$\overline{AB} \cong \overline{DE}$;
$\overline{BC} \cong \overline{EF}$; m∠B > m∠E

   Prove: AC > DF Assume AC ≯ DF. Then either AC = DF or AC < DF.

PRACTICE EXERCISES

Write a statement that contradicts each given statement.

A   **1.** AB = GH AB ≠ GH

   2. m∠FGH = m∠MNP
   m∠FGH ≠ m∠MNP

   3. ∠1 ≇ ∠2 ∠1 ≅ ∠2

   4. XV < HJ XV ≥ HJ

   5. m∠LPM > m∠YOP
   m∠LPM ≤ m∠YOP

   6. m∠7 ≯ m∠5
   m∠7 > m∠5

   7. It is Saturday.
   It is not Saturday.

   8. In my hand, I have $1.25.
   In my hand, I do not have $1.25.

   9. △TRP is isosceles.
   △TRP is not isosceles.

   10. I do not like vanilla ice cream.
   I like vanilla ice cream.

   11. m∠CVF < 90
   m∠CVF ≥ 90

   12. △ADC is not scalene.
   △ADC is scalene.

True or false? If false, tell why.

13. The negation of AB > 5 cm is AB < 5 cm.
false; trichotomy prop.; AB = 5 also possible

14. ∠A is obtuse and ∠B is acute are contradictory statements.
false; ∠B is acute or a rt. ∠.

15. The negation of ∠A is obtuse is ∠A is acute. false; ∠A is a rt. ∠ also possible

16. CD = 7 cm and CD ≠ 7 cm are contradictory statements. true

Write a conclusion that follows from the given information.

17. Given: $\overrightarrow{OQ}$ does not bisect ∠POR.   **Conclusion:** ∠POQ ⟶?⟶ ∠QOR
≠ if $\overrightarrow{OQ}$ is between rays PQ and QR, otherwise not enough information.

18. Given: ∠F is not obtuse.   **Conclusion:** ∠F is ? or ∠F is ?. acute; a rt ∠

19. Given: W, on $\overline{XZ}$, is not the midpoint of $\overline{XZ}$.   **Conclusion:** $\overline{XW}$? $\overline{WZ}$ ≠

20. Given: △ABC, $\overline{AB} \not\cong \overline{BC}$ **Conclusion:** ∠A ? ∠C ≠

Prove each of the following by writing an indirect proof. See Additional
Answers, p. 702.

B   **21. Given:** $\overline{CO} \cong \overline{PI}$; $\overline{OW} \cong \overline{IG}$; ∠O ≇ ∠I
   Prove: $\overline{CW} \not\cong \overline{PG}$

   22. Given: $\overline{CO} \cong \overline{PI}$; $\overline{OW} \cong \overline{IG}$; $\overline{CW} \not\cong \overline{PG}$
   Prove: ∠O ≇ ∠I

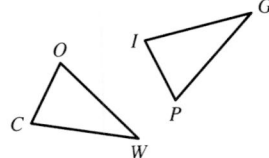

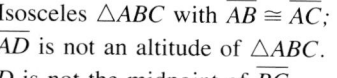

See Additional Answers, p. 702.

23. Given: Isosceles $\triangle ABC$ with $\overline{AB} \cong \overline{AC}$;
$\overline{AD}$ is not a median of $\triangle ABC$.

Prove: $\overline{AD}$ does not bisect $\angle A$.

24. Given: Isosceles $\triangle ABC$ with $\overline{AB} \cong \overline{AC}$;
$\overline{AD}$ is not an altitude of $\triangle ABC$.

Prove: D is not the midpoint of $\overline{BC}$.

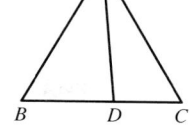

25. Given: $\overline{AD}$ is a median of $\triangle ABC$; $\angle BAD \not\cong \angle CAD$

Prove: $\overline{AB} \not\cong \overline{AC}$

C **26. Prove:** If two angles of a triangle are not congruent, then the sides opposite those angles are not congruent.

27. Write an indirect proof of the first part of the subtraction property of inequality.

Applications

28. Navigation Plane 1 is headed due west at 37,000 ft and Plane 2 is headed due east at 35,000 ft. Use indirect reasoning to show that their courses are represented by parallel lines. Assume the planes are on intersecting courses or skew courses. Then reason to contradictions of meanings of East and West.

29. Law In legal cases, how does an *alibi* compare to an indirect proof? The defense lawyer shows that the prosecutor's argument leads to a contradiction.

TEST YOURSELF

1. If $\overline{PI} \cong \overline{PA}$, name two congruent angles. $\angle I \cong \angle PAI$ 5.1

2. If $\angle APN \cong \angle ANP$, name two congruent segments. $\overline{AP} \cong \overline{AN}$

3. If $\overline{PI} \cong \overline{PA}$ and $m\angle AIP = 80$, then $m\angle API = \underline{\ ?\ }$. 20

4. If $\overline{PI} \cong \overline{PA}$ and $\overline{PA} \cong \overline{AN}$, then $\overline{PI} \ \underline{\ ?\ } \ \overline{AN}$. $\cong$

5. Name an angle with measure greater than $m\angle API$. $\angle NAP$ or $\angle NPI$

6. Name two angles with measures less than $m\angle ANO$. $\angle PAN, \angle NPA$ 5.2

Name the property of inequality illustrated in each statement.

7. If $m\angle A = m\angle B = 80$, $m\angle C = 50$, $m\angle D = 40$, then $m\angle A - m\angle C < m\angle B - m\angle D$. subtraction

8. If $AB \ne CD$, then $AB > CD$ or $AB < CD$. trichotomy

9. Given: $\triangle LUF$ is isosceles with base $\overline{UF}$;
$\angle LFT \cong \angle LUT$.

Prove: $\triangle FUT$ is isosceles.

See Additional Answers, p. 702.

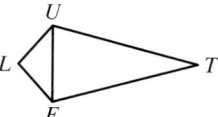

10. Write an indirect proof: If two sides of a triangle are not congruent, then the angles opposite those sides are not congruent.   5.3, 5.4

5.4 Indirect Proof and Inequalities   **193**

Teacher's Resource Book
Follow-Up Investigation, Chapter 5, p. 9

P Name _____ Date _____
Practice: For use after Lesson 5.4, Geometry

Indirect Proof and Inequalities

True or *false*? If false, tell why.

1. The negation of $m\angle X > m\angle Y$ is $m\angle X < m\angle Y$. __False; also possible that $m\angle X = m\angle Y$__
2. The negation of $\overline{AM}$ is a median is $\overline{AM}$ not a median __True__
3. $\triangle XYZ$ is an acute triangle and $\triangle XYZ$ is an obtuse triangle are contradictory statements. __False; $\triangle XYZ$ could be a right triangle.__
4. $PQ > MP$ and $PQ \not> MP$ are contradictory statements. __True__

Write a conclusion that follows from the given information.

5. Given: $\overline{AD}$ is not an altitude of $\triangle ABC$. Conclusion: $\overline{AD}$ __not $\perp$__ $\overline{BC}$.
6. Given: $m\angle Z$ is not 90. Conclusion: $\angle Z$ is __acute__ or $\angle Z$ is __obtuse__.
7. Given: In right $\triangle MNO$, $\overline{MN}$, is not the hypotenuse. Conclusion: $m\angle O$ __$\ne$__ 90.
8. Given: In $\triangle BAG$, $\angle B \ne \angle G$. Conclusion: $\overline{AG}$ __$\ne$__ $\overline{BA}$.

Prove the following by writing an indirect proof.

9. Given: Right triangles ACB and ACD with $\angle B \ne \angle D$
Prove: $\overline{BC} \ne \overline{CD}$
Plan: Assume the negation of $\overline{BC} \ne \overline{CD}$. Show that this leads to a contradiction.

Proof: Assume $\overline{BC} \cong \overline{CD}$ Negation of the conclusion
$\overline{AC} \cong \overline{AC}$ Reflexive property of congruency
$\triangle ACB \cong \triangle ACD$ LL Th.
$\angle B \cong \angle D$ CPCTC

Contradiction: __$\angle B \cong \angle D$__

Conclusion: Since the assumption leads to a contradiction of the given information, the assumption that $\overline{BC} \cong \overline{CD}$ is false. Thus $\overline{BC} \ne \overline{CD}$.

Application

10. **Logic** Use indirect reasoning to prove that it is not snowing if it is not cold outside.

__Assume that it is snowing. Then it must be cold. But this contradicts the fact that it is not cold outside. Since the assumption that it is snowing leads to a contradiction, the assumption must be false, and it is not snowing.__

10   Chapter 5

E Name _____ Date _____
Enrichment: For use after Lesson 5.4, Geometry

Truth Tables and Indirect Proofs

Ordinary logic, which lies at the root of both mathematics and detective stories, is based on the two-valued propositional calculus, the logic in which statements are either true (T) or false (F). Label these propositions as T (true), F (false), or N (not applicable):

1. The sum of the angles in a triangle is 180 degrees.	2. Washington was a better President than Lincoln.	3. Alternate interior angles are supplementary.
T	N	N

In this system a typical proposition is denoted by a letter, such as p. The proposition NOT p is the negation of p. A truth table is a table of "truth values" of propositions, such as this one.

p	NOT p
T	F
F	T

Compound propositions are formed with AND, OR, and IF, THEN: p OR q is true only when either proposition is true; p and q is true only when both propositions are true; IF p, THEN q is false only when the hypothesis is true and the conclusion is false. Complete the table.

	p	q	p and q	p and q	If p, then q.
4.	T	T	T	T	T
5.	T	F	T	F	F
6.	F	T	T	F	T
7.	F	F	F	F	T

8. Why does a false hypothesis lead to any conclusion?
__If p if false, then if p, then q is true.__

A **tautology** is a compound proposition which is always true, no matter what the truth values of the individual propositions.

9. Complete the truth table to show that the compound proposition p OR (NOT p) is a tautology.

p	NOT p	p or (not p)
T	F	T
F	T	T

Chapter 5   11

193

LESSON PLAN

Materials/Manipulatives

Teaching Transparency 32

Technology

Computer
Computer Test Bank, pp. 286–296
The Geometric Supposer: Triangles
Geometry Problems and Projects: Triangles, Worksheets T6, T13

LESSON FOCUS

Review

- Review what students learned in Lesson 5.1 about angle measures in isosceles and equilateral triangles. Also review what is known about the sides opposite two congruent angles of a triangle.
- The Algebra Review, Exercises 29–31, involves solving inequalities.

Alternative Learning Styles

- In the Investigation, students use a kinesthetic approach and inductive reasoning to conclude that the largest and smallest angles of a scalene triangle are opposite the longest and shortest sides, respectively.
- Manipulatives such as straws or long toothpicks can help students realize that the relationship between each angle and the corresponding relationship between each side exists within a triangle and NOT between triangles. Students can work with one triangle at a time or with color-coded triangles to explore the inequality relations in a triangle.

5.5 Inequalities in One Triangle

Objective: To state and apply the inequality relations for one triangle

Congruence relationships exist in isosceles, equilateral, and scalene triangles. Inequality relationships also exist in these figures.

Investigation—*Thinking Critically*

Measure the sides and angles of each of the triangles.

1. Make a table of your findings.

2. What seems to be true regarding the angles of scalene triangles? No 2 ∠s are ≅.

For each triangle, compare the lengths of the sides with the measures of their opposite angles.

3. Make a generalization regarding this comparison. Largest ∠ is opp. longest side; smallest ∠ is opp. shortest side.

4. What kind of reasoning did you use to make this generalization? inductive

5. Discuss ways to prove this generalization.
   Answers may vary. Use the inductive approach by drawing and measuring several more △s.

The following theorems deal with the relationships of noncongruent, or unequal, sides and angles in triangles.

Theorem 5.6 If two sides of a triangle are unequal, then the angles opposite them are unequal and the larger angle is opposite the longer side.

Given: $OY > YT$

Prove: $m\angle OTY > m\angle TOY$

Plan: Add an auxiliary segment, $\overline{TM}$, so that $\overline{YM} \cong \overline{YT}$. Use the Exterior Angle Theorem.

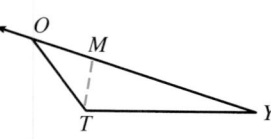

194 Chapter 5 Inequalities in Triangles

Developing Mathematical Power

Cooperative Learning The Enrichment activity, p. 14, in the *Teacher's Resource Book* (see side column, p. 198) can be done with students working in cooperative groups. Challenge the groups to create a similar activity sheet by changing the exercises and the question.

Proof:

Statements	Reasons
1. In $\triangle TOY$, $OY > YT$	1. Given
2. Locate M on $\overrightarrow{YO}$ such that $YM = YT$.	2. On a ray there is exactly one point at a given distance from the endpoint of the ray.
3. $\overline{YM} \cong \overline{YT}$	3. Definition of congruent segments
4. Draw $\overline{TM}$.	4. Two points determine one line.
5. $\triangle YTM$ is isosceles.	5. Definition of an isosceles triangle
6. $\angle YMT \cong \angle YTM$	6. Isosceles Triangle Theorem
7. $m\angle YMT = m\angle YTM$	7. Definition of congruent angles
8. $m\angle OTY = m\angle OTM + m\angle YTM$	8. Definition of a between ray
9. $m\angle OTY > m\angle YTM$	9. Definition of greater than
10. $m\angle OTY > m\angle YMT$	10. Substitution property
11. $m\angle YMT > m\angle TOY$	11. Exterior Angle Theorem
12. $m\angle OTY > m\angle TOY$	12. Transitive property of inequality

Conclusion: In $\triangle TOY$, whenever $OY > YT$, then $m\angle OTY > m\angle TOY$.

EXAMPLE 1 Use $>$, $<$, or $=$ to show the relationship(s) of the measures of the angles in each triangle.

a.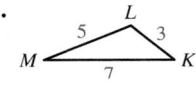

b.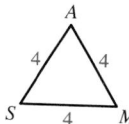

c.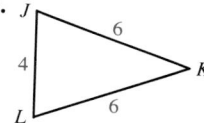

a. $m\angle M < m\angle K < m\angle L$ **b.** $m\angle S = m\angle A = m\angle M$ **c.** $m\angle K < m\angle J$; $m\angle J = m\angle L$

Theorem 5.7 If two angles of a triangle are unequal, then the sides opposite them are unequal and the longer side is opposite the larger angle.

Given: $\triangle PQR$ with $m\angle Q > m\angle R$

Prove: $PR > PQ$

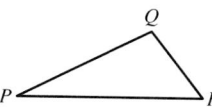

Plan: Assume $PR \not> PQ$. Show that each alternative leads to a contradiction.

(1) *Assume:* $PR = PQ$ Negation of the conclusion
         $\angle Q \cong \angle R$ Isosceles Triangle Theorem
         $m\angle Q = m\angle R$ Definition of congruent angles
     Contradiction: $m\angle Q > m\angle R$

 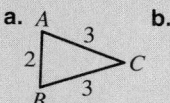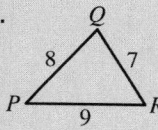

For Example 2

Use > and = to show the relationship(s) of the lengths of the sides in each triangle.

a.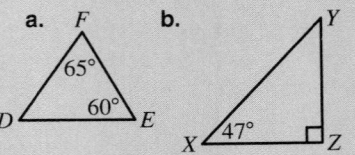

b.

a. $DE > DF > EF$ b. $XY > YZ > XZ$

For Example 3

What can you conclude?

a. **Given:**
  $DC < DB$
b. **Given:**
  $m\angle ADB >$
  $m\angle ABD$
c. **Given:** $BC > AB$
d. $m\angle ADB > \underline{\ ?\ }$
  and $m\angle ADB > \underline{\ ?\ }$

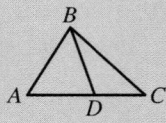

a. $m\angle DBC < m\angle DCB$
b. $AB > AD$
c. $m\angle A > m\angle C$
d. $m\angle C;\ m\angle DBC$

Common Errors

- Students might correlate the size of the angle with one of its adjacent sides, rather than its opposite side. Encourage students to measure actual sides and angles.
- Some students confuse inductive and deductive reasoning. Stress that inductive reasoning uses facts that lead to generalizations.
- See *Teacher's Resource Book* for additional remediation.

LESSON FOLLOW-UP

Assignment Guide

See p. 172B for assignments.

196

---

(2) *Assume:* $PR < PQ$ Negation of the conclusion
              $m\angle Q < m\angle R$ The angle opposite the longer
                                   side is the larger angle.

     Contradiction: $m\angle Q > m\angle R$

Conclusion: The assumption, $PR \not> PQ$, is false. Therefore, in $\triangle PQR$ with $m\angle Q > m\angle R$, $PR > PQ$.

EXAMPLE 2   Use >, <, or = to show the relationship(s) of the lengths of the sides in each triangle.

a. 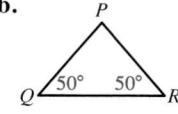   b. 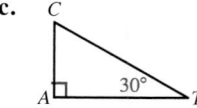   c. 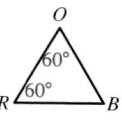   d.

a. $TY > RY > RT$ b. $QR > PQ$;   c. $CT > AT > CA$ d. $OR = OB = RB$
                       $PQ = PR$

EXAMPLE 3   Use the given information to complete each statement.

   a. If $MO = MN$, then $m\angle O \underline{\ ?\ } m\angle MNO$.

   b. If $m\angle O < m\angle MNO$ then $MN \underline{\ ?\ } MO$.

   c. If $m\angle M > m\angle MNP$, then $\underline{\ ?\ } > \underline{\ ?\ }$.

   d. $m\angle OPN > \underline{\ ?\ }$ or $\underline{\ ?\ }$.

   a. =   b. <   c. $NP > PM$ d. $m\angle M$ or $m\angle MNP$

In this figure, $\overleftrightarrow{PQ} \perp \overleftrightarrow{QR}$ at Q and R is any other point on $\overleftrightarrow{QR}$. Why is it true that $m\angle Q > m\angle R$? From Theorem 5.7, it follows that $PR > PQ$, or $PQ < PR$. The rt. $\angle$ is the largest $\angle$ in a rt. $\triangle$.

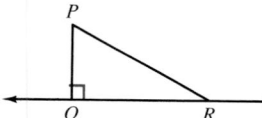

Corollary 1   The perpendicular segment from a point to a line is the shortest segment from the point to the line.

Corollary 2   The perpendicular segment from a point to a plane is the shortest segment from the point to the plane.

CLASS EXERCISES

True or false? If false, explain why.

1. In $\triangle MPQ$, $m\angle M = 55$ and $m\angle P = 75$. The longest side of $\triangle MPQ$ is $\overline{MP}$.
False; $\angle P$ is largest $\angle$, so $\overline{MQ}$ is the longest side.
2. In $\triangle TRS$, $m\angle T = 20$ and $m\angle R = 20$. The shortest side of $\triangle TRS$ is $\overline{TR}$.
False; $\overline{TR}$ is the longest side.

3. In acute $\triangle FGH$ with $\overline{GX} \perp \overline{FH}$, $FG > GX$. true

4. If $\triangle CDE$ is isosceles with base $\overline{DE}$ and $CD > DE$, then $m\angle C > 60$.
false; if $CD > DE$, then $m\angle C < 60$

5. The median of an equilateral triangle is shorter than any of the sides. true

PRACTICE EXERCISES  Use technology where appropriate.

Use $<$, $>$, or $=$ to show the
relationship of the measures of the
given angles, if it can be determined.

A
1. $m\angle 3$ _?_ $m\angle 4$ =   **2.** $m\angle 8$ _?_ $m\angle 5$ >

3. $m\angle 1$ _?_ $m\angle 4$ **4.** $m\angle 2$ _?_ $m\angle 9$ =
cannot be determined
5. $m\angle 6$ _?_ $m\angle 7$ <   **6.** $m\angle 4$ _?_ $m\angle 2$ >

Sketch and label each indicated $\triangle TRS$. Use $>$, $<$, or $=$ to show the
relationship(s) of the measures of the angles of each $\triangle TRS$. Check students' sketches.

7. $TR = 8$ cm; $RS = 20$ cm; $TS = 15$ cm $m\angle S < m\angle R < m\angle T$

8. $TR = \sqrt{12}$ cm; $RS = \sqrt{12}$ cm; $TS = 5$ cm $m\angle T = m\angle S$; $m\angle T < m\angle R$

Sketch and label each indicated $\triangle ABC$. Name the longest side and the
shortest side of each triangle.

9. $m\angle A = 120$; $m\angle B = 40$ **10.** $m\angle C = 30$; $m\angle A = 120$
longest: BC; shortest: AB longest: BC; shortest: $AB \cong AC$
11. $m\angle B = 75$; $m\angle C = 36$ **12.** $m\angle A = 90$; $m\angle C = 20$
longest: AC; shortest: AB longest: BC; shortest: AB

What conclusion follows from the given information?

13. **Given:** $HI > GI$
    Conclusion: _?_ > _?_ $m\angle G$, $m\angle H$

14. **Given:** $m\angle I < m\angle G$
    Conclusion: _?_ < _?_ HG, HI

15. Use the plan to complete a proof.
    Given: $m\angle FEG > m\angle GED$
    Prove: $FG > EF$
    Plan: Show that $m\angle GED > m\angle EGF$. Use
          this fact and the given information to
          show that $FG > EF$ in $\triangle EFG$.
          See Additional Answers, p. 702.

What conclusion may be drawn? Justify your answer by stating a theorem.

B
16. In $\triangle DEF$, $DE > DF$. Conclusion: _?_ $m\angle DFE > m\angle DEF$, Th. 5.6

17. In $\triangle RJC$, $m\angle R < m\angle C$. Conclusion: _?_ $JC < JR$, Th. 5.7

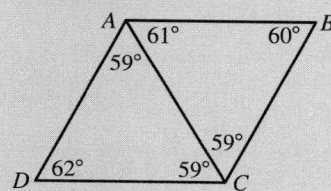

Teacher's Resource Book

Follow-Up Investigation, Chapter 5, p. 12

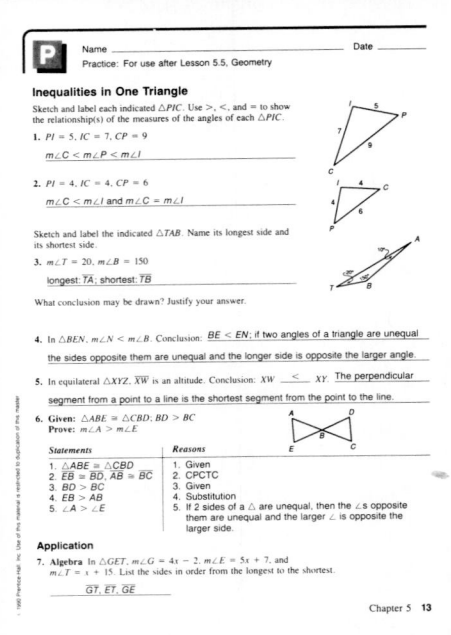

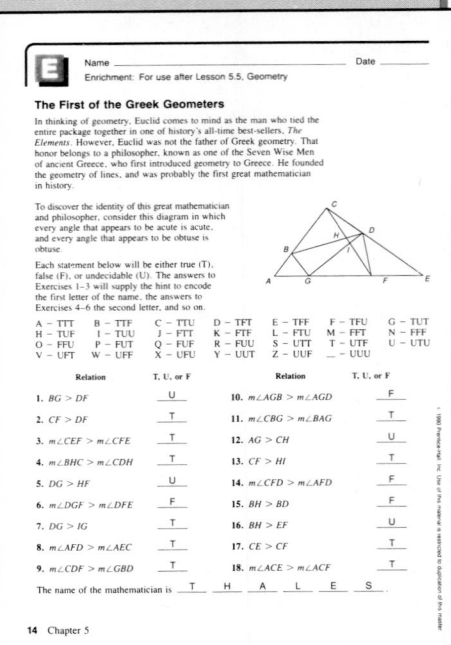

See Additional Answers, p. 702.

Draw and label an appropriate figure and write the hypothesis (Given) and the conclusion (Prove). Do not prove.

18. The exterior angle of isosceles triangle PQR with base $\overline{QR}$ is obtuse.

19. The altitude of an equilateral triangle is shorter than the sides.

20. Either of the two congruent sides of an isosceles triangle is longer than the median to the base of the triangle.

21. The diagonal of a square is longer than the sides of the square.

22. Given: $DF > DG$; $FE > EG$
Prove: $m\angle DGE > m\angle DFE$

23. Given: $\triangle DGF \cong \triangle EGF$; $m\angle 4 > m\angle 3$
Prove: $DF > DG$

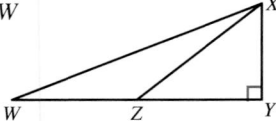

C **24.** Prove that the hypotenuse is the longest side of a right triangle.

25. Given: Right triangle XYZ with $\overrightarrow{YZ}$ extended to W
Prove: $XW > XZ$

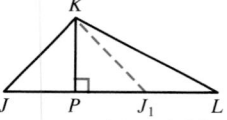

26. Given: $\triangle JKL$ with altitude $\overline{KP}$; $LP > PJ$
Prove: $KL > KJ$

(*Hint:* On $\overline{PL}$ locate J_1 such that $\overline{PJ} \cong \overline{PJ_1}$.)

27. Write a statement that summarizes the results of Exercises 25 and 26.

In the figure, the greater the distance between R and other points of $\overline{MQ}$, the longer the segment joining P to that point.

Applications

28. Technology Using Logo, draw a scalene triangle. Make a chart relating the measure of each angle and the length of the side opposite the angle. What general statement can you make regarding the relationship? The longest side is opp. the largest $\angle$; the shortest side is opp. the smallest $\angle$.

Algebra Review

Solve. Name the property of inequality used in Exercises 29–31.

29. $x + 5 > 9$ $x > 4$, subtr.   **30.** $3a \le 21$ $a \le 7$, div.   **31.** $k - 9 \ge 15$ $k \ge 24$, add.

Developing Mathematical Power

32. Extension In $\triangle ABC$, a, b, and c represent the lengths of the sides with $a < c < b$. Give three equivalent forms of the inequality. Answers may vary; $b > c > a$; $a < c$ and $c < b$; $a \ne c \ne b$

198   Chapter 5 Inequalities in Triangles

5.6 More on Inequalities

Objectives: To state and apply the Triangle Inequality Theorem
To state and apply the inequality relations for two triangles

Which path would you measure to find the distance between points P and Q? $\overline{PQ}$

The distance between two points or a point and a line, or between any two geometric figures, is always the length of the shortest path between them.

Investigation—*Visualizing the Concept*

Three pieces of framing are assembled as shown. If the 2′ and 1′ sections are rotated, is it possible to obtain a triangular frame? Explain your answer. No; when the 2′ and 1′ sections are rotated to meet the horizontal 3′ section, they will coincide with it.

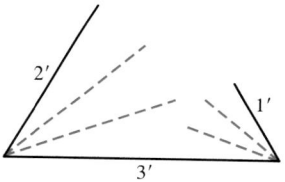

Theorem 5.8   Triangle Inequality Theorem   The sum of the lengths of any two sides of a triangle is greater than the length of the third side.

Given: $\triangle ABC$

Prove: $AB + BC > AC$

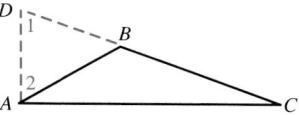

Plan: Extend $\overrightarrow{CB}$ through B to point D, such that $\overline{DB} \cong \overline{AB}$. Draw $\overline{DA}$. Now $\angle 1 \cong \angle 2$. Since $DB + BC = DC$ and $DB = AB$, then $AB + BC = DC$. Since $m\angle DAC > m\angle 2$, $m\angle DAC > m\angle 1$. Thus $DC > AC$ and $AB + BC > AC$. Proved in Practice Exercises 15–17

Inequality relationships exist between two triangles when *two sides* of one triangle are congruent to the corresponding sides of a second triangle, but the *included angles* are not congruent.

Developing Mathematical Power

Cooperative Learning   Working in groups, students can complete the Investigation activity, p. 15, in the *Teacher's Resource Book*. Encourage them to cut straws to the lengths shown and to use the straws to help answer Exercises 2–7.

199

LESSON PLAN

Materials/Manipulatives
Straws cut in different lengths
Teacher's Resource Book,
   Transparency 6
Teaching Transparency 33
Connections, p. 14

Technology
Computer
Computer Test Bank,
   pp. 296–304
The Geometric Supposer:
   Triangles
   Geometry Problems and
   Projects: Triangles, Worksheets
   T5, T12

LESSON FOCUS

Review
Find the indicated measure when $\triangle ABC$ is isosceles with base $\overline{AC}$.
1. If $m\angle A = 40$, $m\angle C = $ _?_ 40
2. If $AB = 8$, $BC = $ _?_ 8
3. If $m\angle B = 70$, $m\angle A = $ _?_ 55

Alternative Learning Styles
• To provide a kinesthetic approach to the Investigation, students could use straws to construct and experiment with the framing. For example, use straws whose lengths in inches are (1, 1, 2), (1, 2, 2), (2, 2, 2), (2, 3, 4).
• To model the Hinge Theorem and its converse, form $\angle BAC$ and $\angle EDF$ from congruent straws.

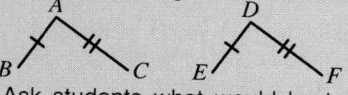

Ask students what would be true about BC and EF if $m\angle A > m\angle D$? $BC > EF$
If $BC > EF$, how would $m\angle A$ compare to $m\angle D$? $m\angle A > m\angle D$

TEACHING SUGGESTIONS

- The proof of Theorem 5.9 is complex. Don't belabor it.
- The indirect proof used for Theorem 5.10 is fairly simple and provides a good example of an indirect proof when more than one alternative must be considered.
- The Hinge Theorem is sometimes called the SAS Inequality Theorem. Help students see the relationship between the SAS Postulate and the Hinge Theorem, as well as the relationship between the converse of the Hinge Theorem and the SSS Postulate.

CHALKBOARD EXAMPLE

• For the Example

Use the given information to fill in the blanks. Justify your answers.

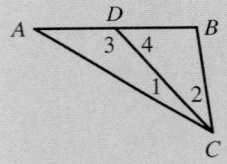

a. If $DB = DA$ and $m\angle 4 < m\angle 3$, then AC _?_ BC.

b. If $CA = CB$ and $m\angle 1 < m\angle 2$, then BD _?_ AD.

c. If DC is a median and $BC < AC$ then $m\angle 4$ _?_ $m\angle 3$.

a. $AC > BC$; Hinge Theorem

b. $BD > AD$; Hinge Theorem

c. $m\angle 4 < m\angle 3$; converse of Hinge Theorem

Critical Thinking

Comparing-Contrasting Have students differentiate among the SAS Postulate, the Hinge Theorem, the SSS Postulate, and the converse of the Hinge Theorem.

The Hinge Theorem, which follows, may be visualized by thinking of a Dutch door. If the top door is opened wider than the bottom door, the triangles formed by ABC and DEF have two pairs of congruent sides ($\overline{AB} \cong \overline{DE}$ and $\overline{BC} \cong \overline{EF}$), but $m\angle ABC > m\angle DEF$. How does AC compare to DF? It appears that $AC > DF$.

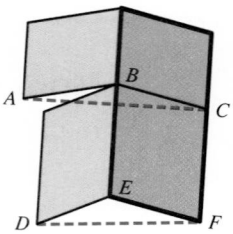

Theorem 5.9   Hinge Theorem   If two sides of one triangle are congruent to two sides of a second triangle, and the included angle of the first is larger than the included angle of the second, then the third side of the first triangle is longer than the third side of the second triangle.

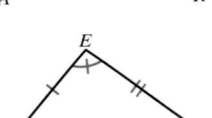

Given: $\triangle ABC$ and $\triangle DEF$ with $\overline{AB} \cong \overline{DE}$; $\overline{BC} \cong \overline{EF}$; $m\angle ABC > m\angle DEF$

Prove: $AC > DF$

Plan: Since $m\angle ABC > m\angle DEF$, locate $\overrightarrow{BR}$ such that $\angle ABR \cong \angle DEF$ and $\overline{BR} \cong \overline{EF}$. Drawing $\overline{AR}$, $\triangle ABR \cong \triangle DEF$. Thus $\overline{AR} \cong \overline{DF}$.

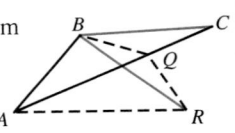

Since $\overline{BC} \cong \overline{EF}$ and $\overline{BR} \cong \overline{EF}$, $\overline{BC} \cong \overline{BR}$. Now let Q be on $\overline{AC}$ such that $\overrightarrow{BQ}$ bisects $\angle RBC$. Drawing $\overline{QR}$, $\triangle BQR \cong \triangle BQC$. Thus $QR = QC$.

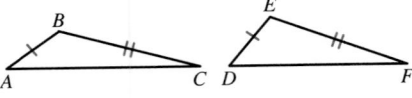

In $\triangle AQR$,	$AQ + QR > AR$	Triangle Inequality Theorem
	$AQ + QC > AR$	Substitution property
	$AQ + QC = AC$	Definition of betweenness
	$AC > AR$	Substitution property

Proved in Practice Exercise 20

Theorem 5.10   Converse of the Hinge Theorem   If two sides of one triangle are congruent to two sides of a second triangle, and the third side of the first is longer than the third side of the second, then the included angle of the first triangle is larger than the included angle of the second triangle.

Given: $\triangle ABC$ and $\triangle DEF$ with $\overline{AB} \cong \overline{DE}$, $\overline{BC} \cong \overline{EF}$, and $AC > DF$

Prove: $m\angle ABC > m\angle DEF$

Developing Mathematical Power

Keeping a Portfolio   Provide students with Reading in Geometry activity (Networks, p. 14, in *Connections*). Have them research networks and summarize their findings in a paragraph. They should include illustrations and answer the question.

Plan: Write an indirect proof to show that the assumption $m\angle ABC \not> m\angle DEF$ leads to a contradiction.

Proof: *Assume:* $m\angle ABC < m\angle DEF$ or $m\angle ABC = m\angle DEF$

$\qquad\qquad$ $AC < DF$ Hinge $\qquad\qquad$ $\triangle ABC \cong \triangle DEF$ SAS
$\qquad$ *Contradiction:* $AC > DF$ Theorem $\qquad\qquad$ $\overline{AC} \cong \overline{DF}$ CPCTC
$\qquad\qquad\qquad\qquad\qquad\qquad\qquad\qquad\qquad$ $AC = DF$ Def. $\cong$ segments
$\qquad\qquad\qquad\qquad\qquad\qquad\qquad$ *Contradiction:* $AC > DF$

Conclusion: Both cases contradict the given fact that $AC > DF$. Therefore, $m\angle ABC \not> m\angle DEF$ must be false. Thus, given $\triangle ABC$ and $\triangle DEF$ with $\overline{AB} \cong \overline{DE}$, $\overline{BC} \cong \overline{EF}$, and $AC > DF$, $m\angle ABC > m\angle DEF$.

EXAMPLE   Use the given information to fill in the blanks. Justify your answers.

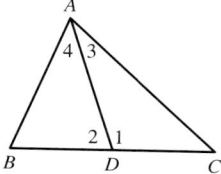

  a. If $BD = DC$ and $m\angle 1 > m\angle 2$, then $AC \underline{\ ?\ } AB$.
  b. If $AB = AC$ and $m\angle 3 > m\angle 4$, then $CD \underline{\ ?\ } BD$.
  c. If AD is a median and $AB < AC$, then $m\angle 2 \underline{\ ?\ } m\angle 1$.

a. $AC > AB$; Hinge Theorem   **b.** $CD > BD$; Hinge Theorem
c. $m\angle 2 < m\angle 1$; converse of the Hinge Theorem

CLASS EXERCISES

Thinking Critically

  1. Read the opening statement in this lesson. Explain how the figure illustrates the Triangle Inequality Theorem. It shows that the shortest distance between P and Q is PQ, not $PR + RQ$; i.e., $PR + RQ > PQ$.
  2. Describe in your own words why Theorem 5.9 is called the *Hinge Theorem*. Think of a hinge on a door. The door opens wider as hinge opens. The hinge is analogous to the included $\angle$; the width of the door opening is analogous to the opp. side of $\triangle$.

Fill in the blanks. Justify your answers.

  3. In $\triangle TUV$, $TV < \underline{\ ?\ } + \underline{\ ?\ }$. *TU; UV;* $\triangle$ Inequality Th.

  4. In $\triangle XYZ$, $m\angle X = 30$ and $m\angle Y = 100$. Then $\underline{\ ?\ }$ is the longest side. $\overline{XZ}$; longest side is opposite largest $\angle$

  5. In $\triangle MNO$, $MN + NO \underline{\ ?\ } MO$. $>$; $\triangle$ Inequality Th.

  6. The length of any side of a triangle $\underline{\ ?\ }$ the sum of the lengths of the other two sides. is less than; $\triangle$ Inequality Th.

  7. The length of any side of a triangle $\underline{\ ?\ }$ the difference of the lengths of the other two sides. is greater than; $\triangle$ Inequality Th.

  8. If $\overline{AM}$ is the median to $\overline{BC}$ of $\triangle ABC$ and $AB < AC$, then $m\angle AMB \underline{\ ?\ } m\angle AMC$. $<$; conv. of Hinge Th.

Common Error

- Students may attempt to apply the Hinge Theorem (or its converse) incorrectly by not satisfying the hypothesis of the theorem. That is, they may attempt to apply it when two pairs of sides are congruent but the angles are not included by the congruent sides. Insist that students label all sides and angles in question, to make certain that they are working with an included angle.
- See *Teacher's Resource Book* for additional remediation.

LESSON FOLLOW-UP

Assignment Guide
See p. 172B for assignments.

Developing Mathematical Power
Thinking Critically Students are to combine two statements (Class Exercises 6 and 7) to create one true statement.

Lesson Quiz

Which sets of numbers could be the lengths of the sides of a triangle?

1. (4, 4, 2)   **2.** (2, 2, 4)

What conclusion follows from the given? Justify your answer.

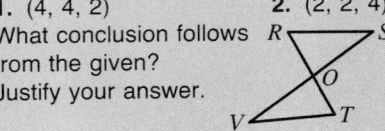

3. Given: O is the midpoint of $\overline{RT}$;
$\overline{RS} \cong \overline{VT}$; $m\angle SRO < m\angle VTO$

4. Given: $\overline{RS} \cong \overline{VT}$; $\overline{OS} \cong \overline{OV}$;
$OR > OT$

5. Given: $\overline{BD}$ is a median of $\triangle ABC$;
$m\angle BDC > m\angle BDA$
Prove: $BC > AB$

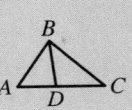

1. Yes   **2.** No
3. $SO < VO$ by the Hinge Theorem.
4. $m\angle S > m\angle V$ by the converse of the Hinge Theorem.
5. Plan: Apply the Hinge Theorem to $\triangle BDC$ and $\triangle BDA$.

Proof:

Statements	Reasons
1. $\overline{BD}$ is a median of $\triangle ABC$.	Given
2. D is the midpoint of $\overline{AC}$.	Def. of median
3. $\overline{AD} \cong \overline{DC}$	Def. of midpt.
4. $\overline{BD} \cong \overline{BD}$	Refl. Prop. of $\cong$
5. $m\angle BDC > m\angle BDA$	Given
6. $BC > AB$	Hinge Theorem

Conclusion: In the given figure, if $\overline{BD}$ is a median of $\triangle ABC$ and if $m\angle BDC > m\angle BDA$, then $BC > AB$.

Enrichment

If $\overline{NR} \cong \overline{PR}$ and $m\angle NRM > m\angle MRP$, what conclusions follow?

$MN > MP$; $m\angle NRO < m\angle PRO$; $NO < PO$

9. In $\triangle ABC$ and $\triangle GHI$, $AB = GH = 4$ cm, $AC = GI = 8$ cm, $m\angle BAC = 60$, and $m\angle HGI = 65$. Then BC _?_ HI. <; Hinge Th.

10. If the median and the altitude are drawn to the same side of a scalene triangle, the length of the median _?_ the length of the altitude.
is greater than; ⊥ is shortest segment from a point to a line

11. In $\triangle KLM$, $m\angle K = 46$ and the measure of the exterior angle at L is 133. The longest side of the triangle is _?_.
$\overline{KL}$; in a $\triangle$, the longest side is opposite the largest $\angle$

PRACTICE EXERCISES   Use technology where appropriate.

Which sets of numbers could be the lengths of the sides of a triangle?

A   **1.** {8, 8, 8} yes   **2.** {12, 20, 13} yes   **3.** {17, 10, 30} no   **4.** {1, 2, 3} no

Complete the statement. Justify your answers.

5. $FL + LA >$ _?_   FA; $\triangle$ Inequality Th.
6. $LA + AR >$ _?_   LR; $\triangle$ Inequality Th.
7. $LO < OA +$ _?_   AL; $\triangle$ Inequality Th.
8. In $\triangle FLA$, $m\angle L$ _?_ $m\angle F$ >; Th 5.6
9. In $\triangle LFA$ and $\triangle LAO$, $m\angle FLA$ _?_ $m\angle ALO$ >; Conv. of Hinge Th.

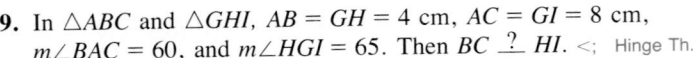

10. Given: $\triangle FRI$
Conclusion: $FR <$ _?_ $+$ _?_   RI   IF $\triangle$ Inequality Th.

11. Given: Right $\triangle RFE$
Conclusion: RE _?_ RF <; Hypotenuse is the longest side of any rt. $\triangle$.

12. Given: $\overline{XY} \cong \overline{XZ}$; $m\angle WXY < m\angle WXZ$
Conclusion: YW _?_ WZ <; Hinge Th.

13. Given: Isosceles $\triangle XYZ$ with base $\overline{YZ}$; $YW < WZ$
Conclusion: $m\angle YXW$ _?_ $m\angle ZXW$ <; conv. of Hinge Th.
See Additional Answers, p. 702.

B   **14. Given:** Regular hexagon $PQRSTU$ with vertices P, R, T joined to form $\triangle PRT$
Prove: The perimeter of $\triangle PRT$ is less than the perimeter of hexagon $PQRSTU$.

15. Use the plan for Theorem 5.8 to justify that $AB + BC > AC$.

16. Write a plan to justify the proof of $BC + CA > AB$ in Theorem 5.8.

17. Write a proof to justify that $CA + AB > BC$ in Theorem 5.8.

18. Prove that the difference between the lengths of any two sides of a triangle is less than the length of the third side.

19. Given: $\overline{QS}$ is a median of $\triangle QRT$; $TQ > RQ$
Prove: $m\angle TSQ > m\angle RSQ$

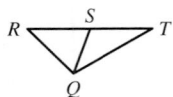

202   Chapter 5 Inequalities in Triangles

20. Write a proof of the Hinge Theorem. Follow the plan for Theorem 5.9.

21. Prove that in a scalene triangle, the angle bisector of any angle of the triangle is longer than the altitude from that vertex.

Applications

22. Technology   Using Logo, write a procedure that demonstrates the Hinge Theorem. See Solutions Manual.

23. Construction   The A-frames of two houses are isosceles triangles with corresponding legs of equal length. If the bases of the A-frames have different lengths, which house has the steeper roof? the house with the shorter base

Developing Mathematical Power

24. Thinking Critically   Combine Class Exercises 6 and 7 into one statement. Answers may vary. The length of any side of a triangle is less than the sum and greater than the difference of the lengths of the other two sides.

CONSTRUCTION

Given: Segments a, b, and c

Construct: $\triangle ABC$ with sides a, b, and c

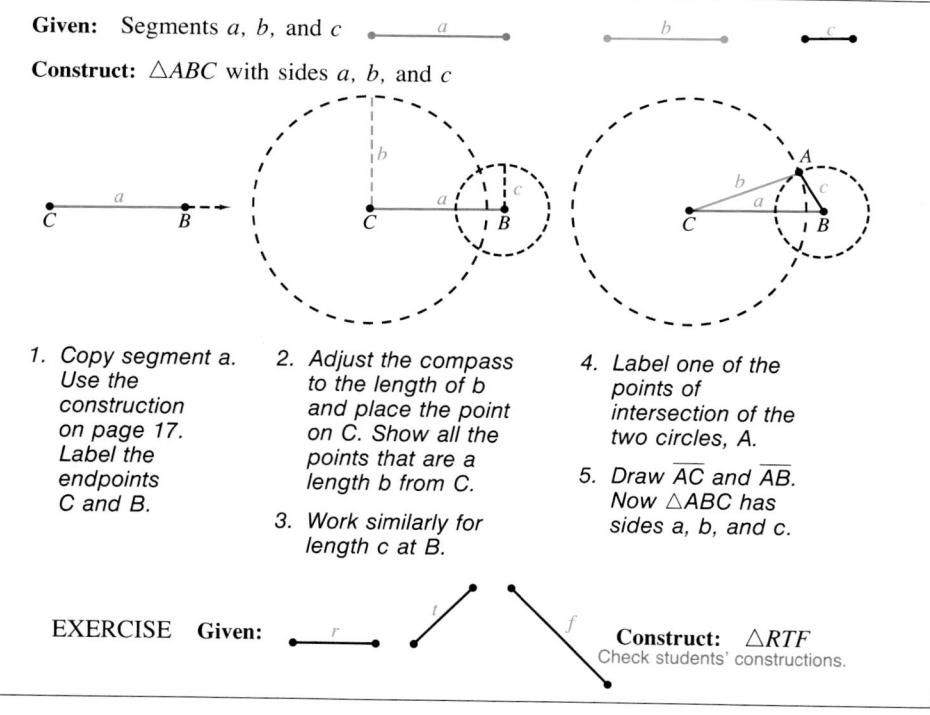

1. Copy segment a. Use the construction on page 17. Label the endpoints C and B.

2. Adjust the compass to the length of b and place the point on C. Show all the points that are a length b from C.

3. Work similarly for length c at B.

4. Label one of the points of intersection of the two circles, A.

5. Draw $\overline{AC}$ and $\overline{AB}$. Now $\triangle ABC$ has sides a, b, and c.

EXERCISE   Given: **Construct:** $\triangle RTF$
Check students' constructions.

5.6 More on Inequalities   **203**

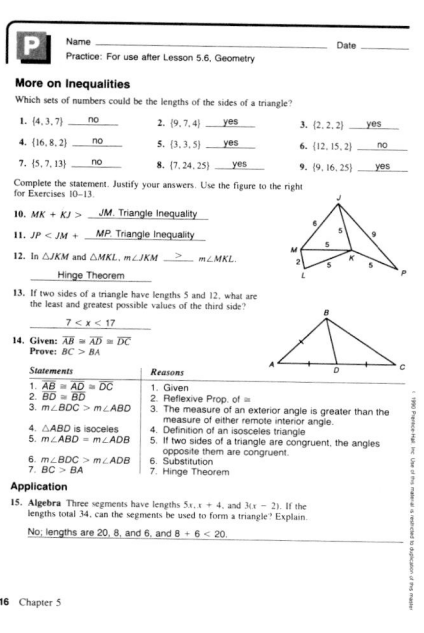
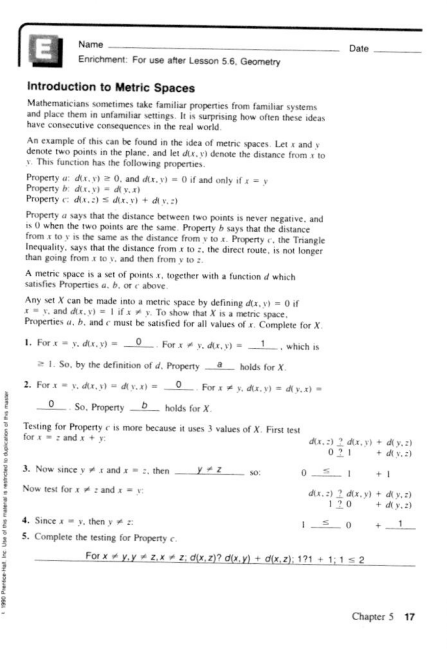

Vocabulary

Adjacent dihedral angles
Dihedral angle
Edge of a dihedral angle
Face of a dihedral angle
Measure of a dihedral angle
Plane angle of a dihedral angle

Materials/Manipulatives

Index cards
Manila file folders
Scissors
Teaching Transparency 34
Connections, p. 17

Technology

Computer Test Bank, pp.
305–316

LESSON FOCUS

Review

• Put this figure on the chalkboard.

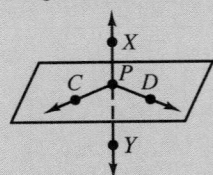

Tell students that $\overleftrightarrow{XY}$ is perpendicular to plane *CPD*. Ask what must be true of $\overleftrightarrow{XY}$, $\overrightarrow{PC}$, and $\overrightarrow{PD}$.
$\overleftrightarrow{XY} \perp \overrightarrow{PC}$ and $\overleftrightarrow{XY} \perp \overrightarrow{PD}$.

• The Chapter Summary and Review, pp. 212–213, gives vocabulary and concepts and review exercises by lesson.

• The end of the chapter features an Algebra Review on p. 216.

Alternative Learning Styles

Some students may need a real-life application of a dihedral angle. Direct their attention to the Investigation. Once sheathing is laid, a dihedral angle is formed.

204

5.7

Congruence in Space: Dihedral Angles

Objective: To identify dihedral angles and their plane angles

In Chapter 1, you learned that a line separates a plane into two *half-planes* and that the line is called the *edge* of each half-plane.

Investigation—*Visualizing the Concept*

The construction workers have put the roof on a house by applying sheets of plywood to the triangular braces, or rafters. The pitch of the roof is the measure of the vertical *rise* divided by the measure of the horizontal *span*.

1. What guarantees that the roof will have the same pitch everywhere? The rafters are ≅. isosceles △.

If plane *P* is thought of as a piece of paper and is folded along line *l*, the resulting noncoplanar half-planes form a figure called a *dihedral angle*.

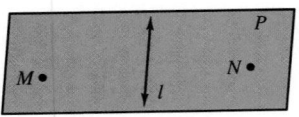

A **dihedral angle** is the union of two noncoplanar half-planes that have the same **edge**. The half-planes are called the **faces** of the dihedral angle. A dihedral angle is named by using, in order, a point in one face, the edge, and a point in the second face. This figure shows dihedral angle $A–\overleftrightarrow{XY}–B$, or $B–\overleftrightarrow{XY}–A$.

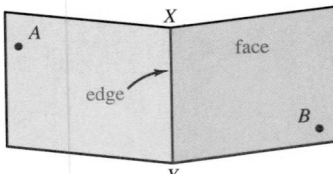

EXAMPLE 1   Name each dihedral angle two ways.

a.

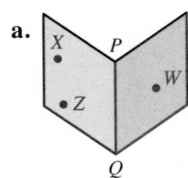

b.

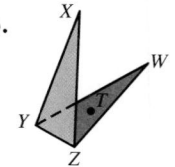

a. $X–\overleftrightarrow{PQ}–W$ or $Z–\overleftrightarrow{PQ}–W$

b. $X–\overleftrightarrow{YZ}–T$ or $X–\overleftrightarrow{YZ}–W$

204   Chapter 5 Inequalities in Triangles

Developing Mathematical Power

Keeping a Portfolio   Provide each student with the Investigation: Fold-up Boxes, p. 18 in the *Teacher's Resource Book*. After completing it, have them write an explanation in their own words of how to name a dihedral angle. They should also include a labeled and named dihedral angle of their own.

Two planes intersect to form four dihedral angles.
Planes AXC and BXD intersect in $\overleftrightarrow{XY}$.
The four dihedral angles are:
$A-\overleftrightarrow{XY}-B$, $A-\overleftrightarrow{XY}-D$, $B-\overleftrightarrow{XY}-C$, and $C-\overleftrightarrow{XY}-D$.
Dihedral angles that share a common edge and
a common face are called **adjacent dihedral angles.**
Which pairs of dihedral angles are adjacent?

$A-\overleftrightarrow{XY}-B$ and $B-\overleftrightarrow{XY}-C$; $B-\overleftrightarrow{XY}-C$ and $C-\overleftrightarrow{XY}-D$; $C-\overleftrightarrow{XY}-D$ and $D-\overleftrightarrow{XY}-A$; $D-\overleftrightarrow{XY}-A$ and $A-\overleftrightarrow{XY}-B$

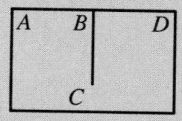

EXAMPLE 2   Name some of the dihedral angles formed.

$C-\overleftrightarrow{AG}-L$, $C-\overleftrightarrow{AE}-I$, $L-\overleftrightarrow{AB}-I$, $F-\overleftrightarrow{BH}-L$, $F-\overleftrightarrow{BI}-E$

Pick a point on the edge of dihedral angle $A-\overleftrightarrow{XY}-B$.
Call it P. If $\overrightarrow{PD}$ and $\overrightarrow{PC}$ are perpendicular to $\overleftrightarrow{XY}$
at P, then $\angle CPD$ is called a *plane angle*
of dihedral angle $A-\overleftrightarrow{XY}-B$.

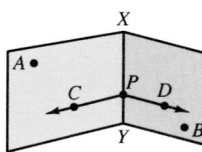

This figure shows a way to visualize the
plane angle, $\angle CPD$.

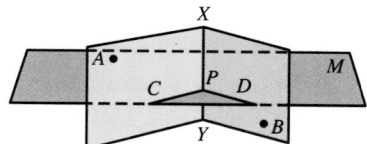

Definition   A **plane angle** of a dihedral angle is the angle formed by the
intersection of the dihedral angle and a plane that is perpendicular to its edge.

The **measure of a dihedral angle** is found by measuring any one of its plane
angles. All plane angles of a dihedral angle have the same measure. Dihedral
angles may be classified as acute, right, or obtuse, depending upon whether
the plane angles of the dihedral angle are acute, right, or obtuse. What is true
about the planes that intersect to form a right dihedral angle? They are ⊥.

- To illustrate dihedral angles, give
  each student two index cards, one
  of which has a slot cut that is perpendicular to the edge and extends
  three-fourths of the way through
  the card. Have the students label
  the cards as shown and insert the
  second card into the first.

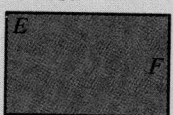

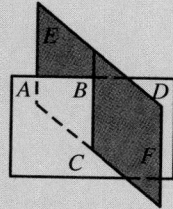

Ask students to name all the dihedral angles.

- Use the Extended Investigation to
  illustrate a plane angle of a dihedral
  angle.

Critical Thinking

1. *Constructing* Ask students to
   model dihedral angles.
2. *Causal Explanation* Have students analyze conditions that are
   true if an angle is a plane angle of a
   dihedral angle.

CHALKBOARD EXAMPLES

- **For Example 1**
  Name the di-
  hedral angle
  two ways.

  $T-\overleftrightarrow{RS}-W$ or $T-\overleftrightarrow{RS}-Z$

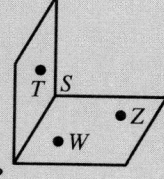

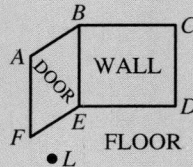
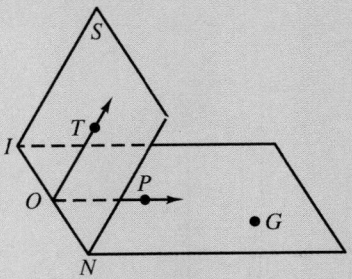
EXAMPLE 3 ∠MPN is a plane angle of dihedral angle $A-\overleftrightarrow{BC}-D$.

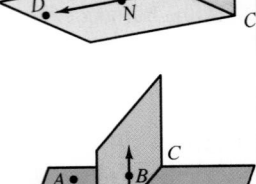

a. If m∠MPN = 105, then the measure of $A-\overleftrightarrow{BC}-D$ = ?.
b. Since ∠MPN is a plane angle, m∠MPB = ?.
c. If m∠MPN = 105, then dihedral angle $A-\overleftrightarrow{BC}-D$ is ?.

a. 105   b. 90   c. obtuse

Be careful about drawing conclusions from pictures. For example, in this figure, ∠BEF may or may not be a plane angle of dihedral angle $B-\overleftrightarrow{CD}-J$. Under what circumstances would you be justified in calling ∠BEF a plane angle? when the plane containing ∠BEF is ⊥ $\overleftrightarrow{DC}$

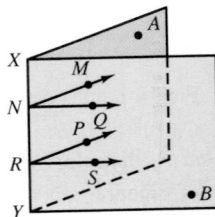

> **Theorem 5.11** All plane angles of the same dihedral angle are congruent. Proved on page 258

If ∠MNQ and ∠PRS are plane angles of dihedral angle $A-\overleftrightarrow{XY}-B$, then ∠MNQ ≅ ∠PRS. Although the meaning of the word *angle* differs in plane angle and dihedral angle, plane angles play an integral part in describing the properties of dihedral angles.

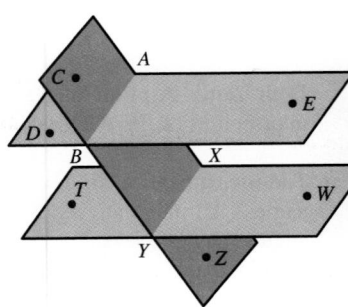

CLASS EXERCISES
Answers may vary. Check students' drawings.

1. Draw an acute dihedral angle.
2. Draw an obtuse dihedral angle.
3. Draw a pair of perpendicular planes. Label a dihedral angle.
4. Draw two parallel planes and a third plane that intersects each of the parallel planes. Label a pair of dihedral angles.

Name two pairs of indicated dihedral angle(s).

5. Vertical dihedral angles with edge $\overleftrightarrow{AB}$
   $C-\overleftrightarrow{AB}-E$ and $D-\overleftrightarrow{AB}-X$; $D-\overleftrightarrow{AB}-C$ and $E-\overleftrightarrow{AB}-X$
6. Supplementary dihedral angles with edge $\overleftrightarrow{AB}$
   $D-\overleftrightarrow{AB}-C$ and $C-\overleftrightarrow{AB}-E$; $D-\overleftrightarrow{AB}-X$ and $E-\overleftrightarrow{AB}-X$
7. Alternate interior dihedral angles.
   $E-\overleftrightarrow{AB}-X$ and $B-\overleftrightarrow{XY}-T$; $D-\overleftrightarrow{AB}-X$ and $A-\overleftrightarrow{XY}-W$
8. Corresponding dihedral angles
   $C-\overleftrightarrow{AB}-E$ and $A-\overleftrightarrow{XY}-W$; $E-\overleftrightarrow{AB}-X$ and $W-\overleftrightarrow{XY}-Z$;
   $D-\overleftrightarrow{AB}-X$ and $T-\overleftrightarrow{XY}-Z$; $C-\overleftrightarrow{AB}-D$ and $B-\overleftrightarrow{XY}-T$

Use the figure at the bottom of page 206 to answer Exercises 9–10.

9. If plane *DAE* is parallel to plane *TXW* and dihedral angle C–$\overleftrightarrow{AB}$–E measures 130, what is the measure of dihedral angle B–$\overleftrightarrow{XY}$–W? 130

10. If dihedral angle B–$\overleftrightarrow{XY}$–T measures 60 and dihedral angle C–$\overleftrightarrow{AB}$–E measures 120, is plane *DAE* parallel to plane *TXW*? Justify. Yes; if B–$\overleftrightarrow{XY}$–T measures 60, then B–$\overleftrightarrow{XY}$–W measures 120. If corr. ∠s are ≅, the planes that form them are ‖.

PRACTICE EXERCISES

The figure below is a cube. *P* is in plane *JKC*. Use the figure to complete the statements in Exercises 1–8.

A

1. $\overrightarrow{JA}$ is the edge of dihedral angle ___?___. P–$\overrightarrow{JA}$–M

2. Name all dihedral angles with *P* on a face.
   P–$\overrightarrow{JA}$–M; P–$\overrightarrow{AC}$–E; P–$\overrightarrow{JK}$–R; P–$\overrightarrow{KC}$–R

3. $\overline{HM}$ is the edge of dihedral angle ___?___. J–$\overrightarrow{HM}$–R

4. Dihedral angle A–$\overrightarrow{ME}$–R has plane angles ___?___ and ___?___. ∠AMH; ∠CER

5. ∠*AME* is a plane angle of dihedral angle ___?___. A–$\overrightarrow{HM}$–E

6. ∠*JKR* is a plane angle of dihedral angle ___?___. P–$\overrightarrow{KC}$–R

7. ∠*ACE* is a plane angle of dihedral angle ___?___. P–$\overrightarrow{KC}$–R

8. What is the intersection of dihedral angles J–$\overleftrightarrow{KR}$–E and R–$\overleftrightarrow{CE}$–A? face *KCER*

Use the figure to the right for Exercises 9–14.

9. If ∠*ABC* is a plane angle of dihedral angle R–$\overleftrightarrow{ST}$–W, what is true about $\overrightarrow{BA}$ and $\overrightarrow{BC}$?
   They are ⊥ to $\overleftrightarrow{ST}$ at B; $\overrightarrow{BA}$ ⊥ $\overleftrightarrow{ST}$; $\overrightarrow{BC}$ ⊥ $\overleftrightarrow{ST}$.

10. If ∠*ABC* is a plane angle of dihedral angle R–$\overleftrightarrow{ST}$–W, $m\angle ABS = $ ___?___. 90

11. If ∠*MON* is a plane angle of dihedral angle Q–$\overleftrightarrow{ST}$–P, what is true about $\overrightarrow{OM}$ and $\overrightarrow{ON}$?
    They are ⊥ to $\overleftrightarrow{ST}$ at O; $\overrightarrow{OM}$ ⊥ $\overleftrightarrow{ST}$; $\overrightarrow{ON}$ ⊥ $\overleftrightarrow{ST}$.

12. If ∠*MON* is a plane angle of dihedral angle Q–$\overleftrightarrow{ST}$–P, $m\angle TON = $ ___?___. 90

13. ∠*MON* is a plane angle of Q–$\overleftrightarrow{ST}$–P, and ∠*ABC* is a plane angle of R–$\overleftrightarrow{ST}$–W. If $m\angle MON = 70$ and $m\angle ABC = 80$, what is the measure of Q–$\overleftrightarrow{ST}$–R? 30

14. If ∠*DEF* and ∠*ABC* are plane angles of dihedral angle R–$\overleftrightarrow{ST}$–W, then $m\angle DEF$ ___?___ $m\angle ABC$. =

True or false? Justify your answers.

B

15. If a plane intersects the edge of a dihedral angle, the intersection is a plane angle of a dihedral angle. false; true if the plane is ⊥ to the edge of the dihedral ∠

16. If a plane intersects the faces of a dihedral angle, the intersection is a plane angle of the dihedral angle. false; true if plane intersects the edge and is ⊥ to the edge

5.7 Congruence in Space: Dihedral Angles   **207**

Assignment Guide
See p. 172B for assignments.

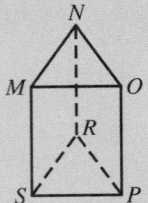
Given the figure and the information shown, is there enough information to conclude that ∠*BAC* is a plane angle of dihedral angle Z–$\overleftrightarrow{XY}$–W? Justify your answers.

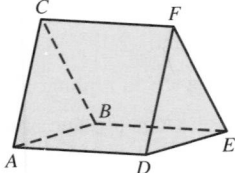

17. **Given:** $\overrightarrow{AB} \perp \overleftrightarrow{XY}$; $\overrightarrow{AC} \perp \overleftrightarrow{XY}$ yes; def. of plane ∠

18. **Given:** $m\angle XAB = 90$ no; not unless $m\angle XAC = 90$

19. **Given:** $m\angle XAB = m\angle CAY = 90$ yes; def. of plane ∠

20. **Given:** $\overrightarrow{AC} \perp \overleftrightarrow{XY}$ no; must know $\overrightarrow{AB} \perp \overleftrightarrow{XY}$ also

21. **Given:** Plane *BAC* is parallel to plane *ZXW*. no; not unless plane ZXW is ⊥ $\overleftrightarrow{XY}$

C 22. ∠*ACB* and ∠*DFE* are plane angles of A–$\overleftrightarrow{CF}$–B. △*ACB* and △*DFE* are congruent isosceles triangles with bases $\overline{AB}$ and $\overline{DE}$. If $m\angle ABC = x$, express the measure of dihedral angle D–$\overleftrightarrow{CF}$–E in terms of x. 180 – 2x

23. **Given:** $\overline{BC} \cong \overline{EF}$; See side column.
∠*ABC* ≅ ∠*DEF*;
∠*ACB* and ∠*DFE* are plane angles of dihedral angle A–$\overleftrightarrow{CF}$–B.

Prove: $\overline{AC} \cong \overline{DF}$

Applications

24. **Art** Study the dihedral angles suggested by this sculpture. Answers may vary.

25. **Architecture** Find an aerial photograph of the Pentagon Building in Washington, D.C. Sketch the building and label the corner posts. Then name as many dihedral angles as you can. Answers may vary.

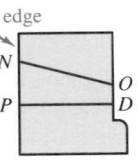

Developing Mathematical Power

Investigation Take a manila file folder and construct line segment *PD* across the front of the folder so that $\overline{PD}$ is perpendicular to the edge of the folder. Now draw segment *NO* that is not perpendicular to the edge. Cut along both line segments from the folded edge to about halfway across the folder.

Stand the folder on end on your desk. Insert another folder into each cut on the original folder.

26. Which inserted folder forms a plane angle congruent to the plane angle formed with the surface of the desk? Why? The one through $\overrightarrow{PD}$; $\overrightarrow{PD}$ is ⊥ to the edge.

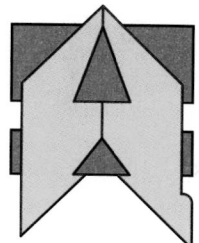

27. Is the other angle that is formed considered a plane angle? Explain your answer. no; not unless $\overrightarrow{NO}$ is ⊥ to the edge

28. How do the two angles that were formed seem to compare? Answers may vary depending on how $\overrightarrow{NO}$ was cut; the ∠s are unequal in measure.

TEST YOURSELF

Justify your answers.

1. If $FA = 4$ cm, $AR = 12$ cm, and $FR = 9$ cm, the largest angle of $\triangle FRA$ is _?_. ∠AFR; largest ∠ is opposite longest side

2. If $\overline{FD} \perp \overline{DA}$, the longest side of $\triangle FDA$ is _?_. FA; hypotenuse is longest side

3. If $m\angle AFE = 110$, the longest side of $\triangle AFE$ is _?_. AE; longest side is opp. largest ∠

4. If $FE > ER$, then $m\angle\underline{?} < m\angle\underline{?}$. EFR; FRE; larger ∠ is opposite longer side

5. In $\triangle FDE$, $FD + DE \underline{?} FE$. >; △ Inequality Th.

6. In $\triangle FER$, if $FE = 6$ cm and $ER = 4$ cm, the greatest possible whole number value of FR is _?_. 9 cm; △ Inequality Th.

5.5

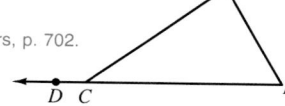

7. Given: $\triangle ABC$ with $\overrightarrow{BC}$ extended through D;
$AC > AB$
Prove: $m\angle DCA > m\angle ACB$ See Additional Answers, p. 702.

8. If $\overline{AB} \cong \overline{DE}$, $\overline{BC} \cong \overline{EC}$, and $\angle B \cong \angle E$, then $AC \underline{?} CD$. =; SAS; CPCTC; ≅ seg.

9. If $\overline{AB} \cong \overline{DE}$, $\overline{AC} \cong \overline{DC}$, and $m\angle D > m\angle A$, then $BC \underline{?} EC$. <; Hinge Th.

10. If $\overline{BC} \cong \overline{EC}$, $\overline{CA} \cong \overline{CD}$, and $AB < DE$, then $m\angle\underline{?} > m\angle\underline{?}$. ECD; BCA; conv. of Hinge Th.

5.6

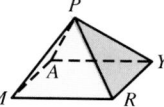

5.7

11. $\overleftrightarrow{PA}$ is the edge of dihedral angle _?_. M−$\overrightarrow{PA}$−Y

12. Name all the dihedral angles in this figure.
A−$\overrightarrow{PY}$−R; R−$\overrightarrow{PM}$−A; P−$\overrightarrow{YR}$−A; P−$\overrightarrow{MA}$−R;
Y−$\overrightarrow{PR}$−M; P−$\overrightarrow{AY}$−R; P−$\overrightarrow{RM}$−A; M−$\overrightarrow{PA}$−Y

5.7 Congruence in Space: Dihedral Angles **209**

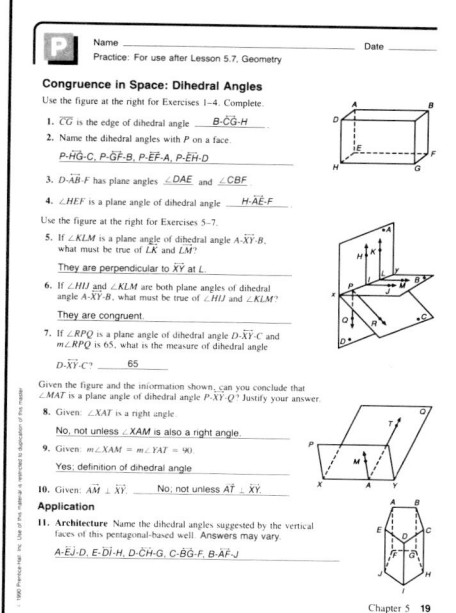

Students should complete the Technology exercises on pp. 90 and 108 prior to this lesson.

See Teacher's Resource Book, Follow-up Technology, pp. 5–6.

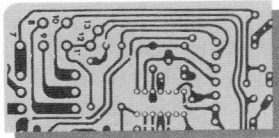

TECHNOLOGY:
Recursion and Tessellations

Recursion happens when a procedure calls itself. The procedure can be stopped by typing in open-apple S. To stop the recursion *within a procedure* (not using open-apple S), use the Logo primitive **stop**. This primitive is used in conjunction with a conditional if statement of the form:

if (something is true) [stop].

EXAMPLE **Type in these procedures and describe each output.**

a. to hello
print [hi! how are you?]
hello
end

b. to hello :counter
if :counter > 20 [stop]
print [hi! how are you?]
hello :counter + 1
end

a. It will print hi! how are you? over and over again on the screen.

b. Provided the original counter was set at 1, it prints hello! how are you? twenty times and then "stops."

The following *polyspi* procedure is a famous example of recursion.

to polyspi :side :angle
forward :side
right :angle
polyspi (:side + 3) :angle
end

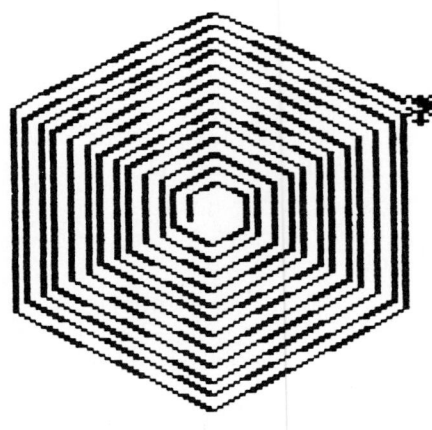

polyspi 10 60

Square tiles can be placed in rows and columns to cover a floor without gaps. However, tiles in the shape of pentagons leave gaps. Creating tessellations is similar to the practical task of covering a floor or wall with tiles. There are three regular tessellations. They are formed by equilateral triangles, squares, and hexagons (Figure 1). However, if regular shapes are mixed, many other kinds of tessellations can be generated (Figure 2) which create pleasing patterns.

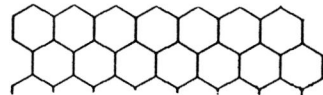

Figure 1

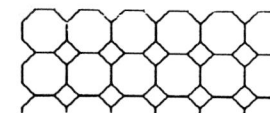

Figure 2

The above tessellations are called *periodic* because the pattern repeats. Regular polygons can be used to generate *nonperiodic* tessellations where the pattern never repeats. Roger Penrose, in the mid-1970s, created two nonregular diamonds from which he generated a nonperiodic tessellation with a fivefold symmetry.

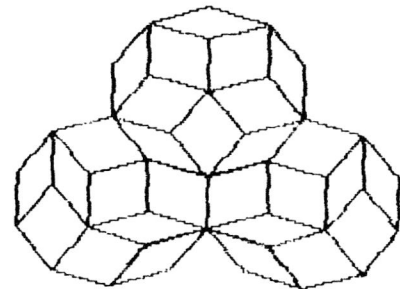

Any Logo drawing can have color—both background color and pencolor. The available colors and their respective number codes are:

black—0, white—1, green—2, violet—3, orange—4, blue—5

The command to change the background is **setbg** followed by a number. The command to change the pencolor is **setc** followed by a number. For example, **setbg 4** sets the background color to orange.

EXERCISES

1. Try different values in the *polyspi* procedure.

2. Change the *polyspi* procedure to stop when the length of a side is larger than 70.

3. Change the *polyspi* procedure so that :**angle** also increases.

4. Change the *polyspi* procedure so that both :**side** and :**angle** decrease.

5. Generate a graphic using recursion. Now add color.

6. Why do equilateral triangles, squares, and regular hexagons form the only regular tessellations?

- See *Teacher's Resource Book, Spanish Chapter Summary and Review*, pp. 9–10.
- See Extra Practice, p. 647.

Vocabulary

adjacent dihedral angles (205)
assumption (185)
base (174)
base angles (174)
contradiction (185)
dihedral angle (204)
edge of a dihedral angle (204)
face of a dihedral angle (204)

indirect proof (184)
legs (174)
measure of a dihedral angle (205)
plane angle of a dihedral angle (205)
remote interior angle (180)
trichotomy property (181)
vertex angle (174)

Congruence in a Single Triangle The base angles of an isosceles triangle are congruent. The bisector of the vertex angle of an isosceles triangle is perpendicular to the base at its midpoint. A triangle is equiangular if and only if it is equilateral.   5.1

Find the indicated measures.

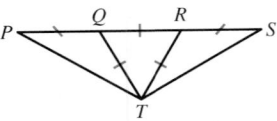

1. $m\angle TQR = \underline{?}$ 60   2. $m\angle QRT = \underline{?}$ 60

3. $m\angle SRT = \underline{?}$ 120   4. $m\angle QTP = \underline{?}$ 30

5. $m\angle PST = \underline{?}$ 30   6. $m\angle PTS = \underline{?}$ 120

Properties of Inequality The algebraic relationships *greater than* and *less than* are the basis for comparing segments that are not congruent and for comparing angles that are not congruent. The measure of an exterior angle of a triangle is greater than the measure of either remote interior angle.   5.2

Identify the property or name a theorem that justifies each conclusion.

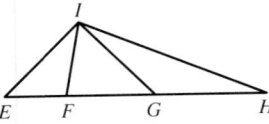

7. $m\angle FIG < m\angle FIH$ 8. $EG > FG$ Th. 5.3
   Th. 5.4
9. If $m\angle HIF > m\angle EIG$, then $m\angle HIG > m\angle EIF$.
   subt. prop. of ≠
10. If $EI \neq GI$, then $EI > GI$ or $EI < GI$. trichotomy

11. If $EF < GH$, then $EG < FH$. add. prop. of ≠

12. $m\angle HGI > m\angle EIG$ Ext. ∠ Th.

Indirect Proof and Inequalities Indirect reasoning often is used to prove theorems about inequalities. To negate statements such as $AB > AC$ or $m\angle CDF < m\angle FGH$, use the trichotomy property, which states that for any two real numbers one must be $<$, $>$, or $=$ the other.   5.3, 5.4

Write the assumption that you would make as the first step in an indirect proof. Identify all the cases that would have to be proven.

13. Prove: $\triangle ABC$ is not isosceles.

14. Prove: $AB = CD$ Assume
$AB \neq CD$. Then (1) $AB < CD$ or (2) $AB > CD$.

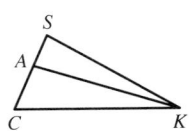

15. Write an indirect proof. See page 724.
    Given: Isosceles $\triangle DEF$ with base $\overline{EF}$;
            $\overline{DG}$ does not bisect $\angle EDF$.
    Prove: $\overline{DG}$ is not perpendicular to $\overline{EF}$.

13. Assume $\triangle ABC$ is isosceles. Then (1)
$AB \cong AC$ (2) $AB \cong BC$ or (3) $AC \cong BC$.

Inequalities in One Triangle In a triangle, an inequality between two   5.5
sides (angles) holds for the angles (sides) opposite those sides (angles).

16. If $m\angle S = 85$ and $m\angle C = 63$,
the longest side of $\triangle SKC$ is __?__. $\overline{CK}$

17. If $SK > SC$, then $m\angle$ __?__ $< m\angle$ __?__. SKC, C

18. Given: Isosceles $\triangle SKA$ with base $\overline{SA}$
     Prove: $CK > SK$
      See side column.

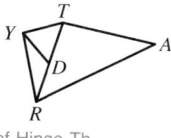

More on Inequalities In any triangle, it is always true that the sum of the   5.6
lengths of any two sides is greater than the length of the third side.
Inequalities that hold between two triangles that have two pairs of congruent
sides are described by the Hinge Theorem and its converse.

Could these sets of positive integers be the lengths of sides of a triangle?

19. $\{5, 9, 15\}$ no   **20.** $\{6, 6, 6\}$ yes   **21.** $\{x, x, 2x\}$ no   **22.** $\{2, x, x+1\}$ yes

Justify each answer.

23. $TR <$ __?__ $+$ __?__ or __?__ $+$ __?__.
YR, YT; AT, AR; $\triangle$ Inequality Th.

24. If $\overline{YT} \cong \overline{YD} \cong \overline{RD}$, and $TD < YR$,
then $m\angle$ __?__ $< m\angle$ __?__. TYD, RDY; conv. of Hinge Th.

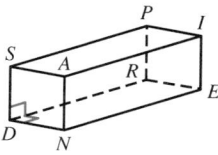

Dihedral Angles Dihedral angles are formed when two noncoplanar   5.7
half-planes share an edge. A plane angle is the angle formed by the intersection
of a plane perpendicular to the edge of the dihedral angle at a given point. A
dihedral angle is measured by measuring any one of its plane angles.

25. $\overline{AN}$ is the edge of dihedral angle __?__. I–$\overleftrightarrow{AN}$–D

26. $\angle SDN$ is a plane angle of dihedral angle __?__.
S–$\overline{DR}$–N

27. The intersection of dihedral angles A–$\overrightarrow{PI}$–R
and P–$\overleftrightarrow{IE}$–N is __?__. face PIRE and $\overleftrightarrow{AI}$

---

18. Plan: Since $\triangle SKA$ is isos., with base SA, $\angle S \cong \angle SAK$. By the Ext. Angle Th., $m\angle SAK > m\angle C$. By subs., $m\angle S > m\angle C$. The conclusion follows by $\triangle$inequality for $\triangle SCK$.

Proof:

Statements	Reasons
1. Isos. $\triangle SKA$; base SA	1. Given
2. $\angle S \cong \angle SAK$	2. Base $\angle$s of an isos. $\triangle$ are $\cong$.
3. $m\angle S = m\angle SAK$	3. Def. of $\cong \angle$s
4. $m\angle SAK > m\angle C$	4. Ext. $\angle$ Th.
5. $m\angle S > m\angle C$	5. Subs. prop.
6. $CK > SK$	6. If the meas. of 2 $\angle$s of a $\triangle$ are unequal, the longer side is opposite the larger $\angle$.

Conclusion: In the given figure, if $\triangle SKA$ is isosceles, then $CK > SK$.

Summary and Review   **213**

Name _____ **Date** _____
Chapter 5 Test: Form A, page 1, Geometry

Chapter Test

Tell whether the given statement is always, sometimes, or never true.

ANSWERS

1. If in △ABC and △DEF, $\overline{AB} \cong \overline{DE}$, then ∠C = ∠F. 1. ___sometimes___

2. If △MNO and △DEF are equilateral and $\overline{MN} \cong \overline{DE}$, then △MNO ≅ △DEF. 2. ___always___

3. In △RST, ST + RT > RS. 3. ___always___

4. If ∠KJR and ∠STU are plane angles of dihedral angle O–AB–P, then m∠KJR = m∠STU. 4. ___always___

5. In △ABC, if AB > BC, then m∠A > m∠C. 5. ___never___

6. If △RST is isosceles and $\overline{RS} \cong \overline{TS}$, then ∠R ≅ ∠T. 6. ___always___

Select the correct answer.

7. If △XYZ is isosceles with base $\overline{XZ}$, then
   a. XY = YZ   c. XZ = YZ
   b. XY = ZY   d. none of these   7. ___b___

8. If ST > BC is to be proven indirectly, then assume
   a. m∠T = m∠B   c. BC > ST
   b. BC < ST   d. none of these   8. ___d___

9. If $\overline{DB} \cong \overline{BE}$, AC < ST, then
   a. AC + DB > ST + BE   c. $\frac{AC}{DB} < \frac{ST}{BE}$
   b. AC − DB > ST − BE   d. AC(BE) < ST(AC)   9. ___c___

10. The following sets of sides can be used to form triangles except
    a. 8, 22, 12   c. 20, 12, 16
    b. 10, 24, 26   d. 16, 30, 34   10. ___a___

Tests **53**

Name _____ **Date** _____
Chapter 5 Test: Form A, page 2, Geometry

Chapter Test

Complete the proofs.

11. Given: $\overline{AB} \cong \overline{DE}$, C is the midpoint of $\overline{AD}$; m∠BAC > m∠EDC
    Prove: BC > EC

    Plan: Show △s have 2 sides ≅ and incl. ∠ is lgr. Use Hinge Theorem.

Statements	Reasons
$\overline{AB} \cong \overline{DE}$, C is the midpoint of $\overline{AD}$; m∠BAC > m∠EDC	12. ___Given___
$\overline{AC} \cong \overline{DC}$	13. ___Def. of midpt.___
BC > EC	14. ___Hinge Th.___

Given: △RST with a point M in the interior.
Prove: RM + MT < RS + ST

Statements	Reasons
Extend $\overline{RM}$ to point Z on $\overline{ST}$	15. ___A line from a vertex to a point in the interior of a △ intersects the opp. side___
RM + MZ < RS + SZ.	Triangle ineq.
MT < MZ + ZT; RM + MZ + MT < RS +	Addition prop. of ineq.
16. ___SZ + MZ + ZT___	
17. ___RM + MT < RS + SZ + ZT___	Subtraction prop. of ineq.
18. ___RM + MT < RS + ST___	Def. of betweenness

Challenge

Prove that the sum of the sides of a quadrilateral is greater than the sum of the diagonals.

Statements	Reasons
1. c + d > h + f; b + c > e + g; a + d > e + g; a + b > f + h	1. Triangle inequality
2. 2a + 2b + 2c + 2d > 2e + 2f + 2g + 2h	2. Addition prop. of inequality
3. a + b + c + d > e + f + g + h	3. Division prop. of inequality
4. a + b + c + d > AC + BD	4. Def. of betweenness

54 Tests

Justify whether the given statement is always, sometimes, or never true.

1. In △JHK and △LMN, if ∠J ≅ ∠L, then $\overline{HK} \cong \overline{MN}$. sometimes; if △ are ≅

2. In △PQR, PQ < PR + RQ. always; △ Inequality Th.

3. In △EFG, if $\overline{EF} \not\cong \overline{FG}$, then m∠G > m∠E. sometimes true; if EF > FG

4. If ∠MNO and ∠PQR are plane angles of dihedral angle X–$\overleftrightarrow{YZ}$–W, then m∠MNO > m∠PQR. never; plane ∠s of a dihedral ∠ are ≅

Select the correct answer.

5. If m∠A > m∠B is to be proven indirectly, then assume
   a. m∠A < m∠B   b. m∠A = m∠B   d
   c. ∠A ≅ ∠B   d. None of these

6. If △ISO is isosceles with base $\overline{SO}$ and altitude $\overline{IA}$, then
   a. IS > IA   b. IS = IA   a
   c. IS < IA   d. Cannot determine

7. **Given:** $\overline{PL} \cong \overline{RA}$; m∠LPR > m∠PRA
   Prove: LR > PA
   Plan: __?__ In △PLR and △RAP, 2 pairs of sides are ≅.
   Proof: Use the included ∠s and Hinge Th. to reach conclusion.

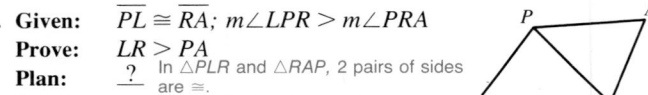

Statements	Reasons
1. $\overline{PL} \cong \overline{RA}$; m∠LPR > m∠PRA	1. Given
2. $\overline{PR} \cong$ __?__ $\overline{RP}$	2. __?__ Refl. prop.
3. LR > PA	3. __?__ Hinge Th.

Conclusion: __?__ If $\overline{PL} \cong \overline{RA}$ and m∠LPR > m∠PRA in the given figure, then LR > PA.

8. **Given:** △PQR with altitude $\overline{QA}$, angle bisector $\overline{QB}$, and median $\overline{QM}$, with B between A and M
   Prove: QA < QB < QM
   See Additional Answers, p. 702.

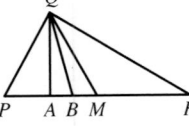

Challenge

Prove the Isosceles Triangle Theorem, using Euclid's proof. The plan is given below.

Given: Isosceles △ABC with $\overline{AB} \cong \overline{AC}$
Prove: ∠ABC ≅ ∠ACB
Plan: Extend $\overrightarrow{AB}$ to D and $\overrightarrow{AC}$ to E such that $\overline{BD} \cong \overline{CE}$.

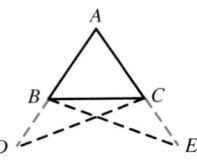

214 Chapter 5 Inequalities in Triangles

Alternative Assessment Have students make a drawing to illustrate each one of the following theorems: Isosceles Triangle theorem, the Exterior Angle theorem, Theorem 5.6, Triangle Inequality theorem, and Hinge Theorem. Have them describe each theorem in their own words.

Directions. In each item, compare a quantity in Column 1 with a quantity in Column 2. Write the letter of the correct answer from these choices:

A. The quantity in Column 1 is greater than the quantity in Column 2.
B. The quantity in Column 2 is greater than the quantity in Column 1.
C. The quantity in Column 1 is equal to the quantity in Column 2.
D. The relationship cannot be determined from the given information.

Notes: A symbol that appears in both columns has the same meaning in each column. All variables represent real numbers. Most figures are not drawn to scale.

Column 1	Column 2

$$3(2x - 7) = x - 1$$

1. $5x - 4$ x^2
C
2. 10% of 500   300% of 14
A

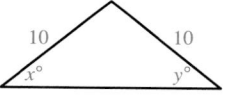

3. x
C

$$-3x > -15$$

4. x 5
B

Use this diagram for 5–6.

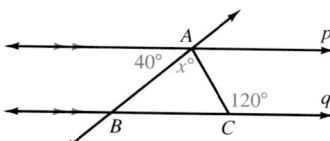

5. 90 x
A
6. AB BC
B

Column 1	Column 2

$$\frac{x + 3}{2} = \frac{x - 3}{4}$$

7. x -8
B

a is an even integer
b is an odd integer
$ab = 36$

8. a b
D
9. $\frac{2}{3}$ of 69 $\frac{3}{2}$ of 30
A

$$\frac{1}{x} > 3$$

10. x 0
A

Use this diagram for 11–12.

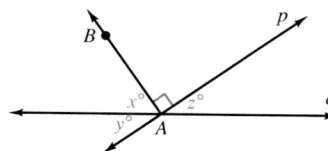

11. x z
D
12. y z
C

The following skills and concepts are reviewed:
Ratio and proportion
Solving fractional equations

Express each ratio in simplest form.

Example   Hope High School has a student population of 1500 boys and 1200 girls. What is the ratio of girls to boys?

$$\frac{girls}{boys} = \frac{1200}{1500} = \frac{4}{5}$$

1. John's monthly salary is $1300 and his wife's monthly salary is $1100. They pay $800 a month rent. What part of their combined salary goes for rent each month? $\frac{1}{3}$

2. What is the ratio of the length of one side of a regular hexagon to its perimeter? $\frac{1}{6}$

Solve.

Example   The measures of an angle and its complement are in a ratio of $2:7$. Find the measure of each angle.

Let $2x$ and $7x$ be the measures of the angle and its complement.
$2x + 7x = 90$
$\qquad 9x = 90$ Check:
$\qquad\quad x = 10$ $20:70 = 2:7$ ✔
The measure of the angle is $2x$, or 20. $20 + 70 = 90$ ✔
The measure of its complement is $7x$, or 70.

3. The measures of two supplementary angles are in a ratio of $5:10$. Find the measure of each angle. 60, 120

4. The ratio of the measures of three angles of a triangle is $1:3:5$. Find the measure of each angle. 20, 60, 100

Solve.

Examples   a. $\frac{15}{3} = \frac{x}{7}$ b. $\frac{3x-2}{x} = \frac{8}{4}$
$\quad 15 \cdot 7 = 3 \cdot x$ $4(3x-2) = 8x$
$\quad\quad 105 = 3x$ $12x - 8 = 8x$
$\quad\quad\quad 35 = x$ $4x = 8$
                             $x = 2$

5. $\frac{2}{7} = \frac{4}{x}$ 14

6. $\frac{3}{4} = \frac{x}{20}$ 15

7. $\frac{x+12}{3} = \frac{3x+4}{5}$ 12

8. $\frac{z-5}{z} = \frac{3}{4}$ 20

9. $\frac{2x-3}{27} = \frac{x-2}{12}$ 6

10. $\frac{2x-4}{37} = \frac{3x}{74}$ 8

216   Chapter 5 Inequalities in Triangles

OVERVIEW • Chapter 6

SUMMARY

In Chapter 6, students define a parallelogram and develop theorems relating its definition to its properties. They extend this understanding to figures containing more than one transversal. The rectangle, rhombus, and square are defined and their properties are explored. Students learn about trapezoids and related properties. Theorems establishing congruent quadrilaterals are then proven.

CHAPTER OBJECTIVES

- To apply the definition of a parallelogram
- To prove and apply theorems relating parallelograms and their properties
- To prove and apply theorems that relate to parallel lines cut by more than one transversal
- To identify and apply special properties of a rectangle, rhombus and square
- To apply the definition of a trapezoid
- To prove and apply theorems relating to properties of trapezoids
- To identify and prove theorems about congruent quadrilaterals
- To learn the basis for clear definitions and necessary and sufficient conditions by discussing *minimal conditions*

CHAPTER HIGHLIGHTS

DEVELOPING MATHEMATICAL POWER

Problem Solving

The strategy lesson incorporates the four problem solving steps into the process of recognizing minimal defining conditions for geometric terms and figures.

Communication

The side column suggests topics for writing and drawing, such as describing congruent quadrilaterals and making a Venn diagram to describe relationships. Alternative learning styles are addressed through using manipulatives. Enrichment exercises from the *Teacher's Resource Book* lend themselves to cooperative learning endeavors, such as describing the vanishing point. There is a Chapter Summary and Review in Spanish in the *Teacher's Resource Book.*

Reasoning

An exercise in Lesson 6.2 asks students to compare and contrast parallelograms and kites. Formal proofs and indirect proofs are used throughout the chapter.

Connections

Real-world applications include such topics as construction, hobbies, and architecture. Dutch artist Maurtis Escher provides an example of the variety of cultural influences on mathematics. Vectors and scalars are featured in the Integrating Geometry section.

Technology

Logo topics are presented in exercises throughout the chapter.

STUDENT TEXT

Chapter Content	Basic	Average	Enriched	NCTM STANDARDS*
6.1 The Parallelogram —A Special Quadrilateral	D; 221/1-13, 22, 23, 37, MR	D: 221/1-13, 22-30, 37, 38, MR	D: 221/1-5, 14-29, 30-36 even, 37, 38, MR	2, 3, 5, 7
6.2 Finding Quadrilaterals That Are Parallelograms	D: 225/1-13, 29, 31 R: 221/14-21	D: 225/1-16, 17-23 odd, 29 R: 221/14-21, 31	D: 225/6-25, 29-32 R: 221/30-36 odd	2, 3, 7
6.3 Parallel Lines and Midpoints	D: 230/1-8, 16-17, 31, MR R: 225/14-16	D: 230/1-19, 20-26 even, 31, MR R: 225/17-23 even	D: 230/1-19, 20-30 even, 31, 32, MR R: 225/26-28	3, 4, 5, 7
6.4 Special Parallelograms	D: 236/1, 2, 3-15 odd, 34 R: 230/9-14	D: 236/1-13, 14-24 even, 35 R: 230/20-26 odd	D: 236/1-24, 25-33 odd, 34, 35 R: 230/20-30 odd	2, 3, 5, 7
6.5 Trapezoids	D: 242/1-15, 32, AR R: 236/3-15 even	D: 242/1-22, 23-27 odd, 32, AR R: 236/14-24 odd, 34	D: 242/1-22, 23-29 odd, 32, 33, AR R: 236/25-33 even	2, 3, 5, 7
6.6 Strategy: Recognize Minimal Conditions	D: 246/1, 2, 3-13 odd R: 242/17-19	D: 246/1, 2, 3-13 odd R: 242/23-27 even	D: 246/1, 2, 3-13 odd R: 242/23-29 even	1, 3
6.7 Congruent Quadrilaterals	D: 250/2-20, 40 R: 246/4-10 even	D: 250/1, 11-33, 40-42 R: 246/4-12 even	D: 250/11-28, 34-42 R: 246/4-12 even	2, 3, 7

D = Daily   R = Review   MR = Mixed Review   AR = Algebra Review

*For a complete list of NCTM Standards, see p. T7.

STUDENT TEXT

Review/Assessment

Mixed Review 222, 232

Algebra Review 243

Summary and Review 256

College Ent. Exam Rev. 259

Cumulative Review 260

Extra Practice 648

Test Yourself 238, 253

Chapter Test 258

Chapter Project 217

Special Features

Technology 222, 227, 238, 243, 253

Devel. Math. Power 227, 253

Applications 222, 227, 232, 238, 243, 253, 254-255

Project 247

RESOURCES

Teacher's Resource Book

Ch. 6: Investigation/Practice/ Enrichment 1-20

Spanish Sum. and Rev. 11-12

Quizzes 57-60

Chapter Tests 61-64

Cumulative Tests 65-68

Perf. Assessment Proj. Ch. 6

Critical Thinking 6

Reading and Writing in Geom. 6

Application—Ch. 6, 21

Technology 7-8

Teaching Aid 6

Transparency 7

Teaching Transparencies 35-41

Computer Test Bank 317-382

PH Graph. Utility

Overhead Manip. Kit

Quadrilaterals

A formidable figure!

Developing Mathematical Power

In the fifth century B.C., ancient Greeks built a temple on the cliffs of Athens. This building, known as the Parthenon, is an example of the architectural use of the Golden Rectangle.

The Golden Rectangle is thought to be the geometric form that is most pleasing to the human eye. Examples of Golden Rectangles are found in art and nature, as well as in architecture. Is there another rectangle that you find more pleasing?

Project

Create the "silver rectangle," your own special rectangle, and describe its ratio of length to width. Draw examples of Golden Rectangles and silver rectangles. Find examples of Golden Rectangles in art, architecture, and nature. Then look for examples of your silver rectangle.

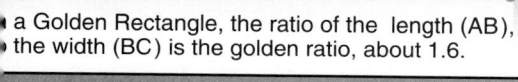

In a Golden Rectangle, the ratio of the length (AB), to the width (BC) is the golden ratio, about 1.6.

217

Vocabulary
Parallelogram

Materials/Manipulatives
Quadrilateral cutouts
Protractors and rulers
Compasses
Teacher's Resource Book,
 Transparency 7
Teaching Transparency 35

Technology
Computer Test Bank, pp.
 317–328

LESSON FOCUS

Review

* Review measures of angles of polygons.
  1. What is the sum of the measures of the interior angles of a pentagon? 540
  2. What is the measure of one interior angle for a regular quadrilateral? 90
  3. What is the sum of the measures of the exterior angles of a hexagon? 360
* The Mixed Review, Exercises 39–46, involves the relationship between angles and sides of triangles and parallel lines.

Alternative Learning Styles

Exploring relationships with manipulatives can aid student understanding. Provide groups with about 10 quadrilaterals with different shapes. Ask them to classify the quadrilaterals according to whether or not they have any parallel sides. Then ask them to measure the sides and angles of each figure and record the information in a table. Students should draw conclusions about the properties of various quadrilaterals.

218

6.1	**The Parallelogram—A Special Quadrilateral**

Objectives: To apply the definition of a parallelogram
To prove and apply theorems about the properties of a parallelogram

Quadrilaterals are four-sided polygons. They can be categorized by the special characteristics and relationships of their sides and angles.

Investigation—*Visualizing the Concept*

A planner is laying out a reconstructed subdivision along historic River Road. East-west streets will be parallel, but at Second Avenue the north-south streets will turn and run parallel to River Road.

1. Compare the shapes of the numbered blocks. They each have 4 sides. Blocks 1 and 2 appear to have the same size and shape; so do blocks 3 and 4.
2. Estimate the measure of each angle in block 2 and in block 4. Check your estimates with a protractor. In block 2, each ∠ appears to measure 90. In block 4, ∠s measure 115 and 65.
3. In what ways are blocks 2 and 4 alike? In what ways are they different? Answers may vary; alike: opp. sides ∥ and = in length; different: consec. ∠s are not ≅ in block 4.

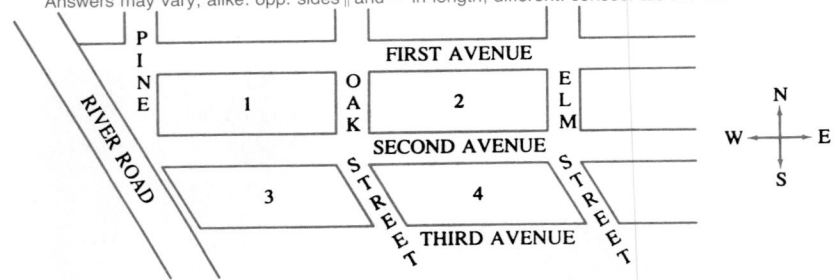

Recall how to name consecutive sides and angles of figures. It is also important to be able to identify and name opposite sides and angles of quadrilaterals.

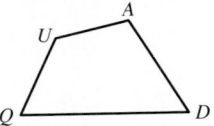

Opposite sides: $\overline{QU}$ and $\overline{AD}$; $\overline{UA}$ and $\overline{DQ}$
Opposite angles: ∠Q and ∠A; ∠U and ∠D

Definition   A quadrilateral is a **parallelogram** (▱) if and only if both pairs of opposite sides are parallel.

218   Chapter 6 Quadrilaterals

Developing Mathematical Power

Cooperative Learning   In addition to their explorations in the activity in Alternative Learning Styles, have the groups of students complete the Investigation, p. 1, in the *Teacher's Resource Book.* Each group should have time to share its findings for both activities with the class.

Parallelograms have several special properties. Drawing an auxiliary line to form two triangles is helpful in proving these properties.

Theorem 6.1 Opposite sides of a parallelogram are congruent.

Given: $\square YTON$

Prove: $\overline{TO} \cong \overline{NY}$ and $\overline{TY} \cong \overline{NO}$

Plan: Draw a diagonal $\overline{YO}$. Use the properties of parallel lines to prove $\triangle TOY \cong \triangle NYO$. Then the sides are congruent by CPCTC.

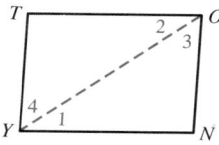

Proof:

Statements	Reasons
1. $\square YTON$	1. Given
2. $\overline{TO} \parallel \overline{NY}$ and $\overline{TY} \parallel \overline{ON}$	2. Definition of parallelogram
3. Draw diagonal $\overline{YO}$.	3. Two points determine a line.
4. $\angle 1 \cong \angle 2$; $\angle 3 \cong \angle 4$	4. If parallel lines have a transversal, then pairs of alternate interior angles are congruent.
5. $\overline{OY} \cong \overline{YO}$	5. Reflexive property of congruence
6. $\triangle TOY \cong \triangle NYO$	6. ASA
7. $\overline{TO} \cong \overline{NY}$ and $\overline{TY} \cong \overline{NO}$	7. CPCTC

Conclusion: In any parallelogram, both pairs of opposite sides are congruent.

An intermediate conclusion in Theorem 6.1 can be stated as Corollary 1.

Corollary 1 A diagonal of a parallelogram forms two congruent triangles.

Corollary 2 If two lines are parallel, then all points on one line are equidistant from the other line. Proved in Practice Exercise 30

You can use Theorem 6.1 to prove Corollary 2 and the following theorem.

Theorem 6.2 Opposite angles of a parallelogram are congruent.
Proved in Practice Exercise 33

6.1 The Parallelogram—A Special Quadrilateral **219**

TEACHING SUGGESTIONS

- Point out how several of the theorems use properties of angles formed by parallel lines cut by a transversal. The transversal might be a diagonal or a side of a parallelogram.
- For Corollary 2 of Theorem 6.1, remind students that the distance from a point to a line was defined as the length of the perpendicular segment from the point to the line.
- Point out that proofs of all theorems, except for Theorem 6.3, require demonstration of at least one triangle congruence as an intermediate goal.
- Ask students to suggest a proof for Theorem 6.2 that does not rely on congruent triangles. In $\square ABCD$, $\overline{AB} \parallel \overline{DC}$, thus $\angle B$ and $\angle C$ are supp. $\overline{BC} \parallel \overline{AD}$, so $\angle A$ and $\angle B$ are supp. Since supplements of the same $\angle$ are $\cong$, $\angle A \cong \angle C$.
- Emphasize the phrase "bisect each other."

Critical Thinking

Creative Thinking Ask students to develop and compare alternate proofs.

CHALKBOARD EXAMPLE

- **For the Example**
  Given $\square ABCD$, complete each statement and justify.

  a. $AD = \underline{?}$
  b. $\overline{AB} \parallel \underline{?}$
  c. $m\angle BAD = \underline{?}$
  d. $m\angle ABC = \underline{?}$
  e. $\triangle ABC \cong \underline{?}$

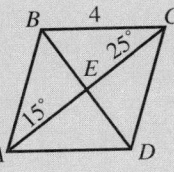

  a. 4; opp. sides $\cong$
  b. $\overline{CD}$; opp. sides are $\parallel$
  c. 40; $m\angle CAD = 25$ ($\overline{BC} \parallel \overline{AD}$ alt. int. $\angle$s $\cong$); $m\angle BAD = 15 + 25 = 40$
  d. 140; consec. $\angle$s supp.
  e. $\triangle CDA$; diag. creates $\cong \triangle$s

219

Common Errors

- Some students may need a great deal of help in identifying congruent alternate interior angles formed by two parallel sides of a parallelogram and a diagonal.
- Students may continue to have difficulty writing proofs. Emphasize planning, including identification of intermediate goals, such as showing two triangles congruent.
- See *Teacher's Resource Book* for additional remediation.

LESSON FOLLOW-UP

Discussion

Preview the next lesson by asking students to think about conditions that would convince them that a given quadrilateral is a parallelogram. For example, would it be enough to know that one pair of sides is congruent? Help students to look for counterexamples for their suggestions where appropriate.

Critical Thinking

Causal Explanation Have students determine conditions that might indicate that a given quadrilateral is a parallelogram.

Assignment Guide

See p. 216B for assignments.

Theorem 6.3 Consecutive angles of a parallelogram are supplementary.
Proved in Practice Exercise 31

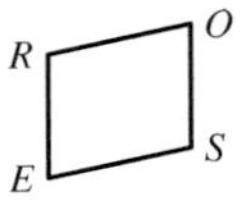

Given: $\square OSER$

Prove: $\angle R$ and $\angle E$ are supplementary.

Plan: Since $OSER$ is a parallelogram, $\overline{RO} \parallel \overline{ES}$ and $\angle R$ and $\angle E$ are supplementary interior angles on the same side of the transversal.

The next theorem describes a relationship between a parallelogram's diagonals.

Theorem 6.4 The diagonals of a parallelogram bisect each other.

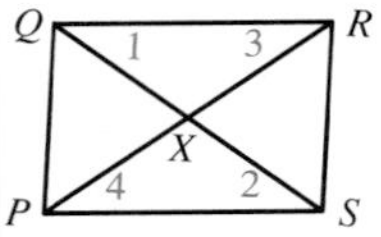

Given: $\square PQRS$ with diagonals $\overline{PR}$ and $\overline{QS}$

Prove: $\overline{PX} \cong \overline{RX}$; $\overline{QX} \cong \overline{SX}$

Plan: Show that $\triangle QRX \cong \triangle SPX$. Then use CPCTC.
Proved in Practice Exercise 32

EXAMPLE **Given $\square$ *NPWS*, complete each statement and justify.**

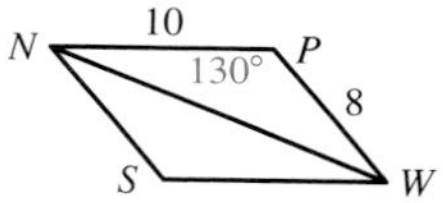

a. $NS = \underline{?}$ **b.** $\overline{SW} \parallel \underline{?}$ **c.** $m\angle NSW = \underline{?}$
d. $\triangle NPW \cong \underline{?}$ **e.** $\overline{WS} \cong \underline{?}$ **f.** $m\angle PNS = \underline{?}$

a. 8; opposite sides $\cong$ **b.** $\overline{NP}$; opposite sides $\parallel$
c. 130; opposite angles $\cong$ **d.** $\triangle WSN$; diagonal creates $\cong$ triangles
e. $\overline{NP}$; opposite sides $\cong$ **f.** 50; consecutive angles supp.

Remember these important facts about parallelograms:

Opposite sides are parallel.
Opposite sides are congruent.
Opposite angles are congruent.
Consecutive angles are supplementary.
A diagonal separates a parallelogram into two congruent triangles.
Diagonals bisect each other.

CLASS EXERCISES

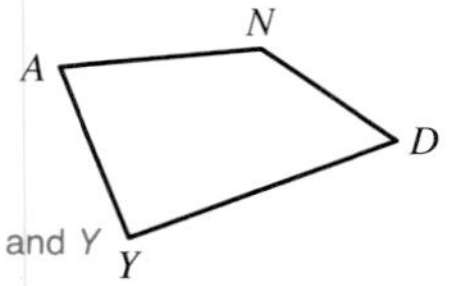

1. Name two pairs of opposite sides. $\overline{AN}$ and $\overline{DY}$; $\overline{ND}$ and $\overline{AY}$
2. Name the vertices that are consecutive to vertex D. N and Y
3. Name the angle opposite $\angle AYD$. Name the other pair of opposite angles. $\angle AND$; $\angle A$ and $\angle D$
4. Name the diagonals. How many are there in all? How many diagonals are there in any quadrilateral? $\overline{AD}$ and $\overline{NY}$; 2; 2

Developing Mathematical Power

Keeping a Portfolio Have students record in their math journals a summary of the properties of parallelograms they learned through investigation and study. They should include diagrams that illustrate each property they describe.

Quadrilateral *OMYT* is a parallelogram.

5. $m\angle OMY =$ _?_ 50   **6.** $m\angle MYT =$ _?_ 130

7. $m\angle YTO =$ _?_ 50   **8.** $TO =$ _?_ 8   **9.** $OM =$ _?_ 5

10. Name two congruent triangles formed by drawing $\overline{OY}$. △OMY ≅ △YTO

11. If $\overline{OY}$ and $\overline{MT}$ are drawn and intersect at *X*, then $\overline{OX} \cong$ _?_ and $\overline{MX} \cong$ _?_.
XY; XT

PRACTICE EXERCISES   Use technology where appropriate.

Given ▱*QUAD*, complete each statement.

A   **1.** If $QD = 16$, then $UA =$ _?_. 16

2. If $DE = 5$, then $UD =$ _?_. 10

3. If $QU = 7.5$, then $AD =$ _?_. 7.5

4. If $m\angle UAD = 98$, then $m\angle ADQ =$ _?_. 82

5. If $UA = 2AD$, and $UA = 15$, then $AD =$ _?_. 7.5

Use ▱*ORKM* to name the following.

6. The side opposite $\overline{KR}$ $\overline{OM}$ **7.** The side parallel to $\overline{MK}$
OR

8. The angle opposite $\angle MOR$ **9.** A consecutive angle to $\angle R$
∠MKR   ∠K or ∠O

10. The congruent triangles   **11.** The congruent triangles
formed by diagonal $\overline{MR}$ formed by diagonal $\overline{KO}$
△KMR ≅ △ORM   △KMO ≅ △ORK

12. Two pairs of congruent sides   **13.** Two pairs of congruent angles
MO ≅ KR; MK ≅ OR   ∠M ≅ ∠R; ∠K ≅ ∠O

Given ▱*OWSN*, complete the statements in Exercises 14–21.

14. _?_ $\cong \angle OWS$ ∠SNO   **15.** $m\angle SNO =$ _?_
60

16. $\triangle NOD \cong \triangle$ _?_ WSD   **17.** $\angle ONW \cong$ _?_ 55°
∠NWS

18. $\triangle$ _?_ $\cong \triangle ODW$ SDN   **19.** $m\angle NOW =$ _?_ 120

20. $m\angle OSW =$ _?_ 65   **21.** $SD = \frac{1}{2}$ _?_ SO

22. Use ▱*XYZW*   **23.** Find QS of ▱*PQRS*,
and find the   if $QT = 6y - 2$
measures of   and $TS = 12 - y$.
all the angles.

See Additional Answers, p. 702.

B   **24.** In ▱*ABCD*, $m\angle B$ is twice $m\angle A$. Find the measures of all the
angles. $m\angle A = 60$, $m\angle B = 120$, $m\angle C = 60$, $m\angle D = 120$

25. In ▱*QUED*, $m\angle D$ is 30 greater than $m\angle E$. Find the measures of each of
the angles. $m\angle E = 75$, $m\angle D = 105$, $m\angle Q = 75$, $m\angle U = 105$

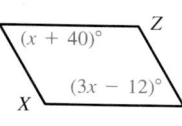
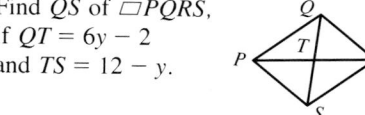

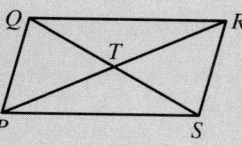
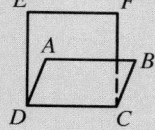
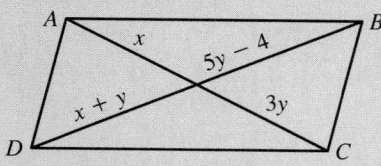

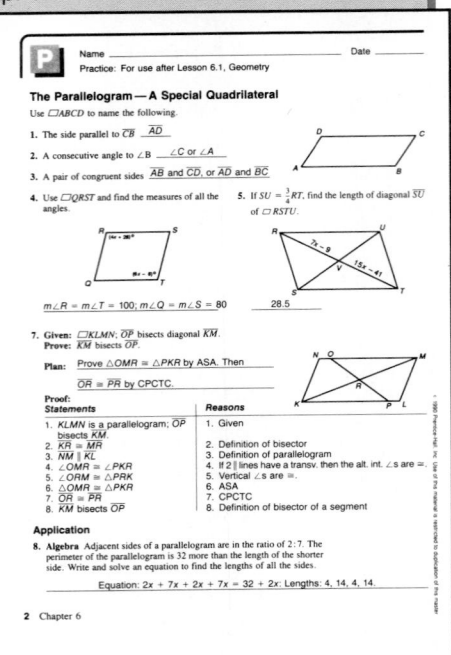

P Name _____ Date _____
Practice: For use after Lesson 6.1, Geometry

The Parallelogram—A Special Quadrilateral
Use □ABCD to name the following.

1. The side parallel to $\overline{CB}$ __AD__
2. A consecutive angle to ∠B __∠C or ∠A__
3. A pair of congruent sides __AB and CD, or AD and BC__
4. Use □QRST and find the measures of all the angles. 5. If $SU = \frac{3}{4}RT$, find the length of diagonal $\overline{SU}$ of □ RSTU.

m∠R = m∠T = 100; m∠Q = m∠S = 80   28.5

7. **Given:** □KLMN; $\overline{OP}$ bisects diagonal $\overline{KM}$.
Prove: $\overline{KM}$ bisects $\overline{OP}$.
Plan: Prove △OMR ≅ △PKR by ASA. Then $\overline{OR} \cong \overline{PR}$ by CPCTC.
Proof:

Statements	Reasons
1. KLMN is a parallelogram; $\overline{OP}$ bisects $\overline{KM}$.	1. Given
2. $\overline{KR} \cong \overline{MR}$	2. Definition of bisector
3. $\overline{NM} \parallel \overline{KL}$	3. Definition of parallelogram
4. ∠OMR ≅ ∠PKR	4. If 2 ∥ lines have a transv. then the alt. int. ∠s are ≅.
5. ∠ORM ≅ ∠PRK	5. Vertical ∠s are ≅.
6. △OMR ≅ △PKR	6. ASA
7. $\overline{OR} \cong \overline{PR}$	7. CPCTC
8. $\overline{KM}$ bisects $\overline{OP}$	8. Definition of bisector of a segment

Application
8. **Algebra** Adjacent sides of a parallelogram are in the ratio of 2:7. The perimeter of the parallelogram is 32 more than the length of the shorter side. Write and solve an equation to find the lengths of all the sides.

Equation: 2x + 7x + 2x + 7x = 32 + 2x; Lengths: 4, 14, 4, 14.

2   Chapter 6

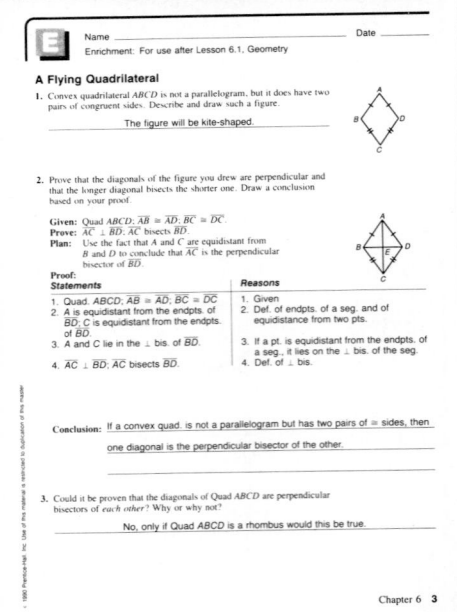

E Name _____ Date _____
Enrichment: For use after Lesson 6.1, Geometry

A Flying Quadrilateral
1. Convex quadrilateral ABCD is not a parallelogram, but it does have two pairs of congruent sides. Describe and draw such a figure.

The figure will be kite-shaped.

2. Prove that the diagonals of the figure you drew are perpendicular and that the longer diagonal bisects the shorter one. Draw a conclusion based on your proof.

Given: Quad ABCD; $\overline{AB} \cong \overline{AD}$; $\overline{BC} \cong \overline{DC}$.
Prove: $\overline{AC} \perp \overline{BD}$; $\overline{AC}$ bisects $\overline{BD}$.
Plan: Use the fact that A and C are equidistant from B and D to conclude that $\overline{AC}$ is the perpendicular bisector of $\overline{BD}$.
Proof:

Statements	Reasons
1. Quad. ABCD; $\overline{AB} \cong \overline{AD}$; $\overline{BC} \cong \overline{DC}$.	1. Given
2. A is equidistant from the endpts. of $\overline{BD}$; C is equidistant from the endpts. of $\overline{BD}$.	2. Def. of endpts. of a seg. and of equidistance from two pts.
3. A and C lie in the ⊥ bis. of $\overline{BD}$.	3. If a pt. is equidistant from the endpts. of a seg., it lies on the ⊥ bis. of the seg.
4. $\overline{AC} \perp \overline{BD}$; $\overline{AC}$ bisects $\overline{BD}$.	4. Def. of ⊥ bis.

Conclusion: If a convex quad. is not a parallelogram but has two pairs of ≅ sides, then one diagonal is the perpendicular bisector of the other.

3. Could it be proven that the diagonals of Quad ABCD are perpendicular bisectors of each other? Why or why not?
No, only if Quad ABCD is a rhombus would this be true.

Chapter 6   3

---

26. If the lengths of two railroad ties between parallel rails can be expressed as $(3x + 32)$ in. and $(6x + 8)$ in., how far apart are the rails? 56 in.

27. If $m \parallel n \parallel p$, with $\overline{BJ}$ and $\overline{FE}$; FBCD is a parallelogram, $\overline{DA} \perp m$, $\overline{BH} \perp n$, △DEG is isosceles with $\overline{DE} \cong \overline{DG}$, and $m\angle IJC = 75$, find the measures of angles 1–12.
See Additional Answers, p. 702.

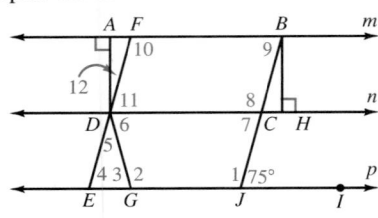

Use this figure and *Given* for Exercises 28 and 29.

Given: □XYZW with M the midpoint of $\overline{XY}$ and N the midpoint of $\overline{WZ}$

28. **Prove:** $\overline{XN} \cong \overline{ZM}$ 29. **Prove:** $\overline{XN} \parallel \overline{MZ}$

30. Prove Corollary 2 of Theorem 6.1.   31. Complete the proof of Theorem 6.3.

C 32. Complete the proof of Theorem 6.4.   33. Prove Theorem 6.2.

34. **Prove:** The line joining the midpoints of two opposite sides of a parallelogram bisects the diagonals of the parallelogram.

35. **Prove:** The bisectors of consecutive angles of a parallelogram are perpendicular.

36. Given a parallelogram in which bisectors of opposite angles do not coincide, prove that those bisectors are parallel.

Applications

37. **Technology**   Use Logo to generate a tessellation based on a parallelogram of your choice. See Solutions Manual.

38. **Construction**   Since the parallelogram is not a rigid figure, it is not usually used in construction. Explain. Answers may vary. Unlike the △, a □ can collapse if pressure is applied. This can be illustrated by making a □ from strips of cardboard.

Mixed Review

Given $\overline{AB} \parallel \overline{ED}$, $\overline{AB} \cong \overline{EC} \cong \overline{ED}$, $AE < CD$, and $CD < EC$, use >, <, or = to complete each statement. Justify your answer.

39. $m\angle ABE \underline{\ ?\ } m\angle CED$
=; Th. 3.2

40. $m\angle ABC \underline{\ ?\ } m\angle BAE$
>; Th. 5.5

41. $m\angle BAE \underline{\ ?\ } m\angle AEB$
<; Th. 5.6

42. $m\angle ECD \underline{\ ?\ } m\angle EDC$
=; Th. 5.1

43. $EB \underline{\ ?\ } EC$
<; Th. 5.3

44. $AE \underline{\ ?\ } ED$
<; trans. prop. and subst.

45. $m\angle ABC + m\angle CED \underline{\ ?\ } 180$
=; Linear Pair Post, Th. 3.2, and subst.

46. $m\angle BAE + m\angle AEB \underline{\ ?\ } m\angle ABC$
=; Th. 3.12

Finding Quadrilaterals That Are Parallelograms

Objective: To prove that certain quadrilaterals are parallelograms

By using the information given about a quadrilateral, you can determine whether or not it is a parallelogram.

Investigation—*Using Manipulatives*

Use a folding ruler to form these figures.

1. What is true about all the figures?
   They are all quadrilaterals.
2. Which figures seem to fit the definition of a parallelogram? 3 and 4
3. What is true about the opposite sides of those figures? They are ≅ and ∥.

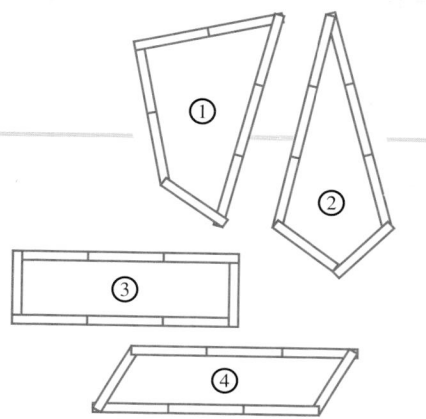

In order to use the definition of a parallelogram to prove that a quadrilateral is a parallelogram, you have to show that both pairs of opposite sides of the quadrilateral are parallel. The next four theorems present other ways to prove that certain quadrilaterals are parallelograms.

> **Theorem 6.5** If both pairs of opposite sides of a quadrilateral are congruent, then the quadrilateral is a parallelogram.

Given: Quadrilateral *YTON* with $\overline{TO} \cong \overline{NY}$ and $\overline{TY} \cong \overline{NO}$

Prove: *YTON* is a parallelogram.

Plan: Show that opposite sides are parallel. Draw diagonal $\overline{YO}$ and prove that $\triangle TOY \cong \triangle NYO$. Then use CPCTC to find the congruent angles necessary to show $\overline{TO} \parallel \overline{NY}$ and $\overline{TY} \parallel \overline{NO}$.

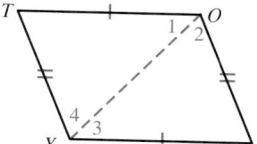

6.2 Finding Quadrilaterals That Are Parallelograms **223**

TEACHING SUGGESTIONS

Go over Plans for proof for Theorems 6.6, 6.7, and 6.8, even if the theorems are not proven in class. As much as possible, get the class involved in developing each Plan.

Critical Thinking

Integration Have students develop Plans for proof.

CHALKBOARD EXAMPLES

- **For the Example**

  Use the given information to decide if *EFGH* is a parallelogram. Justify your answers.

  a. $\overline{EF} \parallel \overline{HG}$; $\overline{FG} \parallel \overline{EH}$

  b. $\overline{FG} \parallel \overline{EH}$; $\overline{FG} \cong \overline{EH}$

  c. $\angle E \cong \angle G$; $\angle F \cong \angle H$

  d. $\overline{EF} \parallel \overline{HG}$; $\overline{FG} \cong \overline{EH}$

  e. $\overline{FG} \cong \overline{EH}$; $\overline{EF} \cong \overline{HG}$

  f. $\overline{EF} \perp \overline{FG}$; $\overline{GH} \perp \overline{FG}$

  a. yes; def. of ▱
  b. yes; pair of opp. sides ∥ and ≅
  c. yes, both pairs of opp. ∠s ≅
  d. no conclusion possible
  e. yes; both pairs of opp. sides ≅
  f. no conclusion possible

Common Errors

- Students may decide that a given quadrilateral is a parallelogram on the basis of insufficient evidence. Have these students make a list of all the ways to show that a quadrilateral is a parallelogram.
- Some students may assume that a quadrilateral is a parallelogram if it has congruent diagonals. Challenge them to draw a kite that has congruent diagonals.
- See *Teacher's Resource Book* for additional remediation.

Proof:

Statements	Reasons
1. Quadrilateral *YTON*; $\overline{TO} \cong \overline{NY}$; $\overline{TY} \cong \overline{NO}$	1. Given
2. Draw diagonal $\overline{YO}$.	2. Two points determine a line.
3. $\overline{OY} \cong \overline{YO}$	3. Reflexive property of congruence
4. $\triangle TOY \cong \triangle NYO$	4. SSS
5. $\angle 1 \cong \angle 3$; $\angle 4 \cong \angle 2$	5. CPCTC
6. $\overline{TO} \parallel \overline{NY}$; $\overline{TY} \parallel \overline{NO}$	6. If 2 lines have a transv. and a pair of ≅ alt. int. ∠s, then the lines are parallel.
7. *YTON* is a parallelogram.	7. Definition of parallelogram

Conclusion: If quadrilateral *YTON* has both pairs of opposite sides congruent, then it is a parallelogram.

Theorem 6.6 If one pair of opposite sides of a quadrilateral is both congruent and parallel, then the quadrilateral is a parallelogram.

Given: Quadrilateral *OKRA* with $\overline{KR} \parallel \overline{AO}$ and $\overline{KR} \cong \overline{AO}$

Prove: *OKRA* is a parallelogram.

Plan: Draw diagonal $\overline{OR}$. Since $\angle 1 \cong \angle 3$, show that $\triangle KRO \cong \triangle AOR$. So $\angle 4 \cong \angle 2$, and then $\overline{OK} \parallel \overline{RA}$.
Proved in Practice Exercise 17

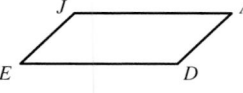

Theorem 6.7 If both pairs of opposite angles of a quadrilateral are congruent, then the quadrilateral is a parallelogram.
Proved in Practice Exercise 24

EXAMPLE **Use the given information to decide if *DAJE* is a parallelogram. Justify your answers.**

a. Given: $\overline{JA} \cong \overline{ED}$; $\overline{JE} \cong \overline{AD}$ **b.** Given: $\overline{JE} \parallel \overline{AD}$; $\overline{JA} \parallel \overline{ED}$

c. Given: $\overline{JA} \parallel \overline{ED}$; $\overline{JA} \cong \overline{ED}$ **d.** Given: $\overline{JA} \parallel \overline{ED}$; $\overline{JE} \cong \overline{AD}$

e. Given: $\angle J \cong D$; $\angle A \cong \angle E$ **f.** Given: $\angle J \cong \angle D$; $\overline{JA} \cong \overline{ED}$

a. Yes; opposite sides are congruent. **b.** Yes; opposite sides are parallel.
c. Yes; one pair of opposite sides is both congruent and parallel.
d. No conclusion **e.** Yes; opposite angles are congruent. **f.** No conclusion

The final theorem involves the diagonals of a quadrilateral.

> **Theorem 6.8** If the diagonals of a quadrilateral bisect each other, the quadrilateral is a parallelogram. Proved in Practice Exercise 25

To determine whether a given quadrilateral is a parallelogram, show any of the following:

Both pairs of opposite sides are parallel.
Both pairs of opposite sides are congruent.
Both pairs of opposite angles are congruent.
One pair of opposite sides is parallel and congruent.
The diagonals bisect each other.

CLASS EXERCISES See side column.

Is the quadrilateral a parallelogram? If not, sketch a counterexample.

1. Two angles of the quadrilateral are congruent. no

2. All pairs of consecutive angles of the quadrilateral are supplementary. yes

3. All pairs of consecutive angles of the quadrilateral are congruent. yes

4. One pair of opposite sides of the quadrilateral is congruent and the other pair of opposite sides is parallel. no

5. The diagonals of the quadrilateral are congruent. no

6. A diagonal of a quadrilateral separates it into two congruent triangles. no

7. One pair of sides of the quadrilateral is parallel and one pair of opposite angles is congruent. yes

8. The quadrilateral has one pair of parallel sides and one of its diagonals bisects the other diagonal. yes

9. One pair of sides of the quadrilateral is parallel, and the diagonals intersect to form one pair of congruent triangles. no

PRACTICE EXERCISES ⟳ Use technology where appropriate.

A **1. Drawing in Geometry** In □*ABCD*, each side is extended by distance *d*. Explain why quadrilateral *MNPQ* is a parallelogram.

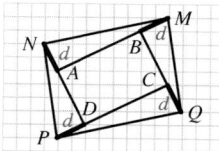

PC = d + DC, MA = d + AB, and DC = AB, so $\overline{PC} \cong \overline{MA}$; ∠NAM and ∠QCP are supplements respectively of ≅ ∠s DAB and DCB, so ∠NAM ≅ ∠QCP; $\overline{NA} \cong \overline{QC}$, so △NAM ≅ △QCP and $\overline{NM} \cong \overline{QP}$ (CPCTC). Similarly, $\overline{PN} \cong \overline{MQ}$, so MNPQ is a □.

6.2 Finding Quadrilaterals That Are Parallelograms **225**

Developing Mathematical Power

Cooperative Learning Working in groups, students can complete Applications, pp. 12 and 13, in *Connections* as a follow-up to Exercise 30. Encourage them to be creative in making their own tessellations and to use color effectively. Display their responses to p. 13 on the bulletin board.

LESSON FOLLOW-UP

Discussion
Ask students to summarize all the ways now known to prove that a given quadrilateral is a parallelogram. Be sure that students include the definition. Discuss with students why the answer to Class Exercise 8 is yes. (Use ASA.)

Assignment Guide
See p. 216B for assignments.

Additional Answers

1.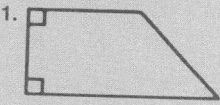

4.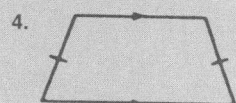

5.

6.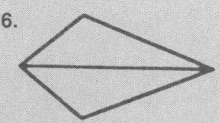

9.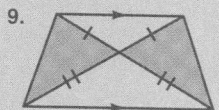

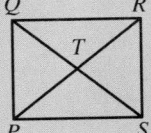
Which figures are parallelograms? Justify your answers.

2.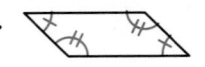

3.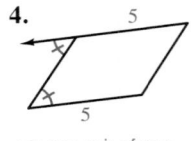

4.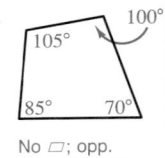

5.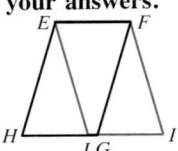

□; both pairs of opp. ∠s are ≅.

□; both pairs of opp. sides are ≅.

□; one pair of opp. sides is ∥ and ≅.

No □; opp. sides are not ∥.

Use the given information to decide if *NAOJ* is a parallelogram. Justify your answer

6. $\overline{JO} \parallel \overline{AN}$; $\overline{JO} \cong \overline{AN}$ **7.** $\triangle JON \cong \triangle ANO$

8. $\overline{ON}$ and $\overline{JA}$ bisect each other. Yes; diag. bis. each other.

9. $m\angle J + m\angle O + m\angle A + m\angle N = 360$

6. Yes; a pair of opp. sides is ∥ and ≅.
7. Yes; by CPCTC, opp. sides ≅.
9. No; this is true for all quad.

Given □*EFGH*, □*EFIJ*, □*ABCD*, and □*EBFG*, complete the conclusions and justify your answers.

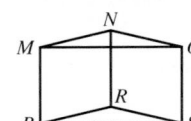

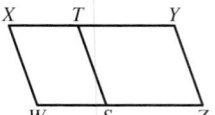

10. $\overline{EJ}$ and $\overline{FI}$ are ? . ≅ and ∥; opp. sides of □ are ≅ and ∥.

11. $\overline{HG}$ and $\overline{JI}$ are ? . ≅; both are ≅ to $\overline{EF}$

12. $\overline{HJ}$ and $\overline{GI}$ are ? . ≅; $HG - JG = JI - JG$

13. $\triangle HEJ$ and $\triangle GFI$ are ? . ≅; SSS

14. $\angle D$ and $\angle G$ are ? . ≅; both are ≅ to $\angle B$.

15. $\angle D$ and $\angle BEG$ are ? . Supp.; $\angle D \cong \angle B$, $\angle B$ is supp. to $\angle BEG$.

16. $\angle D$ and $\angle BFG$ are ? . Supp.; $\angle D \cong \angle B$, $\angle B$ is supp. to $\angle BFG$.

B **17.** Use the plan for Theorem 6.6 to complete a proof. See Additional Answers, p. 702.

18. Given: □*MNRP* and □*MOSP*
Prove: *NOSR* is a □.

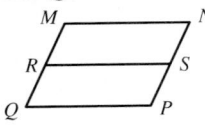

19. Given: □*WXYZ*; $\angle WST \cong \angle SZY$
Prove: *XTSW* is a □.

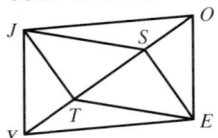

20. Given: □*MNPQ*; *R* is midpoint of $\overline{MQ}$; *S* is midpoint of $\overline{NP}$
Prove: *RSPQ* is a □.

21. Given: □*YEOJ* with diagonal $\overline{OY}$; $\overline{JT} \perp \overline{YO}$; $\overline{ES} \perp \overline{YO}$
Prove: *JSET* is a □.

226   Chapter 6 Quadrilaterals

See Additional Answers, p. 702.

22. Given: $\overline{JE} \cong \overline{EO}$; $\overline{NF} \cong \overline{FH}$; $\overline{JM} \cong \overline{HM}$; $\angle MEO \cong \angle MFN$
Prove: $JNHO$ is a ▱.

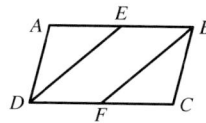

23. Given: ▱$ABCD$; $\angle ADE \cong \angle CBF$
Prove: $DEBF$ is a ▱.

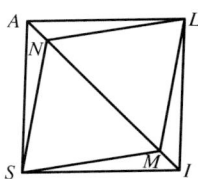

C

24. Prove Theorem 6.7.

25. Prove Theorem 6.8.

26. Given: ▱$MNPQ$; $\overline{MW}$ bisects $\angle M$; $\overline{NX}$ bisects $\angle N$; $\overline{PX}$ bisects $\angle P$; $\overline{QW}$ bisects $\angle Q$.
Prove: $XYWZ$ is a ▱.

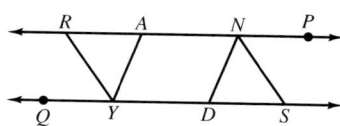

27. Given: ▱$ALIS$; $\overline{AN} \cong \overline{IM}$
Prove: $LMSN$ is a ▱.

28. Given: ▱$AYDN$; $\overline{AN}$ and $\overline{YD}$ extended as shown; $\overline{YR}$ bisects $\angle AYQ$; $\overline{NS}$ bisects $\angle DNP$.
Prove: $RNSY$ is a ▱.

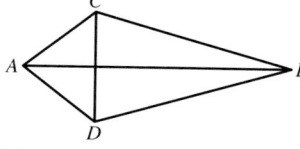

Applications

29. Hobbies How would you rearrange the cross beams $\overline{AB}$ and $\overline{CD}$ of this kite in order to redesign it in the shape of a parallelogram? Reposition $\overline{CD}$ so that $\overline{AB}$ and $\overline{CD}$ bisect each other.

30. Technology A tessellation can be based on any quadrilateral. Why? Use Logo to generate a tessellation based on a quadrilateral that is not a parallelogram. See Solutions Manual.

Developing Mathematical Power

31. Extension Given that $MNRP$ and $MOSP$ are parallelograms, write a plan to prove that $NOSR$ is a parallelogram. Show that ▱$MNRP$ and ▱$MOSP$ contain sides of quad. $NOSR$ that are ∥ and ≅. Therefore, the quad is a ▱.

32. Writing in Mathematics Write a paragraph that explains the similarities and differences between a parallelogram and a kite. Answers may vary. Similarities: 2 pairs of ≅ sides, 2 pairs of ≅ ∠s. Differences: in a kite, only one diagonal is bisected and the ≅ sides are not opposite sides.

6.2 Finding Quadrilaterals That Are Parallelograms **227**

Teacher's Resource Book
Follow-Up Investigation, Chapter 6, p. 4

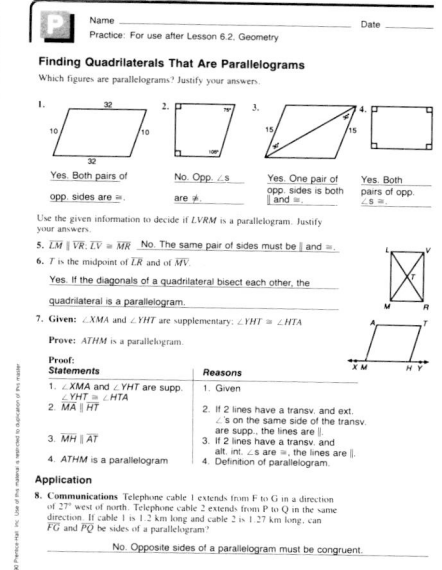

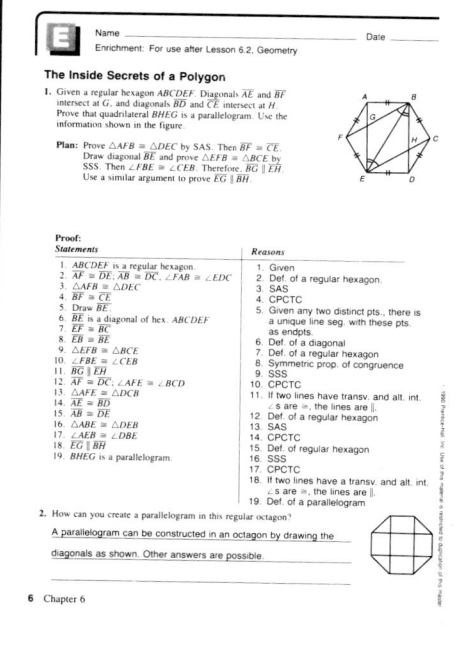

227

Materials/Manipulatives
Lined and unlined paper
Rulers
String
Teaching Transparency 37

Technology
Computer Test Bank, pp. 338–348

LESSON FOCUS

Review

- On the chalkboard draw three parallel lines intersected by a transversal. Review the angle pairs when a transversal cuts two parallel lines and use the transitive property to extend this to three parallel lines.
- The Mixed Review, Exercises 33–40, involves angle relationships in triangles and parallelograms, and the lengths of the sides of a triangle.

Alternative Learning Styles

- Some students will benefit from a concrete approach to Theorem 6.9. Provide students with a piece of string with which to do the activity described in the Investigation. Point out that this method can be used to divide a segment into any number of congruent parts.
- Use the parallel lines on a sheet of lined paper to provide students with a visual interpretation of parallel lines. Have each student draw three transversals. Ask students to measure the lengths of the segments that are cut off on each transversal and make observations about their findings.   On each transversal, the segments cut off by the parallel lines are congruent.

6.3 Parallel Lines and Midpoints

Objective: To prove and apply theorems that relate to parallel lines cut by more than one transversal

The properties of parallelograms can be used to prove theorems about parallel lines and congruent segments.

> **Investigation—*Visualizing the Concept***
>
> An ancient surveyor had to divide a boundary ($\overline{AF}$) into 5 equal lengths. First he made 5 equally spaced knots on a rope (labeled K, J, I, H, and G). Then he arranged them as shown. He marked off segments parallel to $\overline{FG}$ through H, I, J, and K, and located E, D, C, and B. What geometric principle did he use? Equally spaced ∥ lines cut off ≅ segments on a transversal.

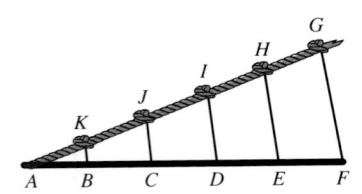

If lines l_1, l_2, l_3, and l_4 are intersected by a transversal, the lines are said to "cut off" segments on the transversal, as this figure shows. When the segments are cut off on the transversal by parallel lines, further conclusions can be made.

Segments $\overline{AB}$, $\overline{BC}$, and $\overline{CD}$ are cut off on transversal t.

> **Theorem 6.9**   If three or more parallel lines cut off congruent segments on one transversal, then they cut off congruent segments on every transversal.

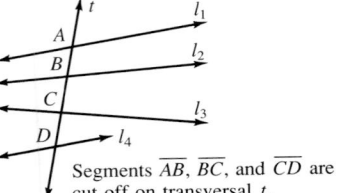

Given: $l_1 \parallel l_2 \parallel l_3$; $\overline{AB} \cong \overline{BC}$;
t and u are transversals of l_1, l_2, and l_3.

Prove: $\overline{EF} \cong \overline{FG}$

Plan: Through E and F, construct $\overline{EI}$ and $\overline{FJ}$ such that $\overline{EI} \parallel \overline{AC}$ and $\overline{FJ} \parallel \overline{AC}$. Thus quadrilaterals $AEIB$ and $BFJC$ are parallelograms. Since $\overline{AB} \cong \overline{BC}$, then $\overline{EI} \cong \overline{FJ}$. Next, show $\angle 1 \cong \angle 2$ and $\angle 3 \cong \angle 4$, so that $\triangle EIF \cong \triangle FJG$. Hence $\overline{EF} \cong \overline{FG}$ by CPCTC.
Proved in Practice Exercise 20
A similar proof is used in cases involving more than three parallel lines.

228   Chapter 6 Quadrilaterals

Developing Mathematical Power

Keeping a Portfolio   To test the general nature of the corollary to Theorem 6.9, students need to experiment with different kinds of triangles. Have them draw the conditions of the hypothesis for scalene and isosceles triangles (one acute, one right, and one obtuse for each) and for an equilateral triangle to demonstrate the corollary.

EXAMPLE 1   **True? Justify your answers.**

    a. $\overline{TU} \cong \overline{VW}$ **b.** $\overline{PQ} \cong \overline{RS}$

    c. $\overline{PR} \cong \overline{QS}$ **d.** $\overline{PQ} \cong \overline{TU}$

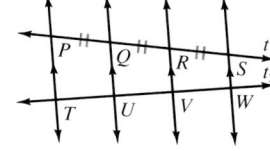

a. True, by Theorem 6.9   **b.** True, by the given information
c. True, since $PQ = RS$ **d.** Insufficient information
    and $PQ + QR = RS + QR$

Corollary   A line that contains the midpoint of one side of a triangle and is parallel to another side bisects the third side.

Given: $\triangle ABC$ with D the midpoint of $\overline{AB}$; $\overleftrightarrow{DE} \parallel \overline{BC}$

Prove: $\overleftrightarrow{DE}$ bisects $\overline{AC}$.

Plan: Construct $\overleftrightarrow{AF}$ through A such that $\overleftrightarrow{AF} \parallel \overline{BC}$. Since $\overleftrightarrow{AF}$, $\overleftrightarrow{DE}$, and $\overline{BC}$ are parallel and cut off congruent segments on transversal $\overline{AB}$, they cut off congruent segments on transversal $\overline{AC}$. Since $\overline{AE} \cong \overline{EC}$, use the definition of a bisector to reach the conclusion.

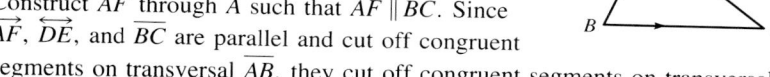

Proved in Practice Exercise 21

EXAMPLE 2   **Find the indicated measure if $l_1 \parallel l_2 \parallel l_3$ and T is the midpoint of $\overline{SE}$.**

    a. If $SE = 12$ cm, $TE = \underline{\ ?\ }$.   **b.** If $NV = 8$ cm, $NE = \underline{\ ?\ }$.

    c. If $\triangle SNE$ is equilateral and if $ST = 5$ cm, then the perimeter of $\triangle SNE$ is $\underline{\ ?\ }$.

    d. If $\triangle SNE$ is isosceles with base $\overline{SN}$ and $m\angle ETV = 40$, then $m\angle SEN = \underline{\ ?\ }$.

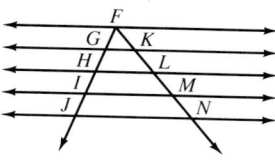

    a. 6 cm   **b.** 16 cm   **c.** 30 cm   **d.** 100

CLASS EXERCISES

For Exercises 1–5, the horizontal lines are equidistant and parallel.

1. If $FK = 9$ cm and $LM = 3x + 6$ cm, then $x = \underline{\ ?\ }$. 1

2. If $FL = 20$ cm, then $FK = \underline{\ ?\ }$. 10 cm

3. If $\overline{KL} \cong \overline{GH}$, then $MN = \underline{\ ?\ }$. Answers may vary; IJ

4. If $KM = 34$ cm and $FL = 4x - 2$ cm, then $x = \underline{\ ?\ }$. 9

5. If $FN = 42$ cm, then $FL = \underline{\ ?\ }$. 21 cm

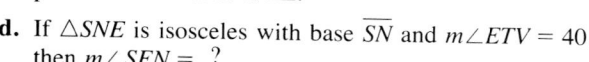

$FG = GH = HI = IJ$

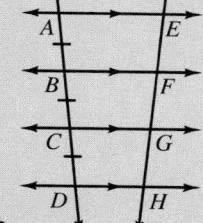
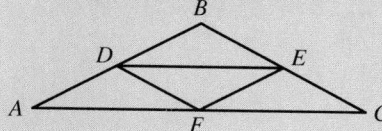

230

Common Error

- Students sometimes confuse the segments on transversals with segments on parallel lines. Diagrams of parallel lines drawn all in one color and transversals in various colors might be a help.
- See *Teacher's Resource Book* for additional remediation.

LESSON FOLLOW-UP

Assignment Guide

See p. 216B for assignments.

Additional Answers

20. Proof:

Statements	Reasons
1. $l_1 \parallel l_2 \parallel l_3$; t and u are transversals.	1. Given
2. Through E and F construct $\overline{EI}$ and $\overline{FJ}$, respectively, such that $\overline{EI} \parallel \overline{AC}$ and $\overline{FJ} \parallel \overline{AC}$.	2. Through a pt. not on a line, there is exactly one line $\parallel$ to the given line.
3. $AEIB$ and $BFJC$ are $\square$s.	3. Def. of $\square$
4. $\overline{AB} \cong \overline{EI}$; $\overline{BC} \cong \overline{FJ}$	4. Opp. sides of a $\square$ are $\cong$.
5. $\overline{AB} \cong \overline{BC}$	5. Given
6. $\overline{EI} \cong \overline{FJ}$	6. Subst. prop.
7. $\angle 1 \cong \angle 2$	7. If $\parallel$ lines have a transv., corr. $\angle$s are $\cong$.
8. $\overline{EI} \parallel \overline{FJ}$	8. 2 lines $\parallel$ to a third line are $\parallel$ to each other.
9. $\angle 3 \cong \angle 4$	9. Same as 7
10. $\triangle EIF \cong \triangle FJG$	10. AAS
11. $\overline{EF} \cong \overline{FG}$	11. CPCTC

Conclusion: If 3 or more $\parallel$ lines cut off $\cong$ segments on a transv., they will cut off $\cong$ segments on any transv. of the lines.

In $\triangle DEF$, $\overline{GH} \parallel \overline{EF}$. Answer each and justify your answers.

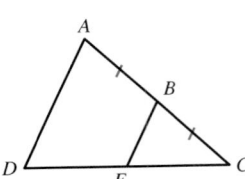

6. If $GE = 5$, $HF = 4$, and $DH = 4$, find DG. 5; a line that contains the midpt. of 1 side of a $\triangle$ and is $\parallel$ to another side bisects the third side.

7. If $DF = 18$, $EG = 6$, and $GD = 6$, find DH. 9; same as Ex. 6

8. If $m\angle GEM = m\angle HMF$ and if $DF = 10$, find HF. 5; same as Ex. 6

9. If $\overline{ED} \parallel \overline{MH}$, then $\overline{DH} \cong \underline{\ ?\ }$. $\overline{HF}$; same as Ex. 6

10. If $DH = HF = 2x + 5$, $DF = 30$, and $GD = x$, find EG. 5; same as Ex. 6

In $\triangle ADC$, $\overline{EB} \parallel \overline{AD}$.

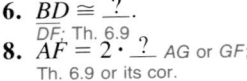

11. If $DE = 4x - 5$ and $EC = 2x + 3$, find the length of DC. 22

12. If the perimeter of $\triangle ADC$ is 50 in., $EC = 10$ in., and $AD = 12$ in., find the length of $\overline{AB}$. 9 in.

13. If $AD = 17.5$, $AB = 14.4$, and $EC = 12.6$, find the perimeter of $\triangle ADC$. 71.5

PRACTICE EXERCISES

A In Exercises 1–8, $\overleftrightarrow{AB} \parallel \overleftrightarrow{CD} \parallel \overleftrightarrow{EF}$ and $\overline{AC} \cong \overline{CE}$. Answer each and justify your answers.

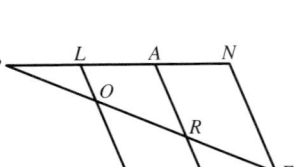

1. If $BD = 9$, $BF = \underline{\ ?\ }$. 18; Th. 6.9 or its cor.

2. $\overline{EH} \cong \underline{\ ?\ }$. $\overline{HB}$; Th. 6.9 or its cor.

3. If $AF = 34$, $AG = \underline{\ ?\ }$. 17; Th. 6.9 or its cor.

4. $\overline{GF} \cong \underline{\ ?\ }$. $\overline{AG}$; Th. 6.9 or its cor.

5. If $BH = 10$, $EH = \underline{\ ?\ }$. 10; Th. 6.9 or its cor.

6. $\overline{BD} \cong \underline{\ ?\ }$. $\overline{DF}$; Th. 6.9

7. If $GF = 13.5$, $AF = \underline{\ ?\ }$. 27; Th. 6.9 or its cor.

8. $AF = 2 \cdot \underline{\ ?\ }$ AG or GF; Th. 6.9 or its cor.

In this figure, $\overline{LS} \parallel \overline{AT} \parallel \overline{NE}$ and $\overline{ST} \cong \overline{TE}$. Find each segment length and justify your answers.

9. If $AN = 16.5$ cm, find LA. $LA = 16.5$ cm; Th. 6.9

10. If $SE = 48$ cm, find ST. $ST = 24$ cm; Th. 6.9

11. If $EO = 32$ cm, find OR. $OR = 16$ cm; Th. 6.9 or its cor.

12. If $EO = 27$ cm, find ER. $ER = 13.5$ cm; Th. 6.9 or its cor.

13. If $OR = 15$ cm, find RE. $RE = 15$ cm; Th. 6.9 or its cor.

14. If $PN = 27$ cm, $PL = 3$ cm, find AN. $AN = 12$ cm; $27 - 3 = 24$, then Th. 6.9

15. Thinking Critically Suppose $\overline{ST} \not\cong \overline{TE}$. Could you conclude that $\overline{LS} \parallel \overline{AT} \parallel \overline{NE}$? Explain your answer. No; the conv. of Th. 6.9 is not true.

$m_1 \parallel m_2 \parallel m_3$ and D is the midpoint of $\overline{AE}$.

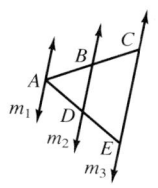

16. If $\triangle CAE$ is equilateral and if $DE = 7$ cm, find the perimeter of $\triangle CAE$. 42 cm

17. If $\triangle CAE$ is isosceles with base $\overline{CE}$ and $m\angle CBD = 110$, find $m\angle CAE$. 40

B 18. If $\overline{XT} \parallel \overline{YU} \parallel \overline{ZV}$, $\overline{XY} \cong \overline{YZ}$, and $\overline{TR} \parallel \overline{UQ} \parallel \overline{VP}$, explain why $\overline{PQ} \cong \overline{QR}$.
$\overline{TU} \cong \overline{UV}$ by Th. 6.9; then $\overline{QR} \cong \overline{PQ}$ by Th. 6.9

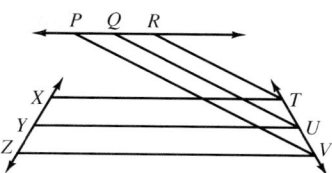

19. If $l_1 \parallel l_2 \parallel l_3 \parallel l_4$ with transversals t_1 and t_2 and the parallel lines cut congruent segments on t_1 and t_2, $\overline{LM} \cong \overline{MN}$ and $\overline{PQ} \cong \overline{QR}$. When could you conclude that $\overline{LM} \cong \overline{PQ}$? when $t_1 \parallel t_2$ or $LO = PS$

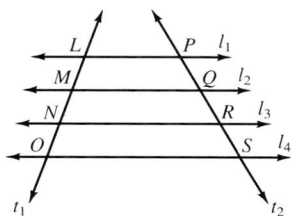

20. Use the *Plan* for Theorem 6.9 to complete a proof. See side column, page 230.

21. Use the *Plan* for the Corollary of Theorem 6.9 to complete a proof.
See Additional Answers, p. 702.

22. **Given:** $\triangle PQR$ with S the midpoint of $\overline{PQ}$; $\angle PST \cong \angle SQR$.
    Prove: $\overline{PT} \cong \overline{TR}$

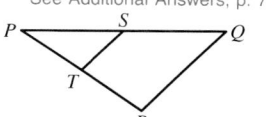

23. **Given:** $\angle GBL \cong \angle BAN$; L is the midpoint of $\overline{IN}$.
    Prove: $\overline{AO} \cong \overline{OI}$

24. **Given:** $\overline{GI} \parallel \overline{BL} \parallel \overline{AN}$; L is the midpoint of $\overline{IN}$.
    Prove: B is the midpoint of $\overline{GA}$.

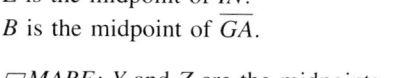

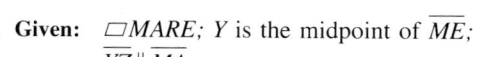

25. **Given:** $\square MARE$; Y and Z are the midpoints of $\overline{ME}$ and $\overline{AR}$, respectively.
    Prove: X is the midpoint of $\overline{MR}$.

26. **Given:** $\square MARE$; Y is the midpoint of $\overline{ME}$; $\overline{YZ} \parallel \overline{MA}$.
    Prove: Z is the midpoint of $\overline{AR}$.

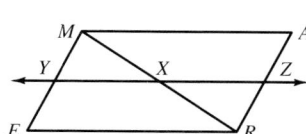

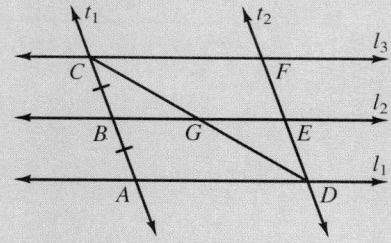
Developing Mathematical Power

Cooperative Learning   Select teams of students to work in cooperative groups to create a display that illustrates the art concepts of *perspective* and the *vanishing point*. When presenting their projects to the class, they should relate what they have learned to the concepts of the lesson.

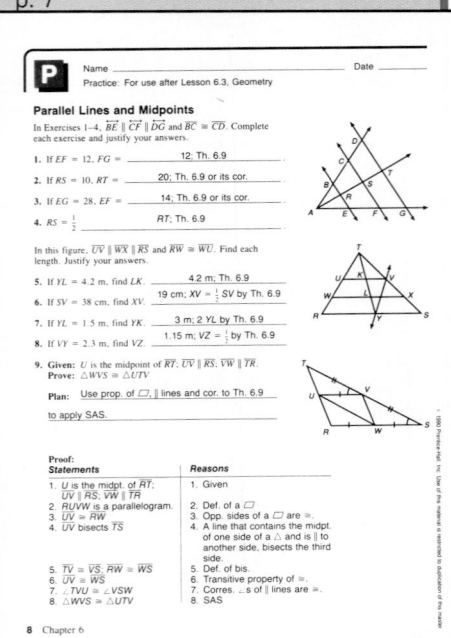

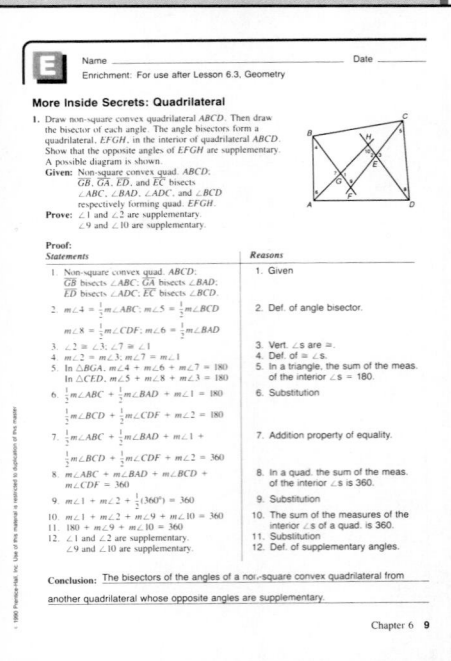

C **27. Given:** Isosceles $\triangle ABC$ with base $\overline{BC}$; D is the midpoint of $\overline{AB}$; $\angle ADE \cong \angle C$.

See Additional Answers, p. 702.

Prove: $\overline{BE}$ is a median of $\triangle ABC$.

28. Given: Isosceles $\triangle ABC$ with $\overline{AB} \cong \overline{AC}$; D is the midpoint of $\overline{AB}$; $\overline{DE} \parallel \overline{BC}$.

Prove: $\overline{DB} \cong \overline{EC}$

29. Given: $\square FDER$; M is the midpoint of $\overline{FR}$; N is the midpoint of $\overline{DE}$.

Prove: $\overline{FI} \cong \overline{IS} \cong \overline{SE}$

30. Given: $\overline{MN} \parallel \overline{TS} \parallel \overline{RP}$; T is the midpoint of $\overline{MR}$.

Prove: $\overline{MN} \cong \overline{PQ}$

Applications   Answers may vary.

31. Art In this photo, which lines appear to be parallel? Which lines appear to be congruent? What geometric theorem justifies your observations?

32. Architecture Discuss the application of Theorem 6.9 in relation to the structure of a bridge.

Mixed Review

What conclusion may be drawn? Justify your answer by stating a property or a theorem.

33. In $\triangle DEF$, $\angle D \cong \angle F$. Conclusion: $\underline{\ ?\ }$. $\overline{DE} \cong \overline{EF}$, Th. 5.2

34. In $\triangle ABC$, $AB > AC$. Conclusion: $\underline{\ ?\ }$. $m\angle C > m\angle B$, Th. 5.6

35. $\triangle GHI \cong \triangle JKL$, $\overline{GI} \underline{\ ?\ } \overline{JL}$. $\cong$, CPCTC

36. In $\square ABCD$, $m\angle C + m\angle D = \underline{\ ?\ }$. 180, Th. 6.3

Which sets of numbers could be lengths of the sides of a triangle?

37. $\{5, 4, 8\}$ yes **38.** $\{3, 3, 8\}$ no **39.** $\{5, 5, 5\}$ yes **40.** $\{8, 12, 15\}$ yes

Special Parallelograms

Objective: To identify and apply special properties of a rectangle, rhombus, and square

LESSON PLAN

Vocabulary
Rectangle   Square
Rhombus

Materials/Manipulatives
Graph paper
Teaching Transparency 38
Connections

Technology
Computer Test Bank, pp. 349–358
The Geometric Supposer: Quadrilaterals, pp. 91, 92

Three special types of parallelograms—rectangles, rhombuses, and squares—have all the properties of parallelograms, as well as their own unique properties.

Investigation—*Coordinate Geometry*

1. Beyond the properties of a parallelogram, what characteristic do
   a. II and IV share? Adj. sides are ⊥.
   b. III and IV share? Adj. sides are ≅.

2. Redraw each figure on graph paper and draw the diagonals. Discuss the results in each case. In I, the diagonals bisect each other; in II and IV, the diagonals are ≅; in III and IV the diagonals are ⊥ to each other, and each diagonal bisects the opposite pair of ∠s.

The special types of parallelograms are defined as follows:

Name	Figure	Definition
Rectangle		A parallelogram is a **rectangle** if and only if it has a right angle.
Rhombus		A parallelogram is a **rhombus** if and only if it has a pair of consecutive congruent sides.
Square		A rectangle is a **square** if and only if it has a pair of consecutive congruent sides.

Applying the properties of a parallelogram:

What is true about all four angles of a rectangle? They are rt. ∠s and therefore ≅.
What is true about all four sides of a rhombus? They are ≅.

Since a square can be classified as a rectangle or as a rhombus, it has all the properties of both figures, as well as all the properties of any parallelogram.

6.4 Special Parallelograms **233**

Developing Mathematical Power

Cooperative Learning   Select teams of students to work on the Critical Thinking activity, p. 15, in *Connections*. Have them use the "Euclidean Series" to create and color a design. Allow time for them to share their generalizations. Use their designs for a bulletin-board display.

LESSON FOCUS

Review
Display these transparency figures.

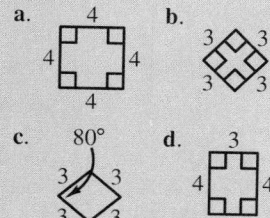

Ask which are parallelograms? All
Which are squares? (a) and (b) Which are rectangles? (a), (b), and (d) Students may need help recognizing that *b* is a square and that *a* and *b* are rectangles as well as squares.

Alternative Learning Styles
• Through coordinate geometry, the Investigation helps students to visualize the similarities and differences among special parallelograms.
• Teaching Transparency 38 provides an aid for the visual learner to understand the relationships among special parallelograms.

Multicultural Opportunity
See Developing Mathematical Power, p. 236.

Given: Quad.
ABCD with
$\overline{AB} \cong \overline{BC}$;

$\overline{AE} \cong \overline{EC}$; $\overline{BE} \cong \overline{ED}$

Prove: ABCD is a rhombus.

Plan: Since the diagonals bisect each other, the quad. is a ▱. Since $\overline{AB} \cong \overline{BC}$, the ▱ is a rhombus.

- Point out that the converses of Theorems 6.10–6.13 (Practice Exercises 30–33) provide ways of showing that figures are special parallelograms. Discuss the Plans for proof.

Critical Thinking

1. *Reasoning* Ask students to plan proofs.
2. *Making Decisions* Have students state converses and determine whether they are true.

CHALKBOARD EXAMPLES

- **For Example 1**

  True or False?

  a. All rhombuses are parallelograms.
  b. All parallelograms are squares.
  c. Every square is a rectangle.
  d. Some rectangles are squares.
  e. Not every parallelogram is a rhombus.
  f. A square is not a rhombus.

  a. True   **b.** False   **c.** True
  d. True   **e.** True   **f.** False

EXAMPLE 1   Use the diagram to decide whether each statement is true or false.

a. All squares are rectangles.

b. Every parallelogram is a rhombus.

c. Some rhombuses are rectangles.

d. All rectangles are squares.

e. Not every rectangle is a rhombus.

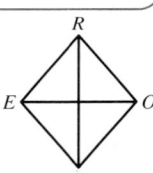

a. True   **b.** False   **c.** True   **d.** False   **e.** True

---

Theorem 6.10   The diagonals of a rectangle are congruent.

Given: Rectangle HNRO with diagonals $\overline{HR}$ and $\overline{ON}$

Prove: $\overline{HR} \cong \overline{ON}$

Plan: Since a rectangle is a ▱, use the properties of a ▱ to show $\triangle HRN \cong \triangle ONR$. Then use CPCTC.
Proved in Class Exercise 17

Theorem 6.11   The diagonals of a rhombus are perpendicular.

Given: Rhombus ESOR with diagonals $\overline{RS}$ and $\overline{EO}$

Prove: $\overline{RS} \perp \overline{EO}$

Plan: Since $\overline{ER} \cong \overline{RO}$ and $\overline{ES} \cong \overline{SO}$, R and S are equidistant from E and O. Thus $\overline{RS}$ is the perpendicular bisector of $\overline{EO}$ and $\overline{RS} \perp \overline{EO}$.
Proved in Practice Exercise 19

Theorem 6.12   Each diagonal of a rhombus bisects two angles of the rhombus.

Given: Rhombus RANF; diagonals $\overline{FA}$ and $\overline{NR}$

Prove: $\overline{NR}$ bisects $\angle R$ and $\angle N$; $\overline{FA}$ bisects $\angle F$ and $\angle A$.

Plan: Since $\overline{RN} \perp \overline{FA}$, show that the four right triangles formed are congruent. Since the two angles formed at each vertex can be shown congruent by CPCTC, the angles at the vertices must be bisected.
Proved in Practice Exercise 20

What properties of a square can be concluded from Theorems 6.10–6.12?
The diagonals are ≅ and ⊥. Each diagonal bisects 2 ∠s.

EXAMPLE 2   Use rhombus *ONET* to answer each question.

If $m\angle TON = 52$, then

a. $m\angle TOY = \underline{?}$

b. $m\angle ONE = \underline{?}$

c. $m\angle YNE = \underline{?}$

If $m\angle ETY = 48$, then

d. $m\angle YNE = \underline{?}$

e. $m\angle TEN = \underline{?}$

f. $m\angle YON = \underline{?}$

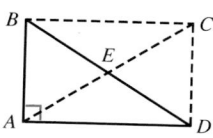

a. 26   b. 128   c. 64   d. 48   e. 84   f. 42

In Theorem 6.13, the properties of a rectangle are used to derive information about right triangles.

> **Theorem 6.13**   The midpoint of the hypotenuse of a right triangle is equidistant from the three vertices. Proved in Practice Exercise 25

CLASS EXERCISES

True or false? If false, sketch a counterexample.

1. A quadrilateral is a parallelogram. false

2. Every rectangle is a parallelogram. true

3. Every parallelogram is a rectangle. false

4. Some parallelograms are rectangles. true

5. A rectangle is an equiangular quadrilateral. true

6. The diagonals of a rhombus are congruent. false

7. A square has diagonals that are congruent and perpendicular. true

8. The median to the hypotenuse of a right triangle is half as long as the hypotenuse. true

Given: *ABCD* is a square and the diagonals intersect at *E*.

9. $\overline{AC} \cong \underline{?}$ $\overline{BD}$

10. $\underline{?} \perp \overline{BD}$ $\overline{AC}$

11. $\overline{AE} \cong \underline{?}$ $\overline{EB}, \overline{EC},$ or $\overline{ED}$

12. $\angle BAE \cong \underline{?}$
Answers may vary;
$\angle ABE$

13. $\angle BCE \cong \underline{?}$
Answers may vary;
$\angle CBE$

14. $\triangle BEC \cong \underline{?}$
$\triangle DEA, \triangle AEB,$ or $\triangle CED$

Given: $\overline{NE}$ is a median of right triangle *LOE* with right angle at *E*.

15. If $ON = 8$, find NL. 8

16. If $EN = y$, then $\underline{?} = y$
ON and NL

6.4 Special Parallelograms   **235**

• **For Example 2**

ABCD is a rhombus. If $m\angle DAC = 47$, then:

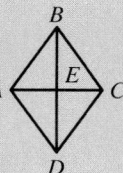

a. $m\angle BCD = \underline{?}$ 94
b. $m\angle ADC = \underline{?}$ 86
If $m\angle ABC = 82$, then:
c. $m\angle DAB = \underline{?}$ 98
d. $m\angle BDC = \underline{?}$ 41
e. $m\angle BEC = \underline{?}$ 90

Common Error
• Students may fail to show that a figure is a parallelogram before trying to show that it is a rectangle, rhombus, or square. Provide examples of quadrilaterals that are not parallelograms but have one right angle and/or two congruent adjacent sides.
• See *Teacher's Resource Book* for additional remediation.

LESSON FOLLOW-UP

Assignment Guide
See p. 216B for assignments.

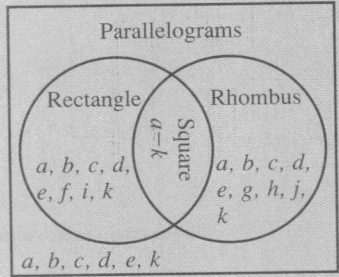

1–2.

Parallelograms

Rectangle — Rhombus — Square (a–k)

Rectangle: a, b, c, d, e, f, i, k

Rhombus: a, b, c, d, e, g, h, j, k

a, b, c, d, e, k

19. Proof:

Statements	Reasons
1. Rhombus *ESOR* with diag. $\overline{RS}$ and $\overline{EO}$	1. Given
2. $\overline{ER} \cong \overline{RO}$; $\overline{SE} \cong \overline{SO}$	2. Def. of rhombus
3. $ER = RO$; $SE = SO$	3. Def. of $\cong$ seg.
4. *R* and *S* are equidistant from *E* and *O*.	4. Def. of equidistant
5. $\overline{RS}$ is the ⊥ bis. of $\overline{EO}$.	5. If 2 points are equidistant from the endpt. of a segment, they lie on the ⊥ bis. of the segment.
6. $\overline{RS} \perp \overline{EO}$	6. Def. of ⊥ bis.

Conclusion: The diag. of a rhombus are ⊥.

---

17. Use the figure, *Given*, *Prove*, and *Plan* of Theorem 6.10 to complete this proof:

Proof:

Statements	Reasons
1. Rectangle *HNRO* with diagonals $\overline{HR}$ and $\overline{ON}$	1. _?_ Given
2. Rectangle *HNRO* is a _?_. □	2. _?_ Def. of rectangle
3. $\overline{HN} \cong$ _?_ $\overline{OR}$	3. Opposite sides of a □ are ≅.
4. $\overline{NR} \cong$ _?_ $\overline{RN}$	4. Reflexive property of congruence
5. $\angle HNR$ and $\angle ORN$ are _?_.	5. _?_ All ∠s of a rectangle are rt. ∠s.
6. _?_ rt. ∠s △HRN and △ONR are rt. △.	6. Definition of a right triangle
7. $\triangle HRN \cong$ _?_ $\triangle ONR$	7. _?_ LL
8. _?_ $\overline{HR} \cong \overline{ON}$	8. _?_ CPCTC

Conclusion: _?_ In rectangle *HNRO*, diagonals $\overline{HR}$ and $\overline{ON}$ are ≅.

PRACTICE EXERCISES 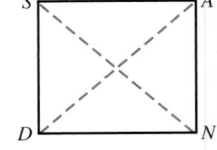 Use technology where appropriate.

A

1. Drawing in Geometry Copy this Venn diagram. Show the relationships of the special parallelograms by adding the labels: Rectangle, Rhombus, and Square.

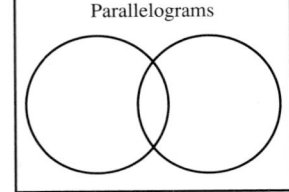

Parallelograms

2. The four regions on the Venn diagram represent the types of parallelograms. In each region write the letter(s) of the properties that characterize that type of parallelogram. See side column.

a. Opposite sides are ∥.
b. Opposite sides are ≅.
c. Opposite angles are ≅.
d. Diagonals form 2 ≅ △.
e. Diagonals bisect each other.
f. Diagonals are ≅.
g. Diagonals are ⊥.
h. Diagonals bisect 2 ∠s.
i. All ∠s are right ∠s.
j. All sides are ≅.
k. Consecutive ∠s are supplementary.

Use the given information to classify □*DNAS* as a rectangle, rhombus, square, or none of these. Use all terms that apply.

3. $\overline{NA} \perp \overline{SA}$ rectangle

4. $\overline{NA} \perp \overline{SA}$; $\overline{NA} \cong \overline{SA}$ rectangle, rhombus, square

5. $\overline{SD} \cong \overline{DN}$ rhombus

6. $\overline{SA} \cong \overline{DN}$; $\overline{SD} \cong \overline{AN}$ none

7. $\overline{SN} \perp \overline{DA}$ rhombus

8. $m\angle SDA = m\angle NDA$ rhombus

9. $m\angle SDN + m\angle DNA = 180$ none

10. $SA = 5$ cm; $SD = 5$ cm; $m\angle S = 89$ rhombus

11. $m\angle N = 90$; $DN = 6$ cm; $DS = 6$ cm rectangle, rhombus, square

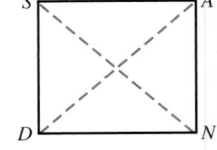

Developing Mathematical Power

Keeping a Portfolio As an extension of Exercise 35, have students prepare a short report on Maurits Escher (1898–1972) and his work. They should include some of the geometrical concepts that he used in creating his tessellations.

12. Given: Right $\triangle TRI$ with median $\overline{TM}$

Conclusion: M is the __?__ of $\overline{RI}$. midpoint

Reason: __?__ Def. of median

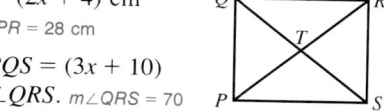

13. Given: Right $\triangle TRI$ with median $\overline{TM}$

Conclusion: __?__ = __?__ = __?__ TM; RM; MI

Reason: __?__ The midpt. of the hyp. of a rt. $\triangle$ is equidistant from the 3 vertices.

In Exercises 14 and 15 show that $\square ACKJ$ is a rhombus.

14. $AC = (6y + 4)$ cm, $CK = (5y + 8)$ cm, and $KJ = (3y + 16)$ cm.
6y + 4 = 5y + 8; y = 4; AC = CK = KJ = 28

15. $JK = (12y - 5)$ cm, $KC = (9y + 4)$ cm, and $JA = (7y + 10)$ cm.
12y − 5 = 9y + 4; y = 3; JK = KC = JA = 31

B

16. If $PQRS$ is a rectangle with $QT = (2x + 4)$ cm and $TS = (3x - 1)$ cm, find PR. PR = 28 cm

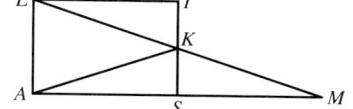

17. If $PQRS$ is a rhombus with $m\angle PQS = (3x + 10)$ and $m\angle SQR = (x + 40)$, find $m\angle QRS$. m∠QRS = 70

18. $PQRS$ is a square with $ST = (x + 8)$ cm and $PR = (4x + 6)$ cm. Find QT.
QT = 13 cm

19. Complete the proof of Theorem 6.11. See side column, page 236.

20. Complete the proof of Theorem 6.12. See Additional Answers, p. 702.

21. Given: Rect. $ASIL$; K is the midpoint of $\overline{IS}$.

Prove: S is the midpoint of $\overline{AM}$.

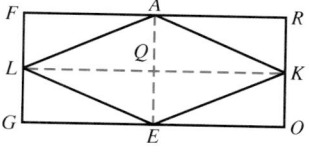

22. Given: Rect. $ASIL$; K is the midpoint of $\overline{IS}$.

Prove: $\overline{AK} \cong \overline{LK}$

23. Given: Rect. $GORF$; L, A, K, and E are midpoints of $\overline{GF}$, $\overline{FR}$, $\overline{RO}$, and $\overline{OG}$, respectively.

Prove: $ALEK$ is a rhombus.

24. Given: Rect. $GORF$; L, A, K, and E are midpoints of $\overline{GF}$, $\overline{FR}$, $\overline{RO}$, and $\overline{OG}$, respectively.

Prove: $\angle LAQ \cong \angle KEQ$

C

25. Prove Theorem 6.13.

26. Prove that a rectangle has four right angles.

27. Prove that the diagonals of a square are perpendicular.

28. Prove that a rhombus has four congruent sides.

29. Prove that the diagonals of a square are congruent.

Prove the converse of each.

30. Theorem 6.10. **31.** Theorem 6.11. **32.** Theorem 6.12. **33.** Theorem 6.13.

6.4 Special Parallelograms **237**

237

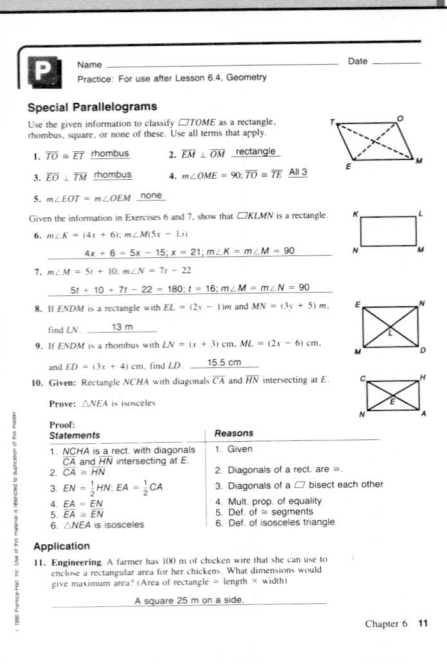

P Name _____ Date _____
   Practice: For use after Lesson 6.4, Geometry

Special Parallelograms

Use the given information to classify ▱TOME as a rectangle,
rhombus, square, or none of these. Use all terms that apply.

1. $\overline{TO} \cong \overline{ET}$ rhombus   2. $\overline{EM} \perp \overline{OM}$ rectangle

3. $\overline{EO} \perp \overline{TM}$ rhombus   4. $m\angle OME = 90; \overline{TO} \cong \overline{TE}$ All 3

5. $m\angle EOT = m\angle OEM$ none

Given the information in Exercises 6 and 7, show that ▱KLMN is a rectangle.

6. $m\angle K = (4x + 6); m\angle M(5x - 15)$
   $4x + 6 = 5x - 15; x = 21; m\angle K = m\angle M = 90$

7. $m\angle M = 5t + 10; m\angle N = 7t - 22$
   $5t + 10 + 7t - 22 = 180; t = 16; m\angle M = m\angle N = 90$

8. If ENDM is a rectangle with $EL = (2y - 1)m$ and $MN = (3y + 5)m$,
   find LN. 13 m

9. If ENDM is a rhombus with $LN = (x + 3)$ cm, $ML = (2x - 6)$ cm,
   and $ED = (3x + 4)$ cm, find LD. 15.5 cm

10. **Given:** Rectangle NCHA with diagonals $\overline{CA}$ and $\overline{HN}$ intersecting at E.
    Prove: △NEA is isosceles

Proof:
Statements	Reasons
1. NCHA is a rect. with diagonals $\overline{CA}$ and $\overline{HN}$ intersecting at E.	1. Given
2. $\overline{CA} \cong \overline{HN}$	2. Diagonals of a rect. are ≅.
3. $EN = \frac{1}{2}HN; EA = \frac{1}{2}CA$	3. Diagonals of a ▱ bisect each other
4. $EA = EN$	4. Mult. prop. of equality
5. $\overline{EA} \cong \overline{EN}$	5. Def. of ≅ segments
6. △NEA is isosceles	6. Def. of isosceles triangle

Application

11. **Engineering** A farmer has 100 m of chicken wire that she can use to
    enclose a rectangular area for her chickens. What dimensions would
    give maximum area? (Area of rectangle = length × width)

    A square 25 m on a side.

Chapter 6 **11**

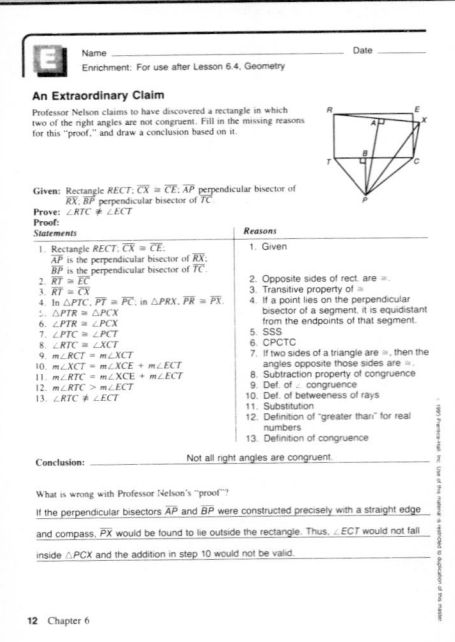

E Name _____ Date _____
   Enrichment: For use after Lesson 6.4, Geometry

An Extraordinary Claim

Professor Nelson claims to have discovered a rectangle in which
two of the right angles are not congruent. Fill in the missing reasons
for this "proof," and draw a conclusion based on it.

Given: Rectangle RECT; $\overline{CX} \cong \overline{CE}$; $\overline{AP}$ perpendicular bisector of
$\overline{RX}$, $\overline{BP}$ perpendicular bisector of $\overline{TC}$.
Prove: $\angle RTC \not\cong \angle ECT$
Proof:
Statements	Reasons
1. Rectangle RECT; $\overline{CX} \cong \overline{CE}$; $\overline{AP}$ is the perpendicular bisector of $\overline{RX}$; $\overline{BP}$ is the perpendicular bisector of $\overline{TC}$.	1. Given
2. $\overline{RT} \cong \overline{EC}$	2. Opposite sides of rect. are ≅.
3. $\overline{RT} \cong \overline{CX}$	3. Transitive property of ≅
4. In △PTC, $\overline{PT} \cong \overline{PC}$; in △PRX, $\overline{PR} \cong \overline{PX}$.	4. If a point lies on the perpendicular bisector of a segment, it is equidistant from the endpoints of that segment.
5. △PTC ≅ △PCX	5. SSS
6. ∠PTC ≅ ∠PCX	6. CPCTC
7. ∠PTC ≅ ∠PCT	7. If two sides of a triangle are ≅, then the angles opposite those sides are ≅.
8. ∠RTC = ∠XCT	8. Subtraction property of congruence
9. $m\angle RCT = m\angle XCT$	9. Def. of ≅ congruence
10. $m\angle XCT = m\angle XCE + m\angle ECT$	10. Def. of betweeness of rays
11. $m\angle RTC = m\angle XCE + m\angle ECT$	11. Substitution
12. $m\angle RTC > m\angle ECT$	12. Definition of "greater than" for real numbers
13. ∠RTC ≇ ∠ECT	13. Definition of congruence

Conclusion: _____ Not all right angles are congruent. _____

What is wrong with Professor Nelson's "proof"?
If the perpendicular bisectors $\overline{AP}$ and $\overline{BP}$ were constructed precisely with a straight edge
and compass, $\overline{PX}$ would be found to lie outside the rectangle. Thus, ∠ECT would not fall
inside △PCX and the addition in step 10 would not be valid.

12 Chapter 6

Applications

34. **Art** What are some examples of parallelograms
    in this artpiece? Answers may vary.

35. **Technology** The Dutch artist Maurits Escher
    created many tessellations based on quadrilaterals.
    Research his work, then use Logo to generate your
    own "Escher" tessellation. Answers may vary.
    See Solutions Manual.

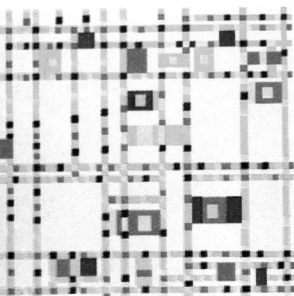

TEST YOURSELF

MNPQ is a parallelogram.

1. Find the measure of $\angle M$; $\angle N$; $\angle NPQ$; $\angle Q$.
   115; 65; 115; 65

2. Find the length of side $\overline{MN}$; $\overline{NP}$; $\overline{QM}$. 10; 7; 7

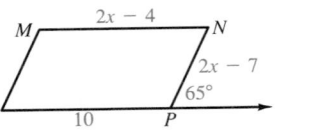

6.1

Is enough information given to conclude that *TORY*
is a parallelogram? Justify your answers.

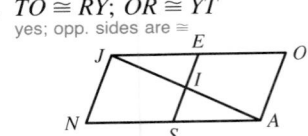

3. $\overline{TO} \parallel \overline{RY}$; $\overline{OR} \parallel \overline{YT}$ yes; def. of ▱   6.2

4. $\angle T \cong \angle R$; $\angle T$ and $\angle O$ are supplementary.

5. $\overline{TO} \cong \overline{RY}$; $\overline{YT} \parallel \overline{OR}$ yes; $\overline{TY} \parallel \overline{OR}$, $\overline{TO} \parallel \overline{YR}$ 6. $\overline{TO} \cong \overline{RY}$; $\overline{OR} \cong \overline{YT}$ 6.3
   no; could be a trapezoid   yes; opp. sides are ≅

7. **Given:** ▱NAOJ with diagonal $\overline{JA}$;
   I is the midpoint of $\overline{JA}$.
   Prove: I is the midpoint of $\overline{ES}$.
   See Additional Answers, p. 702.

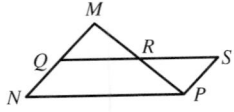

8. **Given:** ▱ABCD; E is the midpoint of $\overline{AB}$;
   G is the midpoint of $\overline{CD}$.
   Prove: EFGH is a parallelogram.

9. **Given:** Q is the midpoint of $\overline{MN}$;   6.3
   R is the midpoint of $\overline{MP}$ and $\overline{QS}$.
   Prove: NQSP is a parallelogram.

Identify each figure as a parallelogram, rectangle, rhombus, square, or   6.4
none of these. Use all terms that apply.

10.   11.   12.   13.
▱, rhombus   ▱, rhombus, rect., square   ▱, rect.   none

6.5 Trapezoids

Objectives: To apply the definition of a trapezoid
To prove and apply theorems about isosceles trapezoids, medians of trapezoids, and the segment that joins the midpoints of two sides of a triangle

The parallelogram is a quadrilateral with specific properties. A *trapezoid* is another special type of quadrilateral.

Investigation—*Visualizing the Concept*

This photograph of a house shows a portion of the roof that has the shape of a quadrilateral.

1. Which sides appear to be parallel?
   The top and the bottom of the roof appear to be ∥.
2. Which appear to be congruent?
   The ends of the roof appear to be ≅. $\overline{AD} \cong \overline{BC}$.
3. What appears to be true about the angles of this figure? ∠s at the top (D and C) appear ≅; ∠s at the bottom (A and B) appear ≅.
4. If *AD* and *CB* were extended to meet at point *E*, what would appear to be true about △*AEB*? △*AEB* would be isos.

The quadrilateral known as a trapezoid has one pair of parallel sides.

Definitions A quadrilateral is a **trapezoid** if and only if it has exactly one pair of parallel sides. The parallel sides of a trapezoid are the **bases**; the nonparallel sides are the **legs**. The angles at the ends of the *bases* are called **base angles**. Two base angles include each base.

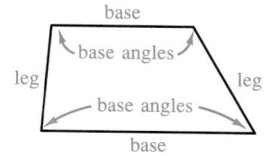

This figure shows a special type of trapezoid, called an *isosceles trapezoid*.

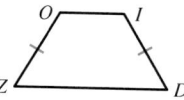

Definition A trapezoid is an **isosceles trapezoid** if and only if its legs are congruent.

Recall that if a triangle is isosceles, the base angles are congruent; conversely, if a triangle has congruent base angles, it is isosceles. This situation also exists with respect to isosceles trapezoids.

6.5 Trapezoids **239**

Developing Mathematical Power

Keeping a Portfolio Have students complete the Critical Thinking activity, p. 6, in the *Teacher's Resource Book*. They should write the defining property that leads from one box to another on the arrow (for example, from rectangles to squares: congruent sides).

LESSON PLAN

Vocabulary
Base angles of a trapezoid
Bases of a trapezoid
Isosceles trapezoid
Legs of a trapezoid
Median of a trapezoid
Trapezoid

Materials/Manipulatives
Models of quadrilaterals
Teaching Transparency 39

Technology
Computer Test Bank, pp. 358–368
The Geometric Supposer: Triangles
Geometry Problems and Projects: Triangles, Worksheet T28, T30

LESSON FOCUS

Review
• Use a transparency for:

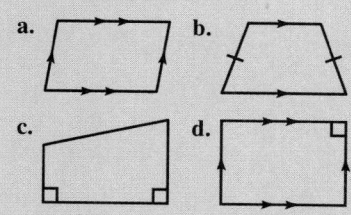

Ask students to identify all parallelograms and special parallelograms. ▱s: a and d; rect.: d **What do b and c appear to have in common?** exactly one pair of ∥ sides
• The Algebra Review, Exercises 34–45, involves rational expressions, radicals, and proportions.

Alternative Learning Styles
Some students will get a better understanding of trapezoids by relating them to real-life occurrences such as that found in the Investigation. Ask students to give other examples.

239

- Provide many opportunities for students to recognize trapezoids and distinguish them from other quadrilaterals. Use actual models cut from paper, diagrams of figures, and examples students create.
- Help students to restate Theorems 6.14 and 6.15 and Theorems 6.16 and 6.17 as biconditionals.
- The Midsegment Theorem is important and has many applications. Compare and contrast it with the corollary of Theorem 6.9. Be sure to demonstrate the theorem using triangles in different orientations.

CHALKBOARD EXAMPLE

- **For the Example**

AYDN is a trap. with median $\overline{LM}$, and P is the midpt. of $\overline{ND}$.

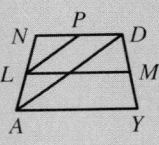

a. If ND = 12 cm and AY = 18 cm, then LM = _?_ cm. 15
b. If AY = 24 cm and LM = 20 cm, then ND = _?_ cm. 16
c. If AD = 22 cm, then LP = _?_ cm. 11
d. If AY = (4x − 1)cm, ND = (3x − 2)cm, and LM = (3x + 3)cm, find x, AY, LM, and ND.

$3x + 3 = (\frac{1}{2})[(4x - 1) + (3x - 2)]$
$6x + 6 = 7x - 3$
$9 = x$
AY = 35 cm, LM = 30 cm, ND = 25 cm

Common Error

- Students may assume that a given triangle is isosceles merely because it appears to be so, or they may make incorrect assumptions about the diagonals and base angles of nonisosceles trapezoids.
- See *Teacher's Resource Book* for additional remediation.

Theorem 6.14 Base angles of an isosceles trapezoid are congruent.

Given: Isosceles trapezoid ARYG

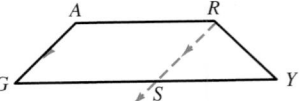

Prove: $\angle G \cong \angle Y$
$\angle A \cong \angle ARY$

Plan: Through R, construct $\overrightarrow{RS}$ parallel to $\overline{AG}$. Then $\angle G \cong \angle RSY$ because they are corresponding angles. Since $\overline{AG} \cong \overline{RS}$, $\overline{RS} \cong \overline{RY}$. Thus $\triangle RSY$ is isosceles and $\angle RSY \cong \angle Y$. By the Transitive property, $\angle G \cong \angle Y$. Also, since $\angle A$ is supplementary to $\angle G$ and $\angle ARY$ is supplementary to $\angle Y$, $\angle A \cong \angle ARY$. Proved in Practice Exercise 23

Theorem 6.15 is the converse of Theorem 6.14.

Theorem 6.15 If the base angles of a trapezoid are congruent, then the trapezoid is isosceles. Proved in Practice Exercise 28

If a trapezoid is isosceles, conclusions can be drawn about its diagonals.

Theorem 6.16 The diagonals of an isosceles trapezoid are congruent.

Theorem 6.17 If the diagonals of a trapezoid are congruent, then the trapezoid is isosceles. Proved in Practice Exercises 29 and 30

Theorem 6.18   The Midsegment Theorem The segment that joins the midpoints of two sides of a triangle is parallel to the third side and its length is half the length of the third side.

Given: $\triangle ABC$; E is the midpoint of $\overline{AB}$; F is the midpoint of $\overline{BC}$.

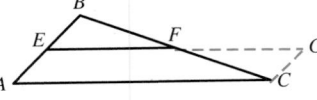

Prove: $\overline{EF} \parallel \overline{AC}$; $EF = \frac{1}{2}AC$

Plan: Extend $\overrightarrow{EF}$ through F to G so that $\overline{FE} \cong \overline{FG}$. Draw $\overline{CG}$. $\triangle BFE \cong \triangle CFG$ by the SAS Postulate, so $\overline{BE} \cong \overline{CG}$. $\overline{BE} \cong \overline{AE}$, so $\overline{AE} \cong \overline{CG}$. By CPCTC, $\angle BEF \cong \angle CGF$; thus $\overline{AB} \parallel \overline{CG}$ and AEGC is a parallelogram. Hence $\overline{EG} \parallel \overline{AC}$ (or $\overline{EF} \parallel \overline{AC}$). Since $EF = \frac{1}{2}EG$ and EG = AC, it also follows that $EF = \frac{1}{2}AC$. Proved in Practice Exercise 24

A segment that often is useful in proving theorems about trapezoids is the *median* of a trapezoid.

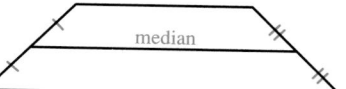

median

Definition   A segment is the **median of a trapezoid** if and only if it joins the midpoints of the legs of the trapezoid.

> **Theorem 6.19**   The median of a trapezoid is parallel to the bases and has a length equal to half the sum of the lengths of the bases.
> Proved in Practice Exercise 31

EXAMPLE   *WXYZ* **is a trapezoid with median** $\overline{EF}$.

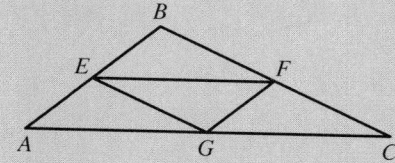

a. If $XY = 15$ cm and $WZ = 11$ cm, then $EF = \underline{\;?\;}$.
b. If $EF = 14$ cm and $WZ = 10$ cm, then $XY = \underline{\;?\;}$.
c. If $EF = 18$ cm, $XY = (5n - 9)$ cm, and
   $WZ = (2n + 3)$ cm, find n, XY, and WZ.
d. If $EF = (2y + 4)$ cm, $XY = (5y + 2)$ cm,
   and $WZ = (-3y + 8)$ cm, find y, EF, XY, and WZ.

a. 13 cm   c. $n = 6$; $XY = 21$ cm; $WZ = 15$ cm
b. 18 cm   d. $y = 1$; $EF = 6$ cm; $XY = 7$ cm; $WZ = 5$ cm

CLASS EXERCISES

Thinking Critically

1. Compare and contrast parallelograms and trapezoids. Answers may vary.

2. Describe the properties of isosceles trapezoids. Answers may vary. The non ∥ sides are ≅, the ∥ sides ≠, the base ∠s are ≅, the diagonals are ≅.

3. Describe at least three methods that can be used to show that a given trapezoid is isosceles. Answers may vary. (1) Show that the base ∠s are ≅, (2) show the diagonals are ≅, or (3) show the non ∥ sides ≅.

Use this figure and the given information to answer each question. Justify your answers.

trapezoid; one pair of ∥ sides
4. If $\overline{IR} \parallel \overline{NO}$, then *INOR* is a/an $\underline{\;?\;}$.

5. If $\overline{IR} \parallel \overline{NO}$ and $\angle N \cong \angle O$, then *INOR* is a/an $\underline{\;?\;}$.
isos. trap.; base ∠s ≅
6. If *INOR* is an isosceles trapezoid, then $\overline{IO} \cong \underline{\;?\;}$.
$\overline{RN}$; diagonals are ≅.
7. If $\overline{PQ}$ bisects $\overline{IN}$ and $\overline{IR}$, then *PQRN* is a/an $\underline{\;?\;}$. trapezoid; Midsegment Th.

8. If *P* and *Q* are the respective midpoints of $\overline{IN}$ and $\overline{IR}$, then $NR = 2 \cdot \underline{\;?\;}$. PQ; Midsegment Th.

6.5 Trapezoids   **241**

LESSON FOLLOW-UP

Discussion

If *E*, *F*, and *G* are the midpoints of the sides of $\triangle ABC$, how does the perimeter of $\triangle EFG$ compare to the perimeter of $\triangle ABC$? Explain.

Since each side of $\triangle EFG$ is half the length of the side of $\triangle ABC$ that it is parallel to, the perimeter of $\triangle EFG$ is half the perimeter of $\triangle ABC$.

Assignment Guide

See p. 216B for assignments.

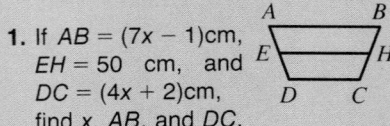
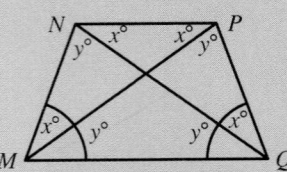
PRACTICE EXERCISES

 Use technology where appropriate.

Trapezoid *WERI* has legs $\overline{WI}$ and $\overline{ER}$.

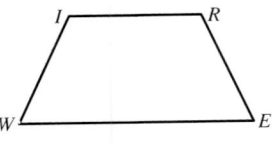

A

1. If *WERI* is isosceles and if $m\angle I = 110$, find $m\angle W$, $m\angle R$, and $m\angle E$.
   $m\angle W = 70$; $m\angle R = 110$; $m\angle E = 70$
2. If *WERI* is isosceles and if $m\angle E = 86$, find $m\angle W$, $m\angle I$, and $m\angle R$. $m\angle W = 86$; $m\angle I = 94$; $m\angle R = 94$
3. If $\overline{WI} \cong \overline{ER}$, $m\angle W = 2x + 55$, and $m\angle E = 7x - 15$, find x and the measures of $\angle W$ and $\angle E$. $x = 14$; $m\angle W = m\angle E = 83$
4. If $\overline{WI} \cong \overline{ER}$, $m\angle I = 6y - 60$, and $m\angle R = 3y + 30$, find y and the measures of $\angle I$ and $\angle R$. $y = 30$; $m\angle I = m\angle R = 120$
5. If $m\angle W = m\angle E = 82$, $WE = 15$ cm, $IR = 10$ cm, and the perimeter of *WERI* is 43 cm, find WI and ER. $WI = ER = 9$ cm
6. If $\angle I \cong \angle R$, $IR = 12$ cm, $WE = 16$ cm, and the perimeter of *WERI* is 38 cm, find WI and ER. $WI = ER = 5$ cm

Trapezoid *ZOID* has diagonals $\overline{ZI}$ and $\overline{DO}$.

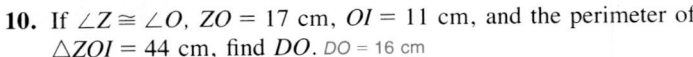

7. If *ZOID* is isosceles and $ZI = 12$ cm, find DO.
   $DO = 12$ cm
8. If *ZOID* is isosceles and $DO = 18$ cm, find ZI.
   $ZI = 18$ cm
9. If $\angle D \cong \angle I$, $ZD = 10$ cm, $DI = 8$ cm, and the perimeter of $\triangle ZID = 30$ cm, find DO. $DO = 12$ cm
10. If $\angle Z \cong \angle O$, $ZO = 17$ cm, $OI = 11$ cm, and the perimeter of $\triangle ZOI = 44$ cm, find DO. $DO = 16$ cm
11. If $\overline{ZI} \cong \overline{DO}$, $ZD = (6x - 5)$ cm, and $OI = (2x + 7)$ cm, find x, ZD, and OI. $x = 3$, $ZD = 13$ cm, $OI = 13$ cm

Trapezoid *NDYA* has median $\overline{LM}$, and P is the midpoint of $\overline{ND}$.

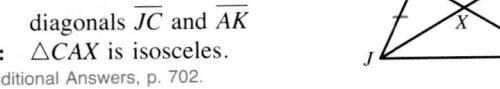

12. If $ND = 12$ and $AY = 18$, then $LM = \underline{?}$. 15
13. If $AY = 27$ and $ND = 22$, then $LM = \underline{?}$. 24.5
14. If $AY = 24$ and $LM = 20$, then $ND = \underline{?}$. 16
15. If $ND = 13$ and $LM = 16$, then $AY = \underline{?}$. 19
16. If $AD = 22$, then $LP = \underline{?}$. 11
17. If $LP = y$, then $AD = \underline{?}$. 2y
18. If $ND = x$, and $AY = y$, then $LM = \underline{?}$. $\frac{1}{2}(x + y)$

B

19. **Given:** Isosceles trapezoid *ACKJ* with diagonals $\overline{JC}$ and $\overline{AK}$
    Prove: $\triangle CAX$ is isosceles.
    See Additional Answers, p. 702.

Trapezoid *PARK* has median $\overline{ED}$.

20. If $ED = 16$ cm, $KR = (3x + 5)$ cm,
and $PA = (5x + 11)$ cm, find x, KR, and PA.
$x = 2$, $KR = 11$ cm, $PA = 21$ cm

21. If $ED = 25$ cm, $PA = (4x - 1)$ cm, and
$KR = (3x + 2)$ cm, find x, PA, and KR.
$x = 7$, $PA = 27$ cm, $KR = 23$ cm

22. If $PA = (5y + 6)$ cm, $KR = (4y + 5)$ cm, and
$ED = (6y - 2)$ cm, find PA, KR, and ED.
$PA = 31$ cm, $KR = 25$ cm, $ED = 28$ cm

23. Complete the proof of Th. 6.14.   **24.** Complete the proof of Th. 6.18.
See Additional Answers, p. 702.

25. Write an indirect proof to justify that if the lower base angles of a
trapezoid are not congruent, the trapezoid is not isosceles.

26. Write an indirect proof to justify that if a trapezoid is not isosceles, its
diagonals are not congruent.

27. Prove that the figure formed by joining in order the midpoints of the sides
of any quadrilateral is a parallelogram.

C **28.** Prove Theorem 6.15. Use a method different from the one used in
proving Theorem 6.14.

29. Prove Theorem 6.16.   **30.** Prove Theorem 6.17.   **31.** Prove Theorem 6.19.

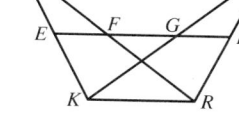

Applications

32. Architecture This office building has surfaces
that are quadrilaterals with at least one pair of
parallel sides. Locate and describe the
quadrilaterals. two rectangles; top and bottom; two
rectangles on the left and right; two isos. trap. on front and back

33. Technology Research the tessellations of Roger Penrose and use Logo to
generate your own "Penrose" tessellation. Answers may vary. See Solutions Manual.

Algebra Review

Simplify.

34. $\dfrac{x}{2xy}$ $\frac{1}{2y}$ **35.** $\dfrac{a^2b}{ab^2}$ $\frac{a}{b}$ **36.** $\dfrac{x - 2}{x^2 - 4}$ $\frac{1}{x+2}$ **37.** $\dfrac{3x + 6}{x^2 + 5x + 6}$ $\frac{3}{x+3}$

38. $\sqrt{81}$ 9   **39.** $\sqrt{50}$ $5\sqrt{2}$ **40.** $\sqrt{9x^2}$ $3x$ **41.** $\sqrt{45y^3}$ $3y\sqrt{5y}$

Solve.

42. $\dfrac{2}{3} = \dfrac{x}{9}$ 6   **43.** $\dfrac{5}{8} = \dfrac{20}{x}$ 32   **44.** $\dfrac{3}{x} = \dfrac{7\frac{1}{2}}{25}$ 10   **45.** $\dfrac{x}{15} = \dfrac{28}{60}$ 7

6.5 Trapezoids **243**

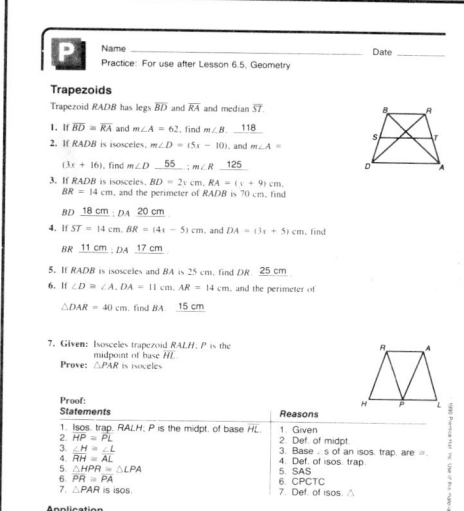
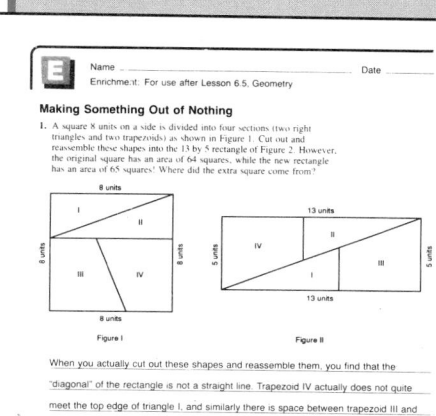

LESSON PLAN

Vocabulary
Circular definition
Minimal conditions

Materials/Manipulatives
Colored pencils
Teaching Transparency 40

Technology
Computer Test Bank, pp.
368–373
The Geometric Supposer:
Quadrilaterals, p. 95

LESSON FOCUS

Review
Review characteristics of quadrilaterals, parallelograms, and trapezoids. Have students identify those characteristics that determine each shape.

Alternative Learning Styles
• Students will benefit from a visual-concrete approach to reorganizing minimal conditions for definitions. Using colored pencils to represent each polygon, students can list the properties of each polygon. Then, referring to the definitions, they can determine those characteristics which are the defining properties for each polygon. Students should remember each defining property by associating it with its color.
• Another visual aid for helping students determine minimal conditions for definitions is Teaching Transparency 40.

6.6   Strategy: Recognize Minimal Conditions

Recall that definitions are *biconditional* and are usually stated in "if and only if" form. Good definitions have other important characteristics.

Good definitions are stated using previously defined terms or undefined terms. This practice avoids *circular* definitions in which one term is described using a second term, and then the second term is described using the first.

Good definitions place the defined term in the nearest class to which it belongs. For example, a rectangle can be classed as a polygon, a quadrilateral, and a parallelogram, but the definition of a rectangle places it in the *nearest* of these classes—that of parallelogram.

Good definitions describe how the term differs from other members of the class. If a term is defined by placing it in its nearest class, the definition must show how the term is different from other members of the class. For example, vertical angles are first placed in the class of all angles, then distinguished from other types of angles by the remaining defining characteristics (nonadjacent angles formed by two intersecting lines).

Good definitions identify the minimal conditions that characterize the term. A good definition gives the least amount of necessary information. For example, other properties of rectangles follow from the properties of parallelograms but are not considered to be defining properties.

EXAMPLE 1   Which of the properties listed are defining properties of the given object?

a. Equilateral triangle

Properties: (1) is a polygon; (2) is a triangle; (3) has three angles; (4) has three congruent sides; (5) has three congruent angles; (6) has angles that measure 60

b. Square

Properties: (1) is a quadrilateral (2) is a parallelogram; (3) is a rhombus; (4) has a right angle; (5) has four right angles; (6) has sides that are perpendicular

a. Defining properties: 2 and 4   **b.** Defining properties: 3 and 4

244   Chapter 6 Quadrilaterals

Developing Mathematical Power
Keeping a Portfolio   Have students write a brief description of the characteristics of a good definition. Then have them select a common, everyday object, such as a pencil, and define the object. Encourage them to check their definitions against the characteristics they described to see if the definitions are good.

EXAMPLE 2 These figures are quadriplexes.

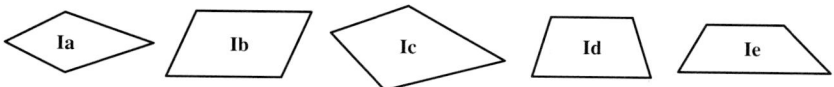

These figures are not quadriplexes.

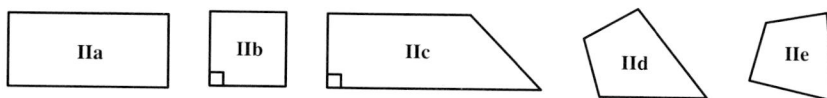

Which of these figures are quadriplexes? Define quadriplex.

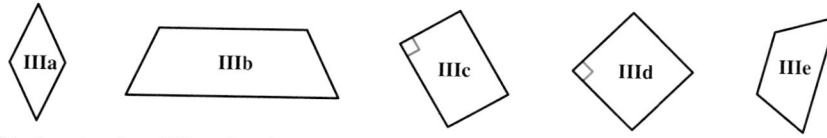

Understand the Problem	**What is given?** Examples of quadriplexes and nonquadriplexes **What is to be determined?** The minimal conditions that can be used to define a quadriplex
Plan Your Approach	**Identify the nearest class of geometric terms to which quadriplexes belong.** Ask what characteristics all quadriplexes share. **Decide what distinguishes the quadriplexes from other members of this class.** Examine the sides and angles of the figures to get some ideas.
Implement the Plan	Since quadriplexes are not necessarily parallelograms or trapezoids, the nearest class is quadrilateral. From the examples, no statement about congruence of sides or angles appears likely. If the angles of each quadriplex are measured, each one is seen to have exactly two obtuse angles. Hence, Figures IIIa, b, and e are quadriplexes. Based on the evidence, it appears that a quadriplex could be defined as a *quadrilateral having exactly two obtuse angles*.
Interpret the Results	Does the definition exhibit the characteristics of a *good definition*? Are other definitions for a quadriplex possible?

6.6 Strategy: Recognize Minimal Conditions **245**

- Point out that a "class" is a group of objects all of which share a common characteristic.
- Discuss the relationship between definitions and theorems. Definitions describe minimal conditions that characterize an object; theorems often describe additional properties of the object that can be derived from the definition.

CHALKBOARD EXAMPLES

- **For Example 1**

  Which of the properties listed are defining properties of a rectangle?

  (1) is a quadrilateral;
  (2) is a polygon;
  (3) has 4 right angles;
  (4) is a parallelogram;
  (5) has 2 pairs of congruent sides;
  (6) has a right angle

  Defining properties: 4 and 6

- **For Example 2**

  These figures are *polypars*.

  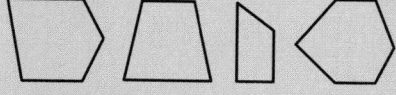

  These figures are not *polypars*.

  Which of these are *polypars*?
  Define *polypar*.

  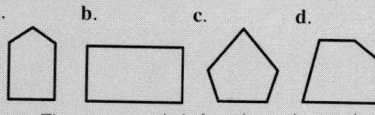

  Figures *a* and *d*; A *polypar* is a polygon having exactly one pair of parallel sides.

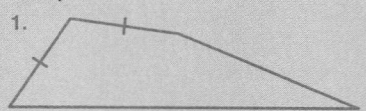
CLASS EXERCISES

Arrange the following terms in the order in which their definitions should be given.

1. Ray, line, segment line, ray, segment
2. Segment, median, midpoint segment, midpoint, median
3. Rectangle, parallelogram, rhombus, quadrilateral quad., ▱, rect., rhombus
4. Polygon, isosceles trapezoid, quadrilateral, trapezoid polygon, quad., trap., isos. trap.
5. Hypotenuse, triangle, right triangle △, rt. △, hyp.

Suppose the word in italics is to be defined. What is wrong with each of the following definitions? Explain.

6. A *dog* is an animal that barks. It does not distinguish dogs from other animals that bark.
7. *Hot* is the opposite of cold. circular
8. A *square* is a polygon with 4 congruent sides and 4 congruent angles. Square should be classed as a rect. or rhombus.
9. A *triangle* is a geometric figure composed of 3 line segments. △ should be classed as a polygon; 3 line segments do not provide minimal conditions.
10. A *rhombus* is an equilateral parallelogram. Too much information in *equilateral*.

PRACTICE EXERCISES

A **Identify the minimal defining conditions from among the properties listed.**

1. Isosceles trapezoid

   (a) quadrilateral; (b) has one pair of congruent sides; (c) has congruent base angles; (d) has one pair of parallel sides; (e) has congruent diagonals a, c, d

2. Rhombus

   (a) is a quadrilateral; (b) has two pairs of congruent sides; (c) is a parallelogram; (d) diagonals bisect angles; (e) has a pair of consecutive sides congruent c, e

The following are not good definitions. Show why by sketching a counterexample. Then rewrite in acceptable form.

3. Parallel lines are lines that do not intersect. ∥ lines are coplanar lines that do not intersect.

4. Adjacent angles are coplanar and have a common vertex and a common side. Adj. ∠s are coplanar, have a common vertex and a common side, and have no interior pts. in common.

5. A rectangle is a quadrilateral having two right angles. A rect. is a ▱ with a rt. ∠.

6. A trapezoid is a polygon having exactly one pair of parallel sides. A trap. is a quad. having exactly one pair of ∥ sides.

7. Supplementary angles are angles whose measures have a sum of 180. Supp. ∠s are 2 ∠s whose measures have a sum of 180.

8. Vertical angles are angles formed by two intersecting lines. Vert. ∠s are pairs of nonadj. ∠s formed by 2 intersecting lines.

9. Congruent triangles have congruent sides and congruent angles. ≅ △s have corr. ≅ sides and ≅ ∠s.

10. A parallelogram is a polygon having two pairs of parallel sides. A ▱ is a quad. having 2 pairs of ∥ sides.

11. A rhombus is a quadrilateral with a pair of consecutive congruent sides. A rhombus is a ▱ with a pair of consecutive ≅ sides.

12. The median of a trapezoid joins the midpoints of two sides. The median of a trap. joins the midpts. of the legs.

13. These figures are duoquads.

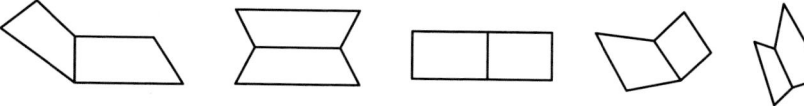

These figures are not duoquads.

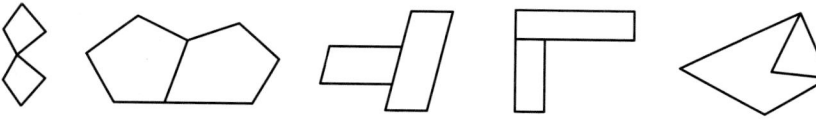

Which of these figures are duoquads? Define duoquad.

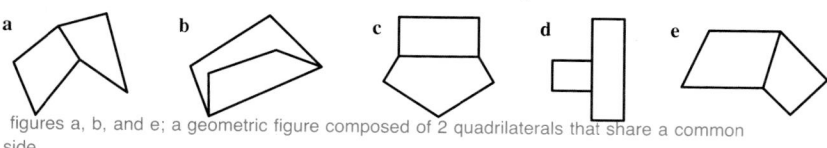

figures a, b, and e; a geometric figure composed of 2 quadrilaterals that share a common side

---

PROJECT

Make up your own nonstandard geometric figure and write a problem similar to Problem 13. Challenge your classmates to define the nonstandard figure.

6.6 Strategy: Recognize Minimal Conditions **247**

Developing Mathematical Power

Cooperative Learning Working in small groups, students can share and critique the definitions they wrote in their portfolios. Then provide time for them to do Exercise 13 and the challenge provided in the Project.

Teacher's Resource Book

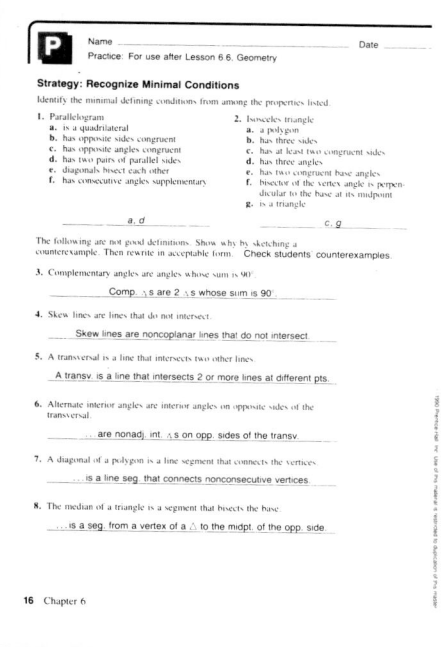

Congruent Quadrilaterals

6.7

Objective: To identify and prove theorems about congruent
 quadrilaterals

Congruent quadrilaterals have the same shape and size. Methods for proving them
congruent are similar to methods for proving triangles congruent.

Investigation—*Thinking Critically*

A construction supervisor instructed each of three workers to construct a
nonrectangular frame that could be used as a mold for pouring concrete. Each
worker was given two 12′ and two 8′ pieces of wood, and this was the result:

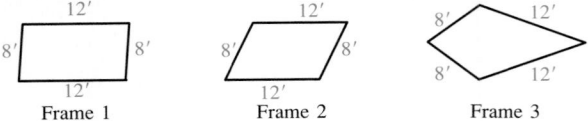

Frame 1   Frame 2   Frame 3

The supervisor had intended that the frames be identical.

1. What instructions should have been given to the workers to guarantee that
 the frames would match? Answers may vary: Put the ≅ pieces of wood next to
 each other at a specific angle.
2. What can be done to make the frames identical? Frame 1 and Frame 2 can be
 made identical by making 1 pair of corr. ∠s ≅.

Definition Two **quadrilaterals are congruent** if and only if there is a
correspondence between the vertices of the quadrilaterals, such that the
corresponding angles and the corresponding sides are congruent.

Quadrilateral *ABCD* is congruent
to quadrilateral *RSTU* because
corresponding angles and
corresponding sides are congruent.

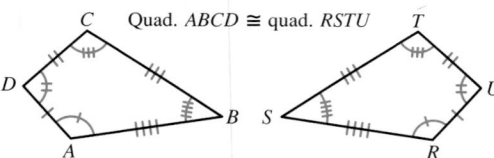

Quad. *ABCD* ≅ quad. *RSTU*

EXAMPLE 1   Quad. *ABCD* ≅ quad. *EFGH*. Complete each statement.

a. $\angle C \cong \angle \underline{\ ?\ }$

b. $\overline{DA} \cong \underline{\ ?\ }$

c. $m\angle D = \underline{\ ?\ }$

d. $BC = \underline{\ ?\ }$

e. $m\angle A = m\angle \underline{\ ?\ } = \underline{\ ?\ }$

a. ∠G   b. $\overline{HE}$ c. 145   d. 10

e. $m\angle E$; 60

Developing Mathematical Power

Keeping a Portfolio Students can demonstrate their understanding of the properties of parallelograms by completing the Reading and Writing in Geometry activity, p. 6, in the *Teacher's Resource Book*. Encourage them to state the theorem or
corollary they used in their explanation.

Two methods can be used to prove any two quadrilaterals congruent:

SASAS Theorem (Side-Included Angle-Side-Included Angle-Side)
ASASA Theorem (Angle-Included Side-Angle-Included Side-Angle)

Theorem 6.20 SASAS Theorem Two quadrilaterals are congruent if any three sides and the included angles of one are congruent, respectively, to the corresponding three sides and the included angles of the other.

Given: $\overline{AB} \cong \overline{EF}$; $\overline{BC} \cong \overline{FG}$, $\overline{CD} \cong \overline{GH}$;
$\angle B \cong \angle F$; $\angle C \cong \angle G$

Prove: Quad. $ABCD \cong$ quad. $EFGH$

Plan: Draw diagonals $\overline{AC}$ and $\overline{EG}$. $\triangle ABC \cong \triangle EFG$ by the SAS Postulate. Show that $\triangle DCA \cong \triangle HGE$. Then the remaining corresponding parts of the quadrilaterals can also be shown congruent.
Proved in Practice Exercise 31

Theorem 6.21 ASASA Theorem Two quadrilaterals are congruent if any three angles and the included sides of one are congruent, respectively, to the three corresponding angles and the included sides of the other. Proved in Practice Exercise 34

In Theorems 6.20 and 6.21, using the included corresponding parts that are called for is *necessary* to guarantee the congruence.

Since parallelograms, rectangles, and squares have special features, fewer conditions need to be verified in order to prove congruence.

EXAMPLE 2 Write a plan and state a conclusion for this proof.

Given: $\square ABCD$ and $\square EFGH$;
$\angle B \cong \angle F$; $\overline{AB} \cong \overline{EF}$; $\overline{BC} \cong \overline{FG}$

Prove: $\square ABCD \cong \square EFGH$

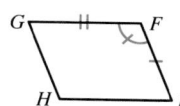

Plan: Use the properties of a parallelogram to show that $\overline{CD} \cong \overline{GH}$ and $\angle C \cong \angle G$. The conclusion follows by SASAS.

Conclusion: Two parallelograms are congruent if two sides and the included angle of one parallelogram are congruent, respectively, to the corresponding parts of the other parallelogram.

6.7 Congruent Quadrilaterals **249**

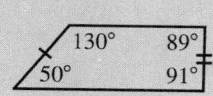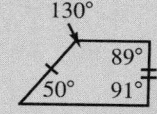
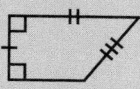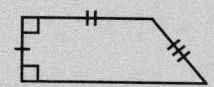
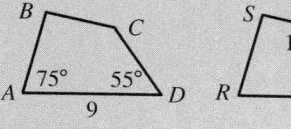
249

• For Example 2

Write a plan and state a conclusion for this proof.

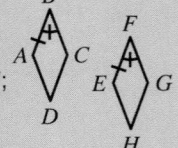

Given: Rhombuses *ABCD* and *EFGH*; $\overline{AB} \cong \overline{EF}$; $\angle B \cong \angle F$

Prove: Rhombus *ABCD* ≅ Rhombus *EFGH*

Plan: Use $\overline{AB} \cong \overline{EF}$ and the fact that all sides of a rhombus are congruent to show $\overline{BC} \cong \overline{FG}$ and $\overline{CD} \cong \overline{GH}$. Use $\angle B \cong \angle F$, the fact that rhombuses are parallelograms, and the fact that consecutive angles of a parallelogram are supplementary to show $\angle C \cong \angle G$. The conclusion follows by SASAS.

Conclusion: If one side and one angle of a rhombus are congruent to the corresponding parts of a second rhombus, then the rhombuses are congruent.

Common Error

• Students may apply the congruence theorems for quadrilaterals inappropriately by failing to use *included sides* or *included angles*. Emphasize the counterexamples shown in the first Teaching Suggestion, p. 249.

• See *Teacher's Resource Book* for additional remediation.

LESSON FOLLOW-UP

Assignment Guide

See p. 216B for assignments.

Developing Mathematical Power

Thinking Critically Students are asked to analyze a figure to find the measures of the angles of a trapezoid.

CLASS EXERCISES

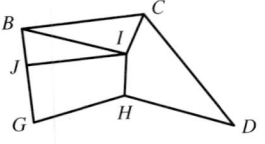

1. Name the angles included by sides $\overline{IC}$, $\overline{CD}$, and $\overline{DH}$ of quadrilateral *HICD*. ∠ICD, ∠CDH

2. Name the sides included by angles *I*, *J*, and *B* in quadrilateral *BCIJ*. $\overline{IJ}$, $\overline{JB}$

3. If quad. *MNOP* ≅ quad. *ABCD*, name all pairs of congruent corresponding angles and all pairs of congruent corresponding sides.
   corr. ∠s ∠M ≅ ∠A   ∠O ≅ ∠C ∠N ≅ ∠B   ∠P ≅ ∠D

   corr. $\overline{MN} \cong \overline{AB}$
   sides $\overline{NO} \cong \overline{BC}$
   $\overline{OP} \cong \overline{CD}$
   $\overline{PM} \cong \overline{DA}$

Identify the congruent quadrilaterals. Justify each congruence.

4.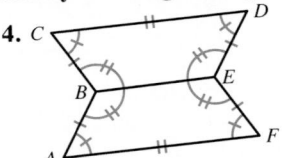

quad. *BCDE* ≅ quad. *BAFE* by def. of ≅ quads., SASAS, or ASASA

5.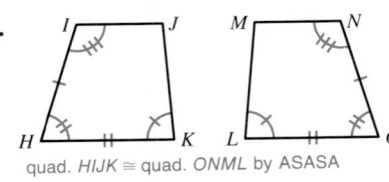

quad. *HIJK* ≅ quad. *ONML* by ASASA

True or false? Justify your answers.

6. Two squares are congruent if a side of one square is congruent to a side of the other. True; ASASA (if one side is ≅, all sides are ≅, and all ∠s are rt∠s.)

7. Two rectangles are congruent if a diagonal of one rectangle is congruent to the corresponding diagonal of the other rectangle.
   False. The sides may not be ≅.

8. Two trapezoids are congruent if the bases and one leg of one trapezoid are congruent to the corresponding parts of the second.
   False; a pair of ≅ corr. ∠s is also needed.

9. Two rectangles are congruent if a pair of consecutive sides of one rectangle is congruent to the corresponding parts of the second. True; ASASA

10. Two rhombuses are congruent if a side of one rhombus is congruent to a side of the other. False; angles are not necessarily ≅.

11. Two rectangles are congruent if a side and diagonal of one rectangle are congruent to the corresponding parts of the other. True; the bases are ≅, which gives SASAS.

12. If three angles of one quadrilateral are congruent to the corresponding angles of another quadrilateral, the fourth angles are congruent. True; sum of the measures of the angles of every quad. is 360.

PRACTICE EXERCISES   ⌣ Use technology where appropriate.

A 1. **Writing in Geometry** A teacher challenges a class to construct a quadrilateral congruent to quadrilateral *CORB*. Explain how this can be done using only a straightedge and a compass.
   See side column.

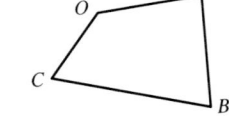

250   Chapter 6 Quadrilaterals

---

1. Methods may vary. Start with a line and a pt. to represent *C'*. Const. an ∠ ≅ to ∠OCB. (∠C') Const. a seg. ≅ $\overline{CB}$. (C'B' ≅ CB). Const. an ∠ ≅ to ∠RBC with vertex *B'*.
Const. a seg. ≅ $\overline{BR}$ (B'R' ≅ BR). Const. an ∠ ≅ ∠R at *R'*. Extend a side of ∠R' to intersect the sides of ∠C' (ASASA).

1.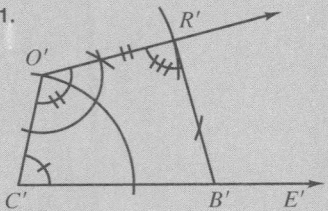

Quad. *AGET* ≅ quad. *UJPM*.

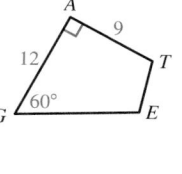
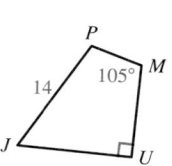

2. $m\angle T = \underline{\ ?\ }$. 105 **3.** $m\angle J = \underline{\ ?\ }$. 60

4. $m\angle E = \underline{\ ?\ }$. 105 **5.** $m\angle P = \underline{\ ?\ }$. 105

6. If the perimeter of *AGET* = 40 cm, then $MP = \underline{\ ?\ }$ cm. 5

7. If the perimeter of *UJPM* = 42 cm, then $TE = \underline{\ ?\ }$ cm. 7

Where enough information is given, write an appropriate congruence statement. Verify the congruence.

8.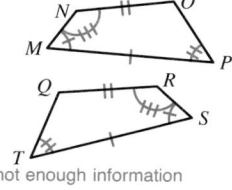
not enough information

9.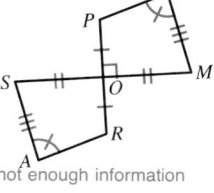
not enough information

10.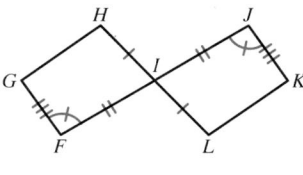
quad. *HIFG* ≅ quad *LIJK* (SASAS)

If there is enough information to determine that quad. *ABCD* ≅ quad. *MNOP*, verify the congruence.

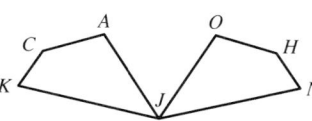

11. $\angle A \cong \angle M$; $\angle B \cong \angle N$; $\angle D \cong \angle P$; $\overline{AB} \cong \overline{MN}$; $\overline{DA} \cong \overline{PM}$ ASASA

12. $\angle B \cong \angle N$; $\angle C \cong \angle O$; $\overline{BC} \cong \overline{NO}$; $\overline{CD} \cong \overline{OP}$; $\overline{AB} \cong \overline{MN}$ SASAS

13. $\overline{CD} \cong \overline{OP}$; $\overline{DA} \cong \overline{PM}$; $\angle D \cong \angle P$; $\angle C \cong \angle O$; $\overline{BC} \cong \overline{NO}$ SASAS

14. $\overline{BC} \cong \overline{NO}$; $\overline{AB} \cong \overline{MN}$; $\angle B \cong \angle N$; $\angle C \cong \angle O$; $\angle D \cong \angle P$
not enough information

15. $\angle D \cong \angle P$; $\overline{DA} \cong \overline{PM}$; $\overline{CD} \cong \overline{OP}$; $\angle A \cong \angle M$; $\overline{BC} \cong \overline{NO}$
not enough information

16. $\angle B \cong \angle N$; $\angle A \cong \angle M$; $\overline{AB} \cong \overline{MN}$; $\overline{DA} \cong \overline{PM}$; $\angle D \cong \angle P$
ASASA

Use the figure and the information in the chart to find the missing congruence statement.

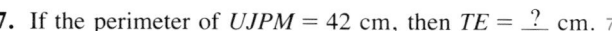

Given	Theorem to Be Used	Missing Congruence
17. $\angle K \cong \angle N$; $\angle KJA \cong \angle NJO$; $\overline{KJ} \cong \overline{NJ}$; $\angle A \cong \angle O$	ASASA	$\underline{\ ?\ }$ $\overline{JA} \cong \overline{JO}$
18. $\overline{AC} \cong \overline{OH}$; $\angle A \cong \angle O$; $\angle C \cong H$; $\overline{JA} \cong \overline{JO}$	SASAS	$\underline{\ ?\ }$ $\overline{CK} \cong \overline{HN}$
19. $\overline{JA} \cong \overline{JO}$; $\overline{AC} \cong \overline{OH}$; $\angle C \cong \angle H$; $\overline{CK} \cong \overline{HN}$	SASAS	$\underline{\ ?\ }$ $\angle A \cong \angle O$
20. $\overline{CK} \cong \overline{HN}$; $\overline{KJ} \cong \overline{NJ}$; $\angle K \cong \angle N$; $\angle C \cong \angle H$	ASASA	$\angle KJA \cong \angle NJO$

6.7 Congruent Quadrilaterals **251**

Lesson Quiz

If enough information is given, write an appropriate congruence statement. Justify the congruence.

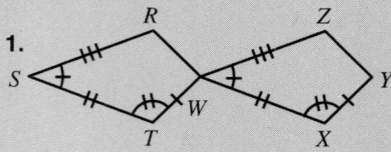

1.

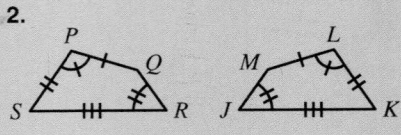

2.

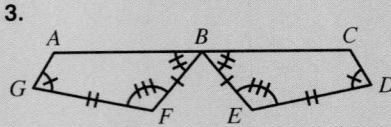

3.

1. Quad. *RSTW* ≅ Quad. *ZWXY* (SASAS)
2. not enough information
3. Quad. *ABFG* ≅ Quad. *CBED* (ASASA)

△*BFE* is equilateral and isosceles trapezoid *ABFG* is congruent to *BCDE*.

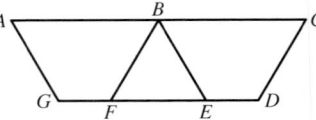

B

21. Find $m\angle BFE$, $m\angle CBE$, $m\angle C$, and $m\angle DEB$.
60; 60; 60; 120

22. Find $m\angle A$, $m\angle G$, $m\angle ABF$, and $m\angle BFG$.
60; 120; 60; 120

23. If $BE = (3x - 7)$ cm and $CD = (x + 6)$ cm, find x, BE, and CD. 6.5, 12.5 cm, 12.5 cm

24. If $AB = (4y + 12)$ cm and $AC = 64$ cm, find y, AB, and BC. 5 cm, 32 cm, 32 cm

25. If $AB = (8y - 6)$ cm, $FG = (4y + 2)$ cm, and $DE = (6y - 8)$ cm, find FE. 12 cm

26. If $AC = (10y + 18)$ cm, $FG = (5y + 2)$ cm, and $DE = (2y + 11)$ cm, find FE. 7 cm

27. If $AC = 54$ cm and $GD = 39$ cm, find GF, FE, and ED. 12 cm, 15 cm, 12 cm

28. If $BC = 38$ cm and $GD = 45$ cm, find GF, FE, and ED. 7 cm, 31 cm, 7 cm
See side column page 251.

29. Given: Isosceles trapezoid *ABCD*; *N* and *M* are respective midpoints of $\overline{BC}$ and $\overline{AD}$.
 Prove: Quad. *ABNM* ≅ quad. *DCNM*

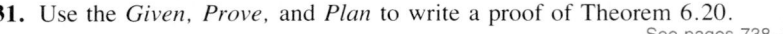

30. Given: Isosceles trapezoid *ABCD*; $\overline{MN}$ is the perpendicular bisector of $\overline{BC}$.
 Prove: Quad. *ABNO* ≅ quad. *DCNO*

31. Use the *Given, Prove,* and *Plan* to write a proof of Theorem 6.20.
See pages 738–740.

32. Given: *TRAP* is an isosceles trapezoid; *M* is the midpoint of $\overline{TP}$; △*MNQ* is isosceles with base $\overline{NQ}$.
 Prove: Quad. *TRNM* ≅ quad. *PAQM*

33. Given: Trapezoid *TRAP*; $\angle R \cong \angle A$; isosceles △*MNQ* with base $\overline{NQ}$; $\overline{RN} \cong \overline{AQ}$.
 Prove: Quad. *TRNM* ≅ quad. *PAQM*

C **34.** Prove Theorem 6.21.

Prove the following statements.

35. If three angles of one quadrilateral are congruent to the corresponding angles of another quadrilateral, the remaining angles are congruent.

36. Two squares are congruent if a side of the first square is congruent to a side of the second square.

37. Two rectangles are congruent if a pair of consecutive sides of one is congruent to the corresponding pair of sides of the other.

38. Two rectangles are congruent if a side and diagonal of one are congruent to the corresponding parts of the other.

39. Two rhombuses are congruent if a side and one angle of one rhombus are congruent to the corresponding parts of the other.

40. Technology In Logo use 6 congruent squares to design a shape and then tessellate that shape.

41. Technology Research the history of quilts. Using Logo, generate a series of historic quilt designs. Include your own new design.

Developing Mathematical Power

42. Logical Reasoning If $\overline{MN} \cong \overline{NP} \cong \overline{PQ}$ and $\overline{MP} \cong \overline{NQ} \cong \overline{MQ}$, find the measures of angles QMN, MNP, NPQ, and PQM. 72; 108; 108; 72

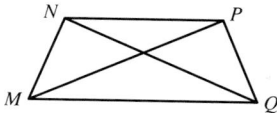

TEST YOURSELF

ABCD is a rectangle with diagonals $\overline{AC}$ and $\overline{BD}$, and FCDE is a trapezoid with median $\overline{GH}$.

1. If $FC = (6y - 10)$ cm, $ED = (3y - 5)$ cm, and $GH = 15$ cm, find FC and ED. 20 cm; 10 cm

6.5

2. If $AD = 36$ cm and $GH = (7y - 3)$ cm, find y. 3

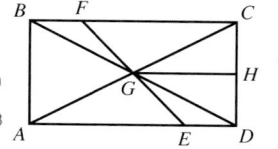

Use the given information to reach conclusions. Justify your answers.
See side column.

3.

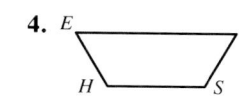

Given: Trapezoid JKLM
with median $\overline{PQ}$

Conclusions: **a.** $PQ = $ _?_
b. $JP = $ _?_
c. _?_ $\parallel \overline{ML}$
d. $\angle KQP \cong$ _?_

4.

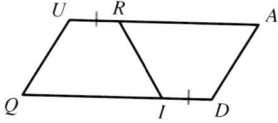

Given: Isosceles trapezoid EBSH
with legs $\overline{HE}$ and $\overline{SB}$

Conclusions: **a.** $\angle$ _?_ $\cong \angle B$
b. $\angle$ _?_ $\cong \angle$ _?_
c. _?_ $\cong$ _?_
d. _?_ $\parallel$ _?_

5. Analyze this statement: A trapezoid is a quadrilateral with a pair of parallel sides. The statement underdetermines a trapezoid, which has only one pair of parallel sides.

6.6

6. Given: $\square QUAD$; $\overline{UR} \cong \overline{DI}$
Prove: Quad. $QURI \cong$ quad. $ADIR$
See Additional Answers, p. 702.

6.7

6.7 Congruent Quadrilaterals **253**

3. a. $\frac{JK + LM}{2}$; median is average of length of bases.
b. PM; a median divides a segment into two equal parts.
c. JK; def. of a trap.; or $\overline{PQ}$; median is $\parallel$ to base.
d. $\angle QLM$; corr. $\angle$s of $\parallel$ lines are $\cong$.

4. a. E; base $\angle$s of isos. trap. are $\cong$.
b. H; S; base $\angle$s of isos. trap. are $\cong$.
c. HE; SB; def. of an isos. trap.
d. HS; EB; def. of a trap.

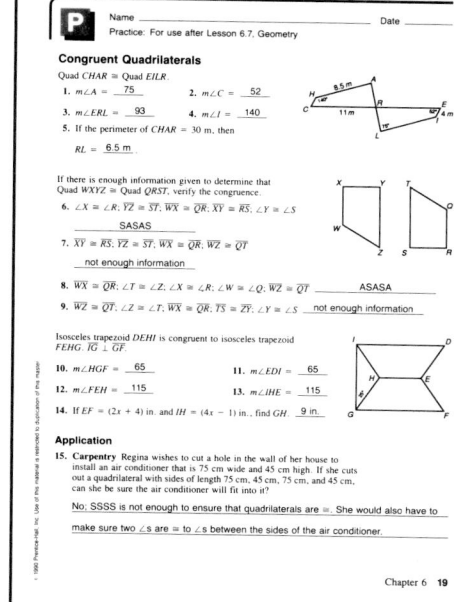
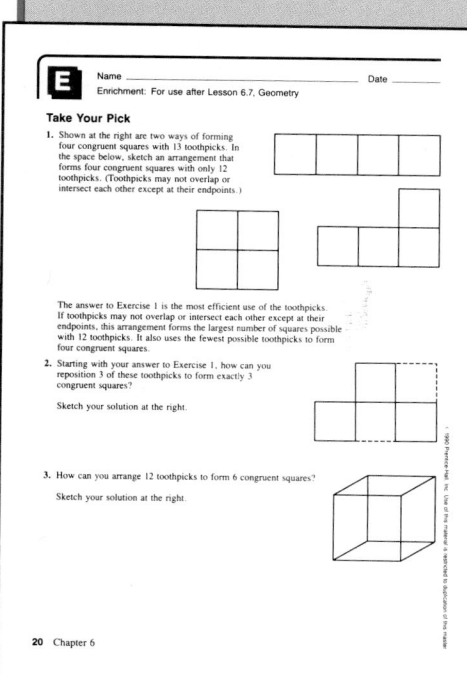

See *Teacher's Resource Book, Follow-up Application*, Chapter 6, p. 21.

INTEGRATING GEOMETRY
Vectors and Scalars

Did you know that a tug of war could be represented by two arrows pointing away from each other, where the length of the arrow represents the amount of strength pulling on each side and the direction of the arrow represents the direction in which the rope is being pulled?

Also, the force of gravity on an apple could be represented by an arrow pointing from the apple towards the earth, with the length of the arrow proportional to the force of gravity. Such arrows have magnitude, given by the length of the arrow, and direction, given by the direction of the arrow, and are called *vector quantities,* or simply *vectors.*

Vectors are used in physics, engineering, and applied mathematics to determine how objects and forces interact with each other. Some of the better known vector quantities are forces such as magnetism, velocity, and acceleration. Although speed has magnitude, it has no direction and is not a vector quantity; velocity, however, represents speed as well as direction. Thus, one's speed is 50 mph, whereas one's velocity is 50 mph in a north-easterly direction.

Quantities that have either magnitude or direction but not both are called *scalar quantities,* or *scalars.* Vectors of the same magnitude and direction that are parallel to each other are congruent. A vector can be moved anywhere in space as long as its length and direction are preserved.

Vectors can be added together to form a new vector, called the *resultant,* by attaching the vectors so that the tip (arrowhead end) of one vector meets the tail (nonarrowhead end) of the other. The sum of two parallel vectors is a vector in the same direction with a magnitude equal to the sum of the magnitudes of the given vectors.

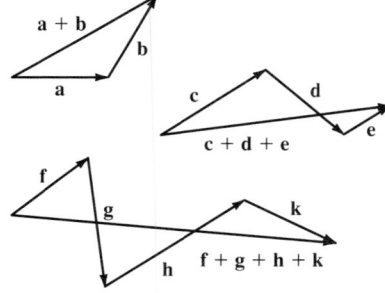

If a vector is positioned at the origin of a coordinate axis, then it can be broken down into components that are parallel to each of the axes by drawing perpendiculars from the tip of the vector to each of the axes.

EXAMPLE 1   Find the components of the given vector.

The components are found by drawing a perpendicular to each axis, then drawing a vector from the origin along each axis to the perpendicular.

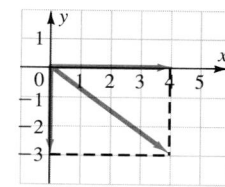

A unit vector has length 1 unit. The unit vector along the x-axis is notated as $\hat{\imath}$, and the unit vector along the y-axis is notated as $\hat{\jmath}$. Thus, a vector on the x-axis that is 6 units long is $6\hat{\imath}$, and a vector on the y-axis that is 7 units long is $7\hat{\jmath}$.

EXAMPLE 2   Determine the vector given by $4\hat{\imath} + 5\hat{\jmath}$.

Starting at the origin, draw a vector 4 units long on the x-axis and another vector 5 units long on the y-axis, then move the second vector 4 units to the right so that the two vectors can be added. Draw the resultant vector.

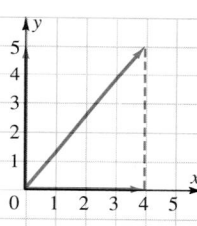

EXERCISES See Solutions Manual.

1. Copy the figure shown and draw the resultant of vectors **a** and **b**. Name the new vector **a** + **b**.

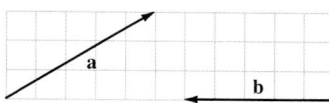

2. Resolve vectors **a** and **b** into horizontal and vertical components, then add the x- and y-components together.
Now find the resultant and compare it to **a** + **b** of Exercise 1.
same resultant as in Exercise 1

3. Use your understanding of vector addition to find the vector **a** − **b**.

4. Copy the figures shown and draw the vector **a** + **b** − **c**.

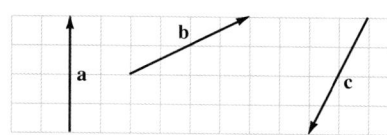

5. A boat sailing due north at 30 mph meets with a head wind of 5 mph. Draw a picture showing the resultant velocity of the boat.

- See *Teacher's Resource Book, Spanish Chapter Summary and Review*, pp. 11–12.
- See Extra Practice, p. 648.

Vocabulary

ASASA Theorem (249)
base angles of a trapezoid (239)
bases of a trapezoid (239)
congruent quadrilaterals (248)
isosceles trapezoid (239)
legs of a trapezoid (239)
median of a trapezoid (241)

Midsegment Theorem (240)
parallelogram (218)
rectangle (233)
rhombus (233)
SASAS Theorem (249)
square (233)
trapezoid (239)

The Parallelogram   A quadrilateral that has any of the following sets of conditions is a parallelogram: both pairs of opposite sides parallel; both pairs of opposite sides congruent; one pair of opposite sides congruent and parallel; both pairs of opposite angles congruent; diagonals that bisect each other.   6.1

In □WAGN

1. $\overline{WA} \parallel$? *NG*   2. ∠NWA ≅ ∠ ? *NGA*   3. ∠A is ? to ∠G. *supp.*   4. ? ≅ *NG* *WA*

Which quadrilaterals are parallelograms? Justify your answers.   6.2

5.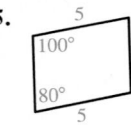
6.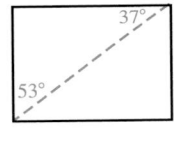
7.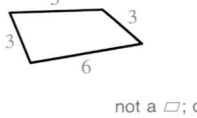

yes; has a pair
of ≅ ∥ sides;

not enough
information

not a □; opp.
sides are ≇

Parallel Lines and Midpoints   Congruent segments will be cut off on any transversal of three or more equidistant parallel lines.   6.3

In this figure, $l_1 \parallel l_2 \parallel l_3$.

8. If $\overline{AE} \cong \overline{ED}$, then $\overline{AB} \cong$? . *BC*

9. If $AE = 6$ cm, $BC = 8$ cm, and $ED = 6$ cm, then $AC = $? cm. *16*

10. If B is the midpoint of $\overline{AC}$, and $AD = 15$ cm, then $AE = $? cm. *7.5*

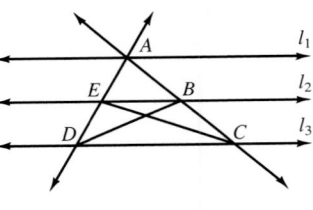

Special Parallelograms   A rectangle is a parallelogram having a right angle; a rhombus is a parallelogram having a pair of consecutive congruent sides; a square may be defined either as an equilateral rectangle or as an equiangular rhombus. The midpoint of the hypotenuse of a right triangle is equidistant from the three vertices of the triangle.   6.4

256   Chapter 6 Quadrilaterals

Use the given information to classify ▱RAMG as a rectangle, rhombus, square, or none of these. Use all terms that apply.

rectangle, square, rhombus

11. $\overline{RG} \perp \overline{RA}$ rectangle

12. $\overline{AM} \cong \overline{MG}$; $\overline{AR} \perp \overline{GR}$

13. $\overline{RA} \cong \overline{AM}$ rhombus

14. $\overline{GA} \perp \overline{RM}$ rhombus

15. WXYZ is a parallelogram. If $\overline{WX} \perp \overline{XY}$, $XZ = (4q - 7)$ cm, and $WT = (q - 1)$ cm, find q and TY.
$q = 2.5$; $TY = 1.5$ cm

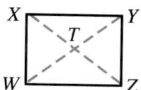

Trapezoids   A trapezoid is a quadrilateral that has exactly one pair of parallel sides. The segment that joins the midpoints of the nonparallel sides of a trapezoid is the median.

6.5

PQRS is an isosceles trapezoid with median $\overline{TU}$ and diagonal $\overline{SQ}$. *W* is the midpoint of $\overline{RS}$.

16. If $m\angle QSR = 48$ and $m\angle PSQ = 61$, find $m\angle P$. 71

17. If $TU = (6x - 5)$ cm, $SR = 11$ cm, and $PQ = (7x + 9)$ cm, find x, TU, and PQ. $x = 6$, $TU = 31$ cm, $PQ = 51$ cm

18. If $UW = (8 - 2y)$ cm and $QS = (19 - 7y)$ cm, find y, UW, and QS.
$y = 1$, $UW = 6$ cm, $QS = 12$ cm

19. **Given:**   Trapezoid *LANK* with median $\overline{EF}$ and diagonal $\overline{AK}$

Prove: $\overline{KH}$ is a median of $\triangle NKG$.
See side column.

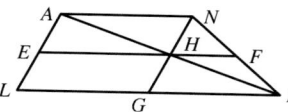

Strategy: Recognize minimal conditions.

6.6

20. Explain why this is a good definition: A trapezoid is a quadrilateral with exactly one pair of parallel sides. It identifies the nearest class, distinguishes trap. from other members of the class, uses only previously defined terms, includes minimal conditions, and is biconditional.

Congruent Quadrilaterals   Two methods for showing quadrilaterals congruent are the SASAS theorem and the ASASA theorem.

6.7

If possible, write and verify a statement of congruence between the figures.

21.

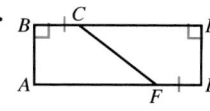

not enough information

22.

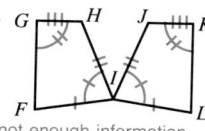

not enough information

23.

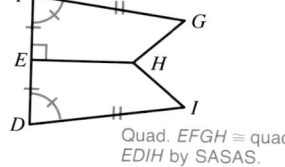

Quad. *EFGH* ≅ quad. *EDIH* by SASAS.

Summary and Review   **257**

19. Plan: Use the def. of median of a trap. and the fact that $\overline{FH}$ contains the midpt. of $\overline{NK}$ and is ∥ to $\overline{LK}$ to show that *H* is the midpt. of $\overline{NG}$.

Proof:

Statements	Reasons
1. Trap. *LANK* with median $\overline{EF}$ and diag. $\overline{AK}$	1. Given
2. *F* is the midpt. of $\overline{NK}$.	2. Def. of median of trap.
3. $\overline{EF} \parallel \overline{LK}$	3. Median of trap. is ∥ to base.
4. $\overline{FH}$ bis. $\overline{NG}$.	4. A line that contains the midpt. of one side of a △ and is ∥ to another side bis. the third side.
5. *H* is the midpt. of $\overline{NG}$.	5. Def. of bis.
6. $\overline{KH}$ is a median of △NKG.	6. Def. of median of △

Conclusion: In trap. *LANK* having median $\overline{EF}$ and diag. $\overline{AK}$, $\overline{KH}$ is a median of △NKG.

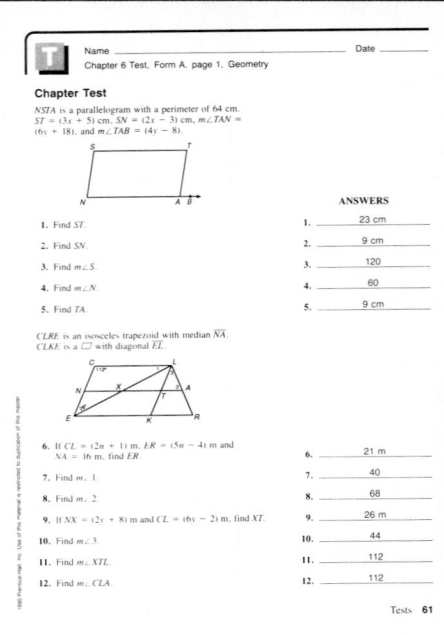

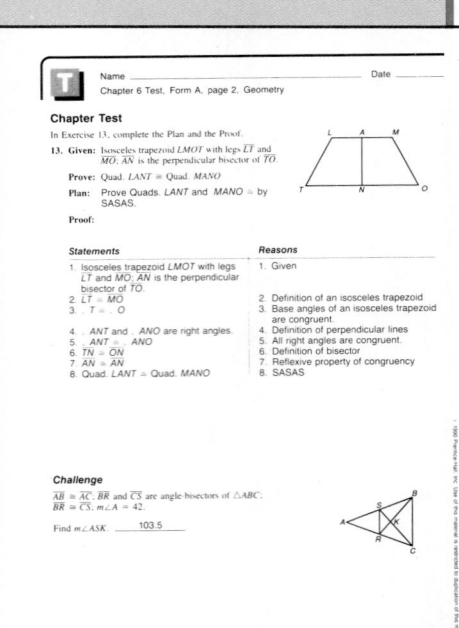

1. *HIJK* is a parallelogram with perimeter 72 cm. The length of $\overline{IJ}$ is twice the length of $\overline{JK}$. Find the measures of all sides and angles. $m\angle I = 65$; $m\angle H = 115$; $m\angle J = 115$; $m\angle JKH = 65$; $IJ = HK = 24$ cm; $IH = JK = 12$ cm

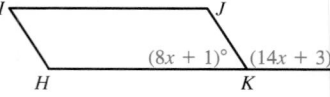

Identify each figure as a parallelogram, rectangle, rhombus, or square. Use all terms that apply.

2. 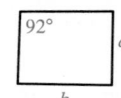 not enough information

3. 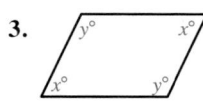 parallelogram

4. 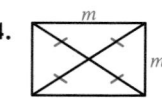 parallelogram; rhombus; square; rectangle

$l_1 \parallel l_2 \parallel l_3$, *ACDF* is an isosceles trapezoid and $\overline{AB} \cong \overline{BC}$.

5. If $DE = 9x - 3$ and $DF = 2(8x + 5)$, find *DE* and *EF*. $DE = EF = 69$

6. If $\overline{DG} \parallel \overline{AC}$, $m\angle 1 = 38$, and $m\angle 6 = 42$, find the measures of the remaining numbered angles. See side column.

7. If $BH = 2y + 4$ and $CD = 3y + 10$, find *HI*. $HI = 8$

8. If $CD = y - 2$, $BE = 4y - 3$, and $AF = 2y + 16$, find *CD*, *BE*, and *AF*. $CD = 2$; $BE = 13$; $AF = 24$

9. **Given:** $\square ROGF$ with diagonal $\overline{RG}$; *L* and *P*, midpoints of $\overline{RF}$ and $\overline{OG}$.
   Prove: $\overline{RE} \cong \overline{GA}$ See page 741.

10. **Given:** Isosceles trapezoid *MNPQ*; *E*, *F*, *G*, and *H* are the respective midpoints of $\overline{MN}$, $\overline{NP}$, $\overline{PQ}$, and $\overline{QM}$.
    Prove: *EFGH* is a rhombus. See page 742.

Challenge See Solutions Manual.

Prove that all plane angles of the same dihedral angle are congruent. (Theorem 5.11)

Given: Dihedral angle $X - \overleftrightarrow{AB} - Y$; plane angles *E* and *H*
Prove: $\angle E \cong \angle H$
(Hint: locate points on the sides of the angles such that $ED = HI$ and $EF = HG$.)

258   Chapter 6 Quadrilaterals

6. $m\angle 2 = 42$; $m\angle 3 = m\angle 7 = m\angle 8 = m\angle 9 = 80$; $m\angle 4 = 100$; $m\angle 5 = 38$

Alternative Assessment   Have students make a drawing of a parallelogram, a rhombus, a rectangle, a square, and an isosceles trapezoid. For each figure they should describe its defining property(ies). Next, have them draw the diagonals in each figure and describe what is true about them.

Select the best choice for each question.

1. In parallelogram *WXYZ*, find the
   B length of the longest side.

   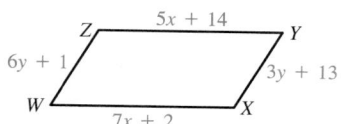

   A. 52   B. 44   C. 37
   D. 25   E. 6

2. Find *x* if $\dfrac{(60 - 10) + (20 + x)}{3} = 58$.
   B

   A. 94   B. 104   C. 124
   D. 174   E. 244

3. The square is made of
   C 4 small congruent
   squares. If the total
   perimeter of the 4 smaller
   squares is 48 cm, find the perimeter
   of the large square.

   A. 16 cm   B. 20 cm   C. 24 cm
   D. 36 cm   E. 48 cm

4. Three of the exterior angles of a
   pentagon have measures of 63, 75,
   and 58. If the other two exterior
   angles are congruent, what is the
   D measure of each?

   A. 16   B. 36   C. 48
   D. 82   E. 96

5. Students decorating a gym for a
   school dance bought 12 rolls of paper
   ribbon at $3.95 a roll and 9 packages
   of crepe paper at $2.99 a package.
   How much did they spend for these
   E supplies?

   A. $75.21   B. $75.31   C. $73.41
   D. $74.21   E. $74.31

6. Solve for *x*: $\dfrac{2x + 3}{5} = \dfrac{3x - 1}{2} + \dfrac{11}{5}$
   D

   A. 2   B. 1   C. $\dfrac{1}{2}$
   D. −1   E. $-\dfrac{3}{2}$

7. In quadrilateral *ABCD*, $\overline{AC} \perp \overline{BD}$,
   $\overline{AC}$ bisects $\overline{BD}$, and $m\angle ABD = 45$.
   A What name can be used for *ABCD*?

   A. kite   B. parallelogram
   C. rectangle   D. rhombus
   E. square

8.
   D

   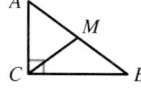

   If $\dfrac{AC}{PQ} = \dfrac{3}{5}$, $\dfrac{BC}{AC} = \dfrac{1}{3}$, and $PQ = 20$,
   find *AB*.

   A. 4   B. 5   C. 6
   D. 8   E. 12

9. If $\overline{AP} \cong \overline{AQ}$, $\overline{BP} \cong \overline{BQ}$,
   E and $AP = 12$,
   what is *BP*?

   A. 24   B. 12
   C. 8   D. 6
   E. It cannot be
      determined from the
      information given.

10. In rt. △ *ABC*, *AC* = 12
    C and *BC* = 16. What is
    the length of the
    median $\overline{CM}$?

    A. 6   B. 8
    C. 10   D. 12
    E. It cannot be determined
       from the information given.

The individual comments provided for
certain problems may help students in
solving them.

3. An alternate method for this problem might be to note that the total
   perimeter of the 4 small squares
   uses the side length of the large
   square 8 times (due to the two inside ones each being used twice).
   A side of the large square thus is
   $\dfrac{48}{8} = 6$, so the perimeter = 24 cm.

7. An abundance of given information
   can be confusing so students need
   experience in sorting out the given
   and determining the possible conclusions which follow.

8. An alternate solution could be to
   assign variable values to the parts
   of the segment as shown.

   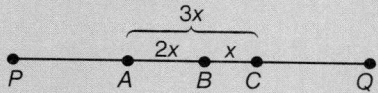

   Then $\dfrac{AC}{PQ} = \dfrac{3}{5}$ becomes $\dfrac{3x}{20} = \dfrac{3}{5}$ and *x* = 4. Then, *AB* = 2*x* = 8.

9. As a contrast to Problem 8, in this
   problem there is not enough given
   imformation and students need the
   experience of coping with this situation.

See *Teacher's Resource Book* for
*Preparing for College Entrance Ex-
ams*.

See *Teacher's Resource Book*, Tests, pp. 65–68.

15. Plan: Since $RT > RS$, $m\angle S > m\angle RTS$. Since $\angle VTR$ is an ext. $\angle$ of $\triangle RST$, $m\angle VTR > m\angle S$. The concl. follows by the trans. prop.

Proof:

Statements	Reasons
1. $\triangle RST$ with $\overrightarrow{ST}$ extended through V, $RT > RS$	1. Given
2. $m\angle S > m\angle RTS$	2. If 2 sides of a $\triangle$ are $\neq$, then the $\angle$s opp. them are $\neq$ and the larger $\angle$ is opp. the longer side.
3. $m\angle VTR > m\angle S$	3. The meas. of an ext. $\angle$ of a $\triangle$ is > than the meas. of either remote int. $\angle$.
4. $m\angle VTR > m\angle RTS$	4. Trans. prop

Concl.: In the given figure, if $RT > RS$, then $m\angle VTR > m\angle RTS$.

16. Plan: Prove $\triangle ABE \cong \triangle DCE$ by ASA. Then $\overline{AE} \cong \overline{DE}$ by CPCTC, so $\overline{BC}$ bis. $\overline{AD}$.

Proof:

Statements	Reasons
1. $\overline{AD}$ bisects $\overline{BC}$; $\angle B \cong \angle C$	1. Given
2. $\overline{BE} \cong \overline{CE}$	2. Def. of bis.
3. $\angle AEB \cong \angle DEC$	3. Vert. $\angle$s are $\cong$.
4. $\triangle ABE \cong \triangle DCE$	4. ASA
5. $\overline{AE} \cong \overline{DE}$	5. CPCTC
6. $\overline{BC}$ bisects $\overline{AD}$.	6. Def. of bis.

Concl.: In the given figure, if $\overline{AD}$ bis. $\overline{BC}$ and $\angle B \cong \angle C$, then $\overline{BC}$ bis. $\overline{AD}$.

Complete.

1. The sum of the measures of the angles of a triangle is _?_. 180 — 3.4

2. If the sum of the measures of two angles is 90°, then they are _?_ of each other. complements — 1.5

3. If two lines are noncoplanar, then they are _?_. skew — 3.1

4. If two planes intersect, then their intersection is a _?_. line — 1.2

5. Write in *if-then* form: Perpendicular lines form right angles. If 2 lines are ⊥, then rt. ∠s are formed. — 2.1

6. If two parallel lines have a transversal, then four angle pairs are formed. Name them. What is the relationship of each pair? alt. int. ∠s, ≅; corr. ∠s, ≅; alt. ext. ∠s, ≅; int. ∠s on same side of transv., supp. — 3.2

7. If two angles of one triangle are congruent to two angles of another triangle, then the third angles are _?_. ≅ — 3.4

8. The sum of the measures of the exterior angles of an n-gon, where $n = 72$ is _?_. 360 — 3.7

9. If $\triangle CAT \cong \triangle DOG$, then $\overline{TA} \cong$ _?_ and $\angle D \cong$ _?_ because _?_. $\overline{GO}$; ∠C; CPCTC — 4.1

10. If two angles of a triangle are congruent, the _?_ are congruent. sides opp. those ∠s — 5.1

11. In $\triangle HOG$, if $HO > HG$ then $m\angle G$ _?_ $m\angle O$, because _?_. >; If 2 sides of a $\triangle$ are ≠, then the ∠s opp. them are ≠ and the larger ∠ is opp. the longer side. — 5.5

12. If a quadrilateral is a parallelogram, then consecutive angles are _?_. supp. — 6.1

13. A regular parallelogram is a _?_. square — 6.4

14. The segment between the midpoints of two sides of a triangle is _?_ to the third side and its length is equal to _?_ the length of the third side. ∥; half — 6.5

Write a two-column proof for each. See side column.

15. **Given:** $\triangle RST$ with $\overrightarrow{ST}$ extended through V; $RT > RS$
   Prove: $m\angle VTR > m\angle RTS$

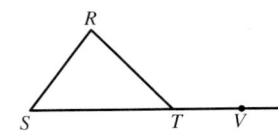

16. **Given:** $\overline{AD}$ bisects $\overline{BC}$, $\angle B \cong \angle C$
   Prove: $\overline{BC}$ bisects $\overline{AD}$.

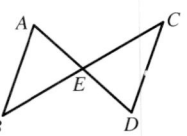

260 Chapter 6 Quadrilaterals

OVERVIEW • Chapter 7

SUMMARY

In Chapter 7, students learn to express ratios in simplest form. Writing and solving proportions are introduced and the geometric mean is defined. The students then apply concepts of proportionality to similar polygons. The AA Similarity Postulate and the SAS and SSS similarity theorems are presented and used for establishing similarity in triangles and proportionality in corresponding parts. Students then prove and apply the Triangle Angle-Bisector Theorem.

CHAPTER OBJECTIVES

- To express a ratio in simplest form
- To identify, write, and solve proportions
- To express a given proportion in an equivalent form
- To find the geometric mean between two numbers
- To identify and apply the properties of similar polygons
- To state and use the AA Similarity Postulate and the SAS and SSS similarity theorems to prove two triangles similar
- To establish and apply theorems relating corresponding parts of similar triangles
- To prove and apply the Triangle Angle-Bisector Theorem
- To approach the problem of solving *inaccessible distances* by using similar triangles and setting up proportions

CHAPTER HIGHLIGHTS

DEVELOPING MATHEMATICAL POWER

Problem Solving

The four problem solving steps are used to apply the concept of triangle similarity to finding inaccessible distances in Lesson 7.6.

Communication

This chapter develops different methods for alternative learning styles and cooperative learning, including looking for patterns that indicate occurrences of the Fibonacci numbers. The *Teacher's Resource Book* offers a Chapter Summary and Review in Spanish. The side column provides topics for students' portfolios such as comparing and contrasting similar and congruent figures.

Reasoning

One thinking critically topic involves drawing conclusions about corresponding medians and altitudes of similar triangles. Formal proofs are used for similar figures and proportional corresponding parts.

Connections

Real-world applications include such topics as recreation, photography, and typing. Algebraic ratios and proportions are used to calculate the lengths of sides of similar figures.

Technology

The Technology feature discusses similarity in computer graphics. The use of a calculator is recommended for solving some proportions.

ASSIGNMENT GUIDE   Meeting Student Needs

STUDENT TEXT

Chapter Content	Basic	Average	Enriched	NCTM STANDARDS*
7.1 Ratio and Proportion	D: 265/1-17 odd, 33, 46, MR	D: 265/1-22, 33-35, 46, MR	D: 265/15-22 odd, 23-35, 46, MR	3, 4, 5, 7
7.2 Properties of Proportions	D: 269/1-16, 32 R: 265/1-17 even	D: 269/1-16, 19-22, 31-36 R: 265/23-28	D: 269/1-22, 25-28, 31-36 R: 265/15-22 even	2, 3, 5, 7, 12
7.3 Similar Polygons	D: 273/1-10, 30-32 R: 269/17, 18	D: 273/1-10, 18-25, 30-32 R: 269/17, 18, 23, 24	D: 273/1-17 odd, 18-22, 26-32 R: 269/23, 24, 29, 30	3, 5, 7, 12
7.4 Similar Triangles	D: 279/1-12, 23-25, AR R: 273/11-15	D: 279/1-16, 23-25, 34, AR R: 273/11-17	D: 279/1-16, 21-25, 34, AR R: 273/23-25	3, 4, 5, 7, 8
7.5 More on Similar Triangles	D: 284/1-11, 30 R: 279/13, 35	D: 284/1-20, 30-32 R: 279/17-19, 35	D: 284/1-20, 27-32 R: 279/17-20, 35	3, 7, 8, 12
7.6 Strategy: Find Inaccessible Distances	D: 289/1-8 R: 284/12-14	D: 289/1-9 R: 284/21-24	D: 289/1-10 R: 284/21-26	1, 3, 4
7.7 Proportional Segments	D: 295/1-15, 30, MR R: 289/9-12	D: 295/5-24, 29, 30, MR R: 289/10-13	D: 295/5-30, MR R: 289/11-14	3, 5, 8

D = Daily   R = Review   MR = Mixed Review   AR = Algebra Review

*For a complete list of NCTM Standards, see p. T7.

STUDENT TEXT

Review/Assessment

Mixed Review 266, 297

Algebra Review 281, 304

Summary and Review 300

College Ent. Exam Rev. 303

Extra Practice 649

Test Yourself 276, 297

Chapter Test 302

Chapter Project 261

Special Features

Technology 266, 276, 281, 286, 297, 298-299

Devel. Math. Power 266, 270, 281, 286

Applications 266, 270, 276, 281, 286, 297

Project 281, 291

RESOURCES

Teacher's Resource Book

Ch. 7: Investigation/Practice/ Enrichment 1-20

Spanish Sum. and Rev. 13-14

Quizzes 69-72

Chapter Tests 73-76

Semester Tests 77-84

Perf. Assessment Proj. Ch. 7

Critical Thinking 7

Reading and Writing in Geom. 7

Technology 9-10

Teaching Aid 7

Transparency 8

Teaching Transparencies 42-48

Computer Test Bank 383-448

PH Graph. Utility

Overhead Manip. Kit

Similarity

What lurks in a shadow?

Developing Mathematical Power

About 3000 years ago, a Greek geometer named Thales astonished Egyptians by using shadows to find the height of the Great Pyramid. First, he measured the length of the pyramid's shadow. Next, he measured a pole and its shadow. Then he used similar triangles to find the height of the pyramid. This method of measurement, sometimes called *shadow reckoning,* is still used today.

Project

Plan and use a procedure that involves shadow reckoning to find the height of your school building. If possible, ask the school administration for the recorded height and compare your result to the actual height.

Thales's method for finding heights

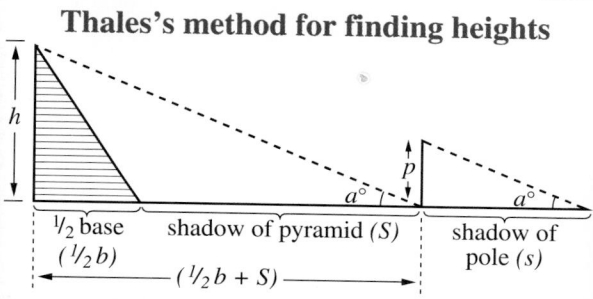

$\frac{1}{2}$ base ($\frac{1}{2}b$)

shadow of pyramid (S)

shadow of pole (s)

($\frac{1}{2}b + S$)

BACKGROUND

Thales measured the length of the Great Pyramid's shadow and added $\frac{1}{2}$ the length of the pyramid's base to that length. He held a pole perpendicular to the ground and measured its shadow. Then he used this proportion to find the height (h) of the pyramid.

$$\frac{h}{\frac{1}{2}b + S} = \frac{p}{s}$$

In the proportion, b is the length of the base of the pyramid, S is the length of the pyramid's shadow, p is the height of the pole, and s is the length of the pole's shadow.

MODELING

Mathematics provides the power to solve real-world problems. This project involves designing a mathematical model for a practical problem. The model is developed by drawing a diagram, measuring, and using mathematical skills.

Cooperative Learning

This project is accomplished through a succession of tasks, each of which is well-suited to a cooperative learning situation. These tasks include:
1. Planning a procedure to find the height of a building.
2. Drawing a diagram.
3. Applying concepts of similar triangles.
4. Performing measurements to obtain data.
5. Writing and solving a proportion.

Alternative Assessment

See *Teacher's Resource Book,* Assessment, Chapter 7. This project and the TRB page may be used as an alternative form of assessment for selected topics in Chapter 7.

261

Vocabulary

Extended	Ratio
proportion	Simplest form
Extremes	Terms of a
Means	proportion
Proportion	

Materials/Manipulatives
Teaching Transparency 42

Technology
Calculators
*Computer Test Bank, pp.
383–390*

LESSON FOCUS

Review

• Review simplifying rational expressions in algebra. Discuss factoring and dividing by a common factor.

$$\frac{15x}{45x^2} = \frac{15x}{15x \cdot 3x^2} = \frac{1}{3x^2}$$

• The Mixed Review, Exercises 36–45, involves the measure of angles and sides under specific conditions.

Alternative Learning Styles

The example in the Investigation provides a real-life application of a proportion. Some students may need to draw a model of the 8 in. wide by 10 in. long photograph to get a visual idea of the actual size of the photo that has to be reduced. They should draw a rectangle $1\frac{3}{5}$ in. wide and 2 in. long next to it. By comparing the lengths, 10 in. and 2 in., and the widths, 8 in. and $1\frac{3}{5}$ ($\frac{8}{5}$) in., they can see that they can get the dimensions of the new photo by dividing *both* dimensions of the original photo by 5.

7.1

Ratio and Proportion

Objectives: To express a ratio in simplest form
To identify, write, and solve proportions

Ratio and *proportion* have important applications in geometry.

Investigation—*Visualizing the Concept*

A layout artist for the local newspaper has an 8 in. wide by 10 in. long photo that must be reduced to fit a slot only 2 in. long.

1. How wide will the reduced photograph be? $1\frac{3}{5}$ in.

2. If the *width* of the newspaper space were 2 in., how long would the picture be? $2\frac{1}{2}$ in.

Two numbers can be compared by writing a *ratio*.

Definition   Given two numbers x and y, $y \neq 0$, a **ratio** is the quotient x divided by y. A ratio can be written as x to y, $x:y$, or $\frac{x}{y}$. All of these ratios are read *x to y*.

To express a ratio in *simplest form*, divide out the common factors. Thus, $\frac{9}{12}$ becomes $\frac{3}{4}$.

EXAMPLE 1   Use $\square ABCD$ to express the ratio
in simplest form.

a. AB to BC **b.** $BC:AD$ **c.** $m\angle A:m\angle D$

a. 1 to 2   **b.** 1:1   **c.** 7:11

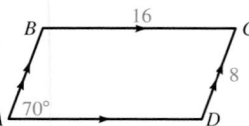

EXAMPLE 2   Write each ratio in simplest form.

a. $\dfrac{3x}{6x^2}$ **b.** $\dfrac{(x-7)}{(2x^2-98)}$

a. $\dfrac{3x}{6x^2} = \dfrac{1}{2x}$ **b.** $\dfrac{(x-7)}{2(x^2-49)} = \dfrac{(x-7)}{2(x+7)(x-7)} = \dfrac{1}{2(x+7)}$

262   Chapter 7 Similarity

Developing Mathematical Power
Cooperative Learning Select teams of students to complete the Enrichment activity, p. 3, in the *Teacher's Resource Book* (see side column, p. 266). It provides a challenge that requires clear and precise thinking. Allow time for them to share proofs.

EXAMPLE 3 The measures of the acute angles of a right triangle are in the ratio 2 to 3. Find their measures.

Since 2 to 3 is a ratio, let $2x$ and $3x$ represent the actual angle measures.

$2x + 3x = 90$ *Acute angles of a right triangle are complementary.*
$5x = 90$ *Distributive property*
$x = 18$ *Division property*

Thus $2x = 2(18) = 36$ and $3x = 3(18) = 54$.

Ratios can be used to compare three or more numbers. The numbers of teeth in these gears are in the ratio $8:12:16$, or $2:3:4$. When you see a ratio in this form, it means that the ratio of the first two numbers is 2 to 3, the ratio of the last two is 3 to 4, and the ratio of the first and third is 2 to 4.

EXAMPLE 4 Find the measures of the angles of a triangle that are in the ratio $3:5:7$.

Since $3:5:7$ is a simplified ratio, let $3x$, $5x$, and $7x$ represent the angle measures.

$3x + 5x + 7x = 180$ *Sum of the angle measures of a triangle is 180.*
$15x = 180$ *Distributive property*
$x = 12$ *Division property*

Then the angle measures are $3(12)$, $5(12)$, and $7(12)$, or 36, 60, and 84.

Definition A **proportion** is the equality of two ratios. In symbols, $\frac{a}{b} = \frac{c}{d}$ ($b \neq 0$, $d \neq 0$), or $a:b = c:d$. It is read *a is to b as c is to d*.

Each number in a proportion is called a *term*.

Terms: 1st 2nd 3rd 4th
$\downarrow \quad \downarrow \qquad \downarrow \quad \downarrow$
$a \; : \; b \; = \; c \; : \; d$

The first and fourth terms are called the *extremes* of a proportion; the second and third terms are called the *means* of the proportion.

means →$b \bowtie d$← extremes
$a \bowtie c$

7.1 Ratio and Proportion   **263**

 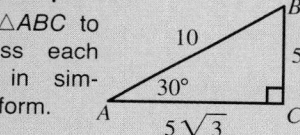

EXAMPLE 5 Find the second term in a proportion whose first, third, and fourth terms are 6, 15, and 10 respectively.

$$\frac{6}{x} = \frac{15}{10}$$ *Let x be the second term.*

$6 \cdot 10 = 15 \cdot x$ *Solve the equation.*

$60 = 15x$

$4 = x$

A calculator can be helpful when solving a proportion.

EXAMPLE 6 Find the fourth term in a proportion whose first, second, and third terms are 2.75, 0.5, and 7.05 respectively.

$$\frac{2.75}{0.5} = \frac{7.05}{x}$$ *Let x be the fourth term.*

$2.75x = 0.5 \cdot 7.05$ *Solve the equation.*

$x = \dfrac{0.5 \cdot 7.05}{2.75}$ *Divide to isolate x. The equation is now calculation-ready.*

$x = 1.2\overline{81}$

When three or more ratios are equal, an *extended proportion* can be written:

$$\frac{a}{b} = \frac{c}{d} = \frac{e}{f}$$

To solve an extended proportion, work with only two ratios at a time.

CLASS EXERCISES

1. Explain why the ratios 3:2 and 2:3 are different. $3:2 = 3 \div 2 = 1.5$; $2:3 = 2 \div 3 = 0.666$

Write each ratio in simplest form.

2. $180:45$ 4:1

3. $10x^2$ to $5x$ 2x:1

4. $12:18:30$ 2:3:5

5. $\dfrac{35}{42}$ 5:6

6. $\dfrac{(3x + 5)(x + 5)}{(3x + 15)}$ (3x + 5):3

7. $\dfrac{(2x^2 - 50)}{(x + 5)}$ 2(x − 5):1

Give each ratio in simplest form.

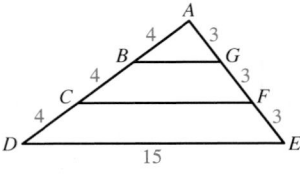

8. $AG:GF$ 1:1

9. $AG:AF$ 1:2

10. $AB:AC$ 1:2

11. $AF:AE$ 2:3

12. $BC:AD$ 1:3

13. $AE:GE$ 3:2

14. $AB:AG:DE$ 4:3:15

15. $AD:AE:DE$ 4:3:5

16. Which ratios are equivalent in Exercises 8–15?
    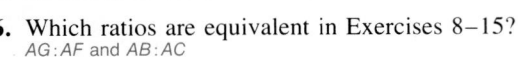
    AG:AF and AB:AC

Identify the means and the extremes. Then find the missing terms. See below.

17. $\dfrac{3}{5} = \dfrac{9}{x}$

18. $7 : x = 3 : 10$

19. $\dfrac{x}{90 - x} = \dfrac{2}{7}$

20. The ratio of the measures of two complementary angles is 7 to 11. What is the measure of each? 35, 55

21. Find the third term of a proportion whose first, second, and fourth terms are 7.6, 0.95, and 17, respectively. 136

PRACTICE EXERCISES 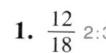 Use technology where appropriate.

Write each ratio in simplest form. Use the figure for Exercises 4–9.

A
1. $\dfrac{12}{18}$ 2:3

2. $15x^3$ to $3x^2$ 5x:1

3. $\dfrac{x^2 - 16}{3x + 12}$ (x − 4):3

4. $AB : BC$ 4:3

5. $AB : AC$ 4:5

6. $BC : BE$ 4:3

7. $DB : AD$ 3:1

8. $DB : BE$ 4:3

9. $AC : EB$ 20:9

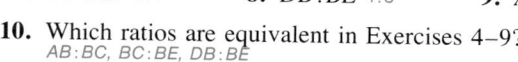

10. Which ratios are equivalent in Exercises 4–9?
AB:BC, BC:BE, DB:BE

Identify the means and the extremes. Then find the missing terms.

11. $4 : 5 = 24 : x$
x = 30

12. $\dfrac{x}{12} = \dfrac{7}{18}$
$x = 4\frac{2}{3}$

13. $\dfrac{x}{180 - x} = \dfrac{3}{7}$
x = 54;
180 − x = 126

14. $\dfrac{4}{x} = \dfrac{x}{9}$
x = 6

Find the angle measures in Exercises 15–17.

B
15. The ratio of the measures of two supplementary angles is 3 to 7. 54, 126

16. The ratio of the measures of two complementary angles is 1 to 5. 15, 75

17. The measures of the angles of a triangle are in the ratio $1 : 2 : 3$. 30:60:90

18. Find the first term in a proportion whose second, third, and fourth terms are 3.9, 6.2, and 1.76, respectively. Round the answer to the nearest hundredth. 13.74

19. The ratio of the measure of a supplement of an angle to the measure of a complement is $4 : 1$. Find the measure of the angle, the complement, and the supplement. 60, 30, 120

20. $k \parallel l$ and the ratio $m\angle 1$ to $m\angle 2$ is 11 to 4; find the measures of all the numbered angles. m∠1 = m∠5 = m∠8 = m∠4 = 132; m∠3 = m∠7 = m∠2 = m∠6 = 48

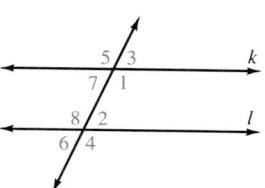

21. $k \parallel l$ and the ratio $m\angle 1$ to $m\angle 7$ is $8 : 1$; find the measures of all the numbered angles. m∠1 = m∠5 = m∠8 = m∠4 = 160; m∠3 = m∠7 = m∠2 = m∠6 = 20

22. $k \parallel l$ and the ratio $m\angle 3$ to $m\angle 4$ is 2 to 3; find the measures of all the numbered angles. m∠1 = m∠5 = m∠8 = m∠4 = 108; m∠3 = m∠7 = m∠2 = m∠6 = 72

7.1 Ratio and Proportion **265**

17. 5, 9 means;
3, x extremes;
x = 15

18. x, 3 means;
7, 10 extremes;
$x = \dfrac{70}{3}$

19. 90−x, 2 means;
x, 7 extremes;
x = 20

265

Solve each proportion.

23. $\sqrt{3}:x = 9:\sqrt{27}$ x = 1
24. $12:\sqrt{8} = \sqrt{18}:y$ y = 1
25. $\dfrac{9}{12} = \dfrac{x}{20} = \dfrac{21}{y}$ x = 15; y = 28
26. $\dfrac{x}{18} = \dfrac{35}{45} = \dfrac{63}{y}$ x = 14; y = 81
27. $\sqrt{9}:3 = x:\sqrt{3}$ x = √3
28. $\sqrt{5}:x = \sqrt{2}:\sqrt{10}$ x = 5

C 29. The ratio of the measure of an interior angle of a regular polygon to the measure of an exterior angle is 2:1. Identify the polygon. hexagon

30. The ratio of the sum of the exterior angles of a regular polygon to the sum of the interior angles is 1:3. Identify the polygon. octagon

31. The perimeter of a rectangle is 50 mm. The ratio of its length to its width is 3:2. Find the length and width. length, 15 mm; width, 10 mm

32. Find x, if $(x - 5):4 = 9:x$. x = 9 or x = −4

Applications

33. **Recreation** The ratio of counselors to five-year-olds at a certain camp must be 2:7. How many counselors are needed for 28 children? 8 counselors

34. **Construction** The ratio of a bunkbed's weight to the weight it can bear is 3:13. How many 70-lb children can a 60-lb bed hold? 3 children

35. **Technology** Use Logo to draw a pair of angles with ratio 7:15.
See Solutions Manual.

Mixed Review

True or false? If false, tell why.

36. If two angles are adjacent, then they are congruent. false; unless they are right angles

37. $\triangle ABC \cong \triangle DEF$, $\overline{AC} \cong \overline{FD}$ true

38. A biconditional combines a conditional and its inverse into one statement. false; conditional and its converse

39. If $a = b$ and $c < d$, then $a - c > b - d$. true

Given: ABCD is a rectangle, and the diagonals intersect at E.

40. $\overline{AB} \perp$ _?_ $\overline{BC}$ or $\overline{AD}$
41. $\overline{BD} \cong$ _?_ $\overline{AC}$
42. $\overline{AE} \cong$ _?_ $\overline{EC}$, $\overline{EB}$, or $\overline{ED}$
43. $\overline{BC} \parallel$ _?_ $\overline{AD}$
44. $\angle BAD \cong$ _?_ $\angle BCD$, $\angle CDA$, or $\angle ABC$
45. $\angle CBD \cong$ _?_ $\angle ADB$, $\angle BCA$, or $\angle DAC$

Developing Mathematical Power

46. **Thinking Critically** Rectangular lot A measures 25 ft by 75 ft. The owners purchase the adjacent lot B. They plan to fence in the double lot, and decide that the ratio of the perimeter of the double lot to the single is 2:1. Explain their error and give the actual ratio.

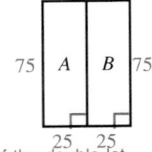

The ratio is 250:200, or 5:4. The common boundary is not included in the perimeter of the double lot.

Properties of Proportions

Objectives: To express a given proportion in an equivalent form
To find the geometric mean between two numbers

Proportions are useful for interpreting and solving a variety of problems in geometry. Such proportions will usually have segment lengths for terms.

Investigation—*Thinking Critically*

Blank cassettes were on sale for $8.75 for 3 cassettes. Alan and Barbara needed to find the cost of 8 cassettes. Alan decided that he should compare cassettes to cassettes and cost to cost, so he wrote this proportion:

$$\frac{3 \text{ cassettes}}{8 \text{ cassettes}} = \frac{\text{cost of 3 cassettes}}{\text{cost of 8 cassettes}} \qquad \frac{3}{8} = \frac{\$8.75}{x}$$

Barbara decided that she should compare each number of cassettes to its cost:

$$\frac{3 \text{ cassettes}}{\text{cost of 3 cassettes}} = \frac{8 \text{ cassettes}}{\text{cost of 8 cassettes}} \qquad \frac{3}{\$8.75} = \frac{8}{x}$$

Who wrote the correct proportion? Explain.
Both are correct; two forms of the same expression.

The *properties of a proportion* show how to rewrite a given proportion in an equivalent form. They can be proven using the rules of algebra.

1. $\frac{a}{b} = \frac{c}{d}$ ($b \neq 0$, $d \neq 0$) is equivalent to $ad = bc$.
   This *means-extremes property* justifies the use of cross products.

2. $\frac{a}{b} = \frac{c}{d}$ is equivalent to $\frac{a}{c} = \frac{b}{d}$ and $\frac{a}{b} = \frac{c}{d}$ is equivalent to $\frac{d}{b} = \frac{c}{a}$.
   Since $ad = bc$, the means or the extremes can be interchanged.

3. $\frac{a}{b} = \frac{c}{d}$ is equivalent to $\frac{b}{a} = \frac{d}{c}$. Thus the reciprocals are equal.

4. $\frac{a}{b} = \frac{c}{d}$ is equivalent to $\frac{a+b}{b} = \frac{c+d}{d}$.

5. If $\frac{a}{b} = \frac{c}{d} = \frac{e}{f} = \cdots$, then $\frac{a+c+e+\cdots}{b+d+f+\cdots} = \frac{a}{b}$.

The last property states that the sum of the numerators and denominators produces an equivalent ratio. Justify this statement.

Since $\frac{a}{b} = \frac{c}{d}, \frac{xa}{xb} = \frac{c}{d}$. Thus, $\frac{a+c}{b+d} = \frac{a+xa}{b+xb} = \frac{a(1+x)}{b(1+x)} = \frac{a}{b}$.

Developing Mathematical Power

Keeping a Portfolio Have students enter the properties of a proportion in their math journals. They should provide numerical examples and a written explanation of what each equivalent proportion represents (see Teaching Suggestions, p. 268) so that the properties become more meaningful.

LESSON PLAN

Vocabulary
Geometric mean
Golden ratio
Means-extremes property
Proportion properties
Radical
Radicand

Materials/Manipulatives
Teaching Transparency 43

Technology
Calculator
Computer Test Bank, pp. 390–400

LESSON FOCUS

Review
Have the students identify the means and extremes and then find the missing terms.

1. $\frac{x}{9} = \frac{21}{27}$ 2. $\frac{5}{8} = \frac{x}{40}$

3. $\frac{2}{3} = \frac{5}{x}$ 4. $\frac{4}{x} = \frac{28}{49}$

1. means: 9, 21; extremes: x, 27; $x =$ 7 2. means: 8, x; extremes: 5, 40; $x =$ 25 3. means: 3, 5; extremes: 2, x; $x =$ $7\frac{1}{2}$ 4. means: x, 28; extremes: 4, 49; $x = 7$

Alternative Learning Styles
- Modeling an abstract concept with a real-world situation can aid student understanding. In the Investigation, students can see that as long as each ratio compares the same things in the same order, the proportions are equivalent.
- The linguistic learner can benefit from verbalizing each equivalent form of the given proportion on Teaching Transparency 43.

Multicultural Opportunity
See Developing Mathematical Power, p. 268.

267

- Students should call the first property the means-extremes property. Help them describe the other properties in words, such as the following. The means of a proportion may be interchanged. Ratios of reciprocals are equal. Adding denominators to numerators produces equivalent ratios.
- To simplify radicals, it is helpful to be familiar with the perfect squares less than 300.

CHALKBOARD EXAMPLES

- **For Example 1**

Complete each statement, given $\frac{AB}{TA} = \frac{OH}{TO}$. Justify.

a. $\frac{TA}{AB} = \frac{?}{?}$

b. $? = AB \cdot TO$

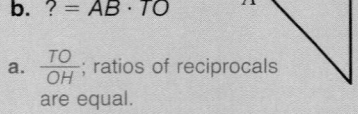

a. $\frac{TO}{OH}$; ratios of reciprocals are equal.

b. $TA \cdot OH$; means-extremes property

- **For Example 2**

Simplify the radicals.

a. $\sqrt{20}$ **b.** $\sqrt{48}$
c. $\sqrt{100}$ **d.** $\sqrt{98}$

a. $2\sqrt{5}$ **b.** $4\sqrt{3}$ **c.** 10 **d.** $7\sqrt{2}$

- **For Example 3**

Find the geometric mean.

a. 2 and 32   **b.** 3 and 7
c. 9 and 6   **d.** 6 and 15

a. 8 **b.** $\sqrt{21}$ **c.** $3\sqrt{6}$ **d.** $3\sqrt{10}$

EXAMPLE 1 Complete each statement, given $\frac{EC}{AE} = \frac{DB}{AD}$. Justify.

a. $\frac{EC}{DB} = \frac{?}{?}$ **b.** $AE \cdot DB = ?$ **c.** $\frac{AC}{AE} = \frac{?}{AD}$

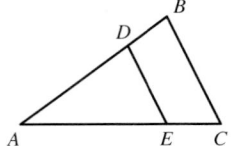

a. $\frac{AE}{AD}$; the means can be interchanged.

b. $EC \cdot AD$; means-extremes property

c. AB: the denominator can be added to each numerator.

The following definition is useful in statistics as well as in geometry.

Definition x is the **geometric mean** between positive numbers p and q if and only if $\frac{p}{x} = \frac{x}{q}$, where $x > 0$.

Applying the means-extremes property to the proportion in the definition, $x^2 = pq$, or $x = \sqrt{pq}$. In other words, the *geometric mean between two positive numbers is the principal square root of their product.*

Recall from algebra that $\sqrt{\ }$ is the symbol for a positive square root. The number under the radical symbol is called the *radicand*. You can simplify a radical, for example $\sqrt{50}$, by finding the largest perfect-square factor of the radicand 50, and then applying the *product property of square roots*.

$$\sqrt{50} = \sqrt{25 \cdot 2} = \sqrt{25} \cdot \sqrt{2} = 5\sqrt{2}$$

EXAMPLE 2 Simplify each radical.

a. $\sqrt{72}$ **b.** $\sqrt{49}$ **c.** $\sqrt{24}$ **d.** $\sqrt{125}$

a. $\sqrt{72} = \sqrt{36 \cdot 2} = \sqrt{36} \cdot \sqrt{2} = 6\sqrt{2}$ **b.** $\sqrt{49} = 7$

c. $\sqrt{24} = \sqrt{4 \cdot 6} = \sqrt{4} \cdot \sqrt{6} = 2\sqrt{6}$ **d.** $\sqrt{125} = \sqrt{25} \cdot \sqrt{5} = 5\sqrt{5}$

EXAMPLE 3 Find the geometric mean between each pair of numbers.

a. 4 and 9   **b.** 5 and 11   **c.** 4 and 10   **d.** 6 and 10

a. 6   **b.** $\sqrt{55}$ **c.** $2\sqrt{10}$ **d.** $2\sqrt{15}$

CLASS EXERCISES

Complete.

1. If $\frac{8}{5} = \frac{9}{x}$, then $8x = \underline{\ ?\ }$. 45

2. If $\frac{11}{x} = \frac{24}{25}$, then $\frac{x}{11} = \frac{?}{?}$. $\frac{25}{24}$

3. If $\frac{12}{x} = \frac{3}{10}$, then $\frac{12}{3} = \frac{?}{?}$. $\frac{x}{10}$

4. If $\frac{7-x}{x} = \frac{12}{20}$, then $\frac{7}{x} = \frac{?}{?}$. $\frac{32}{20}$, or $\frac{8}{5}$

Developing Mathematical Power

Cooperative Learning   Working in groups, students can complete the Reading and Writing in Geometry, p. 7, in the *Teacher's Resource Book.* Each group should prepare a report on a specific occurrence of the Fibonacci numbers and present it to the class. They should provide a visual representation of it for a bulletin board display.

Complete each statement, given $\dfrac{DA}{AR} = \dfrac{LY}{YR}$.

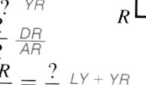

5. $\dfrac{AR}{DA} = \dfrac{?}{?}$ $\tfrac{YR}{LY}$

6. $\dfrac{DA}{LY} = \dfrac{?}{?}$ $\tfrac{AR}{YR}$

7. $\underline{\ ?\ } = AR \cdot LY$ $DA \cdot YR$

8. $\dfrac{?}{?} = \dfrac{LR}{YR}$ $\tfrac{DR}{AR}$

9. $\dfrac{DA}{AR} = \dfrac{DA + LY}{?}$ $AR + YR$

10. $\dfrac{DA + AR}{AR} = \dfrac{?}{?}$ $\tfrac{LY + YR}{YR}$

11. $DA = 6$, $AR = 10$, and $LY = 10$; find YR. $\tfrac{50}{3}$

12. $DA = 18$, $LY = 12$, and $RY = 10$; find DR. 33

Simplify.

13. $\sqrt{121}$ 11

14. $\sqrt{32}$ $4\sqrt{2}$

15. $\sqrt{27}$ $3\sqrt{3}$

Find the geometric mean between each pair.

16. 3 and 15
$3\sqrt{5}$

17. 10 and 12
$2\sqrt{30}$

18. 7 and 10
$\sqrt{70}$

PRACTICE EXERCISES Use technology where appropriate.

A **For Exercises 1–4, use the figure and the proportion $\dfrac{AB}{BC} = \dfrac{DE}{EF}$.**

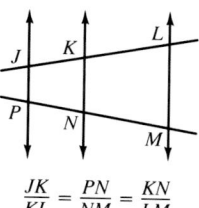

1. $AB \cdot EF = \underline{\ ?\ }$
$BC \cdot DE$

2. $\dfrac{AB}{DE} = \dfrac{?}{?}$ $\tfrac{BC}{EF}$

3. $\dfrac{EF}{BC} = \dfrac{?}{?}$ $\tfrac{DE}{AB}$

4. $\dfrac{DE}{EF} = \dfrac{?}{BC + EF}$ $AB + DE$

Simplify.

5. $\sqrt{54}$ $3\sqrt{6}$

6. $\sqrt{64}$ 8

7. $\sqrt{72}$ $6\sqrt{2}$

8. $\sqrt{76}$ $2\sqrt{19}$

Find the geometric mean between the pair of numbers.

9. 10 and 38 $2\sqrt{95}$ **10.** 9 and 36 18 **11.** 5 and 8 $2\sqrt{10}$ **12.** 8 and 16 $8\sqrt{2}$

Find the missing lengths.

	JK	KL	JL	PN	NM	PM	KN	LM
13.	3	4	$\tfrac{?}{7}$	6	$\tfrac{?}{8}$	$\tfrac{?}{14}$	9	$\tfrac{?}{12}$
14.	2	$\tfrac{?}{3}$	5	6	$\tfrac{?}{9}$	15	$\tfrac{?}{8}$	12
15.	$\tfrac{?}{4}$	$\tfrac{?}{18}$	22	$\tfrac{?}{6}$	$\tfrac{?}{27}$	33	2	9
16.	$\tfrac{?}{9}$	$\tfrac{?}{5}$	14	18	$\tfrac{?}{10}$	28	4.5	$\tfrac{?}{2.5}$

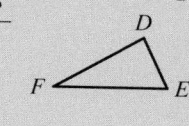

$\dfrac{JK}{KL} = \dfrac{PN}{NM} = \dfrac{KN}{LM}$

B **17.** If $JK = 8$, $NM = 12$, and $KL = PN$, find KL. $4\sqrt{6}$

18. If $KL = KN$, $JK = 8$, and $LM = 18$, find KN. 12

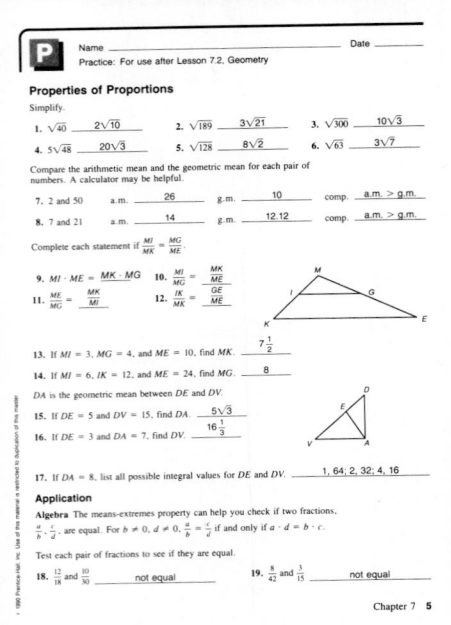

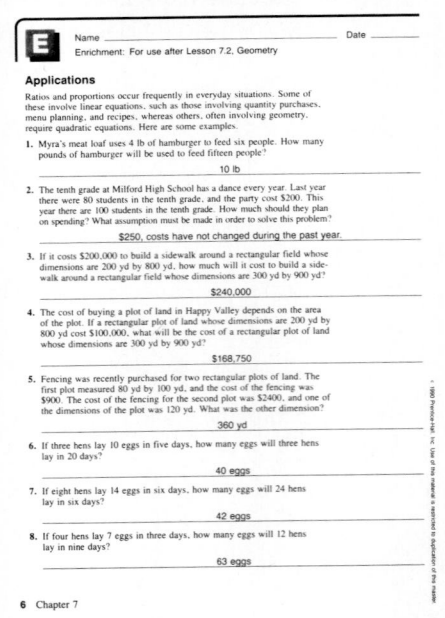

AX is the geometric mean between BX and CX.

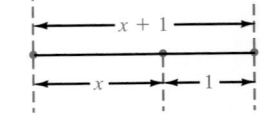

19. If $BX = 2$ and $CX = 8$, $AX =$ _?_. 4

20. If $BX = 3$ and $CX = 8$, $AX =$ _?_. $2\sqrt{6}$

21. If $BX = 2$ and $AX = \sqrt{2}$, $CX =$ _?_. 1

22. If $CX = 9$ and $AX = 9$, $BX =$ _?_. 9

23. $AX = 6$; find all possible integral values for BX and CX.
6, 6; 4, 9; 3, 12; 2, 18; 1, 36

24. $AX = 3\sqrt{2}$; find all possible integral values for BX and CX. 1, 18; 2, 9; 3, 6

Use algebraic properties to prove. See side column pages 269–270.

C

25. If $\dfrac{a}{b} = \dfrac{c}{d}$, then $ad = bc$.

26. If $\dfrac{a}{b} = \dfrac{c}{d}$, then $\dfrac{a}{c} = \dfrac{b}{d}$.

27. If $\dfrac{a}{b} = \dfrac{c}{d}$, then $\dfrac{b}{a} = \dfrac{d}{c}$.

28. If $\dfrac{a}{b} = \dfrac{c}{d}$, then $\dfrac{a+b}{b} = \dfrac{c+d}{d}$.

Find the geometric mean.

29. $\dfrac{4}{(x+1)} = \dfrac{(x+1)}{3x-2}$ 10 or 2

30. $\dfrac{3}{n} = \dfrac{n}{n^2 - n - 3}$ 3

Applications

31. **Algebra** The means-extremes property helps you compare fractions.
$\dfrac{a}{b} < \dfrac{c}{d}$ if and only if $ad < bc$, or $\dfrac{a}{b} > \dfrac{c}{d}$ if and only if $ad > bc$,
$b \neq 0$, $d \neq 0$. Compare $\dfrac{27}{32}$ to $\dfrac{32}{43}$. $\dfrac{27}{32} > \dfrac{32}{43}$

32. **Typing** The accuracy at 30 words per minute on a word processing test is 24 right to 6 wrong. If 15 students are typing, predict the number of mistakes in 3 minutes. 270

Developing Mathematical Power

Extension The geometric mean of three positive numbers is given by the cube root of their product. Find the geometric mean in simplest form.

33. 40, 54, and 5 $6\sqrt[3]{50}$

34. 21, 24, and 3 $6\sqrt[3]{7}$

35. 15, 35, and 50 $5\sqrt[3]{210}$

36. **Investigation** Consider a line segment of a length $x + 1$ such that the ratio of the whole line segment $x + 1$ to the longer segment x is the same as the ratio of the longer segment, x, to the shorter segment, 1. Thus, $\dfrac{(x+1)}{x} = \dfrac{x}{1}$. The resulting quadratic equation is $x^2 - x - 1 = 0$. A positive root of this equation is $\dfrac{\sqrt{5}+1}{2}$, or 1.61803 . . . This irrational number, or its reciprocal $\dfrac{\sqrt{5}-1}{2}$, is known as the Golden Ratio, ϕ *phi*. Read about its use in art or architecture.

27.
$\dfrac{a}{b} = \dfrac{c}{d}$
$\dfrac{bd}{ac} \cdot \dfrac{a}{b} = \dfrac{c}{d} \cdot \dfrac{bd}{ac}$ Mult. prop.
$\dfrac{d}{c} = \dfrac{b}{a}$ Div. prop.
$\dfrac{b}{a} = \dfrac{d}{c}$ Symm. prop.

28.
$\dfrac{a}{b} = \dfrac{c}{d}$
$\dfrac{a}{b} + \dfrac{b}{b} = \dfrac{c}{d} + \dfrac{d}{d}$ Add. prop.
$\dfrac{a+b}{b} = \dfrac{c+d}{d}$ Simplify.

7.3 Similar Polygons

Objective: To identify and apply the properties of similar polygons

Congruent polygons have the same shape and size. *Similar polygons* have the same shape but not necessarily the same size.

Investigation—*Visualizing the Concept*

Ciro made a review transparency for his chemistry class. He worked through the review sheet using the overhead projector. When he projected the review sheet on the wall, the image was five times larger.

1. How do the review sheet and the projected image compare? They are the same shape in different sizes.
2. What can you assume about the projected image? Each length on the image is 5 times longer than the corr. length on the review sheet.

Two polygons are **similar**, ~, if their corresponding angles are congruent and the lengths of their corresponding sides are in proportion.

Trapezoid *ABCD* ~ trapezoid *EFGH*

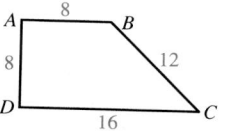

Corresponding angles:
$\angle A \cong \angle E$, $\angle B \cong \angle F$
$\angle C \cong \angle G$, $\angle D \cong \angle H$

Corresponding sides:
$$\frac{AB}{EF} = \frac{BC}{FG} = \frac{CD}{GH} = \frac{DA}{HE}$$

Each ratio in the proportion is $\frac{4}{3}$. This constant ratio is called the **scale factor** of the similarity.

Since similarity is a correspondence between figures, the vertices in a similarity statement must be listed in corresponding order. Thus for the trapezoids above, $BCDA \sim FGHE$, or an equivalent statement, is true, but it is not true that $ABCD \sim FGHE$.

7.3 Similar Polygons **271**

Developing Mathematical Power

Keeping a Portfolio Have students write a short paragraph in which they compare and contrast similarity and congruence both in linguistic usage and mathematical usage. They should discuss whether polygons can be both similar and congruent.

271

TEACHING SUGGESTIONS

- Point out that the scale factor of a similarity is dependent upon the order of the similarity. If $\triangle ABC \sim \triangle DEF$ with scale factor 3:4, then $\triangle DEF \sim \triangle ABC$ with scale factor 4:3.
- Make sure that students understand the meaning of a scale such as 1 in. = 1.5 ft, as in Practice Exercise 30.

CHALKBOARD EXAMPLES

- **For Example 1**

Are the polygons similar? If no, tell why not. If yes, identify the corresponding angles, and give the similarity statement and the scale factor.

a.

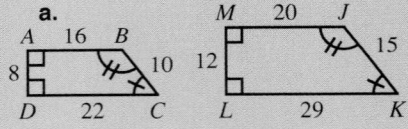

b.

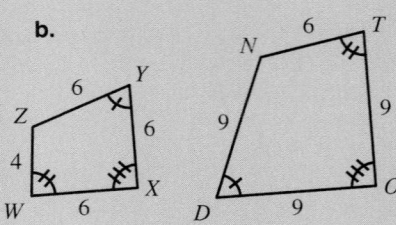

c.

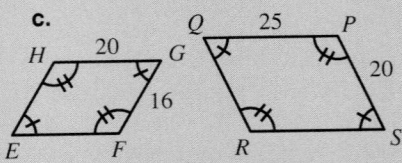

a. No; the sides are not in proportion.
b. yes; $\angle Y \cong \angle D$, $\angle X \cong \angle O$, $\angle W \cong \angle T$, $\angle Z \cong \angle N$; YXWZ ~ DOTN; 2:3
c. yes; $\angle E \cong \angle S$, $\angle G \cong \angle Q$ (or $\angle E \cong \angle Q$, $\angle G \cong \angle S$), $\angle F \cong \angle R$, $\angle H \cong \angle P$ (or $\angle F \cong \angle P$, $\angle H \cong \angle R$); $\square EFGH \sim \square SRQP$ (other possibilities exist); 4:5

EXAMPLE 1 Are the polygons similar? If not, tell why not. If yes, give the corresponding angles, the scale factor, and a similarity statement.

a.

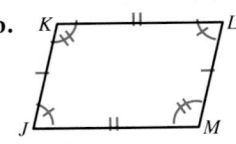

b.

c.

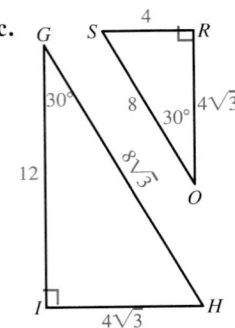

a. Yes; $\angle C \cong \angle F$, $\angle B \cong \angle E$, $\angle A \cong \angle D$; 2:3; $\triangle ACB \sim \triangle DFE$

b. No; the sides are not in proportion.

c. Yes; $\angle G \cong \angle O$, $\angle H \cong \angle S$, $\angle I \cong \angle R$; $\sqrt{3}:1$; $\triangle GHI \sim \triangle OSR$

EXAMPLE 2 These pentagons are similar.

a. Name the corresponding congruent angles.

b. Write a proportion for the lengths of the corresponding sides.

c. Give the scale factor, first to second.

d. $m\angle N = \underline{\ ?\ }$ e. $JX = \underline{\ ?\ }$

f. Write a similarity statement.

g. Find the perimeter of each figure.

h. How does the ratio of the perimeters compare with the scale factor?

a. $\angle G \cong \angle K$, $\angle J \cong \angle N$, $\angle X \cong \angle Y$, $\angle H \cong \angle L$, $\angle I \cong \angle M$

b. $\dfrac{GJ}{KN} = \dfrac{JX}{NY} = \dfrac{XH}{YL} = \dfrac{HI}{LM} = \dfrac{IG}{MK}$

c. $\dfrac{2}{3}$

d. z

e. $\dfrac{JX}{12} = \dfrac{2}{3}$; $3(JX) = 24$; $JX = 8$

f. $GJXHI \sim KNYLM$

g. 38 and 57

h. $\dfrac{38}{57} = \dfrac{2}{3}$; they are equal.

Part *h* of Example 2 suggests that if two polygons are similar, then the ratio of their perimeters is the same as the scale factor of the similarity for the sides. This can be proven.

272 Chapter 7 Similarity

CLASS EXERCISES

1. If two similar polygons have a scale factor of 1, what can you conclude?
Ratio of lengths of sides is 1:1, so corr. sides are ≅ and polygons are ≅.

These pairs of polygons are similar. Give a similarity statement, the scale factor, and the missing lengths. Pent. *ABCDE* ~ Pent. *KLMNO*; scale factor = $\frac{3}{5}$; *AB* = 21; *AE* = 9; *ED* = 18; *NM* = 15

2.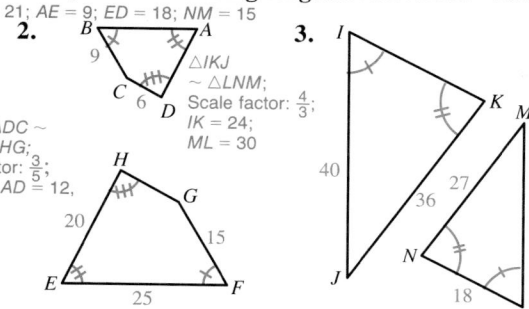
△*IKJ* ~ △*LNM*;
Scale factor: $\frac{4}{3}$;
IK = 24;
ML = 30

Quad. *BADC* ~
Quad. *FEHG*;
Scale factor: $\frac{3}{5}$;
BA = 15, *AD* = 12,
GH = 10

3.

4.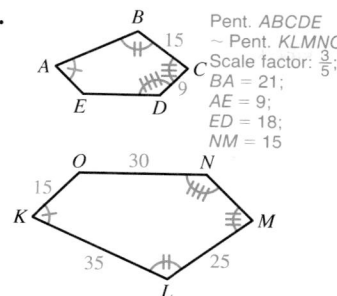
Pent. *ABCDE* ~ Pent. *KLMNO*;
Scale factor: $\frac{3}{5}$;
BA = 21;
AE = 9;
ED = 18;
NM = 15

5. △*SBM* ~ △*TCN*, *SB* = 7, *TC* = 9, and the perimeter of △*SBM* = 63; find the perimeter of △*TCN*. 81

6. The perimeters of similar triangles *JRE* and *KQD* are 28 and 42 respectively, and *DK* = 18; find *EJ*. 12

7. Two regular pentagons have perimeters of 68 and 44 respectively. Are they similar? If so, what is the scale factor of the smaller to the larger? yes; 11:17

True or false? If false, give a counterexample. Counterexamples may vary. See below.

8. All squares are similar. true **9.** All rectangles are similar. false

10. If two triangles are isosceles, then they are similar. false

11. If two polygons are regular pentagons, then they are similar. true

12. If two polygons are similar, then they are congruent. false

13. If two polygons are congruent, then they are similar. true

PRACTICE EXERCISES   ⌖ Use technology where appropriate.

A **1. Thinking Critically** You are given an assignment to make a drawing of this garden. You are given the dimensions, 45 ft by 48 ft, and a choice of scales: 1 in. = 2 ft, 1 in. = 3 ft, and 1 in. = 4 ft. Which makes the calculation simplest? Explain.
1 in. = 3 ft is best, since 45 and 48 are both multiples of 3.

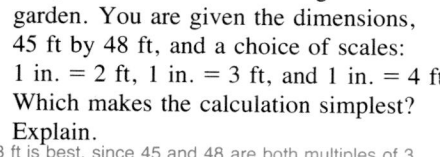

7.3 Similar Polygons **273**

• **For Example 2**
The triangles are similar.

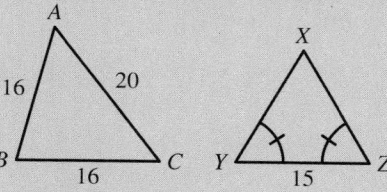

a. Write a similarity statement.
b. Give the scale factor.
c. Find the perimeter of each triangle.
d. How does the ratio of the perimeters compare with the scale factor?

a. △*ABC* ~ △*YXZ* (or △*ABC* ~ △*ZXY*)
b. $\frac{4}{3}$ **c.** 52 and 39
d. $\frac{52}{39} = \frac{4}{3}$; they are equal.

Common Error
• Students may confuse which sides of similar figures correspond. For triangles, first have students identify one pair of corresponding congruent angles, mark them, and then mark the sides opposite those angles. Have them do the same with a second pair of corresponding congruent angles, using double tick marks.
• See *Teacher's Resource Book* for additional remediation.

LESSON FOLLOW-UP

Discussion
Have each student make a scale drawing of the classroom or of a room in his or her home.

Assignment Guide
See p. 260B for assignments.

9.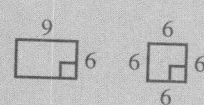

10.

12.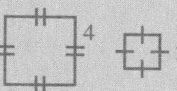

273

Are the polygons similar? If not, tell why not. If yes, give a similarity statement and the scale factor.

2.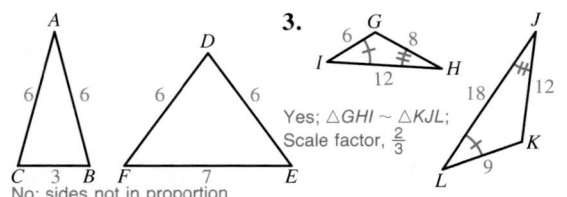

No; sides not in proportion

3. Yes; $\triangle GHI \sim \triangle KJL$; Scale factor, $\frac{2}{3}$

4.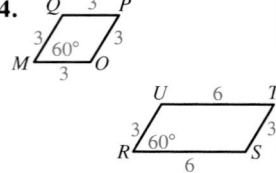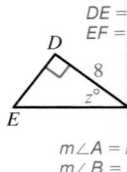

No; sides not in proportion.

The pair of polygons is similar. Find the missing angle measures and side lengths, where possible.

5. Parallelograms *XYZW* and *VSTU*

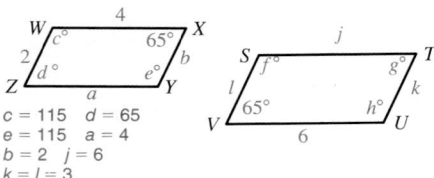

$c = 115 \quad d = 65$
$e = 115 \quad a = 4$
$b = 2 \quad j = 6$
$k = l = 3$
$f = h = 115$
$g = 65$

6. Right triangles *BAC* and *EDF*

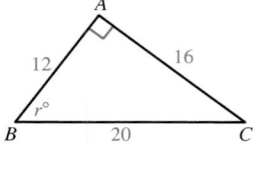

$m\angle C =$
$m\angle E$
$DE =$
$EF =$

7. Quadrilaterals *ABCD* and *HIJK*

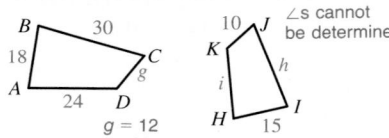

∠s cannot be determined.

$g = 12$
$i = 20$
$h = 25$

8. Trapezoids *ABCD* and *EFGH*

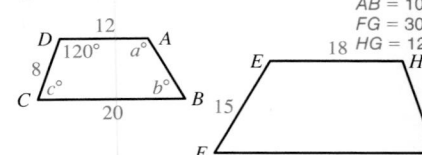

$m\angle A =$
$m\angle B =$
$m\angle C =$
$m\angle H =$
$AB = 10$
$FG = 30$
$HG = 12$

9. If $\triangle MOT \sim \triangle GEN$, $MT = 20$, $GN = 8$, and the perimeter of $\triangle GEN = 18$, then the perimeter of $\triangle MOT = \underline{\;?\;}$. 45

10. If the perimeters of similar triangles *JOA* and *RIT* are 24 and 108, respectively, and $IT = 36$, then $OA = \underline{\;?\;}$. 8

True or false? If false, give a counterexample.

11. If two triangles are equilateral, then they are similar. true

12. If two triangles are equiangular, then they are similar. true

13. If two triangles are similar and one is scalene, then the other is scalene. true

14. All right triangles are similar. false

15. If two quadrilaterals are rhombuses, then they are similar. false

16. If two quadrilaterals are equiangular, then they are similar. false

17. If two pentagons are equiangular, then they are similar.
False; corr. sides may not be in proportion.

B

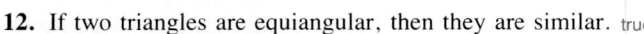
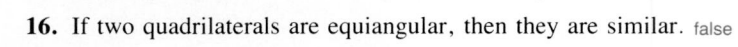
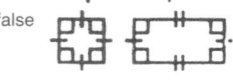

274 Chapter 7 Similarity

17. Counterexample

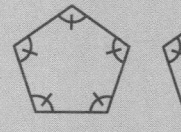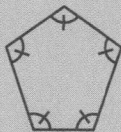

In this figure, $\triangle ABC \sim \triangle ADE$.

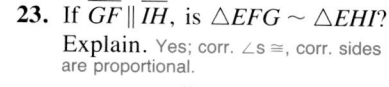

18. Give all the triangle angle measures.
    $m\angle AED = 40$; $m\angle ABC = m\angle ADE = y$; $m\angle CAB = 140 - y$

19. Name the parallel segments. Explain.
    $\overline{BC} \parallel \overline{DE}$; corr. $\angle$s are $\cong$.

20. If $AB = 3$, $AC = 4$, and $AD = 7$, then
    $BD = \underline{\ ?\ }$, $AE = \underline{\ ?\ }$, and $CE = \underline{\ ?\ }$. $4; \frac{28}{3}; \frac{16}{3}$

21. If $AB = 1.5$, $BD = 3$, and $CE = 4$, then $AC = \underline{\ ?\ }$, $AE = \underline{\ ?\ }$, and $AD = \underline{\ ?\ }$.
    $2; 6; 4.5$

22. If $ABCD \sim JMLK$, find the
    missing lengths. $x = 3$, $y = 4.5$, $w = 3$

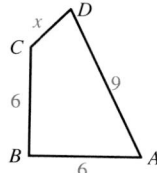 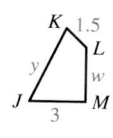

23. If $\overline{GF} \parallel \overline{IH}$, is $\triangle EFG \sim \triangle EHI$?
    Explain. Yes; corr. $\angle$s $\cong$, corr. sides
    are proportional.

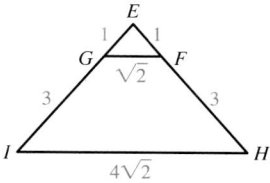

24. Pentagons $ABCDE$ and $RSTUV$ are similar. The sides of $ABCDE$ are 24, 40, 56, 24, and 48. The perimeter of $RSTUV$ is 240; find the lengths of its sides. 30, 50, 70, 30, 60

25. Use this figure to identify
    a pair of similar triangles.
    Find the scale factor. $\triangle ABD \sim \triangle CBA$
    Scale factor $1:\sqrt{3}$

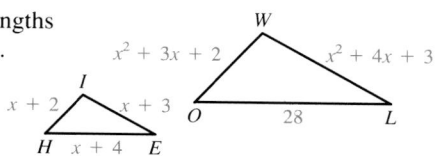

C 26. Prove that for any pair of similar triangles ABC and DEF, the ratio of the perimeters, $(AB + BC + CA):(DE + EF + FD)$, is equal to the ratio of the lengths of any pair of corresponding sides. See side column page 274.

27. A photocopy machine enlarges a picture of a polygon to 135% of its original size. The original is then reduced to 81% of its size. What is the ratio of the side length of the enlargement to the corresponding side length of the reduction? $135:81$, or $5:3$

28. How could the photocopy machine be used to create two similar polygons whose sides are in the ratio 5 to 4? Answers may vary. Enlarge the original to 125%.

29. $\triangle HIE \sim \triangle OWL$. Find x and the lengths
    of all the sides of the two triangles.
    $x = 3$, $HI = 5$, $IE = 6$, $HE = 7$,
    $OW = 20$, $WL = 24$

7.3 Similar Polygons **275**

Lesson Quiz

Are the polygons similar? Why?

1.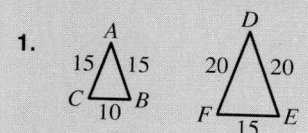

2.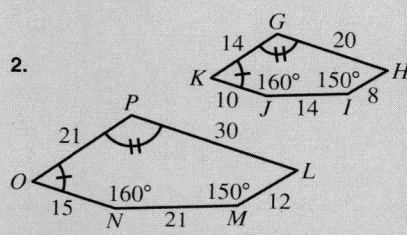

Find all missing lengths and angle measures in these similar polygons.

3.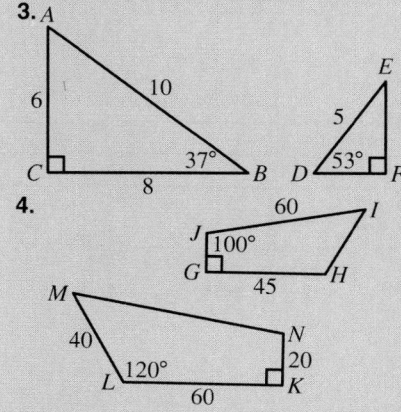

4.

1. no; no proportion of sides
2. yes; corr. $\angle$s $\cong$; corr. sides in prop.
3. $m\angle A = 53$, $m\angle E = 37$, $DF = 3$, $EF = 4$
4. $m\angle H = 120$, $m\angle I = m\angle M = 50$, $m\angle N = 100$, $GJ = 15$, $HI = 30$, $MN = 80$

Enrichment

$\square ABCD \sim \square EFGH$, with $AB = x + 5$,
$BC = x + 2$, $EF = x - 2$, and $FG = x - 3$. Find the perimeters and scale factor.

$\frac{AB}{EF} = \frac{BC}{FG}$; $\frac{x + 5}{x - 2} = \frac{x + 2}{x - 3}$; $x = 5\frac{1}{2}$

$P(ABCD) = 2(10\frac{1}{2}) + 2(7\frac{1}{2}) = 36$.

$P(EFGH) = 2(3\frac{1}{2}) + 2(2\frac{1}{2}) = 12$. Scale factor is $3:1$.

275

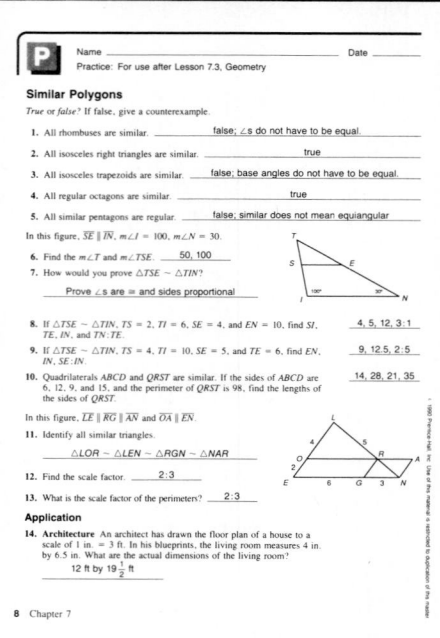

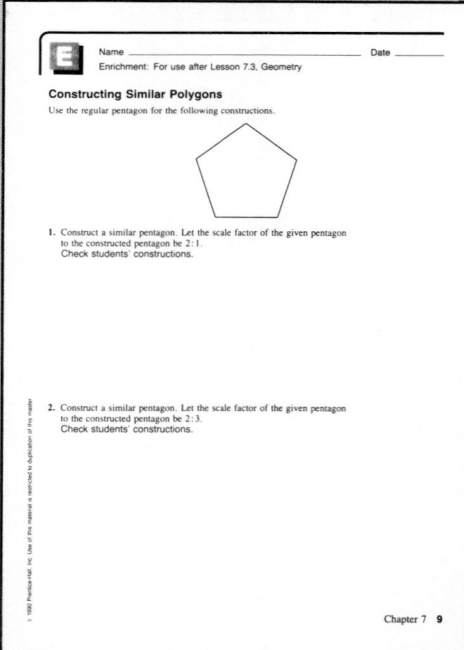

Applications

30. Scale Drawing A student makes a scale drawing of a rectangular room that measures 27 ft by 18 ft. If he uses a scale of 1 in. = 1.5 ft, what are the dimensions of his drawing? 18 in. by 12 in.

31. Photography A studio photo is $3\frac{1}{2}$ in. wide × 5 in. long. If a yearbook print must be 8 in. wide, what will the length be? $11\frac{3}{7}$ in.

32. Technology Use Logo to generate squares within squares. What is the ratio between the side of the largest square and the side of each inner square? See Solutions Manual.

TEST YOURSELF

Write each ratio in simplest form.

1. $90:102$ 15:17

2. $\dfrac{(x^2 + x - 20)}{(6x - 24)}$ $\dfrac{(x+5)}{6}$ 7.1

Identify the means and extremes in each proportion. Solve for x.

3. $\dfrac{4}{x} = \dfrac{x}{9}$ extremes 4, 9; means x, x; $x = \pm 6$

4. $\dfrac{9}{4} = \dfrac{x}{x-5}$ extremes 9, $(x-5)$; means 4, x; $x = 9$

5. The measures of the angles of a triangle are in the ratio $2:3:4$. Find the measure of each angle. 40, 60, 80

6. The ratio of measures of a complement of an angle to its supplement is 3 to 8. Find the measures of the angle, its complement, and its supplement. 36, 54, 144

7. Find the geometric mean in simplest form between 5 and 75. $5\sqrt{15}$ 7.2

$\dfrac{AX}{BX} = \dfrac{AY}{CY}$; **complete each statement. Justify your answer.**

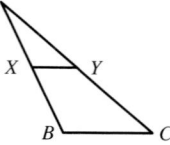

8. $\dfrac{AX}{AY} = \dfrac{?}{}$ $\dfrac{BX}{CY}$
Means may be interchanged.

9. $\dfrac{BX}{AX} = \dfrac{?}{}$ $\dfrac{CY}{AY}$
If $\dfrac{a}{b} = \dfrac{c}{d}$, then $\dfrac{b}{a} = \dfrac{d}{c}$.

10. $\dfrac{AB}{AX} = \dfrac{?}{}$ $\dfrac{AC}{AY}$
If $\dfrac{a}{b} = \dfrac{c}{d}$, then $\dfrac{a+b}{b} = \dfrac{c+d}{d}$.

True or false? If false, give a counterexample. See below.

11. All rectangles are similar. false

12. All squares are similar. true   7.3

13. All isosceles triangles are similar. false

14. All equilateral triangles are similar. true

15. In the given figure, $\square ABCD \sim \square EFGH$. Find all missing lengths and angle measures.

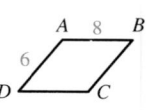
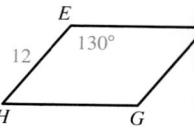

BC = 6
CD = 8
FG = 12
GH = EF = 16

$m\angle A = m\angle C = m\angle G = m\angle E = 130$
$m\angle B = m\angle D = m\angle F = m\angle H = 50$

11.

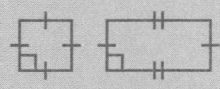

13.

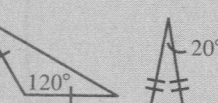

7.4 Similar Triangles

Objectives: To state and use the AA Postulate to prove triangles similar

To deduce information about segments and angles by first proving two triangles similar

Just as there are postulates that provide methods for proving triangles congruent, there is a postulate for *proving triangles similar*.

Investigation—*Visualizing the Concept*

Phil wants to measure inaccessible distances *DF* and *EF*. From the endpoints of a 400-foot segment *DE*, he establishes the lines of sight to *F* with a 67° angle at *D* and a 48° angle at *E*. He then uses the information to make a scale drawing in which the 4-inch segment *GI* corresponds to $\overline{DE}$. He uses a protractor to draw a 67° angle at *G* and a 48° angle at *I*. He labels the intersection point *H*.

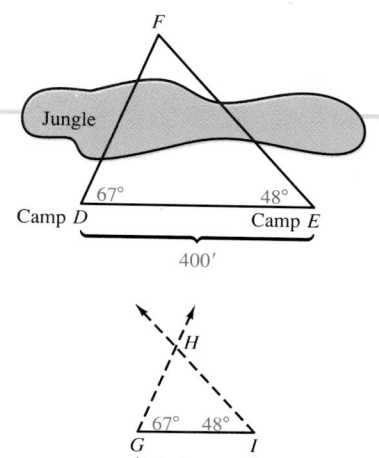

1. Do the figures appear similar? Explain. Yes; corr. ∠s are ≅ and lengths seem proportional.
2. What is the scale factor? How can it be used to find *DF* and *EF*? 1 in. = 100 ft; Measure $\overline{GH}$ and $\overline{HI}$ in inches. Multiply number of inches by 100 ft.

This postulate states the minimal conditions needed to determine that two triangles are similar.

Postulate 17   AA Postulate   If two angles of one triangle are congruent to two angles of a second triangle, then the triangles are similar.

EXAMPLE 1   If the triangles are similar, write a similarity statement.

a.
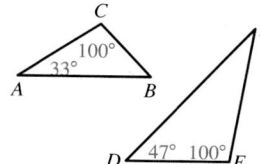

b.
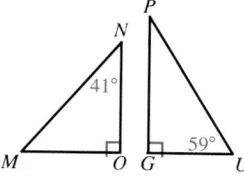

c.
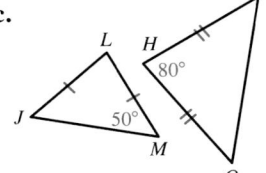

a. $\triangle ABC \sim \triangle FDE$ **b.** No similarity   **c.** $\triangle JLM \sim \triangle QHI$

7.4 Similar Triangles   **277**

Developing Mathematical Power

Cooperative Learning   Assign groups of students to choose two angle measures whose sum is less than 180. Then each member of the group should draw a triangle containing two angles with these measures, but such that the included side has a different length. Have the students record their observations.

LESSON PLAN

Vocabulary
AA Postulate
Similar triangles

Materials/Manipulatives
Protractors and rulers
Teaching Transparency 45

Technology
Computer
Computer Test Bank, pp. 411–422
The Geometric Supposer: Quadrilaterals, p. 100

LESSON FOCUS

Review
• Verify each congruence.

1.
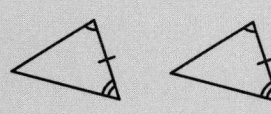

2.

3.
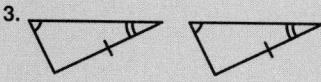

1. SAS   2. ASA   3. AAS

• The Algebra Review, Exercises 26–33, involves solving proportions.

Alternative Learning Styles
• The Investigation provides students with the opportunity to visualize an application of similar triangles to indirect measurement.
• The kinesthetic learner may benefit from using manipulatives to draw other scales, such as *GI* = 2 in. or *GI* = 8 in., and comparing results.

277

TEACHING SUGGESTIONS

- Make sure that students don't assume other polygons to be similar if corresponding angles are congruent. Provide a counterexample, such as two nonsimilar rectangles.
- Students will probably need help seeing *all* the similarities in Class Exercise 5. If necessary, ask what the measure of $\angle MPO$ must be.

CHALKBOARD EXAMPLES

- **For Example 1**
  Are the triangles similar? Justify.

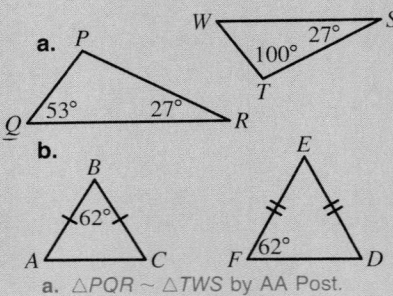

a.

b.

a. $\triangle PQR \sim \triangle TWS$ by AA Post.
b. no similarity

- **For Example 2**
  Give a Plan for proof.

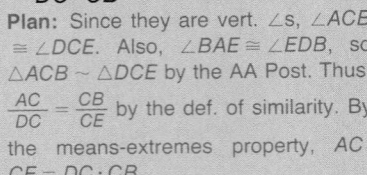

  Given: $\angle BAE \cong \angle EDB$
  Prove: $AC \cdot CE = DC \cdot CB$
  Plan: Since they are vert. $\angle$s, $\angle ACB \cong \angle DCE$. Also, $\angle BAE \cong \angle EDB$, so $\triangle ACB \sim \triangle DCE$ by the AA Post. Thus, $\frac{AC}{DC} = \frac{CB}{CE}$ by the def. of similarity. By the means-extremes property, $AC \cdot CE = DC \cdot CB$.

Common Error

- Some students might assess similarity based upon insufficient information. Have these students fill in all angle measures before making a determination.
- See *Teacher's Resource Book* for additional remediation.

EXAMPLE 2   Complete the proof.

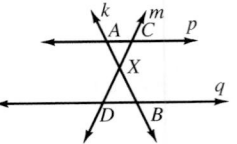

Given: $p \parallel q$; k and m intersect at X.

Prove: $\dfrac{AX}{BX} = \dfrac{CX}{DX}$

Plan: Use alternate interior angles and vertical angles to show $\triangle AXC \sim \triangle BXD$. Use the definition of similar polygons to get $\dfrac{AX}{BX} = \dfrac{CX}{DX}$.

Proof:

Statements	Reasons
1. _?_	1. Given
2. $\angle ACX \cong \angle BDX$	2. _?_
3. _?_	3. Vertical angles are congruent.
4. $\triangle$ _?_ $\sim \triangle$ _?_	4. _?_
5. _?_	5. _?_

Conclusion: _?_

1. $p \parallel q$; k and m intersect at X.   2. If lines are $\parallel$, alt. int. $\angle$s are $\cong$.
3. $\angle AXC \cong \angle BXD$ 4. $\triangle AXC \sim \triangle BXD$; AA Postulate
5. $\dfrac{AX}{BX} = \dfrac{CX}{DX}$; Corr. side lengths of $\sim \triangle$ are in proportion.

Conclusion: In the given figure, if $p \parallel q$, then $\dfrac{AX}{BX} = \dfrac{CX}{DX}$.

CLASS EXERCISES

If the triangles are similar, write a similarity statement.

1.

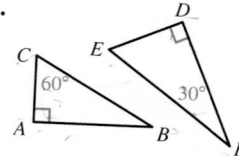

$\triangle ABC \sim \triangle DFE$

2.

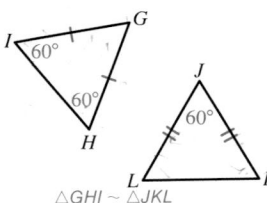

$\triangle GHI \sim \triangle JKL$

3.

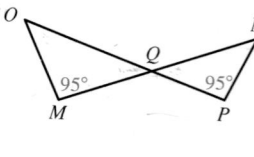

$\triangle MQO \sim PQN$

4.

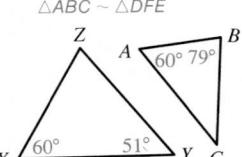

Not $\sim$

5.

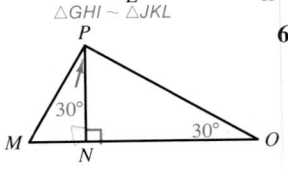

$\triangle NPO \sim \triangle NMP \sim \triangle PMO$

6.

$\triangle XYV \sim \triangle XZW$

7. Supply the statements and reasons.

Given: $\overline{AB} \parallel \overline{CD}$
Prove: $\triangle XAB \sim \triangle XCD$
Proof:

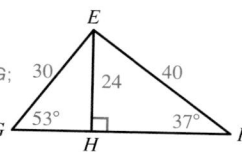

Statements	Reasons
1. <u>?</u> $\overline{AB} \parallel \overline{CD}$	1. Given
2. $\angle XAB \cong \angle XCD$	2. <u>?</u> Corr. $\angle$s of $\parallel$ lines are $\cong$.
3. <u>?</u> $\cong$ <u>?</u> $\angle X$ $\angle X$	3. Reflexive property
4. <u>?</u> $\triangle XAB \sim \triangle XCD$	4. <u>?</u> AA Post.

8. Why is $\triangle HEF \sim \triangle HGE$?
Find GH, HF, and GF.
AA Post.; $\angle EHF \cong \angle EHG$; $\angle HEF \cong \angle G$;
18, 32, 50

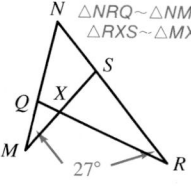

PRACTICE EXERCISES

If the triangles are similar, write a similarity statement.

A **1.** $\triangle NRQ \sim \triangle NMS$;
$\triangle RXS \sim \triangle MXQ$

2. $\triangle ABX \sim \triangle CDX$

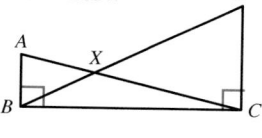

3. $\triangle JDL \sim \triangle HDG$

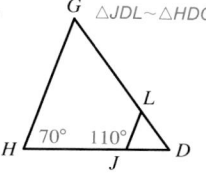

4. If $k \parallel m$, why are the triangles
similar? Find the lengths x and z.
Alt. int $\angle$s are $\cong$ and $\triangle$s are $\sim$ by AA Post.; $x = 9$, $z = 2$

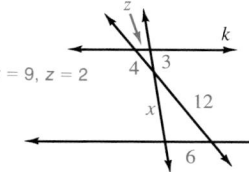

For Exercises 5–8, use this figure to complete each statement.

5. $\triangle JKN \sim$ <u>?</u> $\triangle MLN$

6. $\dfrac{JK}{?} = \dfrac{JN}{?} = \dfrac{KN}{?}$
ML   MN   LN

7. $\dfrac{10}{8?} = \dfrac{?}{6}$ *y* and $\dfrac{10}{?8} = \dfrac{4}{?x}$

8. $x =$ <u>?</u> and $y =$ <u>?</u>.
$3\frac{1}{5}$ $7\frac{1}{2}$

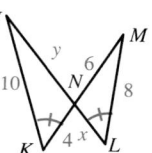

9. If trapezoid $ABCD$ is isosceles, name
a pair of congruent triangles. Name
a pair of similar triangles. $\triangle ABC \cong \triangle BAD$
or $\triangle ADC \cong \triangle BCD$; $\triangle ABE \sim \triangle CDE$

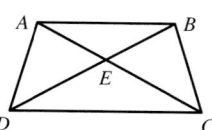

LESSON FOLLOW-UP

Discussion

Ask students if all equilateral triangles
are similar. yes Are all isosceles triangles similar? no

Assignment Guide

See p. 260B for assignments.

Additional Answers for p. 280

12. Proof:

Statements	Reasons
1. $\overline{AB} \perp \overline{BC}$; $\overline{CD} \perp \overline{AD}$	1. Given
2. $\angle D$ and $\angle B$ are rt. $\angle$s.	2. Def. of $\perp$
3. $\angle D \cong \angle B$	3. All rt. $\angle$s are $\cong$.
4. $\angle AXD \cong \angle CXB$	4. Vert. $\angle$s are $\cong$.
5. $\triangle DXA \cong \triangle BXC$	5. AA Post.
6. $\dfrac{DX}{BX} = \dfrac{XA}{XC}$	6. Corr. side lengths of $\sim \triangle$s are in proportion.
7. $DX \cdot XC = BX \cdot XA$	7. Means-extremes prop.

Conclusion: In the given figure, if $\overline{AB} \perp$
$\overline{BC}$ and $\overline{CD} \perp \overline{AD}$, then $DX \cdot XC = BX \cdot XA$.

13. Plan: Since $\overline{PM} \perp \overline{LN}$, $\angle$s PML and
PMN are rt. $\angle$s. $\angle ZLM \cong \angle PNM$,
because they are supp. to $\angle$s 1
and 2. Concl. follows by AA Post.

Proof:

Statements	Reasons
1. $\overline{PM} \perp \overline{LN}$	1. Given
2. $\angle PML$ and $\angle PMN$ are rt. $\angle$s.	2. Def. of $\perp$ lines
3. $\angle PML \cong \angle PMN$	3. All rt. $\angle$s are $\cong$.
4. $\angle 1 \cong \angle 2$	4. Given
5. $\angle ZLM$ and $\angle 2$ are a linear pair as are $\angle PNM$ and $\angle 1$.	5. Def. of linear pair
6. $\angle ZLM$ and $\angle 2$ are supp. as are $\angle PNM$ and $\angle 1$.	6. Linear Pair Post.
7. $\angle ZLM \cong \angle PNM$	7. Supp. of $\cong \angle$s are $\cong$.
8. $\triangle ZML \sim \triangle PMN$	8. AA Post.

Conclusion: In the given figure, if
$\overline{PM} \perp \overline{LN}$ and $\angle 1 \cong \angle 2$, then $\triangle ZML$
$\sim \triangle PMN$.

279

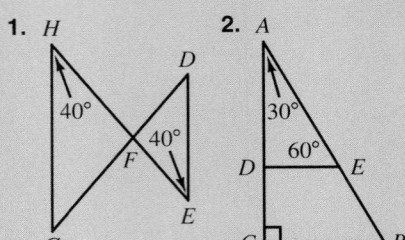
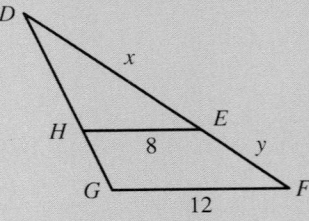
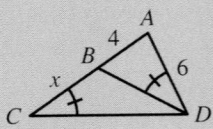
10. $j \parallel l$; find lengths x and y.
$y = 5, x = 10$

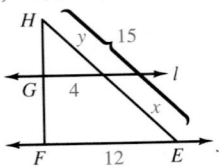

11. Find the height of the building.

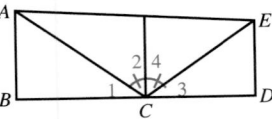

12. Complete the plan and the proof. See side column, p. 279.

Given: $\overline{AB} \perp \overline{BC}$, $\overline{CD} \perp \overline{AD}$
Prove: $DX \cdot XC = BX \cdot XA$
Plan: Prove that $\triangle\underline{?} \sim \triangle\underline{?}$. Set up a proportion using the corresponding side lengths. Then apply the means-extremes property.
DXA BXC

B **13.** **Given:** $\overline{PM} \perp \overline{LN}$; $\angle 1 \cong \angle 2$
Prove: $\triangle ZML \sim \triangle PMN$

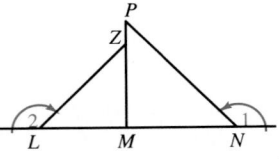

See Additional Answers, p. 702.

14. **Given:** $\overline{AB} \perp \overline{BD}$; $\overline{ED} \perp \overline{BD}$; $\angle 2 \cong \angle 4$; $\angle 2$ is complementary to $\angle 1$. $\angle 4$ is complementary to $\angle 3$.
Prove: $\triangle ABC \sim \triangle EDC$

15. **Given:** $\overline{SR} \perp \overline{TP}$; $\overline{PQ} \perp \overline{ST}$
Prove: $\frac{SM}{MQ} = \frac{PM}{MR}$

16. **Given:** $\overline{SR} \perp \overline{TP}$; $\overline{PQ} \perp \overline{ST}$
Prove: $QT \cdot TS = TP \cdot RT$

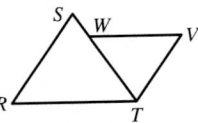

17. **Given:** $\overline{WV} \parallel \overline{RT}$; $\overline{RS} \parallel \overline{TV}$
Prove: $RS \cdot VW = VT \cdot RT$

18. **Given:** $\overline{ZB} \perp \overline{XY}$; $\overline{WA} \perp \overline{UV}$
$\triangle UVW \sim \triangle XYZ$
Prove: $\triangle ZBY \sim \triangle WAV$

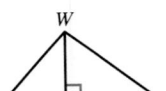 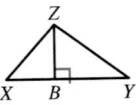

19. $\angle C \cong \angle BDE$; find x and y. $x = 12, y = 12$

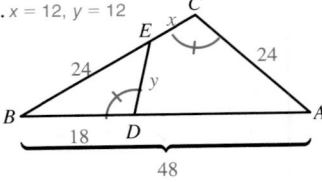

20. **Given:** $\overline{WP}$ and $\overline{XO}$ are altitudes.
   Prove: $\triangle PAX \sim \triangle OYX$

C 21. **Given:** $\overline{WP}$ and $\overline{XO}$ are altitudes.
   Prove: The product of the segment lengths of $\overline{XO}$ equals the product of the segment lengths of $\overline{WP}$.

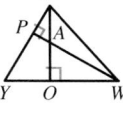

22. **Given:** $\triangle ACP \sim \triangle BAP$, $\triangle CAB$ is a right triangle.
   Prove: $\overline{AP}$ is an altitude of $\triangle ACB$.

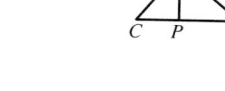

Applications

23. **Surveying** If a surveyor sets up $k \parallel m$ on a levee, find the distances x and y across the river. $33\frac{1}{3}$ yd; 25 yd

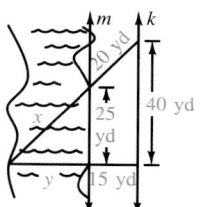

24. **Inaccessible Distances** If $l \parallel k$ along the shoreline, find the distances to the buoy from points A and B. $a = 40$ m; $b = 30$ m

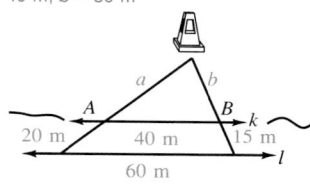

25. **Technology** Use Logo to generate a series of nested similar triangles. Experiment with rotating the turtle to create different visual effects.
   See Solutions Manual.

Algebra Review

Solve the proportion.

26. $\frac{3}{4} = \frac{x}{28}$ 21

27. $\frac{x+1}{10} = \frac{20}{50}$ 3

28. $\frac{x}{20+x} = \frac{30}{70}$ 15

29. $\frac{8}{x-6} = \frac{10}{x}$ 30

30. $\frac{21}{x+5} = \frac{3}{x}$ $5\frac{5}{6}$

31. $\frac{7}{8} = \frac{x+1}{x+5}$ 27

32. $\frac{x}{18} = \frac{x-7}{12}$ 21

33. $\frac{x}{x+10} = \frac{28}{35}$ 40

Developing Mathematical Power

34. **Thinking Critically** It is 3 PM on a sunny day. Your task is to find the height of the flag pole. You have only a meterstick. Explain how you would find the height of the pole and tell why your method works. See below.

35. **Project** A *pantograph* is a mechanical device used to copy to scale similar figures such as maps. Research and construct a pantograph.

7.4 Similar Triangles   **281**

34. Place the meterstick so that the end of its shadow is at the end of the pole's shadow, s. Measure the length, l, of the shadow of the stick. Hence, $\sim\triangle$ are formed, and $\frac{\text{pole length}}{1 \text{ m}} = \frac{s}{l}$.

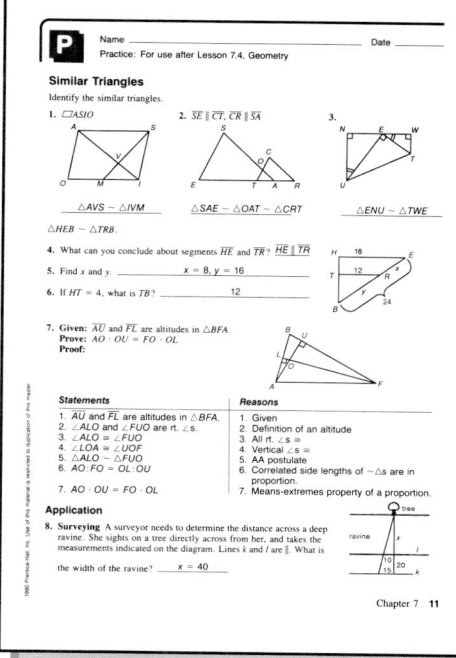
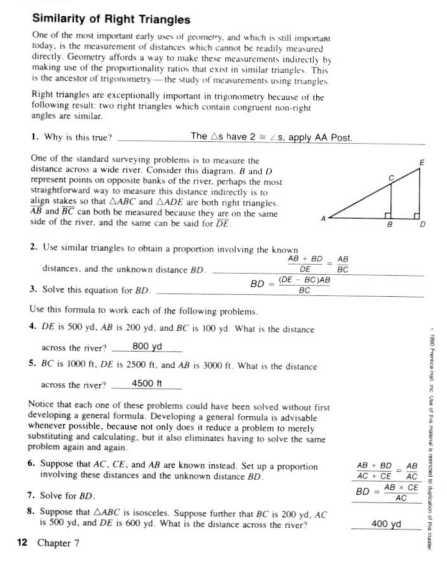

LESSON PLAN

Vocabulary

SAS Theorem   SSS Theorem

Materials/Manipulatives

Compasses and protractors
Metric rulers
Teaching Transparency 46

Technology

Calculator
Computer
Computer Test Bank, pp.
422–430
The Geometric Supposer:
Triangles
   Geometry Problems and
   Projects: Triangles,
   Worksheets T62, T65

LESSON FOCUS

Review

Review the AA postulate for proving
triangles similar.

Alternative Learning Styles

• The Investigation provides students with a kinesthetic approach
to SAS as a condition for similarity
of triangles. Encourage students to
repeat the experiment but to
change one of the given conditions
in △*ABC*; for example, *m*∠*A* = 50.
Ask students to determine how this
will affect △*DEF*. Then have them
draw △*DEF* to verify their conclusion. Are the triangles similar? Students may change the length of
side *AB* or side *BC*, or change the
scale factor.
• You may wish to have students
complete this Investigation using
The Geometric Supposer.
• Some students may benefit from
this hands-on approach to SSS as
a condition for similarity.

7.5 More on Similar Triangles

Objective: To use the SAS and SSS Theorems to prove two triangles
similar

When there is insufficient information to apply the AA Postulate, there are two
theorems that may be used for proving triangles similar.

Investigation—*Constructions*

Use a ruler, a protractor, the information given, and
a scale factor of $\frac{4}{3}$ to draw △*DEF*, a smaller triangle
similar to △*ABC*. Since *AB* = 4 cm, *DE* must be
3 cm. Thus begin with $\overline{DE}$ and copy a 75° angle at
vertex *D*. Now use *AC* and the scale factor to
find *DF*. $\frac{4}{3} = \frac{4.8}{DF}$; *DF* = 3.6. Now on $\overrightarrow{DR}$, measure
3.6 cm and label *F*. Draw $\overline{EF}$.

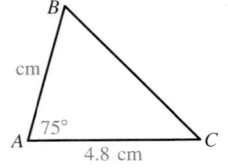

1. Does △*DEF* appear to be similar to △*ABC*? Yes
2. What methods can you use to check your work?
   Use a protractor to measure corr. ∠s.
3. Does the experiment suggest another way to prove
   triangles similar? Yes; see SAS Theorem for ~.

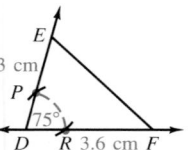

Theorem 7.1   SAS Theorem   If an angle of one triangle is congruent
to an angle of another triangle, and the lengths of the sides including those
angles are in proportion, then the triangles are similar.

Given: ∠*A* ≅ ∠*P*; $\frac{AB}{PQ} = \frac{AC}{PR}$

Prove: △*ABC* ~ △*PQR*

Plan: To apply the AA Postulate, introduce line *k*
parallel to $\overline{QR}$ and intersecting $\overline{PQ}$ at *X*, so
that $\overline{PX} \cong \overline{AB}$. Show △*PXY* ~ △*PQR*.
Use the resulting proportion, $\frac{PX}{PQ} = \frac{PY}{PR}$,

and the given proportion to show $\overline{PY} \cong \overline{AC}$. Then △*ABC* ≅ △*PXY*.
Use corr. parts of ≅ △s to show △*ABC* ~ △*PQR*. Proved in Practice Exercise 25

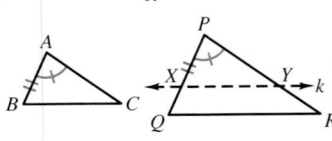

Developing Mathematical Power

Cooperative Learning   Assign groups of students to work on Critical Thinking,
p. 7, of the *Teacher's Resource Book*. Allow time for students to share results and
insights.

In the next theorem, no angles are required to establish triangle similarity.

> **Theorem 7.2   SSS Theorem**   If the corresponding sides of two triangles are in proportion, then the triangles are similar.

Given: $\dfrac{ED}{ST} = \dfrac{DF}{TW} = \dfrac{FE}{WS}$

Prove: $\triangle DEF \sim \triangle TSW$

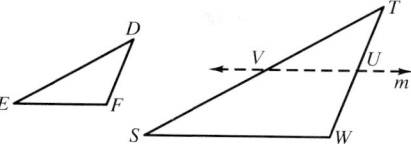

Plan: As in Theorem 7.1, introduce auxiliary line m parallel to $\overline{SW}$ and intersecting $\overline{TS}$ at V such that $\overline{TV} \cong \overline{DE}$. Then show $\triangle TVU \sim \triangle TSW$. Use the resulting proportion $\dfrac{TV}{TS} = \dfrac{TU}{TW}$ with a given proportion to show $\overline{TU} \cong \overline{DF}$. Similarly, $\overline{FE} \cong \overline{UV}$. Then $\triangle DEF \cong \triangle TVU$. Use corresponding congruent angles to show that $\triangle DEF \sim \triangle TSW$.
Proved in Practice Exercise 26

EXAMPLE 1   **Are the triangles similar? If so, write a similarity statement and justify.**

a. 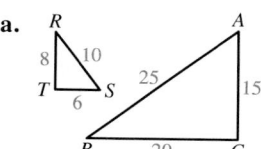   **b.** 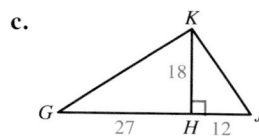   **c.**

a. Yes; $\triangle RTS \sim \triangle BCA$; SSS Th.   **b.** Not enough information
c. Yes; $\triangle GHK \sim \triangle KHJ$; SAS Th.

EXAMPLE 2   **If possible, verify that $\triangle GIH \sim \triangle JLK$.**

a. $\dfrac{GH}{JK} = \dfrac{GI}{JL}$ and $\angle G \cong \angle J$ **b.** $\dfrac{GH}{JK} = \dfrac{GI}{JL} = \dfrac{HI}{KL}$

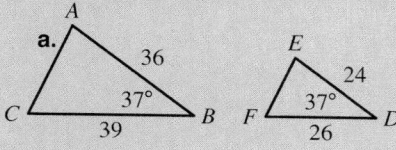

c. $\dfrac{GH}{JK} = \dfrac{GI}{JL}$ and $\angle G \cong \angle K$ **d.** $\dfrac{GH}{JK} = \dfrac{GI}{JL}$

a. Yes; SAS Th.   **b.** Yes; SSS Th.
c. Can't verify.   **d.** Can't verify.

CLASS EXERCISES

1. Distinguish between the statements named the SAS Postulate and SAS Theorem.
SAS Postulate leads to $\cong$ ⌐S⌐; SAS Theorem leads to $\sim$ ⌐S⌐
2. Distinguish between the statements named the SSS Postulate and SSS Theorem.
SSS Postulate leads to $\cong$ ⌐S⌐; SSS Theorem leads to $\sim$ ⌐S⌐

7.5 More on Similar Triangles   **283**

 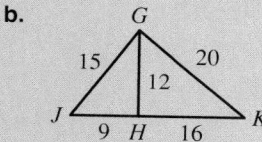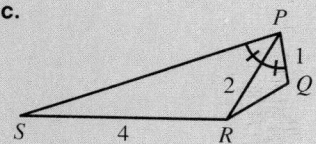
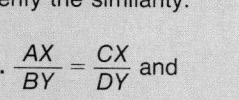
283

LESSON FOLLOW-UP

Assignment Guide

See p. 260B for assignments.

Additional Answers for p. 285

10. Plan: Show $\triangle ABC \sim \triangle ADE$. Thus, $\angle ABC \cong \angle ADE$, and the concl. follows because corr. $\angle$s are $\cong$.

Proof:

Statements	Reasons
1. $\dfrac{AB}{AD} = \dfrac{AC}{AE}$	1. Given
2. $\angle A \cong \angle A$	2. Refl. prop.
3. $\triangle ABC \sim \triangle ADE$	3. SAS Th.
4. $\angle ABC \cong \angle ADE$	4. Corr. $\angle$s of $\sim \triangle$ are $\cong$.
5. $\overline{BC} \parallel \overline{DE}$	5. If $\cong$ corr. $\angle$s, then the lines are $\parallel$.

Conclusion: In the given figure, if $\dfrac{AB}{AD} = \dfrac{AC}{AE}$, $\overline{BC} \parallel \overline{DE}$.

11. Plan: Show $\triangle RST \sim \triangle MVJ$. Thus, $\angle STR \cong \angle VJM$, and the concl. follows because corr. $\angle$s are $\cong$.

Proof:

Statements	Reasons
1. $\dfrac{RS}{MV} = \dfrac{ST}{VJ} = \dfrac{RT}{MJ}$	1. Given
2. $\triangle RST \sim \triangle MVJ$	2. SSS Th.
3. $\angle STR \cong \angle VJM$	3. Corr. $\angle$s of $\sim \triangle$
4. $\overline{ST} \parallel \overline{VJ}$	4. If $\cong$ corr. $\angle$s, then the lines are $\parallel$.

Conclusion: In the given figure, if $\dfrac{RS}{MV} = \dfrac{ST}{VJ} = \dfrac{RT}{MJ}$, then $\overline{ST} \parallel \overline{VJ}$.

3. Why is there an ASA Postulate for congruence, but not an ASA Postulate for similarity? You don't need the side to prove $\sim \triangle$; two $\cong \angle$s are sufficient.

Are the triangles similar? If so, give a similarity statement and verify it.

4.

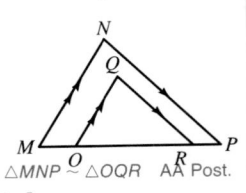

$\triangle XRM \sim \triangle XSN$
SAS Th.

5.

$\triangle ZTY \sim \triangle ZWT$
SAS Th.

6.

$\triangle MNP \sim \triangle OQR$ AA Post.

Give and verify similarity statements. Then, give the indicated measures.

7.

$\triangle ACB \sim \triangle AED$;
AA Post.; $CE = 17.5$; $m\angle D = x$

8.

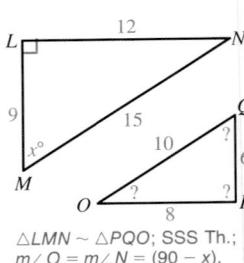

$\triangle JIK \sim \triangle GFH$; SAS Th.;
$m\angle I = 25$; $m\angle J = y$;
$IJ = 24$

9.

$\triangle LMN \sim \triangle PQO$; SSS Th.;
$m\angle O = m\angle N = (90 - x)$,
$m\angle Q = x$, $m\angle P = 90$

10. Supply statements and reasons.

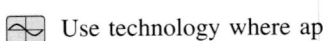

Given: $\overline{AP}$ is an altitude of $\triangle ABC$; $\dfrac{CP}{AP} = \dfrac{AP}{PB}$.

Prove: $\triangle APC \sim \triangle BPA$

Statements	Reasons
1. $\overline{AP}$ is an altitude of $\triangle ABC$.	1. _?_ Given
2. _?_ $\overline{AP} \perp \overline{BC}$	2. Definition of altitude
3. $\angle$_?_ $\cong \angle$_?_ APB CPA	3. _?_ $\angle$s formed by $\perp$ lines are $\cong$.
4. _?_ $\dfrac{CP}{AP} = \dfrac{AP}{PB}$	4. Given
5. $\triangle APC \sim \triangle BPA$	5. _?_ SAS Th.

PRACTICE EXERCISES

Use technology where appropriate.

The two triangles are similar. Find the values of x and y.

A 1.

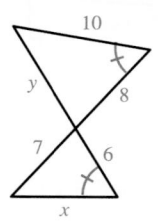

$x = 7\frac{1}{2}$; $y = 9\frac{1}{3}$

2.

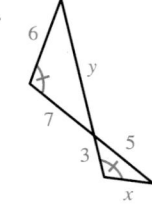

$x = 2\frac{4}{7}$; $y = 11\frac{2}{3}$

3.

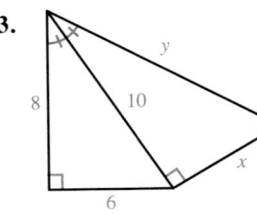

$x = 7\frac{1}{2}$; $y = 12\frac{1}{2}$

Developing Mathematical Power

Keeping a Portfolio Have students write a paragraph about similar triangles. They should analyze conditions that guarantee similarity of triangles and also determine minimal sets of conditions for similarity of triangles.

Are the triangles similar? If so, write a similarity statement and verify.

4.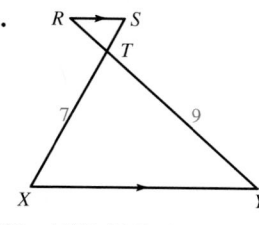

$\triangle RST \sim \triangle YXT$; AA Post.

5.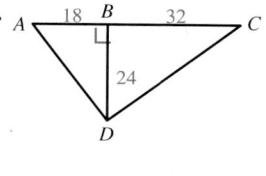

$\triangle ABD \sim \triangle DBC$; SAS Th.

6.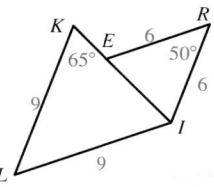

$\triangle IKL \sim \triangle IER$; SAS Th. or AA Post.

Write and verify similarity statements. Then give the indicated angle and side measures.

7.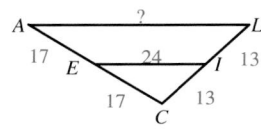

$\triangle ACL \sim \triangle ECI$; SAS Th.; $AL = 48$

8.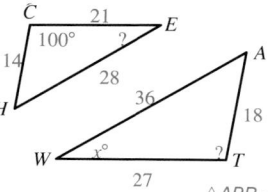

$\triangle CHE \sim \triangle TAW$; SSS Th.; $m\angle E = x$; $m\angle T = 100$

9.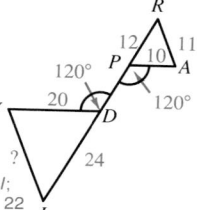

$\triangle APR \sim \triangle YDI$; SAS Th.; $YI = 22$

10. Given: $\dfrac{AB}{AD} = \dfrac{AC}{AE}$

Prove: $\overline{BC} \parallel \overline{DE}$

See side column, p. 284.

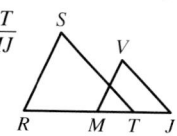

11. Given: $\dfrac{RS}{MV} = \dfrac{ST}{VJ} = \dfrac{RT}{MJ}$

Prove: $\overline{ST} \parallel \overline{VJ}$

Give the missing measure, so that $\triangle ABC \sim \triangle DEF$.

12. $AB = 36$, $BC = 24$, $DE = 48$, $m\angle B = 110$, $m\angle E = 110$; $EF = \underline{?}$ 32

13. $AB = 18$, $BC = 24$, $AC = 30$, $DE = 12$, $EF = 16$; $DF = \underline{?}$ 20

14. $m\angle B = 25$, $m\angle D = 45$, $m\angle E = 25$; $m\angle A = \underline{?}$ 45

B **15.** $AC = 12\sqrt{3}$, $DE = 6\sqrt{2}$, $DF = 8\sqrt{3}$, $m\angle A = m\angle D = 57$; $AB = \underline{?}$ $9\sqrt{2}$

16. $AC = 15$, $DE = 12$, $DF = 20$, $m\angle A = m\angle D = 35$; $AB = \underline{?}$ 9

17. $AB = EF = 15$, $DE = 25$, $BC = 9$, $AC = 12$; $DF = \underline{?}$ 20

18. $AB = EF = 14$, $DE = 4$, $BC = 49$, $AC = 42$; $DF = \underline{?}$ 12

See Additional Answers, p. 702.

19. Given: $\angle 1 \cong \angle 2$; $\dfrac{JM}{TC} = \dfrac{MN}{CN}$

Prove: $\angle J \cong \angle T$

20. Given: $\angle J \cong \angle T$; $\dfrac{JM}{TC} = \dfrac{NJ}{NT}$

Prove: $\dfrac{JM + MN + NJ}{TC + CN + NT} = \dfrac{MN}{CN}$

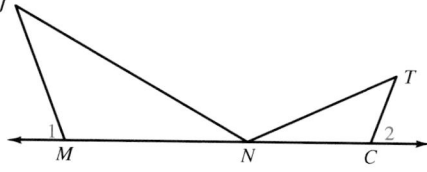

Developing Mathematical Power

Thinking Critically Students are asked to use proportionality of the sides of similar triangles to find the distance run by two players on a playing field.

Lesson Quiz

Are the triangles similar? Verify.

1.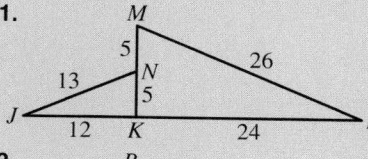

2.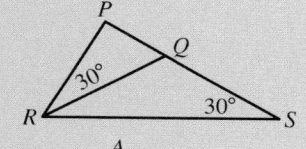

3.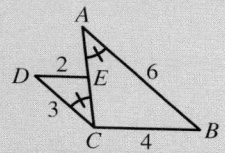

4. Justify the similarity. Find *FH*.

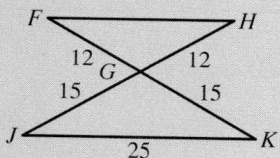

1. yes; $\triangle JKN \sim \triangle LKM$; SSS Th.
2. yes; $\triangle PRQ \sim \triangle PSR$; AA Post.
3. no   4. SAS Th.; $FH = 20$

Teacher's Resource Book
Follow-Up Investigation, Chapter 7, p. 13

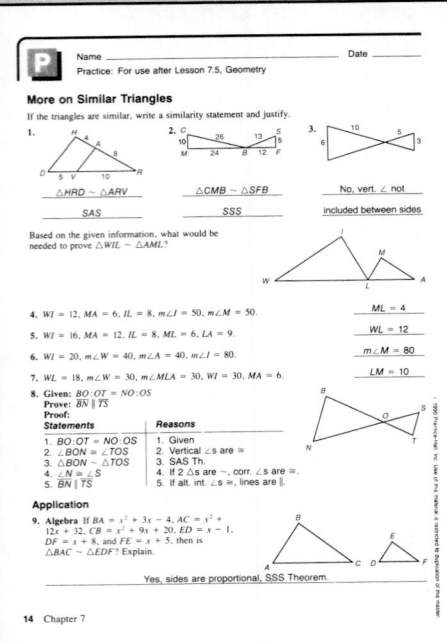

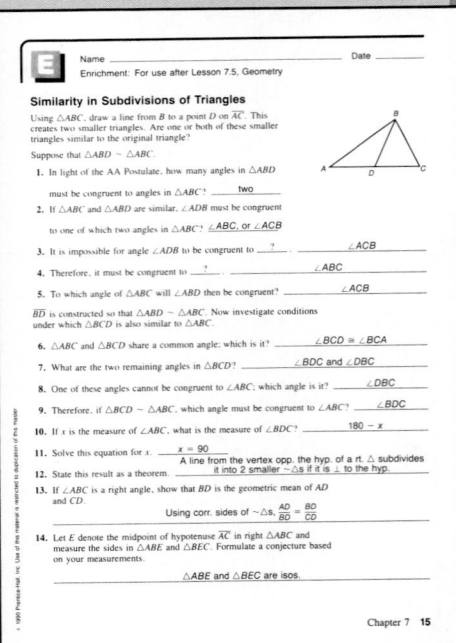

21. Given: $\triangle ABC \sim \triangle DEF$; $\overline{AP}$ and $\overline{DX}$ are medians.
Prove: $\triangle APC \sim \triangle DXF$

22. Given: $\triangle RST \sim \triangle JKM$ $\overline{SP}$ and $\overline{KV}$ are altitudes.
Prove: $\triangle SPT \sim \triangle KVM$

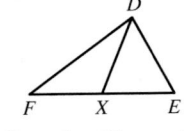

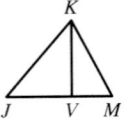

23. Generalize the Exercise 21 proof. See side column.

24. Generalize the Exercise 22 proof.

C **25.** Complete the proof of Theorem 7.1.
See Additional Answers, p. 702.

26. Complete the proof of Theorem 7.2.

27. From point P in the interior of quadrilateral $ABCD$, $\overrightarrow{PA}$, $\overrightarrow{PB}$, $\overrightarrow{PC}$, and $\overrightarrow{PD}$ were drawn through points E, F, G, and H such that $\dfrac{PE}{PA} = \dfrac{PF}{PB} = \dfrac{PG}{PC} = \dfrac{PH}{PD}$.

Prove: $EFGH \sim ABCD$

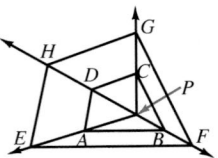

28. P, Q, R, S, T, and U separate $\overline{DF}$, $\overline{FE}$, and $\overline{ED}$ into thirds. Prove that each new triangle formed is similar to $\triangle DFE$.

29. If $\triangle GHI \sim \triangle DFE$ and J, K, L, M, N, and O separate $\overline{GH}$, $\overline{HI}$, and $\overline{IG}$ into thirds, prove that hexagon $PQRSTU$ is similar to $JKLMNO$.

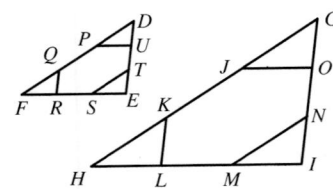

Applications

30. Technology Use Logo to generate $\triangle ABC$ and $\triangle RST$ with $\angle B \cong \angle S$. Is $\triangle RST \sim \triangle ABC$? Explain. See Solutions Manual.

31. Algebra If $RS = x^2 + 4x - 21$, $RT = x^2 + 5x - 24$, $ST = x^2 + 9x - 36$, $AB = x + 7$, $AC = x + 8$, and $BC = x + 9$, then is $\triangle RST \sim \triangle ABC$? Explain. No, the side lengths are not proportional.

Developing Mathematical Power

32. Thinking Critically The distance EF across a rectangular playing field is $50\sqrt{3}$ ft. Use your calculator to approximate EF to the nearest thousandth. J and D show the position of two players with respect to E and F. The player at J runs 50 ft to reach F; how far must the player at D run to reach F? Explain.

86.603 ft; 150 ft; $\triangle EFJ \sim \triangle DFE$ by AA Post.; hence $\dfrac{JF}{EF} = \dfrac{EF}{ED}$

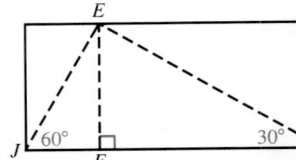

23. If 2 △ are ~ and have medians drawn to corr. sides, then the △ formed in one △ are ~ to the corr. △ formed in the other.

24. If 2 △ are ~ and have altitudes drawn to corr. sides, then the △ formed in one △ are ~ to the corr. △ formed in the other △.

Strategy: Find Inaccessible Distances

If a segment length in one of two similar polygons is unknown, a proportion can be used to find the unknown length. This fact helps technicians such as surveyors and navigators to find distances they cannot measure directly. The problem-solving steps can be helpful in choosing and applying similar-triangle properties to find certain inaccessible distances.

EXAMPLE 1   To find the distance from Q to P across a canyon, a surveyor picks R to be collinear with Q and P, erects perpendiculars at R and Q, and makes S collinear with T and P so that $\overline{QR}$, $\overline{RS}$, and $\overline{QT}$ can be measured. How can the surveyor find QP?

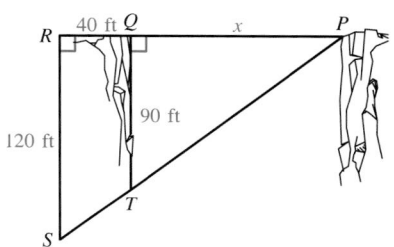

Understand the Problem

What is the question?
What is QP, the distance across the canyon?
What information is given?
The figure shows $\triangle PQT$ and $\triangle PRS$ with certain segment lengths given: $QT = 90$ ft, $RS = 120$ ft, $RQ = 40$ ft.

Plan Your Approach

How are the triangles related?
Since $\overline{RQ} \perp \overline{RS}$ and $\overline{RQ} \perp \overline{QT}$, $\overline{RS} \parallel \overline{QT}$. So, $\triangle PQT \sim \triangle PRS$ by AA.
What similar-triangle proportions involving QP can be written?

$$\frac{QP}{RP} = \frac{QT}{RS} \quad \text{and} \quad \frac{QP}{RP} = \frac{PT}{PS}$$

Enough information is given to solve the first proportion.

Letting $QP = x$, $\dfrac{x}{40 + x} = \dfrac{90}{120}$.

Implement the Plan

Solve the proportion.
$$\frac{x}{40 + x} = \frac{90}{120}$$
$$120x = 3600 + 90x$$
$$30x = 3600$$
$$x = 120$$

Developing Mathematical Power

Cooperative Learning   Bring the activity in the class exercises outside. Have students work in small groups, using a ruler and a meterstick to find *DE* and *XY*. Each group should record and report its findings. Discuss why the measurements among the groups are the same.

LESSON PLAN

Vocabulary
Shadow reckoning

Materials/Manipulatives
Rulers
Metersticks
Teaching Transparency 47

Technology
Calculators
Computer Test Bank, pp. 431–437

LESSON FOCUS

Review
Solve.

1. $\dfrac{x}{9} = \dfrac{25}{45}$ **2.** $\dfrac{x}{x + 3} = \dfrac{120}{150}$

3. $\dfrac{x}{x + 20} = \dfrac{35}{135}$ **4.** $\dfrac{x}{x - 15} = \dfrac{220}{190}$

1. 5   2. 12   3. 7   4. 110

Alternative Learning Styles
- Concrete models of the similar triangles will help students to visualize the overlapping angles. They can make a tracing of $\triangle PQT$ in one color and a separate tracing of $\triangle PRS$ in another color. By separating the triangles and labeling the sides, they can see how to set up the proportion.
- Teaching Transparency 47 provides the visual learner with another diagram configuration that can be used to determine inaccessible distances.

- Have students generate problems in which an inaccessible distance is to be determined, to see what information is needed to solve such problems.
- Remind students that triangles must be shown to be similar *before* proportions are written.
- Point out that sometimes the inaccessible distance is represented by part of a side of a triangle rather than as a side. Insist that students write proportions with names of segments before substituting numerical equivalents.
- The Class Exercises discuss *shadow reckoning*. Point out that these calculations are based on the fact that at any given time of the day, the rays of the sun that fall on two objects "near" each other are virtually parallel. Therefore, if $\overline{AB}$ and $\overline{DE}$ are perpendicular to the ground on which their respective shadows $\overline{BC}$ and $\overline{EF}$ fall, $\overline{AC}$ and $\overline{DF}$ are parallel. Thus, $\angle A \cong \angle D$.

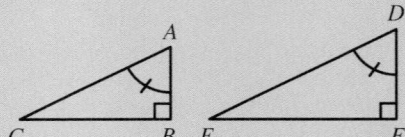

Since $\triangle ABC \sim \triangle DEF$ by AA,
$\dfrac{AB}{DE} = \dfrac{BC}{EF}$.

CHALKBOARD EXAMPLES

- **For Example 1**

  A surveyor knows that the distance WJ across a lake is 500 yd. He also knows the distances shown on the diagram, and wishes to determine the distance of the small island from the western shore of the lake. What is this distance?

288

☐ **Interpret the Results**

Check.
$\dfrac{90}{120} = \dfrac{3}{4}; \quad \dfrac{x}{40 + x} = \dfrac{120}{160} = \dfrac{3}{4}$ ✔

What conclusion(s) can you draw?
1. The distance across the canyon is 120 ft.
2. If an appropriate pair of similar triangles is given, certain inaccessible distances can be found.

EXAMPLE 2 A scout troop chooses a position D and uses a transit to set $m\angle D = 61$. Along one side of $\angle D$ they locate point E 250 m from D. Along the other side, they locate point F 100 m from D. How can they find inaccessible distance EF?

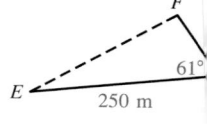

☐ **Understand the Problem**

What is the question?
Find EF, the length of a side of $\triangle DEF$.
What is given?
$DE = 250$ m, $FD = 100$ m, and $m\angle D = 61$

☐ **Plan Your Approach**

How can similar-triangle properties be used to find EF?
If a smaller scale drawing of $\triangle DEF$ could be made, the third side the smaller similar triangle could be measured. Then a proportion involving EF could be written and solved.
Since two sides and an included angle are given, use the SAS Similarity Theorem to justify drawing a $\triangle GHI \sim \triangle DEF$. If the scale 1 mm = 10 m is used, then $HG = 25$ mm, $GI = 10$ mm, and $\overline{HI}$ can be easily measured (22 mm).

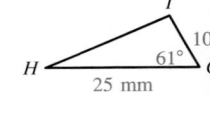

What proportion(s) can be written involving EF?
$$\dfrac{DE}{GH} = \dfrac{EF}{HI} \quad \text{and} \quad \dfrac{DF}{GI} = \dfrac{EF}{HI}$$

☐ **Implement the Plan**

Use the second proportion.
$\dfrac{100}{10} = \dfrac{EF}{22} \qquad EF = 220$ m

☐ **Interpret the Results**

EF of $\triangle DEF$ was found by drawing a similar $\triangle GHI$, measuring $\overline{H}$ and writing and solving a proportion. Since the scale was known to 1 mm = 10 m, EF could have also been found directly after measu $\overline{HI}$: $22 \cdot 10 = 220$.

Problem Solving Reminders

- An inaccessible distance can sometimes be found by considering pairs of similar triangles and writing and solving the related proportions.
- Sometimes an inaccessible distance can be found by using a triangle-similarity postulate or theorem to make a scale drawing.

CLASS EXERCISES

Thinking Critically

Shadows cast by the sun can often be used to find heights of tall objects. To do *shadow reckoning*, take these steps:

a. Measure $\overline{EF}$, the shadow cast by an object of known height DE.

b. Measure $\overline{YF}$, the shadow cast by the object of unknown height XY.

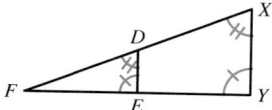

When using shadow reckoning, these two ideas are assumed: the angles at E and Y, formed by the objects with the ground, are congruent; the sun's rays make $\angle FDE \cong \angle X$.

1. Identify all pairs of congruent angles. $\angle F \cong \angle F$, $\angle FDE \cong \angle X$, $\angle FED \cong \angle Y$

2. Which theorem or postulate justifies $\triangle DEF \sim \triangle XYF$? AA Post.

3. Give the three proportions. $\frac{DE}{XY} = \frac{DF}{XF}$, $\frac{DE}{XY} = \frac{EF}{YF}$, $\frac{DF}{XF} = \frac{EF}{YF}$

4. What proportion(s) can be used to find XY? $\frac{DE}{XY} = \frac{EF}{YF}$ or $\frac{XY}{DE} = \frac{YF}{EF}$

5. If a meter stick casts a shadow of 3 m at the same time a building casts a shadow of 36 m, what is the height of the building? 12 m

PRACTICE EXERCISES   Use technology where appropriate.

Find the inaccessible distance x.

1.

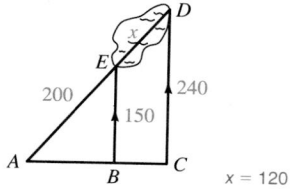

$x = 120$

2.

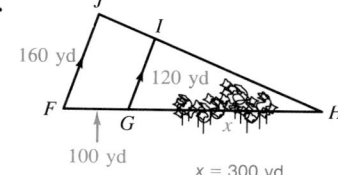

$x = 300$ yd

7.6 Strategy: Find Inaccessible Distances   **289**

Developing Mathematical Power

Keeping a Portfolio   Have students write a short paragraph that describes situations which involve indirect measurement. They should include their own problems and colored diagrams to illustrate them. Have them share their problems with their classmates.

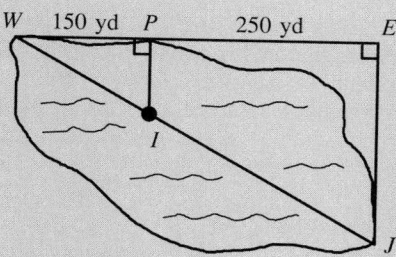

The problem asks for *WI*, the distance from the western shore to the island. Since $\triangle WPI \sim \triangle WEJ$ by AA, it follows that:

$$\frac{WP}{WE} = \frac{WI}{WJ}$$
$$\frac{150}{400} = \frac{WI}{500}$$
$$WI = 187.5 \text{ yd}$$

- **For Example 2**

   To determine an inaccessible distance, a similar triangle was drawn, with scale 1 cm = 15 m. Side $\overline{AC}$ was measured as 7 cm. Find the inaccessible distance corresponding to AC.

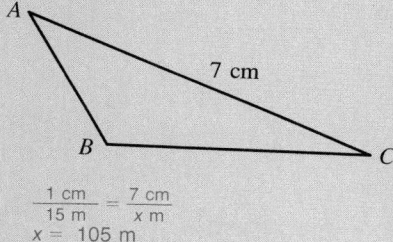

$$\frac{1 \text{ cm}}{15 \text{ m}} = \frac{7 \text{ cm}}{x \text{ m}}$$
$$x = 105 \text{ m}$$

Common Error

- The most likely error will be one in which an incorrect proportion is used. This occurs most often when the inaccessible distance represents part of a side of a triangle. Insist that students write out the proportions used, naming segments with the notations of the problem, before writing numerical equivalents.
- See *Teacher's Resource Book* for additional remediation.

LESSON FOLLOW-UP

Assignment Guide

See p. 260B for assignments.

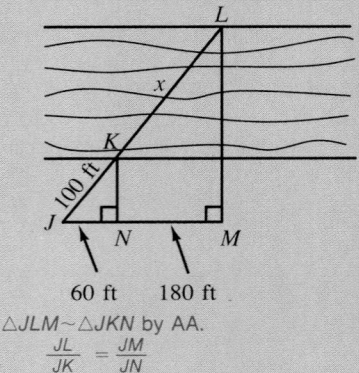
Use the scale drawings to find the inaccessible distances that correspond to the longest side of each triangle.

3.

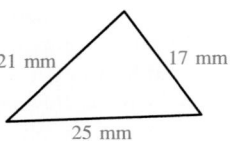

Scale: 1 mm = 10 m

250 m

4.

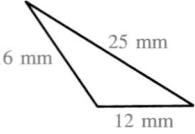

Scale: 1 mm = 50 m

x = 1250 m

5. On level ground, a 5-ft person and a flagpole cast shadows of 10 ft and 60 ft, respectively. What is the height of the flagpole? 30 ft

6. On level ground, a yardstick and a building cast shadows of 5 ft and 125 ft, respectively. What is the building's height? 75 ft

7. A tree stops a surveyor from directly measuring the length XY of a lot boundary. She measures XP = 500 ft and extends it 10 ft to A. YP turns out to be 600 ft and is extended 12 ft to B. Why is $\triangle XPY \sim \triangle APB$? What is the length of the lot boundary? SAS Th.; XY = 50AB

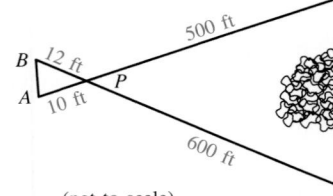

(not to scale)

B

8. A copy machine can enlarge a figure by the ratio 2 to 3. What will be the dimensions and the angle measures if this diagram is copied and enlarged? 72 mm, 48 mm, 36 mm; ∠ measures are the same.

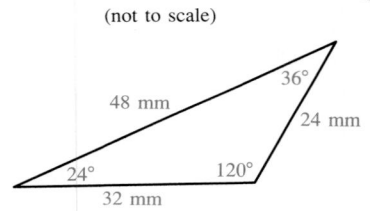

9. On level ground, the base of a tree is 20 ft from the bottom of a 48-ft flagpole. The tree is shorter than the pole. At a certain time, their shadows end at the same point 60 ft from the base of the flagpole. How tall is the tree? 32 ft

10. A yardstick casts a shadow of 24 in. at the same time that a telephone pole casts a shadow of 20 ft 8 in. What is the height of the telephone pole? 31 ft

11. Standing at one side of a room, a person finds that a 1-ft ruler can be held vertically so that the top is in line with the top of the opposite wall and the bottom with the bottom of the wall. If the ruler is 2 ft from the eye and the wall is 8 ft tall, what is the distance across the room? 16 ft

12. A person whose eyes are 5 ft from the ground finds his line-of-sight in line with the top P of a pole and the top B of a building. He knows that the pole is 25 ft tall, his feet are 30 ft from the base of the pole, and the pole is 90 ft from the base of the building. What is the height of the building? 85 ft

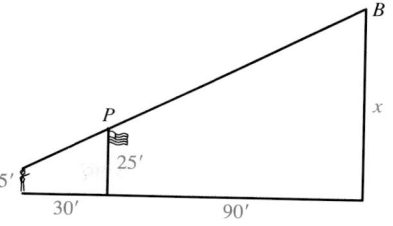

13. A 24-ft high building casts a 4-ft shadow on level ground. A person 5 ft 6 in. tall wants to stand in the shade as far away from the building as possible. What distance is this? 3 ft 1 in.

14. This figure (not drawn to scale) shows the approximate radii and center-to-center distance in miles for the Sun and Earth.

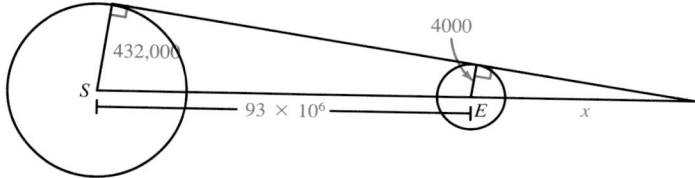

Use a calculator to compute the length x of the Earth's shadow. If the average distance from Earth to its Moon is about 240,000 mi, show why an eclipse of the moon is possible. $x \approx 870{,}000$ mi; $240{,}000 < 870{,}000$

PROJECT

This sighting-by-eye method gives an estimate of the distance to an object:

a. With outstretched arm and left eye closed, line up an object at the unknown distance.

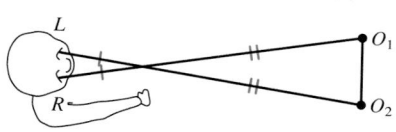

b. With outstretched arm and right eye closed, line up a second object at the unknown distance.

c. Measure the distance from right pupil to left pupil (about 7 cm).

d. Measure eye-to-finger distance along outstretched arm.

e. Estimate the distance from the first object O_1 to the second object O_2.

Use this method to estimate the distance between two objects near school.

7.6 Strategy: Find Inaccessible Distances **291**

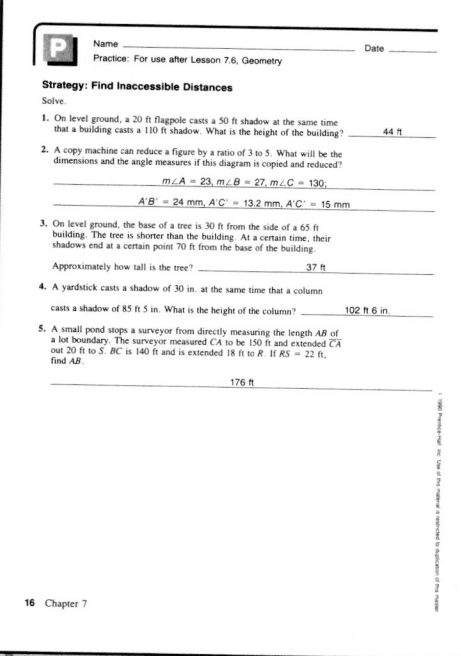
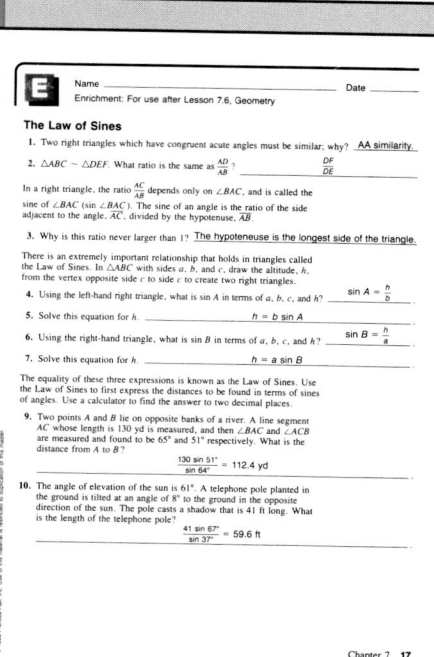

Vocabulary

Divide proportionally
Triangle Angle-Bisector Theorem
Triangle Proportionality Theorem

Materials/Manipulatives

Lined paper
Meterstick
Rulers and protractors
*Teaching Transparencies 48 and
48A*

Technology

Computer
*Computer Test Bank, pp.
438–448*
*The Geometric Supposer:
Triangles*
*Geometry Problems and
Projects: Triangles,
Worksheet T23*

LESSON FOCUS

Review

• The Mixed Review, Exercises
31–32, involves the consecutive
angles of a parallelogram and the
diagonals of a rectangle.
• The Chapter Summary and Review, pp. 300–301, gives vocabulary and concepts and review exercises by lesson.
• The end of the chapter features an
Algebra Review on p. 304.

Alternative Learning Styles

Some students may be better able to
understand the Triangle Angle-Bisector Theorem by verbally explaining
what it means. A visual aid is provided
in Teaching Transparencies 48 and
48A.

Multicultural Opportunity

See *Teacher's Resource Book,* Enrichment (see side column, p. 297).

7.7

Proportional Segments

Objectives: To prove and apply the Triangle Proportionality Theorem
and its related theorems
To prove and apply the Triangle Angle-Bisector Theorem

If X is one-third the distance from A to B and Y is
one-third the distance from D to E, then it is said that the
segments are *divided proportionally* and that $\frac{AX}{XB} = \frac{DY}{YE}$,
or any equivalent proportion, is true.

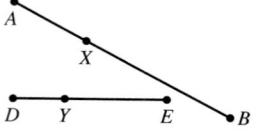

Investigation—*Thinking Critically*

In this plan for a town subdivision, Avenue A
is parallel to Avenue B.

1. What triangles are similar? Why?
   $\triangle RYX \sim \triangle RQP$; AA Post.
2. How can you use the similarity to find the
   distance from X to P? corr. sides of $\sim \triangle$s
   proportional
3. Compare XP to XR and YQ to YR. What
   conclusion(s) can you draw? $\frac{XP}{XR} = \frac{YQ}{YR}$;
   the ∥ line (Ave. A) to the base has divided the △ sides
   into proportional lengths.

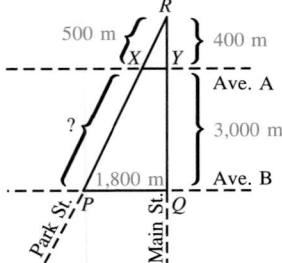

Many facts can be proven by using the properties of similar triangles.

> **Theorem 7.3   Triangle Proportionality Theorem**   If a line parallel
> to one side of a triangle intersects the other two sides, then it divides those
> sides proportionally.

Given: $\triangle ABC$; $\overline{XY} \parallel \overline{BC}$

Prove: $\dfrac{XB}{AX} = \dfrac{YC}{AY}$

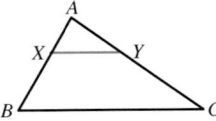

Plan: First prove $\triangle AXY \sim \triangle ABC$. This leads to $\dfrac{AB}{AX} = \dfrac{AC}{AY}$. Use the
definition of betweenness to write $\dfrac{AX + XB}{AX} = \dfrac{AY + YC}{AY}$. Then
apply proportion properties to get $\dfrac{XB}{AX} = \dfrac{YC}{AY}$. Proved in Practice Exercise 16

292   Chapter 7 Similarity

Developing Mathematical Power

Keeping a Portfolio   Have students write a paragraph summarizing what they
learned in this lesson. They should illustrate each theorem and the corollary with a
carefully labeled and color-coded diagram. The Investigation, p. 18, in the *Teacher's Resource Book* provides an opportunity to apply the material.

When three parallel lines are intersected by two transversals, the indicated auxiliary segment produces two triangles. Applying Theorem 7.3 to these triangles produces the following corollary.

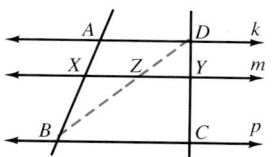

> **Corollary** If three parallel lines have two transversals, then they divide the transversals proportionally. Proved in Practice Exercise 26

EXAMPLE 1 **a.** Complete each proportion.

$$\frac{a}{b} = \underline{\ ?\ } \quad \frac{a}{c} = \underline{\ ?\ } \quad \frac{a+b}{b} = \underline{\ ?\ } \quad \frac{b+a}{a} = \underline{\ ?\ }$$

b. If $a:b = 3:5$ and d is 6 more than c, find c and d.

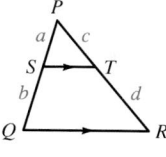

a. $\dfrac{c}{d}$; $\dfrac{b}{d}$; $\dfrac{c+d}{d}$; $\dfrac{d+c}{c}$ **b.** $\dfrac{3}{5} = \dfrac{c}{c+6}$; $c = 9$, $d = 15$

EXAMPLE 2 **a.** Complete each proportion.

$$\frac{XY}{YZ} = \underline{\ ?\ } \quad \frac{XZ}{YZ} = \underline{\ ?\ } \quad \frac{BC}{AB} = \underline{\ ?\ } \quad \frac{AB}{BC} = \underline{\ ?\ }$$

b. If $XY = 24$, $YZ = 16$, and $AC = 30$, then $BC = \underline{\ ?\ }$.

c. If $XY = 15$, $YZ = 25$, and $AB = 10$, then $BC = \underline{\ ?\ }$.

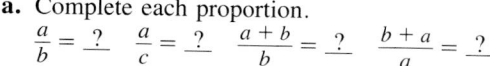

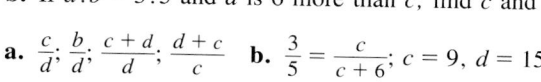

a. $\dfrac{AB}{BC}$; $\dfrac{AC}{BC}$; $\dfrac{YZ}{XY}$; $\dfrac{XY}{YZ}$ **b.** 12 **c.** $\dfrac{50}{3}$

The converse of Theorem 7.3 is also true.

> **Theorem 7.4** If a line divides two sides of a triangle proportionally, then it is parallel to the third side of the triangle. Proved in Practice Exercise 24

The next two theorems deal with medians and altitudes of similar triangles.

> **Theorem 7.5** Corresponding medians of similar triangles are proportional to the corresponding sides.

Given: $\triangle PQR \sim \triangle CTV$; $\overline{QS}$ is a median of $\triangle PQR$; $\overline{TD}$ is a median of $\triangle CTV$.

Prove: $\dfrac{QS}{TD} = \dfrac{PQ}{CT}$

Plan: Use the definition of median and the corresponding parts of the given similar triangles to prove $\triangle QSP \sim \triangle TDC$. The conclusion follows from the definition of similar triangles. Proved in Practice Exercise 17

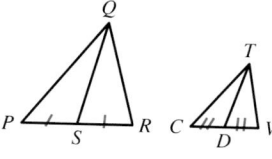

7.7 Proportional Segments **293**

TEACHING SUGGESTIONS

- Model the Triangle Angle-Bisector Theorem by having students work in small groups, with each student drawing a $\triangle ABC$ such that $AB = 2 \cdot AC$. Each student in the group should use a different measure for $\angle A$. Have them bisect $\angle A$ and measure the segments formed. Repeat for a triangle in which $AB = \frac{3}{4} \cdot AC$.

- Go over the Plan for the proof of the Triangle Angle-Bisector Theorem with the class. Students may question reasons for using an auxiliary line such as $\overleftrightarrow{BY}$. Point out how this auxiliary line sets up a situation where the Triangle Proportionality Theorem can be applied.

Critical Thinking

Analysis Ask students to analyze the use of auxiliary lines in proofs.

CHALKBOARD EXAMPLES

- **For Example 1**

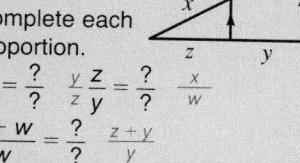

  a. Complete each proportion.

$$\frac{w}{x} = \frac{?}{?} \quad \frac{y}{z}\frac{z}{y} = \frac{?}{?} \quad \frac{x}{w}$$

$$\frac{x+w}{w} = \frac{?}{?} \quad \frac{z+y}{y}$$

  b. If $y:z = 3:2$ and x is 4 less than w, find x and w. $w:(w-4) = 3:2$; $w = 12$, $x = 8$

- **For Example 2**

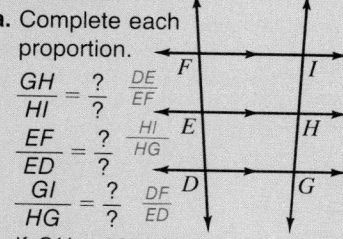

  a. Complete each proportion.

$$\frac{GH}{HI} = \frac{?}{?} \quad \frac{DE}{EF}$$

$$\frac{EF}{ED} = \frac{?}{?} \quad \frac{HI}{HG}$$

$$\frac{GI}{HG} = \frac{?}{?} \quad \frac{DF}{ED}$$

  b. If $GH = 12$, $HI = 8$, and $EF = 10$, then $ED = \underline{\ ?\ }$. 15

  c. If $GH = 18$, $HI = 12$, and $DF = 40$, then $EF = \underline{\ ?\ }$. 16

293

- **For Example 3**

  $\triangle ABC \sim \triangle DEF$; $\overline{AM}$ and $\overline{DN}$ are medians; $\overline{BP}$ and $\overline{ER}$ are altitudes.

  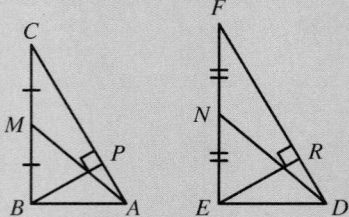

  a. If $AM = 18$, $DN = 27$, and EF $= 33$, find BC. 22

  b. If $BP = 12$, $CA = 24$, and ER $= 16$, find DF. 32

  c. If $ER = 15$, $AM = 14$, and BP $= 10$, find DN. 21

- **For Example 4**

  $\overline{AX}$ bisects $\angle BAC$.

  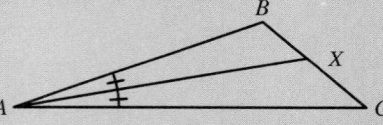

  a. If $AB = 18$, $BX = 6$, and $XC = 8$, find AC. 24

  b. If $AB = 36$, $AC = 45$, and CX $= 20$, find BC. 36

  c. If $BX = 10$ cm, $XC = 15$ cm, and AC is 14 cm longer than AB, find AB and AC. $AB = 28$ cm, AC $= 42$ cm

Common Error

- Students might not realize that a proportion must be written in a particular order. It might be clearer to draw diagrams in colors to show relationships.
- See *Teacher's Resource Book* for additional remediation.

LESSON FOLLOW-UP

Assignment Guide

See p. 260B for assignments.

> **Theorem 7.6**   Corresponding altitudes of similar triangles are proportional to the corresponding sides. Proved in Practice Exercise 18

EXAMPLE 3 $\triangle LIA \sim \triangle RTP$; $\overline{LS}$ and $\overline{RY}$ are medians; $\overline{IM}$ and $\overline{TE}$ are altitudes.

  a. If $LA = 18$, $RP = 12$, and $LS = 15$, find RY.

  b. If $IA = 40$, $TP = 30$, and $TE = 12$, find IM.

  c. If $IM = 24$, $TE = 20$, and $IS = 9$, find TP.

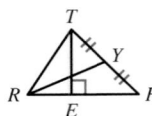 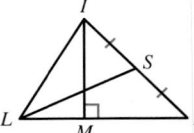

  a. 10   **b.** 16   **c.** 15

> **Theorem 7.7   Triangle Angle-Bisector Theorem**   If a ray bisects an angle of a triangle, then it divides the opposite side into segments proportional to the other two sides of the triangle.

Given: $\overrightarrow{AX}$ bisects $\angle A$ of $\triangle ABC$.

Prove: $\dfrac{BX}{XC} = \dfrac{AB}{AC}$

Plan: To use Theorem 7.3, draw a line through B parallel to $\overrightarrow{AX}$; extend $\overrightarrow{CA}$ so that it intersects that line at point Y. Since $\overrightarrow{BY} \parallel \overrightarrow{AX}$, $\dfrac{BX}{XC} = \dfrac{AY}{AC}$, $\angle 2 \cong \angle 4$ and $\angle 1 \cong \angle 3$. This leads to the fact that $\angle 3 \cong \angle 4$ and $AY = AB$. The conclusion follows by substitution. Proved in Practice Exercise 25

EXAMPLE 4 $\overline{SE}$ bisects $\angle RSO$.

  a. $RE = 8$, $RS = 12$, and $OS = 18$; find EO.

  b. $EO = 12.5$, $OS = 25$, and $RE = 10$; find RS.

  c. $RS = 3$, $OS = 2\sqrt{3}$ and $RE = \sqrt{3}$; find EO.

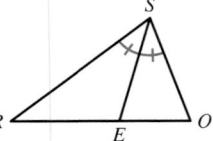

  a. 12   **b.** 20   **c.** 2

CLASS EXERCISES

Thinking Critically

1. If two triangles are similar, can you conclude that corresponding medians are in proportion to corresponding altitudes? Explain.
   Yes; the medians and altitudes are proportional to corr. sides, so they are proportional to each other.

Complete each proportion.

2. $\frac{RS}{ST} = \frac{?}{} \quad \frac{RN}{NM}$ 3. $\frac{RT}{RS} = \frac{?}{} \quad \frac{RM}{RN}$ 4. $\frac{MN}{RM} = \frac{?}{} \quad \frac{ST}{RT}$

5. $RN:MN = 5:4$ and RS is 12 more than ST; find RS and ST.
   60; 48

6. $RM = 30$, $RT = 50$, and $ST = 20$; find NM. 12

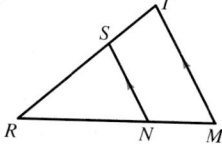

Complete each proportion.

7. $\frac{s}{r} = \frac{?}{} \quad \frac{b}{a}$ 8. $\frac{a+b}{b} = \frac{?}{} \quad \frac{r+s}{s}$ 9. $\frac{r+s}{r} = \frac{?}{} \quad \frac{b+a}{a}$

10. $a = 12$, $b = 9$, and $s = 4$; find r. $\frac{16}{3}$

11. $a = 24$, $s = 6$, and $b = r$; find b and r.
    $b = 12; r = 12$

12. $r + s = 48$, $a + b = 40$, and $r = 32$; find b. $b = \frac{40}{3}$

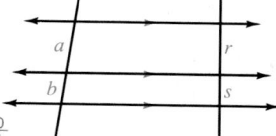

13. $DF = 39$, $DR = 36$, and $AP = 12$; find AC.
    $AC = 13$

14. If $BC = 15$, $EF = 21$, and $AP = 10$, the altitude of the larger triangle is $\underline{?}$. 14

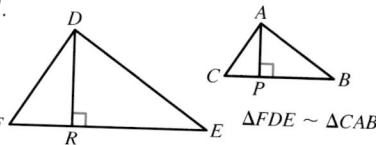

$\triangle FDE \sim \triangle CAB$

PRACTICE EXERCISES   Use technology where appropriate.

Find the measures and complete the statements. See side column.

	AX	BX	AB	AY	YC	AC
1.	6	10	?	21	?	?
2.	10	?	30	?	14	?
3.	4	?	$4 + 2\sqrt{10}$	$\sqrt{10}$	?	?

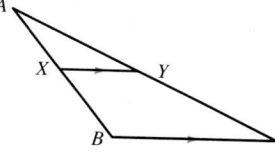

4. $AX:BX = 3:2$ and AY is 2 cm longer than YC; find AY and YC.
   6 cm; 4 cm

	DE	DF	EP	PF	EF
5.	6	21	?	14	?
6.	?	21	10	12	?
7.	3	5	?	?	16
8.	?	$3\sqrt{5}$	$2\sqrt{5}$	5	?
9.	25	35	20	? 28	? 48

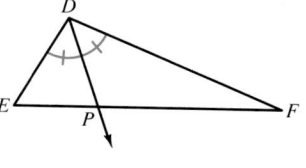

10. If $DE = 30$, $DR = 15$, and $AP = 12$, then $AB = \underline{?}$. 24

11. If $BC = 42$ m, $EF = 63$ m, and $AP = 10$ m, then $DR = \underline{?}$. 15 m

12. If $AC = 7$, and altitudes $\overline{AP}$ and $\overline{DR}$ are in the ratio of 3 to 5, then $DF = \underline{?}$. $\frac{35}{3}$

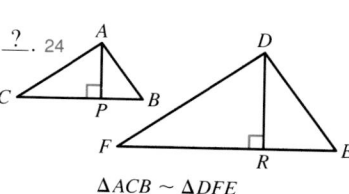

$\triangle ACB \sim \triangle DFE$

7.7 Proportional Segments   **295**

1. 16; 35; 56   2. 20; 7; 21
3. $2\sqrt{10}$; 5; $5 + \sqrt{10}$
5. 4; 18   6. $17\frac{1}{2}$; 22   7. 6; 10
8. 6; $5 + 2\sqrt{5}$

Additional Answers for p. 296

16. Proof:

Statements	Reasons
1. $\overline{XY} \parallel \overline{BC}$	1. Given
2. $\angle AXY \cong \angle ABC$; $\angle AYX \cong \angle ACB$	2. If ∥ lines have a transv., then corr. ∠s are ≅.
3. $\triangle AXY \sim \triangle ABC$	3. AA Post.
4. $\frac{AB}{AX} = \frac{AC}{AY}$	4. Corr. side lengths of ~ △ are in prop.
5. $AB = AX + XB$; $AC = AY + YC$	5. Def. of betw.
6. $\frac{AX + XB}{AX} = \frac{AY + YC}{AY}$	6. Subst. prop.
7. $\frac{XB + AX}{AX} = \frac{XB}{AX}$, $\frac{YC + AY}{AY} = \frac{YC}{AY}$	7. Prop. prop.
8. $\frac{XB}{AX} = \frac{YC}{AY}$	8. Subst. prop.

Conclusion: In $\triangle ABC$, if $\overline{XY} \parallel \overline{BC}$, then $\frac{XB}{AX} = \frac{YC}{AY}$.

17. Proof:

Statements	Reasons
1. $\triangle PQR \sim \triangle CTV$; QS is a median of $\triangle PQR$; TD is a median of $\triangle CTV$.	1. Given
2. $\angle P \cong \angle C$; $\frac{PQ}{CT} = \frac{PR}{CY}$	2. Def. of ~ polygons
3. S is the midpt. of PR; D is the midpt. of CV.	3. Def. of median
4. $PR = 2 \cdot PS$; $CV = 2 \cdot CD$	4. Midpt. Th.
5. $\frac{PQ}{CT} = \frac{2 \cdot PS}{2 \cdot CD}$	5. Subst. prop.
6. $\frac{PQ}{CT} = \frac{PS}{CD}$	6. Equiv. fract.
7. $\triangle QSP \sim \triangle TDC$	7. SAS Th.
8. $\frac{QS}{TD} = \frac{PQ}{CT}$	8. Def. of ~ △

Conclusion: If ~ △ PQR and CTV have corr. median $\overline{QS}$ and $\overline{TD}$, then $\frac{QS}{TD} = \frac{PQ}{CT}$.

Test Yourself

See *Teacher's Resource Book, Tests,* pp. 71–72.

Lesson Quiz

Find x.

1.

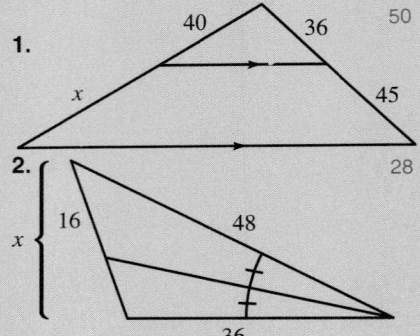
40   36   50
x 45

2.

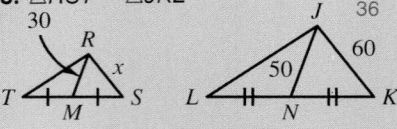
28
16   48
x
36

3. △RST ~ △JKL

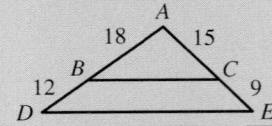
30
R J 36
x 50   60
T S L N K
M

4. Is $\overline{BC} \parallel \overline{DE}$? Explain.

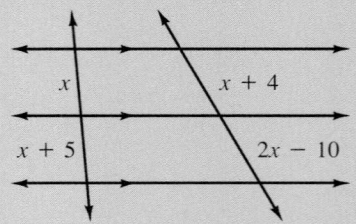
A
18   15
B C
12   9
D E

No; $\overline{BC}$ does not divide $\overline{AD}$ and $\overline{AE}$ proportionally.

Enrichment

Find x.

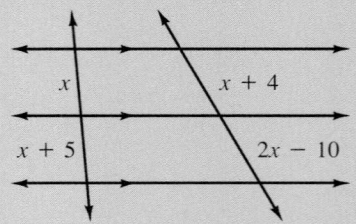
x $x + 4$
$x + 5$ $2x - 10$

$\dfrac{x}{x+5} = \dfrac{x+4}{2x-10}$
$2x^2 - 10x = x^2 + 9x + 20$
$x^2 - 19x - 20 = 0$
$(x - 20)(x + 1) = 0$
$x = 20$ or $x = -1$ (reject)
$x = 20$

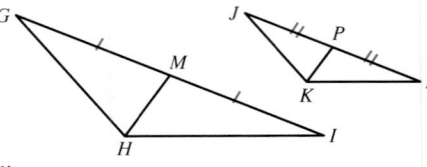
G J P
M K
H I

13. If $IH = 63$ mm, $KP = 15$ mm, and $LK = 42$ mm, then $MH = \underline{\ ?\ }$. $\frac{45}{2}$ mm

14. If $JP = 35$ yd, $MH = 33$ yd, and $PK = 20$ yd, then $GI = \underline{\ ?\ }$. $\frac{231}{2}$ yd

15. Median $\overline{MH}$ is 6 m longer than $\overline{KP}$. $GH:JK = 7:5$; find the length of each median. *MH = 21 m; KP = 15 m*

B **16.** Complete the Theorem 7.3 proof. *See side column page 295.* **17.** Complete the Theorem 7.5 proof.

18. Prove Theorem 7.6. (*Hint:* Study the *Plan* for Theorem 7.5.) *See Additional Answers, p. 702.*

19. △ABD ~ △EFG; find $\overline{BC}$ and $\overline{FH}$. *BC = 12; FH = 9* **20.** For what value of x is $\overline{PQ} \parallel \overline{BC}$? *x = 7*

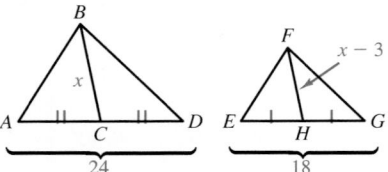
B F $x - 3$
x x
A C D E H G
24   18

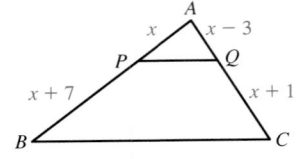
A
x $x - 3$
P Q
$x + 7$ $x + 1$
B C

21. The perimeter of △RXA = 39, $PX = 4$, and $AP = 9$; find RX and RA. *RX = 8; RA = 18*

22. The perimeter of △RXA = 24, $RX = 4.5$, and $RA = 13.5$; find XP and PA. *XP = 1.5; PA = 4.5*

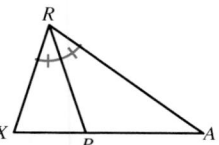
R
X P A

23. Two sides of a triangle measure 8 cm and 12 cm, respectively. A line intersecting those sides separates one into 3 cm and 5 cm, the other into 4.5 cm and 7.5 cm. Why is that line parallel to the third side? $\frac{3}{5} = \frac{4.5}{7.5}$ is a true proportion.

24. Complete this proof of Theorem 7.4.

Given: $\dfrac{QN}{NR} = \dfrac{PM}{MR}$ *See Additional Answers, p. 702.*

Prove: $\overline{NM} \parallel \overline{PQ}$

Q N
P M R

Plan: Use the proportion properties to rewrite the given as $\dfrac{QR}{NR} = \dfrac{PR}{MR}$.
Prove △QRP ~ △NRM by SAS. Use ≅ corr. ∠s to show $\overline{NM} \parallel \overline{PQ}$.

C **25.** Complete the Theorem 7.7 proof. **26.** Prove the Theorem 7.3 corollary.

27. The sides of △RPQ are 5, 12, and 13 in. The angle opposite the shortest side is bisected. Into what lengths does the angle bisector separate that side? $2\frac{2}{5}$ in., $2\frac{3}{5}$ in.

28. Prove: If a ray bisects an exterior angle of a triangle and intersects the line that contains the opposite side, then it separates the opposite side into segments proportional to the other two sides of the triangle. *See Additional Answers, p. 702.*

296   Chapter 7 Similarity

Applications

29. Surveying A triangular plot of land has sides of 240, 300, and 180 ft, respectively. The included angle between the first two sides is bisected by a surveyor's tape. Into what lengths does the tape separate the third side?
80 ft, 100 ft

30. Technology Use Logo to generate a graphic using similar polygons.
See Solutions Manual.

Mixed Review

31. Use $\square ABCD$ and find the measures of all the angles.
65°; 115°

32. $\square CDEF$ is a rectangle, and the diagonals intersect at G.
$CG = 3x - 10$ and $GF = x + 22$.
Find DG. 38

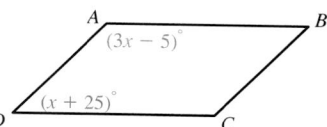
$(3x - 5)^\circ$
$(x + 25)^\circ$

TEST YOURSELF See Additional Answers, p. 702.

1. State the SAS Theorem for similar triangles. 7.5

2. State the Triangle Angle-Bisector Theorem. 7.7

3. Why is $\triangle ABC$ similar to $\triangle XDY$? Write the proportionality statement for side lengths. 7.4

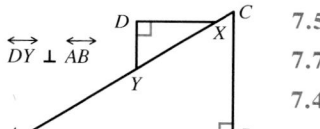
$\overleftrightarrow{DY} \perp \overleftrightarrow{AB}$

Are the triangles similar? If so, write a similarity statement and verify.

4.
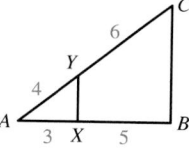
No

5.
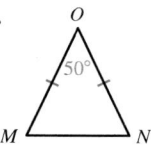
$\triangle MON \sim \triangle TRB$; SAS Th. or AA Post.

6.
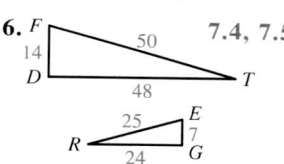
7.4, 7.5
$\triangle GRE \sim \triangle DTF$; SSS Th.

7. A scout sights an object at 40° angles from the endpoints of a 50-yd segment. How can she determine the distance from an endpoint to the object? Make a scale drawing and let 1 yd = 1 in.; distance $\approx 32\frac{1}{2}$ yd. 7.4, 7.6

8. $\overline{AP}$ is the angle bisector of $\angle A$; find the lengths of $\overline{CP}$ and $\overline{BP}$.
$CP = 6$, $BP = 10$
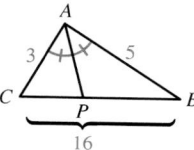

9. $\triangle DEF \sim \triangle GHI$; $GK = \frac{3}{2} DJ$. If $HI = 20$, then $EF = \underline{\ ?\ }$. $\frac{40}{3}$ 7.7
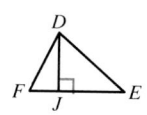 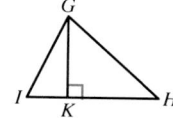

7.7 Proportional Segments **297**

Teacher's Resource Book
Follow-Up Investigation, Chapter 7, p. 18

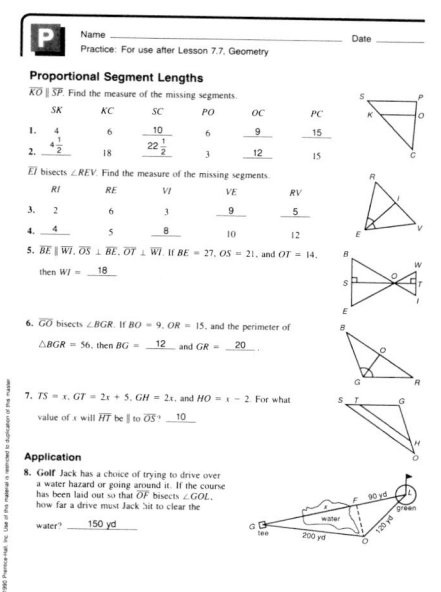

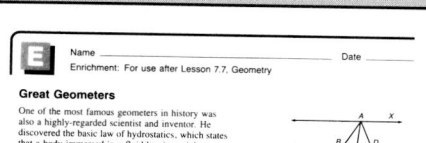

297

See *Teacher's Resource Book,* Follow-up *Technology,* pp. 9–10.

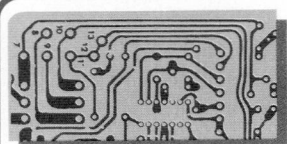

TECHNOLOGY:
Similarity in Computer Graphics

Using ideas of similarity, sophisticated designs and graphics can be generated on the computer. The procedure that defines a regular polygon can be used as the basis for all of the graphics.

The polygon procedure has the two variables:

:number to represent the number of sides you want
:length to represent the length of the side

```
to polygon :number :length
repeat :number [forward :length right 360 / :number]
end
```

polygon 3 80

EXAMPLE **Use recursion with similar polygons to create different spiral effects.**

```
to polyspi :side :angle :number
if :side > 100 [stop]
repeat :number [fd :side rt 360/:number]
lt :angle
polyspi :side + 5 :angle :number
end
```

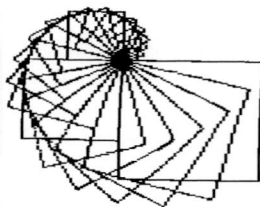

Another way to use the polyspi procedure is to draw only dots at the vertices of the chosen polygon. The dots seem to appear in "arms," either straight arms or spiral arms.

```
to polyspidot :side :angle :number
if :side > 100 [stop]
pu
repeat :number [fd :side drawdot rt 360/:number]
lt :angle
polyspidot :side :angle :number
end

to drawdot
pd fd 1 bk 1 pu
end
```

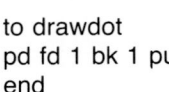

A different way to generate interesting computer graphics using similarity is to overlay or rearrange the figures.

Consider the following design, which is based on similar equilateral triangles. By studying the figure carefully, you can see that there are three different sets of triangles each forming a decagon.

Thus, the building block for this design is again the "polygon" procedure placed within a procedure to draw a decagon:

```
to decagon :number :length
repeat 10 [polygon :number :length forward :length left 36]
end
```

EXERCISES See Solutions Manual.

1. Experiment with different values for the variables in the polyspi procedure to generate a computer graphic of spirals that you like.

2. What happens if you change the recursion to :angle instead of :side? to :number instead of :side?

3. What numbers in the polyspidot procedure create "straight" arms? "curved" arms?

4. What value(s) for :angle will make a sunburst with random length rays?

5. What would be the commands to generate the above graphic based on the decagon?

6. Visit an art department at a college or a computer graphics company to learn about computer graphics and the careers in which computers are used for visual design.

- See *Teacher's Resource Book, Spanish Chapter Summary and Review*, pp. 13–14.
- See Extra Practice, p. 649.

CHAPTER 7   SUMMARY AND REVIEW

Vocabulary

AA Postulate (277)	radical (268)
cross products (267)	radicand (268)
divide proportionally (292)	ratio (262)
extended proportion (264)	SAS Theorem (282)
extremes (263)	scale factor (271)
geometric mean (268)	similar polygons (271)
means (263)	simplest form: radicals (268)
means-extremes property (267)	simplest form: ratio (262)
product property of square roots (268)	SSS Theorem (283)
	terms of a proportion (263)
proportion (263)	Triangle Angle-Bisector Theorem (294)
proportion properties (267)	Triangle Proportionality Theorem (292)

Ratio and Proportion   The ratio of x to y can be expressed as $x:y$, $\frac{x}{y}$, or x to y. A proportion is the equality of two ratios. The first and fourth terms of a proportion are the extremes; the second and third are the means.   **7.1**

Write each ratio in simplest form.

1. $\frac{54}{81}$ $\frac{2}{3}$ **2.** $180:135$ $4:3$ **3.** $\frac{2x^2 - 32}{x + 4}$ $\frac{2(x-4)}{1}$

Identify the means and extremes. Then, find the missing terms.

4. $\frac{4}{9} = \frac{x}{54}$ **5.** $8:x = 12:20$ **6.** $x:4 = 16:x$

means 9, x means x, 12   means 4, 16
extremes 4, 54   extremes 8, 20   extremes x, x
$x = 24$ $x = \frac{40}{3}$ $x = 8$

Properties of Proportions   Five properties can be used to write proportions that are equivalent to a given proportion. The geometric mean between two positive numbers is the principal square root of the product of the two numbers.   **7.2**

Use the proportion $\dfrac{UA}{AM} = \dfrac{UR}{RY}$ to complete the following.

7. $\frac{AM}{UA} = \underline{\ ?\ }$ $\frac{RY}{UR}$ **8.** $AM \cdot UR = \underline{\ ?\ }$ $UA \cdot RY$ **9.** $\frac{UA}{AM} = \frac{UA + UR}{AM + RY}$?

10. If $UA = 9$, $AM = 5$, and $UR = 12$, then $RY = \underline{\ ?\ }$. $\frac{20}{3}$

11. If $UM = 48$, $UR = 20$, and $RY = 12$, then $AM = \underline{\ ?\ }$. 18

12. Find the geometric mean between 6 and 10 in simplest form. $2\sqrt{15}$

Similar Polygons
7.3

Similar polygons have congruent corresponding angles and proportional corresponding side lengths.

Give a similarity statement and the scale factor for these similar polygons.

13.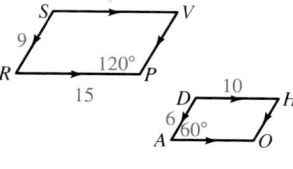

RSVP ~ ADHO;
3:2

14.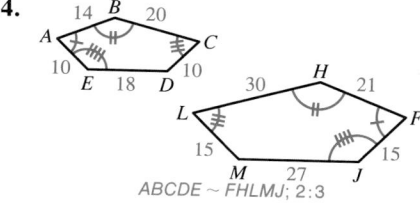

ABCDE ~ FHLMJ; 2:3

Similar Triangles
7.4, 7.5

The AA Postulate and the SAS and SSS Theorems are methods used to prove triangles similar.

Are the triangles similar? If so, write a similarity statement and verify.

15.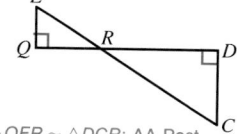

△QER ~ △DCR; AA Post.

16.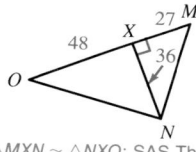

△MXN ~ △NXO; SAS Th.

17.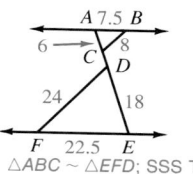

△ABC ~ △EFD; SSS Th.

Strategy: Find Inaccessible Distances

18. On level ground, a 6-ft person and a flagpole cast shadows of 10 ft and 60 ft, respectively. What is the height of the flagpole? 36 ft
7.6

Proportional Segments
7.7

Five theorems and a corollary give information about the proportionality of segment lengths associated with triangles.

19. If $AC = 40$, $AX = 3$, and $BX = 5$, then $AY = \underline{\ ?\ }$. 15

20. If $AX = 4$, $XB = 5$, $AY = 12$, and $YC = 15$, is $\overline{XY} \parallel \overline{BC}$? Explain. Yes; if a line divides 2 sides of a △ proportionally, then it is ∥ to the 3rd side of the △.

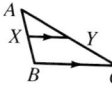

21. △GHI ~ △JKL. If $JY = 6$, $HI = 12$, and $KL = 18$, then $GX = \underline{\ ?\ }$. 4

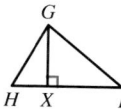
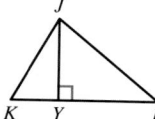

22. $RT:TS = 3:7$ and QS is 28 cm longer than QR; find QR and QS. QR = 21, QS = 49

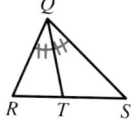

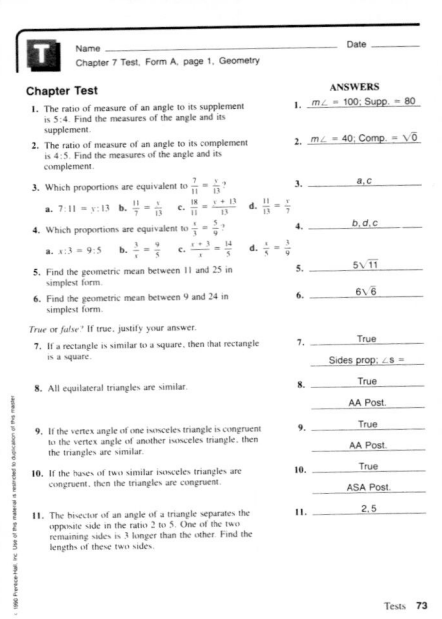

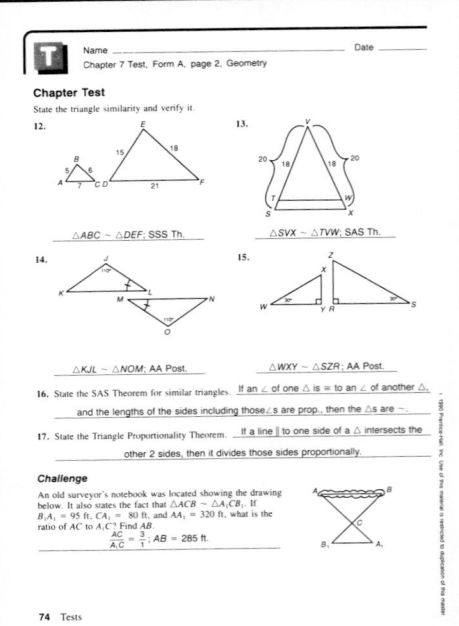

1. The ratio of the measure of an angle to its supplement is 7 to 3. Find the measures of the angle and its supplement. angle = 126, supplement = 54

2. Which proportions are equivalent to $\dfrac{2}{9} = \dfrac{m}{12}$?

   a. $9:2 = 12:m$ **b.** $\dfrac{2+12}{9} = \dfrac{m+12}{12}$ **c.** $\dfrac{11}{9} = \dfrac{m+12}{12}$ **d.** $\dfrac{2}{9} = \dfrac{m+2}{21}$

   a, c, d

3. Find the geometric mean between 6 and 18 in simplest form. $\sqrt{108} = 6\sqrt{3}$

True or false? If false, give a counterexample.

4. If a rhombus is similar to a square, then that rhombus is a square. true

5. All isosceles triangles are similar.
   False; two isos. △s may have different vertex ∠ measures.

6. If an acute angle of one right triangle is congruent to an acute angle of a second right triangle, then the right triangles are similar. true

7. If an acute angle of one right triangle is congruent to an acute angle of a second right triangle, then the right triangles are congruent.
   False; even if the ∠s are ≅, corr. sides may differ in length.

State the triangle similarity and verify it.

8.

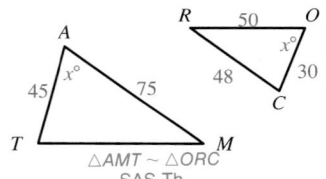

△AMT ~ △ORC
SAS Th.

9.

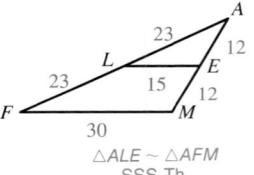

△ALE ~ △AFM
SSS Th.

10. The bisector of an angle of a triangle separates the opposite side in the ratio 7 to 11. One of the two remaining sides is 8 cm longer than the other. Find the lengths of these two sides. 14 cm, 22 cm

11. Point X separates side $\overline{AB}$ of △ABC so that $AX:BX = 1:3$. Point Y separates $\overline{AC}$ so that $AY = 3.5$ in. and $CY = 10.5$ in. Is $\overline{XY} \parallel \overline{BC}$? Explain.
    Yes; $\dfrac{AX}{BX} = \dfrac{AY}{YC} = \dfrac{1}{3}$; since the sides divide proportionally, lines are ∥.

Challenge

The sides of △RXA are parallel to corresponding sides of △SYB. Prove that the triangles are similar.
See Additional Answers, p. 702.

Alternative Assessment   Have students use a ruler and a protractor to draw two similar triangles and to describe the three ways to prove triangle similarity. Have students write a test question for Lesson 7.7.

Solve. Grid in your responses on the answer sheet.

1. Point W is in the interior of $\angle XYZ$. If $m\angle ZYW = 27$ and $m\angle XYZ = 118$, find $m\angle XYW$. 91

2. If $\triangle ABC \sim \triangle XYZ$ and $AB = 8$, $BC = 12$, $AC = 16$, and $XY = 12$, what is the perimeter of $\triangle XYZ$? 54

3. The first of four identical glasses is $\frac{1}{2}$ full of water, the second is $\frac{3}{4}$ full, the third is $\frac{7}{8}$ full, and the fourth is $\frac{15}{16}$ full. After water is poured from the fourth glass to fill each of the first three glasses, what fraction of the fourth glass will be full? $\frac{1}{16}$

4. If the average of the measures of three angles of a quadrilateral is 78, what is the measure of the fourth angle? 126

5. In a biology class, each student measured his or her hand span in inches. They then combined the results into the table below.

span	6.5	7	7.25	7.5	7.75	8
number	2	3	8	10	4	3

   What was the average hand span in inches for these students? 7.4

6. The sum of the perimeters of two similar triangles is 18 in. The ratio of two corresponding sides is $1:2$. What is the perimeter in inches of the smaller triangle? 6

Use the diagram below for 7–8.

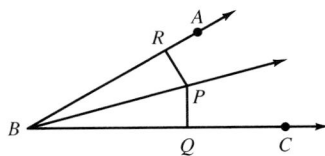

Given: $\overline{PR} \perp \overleftrightarrow{AB}$; $\overline{PQ} \perp \overleftrightarrow{CB}$; $\overline{PR} \cong \overline{PQ}$

7. If $m\angle ABC = 30$, then what is $m\angle ABP$? 15

8. If $BR = 8$, find the length of BQ. 8

Use this definition for 9–10.

ⓐ is defined by ⓐ $= a^3 - a^2$
For example: ③ $= 3^3 - 3^2 = 18$
$$-2 = (-2)^3 - (2)^2$$
$$= -8 - 4 = -12$$

9. Find ⑤. 100

10. Find ⑥ $-$ ④. 132

11. An angle has a measure of $2x + 20$, and its vertical angle has a measure of $5x - 34$. What is the measure of each angle? 56

12. If an angle of a right triangle has a measure of 38, what is the measure of the other acute angle? 52

13. An angle has a measure of $2x + 25$, and its complement has a measure of $8x - 15$. What is the measure of the complement? 49

According to the College Entrance Examination Board and the Educational Testing Service, the 1994 revision of the SAT will include a section of problems that require students to produce and grid in their own answers.

See *Teacher's Resource Book,* Preparing for College Entrance Exams, for grids.

The following skills and concepts are reviewed:

Simplifying radicals
Operating with radicals
Solving radical equations

Simplify.

Examples **a.** $\sqrt{98} = \sqrt{49 \cdot 2} = \sqrt{49} \cdot \sqrt{2} = 7\sqrt{2}$

    b. $\dfrac{\sqrt{72}}{\sqrt{20}} = \sqrt{\dfrac{72}{20}} = \sqrt{\dfrac{18}{5}} = \dfrac{\sqrt{9} \cdot \sqrt{2}}{\sqrt{5}} \cdot \dfrac{\sqrt{5}}{\sqrt{5}} = \dfrac{3\sqrt{10}}{5}$

    c. $(2\sqrt{6})^2 = 2\sqrt{6} \cdot 2\sqrt{6} = 4 \cdot 6 = 24$

1. $\sqrt{36}$ 6   **2.** $-\sqrt{81}$ -9 **3.** $\sqrt{32}$ $4\sqrt{2}$ **4.** $4\sqrt{75}$ $20\sqrt{3}$

5. $\sqrt{5^2}$ 5   **6.** $-(\sqrt{6^2})$ -6 **7.** $\dfrac{\sqrt{21}}{\sqrt{18}}$ $\dfrac{\sqrt{42}}{6}$ **8.** $\left(\dfrac{\sqrt{10}}{2}\right)^2$ $\dfrac{5}{2}$

Simplify.

Examples **a.** $\sqrt{2} \cdot 3\sqrt{2} = 3\sqrt{2 \cdot 2} = 6$

    b. $\sqrt{3}(2 - \sqrt{5}) = \sqrt{3} \cdot 2 - \sqrt{3} \cdot \sqrt{5} = 2\sqrt{3} - \sqrt{15}$

    c. $2\sqrt{28} - 5\sqrt{63} = 2\sqrt{4 \cdot 7} - 5\sqrt{9 \cdot 7} = 4\sqrt{7} - 15\sqrt{7} = -11\sqrt{7}$

9. $\sqrt{\dfrac{4}{7}} \cdot \sqrt{\dfrac{7}{4}}$ 1   **10.** $\sqrt{m}(\sqrt{m^3} + 5)$ $m^2 + 5\sqrt{m}$ **11.** $(\sqrt{x} + \sqrt{3})(\sqrt{x} - \sqrt{3})$ $x - 3$

12. $4\sqrt{45} - 3\sqrt{5}$ $9\sqrt{5}$ **13.** $4\sqrt{32} + 3\sqrt{18}$ $25\sqrt{2}$ **14.** $(7\sqrt{2} - \sqrt{3})^2$ $101 - 14\sqrt{6}$

Solve.

Examples **a.** $\sqrt{x} = 10$ **b.** $a^2 + (2\sqrt{3})^2 = 4^2$ **c.** $x^2 - x - 12 = 0$

    $(\sqrt{x})^2 = 10^2$ $a^2 + 12 = 16$ $(x - 4)(x + 3) = 0$

        $x = 100$ $a^2 = 4$ $x - 4 = 0$

                              $a = \pm 2$ or $x + 3 = 0$

                                            $4, -3$

15. $\sqrt{x} + 2 = 9$ $x = 49$ **16.** $\sqrt{2m} = 8$ $m = 32$ **17.** $x^2 = 49$ $x = \pm 7$

18. $x^2 + 4x + 4 = 9$ **19.** $\dfrac{x}{4} = \dfrac{6}{x}$ $x = \pm 2\sqrt{6}$ **20.** $12^2 + x^2 = 169$ $x = \pm 5$
$x = -5, 1$

21. $\dfrac{x}{6} = \dfrac{12}{7x + 3}$ $x = -\dfrac{24}{7}, 3$ **22.** $2y^2 - 6y - 8 = 0$ $y = 4, -1$ **23.** $3\sqrt{6^2} + x^2 = 9^2$ $x = \pm 3\sqrt{7}$

OVERVIEW • Chapter 8

SUMMARY

In Chapter 8, right triangle similarity is introduced by drawing an altitude to the hypotenuse of a right triangle. Students learn to apply the Pythagorean Theorem and its converse, as well as related theorems. They then study relationships in 30°–60°–90° triangles and in 45°–45°–90° triangles. The tangent, sine, and cosine ratios are defined and used in solving problems involving these ratios. Students also learn to use trigonometric tables.

CHAPTER OBJECTIVES

- To state and apply the relationships that exist when the altitude is drawn to the hypotenuse of a right triangle

- To state and apply the Pythagorean Theorem, its converse, and related theorems about obtuse and acute triangles

- To state and apply the relationships in special right triangles

- To define and compute the tangent, sine, and cosine ratios for an acute angle

- To use trigonometric tables

- To develop skills in *estimating and calculating roots* when solving for one side of a right triangle

- To use trigonometric ratios to solve real-world problems

CHAPTER HIGHLIGHTS

DEVELOPING MATHEMATICAL POWER

Problem Solving

The four problem solving steps are used to estimate and calculate square roots in Lesson 8.5, and, in Lesson 8.7, to use trigonometric ratios.

Communication

The side column has suggestions for alternative learning styles and cooperative learning activities. Students are asked to write about and draw right triangles. The *Teacher's Resource Book* offers a Chapter Summary and Review in Spanish. The side column provides topics such as a biography of Pythagoras for students' portfolio entries.

Reasoning

In Lesson 8.2, students investigate Pythagorean triples by drawing conclusions from patterns found when evaluating expressions. Throughout the chapter, students are asked to write formal proofs.

Connections

Real-world applications include such topics as physics, recreation, and carpentry. The Integrating Geometry feature discusses using geometry to measure astronomical distances.

Technology 〰️

Logo topics are presented in exercises throughout the chapter. Where appropriate, calculators are suggested for deriving square roots and finding trigonometric measures.

STUDENT TEXT

Chapter Content	Basic	Average	Enriched	NCTM STANDARDS*
8.1 Right Triangle Similarity	D_1: 308/1-14, 25, 43 D_2: 308/15-24	D_1: 308/1-24, 43 D_2: 308/25-34, 44, 45	D_1: 308/15-25, 38-41 D_2: 308/26-34, 42-45	1, 3, 4, 5, 7, 8
8.2 Pythagorean Theorem	D: 314/1-14, 28, MR R: 308/26-29	D: 314/1-22, 28, 29, MR R: 308/35-37	D: 314/1-20, 26-29, MR R: 308/35-37	2, 3, 4, 7, 8
8.3 Converse of the Pythagorean Theorem	D: 318/1-17, 32, 38 R: 314/15-17	D: 318/1-23, 32-38 R: 314/23, 24	D: 318/1-21, 29-38 R: 314/21-25	3, 4, 5, 8, 12
8.4 Special Right Triangles	D: 324/1-15 even, 29, AR R: 318/18, 19	D: 324/1-17, 29, 30, AR R: 318/24-27	D: 324/4-17, 21-30, AR R: 318/22-28	3, 4, 6, 8, 12
8.5 Strategy: Estimate and Calculate Roots	D: 328/1-17 odd R: 324/1-15 odd	D: 328/1-21 odd R: 324/18-20	D: 328/1-25 odd R: 324/18-20	1, 4, 6
8.6 Trigonometric Ratios	D: 335/1-10, 33 R: 328/6-12 even	D: 335/1-14, 20-26, 31-34 R: 328/6-12 even	D: 335/1-14, 20-34 R: 328/8-14 even	1, 4, 8, 9
8.7 Strategy: Use Trigonometric Ratios	D: 339/1-8 R: 335/11-13	D: 339/1-10 R: 335/15-19	D: 339/1-12 R: 335/15-19	1, 4, 8, 9

D = Daily   R = Review   MR = Mixed Review   AR = Algebra Review   *For a complete list of NCTM Standards, see p. T7.

STUDENT TEXT

Review/Assessment

Mixed Review 315
Algebra Review 325
Summary and Review 344
College Ent. Exam Rev. 347
Cumulative Review 348

Extra Practice 650
Test Yourself 320, 341
Chapter Test 346
Chapter Project 305

Special Features

Construction 310
Technology 310, 315, 320, 325, 336
Devel. Math. Power 320, 336
Applications 310, 315, 320, 325, 336, 342-343
Project 330, 341

RESOURCES

Teacher's Resource Book

Ch. 8: Investigation/Practice/ Enrichment 1-19
Spanish Sum. and Rev. 15-16
Quizzes 85-88
Chapter Tests 89-92
Perf. Assessment Proj. Ch. 8
Critical Thinking 8

Reading and Writing in Geom. 8
Application—Ch. 8, 20
Teaching Aid 8
Transparencies 9-12

Teaching Transparencies 49-55
Computer Test Bank 449-520
Connections 9-17
PH Graph. Utility
Overhead Manip. Kit

Right Triangles

Tracking time!

Developing Mathematical Power

If you have ever observed your own shadow, you know that your shadow changes in length and direction through-out the day. Before there were clocks, the passage of time was measured by observing shadows. People estimated the hour by measuring the length of their shadows with their footsteps.

The table below, developed by the Venerable Bede in about A.D. 700, was used to tell time. In Bede's day, the hours were counted from dawn, so "6" means the end of the sixth hour after dawn. The time from dawn to sunset was divided into 12 equal hours. This method led to "unequal hours"—longer hours in the summer and shorter hours in the winter.

Project

Measure the length of your own shadow with your feet. What is the time according to Bede's table? Compare that time with the time shown by a clock. Then develop a table that gives the hours of one day based on the length and direction of your shadow.

Length of One's Shadow in "Feet" at Various Hours of the Day at Various Times of the Year

hour of the day	Jan. Dec.	Feb. Nov.	Mar. Oct.	Apr. Sept.	May Aug.	June July
1 or 11	29	27	25	23	21	19
2 or 10	19	17	15	13	11	9
3 or 9	17	15	13	11	9	7
4 or 8	15	13	11	9	7	5
5 or 7	13	11	9	7	5	3
6	11	9	7	5	3	1

305

MODELING

Mathematics provides the power to make everyday living easier. This project involves using a mathematical model for a practical problem. The model is developed by compiling and analyzing data and by using mathematical skills.

Cooperative Learning

This project is accomplished through a succession of tasks, each of which is well-suited to a cooperative learning situation. These tasks include:

1. Testing information in a given table for accuracy.
2. Applying concepts of right triangles and their parts.
3. Keeping a record of data.
4. Organizing data in a table.
5. Analyzing data in a table.

Alternative Assessment

See the *Teacher's Resource Book*, Assessment, Chapter 8. This project and the TRB page may be used as an alternative form of assessment for selected topics in Chapter 8.

Materials/Manipulatives

Geoboard
Graph paper
Teacher's Resource Book,
  Teaching Aid 8
  Transparency 9
  Teaching Transparency 49

Technology
Computer Test Bank, pp.
  449–460

LESSON FOCUS

Review

- Review the meaning of *geometric mean.* Then ask students to answer the following questions.
  1. What is the geometric mean of 5 and 20?
  2. What is the geometric mean of 14 and 35?
  3. 15 is the geometric mean of 9 and what number?

  1. 10   2. $7\sqrt{10}$ 3. 25

- Review simplifying radicals. For example,
  $\sqrt{48} = \sqrt{16 \cdot 3} = \sqrt{16} \cdot \sqrt{3} = 4\sqrt{3}$
  Have students simplify each of the following.
  1. $\sqrt{75}$ **2.** $\sqrt{18}$ **3.** $\sqrt{20}$
  1. $5\sqrt{3}$ 2. $3\sqrt{2}$ 3. $2\sqrt{5}$

Alternative Learning Styles

The Investigation provides a kinesthetic approach to Theorem 8.1. If students use manipulatives such as a geoboard or graph paper to experiment with other right triangles of varying sizes and orientations, they should see that the three triangles formed by the altitude to the hypotenuse *must* be similar because of the AA Postulate.

306

8.1 Right Triangle Similarity

Objective: To state and apply the relationships involving the altitude to the hypotenuse of a right triangle

Auxiliary lines often help reveal the relationships within geometric figures. Drawing an altitude in any triangle shows two smaller right triangles.

Investigation—*Thinking Critically*

Sketch right triangle *ABC* and then measure and label the acute angles. Draw altitude $\overline{BD}$ to the hypotenuse and then measure the acute angles in each of the smaller triangles.

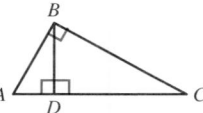

1. What relationship seems to exist between the two smaller triangles? They appear ~ (by the AA Post.).
2. What relationship seems to exist between △*ABC* and each of the smaller triangles? It seems ~ to each of the others (by the AA Post.)
3. Try the same experiment with another right triangle, △*EFG*. Compare the results of the two experiments. The results are the same.

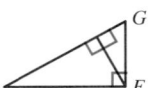

Three triangle similarities can be proven when the altitude to the hypotenuse of a right triangle is drawn.

Theorem 8.1   The altitude to the hypotenuse of a right triangle forms two triangles that are similar to the original triangle and to each other.

Given: Right △*ACB* with altitude $\overline{CP}$

Prove: △*ACP* ~ △*CBP* ~ △*ABC*

Plan: Each of the smaller triangles is similar to △*ABC* by the AA Postulate. Since ∠*A* is complementary to both ∠*B* and ∠*PCA*, ∠*B* ≅ ∠*PCA*. It follows that the two smaller triangles are similar. Proved in Practice Exercise 25

The triangle similarities stated in this theorem lead to two important corollaries about the segment lengths in right triangles.

306   Chapter 8 Right Triangles

Developing Mathematical Power

Keeping a Portfolio   Have students write in their journals the conclusion that can be reached if the altitude to the hypotenuse of a right triangle bisects the hypotenuse. They should justify their responses with illustrations of various triangles for which this is true and show how it follows from Corollary 2.

Corollary 1 The length of the altitude drawn to the hypotenuse of a right triangle is the geometric mean between the lengths of the segments of the hypotenuse. Proved in Practice Exercise 37

Corollary 2 The altitude to the hypotenuse of a right triangle intersects it so that the length of each leg is the geometric mean between the length of its adjacent segment of the hypotenuse and the length of the entire hypotenuse. Proved in Practice Exercise 38

In right $\triangle ACB$, $\overline{CD}$ is the altitude to the hypotenuse, $\overline{AD}$ is the segment of the hypotenuse that is adjacent to leg $\overline{AC}$, and $\overline{BD}$ is the segment of the hypotenuse that is adjacent to leg $\overline{CB}$.

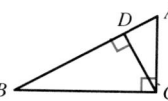

Thus by Corollary 1, $\dfrac{BD}{CD} = \dfrac{CD}{DA}$, and by Corollary 2, $\dfrac{BD}{BC} = \dfrac{BC}{BA}$ and $\dfrac{AD}{AC} = \dfrac{AC}{AB}$.

EXAMPLE 1 How long is the altitude of a right triangle that separates the hypotenuse into lengths 2 and 10?
$\dfrac{2}{h} = \dfrac{h}{10}$; $h^2 = 20$; $h = \sqrt{20} = 2\sqrt{5}$

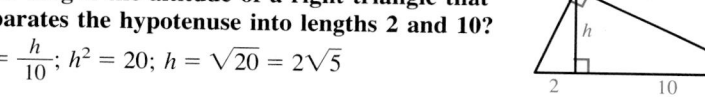

EXAMPLE 2 Find the missing lengths.
$\dfrac{12}{6} = \dfrac{6}{x}$; $12x = 36$; $x = 3$, so $y = 9$.
Since $x = 3$, $\dfrac{3}{h} = \dfrac{h}{9}$; $h^2 = 27$; $h = \sqrt{27} = 3\sqrt{3}$.
Since $y = 9$, $\dfrac{12}{b} = \dfrac{b}{9}$; $b^2 = 108$; $b = \sqrt{108} = 6\sqrt{3}$.

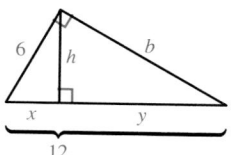

Right triangle similarity statements and the resulting proportions are very helpful in solving geometry problems.

CLASS EXERCISES

Name the following.

1. Angles complementary to $\angle Q$ $\angle R$, $\angle SPQ$

2. Angles complementary to $\angle RPS$ $\angle R$, $\angle SPQ$

3. One angle congruent to $\angle RPS$ $\angle Q$

4. Two angles congruent to $\angle PSR$ $\angle PSQ$, $\angle RPQ$

5. A side-length proportion for $\triangle PSQ \sim \triangle RPQ$ $\dfrac{SQ}{PQ} = \dfrac{PQ}{RQ} = \dfrac{PS}{RP}$

6. A side-length proportion for $\triangle PSQ \sim \triangle RSP$ $\dfrac{PS}{RS} = \dfrac{SQ}{SP} = \dfrac{PQ}{RP}$

8.1 Right Triangle Similarity   **307**

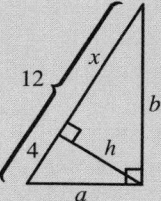

LESSON FOLLOW-UP

Discussion

Ask students to find h for each of the following.

a.

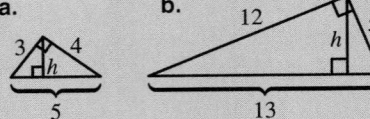

b.

Use Cor. 2 to find x and y (the lengths of the segments of the hypotenuse). Then use Cor. 1 to find h.   a. $h = \frac{12}{5}$ b. $h = \frac{60}{13}$

Then draw a right triangle whose sides have lengths 7, 24, 25, and ask students if they can guess what the length of the altitude to the hypotenuse is without actually calculating. $h = \frac{a \cdot b}{c} = \frac{7 \cdot 24}{25} = \frac{168}{25}$ Have students calculate h to check their guesses.

Critical Thinking

Reasoning Have students determine patterns in the relationship between the lengths of the sides of a right triangle and the length of the altitude to the hypotenuse.

Assignment Guide

See p. 304B for assignments.

Additional Answers

9. $\frac{BT}{AT} = \frac{BA}{AR} = \frac{TA}{TR}$
12. $\frac{RT}{TA} = \frac{TA}{BT}$
13. $\frac{RT}{AR} = \frac{AR}{RB}$
14. $\frac{BT}{AB} = \frac{AB}{BR}$
15. $c = 29; h = 10; a = 2\sqrt{29}; b = 5\sqrt{29}$
16. $y = 9; c = 13; a = 2\sqrt{13}; b = 3\sqrt{13}$
19. $x = 4; h = 4\sqrt{3}; a = 8; b = 8\sqrt{3}$
20. $c = 25; h = 2\sqrt{21}; a = 10; b = 5\sqrt{21}$

Give the indicated proportions.

7. The altitude is a geometric mean. $\frac{FP}{PE} = \frac{PE}{PD}$

8. The horizontal leg is a geometric mean. $\frac{PD}{DE} = \frac{DE}{DF}$

9. The vertical leg is a geometric mean. $\frac{PF}{FE} = \frac{FE}{DF}$

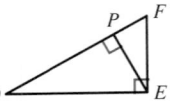

Find the missing lengths.

10. $x = 9; y = 25$ $c = 34;$ $h = 15; a = 3\sqrt{34}; b = 5\sqrt{34}$

11. $c = 1.2; x = 0.3$ $y = 0.9;$ $b = 0.6\sqrt{3}; a = 0.6; h = 0.3\sqrt{3}$

12. $x = 9; y = 11$ $c = 20;$ $h = 3\sqrt{11}; b = 2\sqrt{55}; a = 6\sqrt{5}$

13. $b = 8; y = 4$ $c = 16;$ $x = 12; h = 4\sqrt{3}; a = 8\sqrt{3}$

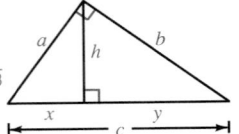

PRACTICE EXERCISES   ⟳ Use technology where appropriate.

Find the lengths.

A   1. $x = \underline{\ ?\ }$ $2\sqrt{3}$
   $y = \underline{\ ?\ }$ 4
   $z = \underline{\ ?\ }$ $4\sqrt{3}$

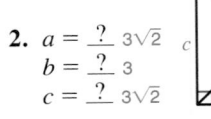

2. $a = \underline{\ ?\ }$ $3\sqrt{2}$
   $b = \underline{\ ?\ }$ 3
   $c = \underline{\ ?\ }$ $3\sqrt{2}$

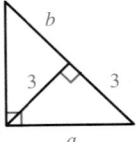

Use $\triangle RBA$ below for Exercises 3–14. Name the following.

3. Two complements of $\angle R$
   $\angle TAR, \angle B$

4. Two complements of $\angle TAB$
   $\angle B, \angle TAR$

5. An angle congruent to $\angle TAB$
   $\angle R$

6. An angle congruent to $\angle B$
   $\angle TAR$

7. Two angles congruent to $\angle BTA$
   $\angle RTA, \angle RAB$

8. Two triangles similar to $\triangle TAR$
   $\triangle ABR, \triangle TBA$

9. A side-length proportion for $\triangle BTA \sim \triangle ATR$ See side column.

10. The segment of the hypotenuse adjacent to leg $\overline{AR}$
    $\overline{RT}$

11. The segment of the hypotenuse adjacent to leg $\overline{AB}$
    $\overline{BT}$

12. A proportion in which TA is a geometric mean

13. A proportion in which AR is a geometric mean

14. A proportion in which AB is a geometric mean

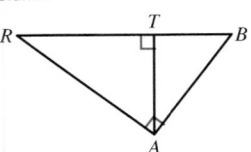

Find the missing lengths.

15. $x = 4; y = 25$

16. $x = 4; h = 6$

17. $y = 3; h = 3\sqrt{3}$ $x = 9;$ $c = 12; a = 6\sqrt{3}; b = 6$

18. $x = 40; c = 50$ $y = 10;$ $h = 20; a = 20\sqrt{5}; b = 10\sqrt{5}$

19. $y = 12; c = 16$ See side column.

20. $x = 4; y = 21$

21. $x = 5; h = 10$ $a = 5\sqrt{5};$ $b = 10\sqrt{5}; c = 25; y = 20$

22. $h = 4\sqrt{3}; y = 6$ $a = 4\sqrt{7};$ $b = 2\sqrt{21}; c = 14; x = 8$

23. $a = 6; c = 12$ $b = 6\sqrt{3};$ $x = 3; y = 9; h = 3\sqrt{3}$

24. $b = 8; c = 32$ $a = 8\sqrt{15};$ $x = 30; y = 2; h = 2\sqrt{15}$

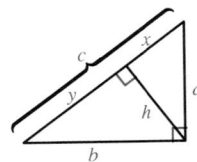

25. Use the figure, *Given*, *Prove*, and *Plan* for Theorem 8.1 to complete these statements and reasons.

Statements	Reasons
1. _?_ Rt. △*ABC*; rt. ∠*BCA*; $\overline{CP}$ is an altitude to $\overline{AB}$.	1. Given
2. _?_ $\overline{CP} \perp \overline{AB}$	2. Definition of altitude
3. ∠*BPC* and ∠*CPA* are rt. angles.	3. _?_ Def. of ⊥ lines
4. ∠*BPC* ≅ ∠*CPA* ≅ ∠*BCA*	4. _?_ All rt. ∠s are ≅.
5. ∠*B* ≅ ∠*B*; ∠*A* ≅ ∠*A*	5. _?_ Refl. Prop.
6. △ _?_ ~ △*ABC*	6. _?_ AA Post.
△ _?_ ~ △*ABC* *ACP; CBP*	
7. ∠*B* is complementary to ∠*A*; ∠*PCA* is complementary to ∠*A*.	7. _?_ Acute ∠s of a rt. △ are comp.
8. ∠ _?_ ≅ ∠ _?_ *B; PCA*	8. _?_ ∠s comp. to the same ∠ are ≅.
9. _?_ ~ _?_ △*PBC* ~ △*PCA*	9. _?_ AA Post.

B   **26.** Find *BC* if *AP* = $3\sqrt{3}$ and *CP* = 9.
  BC = 12
  27. Find *BC* if *AP* = $5\sqrt{2}$ and *BP* = 12.5.
  BC = 16.5
  28. Find *BP* if *AC* = $\sqrt{5}$ and *CP* = 1.
  BP = 4
  29. Find *PC* if *AB* = $4\sqrt{3}$ and *BP* = 6.
  PC = 2
  30. Find *AC* and *AB* if *CP* = 20 and *BP* = 5. *AC* = $10\sqrt{5}$; *AB* = $5\sqrt{5}$

  31. Find *AC* and *AB* if *BC* = 9 and *BP* = 5. *AC* = 6; *AB* = $3\sqrt{5}$

  32. Find *BP* if *AP* = $\sqrt{2}$ and *BC* = 3.
  BP = 2 if *PC* = 1, or *BP* = 1 if *PC* = 2.
  33. The altitude to the hypotenuse of a right triangle has length 2 cm. If it separates the hypotenuse into 4 cm and 1 cm, find the lengths of the legs. $\sqrt{5}$ cm, $2\sqrt{5}$ cm

  34. The altitude to the hypotenuse of a right triangle separates it into lengths 9 m and 3 m. Find the lengths of the legs. 6 m, $6\sqrt{3}$ m

  35. In a right triangle, the altitude to a 6-ft hypotenuse bisects the hypotenuse. Find the length of the altitude and each leg. alt = 3 ft, each leg = $3\sqrt{2}$ ft

  36. The altitude to the hypotenuse of a right triangle is 8 cm. It separates the hypotenuse in the ratio of 16 to 1. What is the length of each segment of the hypotenuse? 2 cm, 32 cm

  37. Complete this proof of Corollary 1 of Theorem 8.1.
  Given: Right △*BCA*; See side column.
  $\overline{CD}$ is an altitude.
  Prove: $\dfrac{BD}{CD} = \dfrac{CD}{DA}$

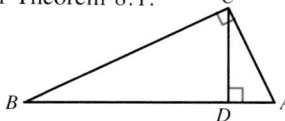

C   **38.** Prove Corollary 2 of Theorem 8.1. See Additional Answers, p. 702.

  39. Find the length of the altitude to the hypotenuse of a right triangle whose legs and hypotenuse measure 3, 4, and 5, respectively. $h = \frac{12}{5}$, or 2.4

Construction

This *Construction* allows students to create the Golden Ratio; however, it can be assigned with the basic constructions presented in Chapter 10.

Lesson Quiz

Find the missing lengths.

1. *x* = 9; *y* = 16
2. *x* = 2; *h* = $2\sqrt{3}$
3. *x* = 8; *a* = 12

1. *a* = 15, *b* = 20, *h* = 12, *c* = 25
2. *y* = 6, *a* = 4, *b* = $4\sqrt{3}$, *c* = 8
3. *c* = 18, *y* = 10, *b* = $6\sqrt{5}$, *h* = $4\sqrt{5}$

Additional Answers

37. Plan: Use Th. 8.1 to prove △*BDC* ~ △*CDA*. The concl. follows by the def. of ~ △s.

Proof:

Statements	Reasons
1. Rt. △*BCA*; $\overline{CD}$ is an alti.	1. Given
2. △*BDC* ~ △*CDA*	2. Th. 8.1
3. $\dfrac{BD}{CD} = \dfrac{CD}{DA}$	3. Def. of ~ △s.

Conclusion: In rt. △*BCA*, if $\overline{CD}$ is an alt. to the hyp., then $\dfrac{BD}{CD} = \dfrac{CD}{DA}$.

40. Prove: The product of the lengths of the legs of a right triangle is equal to the product of the lengths of the hypotenuse and the altitude to the hypotenuse.

41. Find the distance from P of altitude $\overline{CP}$ to Q of angle bisector $\overrightarrow{CQ}$ on hypotenuse $\overline{AB}$ of right $\triangle ABC$. $\frac{12}{35}$ ft

42. Prove that the ratio of the segment lengths created by altitude $\overline{CP}$ is equal to the square of the ratio of the segment lengths created by angle bisector $\overrightarrow{CQ}$.

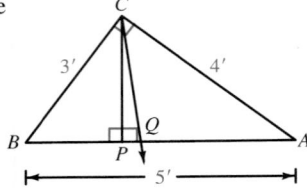

Applications

43. Recreation Two sides of an open tent form a $90°$ angle at the peak. An 8-ft support post, placed at a $90°$ angle with the ground, divides the ground line in a 1-to-4 ratio. Find the length of the ground line. 20 ft

Technology Logo has a primitive SQRT which allows you to find the square root of any number. The format is SQRT (number). For the given triangle: See Solutions Manual.

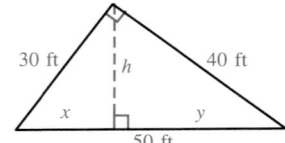

44. Write a procedure which enables you to find x and y.

45. Write a procedure which enables you to find h.

CONSTRUCTION

This construction divides a segment so that the ratio of the length of the whole segment to the longer part equals the ratio of the longer part to the shorter part. The ratio is the **Golden Mean** and is named φ (1.61803 . . .).

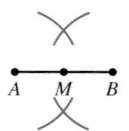 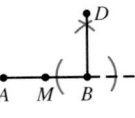 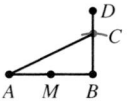 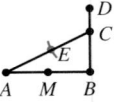 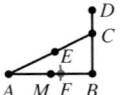

| Mark $\overline{AB}$. Bisect $\overline{AB}$. Mark M. | Construct $\overline{BD} \perp$ to $\overline{AB}$ at B. | With radius $\overline{MB}$ and center B, draw the arc intersecting $\overline{BD}$. Mark C. Draw $\overline{AC}$. | With radius $\overline{BC}$ and center C, draw the arc intersecting $\overline{AC}$. Mark E. | With radius $\overline{AE}$ and center A, draw the arc intersecting $\overline{AB}$. Mark F. |

The Golden Mean is $\dfrac{AB}{AF} = \dfrac{AF}{FB} = \phi$.

EXERCISE Draw $\overline{XY}$ and divide it according to the Golden Mean. Check students' constructions.

Teacher's Resource Book

Follow-Up Investigation, Chapter 8, p. 1

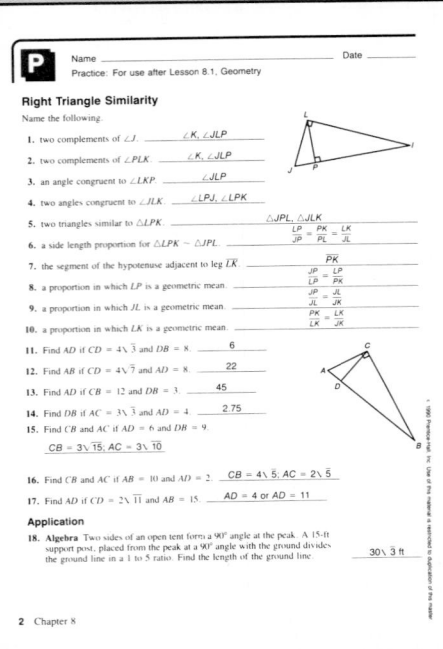

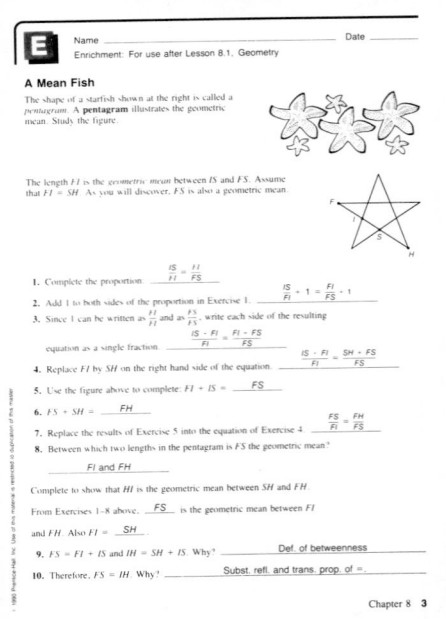

Developing Mathematical Power

Cooperative Learning Assign groups of students to complete the Enrichment activity, p. 3, in the *Teacher's Resource Book* (see side column). When they finish, have them use the pentagram proportions they found to create a design using pentagrams. Encourage them to color and embellish the basic figure.

Pythagorean Theorem

Objective: To state and apply the Pythagorean Theorem

LESSON PLAN

Materials/Manipulatives
Teacher's Resource Book,
Transparency 10
Teaching Transparency 50

Technology
Calculator
Computer
Computer Test Bank, pp.
461–471
Connections, p. 16
The Geometric Supposer:
Triangles
Geometry Problems and
Projects: Triangles,
Worksheet T11

There is a special relationship among the lengths of the sides of any right triangle. This relationship is often used to calculate distances in real-life problems.

Investigation—*Visualizing the Concept*

These four congruent right triangles have sides with lengths *a, b,* and *c,* where $a = 3$, $b = 4$, and $c = 5$.

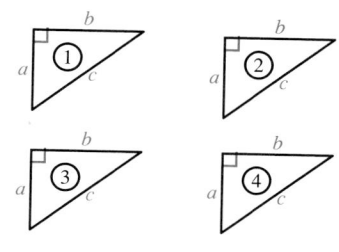

Study the two arrangements of triangles 1 to 4 below. In the first arrangement, the sides have been extended to form the shaded squares.

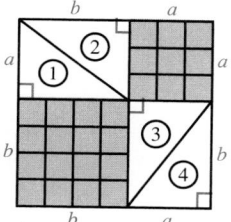
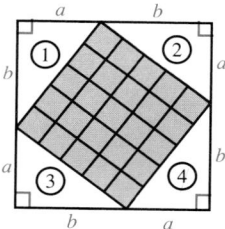

1. What relationship exists between the large squares formed by each triangle arrangement? Justify your answer. They have the same area, with each having $a + b$ as the length of each side.

2. Count the number of unit squares covered in each shaded square. Using *a, b,* and *c,* write an algebraic equation that relates the shaded regions in each arrangement. 9, 16, and 25; $a^2 + b^2 = c^2$

3. How do the sides of the shaded squares relate to the sides of the triangles? The number of shaded squares along each side of the △ denotes the length of that side.

4. What conclusion can you draw about the side lengths of the right triangles? $a^2 + b^2 = c^2$

Named for Pythagoras, a Greek mathematician of the sixth century BC, the *Pythagorean Theorem* is important to mathematics and its applications. Theorem 8.2 states this theorem, which can be used to find a missing side length in a right triangle.

LESSON FOCUS

Review
• Review Corollary 2 of Theorem 8.1 by asking students to find *c* in the following triangle.

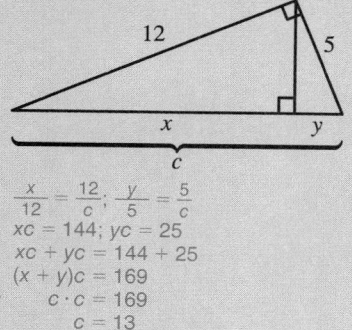

$\frac{x}{12} = \frac{12}{c}; \frac{y}{5} = \frac{5}{c}$
$xc = 144; yc = 25$
$xc + yc = 144 + 25$
$(x + y)c = 169$
$c \cdot c = 169$
$c = 13$

• Exercises 30–36 provide a Mixed Review.

Alternative Learning Styles
The Investigation provides a kinesthetic approach to the Pythagorean Theorem. Some students may need to trace triangles 1–4, cut them out, and manipulate them on graph paper as shown to visualize the Pythagorean Theorem.

Developing Mathematical Power

Cooperative Learning   Working in groups, students can investigate other proofs of the Pythagorean Theorem. Provide them with the Reading and Writing activity, p. 8, in the *Teacher's Resource Book* as a guide to the concept of dissections; or, you may wish to refer students to Elisha Scott Loomis's *The Pythagorean Proposition,* which contains over 300 proofs of the Pythagorean Theorem. Have them illustrate their proofs and use them as a bulletin-board display.

Discuss with students why the negative solution in Example 3 must be rejected.

CHALKBOARD EXAMPLES

• **For Example 1**

Each side of a square is 4 m long. Find the length of a diagonal of the square. $d^2 = 4^2 + 4^2 = 4\sqrt{2}$ m

• **For Example 2**

Find the length of the diagonal $\overline{AC}$ of a cube that is 6 in. on an edge.

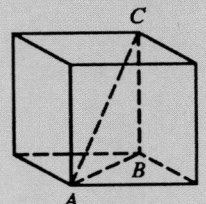

$(AB)^2 = 6^2 + 6^2$; $AB = \sqrt{72} = 6\sqrt{2}$;
$(AC)^2 = 6^2 + (6\sqrt{2})^2 = 36 + 72 = 108$;
$AC = 6\sqrt{3}$ in.

• **For Example 3**

Find the value of x.

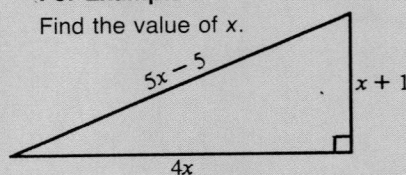

$(4x)^2 + (x + 1)^2 = (5x - 5)^2$
$16x^2 + x^2 + 2x + 1 = 25x^2 - 50x + 25$
$0 = 8x^2 - 52x + 24$
$0 = 2x^2 - 13x + 6$
$0 = (2x - 1)(x - 6)$
$x = \frac{1}{2}$(reject), or $x = 6$

Common Error

• Some students may not notice that a certain value of a variable would make a length negative, and hence that value must be rejected. Have students check their answers by sketching a right triangle with the dimensions in centimeters.

• See *Teacher's Resource Book* for additional remediation.

312

Theorem 8.2 Pythagorean Theorem In a right triangle, the square of the length of the hypotenuse is equal to the sum of the squares of the lengths of the legs.

Given: Right $\triangle BCA$ with leg lengths a and b and hypotenuse length c

Prove: $c^2 = a^2 + b^2$

Plan: Draw altitude $\overline{CP}$ to the hypotenuse. Use Corollary 2 of Theorem 8.1 and then apply algebraic properties.

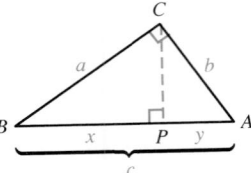

Proof:

Statements	Reasons
1. Draw altitude $\overline{CP}$ to the hypotenuse.	1. From a point not on a line, exactly one $\perp$ can be drawn to the line.
2. $\dfrac{c}{a} = \dfrac{a}{x}$; $\dfrac{c}{b} = \dfrac{b}{y}$	2. The length of each leg is the geom. mean between the length of its adjacent seg. of the hypotenuse and the entire hypotenuse.
3. $cx = a^2$; $cy = b^2$	3. Means-extremes property
4. $cx + cy = a^2 + b^2$	4. Addition property
5. $c(x + y) = a^2 + b^2$	5. Distributive property
6. $c^2 = a^2 + b^2$	6. Substitution property

Conclusion: If a right triangle has legs of length a and b and hypotenuse of length c, then $c^2 = a^2 + b^2$.

EXAMPLE 1 **Find the width of this rectangle.**

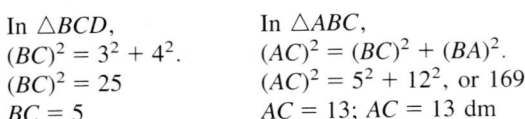

$a^2 + b^2 = c^2$ *Apply the Pythagorean Theorem.*
$x^2 + 12^2 = 13^2$ *Use algebraic methods to solve.*
$x^2 = 169 - 144$
$x = \sqrt{25} = 5$ The width is 5 cm.

EXAMPLE 2 **In this rectangular box, what is the length of $\overline{AC}$?**

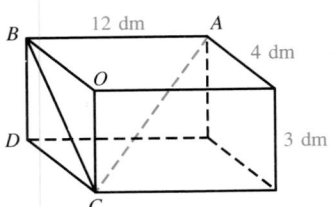

In $\triangle BCD$,
$(BC)^2 = 3^2 + 4^2$.
$(BC)^2 = 25$
$BC = 5$

In $\triangle ABC$,
$(AC)^2 = (BC)^2 + (BA)^2$.
$(AC)^2 = 5^2 + 12^2$, or 169
$AC = 13$; $AC = 13$ dm

EXAMPLE 3 **Find the value of _x_.**

Apply the Pythagorean Theorem and solve.

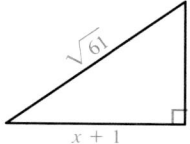

$$x^2 + (x + 1)^2 = (\sqrt{61})^2$$
$$x^2 + (x^2 + 2x + 1) = 61$$
$$2x^2 + 2x - 60 = 0$$
$$x^2 + x - 30 = 0$$
$$(x + 6)(x - 5) = 0$$
$$x = -6, x = 5$$
$$\text{Thus, } x = 5.$$

When applying the Pythagorean Theorem, as in Example 3, remember that a segment length is a positive number.

CLASS EXERCISES

Thinking Critically

Explain why the given equation will lead to the solution of the problem. Then find the solution.

1. A rectangular plot of land is 100 ft long and 50 ft wide. How long is a walkway along the diagonal? The diag. cuts the rect. into 2 rt. ᴤ. Thus, you can use the Pyth. Th. to solve for x; $50\sqrt{5}$ ft.

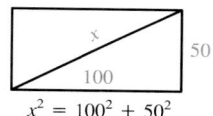

$$x^2 = 100^2 + 50^2$$

2. The length of a rectangular painting is 3 in. longer than its width. If the diagonal is 15 in. long, what are the dimensions of the painting? The diag. cuts the rect. painting into 2 rt. ᴤ. Thus, you can use the Pyth. Th. to solve the problem; 9 in. × 12 in.

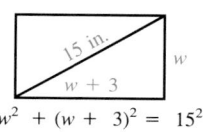

$$w^2 + (w + 3)^2 = 15^2$$

Find the missing lengths.

	_a_	_b_	_c_
3.	7	24	_?_ 25
4.	4	6	_?_ $2\sqrt{13}$
5.	7	9	_?_ $\sqrt{130}$
6.	8	_?_ 6	10
7.	$6\sqrt{3}$	_?_ 6	12
8.	_?_ 6	9	$3\sqrt{13}$

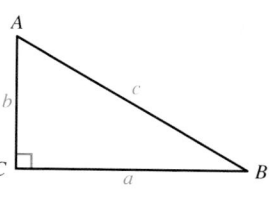

Discussion

To preview the next section, draw on the chalkboard a △*ABC* that looks like it might be a right triangle, and label the lengths of the sides as _a_, _b_, and _c_ (with _c_ as the longest length). Write "Given: $a^2 + b^2 = c^2$" and ask students what they think is true. The triangle is a right △, with the right ∠ opp. the longest side. Write "If $a^2 + b^2 = c^2$, then △*ABC* is a right triangle," and ask how this statement is related to the Pythagorean Theorem. It is the converse of the Pythagorean Theorem. Ask students to suggest a Plan for proving this converse. As necessary, ask leading questions such as "If we drew △*DEF* such that $m\angle F = 90$, $DF = b$, and $EF = a$, what would be true?" Then $(DE)^2 = a^2 + b^2 = c^2$, so $DE = c$. △*ABC* ≅ △*DEF* by SSS, so $m\angle C = m\angle F = 90$.

Critical Thinking

1. *Predicting Consequences* Have students draw conclusions.
2. *Identification* Have students identify the converse of a given theorem.
3. *Reasoning* Ask students to plan proofs.

Assignment Guide

See p. 304B for assignments.

Lesson Quiz

Find the missing lengths in right $\triangle ABC$, with hypotenuse $\overline{AB}$.

1. $AC = 7$, $BC = 14$
2. $AC = 15$, $AB = 17$
3. Find the length of the diagonal of a rectanglular box whose edges are 6 cm, 8 cm, and 10 cm long.

    1. $7\sqrt{5}$ **2.** 8 **3.** $10\sqrt{2}$ cm

Enrichment

Two sides of a right triangle have lengths 9 and 12. What is the length of the third side? Either 15 (if 9 and 12 are lengths of legs), or $3\sqrt{7}$ (if 12 is the length of the hypotenuse).

Additional Answers for p. 315

Mixed Review
30. $\angle ABD$; alt. int. $\angle$s are $\cong$.
31. AC; def. of altitude
32. 180; $\angle EBA$ and $\angle FBA$ are linear pairs; use alt. int. $\angle$s are $\cong$ and subst.
33. $m\angle DBC$; remote int. $\angle$s
34. $\triangle ADB$; $\triangle BDC$; Th. 8.1
35. $\angle SBD$; corr. $\angle$s of $\sim \triangle$s
36. DC; $\triangle$Inequality Th.

PRACTICE EXERCISES   Use technology where appropriate.

A   **1. Writing in Geometry**
Write a paragraph that explains how this figure illustrates the Pythagorean Theorem. Compare this illustration to the one given in the Investigation at the beginning of this lesson. Answers may vary. A square rests on each side of the rt. $\triangle$; $6^2 + 8^2 = 10^2$

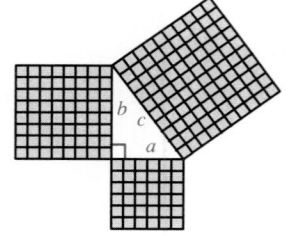

Find the missing lengths.

	Leg	Leg	Hypotenuse			Leg	Leg	Hypotenuse
2.	8	15	? 17		**3.**	11	60	? 61
4.	6	? $\sqrt{13}$	7		**5.**	9	? 40	41
6.	5	15	? $5\sqrt{10}$		**7.**	1	1	? $\sqrt{2}$
8.	? $2\sqrt{6}$	1	5		**9.**	? 6	17.5	18.5

10. Find UR.
$2\sqrt{29}$

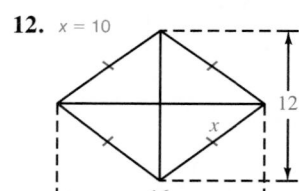

11. Find JQ.
$5\sqrt{3}$

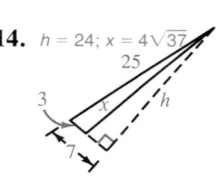

Find the missing lengths.

12. $x = 10$

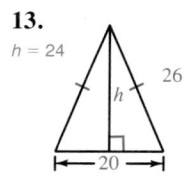

13.
$h = 24$

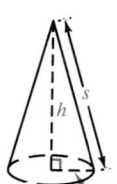

14. $h = 24$; $x = 4\sqrt{37}$

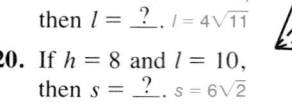

B   **15.** If $r = 6$ and $h = 15$, then $s = \underline{\ ?\ }$. $s = 3\sqrt{29}$

16. If $s = 9$ and $h = 6$, then $r = \underline{\ ?\ }$. $r = 3\sqrt{5}$

17. If $r = 4$ and $s = 12$, then $h = \underline{\ ?\ }$. $h = 8\sqrt{2}$

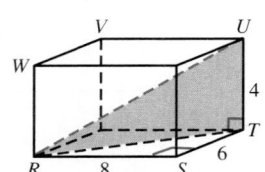

18. If $l = 13$ and $s = 5\sqrt{2}$, then $h = \underline{\ ?\ }$. $h = 12$

19. If $s = 8$ and $h = 12$, then $l = \underline{\ ?\ }$. $l = 4\sqrt{11}$

20. If $h = 8$ and $l = 10$, then $s = \underline{\ ?\ }$. $s = 6\sqrt{2}$

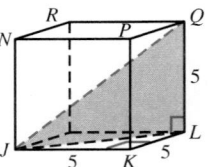

314   Chapter 8 Right Triangles

Developing Mathematical Power

Keeping a Portfolio Have students research and write a brief essay on Pythagoras. They should include data on the time in which he lived, the mathematical thinking of the time and how he was influenced by it, and his mathematical contributions.

21. If $w = 9$, $l = 12$, and $h = 30$, then $AG = \underline{\ ?\ }$. $AG = 15\sqrt{5}$

22. If $h = 24$, $AH = 25$, and $CH = 26$, then $AC = \underline{\ ?\ }$. $AC = \sqrt{149}$

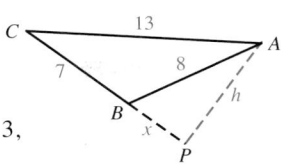

23. Find the length of altitude $\overline{AP}$ of $\triangle ABC$. $h = AP = 4\sqrt{3}$

24. Find the length of altitude $\overline{AP}$ of obtuse $\triangle ABC$ if $AB = 2\sqrt{37}$, $BC = 3$, and $AC = 13$. $h = AP = 12$

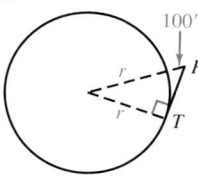

C **25.** A rectangular box has a square base whose area is 64 cm^2. The height of the box is 12 cm; find the length of the interior diagonal of the box. $4\sqrt{17}$ cm

26. Show that the formula for the length d of the diagonal of any square is $d = s\sqrt{2}$, where s is the side of the square. See side column.

27. Show that $p^2 + q^2 = 4s^2$ is the formula for the length s of the side of any rhombus in terms of its diagonals p and q. Four rt. △ Are formed with hyp. s and legs $\frac{p}{2}$ and $\frac{q}{2}$. Thus, by the Pyth. Th., $(\frac{p}{2})^2 + (\frac{q}{2})^2 = s^2$, or $p^2 + q^2 = 4s^2$.

Applications

28. Technology Use Logo to find the diagonal of a rectangular box which is 7 cm wide, 24 cm long, and 25 cm high. See Solutions Manual.

29. Navigation Here is a sketch of the earth, showing the circular disk created by its intersection with a plane through the earth's center. A ship at T is sighted by an observer 100 ft above sea level at P. The length of $\overline{PT}$ approximates how far the navigating officer can see in all directions at sea level. Find PT to the nearest foot. $PT \approx 64{,}944$ ft

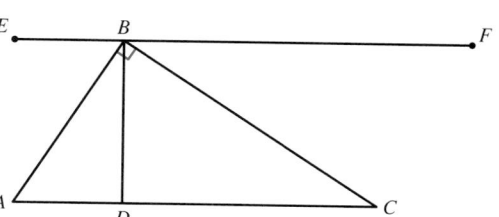

$r \approx 4{,}000$ mi

Mixed Review

$\overline{EF} \parallel \overline{AC}$, and $\overline{BD}$ is an altitude. **Complete. Justify each answer.** See side column, p. 314.

30. $\angle FBC \cong \underline{\ ?\ }$

31. $\overline{BD} \perp \underline{\ ?\ }$

32. $m\angle FBA + m\angle BAD = \underline{\ ?\ }$

33. $m\angle BDA = m\angle DCB + \underline{\ ?\ }$

34. $\triangle ABC \sim \underline{\ ?\ }$

35. $\angle BAD \cong \underline{\ ?\ }$

36. $BC + BD > \underline{\ ?\ }$

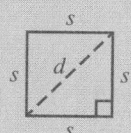

26. $s^2 + s^2 = d^2$
$2s^2 = d^2$
$\sqrt{2s^2} = d$
$s\sqrt{2} = d$

Teacher's Resource Book

Follow-Up Investigation, Chapter 8, p. 4

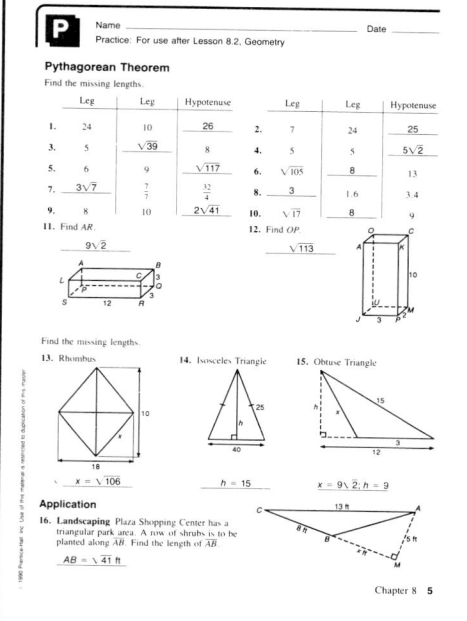

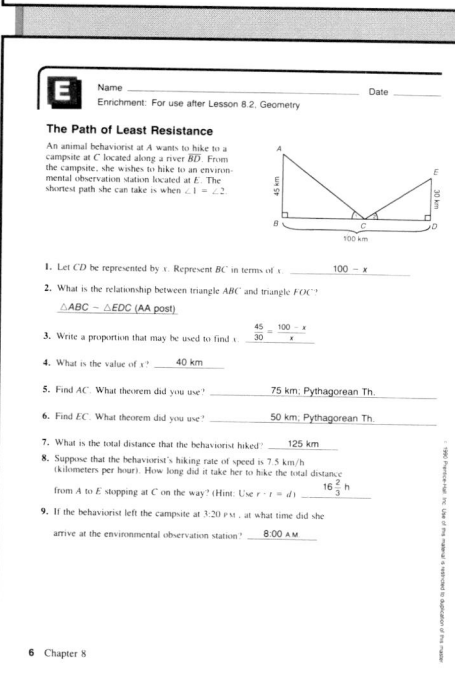

316

8.3

Converse of the Pythagorean Theorem

Objectives: To state and apply the converse of the Pythagorean Theorem

To state and apply related theorems about obtuse and acute triangles

While carpenters and surveyors use T-squares and transits to produce right triangles, desktop publishers use computer graphics to draw right triangles.

Investigation—*Visualizing the Concept*

On graph paper, draw triangles with side lengths 3, 4, and 5 units, such that one side lies on a horizontal line and one side lies on a vertical line.

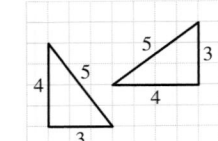

1. Classify the triangles that you drew.

Now in the same manner, try drawing triangles with sides 4, 5, and 6 units.
The first set of △s are rt. △s. You can't draw a 4-5-6 rt. △.

2. Compare these to the first set of triangles.
These △s were acute △s.

3. Why did only one set of the above side lengths produce right triangles?
Only that set of side lengths satisfied the Pyth. Th.

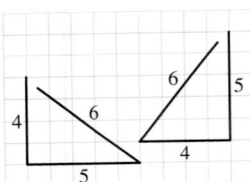

> **Theorem 8.3 Converse of Pythagorean Theorem** If the sum of the squares of the lengths of two sides of a triangle is equal to the square of the length of the third side, then the triangle is a right triangle.

Given: $\triangle ABC$ with $a^2 + b^2 = c^2$

Prove: $\triangle ABC$ is a right triangle with right $\angle C$.

Plan: Draw right $\triangle DEF$ with right $\angle F$ and legs of length a and b. Since $a^2 + b^2 = (DE)^2$, $(DE)^2 = c^2$. $\triangle ABC \cong \triangle DEF$ and the conclusion follows.
Proved in Practice Exercise 17

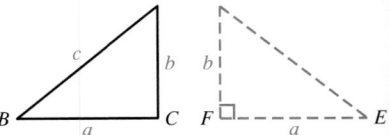

316   Chapter 8 Right Triangles

Developing Mathematical Power

Keeping a Portfolio   Have students write an explanation of why the theorems of the lesson do not apply to equilateral triangles. They should also explain, in their own words, why the relationship of c^2 to $a^2 + b^2$ determines what kind of a triangle it is.

EXAMPLE 1   **Is the triangle with the given dimensions a right triangle? If so, which angle is the right angle?**

a. $\triangle PQR$ with $PQ = 5$, $QR = 5\sqrt{3}$, and $RP = 10$

b. $\triangle STU$ with $TU = 5$, $US = 8$, and $ST = 10$

a. $5^2 + (5\sqrt{3})^2 \underline{\;?\;} 10^2$
$25 + 75 \underline{\;?\;} 100$
$100 = 100$
Yes, right $\triangle PQR$ has right $\angle Q$.

b. $5^2 + 8^2 \underline{\;?\;} 10^2$
$25 + 64 \underline{\;?\;} 100$
$89 \neq 100$
$\triangle STU$ is *not* a right triangle.

If a triangle is not a right triangle, the next two theorems will help you to find out whether it is acute or obtuse.

Theorem 8.4   If the square of the length of the longest side of a triangle is greater than the sum of the squares of the lengths of the other two sides, then the triangle is an obtuse triangle.

Given: $\triangle ABC$ with $c^2 > a^2 + b^2$

Prove: $\triangle ABC$ is an obtuse $\triangle$.

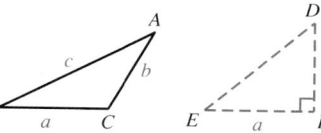

Plan: Introduce auxiliary figure, right $\triangle DEF$, with right $\angle F$ and legs of length a and b. By the Pythagorean Theorem, $(DE)^2 = a^2 + b^2$. Since $c^2 > (DE)^2$, by the converse of the Hinge Theorem, $m\angle C > m\angle F$ and the conclusion follows. Proved in Practice Exercise 28

A similar plan can be used to prove the next theorem.

Theorem 8.5   If the square of the length of the longest side of a triangle is less than the sum of the squares of the lengths of the other two sides, then the triangle is an acute triangle. Proved in Practice Exercise 29

EXAMPLE 2   **Classify the triangle with these side dimensions:**
a. 5, 8, 10   **b.** 5, 6, 7   **c.** 5, 12, 13

a. $10^2 \underline{\;?\;} 8^2 + 5^2$
$100 \underline{\;?\;} 64 + 25$
$100 > 89$
Obtuse triangle

b. $7^2 \underline{\;?\;} 6^2 + 5^2$
$49 \underline{\;?\;} 36 + 25$
$49 < 61$
Acute triangle

c. $13^2 \underline{\;?\;} 12^2 + 5^2$
$169 \underline{\;?\;} 144 + 25$
$169 = 169$
Right triangle

8.3 Converse of the Pythagorean Theorem   **317**

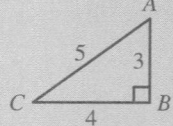
CLASS EXERCISES

Drawing in Geometry See side column.

In $\triangle ABC$, $AB = 3$ and $BC = 4$. Sketch a figure. Justify your answer with a theorem from this lesson or with the Triangle Inequality Theorem.

1. For what value of CA must $\angle B$ be a right angle? 5; Th. 8.3

2. What is the smallest integral value of $CA > 5$ for which there is no $\triangle$? 7; $\triangle$ Ineq. Th.

3. For what values of CA must $\angle B$ be an obtuse angle? $5 < CA < 7$; Th. 8.3 and Th. 8.4

4. What is the largest integral value of $CA < 5$ for which there is no $\triangle$? 1; $\triangle$ Ineq. Th.

5. For what values of CA must $\triangle ABC$ be an acute triangle? $\sqrt{7} < CA < 5$; Th. 8.3 and Th. 8.5

Is the triangle with the given side lengths right, obtuse, or acute?

6. 3, 4, 5 rt.   7. 3, 4, 6 obt.   8. 5, 12, 12 acute   9. 5, 12, 13 rt.

10. 3, 5, $\sqrt{34}$ rt.   11. 4, $2\sqrt{5}$, 6 rt.   12. 4, 4, $4\sqrt{2}$ rt.   13. 5, 5, 5 acute

Identify the $\triangle$ as right or obtuse. Then identify the right or obtuse $\angle$.

14. $AB = 1$, $BC = \sqrt{12}$, $CA = \sqrt{13}$ rt. $\triangle$; rt. $\angle B$ 15. $QR = 4$, $RP = 7.5$, $PQ = 9$ obt. $\triangle$; obt. $\angle R$

PRACTICE EXERCISES   Use technology where appropriate.

Is it possible to form a triangle with these side lengths? If so, tell whether the triangle is *acute*, *right*, or *obtuse*.

A
1. 6, 8, 10 yes; rt.
2. 2, 2, 2 yes; acute
3. 7, 24, 25 yes; rt.
4. 3, 3, $3\sqrt{2}$ yes; rt

5. 3, 3, $3\sqrt{3}$ yes; obt.
6. 1, 2, 3 no
7. 1, $\sqrt{3}$, 2 yes; rt.
8. 6, 7, 8 yes; acute

9. 10, 15, 20 yes; obt.
10. 10, 24, 26 yes; rt.
11. $\sqrt{3}$, $\sqrt{4}$, $\sqrt{5}$ yes; acute
12. $\sqrt{2}$, $\sqrt{3}$, $\sqrt{4}$ yes; acute

13. 5, 5, 12 no
14. $\sqrt{5}$, $\sqrt{6}$, $\sqrt{9}$ yes; acute
15. 3, 6, $3\sqrt{3}$ yes; right
16. 4, 6, 10 no

B
17. Use the figures, *Given*, *Prove*, and *Plan* of Th. 8.3 to complete the proof.

Proof:

Statements	Reasons
1. In $\triangle ABC$, $AB = c$, $BC = a$, $CA = b$, and $a^2 + b^2 = c^2$	1. ? Given
2. Draw right $\triangle DEF$ with right $\angle F$, $EF = a$, and $FD = b$.	2. ? Const.
3. ? $a^2 + b^2 = (DE)^2$	3. Pythagorean Theorem
4. $(DE)^2 = c^2$	4. ? Trans. prop.
5. ? $DE = c$	5. Square root property of equality
6. $\triangle$? $\cong \triangle$? $\triangle ABC \cong \triangle DEF$	6. ? SSS
7. $\angle C \cong$? $\angle F$	7. ? CPCTC
8. $\angle C$ is a ? rt. $\angle$	8. ? Def. of rt. $\angle$ and subst. prop.
9. ? $\triangle ABC$ is a rt. $\triangle$.	9. ? Def. of rt. $\triangle$

Conclusion: ? If the sum of the squares of the lengths of 2 sides of a $\triangle$ is = to the square of the length of the third side, then it is a rt. $\triangle$.

4. |—— 3 ——|— 1 —|

   |———— 4 ————|

5.
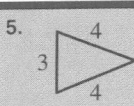

18. For what value of AC will $\square ABCD$ be a rectangle? $AC = 10$

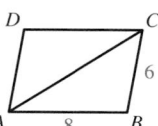

19. For what value of AC will rhombus $ABCD$ be a square? $AC = \sqrt{128} = 8\sqrt{2}$

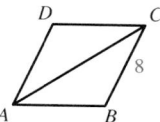

Use integral values when answering Exercises 20–23.

20. What is the smallest value of RT for which $\square RSTU$ will have an obtuse angle at S? $RT = 14$

21. What is the largest value of RT for which $\square RSTU$ will have an acute angle at S? $RT = 12$

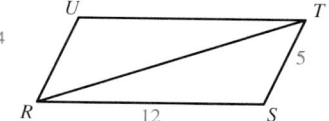

22. What is the largest value of MP for which rhombus $MNPQ$ will have an obtuse angle at Q? $MP = 17$

23. What is the smallest value of MP for which rhombus $MNPQ$ will have an acute angle at Q? $MP = 1$

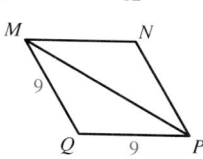

24. The length of the hypotenuse of a right triangle is 26 cm. One leg is 14 cm longer than the other. Find the length of each leg. 10 cm, 24 cm

25. The longest side of an acute triangle measures 15 cm. One of the shorter sides is 3 cm less than the other. Find the possible lengths of these two sides. $9 <$ side 1 < 12; $12 <$ side 2 < 15

26. In $\triangle PQR$, $RP = 15$ cm, $PQ = 13$ cm, and the altitude from P to a point S on QR measures 12 cm. Find RS and SQ. $RS = 9$ cm; $SQ = 5$ cm

27. Show that $\triangle PQR$ in Exercise 26 is acute. $13^2 + 14^2 > 15^2$; thus according to Th. 8.5, $\triangle PQR$ is acute.

C **28.** Complete the proof of Theorem 8.4. See Additional Answers, p. 702.

29. Prove Theorem 8.5.

30. Given: CP is the geometric mean between BP and AP.
   Prove: $\triangle ABC$ is a right triangle.

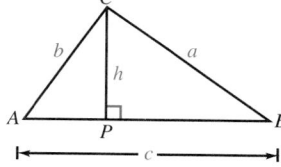

31. Use the converse of the Pythagorean Theorem to prove that the expressions $m^2 - n^2$, $2mn$, and $m^2 + n^2$ generate Pythagorean triples. (See Technology, page 320, for a definition of Pythagorean triple.)

Applications

32. Carpentry A decorator wants the sides of a rectangular picture frame to be in the ratio 7 to 24. If the diagonal is 100 cm long, what should the lengths of the sides be? 28 cm, 96 cm

8.3 Converse of the Pythagorean Theorem   **319**

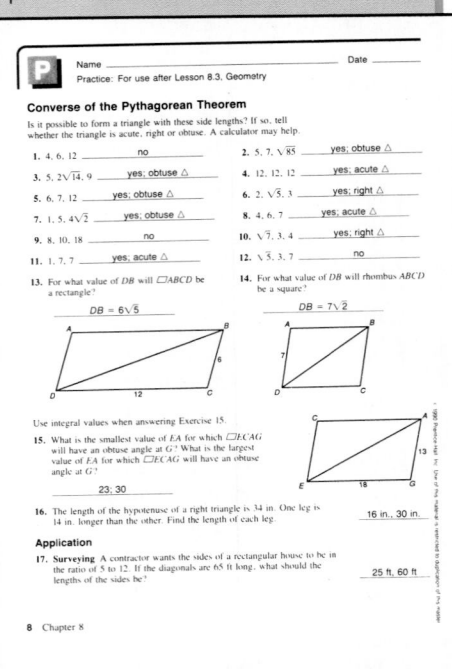

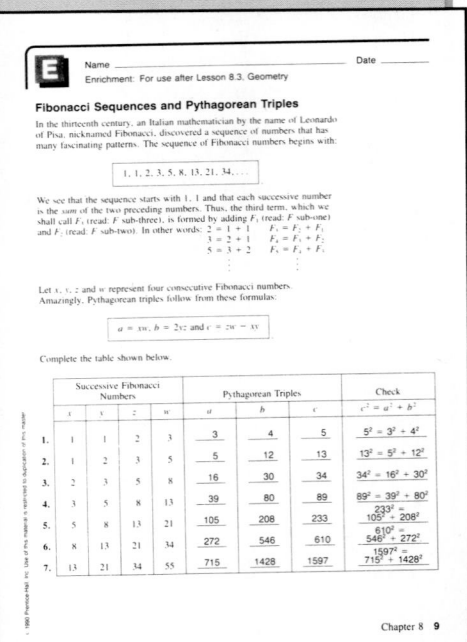

Technology The integral side lengths of a right triangle are called a *Pythagorean triple.* Pythagorean triples can be generated by the expressions $m^2 - n^2$, $2mn$, and $m^2 + n^2$, where $m > n \geq 1$. Logo has a make command to define a variable within a procedure. For example:

```
to pythagorean.triple :m :n
make "a (:m*:m) – (:n*:n)
make "b 2*:m*:n          Note the special use of "
make "c (:m*:m) + (:n*:n)   when defining a variable.
pr (se :a :b :c)
end
```

Use the above procedure to see if the following values generate a Pythagorean triple. If so, find it.

33. $m = 2$,
$n = 1$
yes; 3, 4, 5

34. $m = 3$,
$n = 2$
yes; 5, 12, 13

35. $m = 3$,
$n = 4$
no

36. $m = 4$,
$n = 2$
yes; 12, 16, 20

37. $m = 4$,
$n = 1$
yes; 8, 15, 17

Developing Mathematical Power

38. Investigation Evaluate the expressions $2n^2 + 2n$, $2n^2 + 2n + 1$, and $2n + 1$, with n an odd number from 1 to 10. Draw a conclusion.
The evaluated expressions are Pythagorean triples

TEST YOURSELF

1. Find x if $y = 5$ and $h = 10$. $x = 20$

2. Find h if $x = 2$ and $y = 18$. $h = 6$

3. Find y and c if $x = 9$ and $h = 12$.
$y = 16$; $c = 25$

4. Find a if $x = 4$ and $c = 28$.
$a = \sqrt{112} = 4\sqrt{7}$

8.1

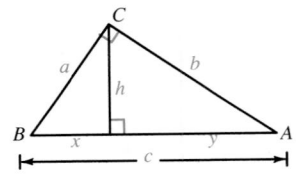

In Exercises 5–7, the lengths of the hypotenuse and the legs of a right triangle are h, a, and b, respectively.

5. $a = 6$, $b = 8$, $h = \underline{\ ?\ }$ **6.** $h = 13$, $b = 5$, $a = \underline{\ ?\ }$ **7.** $h = 20$, $a = 10$, $b = \underline{\ ?\ }$ 8.2
10   12 $10\sqrt{3}$

8. Find the length of the congruent sides of isosceles triangle *DEF*.
each side = 5

9. Find the length of the perimeter of the square. perimeter = 28

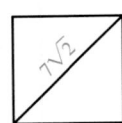

In Exercises 10–12, can the given dimensions be the side lengths of a triangle? If so, is it a right triangle?

10. 10 cm, 24 cm, 26 cm   **11.** 5 ft, 5 ft, $5\frac{1}{2}$ ft   **12.** 2 m, 4 m, 6 m   8.3
yes; yes   yes; no   no

13. Which, if any, of the triangles in Exercises 10–12 is (are) isosceles?
Exercise 11

Developing Mathematical Power

Cooperative Learning The Enrichment activity, p. 9, in the *Teacher's Resource Book* (see side column) can be done by students working in cooperative groups. Encourage them to correlate the algebraic expressions involved with the algebraic expressions in Practice Exercises 33–37. Challenge them to devise another algebraic manipulation that works.

Special Right Triangles

Objective: To state and apply the relationships in special right triangles

When the Pythagorean Theorem is applied to two special triangles, useful relationships among the side lengths emerge.

Investigation—*Visualizing the Concept*

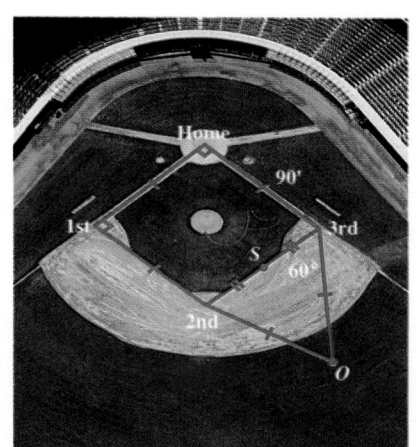

1. What kinds of triangles are formed by a line segment drawn from 1st to 3rd base? isos. rt. △

2. Find the length of the segment. Show your answer in radical form. $90\sqrt{2}$ ft

3. How does that length relate to the sides of the triangles formed? side $\cdot \sqrt{2}$

4. What kinds of triangles are formed by a segment from the outfielder at O to the shortstop at S? 30°-60°-90° △

5. Find the length of $\overline{OS}$. Leave the answer in radical form. $45\sqrt{3}$ ft

6. How does that length relate to each side of the triangles formed? See below.

The following theorem provides a method for determining the side lengths of a 45°-45°-90° triangle, known as an *isosceles right triangle*.

Theorem 8.6   45°-45°-90° Theorem   In a 45°-45°-90° triangle, the length of the hypotenuse is $\sqrt{2}$ times the length of a leg.

Given: △ABC, a 45°-45°-90° triangle

Prove: When $AC = BC = s$, then $AB = s\sqrt{2}$.

Plan: Let s be the length of either leg. Use the Pythagorean Theorem to find AB, the length of the hypotenuse, in terms of s.
Proved in Practice Exercise 23

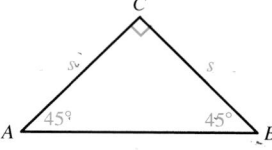

6. longer leg = (hyp.) $\cdot \dfrac{\sqrt{3}}{2}$; longer leg = (shorter leg) $\cdot \sqrt{3}$

8.4 Special Right Triangles   **321**

Developing Mathematical Power

Cooperative Learning   Working in groups, students can "play ball" by completing the Investigation, p. 10, in the *Teacher's Resource Book*. Challenge them to create other problems (they can augment the diagram with other players in other positions or even with fans in the stands!). They can compete with other groups in a classroom "World Series."

- Since these special triangles occur so often in mathematics and its applications, emphasize that it is important that students learn these relationships.
- Note that Lesson 8.5 will cover estimating and calculating roots, including $\sqrt{2}$ and $\sqrt{3}$.

CHALKBOARD EXAMPLES

- **For Example 1**
  a. One leg of a 45°-45°-90° triangle is 45 cm long. How long are the other two sides?
  b. Find the length of each leg of an isosceles right triangle whose hypotenuse is 10 cm long.

  a. hyp. $= \text{leg} \cdot \sqrt{2} = 45\sqrt{2}$ cm, other leg $= 45$ cm
  b. leg $= \dfrac{\text{hyp.}}{\sqrt{2}} = \dfrac{10}{\sqrt{2}} = \dfrac{10}{\sqrt{2}} \cdot \dfrac{\sqrt{2}}{\sqrt{2}}$
  $= 5\sqrt{2}$

- **For Example 2**
  An altitude of an equilateral triangle is 15 ft long. Find the length of a side of the triangle in simple radical form. Then use a calculator to find it to the nearest hundredth.
  $\sqrt{3}(\frac{s}{2}) = 15$; $s = \dfrac{30}{\sqrt{3}} \cdot \dfrac{\sqrt{3}}{\sqrt{3}} = 10\sqrt{3}$ ft;
  $s \approx 17.32$ ft

Common Error

- Some students will still have trouble simplifying radicals such as $\dfrac{10}{\sqrt{2}}$. Have them use a calculator to compare their final answer and the original radical.
- See *Teacher's Resource Book* for additional remediation.

Thus in an isosceles right triangle, multiply the length of a leg by $\sqrt{2}$ to find the length of the hypotenuse and divide the length of the hypotenuse by $\sqrt{2}$ to find the length of a leg.

EXAMPLE 1 **a.** Find the length of the hypotenuse of an isosceles right triangle with a leg $7\sqrt{2}$ cm long.

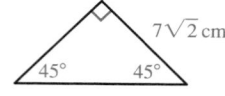

b. Find the length of each leg of a 45°-45°-90° triangle with a hypotenuse 12 cm long.

a. hypotenuse $= \text{leg} \cdot \sqrt{2} = 7\sqrt{2} \cdot \sqrt{2} = 7 \cdot 2 = 14$ cm

b. $\text{leg} = \dfrac{\text{hypotenuse}}{\sqrt{2}} = \dfrac{12}{\sqrt{2}} = \dfrac{12}{\sqrt{2}} \cdot \dfrac{\sqrt{2}}{\sqrt{2}} = \dfrac{12\sqrt{2}}{2} = 6\sqrt{2}$ cm

> **Theorem 8.7 30°-60°-90° Theorem** In a 30°-60°-90° triangle, the length of the hypotenuse is twice the length of the shorter leg, and the length of the longer leg is $\sqrt{3}$ times the length of the shorter leg.

Given: $\triangle ABC$, a 30°-60°-90° triangle

Prove: If $BC = s$, then $AB = 2s$ and $AC = s\sqrt{3}$.

Plan: Draw 30°-60°-90° $\triangle ACD$ that shares $\overline{AC}$ with $\triangle ABC$. Show that $\triangle ABD$ is equiangular and therefore equilateral. Then $\overline{AC}$ bisects $\overline{BD}$ and $BD = AB = 2s$. Applying the Pythagorean Theorem, $AC = s\sqrt{3}$.
Proved in Practice Exercise 24

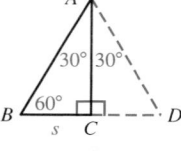

EXAMPLE 2 **a.** How tall is the pole? How long is the cable?

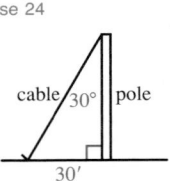

b. Find HL and SL.

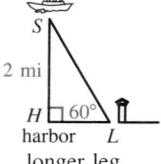

a. longer leg $= $ shorter leg $\cdot \sqrt{3}$
pole height $= 30 \cdot \sqrt{3} = 30\sqrt{3}$
Using a calculator, $30\sqrt{3} \approx 52.0$.
hypotenuse $= $ shorter leg $\cdot 2$
cable length $= 30 \cdot 2 = 60'$

b. shorter leg $= \dfrac{\text{longer leg}}{\sqrt{3}}$
$HL = \dfrac{2}{\sqrt{3}} = \dfrac{2}{\sqrt{3}} \cdot \dfrac{\sqrt{3}}{\sqrt{3}} = \dfrac{2\sqrt{3}}{3}$
$SL = \dfrac{2\sqrt{3}}{3} \cdot 2 = \dfrac{4\sqrt{3}}{3}$

$HL \approx 1.2$ mi and $SL \approx 2.3$ mi.

A calculator can be used to provide a decimal approximation for a radical expression. In Example 2b, an 8-place calculator shows 2.3094011 for $\frac{4\sqrt{3}}{3}$. The answer for SL has been rounded to the nearest tenth of a mile.

CLASS EXERCISES

1. Use a protractor and a ruler to draw a right angle. Mark a point on each side 5 cm from vertex C. Connect the two points. What should the measures of the acute angles be? How long should the hypotenuse be, to the nearest millimeter? Check your answer with a ruler. 45; 71 mm

Find the missing lengths x and y.

2.
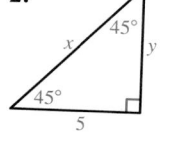
$x = 5\sqrt{2}$
$y = 5$

3.
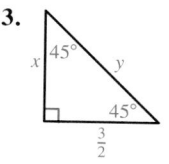
$x = \frac{3}{2}$
$y = \frac{3\sqrt{2}}{2}$

4.
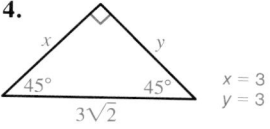
$x = 3$
$y = 3$

5.
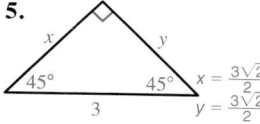
$x = \frac{3\sqrt{2}}{2}$
$y = \frac{3\sqrt{2}}{2}$

6.
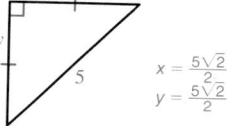
$x = \frac{5\sqrt{2}}{2}$
$y = \frac{5\sqrt{2}}{2}$

7.
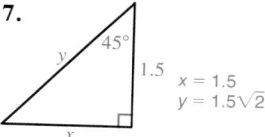
$x = 1.5$
$y = 1.5\sqrt{2}$

8.
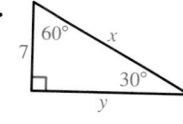

9.
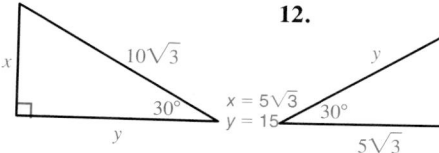
$x = 14$
$y = 7\sqrt{3}$

10.
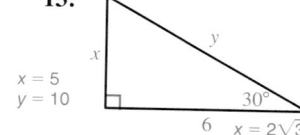
$x = 5$
$y = 5\sqrt{3}$

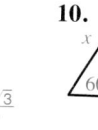
$x = \frac{3}{2}$
$y = \frac{3\sqrt{3}}{4}$

11.
$x = 5\sqrt{3}$
$y = 15$

12.
$x = 5\sqrt{3}$
$y = 15$

13.
$x = 5$
$y = 10$

$x = 2\sqrt{3}$
$y = 4\sqrt{3}$

14. How far up the side of the house will this 18-ft ladder touch if the measure of $\angle A$ is 45? 60? 30? Give answers in simplified radical form and in decimal form to the nearest hundredth.
$9\sqrt{2}$ ft $\approx$ 12.73 ft; $9\sqrt{3}$ ft $\approx$ 15.59 ft; 9 ft = 9.00 ft

LESSON FOLLOW-UP

Discussion

Ask students to find h, x, and y.

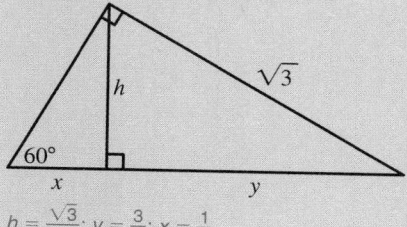

$h = \frac{\sqrt{3}}{2}; y = \frac{3}{2}; x = \frac{1}{2}$

Assignment Guide

See p. 304B for assignments.

Lesson Quiz

Find the missing lengths.

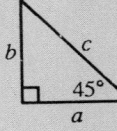

	a	b	c
1.	?	$4\sqrt{2}$	?
2.	?	?	6

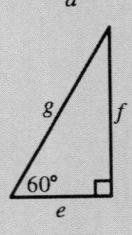

	e	f	g
3.	3	?	?
4.	?	3	?
5.	?	?	3

1. $4\sqrt{2}$; 8   2. $3\sqrt{2}$; $3\sqrt{2}$ 3. $3\sqrt{3}$; 6

4. $\sqrt{3}$; $2\sqrt{3}$ 5. $\frac{3}{2}, \frac{3\sqrt{3}}{2}$

Enrichment

a. Each triangle shown is a 45°-45°-90° triangle and $AB = 1$. Find BC.
$BC = 15$

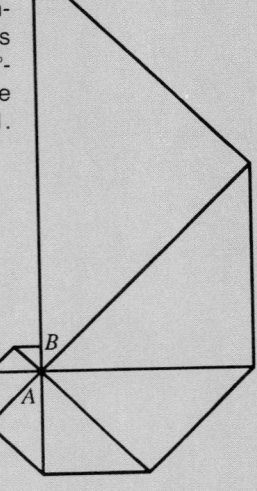

b. Find x.

$x = \frac{32}{9}$

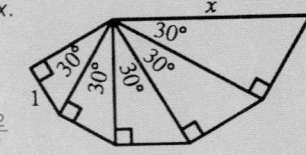

Coordinate Geometry Find the three missing lengths for each triangle.

A **1.** $\triangle ABC$ $a = 3$; $b = 3$; $c = 3\sqrt{2}$

2. $\triangle UVW$ $u = 4\sqrt{3}$; $v = 8$; $w = 4$

3. $\triangle XYZ$ $x = 5\sqrt{3}$; $y = 5$; $z = 10$

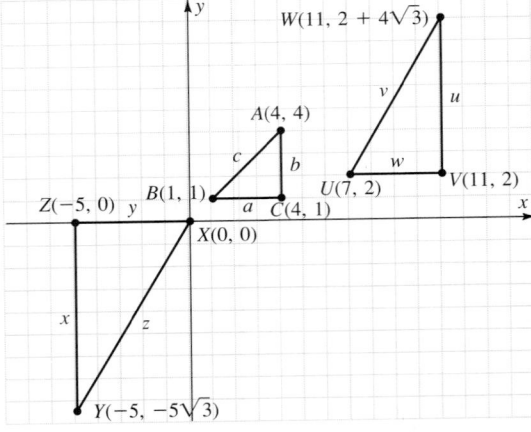

Find the missing lengths.

	a	b	c
4.	12	? 12	? $12\sqrt{2}$
6.	0.7	? 0.7	? $0.7\sqrt{2}$
8.	? $\frac{9\sqrt{2}}{2}$	? $\frac{9\sqrt{2}}{2}$	9

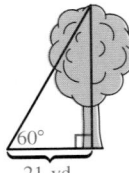

	a	b	c
5.	? $\frac{3}{4}$	$\frac{3}{4}$	? $\frac{3\sqrt{2}}{4}$
7.	? 9	? 9	$9\sqrt{2}$
9.	? $2\sqrt{30}$	? $2\sqrt{30}$	$4\sqrt{15}$

	d	e	f
10.	12	? $12\sqrt{3}$	? 24
12.	? 3	? $3\sqrt{3}$	6
14.	? $\frac{9}{2}$	? $\frac{9\sqrt{3}}{2}$	9

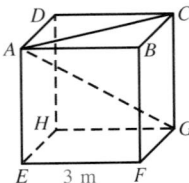

	d	e	f
11.	$12\sqrt{3}$	? 36	? $24\sqrt{3}$
13.	? 6	$6\sqrt{3}$	? 12
15.	$\frac{3}{4}$	? $\frac{3\sqrt{3}}{4}$	? $\frac{3}{2}$

Answer Exercises 16–18 in radical form. Then calculate to the nearest hundredth.

B **16.** Find the height of the tree.
$21\sqrt{3}$ yd ≈ 36.37 yd

17. Find the length of the diagonal of the face of the cube.
$3\sqrt{2}$ m ≈ 4.24 m

18. Find the length of $\overline{AG}$ in the cube.
$3\sqrt{3}$ m ≈ 5.20 m

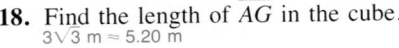

19. Find the perimeter of an equilateral triangle with an altitude $6\sqrt{3}$ inches. 36 in.

20. The legs of an isosceles triangle are $10\sqrt{3}$ cm long. The vertex angle has a measure of 120. Find the length of the base of the triangle and the length of the altitude from the vertex angle. 30 cm; $5\sqrt{3}$ cm

324   Chapter 8 Right Triangles

Developing Mathematical Power

Keeping a Portfolio Have students assign the value *h* to the hypotenuse of a 45°-45°-90° triangle and derive the formula for the legs in terms of *h*. Then they should assign the value *l* to the longer leg of a 30°-60°-90° triangle and express the shorter leg and the hypotenuse in terms of *l*.

21. Find the height of the tree. 15 ft

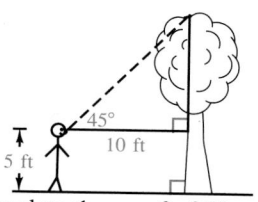

5 ft
45°
10 ft

22. Find c, d, e, f, and g in this corner.
$e = 10$, $g = 10\sqrt{2}$,
$d = 10\sqrt{3}$, $c = 20$,
$f = 20$

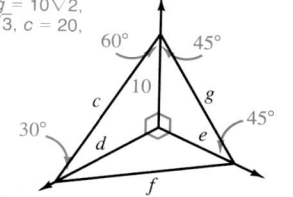

60°   45°
10
30° c g 45°
d e
f

C
23. Complete the proof of Theorem 8.6.
See Additional Answers, p. 702.

24. Complete the proof of Theorem 8.7.

25. Each side of a regular hexagon
PQRSTU measures 10 in. Find the
lengths of the diagonals from *P*.
$PS = 20$ in. $PR = PT = 10\sqrt{3}$ in.

26. Find a formula for the length of the
internal diagonal of any cube having
an edge of length s. $d = s\sqrt{3}$

27. In this triangular disk, the center of
gravity is two-thirds of the way
from *C* along altitude $\overline{CP}$. Find its
distance from *C*.
$\dfrac{10\sqrt{2}}{3}$

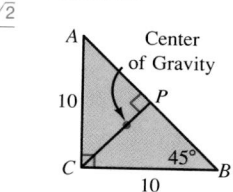

A   Center
of Gravity
10   P
C   45°   B
10

28. Find the coordinates of *A* if $c = -2$
and $a = -5$. Leave the answer in
radical form. $(-5, 3\sqrt{3})$

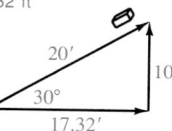

$A(a, b)$ y
$B(a, 0)$ 60° x
$C(c, 0)$ $(0, 0)$

Applications   vertical: $\frac{1}{2}(20 \text{ ft}) = 10$ ft; horizontal: $\frac{1}{2}(20 \text{ ft})\sqrt{3} \approx 10 \cdot 1.732 = 17.32$ ft

29. Physics   A body is displaced 20 ft in a direction 30° above the
horizontal. This has the same result as a displacement of 17.32
ft along the horizontal followed by a move of 10 ft
along the vertical. Verify that 17.32′ and 10′ are correct.

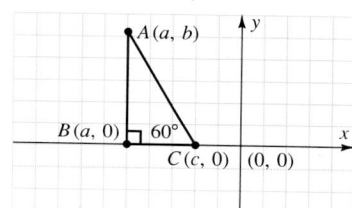

20′   10′
30°
17.32′

30. Technology   Use Logo and your knowledge of special right triangles to
draw houses and rockets. Experiment with tessellations of your drawings.
See Solutions Manual.

Algebra Review

Simplify.

31. $\sqrt{169}$ 13   **32.** $\sqrt{484}$ 22   **33.** $\sqrt{1225}$ 35   **34.** $\sqrt{625}$ 25   **35.** $\sqrt{961}$ 31

Rationalize the expression.

36. $\dfrac{8}{\sqrt{3}}$ $\frac{8\sqrt{3}}{3}$ **37.** $\dfrac{3}{\sqrt{5}}$ $\frac{3\sqrt{5}}{5}$ **38.** $\dfrac{12}{\sqrt{2}}$ $6\sqrt{2}$ **39.** $\dfrac{21}{\sqrt{3}}$ $7\sqrt{3}$ **40.** $\dfrac{35}{\sqrt{7}}$ $5\sqrt{7}$

Solve for the positive root.

41. $x^2 = 225$ 15   **42.** $x^2 - 25 = 0$ 5   **43.** $x^2 + 3x - 10 = 0$ 2   **44.** $x^2 - 6x = 7$ 7

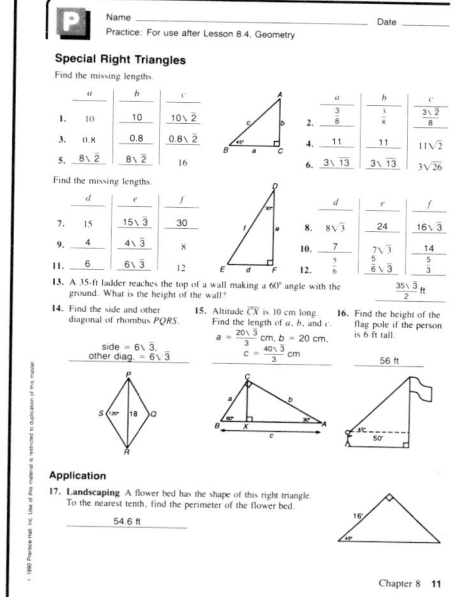

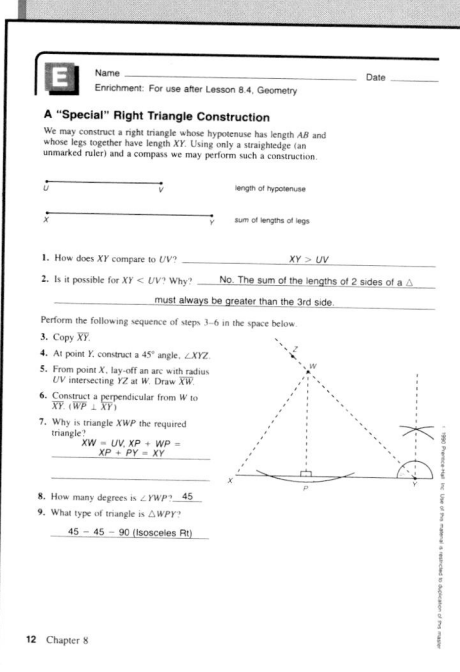

Materials/Manipulatives
Sand timer
Teaching Transparency 53

Technology
*Computer Test Bank, pp.
496–504*

LESSON FOCUS

Review
Review the Pythagorean Theorem and the formulas for finding missing lengths in a 45°-45°-90° triangle and a 30°-60°-90° triangle.

Alternative Learning Styles
Students may benefit from using a calculator when making difficult or tedious calculations. Caution them that they must pay particular attention to the reasonableness of the answer when using a calculator. Encourage them to use estimation to determine the reasonableness of the answer by determining between which two numbers the square root lies. For example, $\sqrt{1030}$ is between $\sqrt{900}$ and $\sqrt{1600}$, that is, between 30 and 40, but closer to 30.

8.5 Strategy: Estimate and Calculate Roots

When applying the Pythagorean Theorem, calculators provide a convenient way to find square roots. When a calculator is not available, estimating can be used to find a reasonable approximation. The problem solving steps can be applied to develop a strategy for estimating roots.

EXAMPLE 1   To find the distance across a pond, a scout troop sets up a right triangle which the hypotenuse is the unknown distance. Using a yard-long pace, they estimate the lengths of the right triangle's legs to be 32 and 44 yd. What is an estimate of the pond's width, to the nearest yard?

Understand the Problem   **Draw a figure.**
Make the hypotenuse the distance across the pond. Label it x.

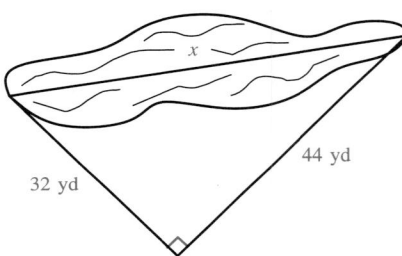

What information is given?
The leg lengths of the right triangle are 32 yd and 44 yd. By the Pythagorean Theorem,

$$x^2 = 32^2 + 44^2$$
$$x^2 = 2960$$

What is the question?
Find x, the distance across the pond, to the nearest yard. That is, find $\sqrt{2960}$ to the nearest integer.

How can the question be restated?
Which positive integer has a square that is closest to 2960?

Developing Mathematical Power
Cooperative Learning   Select teams of students to challenge each other to estimate the square root of a number before the sand runs out in a sand timer. After the teams have practiced, conduct an Estimation Elimination with members from different teams competing.

Plan Your Approach

Find squares near 2960.

The squares of multiples of 10 are easily found.

Number	10	20	30	40	50
Square	100	400	900	1600	2500

There is a pattern that relates a number whose ones digit is 5 with the square of the number.

Number	15	25	35	45
Square	225	625	1225	2025
	1·2	2·3	3·4	4·5

Thus, 5625 is a square because its last two digits form the number 25 and the digits preceding 25 represent the product of two consecutive integers, $7 \cdot 8$. The square root is the smaller integer 7 followed by 5, or 75.

Use the known squares to estimate $\sqrt{2960}$.

Implement the Plan

Estimate and check by multiplying.

2960 lies between 50^2 and 55^2.

$$50^2 < 2960 < 55^2$$

2960 is closer to 55^2 (3025) than to 50^2 (2500).
Choose an estimate closer to 55.

$$\sqrt{2960} \approx 54$$
$$54^2 = 2916$$

54^2 (2916) is closer to 2960 than to 55^2 (3025).

Interpret the Results

Since 2960 is between 54^2 and 55^2 and is closer to 54^2, a good estimate of $\sqrt{2960}$ is 54. So the distance across the pond is about 54 yd.

 A calculator can be used to check the estimate: $\sqrt{2960} \approx 54.405882$.

Estimation problems involving 30°-60°-90° triangles and 45°-45°-90° triangles can be simplified by recalling that $\sqrt{2} \approx 1.4$ and $\sqrt{3} \approx 1.7$.

EXAMPLE 2 A navigator estimates an inaccessible distance EF by setting up 30°-60°-90° $\triangle DEF$ and measuring $\overline{DF}$. If $DF = 42$ m, how can he find EF?

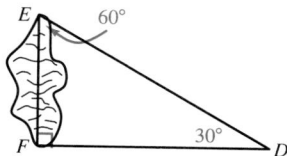

8.5 Strategy: Estimate and Calculate Roots **327**

Developing Mathematical Power

Keeping a Portfolio Have students outline the steps involved in estimating the square root of a number. They should provide several examples to illustrate their lists and explain which step they think is most critical and why.

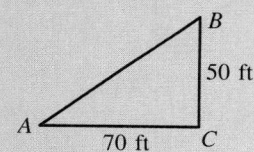
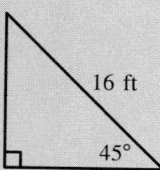

Common Errors

- Some students will need a great deal of practice before their estimates are reasonable. Remind students that estimation is not random guessing. The strategies of the lesson enable one to make appropriate estimates.
- Some students will accept a number produced by a calculator as correct, no matter what. Encourage students to be alert to reasonableness of results through examples of very obvious errors, to help alleviate this difficulty.
- See *Teacher's Resource Book* for additional remediation.

LESSON FOLLOW-UP

Assignment Guide

See p. 304B for assignments.

☐ **Understand the Problem**

$\overline{EF}$ is the shorter leg (the leg opposite the 30° angle) of a 30°-60°-90° triangle. The length of the longer leg $\overline{DF}$ is 42 m. The ratio of the shorter leg to the longer leg in a 30°-60°-90° triangle is always $1:\sqrt{3}$

☐ **Plan Your Approach**

How can the ratio be used?

$$\frac{EF}{42} = \frac{1}{\sqrt{3}}$$

☐ **Implement the Plan**

Solve for *EF*.

$$EF\sqrt{3} = 42$$
$$EF = \frac{42}{\sqrt{3}} = \frac{42}{\sqrt{3}} \cdot \frac{\sqrt{3}}{\sqrt{3}} = \frac{42\sqrt{3}}{3} = 14\sqrt{3} \approx 24 \text{ m}$$

☐ **Interpret the Results**

The inaccessible distance, the shorter leg of a 30°-60°-90° triangle, is about 24 m. Rationalizing the denominator resulted in a multiplication rather than a division by 1.7.

By using the Distributive property, a mental calculation was possible:

$$14(1.7) = 14(1 + 0.7)$$
$$= 14 + 9.8 \approx 24$$

Problem Solving Reminders

- Use the known squares of integers (such as multiples of 5 and 10) to estimate an unknown square root.
- Check your estimate by multiplying. If it is not close enough, choose another estimate.
- If a problem involves finding a side length of a 30°-60°-90° triangle or a 45°-45°-90° triangle, use the ratios of the side lengths and the estimates $\sqrt{3} \approx 1.7$ and $\sqrt{2} \approx 1.4$.

CLASS EXERCISES

Estimate to the nearest integer.

1. $\sqrt{1030}$ ₃₂   2. $\sqrt{2114}$ ₄₆   3. $\sqrt{4625}$ ₆₈

Rationalize the radical expression. Then estimate to the nearest integer. Use mental calculation whenever possible.

4. $\dfrac{16}{\sqrt{2}}$ 11   5. $\dfrac{52}{\sqrt{2}}$ 37   6. $\dfrac{61}{\sqrt{2}}$ 43

7. $\dfrac{24}{\sqrt{3}}$ 14   8. $\dfrac{63}{\sqrt{3}}$ 36   9. $\dfrac{46}{\sqrt{3}}$ 27

10. *AB* can be found by setting up 45°-45°-90° △*ABC* and measuring $\overline{BC}$. If *BC* = 64, what is the distance *AB*?

$64\sqrt{2} \approx 91$

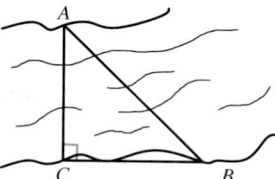

PRACTICE EXERCISES

A

Estimate to the nearest integer.

1. $\sqrt{590}$ 24   **2.** $\sqrt{3130}$ 56   **3.** $\sqrt{5050}$ 71   **4.** $\sqrt{7700}$ 88

Estimate to the nearest integer. Use mental calculation whenever possible.

5. $\dfrac{28}{\sqrt{2}}$ 20   **6.** $\dfrac{73}{\sqrt{2}}$ 52   **7.** $\dfrac{72}{\sqrt{3}}$ 42   **8.** $\dfrac{38}{\sqrt{3}}$ 22

Sketch a right △*ABC* with right ∠*C* for each of Exercises 9–16. Estimate each answer to the nearest integer. Use mental calculation whenever you can.

9. Estimate *AB*, given *BC* = 35 and *CA* = 45. 57

10. Estimate *CA*, given *AB* = 86 and *BC* = 85 13

11. Estimate *AB*, given *BC* = 52 and △*ABC* is a 45°-45°-90° triangle. 74

12. Estimate *BC*, given *CA* = 41 and *m*∠*A* = 60. 71

13. Estimate *BC*, given *CA* = 66 and *m*∠*B* = 30. 114

14. Estimate *BC*, given *AB* = 84 and △*ABC* is a 45°-45°-90° triangle. 59

15. Estimate *AB*, given *AC* = 45 and *m*∠*B* = 60. 52

16. Estimate *BC*, given *AC* = 36 and *m*∠*B* = 60. 21

Where possible, use mental calculation to find the estimates.

17. At a position of 25 m from the base of a tree, the measure of the angle formed by the horizontal and the sight-line to the top of the tree is 60. Estimate the height of the tree to the nearest integer. 43 m

18. A surveyor is 220 m from the base of a perpendicular cliff. The angle formed by the horizontal and the line of sight to the top of the cliff measures 60°. What should be the surveyor's estimate of the height of the cliff? 381 m

8.5 Strategy: Estimate and Calculate Roots **329**

19. At a lumberjack's position 60 ft along the horizontal from the base of a tree, the angle from the horizontal to the tree top measures 60°. Is the tree more than 100 ft tall? $60\sqrt{3} \approx 104$ ft; yes

20. A cable is needed to support a 25-ft pole. The triangle formed by the pole, the horizontal, and the cable is a 45°-45°-90° triangle. Estimate the length of the cable. 35 ft

21. A 20-ft ladder just reaches the top of a house when perched at an angle of 45° with the horizontal. Estimate the height of the house to the nearest tenth of a foot. 14.1 ft

22. An inaccessible distance is the length of the hypotenuse of a right triangle whose legs measure 35 m and 85 m, respectively. Estimate the unknown length. 92 m

Justify each equation.

23. $\frac{\sqrt{300}}{10} = \sqrt{3}$ $\frac{\sqrt{300}}{10} = \frac{\sqrt{3}\cdot\sqrt{100}}{10} = \frac{\sqrt{3}\cdot 10}{10} = \sqrt{3}$

24. $\frac{\sqrt{20,000}}{100} = \sqrt{2}$ $\frac{\sqrt{20,000}}{100} = \frac{\sqrt{2}\cdot\sqrt{10,000}}{100} = \frac{\sqrt{2}\cdot 100}{100} = \sqrt{2}$

C **Solve.**

25. A scout troop finds that the legs of a right triangle measure 33 yd and 44 yd, respectively. Hence, x, the length of the hypotenuse, can be found by solving $x^2 = 33^2 + 44^2$. One of the scouts claims that x can be found by factoring and with almost no calculation. Find a way to do so. See side column.

26. An engineer needs a quick estimate of the length of supporting truss, $\overline{CP}$, the altitude in the right-triangular bridge frame, $\triangle ABC$. $BP = 32$ ft and $PA = 96$ ft. Estimate CP to the nearest integer by mental calculation. 55 ft

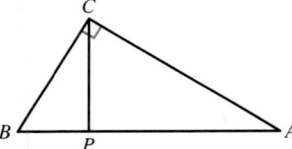

Find the number of digits in each square root. Then make a generalization based on the number of digits in the radicand.

27. $\sqrt{45,670}$ 3 digits

28. $\sqrt{12,345,678}$ 4 digits

Mark off digits in sets of two; the number of sets equals the number of digits. 04 56 70 = 3 digits; 12 34 56 78 = 4

PROJECT

Research the traditional method of computing square root and how this method is related to writing a perfect square trinomial as a binomial squared.

330 Chapter 8 Right Triangles

25. $x^2 = 11^2 \cdot 3^2 + 11^2 \cdot 4^2$
$= 11^2(3^2 + 4^2)$
$= 11^2 \cdot 5^2$
$x = 11 \cdot 5 = 55$

Trigonometric Ratios

Objectives: To define and compute the tangent, sine, and cosine
ratios for an acute angle

LESSON PLAN

Vocabulary
Cosine (cos)   Tangent (tan)
Sine (sin)   Trigonometry

Materials/Manipulatives
Teacher's Resource Book,
Teaching Aid 8
Transparency 12
Teaching Transparency 54

Technology
Graphing calculator
Computer
Computer Test Bank, pp.
504–515
Using the Graphics Calculator 1,
Lesson 15
The Geometric Supposer:
Triangles
Geometry Problems and
Projects: Triangles,
Worksheet T67

Important ratios related to each of
the acute angles in a right triangle
are part of the branch of mathematics
known as *trigonometry*. Note
the right triangles formed
on this radar screen.

Investigation—*Visualizing the Concept*

Use a straightedge and a
protractor to draw three 30°-60°-90°
triangles of different sizes.
Measure and label the sides.
Then complete this chart.

Answers will vary with student drawings, but are approximated by

Ratio	△I	△II	△III
$\dfrac{\text{length of the side opposite the 60° angle}}{\text{length of the hypotenuse}}$	? $\frac{\sqrt{3}}{2}$	?	?
$\dfrac{\text{length of the side adjacent to the 60° angle}}{\text{length of the hypotenuse}}$	? $\frac{1}{2}$	?	?
$\dfrac{\text{length of the side opposite the 60° angle}}{\text{length of the side adjacent to the 60° angle}}$	? $\frac{\sqrt{3}}{1}$	?	?

1. What seems to be true about each set of ratios? They are =.

2. Make a generalization. What kind of reasoning did you use? Using inductive
reasoning, the ratios for the 60°∠ are constant for all sizes of 30°-60°-90° △.

LESSON FOCUS

Review
• Draw and label two similar triangles on the chalkboard. Have students identify the corresponding
angles and write the equivalent ratios for the corresponding sides.
• The Chapter Summary and Review, pp. 344–345, gives vocabulary and concepts and review exercises by lesson.
• The end of chapter features a Cumulative Review on pp. 348–350.

Alternative Learning Styles
• The Investigation provides a kinesthetic approach to the trigonometric
functions and helps students to discover that the trigonometric ratios
for any one angle are constant.
• Some students may benefit from
the use of a mnemonic such as
SOHCAHTOA to help them to remember the trigonometric ratios.

Since these three right triangles are similar, certain ratios remain
constant. The following ratio refers to the 30° angle.

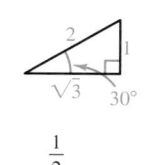 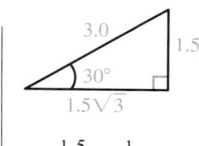 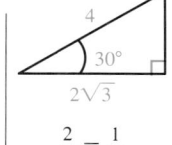

$\dfrac{\text{length of opposite side}}{\text{length of hypotenuse}}$	$\dfrac{1}{2}$	$\dfrac{1.5}{3.0} = \dfrac{1}{2}$	$\dfrac{2}{4} = \dfrac{1}{2}$

Developing Mathematical Power

Cooperative Learning   Working in groups, students can "Measure and Discover!"
by completing the Enrichment activity, p. 17, in the *Teacher's Resource Book* (see
side column, p. 336). Have them draw various-sized circles and various-sized triangles within them and use their drawings to verify that the law of sines works for all
triangles.

332

TEACHING SUGGESTIONS

- Point out that most of the entries in the table are approximations. The exceptions are sin 30° = cos 60° = 0.5 and tan 45° = 1.
- Make sure students see how to determine which table entry a trigonometric ratio is closer to when it falls between two entries.

CHALKBOARD EXAMPLES

- **For Example 1**

  Find sin *A*.

  a. 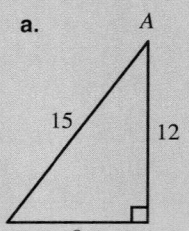   **b.**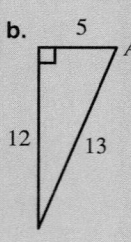

  a. sin A = $\frac{9}{15}$ = 0.6

  b. sin A = $\frac{12}{13}$ ≈ 0.9231

- **For Example 2**

  Use the table on p. 658 to find the value for sin 27°.   sin 27° ≈ 0.4540

A ratio such as the one for 30° exists for *any* acute angle in a right triangle. This ratio has the special name, *sine,* and is very useful in mathematics and its applications. For any given acute angle, the sine ratio will be constant, regardless of the size of the right triangle containing the angle.

Definition   For any acute angle of measure *x* in any right triangle,

$$\text{sine } x = \frac{\text{length of the side opposite the angle}}{\text{length of the hypotenuse}}$$

The word sine is abbreviated *sin.*

If ∠*A* is an acute angle of right △*ABC*, sin A will mean *the sine of the measure of* ∠*A.*

EXAMPLE 1   Find the sine of the indicated angle. Where necessary, give the answer as a simplified radical and then calculate and round to the nearest ten-thousandth.

a. 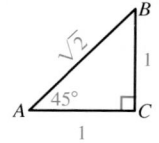   **b.** 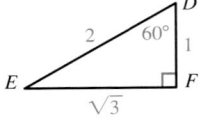   **c.**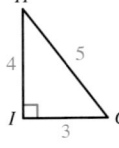

sin A = _?_   sin D = _?_   sin G = _?_

 a. sin 45° = $\frac{1}{\sqrt{2}} \cdot \frac{\sqrt{2}}{\sqrt{2}} = \frac{\sqrt{2}}{2}$ **b.** sin 60° = $\frac{\sqrt{3}}{2}$ **c.** sin G = $\frac{4}{5}$

sin 45° ≈ 0.7071   sin 60° ≈ 0.8660   sin G = 0.8000

The symbol ≈ is used to show that the value is approximate.

Since the sine ratio for any given acute angle is constant, the sine ratios for all acute angles have been made available in tables and on scientific calculators.

EXAMPLE 2   Use the table on page 658 to find the value for sin 51°.

Find 51° in the **Angle** column, and then look under **Sine** for the ratio. Sin 51° ≈ 0.7771. Compare this with the calculator value for sin 51°.

Angle	Sine
50°	0.7660
51°	0.7771
52°	0.7880

332   Chapter 8 Right Triangles

Developing Mathematical Power

Keeping a Portfolio Have students complete the Investigation, p. 15, in the *Teacher's Resource Book.* They should repeat Exercises 5 and 6 for other pairs of complementary angles. Have them generalize their findings about the relationship of the sine and cosine of complementary angles.

EXAMPLE 3   Sin $x = 0.6$; find x to the nearest degree.

Find 0.6000 in the **Sine** column. Since 0.6000 is between 0.5878 for 36° and 0.6018 for 37°, but is closer to 0.6018, $x \approx 37°$.

Angle	Sine
36°	0.5878
37°	0.6018

EXAMPLE 4   Find the missing x and y measures. Check with a calculator.

a.

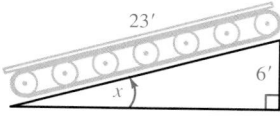

b.

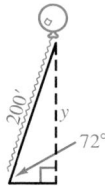

a. $\sin x = \dfrac{6}{23}$

$\sin x \approx 0.2609$
From the table, $x \approx 15°$

b.

$\sin 72° = \dfrac{y}{200 \text{ ft}}$

$0.9511 \approx \dfrac{y}{200 \text{ ft}}$

$200' \cdot 0.9511 \approx y$

$y \approx 190.22 \text{ ft}$

The sine of an angle's complement is called the *cosine* of the angle.

Definition   For any acute angle of measure x in any right triangle,

$$\textbf{cosine } x = \frac{\text{length of the side adjacent to the angle}}{\text{length of the hypotenuse}}$$

The abbreviation for cosine is *cos*. If $\angle B$ is an acute angle of a right triangle, what is the meaning of cos B? the cosine of the measure of $\angle B$

Another frequently used trigonometric ratio is the *tangent*.

Definition   For any acute angle of measure x in any right triangle,

$$\textbf{tangent } x = \frac{\text{length of the side opposite the angle}}{\text{length of the side adjacent to the angle}}$$

Tan is the abbreviation for tangent. What does tan B mean if $\angle B$ is an acute angle of a right triangle? You can use tables and scientific calculators to find an approximation of a tangent ratio. the tangent of the measure of $\angle B$

8.6 Trigonometric Ratios   **333**

• **For Example 3**

If sin x = 0.3100, find x to the nearest degree.
In the table; sin 18° ≈ 0.3090
        sin 19° ≈ 0.3256
Since 0.3100 is closer to 0.3090 than to 0.3256, x ≈ 18°.

• **For Example 4**

Find x to the nearest degree and y to the nearest unit.

a. 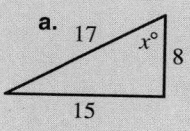 **b.**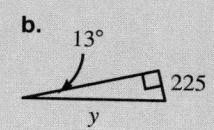

a. Since 17² = 15² + 8², the ∠ opp. 17 is a rt. ∠.
sin x = $\frac{15}{17}$
sin x ≈ 0.8824
    x ≈ 62°
b. sin 13° = $\frac{225}{y}$

$y ≈ \frac{225}{0.2250}$
$y ≈ 1,000$

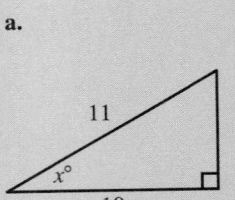
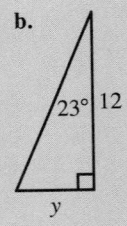
EXAMPLE 5   Find each answer and verify with right triangle properties.

a. Use the cosine ratio to find AC to the nearest integer.

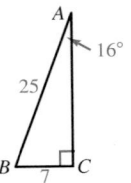

b. Use the tangent ratio to find $m\angle F$ to the nearest degree.

a. $\cos 16° = \dfrac{\text{adjacent side}}{25}$

$0.9613 \approx \dfrac{AC}{25}$

$25 \cdot 0.9613 \approx AC$

$AC \approx 24$

By the Pythagorean Theorem,
$(AB)^2 = (BC)^2 + (AC)^2$
$(AC)^2 = 25^2 - 7^2$
$AC = \sqrt{576} = 24$

b. $\tan x = \dfrac{7}{25}$

$\tan x = 0.28$
$x \approx 16°$
Since acute angles of a right $\triangle$ are complementary,
$90 = 16 + m\angle F,$
$m\angle F = 90 - 16 = 74$

CLASS EXERCISES

Find sin P, cos P, tan P, sin Q, cos Q, and tan Q in fraction form.

1.

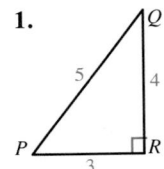

$\sin P = \frac{4}{5}$
$\cos P = \frac{3}{5}$
$\tan P = \frac{4}{3}$
$\sin Q = \frac{3}{5}$
$\cos Q = \frac{4}{5}$
$\tan Q = \frac{3}{4}$

2.

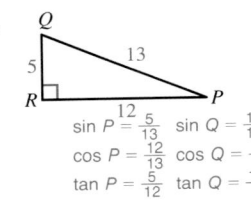

$\sin P = \frac{5}{13}$ $\sin Q = \frac{12}{13}$
$\cos P = \frac{12}{13}$ $\cos Q = \frac{5}{13}$
$\tan P = \frac{5}{12}$ $\tan Q = \frac{12}{5}$

3.

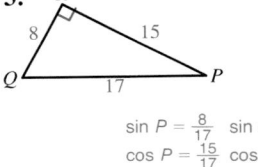

$\sin P = \frac{8}{17}$ $\sin Q =$
$\cos P = \frac{15}{17}$ $\cos Q =$
$\tan P = \frac{8}{15}$ $\tan Q =$

Use the table on page 658 to find each ratio.

4. $\tan 36°$ 0.7265   **5.** $\tan 87°$ 19.0811   **6.** $\sin 10°$ 0.1736

7. $\sin 44°$ 0.6947   **8.** $\cos 46°$ 0.6947   **9.** $\cos 80°$ 0.1736

Use the table on page 658 to find each angle measure to the nearest degree.

10. $\tan x \approx 0.5774$ 30°   **11.** $\tan x = 0.6000$ 31°   **12.** $\sin x = 0.5000$ 30°

13. $\sin x = 0.8000$ 53°   **14.** $\cos x \approx 0.7071$ 45°   **15.** $\cos x = 0.6000$ 53°

Set up a ratio and find x to the nearest hundredth.

16.

$\tan 35° = \frac{x}{20}$
$x \approx 14.00$

17.

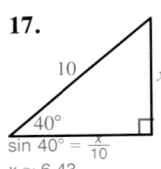

$\sin 40° = \frac{x}{10}$
$x \approx 6.43$

18.

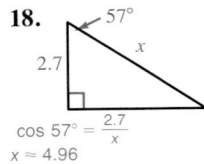

$\cos 57° = \frac{2.7}{x}$
$x \approx 4.96$

334   Chapter 8 Right Triangles

Decide which trigonometric ratio to use. Then use the table on page 658 to find *y* to the nearest hundredth. Find *x* to the nearest degree.

A **1.**
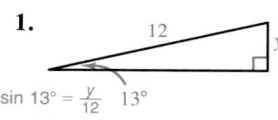

$\sin 13° = \frac{y}{12}$ 13°

$y \approx 2.70$

2.
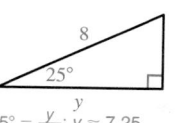

$\cos 25° = \frac{y}{8}$; $y \approx 7.25$

3.
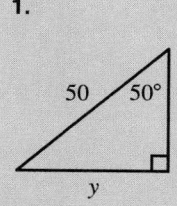

$\tan x = \frac{50}{30}$

$x \approx 59°$

4.
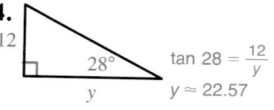

$\tan 28 = \frac{12}{y}$

$y \approx 22.57$

5.
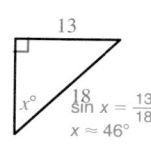

$\sin x = \frac{13}{18}$

$x \approx 46°$

6.
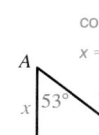

$\cos x = \frac{9}{12}$

$x \approx 41°$

7. Use the cosine ratio to find *x*. Check your answer by using the Pythagorean Theorem. $x \approx 9.03$; $x^2 + 12^2 = 15^2$; $x = 9$

8. Use the tangent ratio to find *x*. Compare your answer with Exercise 7. $x = 9.04$ The answers are different by one hundredth.

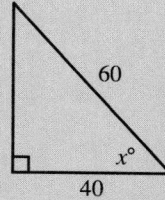

Find *x* to the nearest degree.

9. Use the sine ratio. Check that the acute angles are complements. $\sin x = \frac{5}{13}$, $x \approx 23°$
$23° + 67° = 90°$

10. Use the Pythagorean Theorem to find *EF*, then use the tangent ratio. Compare your methods with those for Exercise 9. $5^2 + (EF)^2 = 13^2$; $25 + (EF)^2 = 169$; $(EF)^2 = 144$; $EF = 12$; $\tan x = \frac{5}{12}$; $\tan x \approx 0.4167$; $x \approx 23°$ Using the sine ratio takes fewer steps.

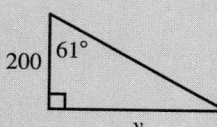

Find *x* and/or *y*. If measures are lengths, round to the nearest hundredth; if angle measures, round to the nearest degree.

B **11.**
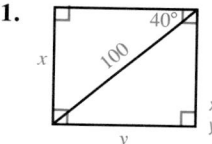

$x \approx 64.28$; $y \approx 76.60$

12.
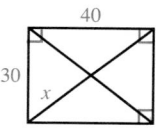

$x \approx 53°$

13.
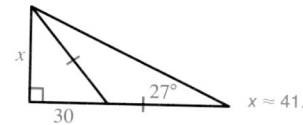

$x \approx 41.29$

14. The shorter diagonal of a rhombus is 50 mm long. Each of its obtuse angles measures 140°. Find the length of each side. each side is 73.10 mm

15. Each base angle of an isosceles triangle measures 50° and the altitude to the base is 26 cm long. Find the length of the base to the nearest centimeter. 44 cm

16. The base of an isosceles triangle is 12 cm long. Its vertex angle measures 70°. Find the length of each congruent side. 10.46 cm

Sketch △*ABC* with *m∠C* = 90. Label *m∠A* as *x*. Write a general expression for each in terms of *a*, *b*, and *c*.

17. $\sin x \frac{a}{c}$

18. $\cos x \frac{b}{c}$

19. $\tan x \frac{a}{b}$

8.6 Trigonometric Ratios   **335**

33. In a rt. △, as ∠ meas. increases, the value of sin increases, the value of cos decreases, and the value of tan increases.
As the ∠ meas. increases, the length of the opp. side increases and the length of the adj. side decreases; so sin ($\frac{opp.}{hyp.}$) will increase, cos ($\frac{adj.}{hyp.}$) will decrease, and tan ($\frac{opp.}{adj.}$) will increase.

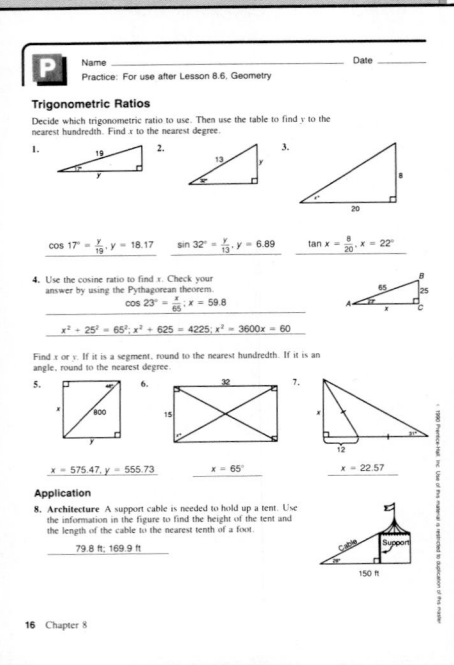

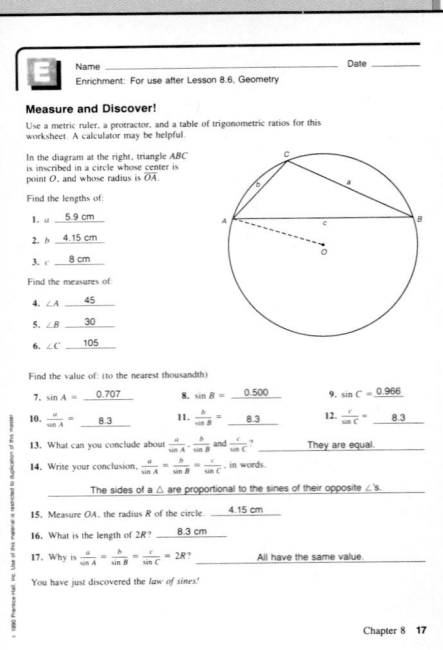

Complete each trigonometric ratio for any equilateral triangle whose side measure is s. Draw an altitude and express segments in terms of s. Then compare each value with the value found in the table on page 658.

20. $\tan 60° = \underline{\ ?\ } \sqrt{3} \approx 1.7321$
trig. table: 1.7321

21. $\sin 60° = \underline{\ ?\ } \frac{\sqrt{3}}{2} \approx 0.8660$
trig. table: 0.8660

22. $\cos 60° = \underline{\ ?\ } \frac{1}{2} = 0.5000$
trig. table: 0.5000

Compare $\sin x$ with $\cos(90° - x)$ when x has the given measure.

23. $x = 30°$ $\sin 30° \approx 0.5$
$\cos 60° = 0.5$

24. $x = 45°$ $\sin 45° \approx 0.7071$
$\cos 45° \approx 0.7071$

25. $x = 60°$ $\sin 60° \approx 0.8660$
$\cos 30° \approx 0.8660$

26. How do $\cos x$ and $\sin(90° - x)$ compare? Explain. They are =.

C **27.** The length of one rectangular face of this prism is twice the width. Find the dimensions to the nearest foot.
width ≈ 19 ft
length ≈ 38 ft

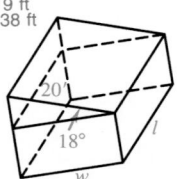

28. $AB = 300$ ft, $m\angle FAP = 4$, and $m\angle PAB = 28$. Find the length of the flagpole to the nearest foot. 28 ft

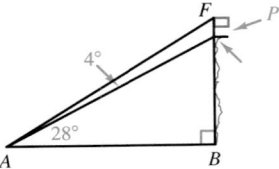

Use the general expressions from Exercises 17–19 to prove the following.
See side column, p. 335.

29. Prove $\sin^2 x + \cos^2 x = 1$.

30. Prove $\tan x = \dfrac{\sin x}{\cos x}$.
See Additional Answers, p. 702.

Applications See Solutions Manual.

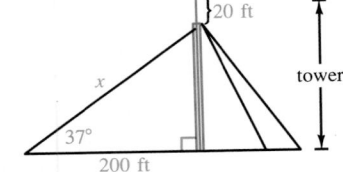

31. Technology Write a procedure to find the height of the radio tower to the nearest tenth of a foot. 170.7 ft

32. Technology Write a procedure to find the length of the support cable x to the nearest tenth of a foot. 250.43 ft

33. Technology Use the Logo commands SIN and COS to create a Table of Trigonometric Ratios. What happens to the values of the sine, cosine, and tangent as angle measures increase from 1 to 89? Explain your answer in terms of the side lengths of a right triangle. See side column.

Developing Mathematical Power

34. Extension The *reciprocals* of sine, cosine, and tangent are often used:

cosecant   secant   cotangent

$$\csc x = \frac{1}{\sin x} \qquad \sec x = \frac{1}{\cos x} \qquad \cot x = \frac{1}{\tan x}$$

Find an equation relating $\tan^2 x$ and $\sec^2 x$, and another relating $\cot^2 x$ and $\csc^2 x$.
See Additional Answers, p. 702.

336 Chapter 8 Right Triangles

Strategy: Use Trigonometric Ratios

LESSON PLAN

Vocabulary
Angle of depression
Angle of elevation

Materials/Manipulatives
Teaching Transparency 55

Technology
Scientific calculator
Computer Test Bank, pp.
515–519

In trigonometry you are often asked to solve problems involving the *angle of elevation* or the *angle of depression*.

When a pilot at *P* sees a control tower at *T* at an angle of 25° *down from the horizontal* of the plane, that angle is an **angle of depression**. When the traffic controllers at *T* see the plane at *P* at an angle of 25° *up from the horizontal* of the control tower, that angle is an **angle of elevation.**

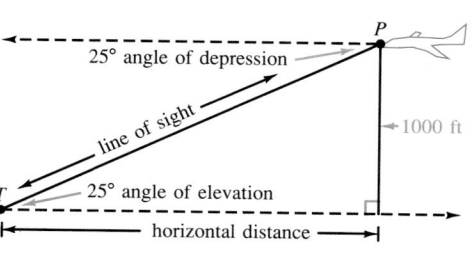

LESSON FOCUS

Review
Review the trigonometric ratios. Draw △*ABC* on the chalkboard. Have students find the missing measures to the nearest tenth.

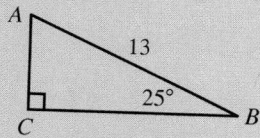

1. *BC* = _?_ 2. *m∠A* = _?_
3. *AC* = _?_

1. 11.8 2. 65 3. 5.5

EXAMPLE 1 Find the horizontal distance from the airplane to the control tower.

Understand The Problem
Study the figure. A right triangle is formed, so calculate the distance by using the angle of elevation or the angle of depression and a trigonometric ratio.

Plan Your Approach
You have a choice of ratios to use: sine, cosine, or tangent. To use the sine or cosine ratios, you need the hypotenuse length, which you could use to find the horizontal distance. But the tangent uses both sides of the triangle, one which is given as 1000 ft and the other which represents the horizontal distance. Thus the tangent is the best choice. Use tan 25°, since the angle of elevation is given as 25°.

Implement The Plan

$$\tan 25° = \frac{1000}{x}$$
$$0.4663 \approx \frac{1000}{x}$$
$$0.4663x \approx 1000$$
$$x \approx 2144.5421 \text{ ft}$$

A calculator or the trigonometric table can be used to find tan 25°.

The equation is now calculation-ready.

Interpret The Results
Unless the problem specifies otherwise, round your answer to the nearest integer. The horizontal distance is 2145 ft.

Sometimes different methods will *not* give precisely the same answer, since trigonometric ratio values are rounded in tables and by calculators.

Alternative Learning Styles
• The visual learner will benefit from using different colors to distinguish between the angle of depression and the angle of elevation. Point out that in Example 3, the angle of inclination can be thought of as the angle of elevation.
• A linguistic learner may benefit by associating an angle of depression with low spirits or feeling *down*, and by associating an angle of elevation with a high place or height *above* a surface.

8.7 Strategy: Use Trigonometric Ratios **337**

Developing Mathematical Power
Cooperative Learning Assign small groups of students to create their own word problems which require the use of trigonometric ratios to solve. Have them write each problem on one side of a card and a worked-out solution on the other side. They can be used for review, testing, or a class competition.

Point out that Example 1 could be set up as $\tan 65° = \dfrac{x}{1000}$ to convert the arithmetic involved into a relatively easy multiplication problem, rather than a division problem.

Critical Thinking

Comparison Ask students to compare different approaches to the same problem.

CHALKBOARD EXAMPLES

- **For Example 1**

  The angle of elevation to the top of a building from a point 2000 ft from the base of the building is 10°. Find the height of the building to the nearest integer. Since the length of one leg of a rt. △ is known and the length of the other leg is to be found, use tan 10°.

  $\tan 10° = \dfrac{h}{2000}$

  $h \approx 2000 \cdot 0.1763 \approx 353$ ft

- **For Example 2**

  To the nearest foot, what is the altitude of a kite whose 450 ft of string forms an angle of elevation of 31°? Since the length of the hypotenuse is known and the length of the side opposite the 31° angle is to be found, use $\sin 31° = \dfrac{x}{450}$.

  $x \approx 450 \cdot 0.5150 \approx 232$ ft

- **For Example 3**

  A woman is standing 50 ft from the base of a building and sights a point 12 ft up the side of the building. If her eyes are 5 ft 6 in. from the ground, what is the measure of the angle of elevation of her sight line to the nearest degree?

  5 ft 6 in. = 66 in.

  12 ft = 144 in.

  50 ft = 600 in.

  144 − 66 = 78

  $\tan x = \dfrac{78}{600} = 0.13; \; x \approx 7°$

EXAMPLE 2 **A 30-m steel wire supports a pole. The angle of elevation from S is 35°. Find the height of the pole.**

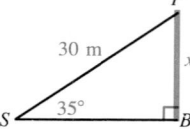

☐ Understand The Problem	Draw and label a figure. Since the length of the hypotenuse is given, sine or cosine can be used.	

☐ **Plan Your Approach**   Use $\sin 35° = \dfrac{x}{30}$ or $\cos 55° = \dfrac{x}{30}$.

☐ **Implement The Plan**

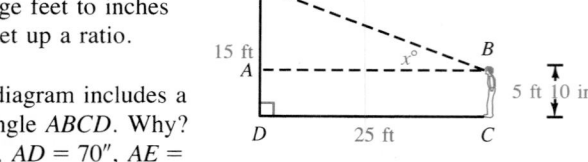

$$\sin 35° = \frac{x}{30} \quad \text{or} \quad \cos 55° = \frac{x}{30}$$
$$0.5736 \approx \frac{x}{30} \qquad\qquad 0.5736 \approx \frac{x}{30}$$
$$30(0.5736) \approx x \qquad 30(0.5736) \approx x$$
$$17\ \text{m} \approx x \qquad\qquad 17\ \text{m} \approx x$$

☐ **Interpret The Results**   The results are identical, since $\sin 35° = \cos(90° - 35°)$. The height of the pole is 17 m.

In some problems, angle measures must be found.

EXAMPLE 3   **A man is standing 25 ft from the foot of a wall. He sights a point 15 ft up the side of the wall. If his eyes are 5 ft 10 in. from the bottom of his feet, what is the measure of the angle of elevation x of his sight line to the nearest degree?**

☐ **Understand The Problem**   Draw and label a figure. Change feet to inches and set up a ratio.

☐ **Plan Your Approach**   The diagram includes a rectangle $ABCD$. Why? Thus, $AD = 70''$, $AE = 180 - 70$ or $110''$, and $\tan x = \dfrac{EA}{DC}$. *Horizontal and vertical lines meet to form right angles.*

☐ **Implement The Plan** $\tan x = \dfrac{110}{300}$

$\tan x \approx 0.3667$ *Use a calculator or the trigonometric table.*

$x \approx 20°$

☐ **Interpret The Results**   The problem shows a way of finding the angle of elevation to a point on a wall without using a transit.

> **Problem Solving Reminders**
>
> • Use the trigonometric ratio that is the most convenient to solve.
> • Use a table or a scientific calculator to help you solve the ratio.

LESSON FOLLOW-UP

Assignment Guide

• See p. 304B for the assignments.
• See *Teacher's Resource Book*, Critical Thinking, p. 8.

CLASS EXERCISES

Write an equation to find x. Then solve to the nearest whole number.

1.

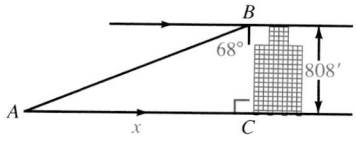

$\tan 68° = \frac{x}{808}$

$x \approx 2000$ ft

2.

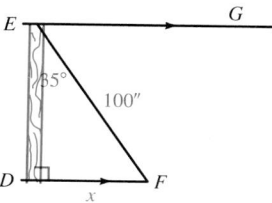

$\sin 35° = \frac{x}{100}$

$x \approx 57''$

3. In Exercise 1, name the angle of elevation from point A and its measure. ∠A; 22

4. In Exercise 2, name the angle of depression from point E and its measure. ∠GEF; 55

5. A surveyor must find the angle denoted by x. Write and solve an equation to find x to the nearest degree. $\tan x = \frac{40}{30}$, $x \approx 53°$

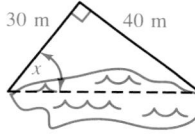

PRACTICE EXERCISES   Use technology where appropriate.

Find the distance to the nearest whole number and the angle measure to the nearest degree.

1. A 110-ft crane set at an angle of 45° to the horizontal can raise building material to what height? 78 ft

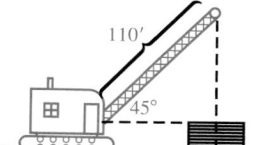

2. The angle of elevation from a ship to the top of a lighthouse is 3°. If the ship is 1000 m from the lighthouse, how tall is the lighthouse? 52 m

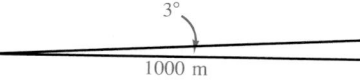

3. A ship's pilot knows that a building on the coast is 100 m tall. If he finds the angle of elevation to be 2°, how far is the ship from the coastline? 2864 m

8.7 Strategy: Use Trigonometric Ratios   **339**

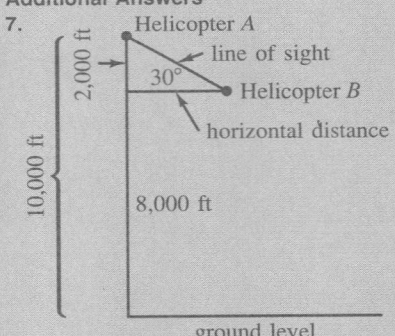
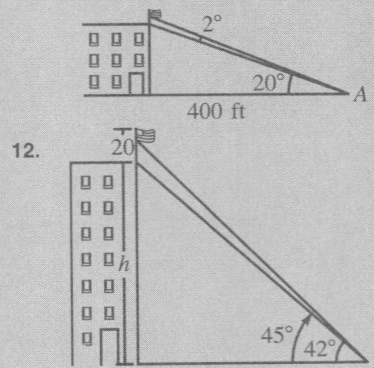
4. A pilot at an altitude of 2000 ft is over a spot 8020 ft from the end of an airport's runway. At what angle of depression should the pilot see the end of the runway? 14°

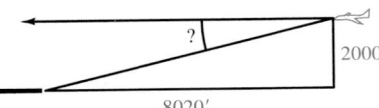

5. A ranger is at the top of a 200-ft lookout tower located on a flat plain. She spots a fire at an angle of depression of 3° from the top of her tower. How far away is the fire?
3817 ft

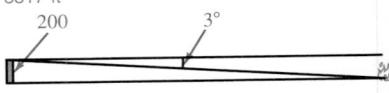

6. At a point 500 m north of a ship, the shoreline runs east and west. West of that point, the navigator sights a lighthouse at an angle of 60°. How far is the ship from the lighthouse? 1000 m

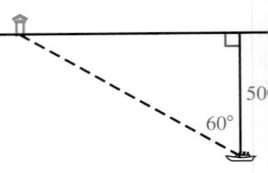

Solve. Draw a figure when necessary. See side column.

B

7. The pilot of a helicopter at an altitude of 10,000 ft sees a second helicopter at an angle of depression of 30°. The altitude of the second helicopter is 8000 ft. What is the distance from the first to the second along the line of sight? What is the horizontal distance between them? Find both answers to the nearest hundred feet. line of sight = 4000 ft; horizontal distance = 3500 ft

8. A flagpole is at the top of a building. Four hundred feet from the base of the building, the angle of elevation of the top of the pole is 22°, and the angle of elevation of the bottom of the pole is 20°. Sketch a figure. To the nearest foot, find the length of the flagpole. 16 ft

9. From a lighthouse 1000 ft above sea level, the angle of depression to a boat at B_1 is 29°. One minute later, the boat is at B_2 and the angle of depression measures 44°. How far to the nearest foot has the boat traveled? What is its speed in feet per hour?
769 ft; 46,140 ft/h

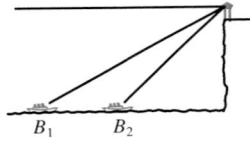

10. The included angle between the 10-m and 15-m sides of a triangular garden plot measures 31°. Find the length to the nearest meter of the altitude to the shorter side. 8 m

11. The diagonals of a rhombus measure 10 cm and 24 cm. To the nearest degree, find the measures of the angles of the rhombus. 45° and 135°

C 12. A 20-ft flagpole is erected at the top of a building of height h. From a distance d, the angle of elevation to the top of the pole is 45° and to the bottom is 42°. Find h and d to the nearest foot. $h = 181$ ft; $d = 201$ ft

13. The base of this regular pyramid is a square. $\overline{XQ}$ is 50 m long and its angle with altitude $\overline{XP}$ measures 20°. Find the length of a side of the base to the nearest meter. 34 m

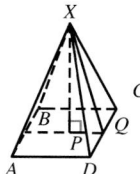

PROJECT

The Logo command arctan outputs the angle defined by $\dfrac{\text{opposite side}}{\text{adjacent side}}$. For example, arctan $\dfrac{1}{1}$ is 45°. Use Logo to draw any right triangle. How would you rewrite your procedure to draw any isosceles triangle? See Solutions Manual.

TEST YOURSELF

1. In a 45°-45°-90° triangle, the hypotenuse is how many times as long as each leg? $\sqrt{2}$ 8.4, 8.5

2. In a 30°-60°-90° triangle, what is the ratio of the length of the longer leg to the shorter leg? $\sqrt{3}:1$

3. One leg of a 45°-45°-90° triangle is 10 cm long. Find the length of the other leg and the hypotenuse. leg = 10 cm; hyp. = $10\sqrt{2}$ cm

4. The hypotenuse of a 30°-60°-90° triangle is 30 mm long. What is the length of the shorter leg? the longer leg? 15 mm; $15\sqrt{3}$ mm

5. State the definition of the sine ratio in a right triangle. $\sin x = \dfrac{\text{leg opp. } \angle x}{\text{hyp.}}$ 8.6

Use the table of trigonometric ratios (p. 658) to find the following.

6. sin 35° 0.5736   **7.** cos 52° 0.6157   **8.** tan 81° 6.3138

9. x to the nearest degree, where sin $x \approx 0.4300$ 25°

10. Find sin 30° without the table. Then check against the table. 0.5

11. Find cos 30° in radical form without using the table. Use a calculator to change to decimal form. Check the values in the table. $\dfrac{\sqrt{3}}{2}$ = 0.8660254; table:0.8660

12. Write an equation to find BC if $m\angle A = 43$ and $AC = 40$ ft. Find BC to the nearest integer. tan 43° = $\dfrac{BC}{40}$; $BC \approx 37$ ft   8.7

13. $AC = 50$ and $AB = 90$. Find $m\angle B$ to the nearest degree. 34

8.7 Strategy: Use Trigonometric Ratios   **341**

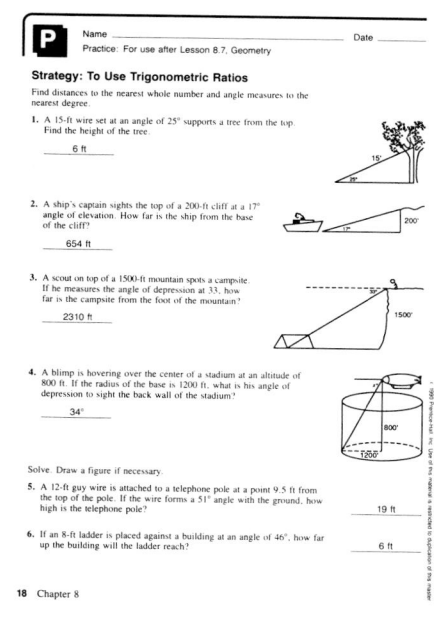

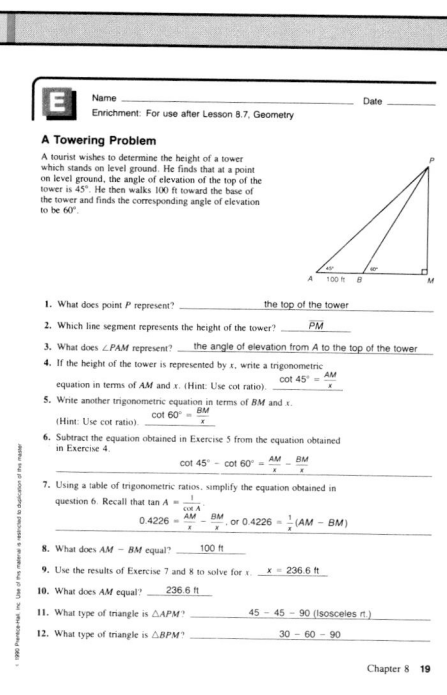

See *Teacher's Resource Book*, Follow-Up Application, *Chapter 8*, p. 20.

INTEGRATING GEOMETRY
Astronomy

Did you know that trigonometry can help you measure the distances to some nearby stars? By using the diameter of the Earth's orbit around the sun and minute angles measured with the help of a telescope, you can create a triangle whose dimensions can be calculated trigonometrically.

Just as an object such as your thumb appears to "move" when viewed from each of your eyes individually, so does a nearby star "move" minutely when sighted from two different points on the Earth's orbit. This movement, or difference in position, is called *parallax*.

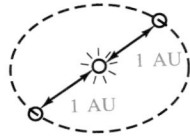

The Earth orbits the sun in an elliptical path. The average distance of the Earth from the sun is approximately 93 million mi, or 150 million km, which is called *one astronomical unit* (1 AU).

A *parallax triangle* is created with the diameter of the Earth's orbit as one side (2 AU's). The other two sides (theoretically equal) are the distances from the earth to the star during the two different sightings.

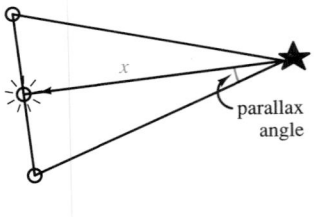

These sightings are made at six-month intervals, when the Earth has reached opposite ends of its orbit. The parallax triangle is thus assumed to be isosceles; the distance from the sun to the star is its altitude to the base; the angle between the two different star sightings is its vertex angle. The *angle of parallax* is one-half the vertex angle.

The measures of the base angles (theoretically equal) of the parallax triangle are calculated using telescopes and other scientific instruments. How does this information enable you to determine the vertex angle and the angle of parallax?

The tangent ratio is then used to
calculate the length of the altitude, or
the distance from the sun to the star.

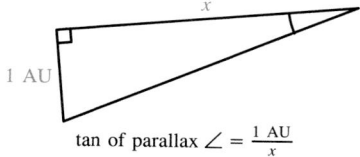

$$\text{tan of parallax} \angle = \frac{1 \text{ AU}}{x}$$

Astronomers use another convenient unit of distance called a *parsec*. One
parsec is the distance to a star that has a parallax angle of one second (1″), or
$\frac{1}{3600}$ of a degree. To find the number of miles in 1 parsec, use the tangent
ratio.

$$\text{tan } 1'' = \frac{1 \text{ AU}}{1 \text{ parsec}}$$

In calculation-ready form,

$$1 \text{ parsec} = \frac{1 \text{ AU}}{\text{tan } 1''} = \frac{93 \text{ million}}{0.000004848} = 19.2 \text{ trillion mi}$$

EXAMPLE **Find the distance from the given star to
the sun if its angle of parallax is 2″.**

$$\text{tan } 2'' = \frac{1 \text{ AU}}{x}$$

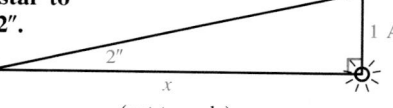

(not to scale)

In calculation-ready form,

$$x = \frac{1 \text{ AU}}{\text{tan } 2''} = \frac{93 \text{ million}}{0.000009696} = 9.5 \text{ trillion mi, or } 0.5 \text{ parsec}$$

EXERCISES   Use technology where appropriate.

1. The angle of parallax for a given star is 0.3″. Find the distance from the
   star to the sun. 6.4 trillion mi, or 3.3 parsec

2. The angle of parallax for a given star is 2.5″. Find the distance from the
   star to the sun. 7.7 trillion mi, or 0.4 parsec

3. What is the angle of parallax for a star that is 4.8 trillion mi from the
   sun? 4″

4. What is the upper limit of the measure of a base angle of a parallax
   triangle? 90

5. Could you use the isosceles triangle model
   to find the distance from the sun to the star
   in this figure? Why or why not?
   No; the base angles would never be equal.

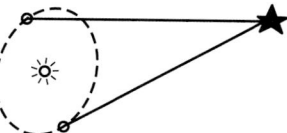

- See *Teacher's Resource Book, Spanish Chapter Summary and Review*, pp. 15–16.
- See Extra Practice, p. 650.

CHAPTER 8 SUMMARY AND REVIEW

Vocabulary

adjacent segment (307)
adjacent side (333)
altitude (306)
angle of depression (337)
angle of elevation (337)
cos *x* (333)
cosine (333)
45°-45°-90° triangle (321)
horizontal line of sight (337)

longer leg (322)
opposite side (332)
shorter leg (322)
sin *x* (332)
sine (332)
tan *x* (333)
tangent (333)
30°-60°-90° triangle (322)
trigonometry (331)

Right Triangle Similarity   The altitude to the hypotenuse of a right triangle   8.1
creates two right triangles, each similar to the other and to the original
triangle. In the original triangle, the length of the altitude is the geometric
mean between the lengths of the segments of the hypotenuse; also, the length
of each leg is the geometric mean between the length of the adjacent segment
of the hypotenuse and the length of the entire hypotenuse.

1. Find the length of the altitude if it separates the hypotenuse into segments measuring 5 cm and 9 cm, respectively. $3\sqrt{5}$ cm

2. Find the length of the hypotenuse if one leg measures 10 in. and the adjacent segment on the hypotenuse measures 5 in. 20 in.

Pythagorean Theorem and Its Converse   The Pythagorean Theorem   8.2, 8.3
can be stated as follows:

> In a right triangle, the square of the length of the hypotenuse is equal to the sum of the squares of the lengths of the legs.

The converse of the Pythagorean Theorem is also true.

3. Find the length of one leg of a right triangle when the other leg and the hypotenuse measure 5 and 9, respectively. $2\sqrt{14}$

4. How long is the diagonal of a rectangle if its length is 10 ft and its width is 24 ft? 26 ft.

Can these sets of numbers be lengths of the sides of a right triangle? Explain.

5. $4\sqrt{3}$, 4, 8   yes; $8^2 = 4^2 + (4\sqrt{3})^2$

6. 4, 5, 6   no; $6^2 \neq 4^2 + 5^2$

Special Right Triangles   In any right triangle whose acute angles are 45°   8.4
each, the length of the hypotenuse is always $\sqrt{2}$ times the length of either leg.
In any right triangle whose acute angles are 30° and 60°, the length of the
hypotenuse is twice the length of the shorter leg and the length of the longer
leg is $\sqrt{3}$ times the length of the shorter leg.

7. Give the lengths of the sides of a 30°-60°-90° triangle in which the shorter
   leg measures 12 cm. 12 cm, 12√3 cm, 24 cm

8. Give the lengths of the sides of a square in which the length of the
   diagonal is 12 mm. 6√2 mm

Strategy: Estimate and Calculate Roots   8.5

9. Estimate $\sqrt{1390}$ to the nearest integer. 37

10. Use mental calculation to estimate $\frac{36}{\sqrt{3}}$ to the nearest integer. 20

Trigonometric Ratios   For any acute angle of measure x in any   8.6, 8.7
right triangle:

$$\sin x = \frac{\text{length of the side opposite the angle}}{\text{length of the hypotenuse}}$$

$$\cos x = \frac{\text{length of the side adjacent to the angle}}{\text{length of the hypotenuse}}$$

$$\tan x = \frac{\text{length of the side opposite the angle}}{\text{length of the side adjacent to the angle}}$$

An angle of depression (elevation) is the angle down (up) from the horizontal.
If a calculator is not available, a table of trigonometric ratios can be used.

**Use the known ratios for the 30°-60°-90° triangle and for the 45°-45°-90°
triangle to find the following:**

11. $\cos 30°$ $\frac{\sqrt{3}}{2}$ 12. $\tan 45°$ 1   13. $\sin 60°$ $\frac{\sqrt{3}}{2}$

14. Find the height of the cliff
    to the nearest integer. 84 m

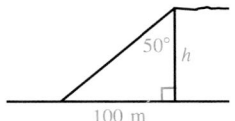

100 m

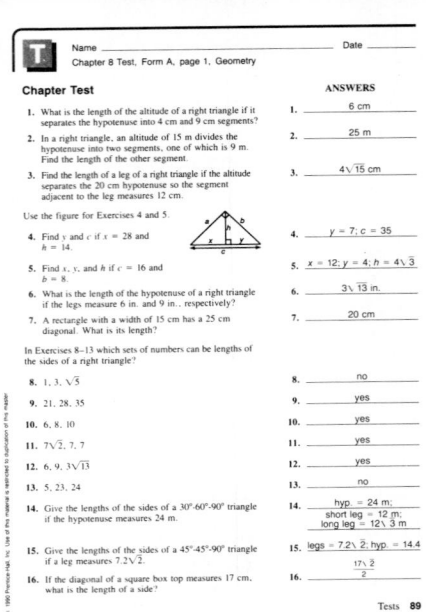

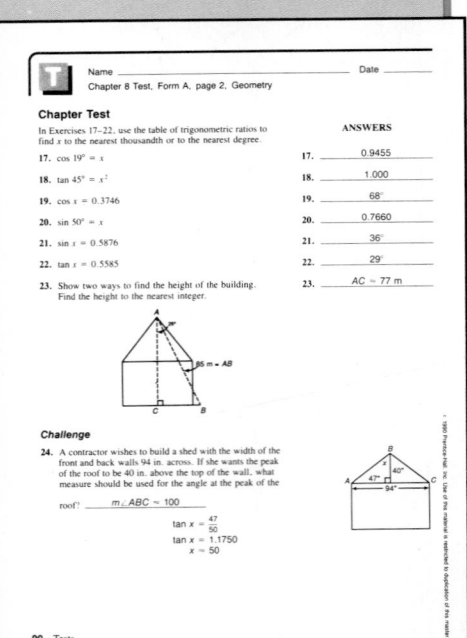

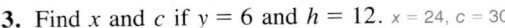

1. What is the length of the altitude of a right triangle if it separates the hypotenuse into 14 mm and 8 mm segments? $4\sqrt{7}$ mm

2. Find the length of one leg of a right triangle if the altitude separates the 45-m hypotenuse so that the segment adjacent to the leg measures 9 m. $9\sqrt{5}$ m

3. Find x and c if $y = 6$ and $h = 12$. $x = 24$, $c = 30$

4. What is the length of the nypotenuse of a right triangle if the legs measure 3 ft and 6 ft, respectively? $3\sqrt{5}$ ft

5. A rectangle with a width of 9 cm has a 15-cm diagonal. What is its length? 12 cm

Can the set of numbers be lengths of the sides of a right triangle?

6. $5\sqrt{2}$, 5, 5 yes   **7.** 1, 2, $\sqrt{2}$ no   **8.** 5, 24, 25 no

9. Give the lengths of the sides of a 30°-60°-90° triangle if the hypotenuse measures 16 cm. 8 cm, $8\sqrt{3}$ cm, 16 cm

10. Give the lengths of the sides of a 45°-45°-90° triangle if a leg measures $6\sqrt{2}$ cm. $6\sqrt{2}$ cm, $6\sqrt{2}$ cm, 12 cm

11. If the diagonal of a square box top measures 25 in., what is the length of a side? $\frac{25\sqrt{2}}{2}$ in.

Use the table of trigonometric ratios on page 658 to find x to the nearest ten-thousandth or to the nearest degree.

12. $\cos 35° = x$ 0.8192   **13.** $\tan 58° = x$ 1.6003   **14.** $\sin x = 0.9955$ 85°

art 8-T-53-1
h: 5ll w: 6 pi
50 m   35°

15. Show two ways to find the height of the building. Find the height to the nearest integer.

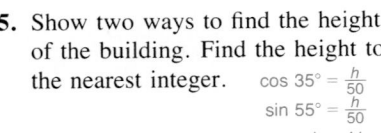
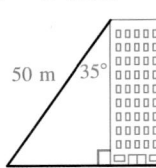

$\cos 35° = \frac{h}{50}$

$\sin 55° = \frac{h}{50}$

$h \approx 41$ m

Challenge

In $\triangle JKL$, $m\angle J = 45$, $m\angle K = 60$, and the shortest side measures 8 cm. Find the other side lengths to the nearest tenth of a centimeter. $JL = 9.8$ cm, $JK = 10.9$ cm

Alternative Assessment   Draw $\triangle ABC$ with right angle C and $\overline{CD} \perp \overline{AB}$. Have students explain how CD can be found using:

1. AD and DB
2. the Pythagorean Theorem
3. a 30°-60°-90° relationship
4. a trigonometric ratio

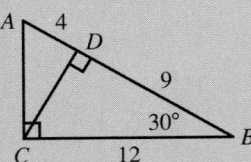

Select the best choice for each question.

1. If $\angle A$ is complementary to $\angle B$,
A   which *must* be true?

    I. $\angle A$ is acute
    II. $\angle A \cong \angle B$
    III. $\angle A$ is adjacent to $\angle B$

A. I only   **B.** III only
C. I, II only   **D.** I, III only
E. I, II, III

2. Which set of numbers could *not* be
the measures of the sides of a right
E   triangle?

A. 4.5, 6, 7.5   **B.** 5, 12, 13
C. $\sqrt{17}, \sqrt{21}, \sqrt{38}$ **D.** 9, 40, 41
E. $\sqrt{131}, 9, \sqrt{211}$

3. Which number is divisible by both
D   3 and 4?

A. 8,033,612   **B.** 108,734
C. 9,158   **D.** 517,236
E. 200,010

4. In $\triangle ABC$, if $m\angle A = 4x - 2$,
$m\angle B = 2x + 11$, and $m\angle C =$
B $3x - 36$, then $\angle A$ is a(n):

A. acute $\angle$ **B.** right $\angle$
C. obtuse $\angle$ **D.** straight $\angle$
E. It cannot be determined from
the information given.

5. If 25% of a number is 48 less than
C   35% of it, the number is:

A. 48   **B.** 80   **C.** 480
D. 800   **E.** 4,800

6. Solve for x if $3x + 5 \le 6x - 16$.
B
A. $x \le 7$ **B.** $x \ge 7$ **C.** $x \ge 3\frac{2}{3}$
D. $x \le -7$ **E.** $x \ge -7$

7. *PQRS* is a trapezoid with $\overline{PQ}$ a
base. Median $\overline{MN}$ intersects the
diagonals at X and Y. If $SR = 12$
C   and $XY = 3$, find PQ.

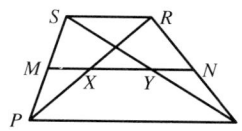

A. 15   **B.** 16   **C.** 18
D. 21   **E.** 24

8. How many different line segments
are determined by 5 points, 4 of
B   which are collinear?

A. 20   **B.** 10   **C.** 8
D. 7   **E.** 5

9. In right triangle ABC, $m\angle A = 60$
and $AB = 12$. Find the length of the
B   altitude to hypotenuse $\overline{AB}$.

A. $2\sqrt{3}$ **B.** $3\sqrt{3}$ **C.** $4\sqrt{3}$
D. 3   **E.** 4

10. In $\triangle ABC$, $\angle B$ is a right angle and
$\overline{ED}$ is drawn perpendicular to $\overline{AC}$ as
shown. If $AC = 33$, $AE = 11$, and
A $BE = 10$, find AD.

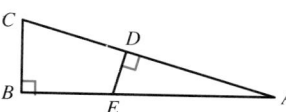

A. 7   **B.** 9   **C.** 13   **D.** 17
E. It cannot be found from the
information given.

The individual comments provided for
certain problems may help the students in solving them.

1. The solution given for this problem
assumes that students have been
taught that, in geometry, for any
angle A, $0 < m\angle A \le 180$.
2. It is useful to encourage students to
learn to recognize and look for Pythagorean Triples.
3. By this stage in the study of mathematics, most of the simple tests for
divisibility should be used regularly.
7. An alternate solution is to use the
fact that $XY = \frac{1}{2}(PQ - SR)$. Then
$3 = \frac{1}{2}(PQ - 12)$ and it follows that
$PQ = 18$.
8. Since the fact that 4 of the points
are collinear has no effect on the
solution, the problem can be answered by thinking of connecting
each of 5 points to each of 4 points,
then taking half the result to eliminate duplicates, giving $\frac{4 \cdot 5}{2} = 10$.
9. The right triangle proportionality
theorem could also be used for this
problem. Using $m\angle B = 30$ and
$AC = 6$,

$$(AC)^2 = AD \cdot AB$$
$$6^2 = AD \cdot 12$$
$$3 = AD$$
then $BD = 9$
Then $(CD)^2 = BD \cdot DA$
$$= 9 \cdot 3$$
$$(CD)^2 = 27$$
$$CD = 3\sqrt{3}$$

See *Teacher's Resource Book* for
Preparing for College Entrance Exams.

You may wish to use the *Teacher's Resource Book*, Tests, pp. 77–84.

Additional Answers for p. 350

43. Plan: Use the given information to prove $\triangle ESP \cong \triangle RSA$ by SAS. Then EP and RA are $\cong$ corr. parts.

Proof:

Statements	Reasons
1. $\overline{ES}$ is a median of $\triangle EPA$; $\overline{AS}$ is a median of $\triangle AER$.	1. Given
2. S is the midpt. of $\overline{ER}$; S is the midpt. of $\overline{PA}$.	2. Def. of median
3. $\overline{ES} \cong \overline{RS}$; $\overline{PS} \cong \overline{AS}$	3. Def. of midpt.
4. $\angle ESP \cong \angle RSA$	4. Vert. $\angle$s are $\cong$.
5. $\triangle ESP \cong \triangle RSA$	5. SAS
6. $\overline{EP} \cong \overline{RA}$	6. CPCTC

Concl.: In the given figure, if $\overline{ES}$ and $\overline{AS}$ are triangle medians, then $\overline{EP} \cong \overline{RA}$.

44. Plan: Prove $\triangle CSA \cong \triangle TSA$ by ASA. Then $\angle C$ and $\angle T$ are $\cong$ corr. parts.

Proof:

Statements	Reasons
1. $\overline{SA}$ bisects $\angle CST$ and $\angle CAT$.	1. Given
2. $\angle CSA \cong \angle TSA$; $\angle CAS \cong \angle TAS$	2. Def. of bis.
3. $\overline{SA} \cong \overline{SA}$	3. Refl. prop.
4. $\triangle CSA \cong \triangle TSA$	4. ASA
5. $\angle C \cong \angle T$	5. CPCTC

Concl.: In the given figure, if SA bisects $\angle CST$ and $\angle CAT$, then $\angle C \cong \angle T$.

45. Plan: Prove $\triangle CSA \cong \triangle TSA$ by AAS. Then $\angle CAS \cong \angle TAS$ by CPCTC, so $\overline{SA}$ bisects $\angle CAT$.

Proof:

Statements	Reasons
1. $\angle C \cong \angle T$; $\overline{AS}$ bisects $\angle CST$.	1. Given
2. $\angle CSA \cong \angle TSA$	2. Def. of bis.
3. $\overline{SA} \cong \overline{SA}$	3. Refl. prop.
4. $\triangle CSA \cong \triangle TSA$	4. AAS
5. $\angle CAS \cong \angle TAS$	5. CPCTC
6. $\overline{SA}$ bisects $\angle CAT$.	6. Def. of bis.

Concl.: In the given figure, if $\angle C \cong \angle T$ and AS bisects $\angle CST$, then $\overline{SA}$ bisects $\angle CAT$.

In Exercises 1–17, answer *true* or *false*. Justify each answer.

1. A scalene triangle may be equiangular. False; an equiangular $\triangle$ is equilateral   **3.4**

2. An isosceles trapezoid has two pairs of congruent angles.   **6.5**
true; base $\angle$s of an isos. trap. are $\cong$

In quadrilateral *ABCD*,   **3.1, 6.1**

3. $\overline{AB} \cong \overline{CD}$ true; opp sides of a $\square$ are $\cong$
4. $\angle 8 \cong \angle 3$ false; $\angle$ pair not related with $\parallel$ lines
5. $\angle 5 \cong \angle 1$ true; alt. int. $\angle$s are $\cong$
6. $\overline{AD} \cong \overline{CD}$ false; true only if $\square ABCD$ is a rhombus
7. $m\angle 1 + m\angle 2 = m\angle 3 + m\angle 4$ false; $\angle D$ is supp. to $\angle C$
8. $\angle 3 \cong \angle 4$ false; adj. $\angle$s are not nec. $\cong$
9. $\overline{AE} \cong \overline{EC}$ true; diag. of $\square$ bisect each other
10. $AE + EB > AB$ true; sum of the lengths of 2 sides of a $\triangle$ is > length of 3rd side
11. $m\angle 7 + m\angle 8 + m\angle 6 + m\angle 5 = 180$ true; $\angle A$ and $\angle B$ are supp.
12. $AE \perp EB$ false; true only if $\square ABCD$ is a rhombus
13. $\triangle ADC \cong \triangle CBA$ true; diag. of $\square$ forms 2 $\cong \triangle$s
14. $\triangle AED \cong \triangle CEB$ true; SAS

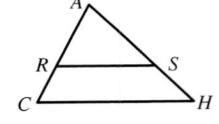

15. If a triangle has sides that measure 2, 3, and 4, then it is a right triangle. false by Pyth. Th.   **8.3**

If $\triangle ARS \sim \triangle ACH$, then   **7.3**

16. $\dfrac{AR}{AC} = \dfrac{RS}{CH}$ true; corr. side lengths of $\sim \triangle$s are in prop.

17. $\dfrac{AR}{AC} = \dfrac{AH}{AS}$ false; $\dfrac{AR}{AC} = \dfrac{AS}{AH}$

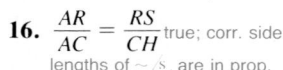

Is each statement true *always*, *sometimes*, or *never*? Justify each answer.

18. If $\overline{AB} \cong \overline{BC}$, then B is $\underline{\ ?\ }$ the midpoint of $\overline{AC}$. sometimes; when A, B and C are coll.   **1.3**

19. If two parallel lines have a transversal, then any pair of angles is $\underline{\ ?\ }$ either congruent or supplementary. always   **3.2**

20. If a quadrilateral has two pairs of supplementary angles, then it will $\underline{\ ?\ }$ be a parallelogram. sometimes; it could also be a trap.   **6.1, 6.5**

21. In a right triangle, the sine of one acute angle is $\underline{\ ?\ }$ equal to the cosine of the other acute angle. always   **8.6**

22. If $\triangle CAT \cong \triangle DOG$, then it is $\underline{\ ?\ }$ true that $\triangle ATC \cong \triangle ODG$. sometimes; if $\overline{AT}$ is $\cong$ to both $\overline{OG}$ and $\overline{OD}$ **4.1**

23. An angle $\underline{\ ?\ }$ has a complement. sometimes; if the $\angle$ is acute   **1.5**

24. Vertical angles are $\underline{\ ?\ }$ adjacent. never; def. of vert. $\angle$s   **1.5**

25. Three given points are $\underline{\ ?\ }$ collinear and $\underline{\ ?\ }$ coplanar. sometimes; always   **1.1**

26. The sine of an acute angle is __?__ greater than 1. never; leg. of a rt. △ is never longer than hyp.　8.6

27. The ratio of the sides of a 30°-60°-90° triangle is __?__ $r:r\sqrt{3}:2r$. always　8.4

Complete.

28. If the sides of one triangle are congruent to the sides of another triangle, then the corresponding angles are __?__. ≅　4.2

29. The supplement of an acute angle is a(n) __?__ angle. obtuse　1.5

30. If a triangle has sides of length a, a, and $a + 1$, then it is a(n) __?__ triangle. isos.　3.4

31. If a line intersects two sides of a triangle and is parallel to the third side, then the triangle formed and the original triangle are __?__. ~　7.7

32. If the diagonals of a rhombus have lengths of 24 and 18, then the lengths of the sides are __?__. 15　8.2, 6.4

33. The altitude to the hypotenuse of a 30°-60°-90° triangle divides the hypotenuse into two segments whose ratio is __?__. 1:3　8.4

34. In △RAT, if $m\angle R = 61$ and $m\angle T = 51$, then the longest side is __?__ and the shortest side is __?__. $\overline{RT}$ $\overline{RA}$　5.5

35. The geometric mean between 8 and 18 is __?__. 12　7.2

36. Given right triangle ABC:　8.6

$\sin A = $ __?__ $\frac{4}{5}$　$\tan A = $ __?__ $\frac{4}{3}$

$\tan B = $ __?__ $\frac{3}{4}$　$\cos B = $ __?__ $\frac{4}{5}$

$\cos A = $ __?__ $\frac{3}{5}$　$\sin B = $ __?__ $\frac{3}{5}$

37. In this right triangle,　8.1

$x = $ __?__ $2\sqrt{10}$

$y = $ __?__ $2\sqrt{6}$

$z = $ __?__ $2\sqrt{15}$

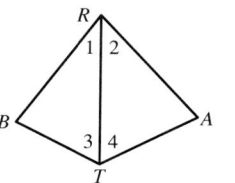

38. If quad. ABCD ≅ quad. MNPQ, then $\angle B \cong$ __?__, $\angle Q \cong$ __?__, and $\overline{DA} \cong$ __?__. ∠N; ∠D; $\overline{QM}$　6.6

Use <, >, or = to complete each statement.

39. If $\overline{BR} \cong \overline{AR}$, and $m\angle 1 > m\angle 2$, then BT __?__ TA. >　5.6

40. If $\overline{BT} \cong \overline{TA}$, and $m\angle 3 < m\angle 4$, then RA __?__ RB. >　5.6

41. If $m\angle 2 < m\angle 4$, then TA __?__ RA. <　5.5

42. If $\angle A \cong \angle B$ and $\angle 3 \cong \angle 4$, then RA __?__ RB. =

Cumulative Review **349**

---

46. Plan: Prove rt. △s MAH and JBK ≅.
Then $\overline{MA}$ and $\overline{JB}$ are ≅ corr. parts.

Proof:

Statements	Reasons
1. ▱HJKM; $\overline{HA}$ ⊥ $\overline{MK}$; $\overline{KB}$ ⊥ $\overline{JH}$	1. Given
2. $\angle MAH$ and $\angle JBK$ are rt. ∠s.	2. Def. of ⊥
3. △MAH and △JBK are rt. △s.	3. Def. of rt. △.
4. $\angle M \cong \angle J$	4. Opp. ∠s of a ▱ are ≅.
5. $\overline{MH} \cong \overline{JK}$	5. Opp. sides of a ▱ are ≅.
6. △MAH ≅ △JBK	6. HA
7. $\overline{MA} \cong \overline{JB}$	7. CPCTC

Concl.: In the given figure, if HJKM is a ▱ and $\overline{HA}$ ⊥ $\overline{MK}$ and $\overline{KB}$ ⊥ $\overline{JH}$, then $\overline{MA} \cong \overline{JB}$.

47. Plan: Show that △MAH ≅ △JBK by HL. Then use the def. of betweenness to show $HJ = MK$. Concl. follows because both pairs of opp. sides of HJKM are ≅.

Proof:

Statements	Reasons
1. HBKA is a rectangle; $\overline{HM} \cong \overline{JK}$.	1. Given
2. $\angle HAK$ and $\angle HBK$ are rt. ∠s.	2. A rect. has 4 rt. ∠s.
3. $\angle HAK \cong \angle HBK$	3. All rt. ∠s are ≅.
4. $\angle MAH \cong \angle JBK$	4. Suppl. of ≅ ∠s are ≅.
5. $\angle MAH$ and $\angle JBK$ are rt. ∠s.	5. Supp. of a rt. ∠ is a rt. ∠.
6. △MAH and △JBK are rt. △s.	6. Def. of rt. △
7. $\overline{HA} \cong \overline{BK}$	7. Opp. sides of a rect. are ≅.
8. △MAH ≅ △JBK	8. HL
9. $\overline{MA} \cong \overline{JB}$	9. CPCTC
10. $\overline{AK} \cong \overline{HB}$	10. Opp. sides of a rect. are ≅.
11. $MA = JB$; $AK = HB$	11. Def. of ≅ segments
12. $MA + AK = JB + HB$	12. Add. prop.
13. $MK = HJ$	13. Def. of betw. and subst.
14. $\overline{MK} \cong \overline{HJ}$	14. Def. of ≅ segments
15. HJKM is a ▱.	15. If both pairs of opp. sides of a quad. are ≅, the quad. is a ▱.

349

---

48. Plan: Show △AMC ≅ △ANC by SSS. Then ∠1 ≅ ∠2 by CPCTC.

Proof:

Statements	Reasons
1. $\overline{AM} \cong \overline{AN}$; $\overline{MC} \cong \overline{NC}$	1. Given
2. $\overline{AC} \cong \overline{AC}$	2. Refl. prop.
3. △AMC ≅ △ANC	3. SSS
4. ∠1 ≅ ∠2	4. CPCTC

Concl.: If $\overline{AM} \cong \overline{AN}$ and, $\overline{MC} \cong \overline{NC}$, then ∠1 ≅ ∠2.

49. Plan: Show $\triangle ADM \cong \triangle ABN$ by ASA.
Then $\overline{AM} \cong \overline{AN}$ by CPCTC.

Proof:

Statements	Reasons
1. $ABCD$ is a rhombus.	1. Given
2. $\angle DAC \cong \angle BAC$	2. Each diag. of a rhombus bisects two $\angle$s of the rhombus
3. $m\angle DAC = m\angle BAC$	3. Def. of $\cong \angle$s.
4. $\frac{1}{2}m\angle DAC = \frac{1}{2}m\angle BAC$	4. Mult. prop.
5. $\overline{AM}$ bisects $\angle DAC$; $\overline{AN}$ bisects $\angle BAC$.	5. Given
6. $m\angle DAM = \frac{1}{2}m\angle DAC$; $m\angle BAN = \frac{1}{2}m\angle BAC$	6. Angle Bis. Th.
7. $m\angle DAM = m\angle BAN$	7. Subst. prop.
8. $\angle DAM \cong \angle BAN$	8. Def. of $\cong \angle$s
9. $\overline{DA} \cong \overline{BA}$	9. Def. of rhombus
10. $\angle D \cong \angle B$	10. Opp. $\angle$s of a $\square$ are $\cong$
11. $\triangle ADM \cong \triangle ABN$	11. ASA
12. $\overline{AM} \cong \overline{AN}$	12. CPCTC

Concl.: If $ABCD$ is a rhombus and $\overline{AM}$ bisects $\angle DAC$ and $\overline{AN}$ bisects $\angle BAC$, then $\overline{AM} \cong \overline{AN}$.

53. Plan: Show $\triangle DAC \sim \triangle BDC$ by AA.
Hence, $\frac{CA}{CD} = \frac{CD}{BC}$ and the concl. follows.

Proof:

Statements	Reasons
1. $\angle A \cong \angle 1$	1. Given
2. $\angle DCA \cong \angle BCD$	2. Refl. prop.
3. $\triangle DAC \sim \triangle BDC$	3. AA
4. $\frac{CA}{CD} = \frac{CD}{BC}$	4. If 2 $\triangle$s are $\cong$, corr. side lengths are in proportion.
5. CD is the geometric mean between BC and CA.	5. Def. of geometric mean

Concl.: In the given figure, if $\angle A \cong \angle 1$, then CD is the geometric mean between BC and CA.

54. Given: $\overline{XY} \not\cong \overline{YZ}$
Prove: $\angle X \not\cong \angle Z$

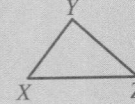

350

See side column pages 348–350.

43. Given: $\overline{ES}$ is a median of $\triangle EPA$
$\overline{AS}$ is a median of $\triangle AER$
Prove: $\overline{EP} \cong \overline{RA}$

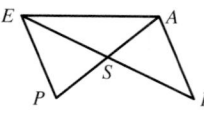

44. Given: $\overline{SA}$ bisects $\angle CST$ and $\angle CAT$
Prove: $\angle C \cong \angle T$

45. Given: $\angle C \cong \angle T$, $\overline{AS}$ bisects $\angle CST$
Prove: $\overline{SA}$ bisects $\angle CAT$.

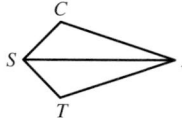

46. Given: $\square HJKM$, $\overline{HA} \perp \overline{MK}$, $\overline{KB} \perp \overline{JH}$
Prove: $\overline{MA} \cong \overline{JB}$

47. Given: $HBKA$ is a rectangle, $\overline{HM} \cong \overline{JK}$
Prove: $HJKM$ is a $\square$.

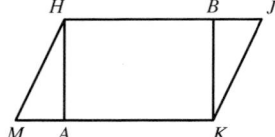

48. Given: $\overline{AM} \cong \overline{AN}$, $\overline{MC} \cong \overline{NC}$
Prove: $\angle 1 \cong \angle 2$

49. Given: $ABCD$ is a rhombus, $\overline{AM}$ bisects $\angle DAC$, $\overline{AN}$ bisects $\angle BAC$
Prove: $\overline{AM} \cong \overline{AN}$

50. Given: $ABCD$ is a rhombus, $\overline{AM}$ is a median of $\triangle DAC$, $\overline{AN}$ is a median of $\triangle BAC$
Prove: $\overline{AM} \cong \overline{AN}$ See page 749.

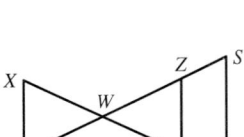

51. Given: $\overline{XY} \parallel \overline{ST}$
Prove: $\triangle XYW \sim \triangle TSW$

52. Given: $\triangle XYW \sim \triangle VZW$
Prove: $XW \cdot ZW = YW \cdot VW$

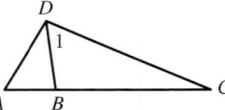

See side column.

53. Given: $\angle A \cong \angle 1$
Prove: CD is the geometric mean between BC and CA.

54. Write an indirect proof for this statement: If two sides of a triangle are not congruent, then the angles opposite those sides are not congruent.

Plan: Assume the negation of $\angle X \not\cong \angle Z$ and show that this leads to a contradiction.
Proof: Assume: $\angle X \cong \angle Z$ Negation of the conclusion
        $\overline{XY} \cong \overline{YZ}$ Conv. of Isos. $\triangle$ Th.
     Contradiction: $\overline{XY} \not\cong \overline{YZ}$
Concl.: Since the assumption $\angle X \cong \angle Z$ leads to a contradiction, then $\angle X \cong \angle Z$ must be false. Therefore, $\angle X \not\cong \angle Z$.

OVERVIEW · Chapter 9

SUMMARY

In Chapter 9, students define a circle, a sphere, and related terms. They apply this information to circumscribed and inscribed polygons and circles. Concentric circles, inscribed angles, tangents, arcs, and chords are introduced, and related theorems are developed and used. Students then learn relationships among lengths of chords, secant segments, and tangent segments for a given circle.

CHAPTER OBJECTIVES

- To define a circle, a sphere, and terms related to them

- To recognize circumscribed and inscribed polygons and circles

- To identify concentric circles and inscribed angles

- To prove and apply theorems relating tangents and radii and theorems about chords of a circle

- To define and apply properties of arcs and central angles

- To solve problems and prove statements about inscribed angles and angles formed by chords, secants and tangents

- To prove and apply theorems relating lengths of chords, secant segments, and tangent segments

- To solve more complex proofs and problems by *using auxiliary figures*

CHAPTER HIGHLIGHTS

DEVELOPING MATHEMATICAL POWER

Problem Solving

Lesson 9.6 shows how the four problem solving steps can be used for determining the auxiliary figures to be used in a proof.

Communication

This chapter develops different methods for alternative learning styles and cooperative learning activities, including measuring inscribed angles to make a generalization. The *Teacher's Resource Book* offers a Chapter Summary and Review in Spanish. The side column provides topics for students' portfolios such as comparing and contrasting internal and external tangents of the same or tangent circles.

Reasoning

Thinking critically topics include comparing measures of angles inscribed in a circle and writing an alternate proof of the sum of measures of angles of a triangle using a triangle inscribed in a circle.

Connections

Real-world applications include such topics as astronomy, gardening, and design. Students use algebra to find lengths of segments and measures of angles. They are asked to write about the relationship of tangents to solar and lunar eclipses.

Technology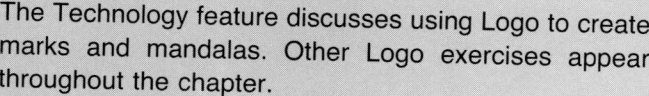

The Technology feature discusses using Logo to create marks and mandalas. Other Logo exercises appear throughout the chapter.

STUDENT TEXT

Chapter Content	Basic	Average	Enriched	NCTM STANDARDS*
9.1 Circles, Segments, and Congruency	D: 355/1-15, 20, 21, 31	D: 355/1-21, 31	D: 355/1-23, 27-32	2, 3, 4, 7
9.2 Properties of Tangents	D: 360/1-16, 28 R: 355/16-19	D: 360/1-21, 30-32 R: 355/22-26	D: 360/1-21, 25-32 R: 355/24-26	2, 3, 7
9.3 Arcs, Chords, and Central Angles	D: 365/1-15, 35, MR R: 360/17-20	D: 365/4-25, 35, 36, MR R: 360/22-24	D: 365/8-30, 35, 36, MR R: 360/22-24	3, 7
9.4 Inscribed Angles	D: 371/1-14, 33, 36 R: 365/16-20	D: 371/1-22, 33-36 R: 365/26-28	D: 371/1-29, 33-36 R: 365/31-34	2, 3, 4, 5, 7
9.5 Tangents, Secants, and Angles	D: 375/1-10, 24, AR R: 371/15-19	D: 375/1-15, 23, 24, AR R: 371/23-28	D: 375/1-15, 20-24, AR R: 371/30-32	2, 3, 5, 8, 12
9.6 Strategy: Use an Auxiliary Figure	D: 381/1-5 R: 375/11-13	D: 361/1-5 R: 375/16-19	D: 381/1-6 R: 375/16-19	1, 3, 7
9.7 Circles and Segment Lengths	D: 385/1-11, 22 R: 381/7, 8	D: 385/1-18, 22-24 R: 381/6-8	D: 385/1-24 R: 381/7, 8	4, 5, 7, 8

D = Daily   R = Review   MR = Mixed Review   AR = Algebra Review

*For a complete list of NCTM Standards, see p. T7.

STUDENT TEXT

Review/Assessment

Mixed Review 367

Algebra Review 377, 394

Summary and Review 390

College Ent. Exam Rev. 393

Extra Practice 651

Test Yourself 367, 387

Chapter Test 392

Chapter Project 351

Special Features

Constructions 356, 377

Technology 356, 361, 367, 372, 377, 388-389

Devel. Math. Power 361, 372

Applications 356, 361, 366, 372, 377, 386-387

Project 381

RESOURCES

Teacher's Resource Book

Ch. 9: Investigation/Practice/ Enrichment 1-20

Spanish Sum. and Rev. 17-18

Quizzes 93-96

Chapter Tests 97-100

Perf. Assessment Proj. Ch. 9

Critical Thinking 9

Reading and Writing in Geom. 9

Technology 11-12

Teaching Aid 9

Transparencies 13-14

Teaching Transparencies 56-62

Computer Test Bank 521-592

Connections 25-26

PH Graph. Utility

Overhead Manip. Kit

Circles

Measuring up!

Developing [Mat]hematical Power

[I]n navigation involves [us]e of radar, sonar, and [compu]ters. Pilots can key in their destinations, and a computer will plot the course, steer the plane, and make corrections as necessary.

Throughout history, people have used many different navigational tools. The sun and the moon were probably the earliest navigational aids. Then people learned to use the North Star as a directional guide. In medieval times, the astrolabe was used to measure the altitude of stars and other celestial bodies. Until the invention of the sextant in the 18th century, mariners used the astrolabe to determine latitude and longitude.

Project

Build an astrolabe and then use it to determine your town's latitude. Consult a map and compare your results to the actual latitude.

[An]cient Astrolabe

351

Alternative Assessment

See the *Teacher's Resource Book,* Assessment, Chapter 9. This project and the TRB may be used as an alternative form of assessment for selected topics in Chapter 9.

BACKGROUND

- The latitude of a place is the angle that the Celestial Pole makes with the horizon. Since the North Star revolves in a circle no greater than 1° from the Celestial Pole, using the North Star to find latitude will result in an error no greater than ± 1°.
- Students can locate the North Star by finding the Big Dipper and following an imaginary line along the far side of the dipper to the bright North Star.

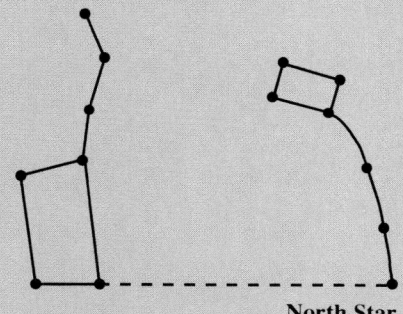

North Star

Modeling

Mathematics provides the power to measure and describe natural phenomena. This project involves building a measuring tool, collecting data, and using mathematical skills.

Cooperative Learning

This project is accomplished through a succession of tasks, each of which is well-suited to a cooperative learning situation. These tasks include:

1. Building a measuring tool.
2. Using a measuring tool to collect data.
3. Determining the latitude of a place.
4. Comparing results with a map.

Vocabulary

Center	Exterior of a
Chord	circle
Circle	Great circle
Circumscribed	Inscribed
Concentric	polygon
circles	Interior of a
Congruent	circle
circles	Radius
Diameter	Secant
	Sphere

Materials/Manipulatives

Globe
Compasses and straightedges
Teacher's Resource Book,
  Transparency 13
Teaching Transparency 56

Technology

Computer
Computer Test Bank pp.
  521–532
The Geometric Supposer:
  Circles, p. 90

LESSON FOCUS

Review

This lesson introduces vocabulary associated with a circle. Draw and label a circle to review familiar terms and to introduce secant.

Alternative Learning Styles

• Using a globe will help students to visualize the lines of latitude and the lines of longitude as circles around the Earth.

• Manipulatives can be particularly effective when used to introduce or reinforce geometric concepts. Using a compass and a straightedge, students can draw and label a circle with each of its associated lines and segments as they are discussed in this lesson.

9.1 Circles, Segments, and Congruency

Objectives: To define a circle, a sphere, and terms related to them
To recognize circumscribed and inscribed polygons and circles
To identify concentric circles

Circles and spheres and their related segments appear throughout everyday life. The globe is a common example.

Investigation—*Visualizing the Concept*

On this world map, the vertical lines represent longitudes and the horizontal lines represent latitudes. See Solutions Manual.

1. What kinds of lines are they?
2. On a globe, do any latitudes intersect? Do any longitudes intersect?
3. Compare the sizes of the longitudes. Compare the sizes of the latitudes. Explain the difference.
4. Visualize the latitudes from the North Pole. How would you show them on a map?

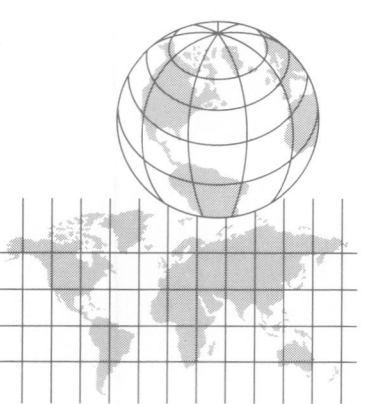

A **circle** is the set of all points in a plane that are a given distance from a given point called the **center.** The given distance, *r*, is the *length of any radius* of the circle.

A **radius** is a segment extending from the center to any point on the circle. Why must all radii in a given circle be congruent? by def. of ⊙ and of radius

The **interior** of circle *O* is the set of all points *I* in the plane of the circle such that $OI < r$.

The **exterior** of circle *O* is the set of all points *E* in the plane of the circle such that $OE > r$.

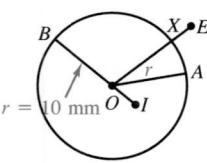

In circle *O*, written as $\odot O$, with radius length *r*:
$r = OB = 10$ mm $OA = OB = OX$
$OI < 10$ mm $OE > 10$ mm

352   Chapter 9 Circles

Developing Mathematical Power

Keeping a Portfolio   Have students write a short paragraph in which they compare and contrast chords, diameters, radii, and secants of a circle, and congruent and concentric circles. Then have them use colored pencils to draw interesting designs made of circles and circle parts.

EXAMPLE 1   ***Q* is the center of this circle.**

a. Name the circle.   **b.** Name two radii of the circle.

c. What is the length of any radius of $\odot Q$?

d. Name three interior points of $\odot Q$.

e. Compare QS and QX to the length of any radius.

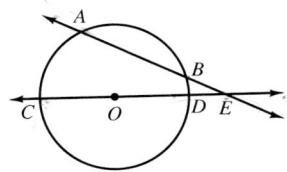

a. $\odot Q$ **b.** $\overline{QP}$ and $\overline{QT}$ **c.** 16 mm   **d.** Q, R, and S **e.** $QS < 16$; $QX > 16$

A **chord** is a segment that joins two points on the circle. A **diameter** d is any chord that contains the center. The length of a diameter of a circle is twice the length of a radius, or $d = 2r$. A **secant** is any line, ray, or segment that contains a chord.

Chords	Diameter	Secants
$\overline{AB}$, $\overline{CD}$	$\overline{CD}$	$\overleftrightarrow{AB}$, $\overrightarrow{AB}$, $\overrightarrow{BA}$, $\overline{AE}$ $\overleftrightarrow{CD}$, $\overrightarrow{DC}$, $\overrightarrow{CD}$, $\overline{CE}$

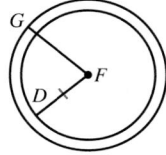

Two or more circles having congruent radii are **congruent circles.**
Two or more coplanar circles having the same center are
concentric circles.

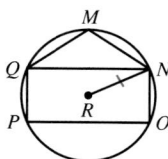

Congruent Circles: **Concentric Circles:**

$\odot F$ with radius $\overline{FD}$ $\odot F$ with radius $\overline{FD}$

$\odot R$ with radius $\overline{RN}$ $\odot F$ with radius $\overline{FG}$

If every vertex of a polygon is a point on a circle, the polygon is **inscribed in the circle** and the circle is **circumscribed about the polygon.** Triangle MQN, quadrilateral $NOPQ$, and pentagon $MQPON$ are inscribed in $\odot R$, and $\odot R$ is circumscribed about these figures.

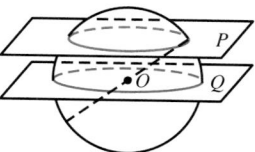

A **sphere** is the set of all points in space that are a given distance from a given point. Every sphere has a center, interior and exterior points, radii, diameters, chords, and secants, and their definitions are similar to those of a circle.

If a plane intersects a sphere in more than one point, then the intersection is a circle. If the sphere's center is a point of the plane, then the intersection is a **great circle.** The intersection of plane P and sphere O is a *circle*; the intersection of plane Q and sphere O is a *great circle*.

9.1 Circles, Segments, and Congruency   **353**

Investigation

3. Longitudes are all the same size $\odot$s. Latitudes are $\odot$s of various sizes. The latitudes are $\odot$s in ‖ planes. They get smaller as their distance from the equator increases. The longitudes are ≅ $\odot$s, all of which intersect at the North and South Poles.

TEACHING SUGGESTIONS

- Point out that although the Earth is not a perfect sphere, it provides a reasonable model of one.
- Emphasize that when a sphere and a plane intersect in more than one point, the intersection is a circle.
- Students should practice using a compass to draw a circle, and to draw congruent and concentric circles.
- You may wish to discuss Exercises 28 and 30 with students before they read about the construction on p. 356. Given any two points A and B, any point on the perpendicular bisector of $\overline{AB}$ is the center of a circle that contains A and B.

CHALKBOARD EXAMPLES

- **For Example 1**

  The center of the circle is P.

  a. Name the circle.

  b. Name as many radii as possible.

  c. Name as many interior points as possible.

  d. Name as many exterior points as possible.

  e. What is the length of any radius?

  f. Compare PW and PV to the length of a radius.

  a. $\odot P$ **b.** $\overline{PQ}$, $\overline{PS}$, $\overline{PT}$ **c.** P, V
  d. W **e.** 5   **f.** $PW > 5$; $PV < 5$

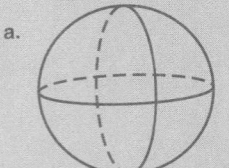
EXAMPLE 2   Study the globe to answer a–e.

a. Which is represented by a great circle: Equator, Tropic of Cancer, or Prime Meridian?

b. Name 5 radii and 2 diameters.

c. What is the length of the radius? of the diameter?

d. Name 2 secants.

e. Are there any concentric circles in the figure? any congruent circles?

a. Equator   b. $\overline{OD}$, $\overline{OE}$, $\overline{OC}$, $\overline{ON}$, $\overline{OS}$; $\overline{NS}$, $\overline{CD}$

c. 3950 mi; 7900 mi   d. $\overleftrightarrow{CD}$, $\overleftrightarrow{NS}$ e. no; $\odot A \cong \odot B$

CLASS EXERCISES

1. Draw a circle with center R. Draw larger and smaller concentric circles. Explain your procedure. Answers may vary.

Use the figure to identify the following.

2. 4 chords $\overline{AD}$, $\overline{AB}$, $\overline{BC}$, $\overline{DC}$ 3. 3 radii $\overline{OB}$, $\overline{OC}$, $\overline{OD}$

4. 1 diameter $\overline{DC}$ 5. 1 secant line $\overleftrightarrow{AB}$

6. 2 secant rays $\overrightarrow{CB}$, $\overrightarrow{AB}$ 7. An inscribed polygon quad. ABCD

8. Two polygons that are not inscribed in $\odot O$ quad. ABOD, △BOC

9. State the definitions of these basic terms with reference to a sphere.
   a. radius   b. diameter   c. chord   d. secant
   See side column.

10. How many concentric circles are pictured? Identify each by naming its center and one point of the circle. 3; O, A; O, B; O, C

11. Give the length of any radius of each circle. OA = 2; OB = 4; OC = 6; QR = 2

12. Give the length of the diameter of each circle with center O. 4, 8, 12

13. Identify the circle(s) that is(are) congruent to $\odot Q$. $\odot O$ containing pt. A

Find the length of a circle's diameter for the given length of the radius.

14. 10 cm 20 cm   15. 3 mm 6 mm   16. $\frac{3}{4}$ in. $\frac{3}{2}$ in.   17. x 2x

Find the length of a circle's radius for the given length of the diameter.

18. 8 m 4 m   19. 3 mm $\frac{3}{2}$ mm   20. $\frac{3}{4}$ in. $\frac{3}{8}$ in.   21. $y \frac{1}{2}y$

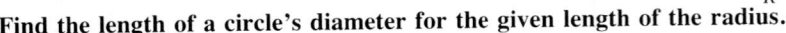

PRACTICE EXERCISES 📈 Use technology where appropriate.

Drawing in Geometry

A **1.** Sketch ⊙O and any two noncollinear radii $\overline{OA}$ and $\overline{OB}$. What kind of triangle is △OAB? Explain. Isosceles; the radii (sides of the △) are ≅. See side column.

2. Sketch ⊙Q and any two radii $\overline{QC}$ and $\overline{QD}$ such that $m\angle CQD = 60$. What kind of triangle is △QCD? Explain. Equilateral; an isos. △ with vert. ∠ of 60° is equilat.

3. Make a generalization based on Exercises 1 and 2.
A △ with 2 noncoll. radii of a ⊙ as 2 of its sides is isos.

4. Name 4 radii of ⊙O. $\overline{OR}$, $\overline{OT}$, $\overline{OX}$, $\overline{OY}$

5. Name all pictured radii of ⊙Q. $\overline{QW}$, $\overline{QS}$, $\overline{QU}$

6. Name a diameter for each circle. $\overline{TR}$; $\overline{SU}$

7. Name a chord that is not a diameter for each circle. $\overline{XY}$; $\overline{SY}$

8. Name a common secant of the circles. $\overleftrightarrow{XY}$

9. Name a ray that is a secant of ⊙Q but *not* of ⊙O. $\overrightarrow{SY}$

10. What kind of triangle is △OXY? isos.   **11.** What kind of triangle is △QRW? rt.

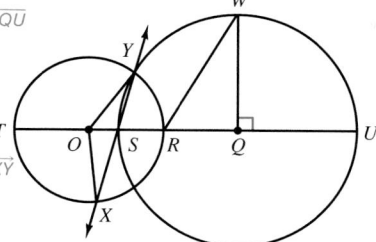

Tell whether the statements in Exercises 12–20 are true or false. If false, sketch a counterexample.

12. If a segment is a chord of a circle, then it is also a diameter. false

13. If a segment is a diameter of a sphere, then it is also a chord. true

14. If a segment is a radius of a circle, then it is also a chord. false

15. If two circles are concentric, then their radii are congruent. false

16. If two circles are congruent, then their diameters are congruent. true

17. A sphere has exactly two diameters. false

18. If two spheres have the same center, then they are concentric. true

B **19.** If $\overline{AB}$ is a chord of a sphere, then $\overrightarrow{AB}$ is also a secant of the sphere. true

20. If $\overleftrightarrow{AB}$ is a secant of a circle, then $\overline{AB}$ is also a chord of the circle. False; see side column.

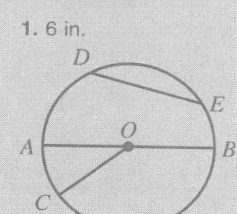
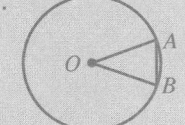
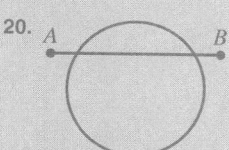

Find *x*.

21.
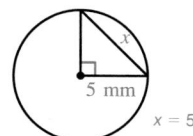 $x = 5\sqrt{2}$ mm

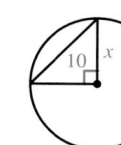 $x = 5\sqrt{2}$

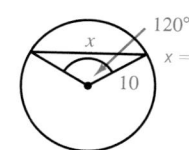 120° $x = 10\sqrt{3}$

9.1 Circles, Segments, and Congruency **355**

Developing Mathematical Power

Cooperative Learning Assign groups of students to research non-Euclidean geometry and its theories on circles and parallel lines. Each group should prepare a brief presentation that compares the approaches of each of the geometries to circles and parallel lines. Their reports should include visual aids.

Construction

Point out that the construction is related to Exercises 28 and 30. (See last Teaching Suggestion.) Since the center of the circumscribed circle is on the perpendicular bisector of each side, it is the point of intersection of the perpendicular bisectors of two sides.

Lesson Quiz

Find the length of a radius of a circle if the length of a diameter is:

1. 12 in.   **2.** 2.4 m

Draw a circle, then name and label the following: Answers may vary.

3. 1 diameter   **4.** 3 radii
5. 2 chords

1. 6 in.   **2.** 1.2 m
3. $\overline{AB}$
4. $\overline{OA}$, $\overline{OB}$, $\overline{OC}$
5. $\overline{AB}$, $\overline{DE}$

Additional Answers

1.

2.

20.

355

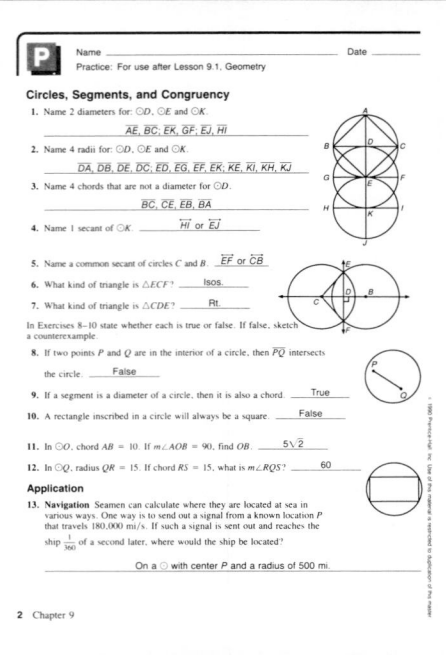

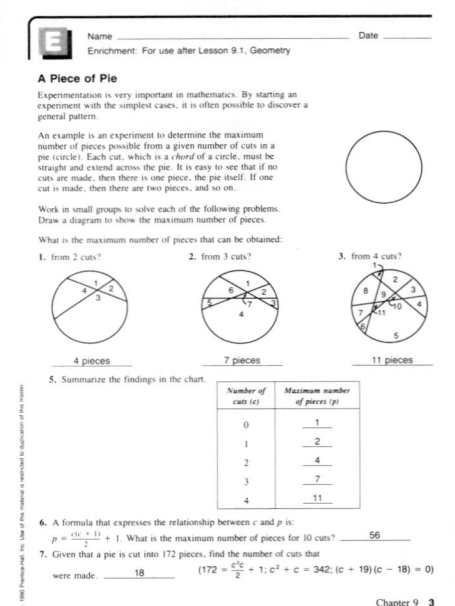

24. In ⊙P, $\overline{AB}$ is a diameter and $\overline{PX} \parallel \overline{BC}$. If AB = 10 mm and AC = 8 mm then XC = __?__. 4 mm

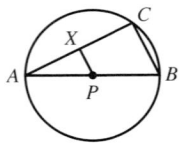

25. In ⊙O, $\overline{OA}$ and $\overline{OB}$ are radii such that m∠AOB = 60. Find OA and OB if AB = $4\sqrt{3}$ cm. OA = OB = $4\sqrt{3}$ cm

26. In ⊙Q, $\overline{QC}$ and $\overline{QD}$ are radii such that m∠CQD = 120. Find QC if CD = 24. QC = $8\sqrt{3}$

C   27. Given: $\overline{PR}$ and $\overline{QS}$ are diameters.
    Prove: $\overline{PQ} \cong \overline{RS}$. See Additional Answers, p. 702.

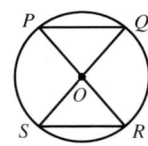

28. Given: $\overline{OA} \perp \overline{BC}$
    Prove: $\overline{OA}$ bisects $\overline{BC}$.

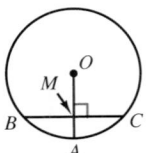

29. Prove that a diameter of a circle is longer than any chord of the circle that does not contain the center of the circle.

30. How many coplanar circles may be drawn through 2 points? infinitely many

Applications

31. **Astronomy** The equatorial diameter of Saturn is 120,660 km and the distance from the center of Saturn to one of its rings is 294,700 km. How far is the ring from the planet? 234,370 km

32. **Technology** Using Logo, draw a series of concentric circles. Then, experiment with the graphic by changing the turtle's heading and having the circles intersect. See Solutions Manual.

CONSTRUCTION

Given: △ABC   Construct: ⊙O containing A, B, and C.

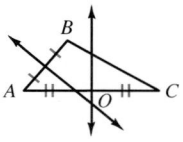
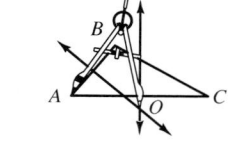
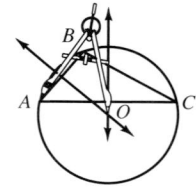

1. Construct the ⊥ bis. of $\overline{AB}$ and $\overline{AC}$. Extend them to intersect at O.

2. With O at center, place the pencil end on A.

3. Draw circle O using $\overline{OA}$ as a radius.

EXERCISE   Given: Acute △RST   Construct: ⊙P containing R, S, and T
Check students' constructions.

356   Chapter 9   Circles

356

Properties of Tangents

Objective: To prove and apply theorems that relate tangents and radii

The concept *tangent* is important throughout mathematics. In one use, the term *tangent* names a line that is associated with circles.

Investigation—*Thinking Critically*

In this figure, the line of sight from the tower looking to the horizon is described by $\overrightarrow{TX}$. Assuming that the earth is a sphere, *X* and *M* are points on a great circle.

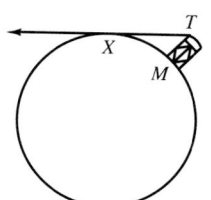

1. Give the intersection of the great circle and $\overrightarrow{TX}$. pt. X

2. Explain why $\overrightarrow{TX}$ cannot be called a secant.
   It does not contain a chord of the great ⊙.

A **tangent** to a circle lies in the plane of the circle and intersects the circle in exactly one point. That point is called the *point of tangency*. In this figure, $\overleftrightarrow{TH}$ is a tangent with point of tangency *H*; $\overrightarrow{TH}$ is a *tangent ray*; and $\overline{TH}$ is a *tangent segment*.

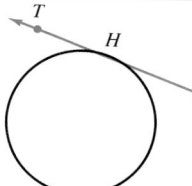

> **Theorem 9.1** If a line is tangent to a circle, then the line is perpendicular to the radius at the point of tangency.

Given: *l* is tangent to ⊙*O* at point *A*.

Prove: $\overline{OA} \perp l$

Plan: Use an indirect proof. Show that the negation of $\overline{OA} \perp l$ leads to a contradiction.

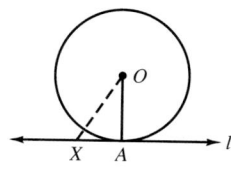

Proof:

Assume: $\overline{OA}$ is not $\perp l$.
    Choose another point, *X*,
      on *l* such that $\overline{OX} \perp l$.
    $OX < OA$.

Negation of the conclusion.
Through a point not on a line there is exactly one ⊥ to the line.
The ⊥ segment from a point to a line is the shortest segment from the point to the line.

LESSON PLAN

Vocabulary

Circumscribed polygon	Internal tangent
Common tangent	Point of tangency
External tangent	Tangent
	Tangent ray
Inscribed circle	Tangent segment

Materials/Manipulatives

Globe, string, small object
Compasses and straightedges
Teaching Transparency 57

Technology

Computer Test Bank, pp. 533–544

LESSON FOCUS

Review
Review the definition of *secant*. Ask students in how many points a secant intersects a circle.

Alternative Learning Styles
To further investigate tangents, use a kinesthetic approach by having students examine the area of the Earth that can receive a transmission from a communication satellite. Using a globe, string, and a small object above the globe as a model of the satellite, stretch the string from the satellite tangent to the globe. As the string is moved to determine all the points of tangency, note that the points form a circle that is the boundary on the Earth's surface.

Developing Mathematical Power

Cooperative Learning Working in groups, students can create original designs using circles and tangents. Encourage them to use color to enhance their drawings. Use the designs as the basis for a bulletin-board display.

- Students might be asked to write Theorems 9.1 and 9.2 as an if-and-only-if statement.
- Point out that the proofs of Theorems 9.1 and 9.2 illustrate once again the usefulness of indirect proofs.

CHALKBOARD EXAMPLES

- **For Example 1**
$\overline{AB}$ and $\overline{AC}$ are tangent segments. $AB = 12$, $AO = 13$, and $m\angle BAO = 23$.

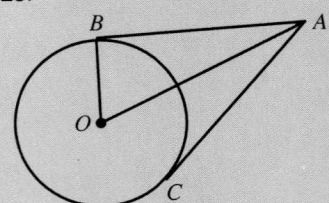

a. Find the length of a radius.
b. Find AC.
c. Find $m\angle CAO$.

a. By Th. 9.1, $m\angle B = 90$. By the Pyth. Th., $OB^2 = 13^2 - 12^2 = 25$. $OB = 5$
b. By Cor. 1, $AC = 12$.
c. By Cor. 2, $m\angle CAO = 23$.

- **For Example 2**
$\triangle GHI$ circumscribes $\odot O$. $GK:HL:IJ = 5:2:3$, the perimeter of $\triangle GHI$ is 100, and $m\angle I = 63$.

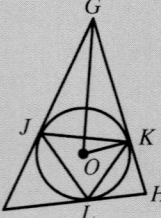

a. Find GK, HL, and IJ.
b. Name 3 isosceles triangles.
c. What kind of triangle is GKO?
d. Find $m\angle IJL$.

a. $2(5x + 2x + 3x) = 100$; $x = 5$; $GK = 25$; $HL = 10$; $IJ = 15$
b. $\triangle GJK$, $\triangle IJL$, $\triangle HLK$
c. right triangle
d. $m\angle IJL = 58.5$

358

Contradiction: $OA < OX$, since all points of tangent l are external to $\odot O$ except for A, which was given as being on the circle.

Conclusion: Since the assumption that $\overline{OA}$ is not $\perp l$ leads to a contradiction of the definition of tangent, it must be true that $\overline{OA} \perp l$.

Corollary 1 Two tangent segments from a common external point are congruent.
Proved in Practice Exercise 22

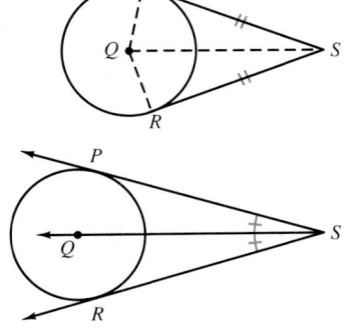

Corollary 2 The two tangent rays from a common external point determine an angle that is bisected by the ray from the external point to the center of the circle.
Proved in Practice Exercise 23

The next theorem is the converse of Theorem 9.1.

Theorem 9.2 If a line in the plane of a circle is perpendicular to a radius at its endpoint on the circle, then the line is tangent to the circle.

Given: $l \perp \overline{OA}$ at A.

Prove: l is tangent to $\odot O$.

Plan: Use an indirect proof. Assume that l is not tangent to $\odot O$, but intersects $\odot O$ at another point, X.
Proved in Practice Exercise 28

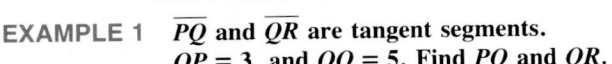

EXAMPLE 1 $\overline{PQ}$ and $\overline{QR}$ **are tangent segments.** $OP = 3$, **and** $OQ = 5$. **Find** PQ **and** QR.

$\triangle OPQ$ is a right triangle by Theorem 9.1.
By the Pythagorean Theorem, $PQ^2 = 5^2 - 3^2$, and $PQ = 4$.
$QR = 4$ by Corollary 1 (Theorem 9.1).

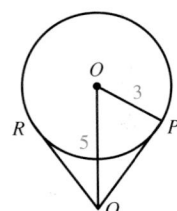

Coplanar circles may have *common tangent lines* and the *circles themselves may also be tangent*.

Developing Mathematical Power

Keeping a Portfolio Have students write a brief paragraph in which they compare and contrast internal and external tangents, and circles that are internally or externally tangent. Then have them explain if it is possible for two tangents to a circle to be parallel; to be perpendicular.

Common tangent lines are: internal tangents	if they intersect the segment joining the centers of the two coplanar circles.	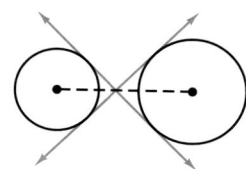
Common tangent lines are: external tangents	if they do *not* intersect the segment joining the centers of the two coplanar circles.	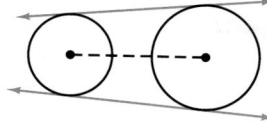
Tangent circles are: internally tangent	if one circle is in the *interior* of the other, except for the point where the circles are tangent to the same line.	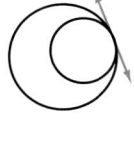
Tangent circles are: externally tangent	if all the points of one circle are *exterior* to those of the other, except the point where the circles are tangent to the same line.	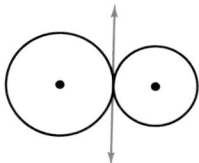

Common Error
- Students may confuse the various kinds of common tangents. Ask students to draw two circles with:

  a. exactly one common tangent.
  b. two common tangents.
  c. three common tangents.
  d. four common tangents.

  Have them identify each case as to types of tangents, and tell whether the circles are tangent and, if so, in which way.
- See *Teacher's Resource Book* for additional remediation.

LESSON FOLLOW-UP

Assignment Guide
See p. 350B for assignments.

When a polygon is *circumscribed* about a circle, each side is a tangent segment to the circle and the circle is *inscribed* in the polygon.

EXAMPLE 2 ⊙*O* is inscribed in △*ABC*. *AD* = 30, *BE* = 50, and *CF* = 20.

a. What kind of triangle is △*ADF*?

b. What kind of triangle is △*ADO*?

c. If *m∠EFC* is 50, find *m∠C*.

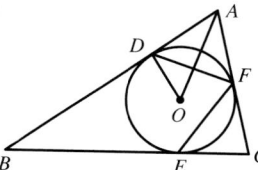

a. isosceles   b. right   c. *m∠C* = 80.

CLASS EXERCISES

Classify each triangle. Justify. Then find the missing angle measures.

1.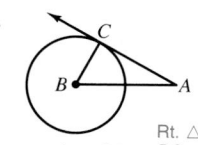

2.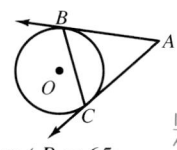

3.

Rt. △;
BC ⊥ *CA* (Th. 9.1);
thus, △*ABC* is
a rt. △. *m∠B* = 60

m∠A = 30;
m∠B = __?__.

Isos. △;
AB ≅ *AC*;
thus △*ABC*
is isos.
m∠C = 65

m∠B = 65;
m∠C = __?__.

m∠BCD = 120;
m∠BCA = __?__.

3. Rt. △; *BC* ⊥ *AB*, *CD* ⊥ *AD*; thus △*ABC* and △*ACD* are rt. △. *m∠BCA* = 60

9.2 Properties of Tangents   **359**

359

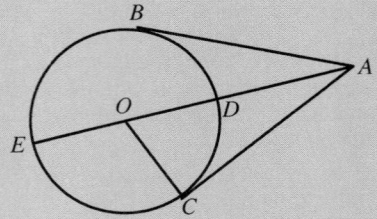
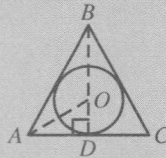
PRACTICE EXERCISES Use technology where appropriate.

How many common tangents can be drawn to the two circles?

A 1. 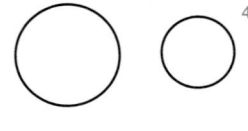 4 **2.** 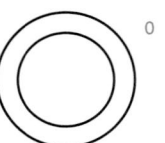 0 **3.** 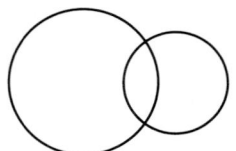 2

4. 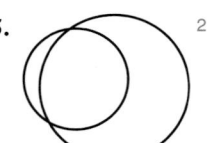 1 **5.** 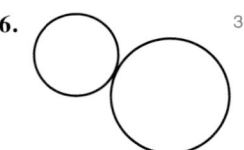 2 **6.** 3

$\overleftrightarrow{RP}$ and $\overline{PS}$ are tangents of $\odot O$.

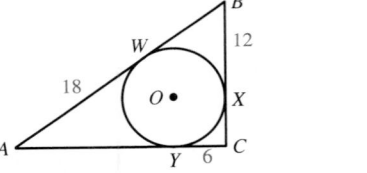

7. If $OR = 3$ and $OP = 5$, $RP = \underline{?}$. 4
8. If $OR = 6$ and $OP = 10$, $PS = \underline{?}$. 8
9. If $QO = 5$ and $RP = 12$, $OP = \underline{?}$. 13
10. If $OR = \sqrt{3}$ and $PS = 3\sqrt{2}$, $OP = \underline{?}$. $\sqrt{21}$
11. If $OR = 5$ and $m\angle ROP = 60$, $OP = \underline{?}$. 10
12. If $OP = 5\sqrt{2}$ and $m\angle ROP = 45$, $OR = \underline{?}$. 5
13. If $m\angle RPT = 50$, $m\angle ROP = \underline{?}$. 40 **14.** If $m\angle PSR = 62$, $m\angle PRS = \underline{?}$. 62

In this figure, $\odot O$ is inscribed in $\triangle ABC$.
$BX = 12$, $CY = 6$, and $AW = 18$.

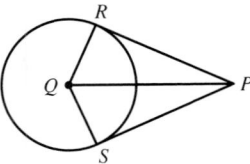

15. Find the perimeter of $\triangle ABC$. 72
16. What kind of triangle is $\triangle ABC$? Why? Rt. $\triangle$; $BC^2 + CA^2 = AB^2$

$\overleftrightarrow{PR}$ is in the plane of $\odot O$, which has a radius of length 5 mm. In each case, in how many points can $\overleftrightarrow{PR}$ intersect $\odot O$?

17. $OP = 6$ mm; $OR = 3$ mm 2 pts. **18.** $OP = 3$ mm; $OR = 3$ mm 2 pts.
19. $OP = 5$ mm; $OR = 13$ mm 1 or 2 pts. **20.** $OP = 13$ mm; $OR = 13$ mm 0, 1, or 2 pts.

B 21. **Given:** $\overline{PR}$ and $\overline{PS}$ are tangent segments.
    Prove: $\angle RPS$ and $\angle RQS$ are supplementary.
    See Additional Answers, p. 702.

22. Prove Corollary 1 of Theorem 9.1.   **23.** Prove Corollary 2 of Theorem 9.1.

See Additional Answers, p. 702.

24. Given: $\overline{WX}$ and $\overline{YZ}$ are common tangent segments to noncongruent circles O and Q.

Prove: $\overline{WX} \cong \overline{YZ}$ (*Hint:* Extend $\overline{WX}$ and $\overline{YZ}$.)

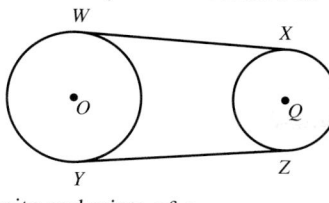

C   **25. Prove:** If two lines are tangent to a circle at opposite endpoints of a diameter, then the lines are parallel.

26. $\triangle ABC$ is circumscribed about $\odot O$, $AB = 46$, $BC = 43$, and $CA = 49$. Find AP, BQ, and CR.

26, 20, 23

27. Quadrilateral $MNTP$ is circumscribed about $\odot G$, $MN = 20$, $NT = 11$, and $TP = 9$. Find PM. 18

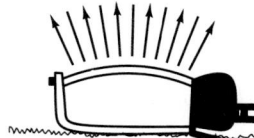

28. Complete the proof of Theorem 9.2. See Additional Answers, p. 702.

29. Prove that the sums of the lengths of the opposite sides of a circumscribed quadrilateral are equal.

Applications

30. Technology   Using Logo, draw two tangent circles. Then draw two more circles tangent to the first set of circles. Connect the centers of your tangent circles. What figure do you have?
See Solutions Manual.

31. Gardening   This oscillating lawn sprinkler sprays water in a straight line rather than in a circular pattern. Describe the line.

Developing Mathematical Power

32. Writing in Mathematics   The figure (not to scale) shows the sun, earth, and moon in the positions for two types of eclipses. Explain how the common tangents can be used to determine whether each eclipse is total or partial. See below.

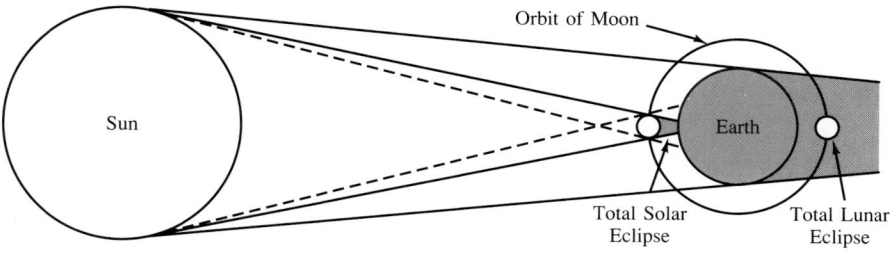

Orbit of Moon

Sun

Earth

Total Solar Eclipse   Total Lunar Eclipse

9.2 Properties of Tangents   **361**

32. A solar eclipse will be total at all points on the Earth that are between the common external tangents. It will be partial at all points between the common internal tangents but not between the common external tangents. A lunar eclipse is total at all points when the moon is between the common external tangents.

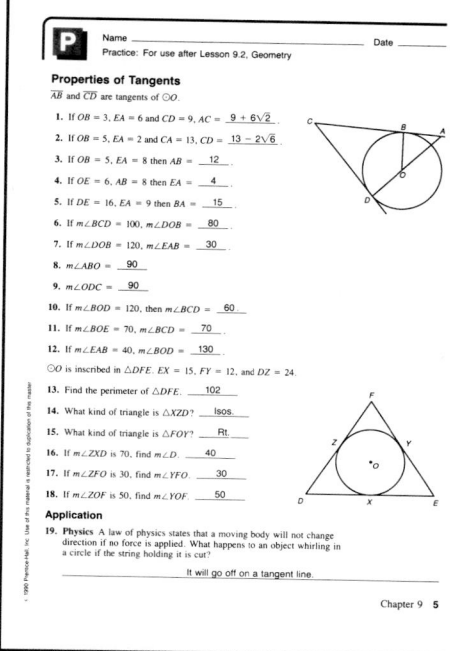

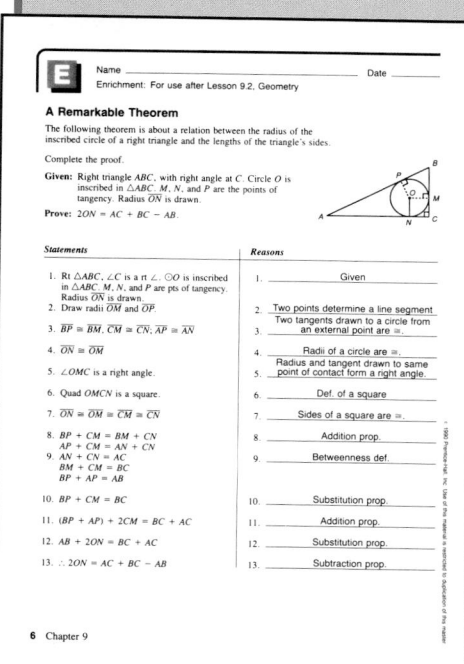

Vocabulary
Adjacent nonoverlapping arcs
Central angle   Major arc
Congruent arcs   Minor arc
Congruent chords   Semicircle

Materials/Manipulatives
Teaching Transparency 58

Technology
Computer
Computer Test Bank, pp.
544–555
The Geometric Supposer:
Circles, pp. 94–97

LESSON FOCUS

Review

• Classify the angles with the following measures.
  1. $m\angle A = 55$ **2.** $m\angle B = 107$
  3. $m\angle C = 90$

  1. acute 2. obtuse
  3. right

• The Mixed Review, Exercises 37–43, involves concepts in Chapters 7–9.

Alternative Learning Styles

• In the Investigation, students can see that the spinner point traces a circle as the spinner moves through four 90° angles. Thus, they discover that the sum of the measures of arcs that make up a circle is 360.

• The visual learner will benefit from drawing a diagram for each theorem in the lesson. By writing each of the geometric terms in the theorem in color and then using the same color for that element on the drawing, students enhance their understanding of the concepts presented.

362

Arcs, Chords, and Central Angles

Objectives: To define and apply properties of arcs and central angles
To prove and apply theorems about chords of a circle
To apply inequality relationships to circles

Circles can be separated into parts called **arcs** ($\overarc{AB}$, $\overarc{BD}$). When the endpoints of an arc are also the endpoints of a diameter, the arc is a **semicircle** ($\overarc{ABD}$).

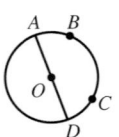

Investigation—*Visualizing the Concept*

A spinner has been placed over the coordinate plane.

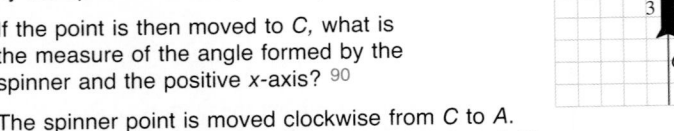

1. If the point of the spinner is moved from *A* to *B*, what is the measure of the angle formed by the spinner and the positive *y*-axis? 90

2. If the point is then moved to *C*, what is the measure of the angle formed by the spinner and the positive *x*-axis? 90

3. The spinner point is moved clockwise from *C* to *A*. What is the sum of the measures of angles 3 and 4?
   180

4. What is the sum of the measures of all four angles? Would this answer be different if the spinner were 1 cm longer? 1 cm shorter? 360; no; no

5. What kind of figure has the spinner point traced? a circle

The **measure of a semicircle** is 180. When an arc is not a semicircle, it is either a *minor arc* or a *major arc*.

An angle is a **central angle** of a circle if its vertex is the center of the circle. $\angle DPE$ is a central angle of $\odot P$. The **minor arc** *DE*, $\overarc{DE}$, consists of endpoints *D*, *E*, and all points of $\odot P$ in the interior of central $\angle DPE$. The **measure of a minor arc** is the measure of its central angle. Since $m\angle DPE = 60$, $m\overarc{DE} = 60$.

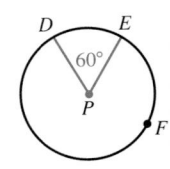

The **major arc** *DFE*, named $\overarc{DFE}$, consists of *D*, *E*, and all points of $\odot P$ in the exterior of its central $\angle DPE$. To distinguish a major arc from its related minor arc, it is named by using three letters. Three letters are also used in naming a semicircle. Why is this helpful? The **measure of a major arc** is the difference between the measure of its related minor arc and 360, which is the measure of the complete circle. Thus, $m\overarc{DFE} = 300$. Three letters indicate which semicircle.

Developing Mathematical Power

Cooperative Learning The Enrichment activity, p. 9, in the *Teacher's Resource Book* (see side column, p. 367) can be done with students working in cooperative groups. Have them draw and color illustrations for Exercises 1–5 and then use the pattern for 7–10 points. Allow enough time for groups to share their responses to Exercise 9.

In the same circle or in congruent circles, **two arcs** are **congruent** if and only if they have equal measures. Thus, in $\odot O$, $\overset{\frown}{QR} \cong \overset{\frown}{RS}$ if $m\overset{\frown}{QR} = m\overset{\frown}{RS}$. Two arcs of a circle are **adjacent nonoverlapping arcs** if they have exactly one point in common. What is true when two arcs of a circle have exactly two points in common? $\overset{\frown}{PQ}$ and $\overset{\frown}{QR}$ are adjacent nonoverlapping arcs; $\overset{\frown}{PR}$ and $\overset{\frown}{QR}$ are not. They form a circle.

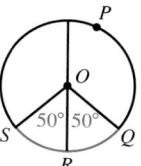

Postulate 18   The measure of an arc formed by two adjacent nonoverlapping arcs is the sum of the measures of those two arcs.

Thus in $\odot O$, $m\overset{\frown}{PQ} + m\overset{\frown}{QR} = m\overset{\frown}{PR}$ and $m\overset{\frown}{PS} + m\overset{\frown}{SR} = m\overset{\frown}{PSR}$.

EXAMPLE 1 $\overline{AD}$ and $\overline{EG}$ are diameters of the concentric circles; $m\angle AOB = 35$ and $m\overset{\frown}{CD} = m\overset{\frown}{AB}$.

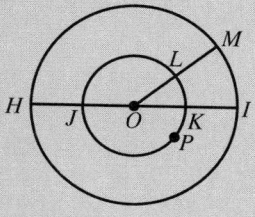

  a. Find $m\overset{\frown}{AB}$, $m\overset{\frown}{BD}$, $m\overset{\frown}{BC}$, $m\overset{\frown}{EF}$, $m\overset{\frown}{FG}$, $m\overset{\frown}{EGF}$, and $m\overset{\frown}{AXC}$.

  b. State the relationship between $\overset{\frown}{AB}$ and $\overset{\frown}{EF}$; between $\overset{\frown}{AB}$ and $\overset{\frown}{CD}$.

  c. If $m\overset{\frown}{AX} = 20$, find $m\angle AOX$ and $m\overset{\frown}{XD}$.

  a. 35; 145; 110; 35; 145; 325; 215

  b. $m\overset{\frown}{AB} = m\overset{\frown}{EF}$, but $\overset{\frown}{AB} \not\cong \overset{\frown}{EF}$; $m\overset{\frown}{AB} = m\overset{\frown}{CD}$ and $\overset{\frown}{AB} \cong \overset{\frown}{CD}$

  c. $m\angle AOX = 20$; $m\overset{\frown}{XD} = 160$

Theorem 9.3   In the same circle, or in congruent circles, two minor arcs are congruent if and only if their central angles are congruent.
Proved in Practice Exercises 19 and 20

Theorem 9.4   In the same circle, or in congruent circles, two minor arcs are congruent if and only if their chords are congruent.
Proved in Practice Exercise 29

Theorem 9.5   If a diameter is perpendicular to a chord, then it bisects the chord and its arc.

Given: Diameter $\overline{CD} \perp$ chord $\overline{AB}$

Prove: $\overline{AX} \cong \overline{BX}$, $\overset{\frown}{AD} \cong \overset{\frown}{DB}$ and $\overset{\frown}{AC} \cong \overset{\frown}{BC}$.

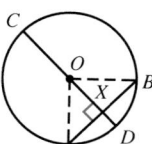

Plan: Draw radii $\overline{OA}$ and $\overline{OB}$. Show $\triangle AOX \cong \triangle BOX$. By CPCTC, $\overline{AX} \cong \overline{BX}$ and $\angle AOX \cong \angle BOX$; therefore $\overset{\frown}{AD} \cong \overset{\frown}{DB}$, and $\overset{\frown}{AC} \cong \overset{\frown}{BC}$.
Proved in Class Exercise 9

TEACHING SUGGESTIONS

- Involve students in discussions of Plans for proofs of the theorems.
- Students can do the proofs of the theorems in small groups.

CHALKBOARD EXAMPLES

- **For Example 1**

  $\overline{JK}$ and $\overline{HI}$ are diameters of these concentric circles. $m\angle HOM = 150$ and $m\overset{\frown}{KP} = m\overset{\frown}{KL}$.

  a. Find $m\overset{\frown}{HM}$, $m\overset{\frown}{MI}$, $m\overset{\frown}{IH}$, $m\overset{\frown}{JL}$, $m\overset{\frown}{LK}$, and $m\overset{\frown}{LJP}$.

  b. Identify two pairs of congruent minor arcs.

  c. Identify two arcs that are not congruent, but whose measures are equal.

    a. 150; 30; 180; 150; 30; 300
    b. $\overset{\frown}{LK} \cong \overset{\frown}{KP}$; $\overset{\frown}{LJ} \cong \overset{\frown}{JP}$
    c. $\overset{\frown}{LK}$ and $\overset{\frown}{MI}$ (answers may vary)

For Example 2

- **For Example 2**
  The length of a radius of ⊙O is 10.
  $AB = AC = 10$ and $OX = 6$.
  a. Find DE. **b.** Find OY.
  c. Are any two chords equidistant from O?

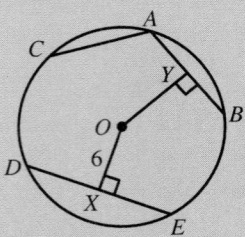

  a. $XE^2 = 10^2 - 6^2 = 64$
  $XE = 8$; $DE = 16$
  b. $OY^2 = 10^2 - 5^2 = 75$; $OY = 5\sqrt{3}$
  c. yes; $\overline{AB}$ and $\overline{AC}$

Common Error

- Students may not see the need for "or in congruent circles" in Theorems 9.3 and 9.4. Example 1b shows arcs that have the same measure, but are not congruent. To illustrate the importance of the phrase in Theorem 9.4, ask students if $\overset{\frown}{ACB}$ is congruent to $\overset{\frown}{AOB}$ in this figure.

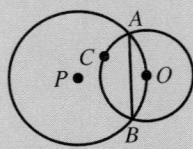

- See *Teacher's Resource Book* for additional remediation.

LESSON FOLLOW-UP

Assignment Guide
See p. 350B for assignments.

Theorem 9.6 In the same circle or in congruent circles, two chords are equidistant from the center(s) if and only if they are congruent.
Proved in Practice Exercise 30

Thus in ⊙O, if $OX = OY$, then $\overline{PQ} \cong \overline{RS}$. Also, if $\overline{PQ} \cong \overline{RS}$, then $\overline{PQ}$ and $\overline{RS}$ are equidistant from center O (or, $OX = OY$).

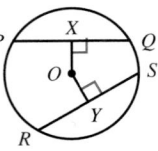

EXAMPLE 2 The length of any radius of ⊙O is 25 mm.
Chord $\overline{AB}$ is 7 mm from O and chord $\overline{CD}$ is 15 mm from O. Which chord is longer? by how much?

$BX^2 = BO^2 - OX^2$	$DY^2 = DO^2 - OY^2$
$BX^2 = 625 - 49$	$DY^2 = 625 - 225$
$BX = \sqrt{576} = 24$	$DY = \sqrt{400} = 20$

Thus $AB = 48$ mm, $DC = 40$ mm, and AB is 8 mm longer.

Example 2 suggests the next two theorems.

Theorem 9.7 If two chords of a circle are unequal in length, then the longer chord is nearer to the center of the circle. Proved in Practice Exercise 31

Theorem 9.8 If two chords of a circle are not equidistant from the center, then the longer chord is nearer to the center of the circle.
Proved in Practice Exercise 32

CLASS EXERCISES

Drawing in Geometry

Draw a figure that shows $\overline{PQ}$ and $\overline{RS}$ are chords of ⊙O, with $PQ < RS$, and $\overline{OX} \perp \overline{PQ}$. Conclude whether Exercises 1–3 are true or false. Justify.

1. $\overline{PQ}$ can be a diameter.   **2.** $\overline{RS}$ is closer to O.   **3.** $\overline{PX} \cong \overline{XQ}$
False; a diam. is the longest chord of a ⊙.   true; $RS > PQ$; Th. 9.7   true; Th. 9.5

In ⊙O, $\overline{AB}$ and $\overline{CD}$ are diameters; $\overline{XO} \perp \overline{CD}$; $m\overset{\frown}{AC} = 20$.

4. Name 8 minor arcs. $\overset{\frown}{CA}, \overset{\frown}{CX}, \overset{\frown}{CB}, \overset{\frown}{XA}, \overset{\frown}{AD}, \overset{\frown}{XB}, \overset{\frown}{DB}, \overset{\frown}{XD}$

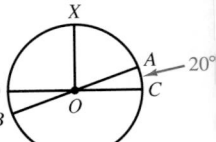

5. Name 3 pairs of congruent arcs.   Answers may vary;
$\overset{\frown}{AC} \cong \overset{\frown}{DB}; \overset{\frown}{CX} \cong \overset{\frown}{DX}; \overset{\frown}{AD} \cong \overset{\frown}{BC}$

6. Find $m\angle AOC$, $m\overset{\frown}{DB}$, $m\overset{\frown}{XD}$, $m\overset{\frown}{BX}$, $m\overset{\frown}{AX}$, $m\angle BOX$, and $m\overset{\frown}{XAB}$.
20   20   90   110   70   110   250

In ⊙Q, CD = 30, QX = 24, **and the length of any radius is 25.**

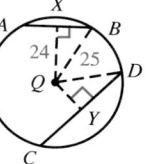

7. Find QY. 20   **8.** Find AB. 14

9. Use the figure, *Given*, *Prove*, and *Plan* to prove Theorem 9.5. See side column.

10. State the two conditionals needed in order to prove Theorem 9.3. If 2 central
∠s of a ⊙, or of ≅ ⊙s, are ≅, then their minor arcs are ≅.
If 2 minor arcs of a ⊙, or of ≅ ⊙s, are ≅, then their central ∠s are ≅.

PRACTICE EXERCISES

 Use technology where appropriate.

In ⊙Q, $\overline{AG}$ is a diameter. Identify the following.

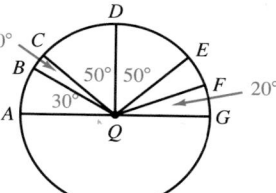

A

1. Five minor arcs Answers may vary; $\widehat{AB}$, $\widehat{BC}$, $\widehat{CD}$, $\widehat{DE}$, $\widehat{EF}$.

2. Five pairs of congruent arcs Answers may vary;
$\widehat{AC} \cong \widehat{EG}$, $\widehat{EF} \cong \widehat{FG}$; $\widehat{CD} \cong \widehat{DE}$, $\widehat{AD} \cong \widehat{DG}$, $\widehat{AE} \cong \widehat{CG}$.

3. Five pairs of congruent angles ∠FQG ≅ ∠FQE,
∠AQC ≅ ∠GQE, ∠CQD ≅ ∠DQE, ∠AQD ≅ ∠GQD,
∠AQE ≅ ∠CQG

Use ⊙O for Exercises 4–7.

4. Explain why there are no congruent chords.
None of the arcs shown are ≅.

5. List all the minor arcs and their measures.
See below.

6. Starting with $\overline{AE}$ and ending with $\overline{AB}$, list 4 chords with endpoint A in order of their distance from the center O. $\overline{AE}$, $\overline{AD}$, $\overline{AC}$, $\overline{AB}$

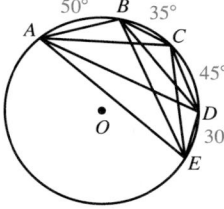

7. $\overline{AE}$, $\overline{AD}$, $\overline{BE}$, $\overline{AC}$, $\overline{BD}$, $\overline{CE}$, $\overline{AB}$, $\overline{CD}$, $\overline{BC}$, $\overline{DE}$

7. List all the chords in order from longest to shortest.

5. $m\widehat{AB} = 50$, $m\widehat{AC} = 85$, $m\widehat{AD} = 130$, $m\widehat{AE} = 160$, $m\widehat{BC} = 35$,
$m\widehat{BD} = 80$, $m\widehat{BE} = 110$, $m\widehat{CD} = 45$, $m\widehat{CE} = 75$, $m\widehat{DE} = 30$

Use ⊙R for Exercises 8–18.

8. Name 2 pairs of congruent segments. $\overline{AP} \cong \overline{PB}$, $\overline{CQ} \cong \overline{QD}$

9. If $\overline{RP} \cong \overline{RQ}$, then $\overline{AB}$ _?_ $\overline{CD}$ and $\widehat{AB}$ _?_ $\widehat{CD}$. ≅; ≅

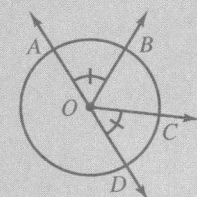

10. If $\overline{RP} \cong \overline{RQ}$, then $\overline{CQ}$ _?_ $\overline{AP}$ and $\widehat{AB}$ _?_ $\widehat{CD}$. ≅; ≅

11. If $RP > RQ$, then AB _?_ CD. <

12. If $RP > RQ$, then CQ _?_ AP. >

13. If $CD < AB$, then RQ _?_ RP. >   **14.** If $CD < AB$, then CQ _?_ AP. <

15. If the length of any radius is 10 and $RP = 6$, then $AP =$ _?_ and $AB =$ _?_.
8; 16

16. If $CQ = 5$ and $RQ = 12$, find the length of any radius. 13

17. The lengths of a diameter and AB are 50 and 48, respectively. Find RP. 7

18. If $RC = \sqrt{2}$ and $CQ = RQ$, then find CQ, DQ, and CD. 1; 1; 2

9.3 Arcs, Chords, and Central Angles   **365**

Developing Mathematical Power

Keeping a Portfolio Have students rewrite Theorems 9.7 and 9.8 as a biconditional statement. Then have them draw a variety of situations to illustrate Theorems 9.6–9.8 and verify each theorem by measuring the chords and the distance of the perpendicular from the center of each circle to each chord.

Lesson Quiz

1. A chord is 15 cm from the center of a circle whose radius has length 25 cm. What is the length of the chord?

2. $m\widehat{AD} = 55$. Find $m\widehat{AC}$, $m\widehat{AB}$, and $m\widehat{ABC}$.

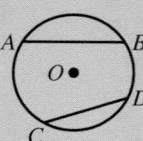

3. $CD = 20$ mm, $\overline{CD} \perp \overline{AB}$, and $m\widehat{BD} = 60$. Find AB.

1. 40 cm

2. $m\widehat{AC} = 125$; $m\widehat{AB} = 110$; $m\widehat{ABC} = 235$

3. $10\sqrt{3}$ mm

Enrichment

a. Give a Plan for proof:

If two chords of a circle are not congruent, then the longer chord has the arc with the greater measure.

Given: ⊙O with chords $\overline{AB}$ and $\overline{CD}$; $AB >$ CD

Prove: $m\widehat{AB}$ $> m\widehat{CD}$

b. How would you prove the converse of the statement in part (a)?

a. Plan: Draw $\overline{OA}$, $\overline{OB}$, $\overline{OC}$, and $\overline{OD}$. By the converse of the Hinge Th., $m\angle AOB$ $> m\angle COD$; thus, $m\widehat{AB} > m\widehat{CD}$.

b. Draw the radii and use the Hinge Th.

---

19. Draw a figure and write the *Given, Prove,* and *Plan* for this part of Theorem 9.3: In a circle, if two central angles are congruent, then their minor arcs are congruent.
See side column page 365.

20. Write a plan for the converse of the statement given in Exercise 19.

In Exercises 21–26, let $\overline{AB}$ be any chord except a diameter in ⊙O.

B **21.** What kind of a triangle is $\triangle AOB$? isos. △

22. Suppose $\overline{OA} \cong \overline{AB}$. What kind of a triangle is $\triangle AOB$? equilateral

23. Find the measures of all the angles of $\triangle AOB$ if $m\widehat{AB} = 50$.
$m\angle OAB = m\angle OBA = 65$, $m\angle AOB = 50$

24. Find the measures of all the angles of $\triangle AOB$ if $m\widehat{AB} = 100$.
$m\angle OAB = m\angle OBA = 40$, $m\angle AOB = 100$

25. Suppose $m\angle AOB = 70$. Find $m\widehat{AB}$, $m\angle A$, and $m\angle B$. $m\widehat{AB} = 70$, $m\angle A = m\angle B = 55$

26. Suppose $m\angle A = 20$. Find $m\angle B$, $m\angle O$, and $m\widehat{AB}$. $m\angle B = 20$, $m\angle O = 140$, $m\widehat{AB} = 140$

27. Given: $\triangle ABC$ is equilateral.
Prove: $m\widehat{AB} = m\widehat{BC} = m\widehat{CA}$
See Additional Answers, p. 702.

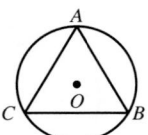

28. Given: Chords $\overline{AB}$ and $\overline{CD}$ are $\cong$.
Prove: $BD = AC$

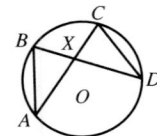

Prove each theorem.

C **29.** Theorem 9.4   **30.** Theorem 9.6   **31.** Theorem 9.7   **32.** Theorem 9.8

33. Given: Diameters $\overline{EG}$ and $\overline{FH}$ of ⊙O
Prove: Quadrilateral $EFGH$ is a parallelogram.

34. Prove: In a plane, the perpendicular bisector of any chord of a circle is a diameter of the circle.

Applications

35. Industry When a wheel with a 25-cm radius is dipped in a vat of cleaning solution, the level of the solution rises to the level shown by the given chord. If the length of the chord determined by the wheel is 48 cm, what is the level of the solution? 32 cm

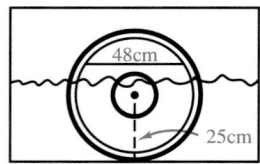

---

36. Technology   Use Logo to generate any size sector of a circle. Then use your procedure to generate a pie chart based on the budget of a school project. See Solutions Manual.

Mixed Review

$\overline{CA}$ is tangent to ⊙B at point C. $\overline{CD} \perp \overline{BD}$, BC = 5, and $m\overgroup{CE} = 60$.
Complete each statement.

37. △ABC is a _?_ triangle. right

38. △ABC ~ _?_ ~ _?_   △ACD; △CBD

39. CD = _?_ 2.5√3

40. m∠A = _?_ 30

41. AB = _?_ 10

42. CA = _?_ 5√3

43. BD = _?_ 2.5

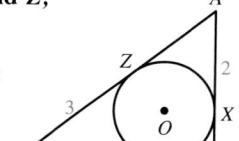

TEST YOURSELF

1. Define *circle*. A ⊙ is the set of pts. in a plane, every one of which is at a given distance from a given pt.   **9.1**

Use ⊙O to name the following.

2. Radii $\overline{OA}, \overline{OB}, \overline{OC}$

3. Diameter $\overline{BC}$

4. Chords $\overline{AC}, \overline{AB}, \overline{CB}$

5. Inscribed polygon △ABC

6. Complete: "If a line in the plane of a circle is perpendicular to a radius at its endpoint on the circle, then _?_." The line is tan. to the ⊙ at that pt.   **9.2**

7. Make a sketch of two circles having no common internal tangents and one common external tangent.

7.

$\overline{AB}, \overline{BC}$, and $\overline{CA}$ are tangent at X, Y, and Z, respectively.

8. Find the perimeter of triangle ABC. 12

9. Find the measure of ∠B. 90

10. Find the length of the radius of ⊙O. 1

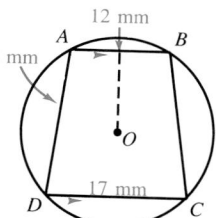

11. Define *central angle*. an ∠ that has its vertex at the center of the ⊙   **9.3**

12. Complete: If _?_, then the diameter bisects the chord and its arc. a diam. is ⊥ to a chord

ABCD is an isosceles trapezoid.

13. Name the pairs of congruent arcs. $\overgroup{BC} \cong \overgroup{AD}, \overgroup{ABC} \cong \overgroup{DAB}, \overgroup{BCD} \cong \overgroup{ADC}, \overgroup{ACD} \cong \overgroup{BDC}$

14. Starting with the closest, list $\overline{AB}, \overline{BC}$, and $\overline{CD}$ in order of their distance from O. $\overline{BC}, \overline{DC}, \overline{AB}$

15. If the length of any radius is 10, how far is $\overline{AB}$ from the center? 8

9.3 Arcs, Chords, and Central Angles   **367**

Teacher's Resource Book
Follow-Up Investigation, Chapter 9, p. 7

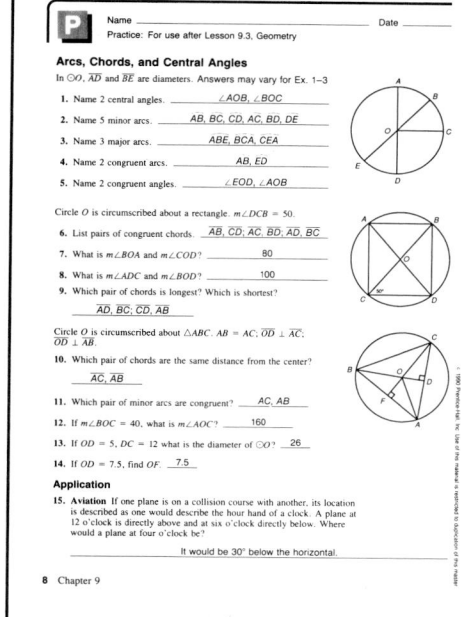

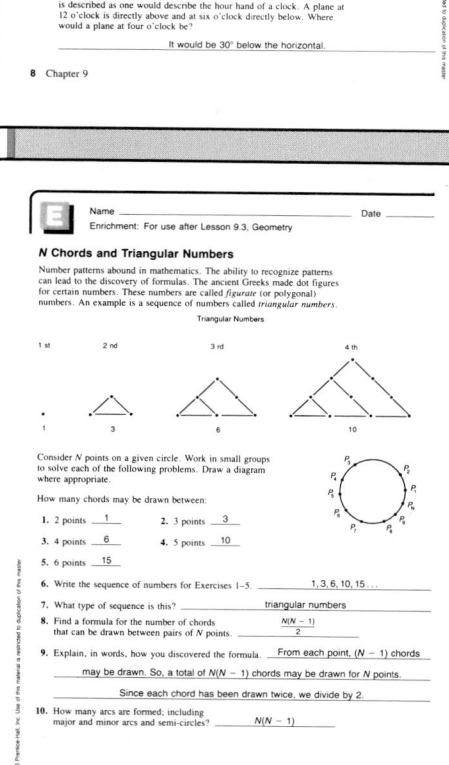

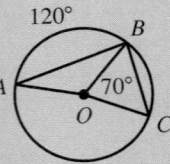
368

9.4 Inscribed Angles

Objectives: To identify inscribed angles
To solve problems and prove statements about inscribed
angles

A central angle has its vertex at the center of a circle. An *inscribed angle* has
its vertex on the circle.

Investigation—*Thinking Critically*

Copy this chart. Complete the chart as you answer Questions 1–6.

$m\angle ACB$	$m\widehat{AB}$	$m\angle D$	$m\angle E$	$m\angle F$
? 60	? 60	? 30	? 30	? 30

$\angle ACB$ is a central angle of ⊙C.

1. Use a protractor to measure $\angle ACB$. 60

2. What is $m\widehat{AB}$? 60

3. How are $\angle D$, $\angle E$, and $\angle F$ alike? Each intercepts $\widehat{AB}$
and each has its vertex on the ⊙.

4. What do these angles have in common with $\angle ACB$?
They all intercept $\widehat{AB}$.

5. Use a protractor to measure $\angle D$, $\angle E$, and $\angle F$.
What appears to be true? $m\angle D = m\angle E = m\angle F = \frac{1}{2}m\angle ACB = \frac{1}{2}m\widehat{AB} = 30$

6. Study the chart and make a generalization. What
kind of reasoning did you just use? Using inductive reasoning,
in a ⊙ the meas. of an inscribed ∠ is ½ the meas.
of a central ∠ that intercepts the same arc.

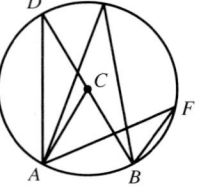

An angle is called an **inscribed angle** of a circle if and only if its vertex is on
the circle and its sides contain chords of the circle. All inscribed angles
intercept arcs.

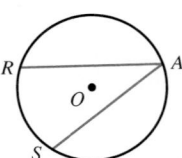

$\angle A$ intercepts
minor $\widehat{RS}$.

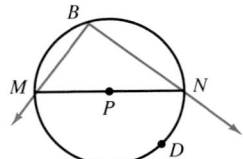

$\angle B$ intercepts
semicircle $\widehat{MDN}$.

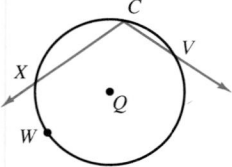

$\angle C$ intercepts
major $\widehat{XWV}$.

Theorem 9.9 and its corollaries state the relationship between any inscribed
angle and its intercepted arc.

Developing Mathematical Power

Cooperative Learning   Select teams of students to complete the Investigation,
p. 10, in the *Teacher's Resource Book.* Have them provide the illustrations they
used to determine their responses. Provide time for the groups to share their strategies and their responses.

Theorem 9.9 The measure of an inscribed angle is equal to one-half the measure of its intercepted arc.

Given: Inscribed $\angle RST$ in $\odot O$

Prove: $m\angle S = \frac{1}{2}m\widehat{RT}$

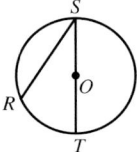 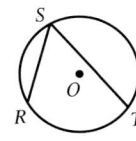 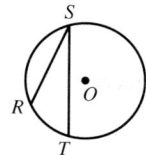

Case 1: Center O on $\angle RST$ Case 2: O in interior of $\angle RST$ Case 3: O in exterior of $\angle RST$

Plan (Case 1): Draw radius $\overline{RO}$. Thus $m\angle ROT = m\widehat{RT}$. By the Exterior Angle Theorem, $m\angle ROT = m\angle R + m\angle S$. Since $\triangle ROS$ is isosceles, $m\angle R = m\angle S$. Thus $m\angle ROT = m\angle S + m\angle S$, and $m\angle S = \frac{1}{2} m\angle ROT$. $m\angle ROT = m\widehat{RT}$, so the conclusion follows.

Case 1 proved in Class Exercise 11; Cases 2 and 3 planned in Class Exercise 12

Corollary 1 If two inscribed angles of a circle intercept the same arc or congruent arcs, then the angles are congruent. Proved in Practice Exercise 25

Corollary 2 If a quadrilateral is inscribed in a circle, then its opposite angles are supplementary. Proved in Practice Exercise 26

Corollary 3 If an inscribed angle intercepts a semicircle, then the angle is a right angle. Proved in Practice Exercise 27

Corollary 4 If two arcs of a circle are included between parallel segments, then the arcs are congruent. Proved in Practice Exercise 28

EXAMPLE 1 Quadrilateral $ABCD$ is inscribed in $\odot O$, with diagonal $\overline{BD}$ containing O.
$m\angle E = 30$. $m\widehat{AD} = 80$.
Find the measures of angles 1–6.

$m\angle 1 = 90$ $m\angle 2 = 40$ $m\angle 3 = 30$
$m\angle 4 = 90$ $m\angle 5 = 60$ $m\angle 6 = 50$

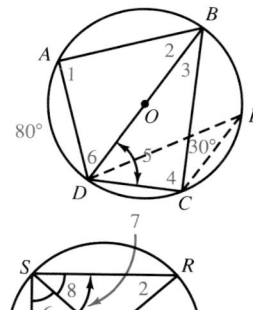

EXAMPLE 2 $\overline{RT}$ is a diameter of $\odot P$, $\overline{RS} \parallel \overline{VT}$, and $m\widehat{TS} = 70$.
Find the measures of angles 1–8.

$m\angle 1 = 70$ $m\angle 2 = 35$ $m\angle 3 = 110$ $m\angle 4 = 35$
$m\angle 5 = 55$ $m\angle 6 = 55$ $m\angle 7 = 90$ $m\angle 8 = 35$

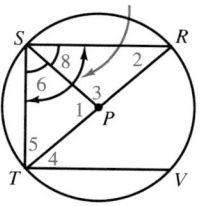

9.4 Inscribed Angles   **369**

Developing Mathematical Power

Keeping a Portfolio Have students choose five exercises (excluding proving theorems) that together they think cover all of the concepts in this lesson. For each exercise, they should write the question, the concepts needed to answer it, and a detailed answer. Allow time for discussion.

TEACHING SUGGESTIONS

- After discussing Theorem 9.9, introduce Corollary 2 by drawing a quadrilateral inscribed in a circle. Ask students what they can deduce about the angles. It may be necessary to ask them to focus on *opposite* angles.
- To apply Corollary 3, draw a circle on the chalkboard, mark the center, and ask students how they could draw a right angle using only the circle and a straightedge. Draw any diagonal and connect its endpoints to any other point of the circle.

Critical Thinking

1. *Reasoning* Lead students to deduce that opposite angles of a quadrilateral inscribed in a circle are supplementary.
2. *Application* Instruct students to apply Corollary 3 to drawing a right angle without using a protractor.

CHALKBOARD EXAMPLES

- **For Example 1**

  Quadrilateral *FGHI* is inscribed in $\odot O$. $\overline{FH}$ is a diagonal, $m\widehat{FI} = 80$, and $m\widehat{GH} = 50$. Find all angle measures.

  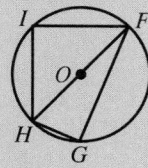

  $m\angle G = m\angle I = 90$
  $m\angle GFI = 75$
  $m\angle IHG = 105$
  $m\angle HFG = 25$
  $m\angle HFI = 50$
  $m\angle FHG = 65$
  $m\angle FHI = 40$

- **For Example 2**

  $\overline{MK}$ is a diameter of $\odot O$, $\overline{ML} \parallel \overline{JK}$, and $m\widehat{ML} = 120$. Find all angle measures.

  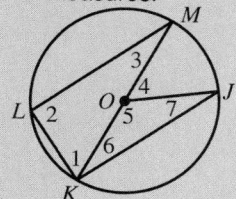

  $m\angle 1 = 60$
  $m\angle 2 = 90$
  $m\angle 3 = 30$
  $m\angle 4 = 60$
  $m\angle 5 = 120$
  $m\angle 6 = 30$
  $m\angle 7 = 30$

369

CLASS EXERCISES   See side column.

$\triangle ABC$ is inscribed in $\odot O$. Find the measures of the minor arcs and the angles of the triangle using the information given in each exercise.

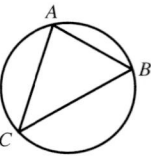

1. $m\angle A = 50$ and $m\angle C = 70$.
2. $m\widehat{AB} = 120$ and $m\widehat{AC} = 110$.
3. $m\angle A = 50$ and $\overline{AB} \cong \overline{BC}$.
4. $m\widehat{AC} = 112$ and $\angle A \cong \angle C$.
5. Center O lies on $\overline{BC}$ and $m\widehat{AC} = 60$.
   $m\widehat{BC} = 180$; $m\widehat{AB} = 120$; $m\angle A = 90$; $m\angle B = 30$; $m\angle C = 60$

Quadrilateral $ABCD$ is inscribed in $\odot O$. Find the measures of the minor arcs and the angles of the quadrilateral using the information given.

6. $m\widehat{AB} = 70$, $m\widehat{BC} = 120$, and $m\widehat{CD} = 80$.
7. $m\angle A = 110$; $m\angle B = 80$, and $m\widehat{CD} = 80$.

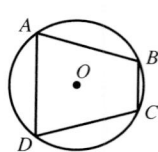

8. $m\angle C = 70$, $m\angle D = 100$, and $\overline{AB} \cong \overline{AD}$.
9. Center O lies on diagonal $\overline{BD}$; $m\widehat{CD} = 80$ and $m\widehat{AB} = \frac{1}{2}m\widehat{AD}$.
10. $\overline{AB} \parallel \overline{DC}$, $m\widehat{BC} = 50$, and $m\angle C = 75$.

11. Supply the missing statements and reasons in this proof of Case 1 of Theorem 9.9.

Statements	Reasons
1. Draw radius $\overline{RO}$.	1. $\underline{?}$ Two pts. determine 1 line.
2. $m\angle ROT = m\widehat{RT}$	2. $\underline{?}$ The meas. of an arc = the meas. of its central $\angle$.
3. $\underline{?} = m\angle R + m\angle S$ $_{m\angle ROT}$	3. $\underline{?}$ Ext. $\angle$ Th.
4. $\overline{RO} \cong \overline{SO}$	4. $\underline{?}$ Radii of a $\odot$ are $\cong$.
5. $\angle R \cong \angle S$	5. $\underline{?}$ Base $\angle$s of an isos. $\triangle$ are $\cong$.
6. $\underline{?}$ $_{m\angle R = m\angle S}$	6. Definition of congruent angles
7. $m\angle ROT = m\angle S + m\angle S$	7. $\underline{?}$ Subst. prop.
8. $\underline{?}$ $_{m\angle ROT = 2m\angle S}$	8. Distributive property
9. $\frac{1}{2}m\angle ROT = \underline{?}$ $_{m\angle S}$	9. Multiplication property
10. $\underline{?}$ $_{m\angle S = \frac{1}{2}m\widehat{RT}}$	10. $\underline{?}$ Subst. prop.

12. Write plans for Cases 2 and 3 of Theorem 9.9. (*Hint:* For each, draw the diameter from S, then follow the reasoning in the plan for Case 1.)

PRACTICE EXERCISES 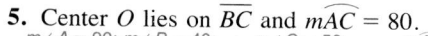 Use technology where appropriate.

Find the measures of the minor arcs and the angles of the triangle using the figure and information given in each exercise.

A

1. $m\angle A = 80$ and $m\overarc{AC} = 140$. $m\angle B = 70;$
   $m\angle C = 30;$ $\qquad m\overarc{AB} = 60; m\overarc{BC} = 160$
2. $m\overarc{BC} = 100$ and $m\overarc{AC} = 90$.
   $m\angle A = 50; m\angle B = 45; m\angle C = 85; m\overarc{AB} = 170$
3. $\triangle ABC$ is isosceles; vertex $\angle A$ measures $80°$.
   See side column.
4. $\overline{AB} \cong \overline{AC}$ and $m\overarc{BC} = 50$.

5. Center O lies on $\overline{BC}$ and $m\overarc{AC} = 80$.
   $m\angle A = 90; m\angle B = 40;$ $\qquad m\angle C = 50; m\overarc{AB} = 100; m\overarc{BC} = 180$
6. Center O lies on $\overline{AC}$ and $m\angle A = \frac{1}{2}m\angle C$.
   $m\angle A = 30; m\angle B = 90; m\angle C = 60;$ $\frac{1}{2} m\overarc{AB} = 120; m\overarc{AC} = 180; m\overarc{BC} = 60$
7. The measures of $\angle A$, $\angle B$, and $\angle C$ are in the ratio of $1:2:3$.
   $m\angle A = 30; m\angle B = 60;$ $\qquad m\angle C = 90; m\overarc{AB} = 180; m\overarc{AC} = 120; m\overarc{BC} = 60$
8. The measures of $\overarc{AB}$, $\overarc{BC}$, and $\overarc{CA}$ are in the ratio of $2:3:4$.
   $m\angle A = 60; m\angle B = 80;$ $\qquad m\angle C = 40; m\overarc{AB} = 80; m\overarc{BC} = 120;$ $m\overarc{CA} = 160$
9. $m\angle A = 50$ and $m\overarc{BC} = \frac{2}{5} m\overarc{AB}$.
   See side column.
10. $m\angle B = 90$ and $m\overarc{AB} = 10$.
    $m\angle A = 85; m\angle C = 5; m\overarc{AC} = 180; m\overarc{BC} = 170$

$\odot O$ **has chords** $\overline{AD}$, $\overline{AC}$, $\overline{BD}$, **and** $\overline{BC}$.

They intercept the same arc. They intercept the same arc.
11. Why is $\angle A \cong \angle B$? 12. Why is $\angle D \cong \angle C$?

13. If $\overline{AD} \parallel \overline{BC}$, which arcs are congruent? $\overarc{AB} \cong \overarc{DC}$

14. Name the similar triangles. Why aren't they congruent?
    $\triangle ADE \sim \triangle CBE$; corresponding sides $\ne$.

Quadrilateral $PQRS$ **is inscribed in** $\odot O$. **Find the measures of the minor arcs and of the angles of the quadrilateral using the information given.**

15. $m\overarc{RS} = 120$, $m\overarc{SP} = 50$, and $m\overarc{PQ} = 40$.
    $m\angle P = 135, m\angle Q = 85, m\angle R = 45, m\angle S = 95, m\overarc{QR} = 150$
16. $m\angle R = 64$, $m\angle S = 80$, $m\angle Q = 100$, and $m\overarc{RS} = 110$.
    $m\angle P = 116, m\overarc{PS} = 90, m\overarc{PQ} = 38,$ $\qquad m\overarc{QR} = 122$
17. $m\angle R = 70$, $m\angle S = 80$, and $m\overarc{PS} = 80$. See side column.

18. $m\angle R = 60$, $m\angle S = 70$, and $m\overarc{PS} = m\overarc{PQ}$.

B
19. $m\angle R = 60$, $m\angle S = 70$, and $m\overarc{PS} = m\overarc{PQ} + 10$.
    $m\angle P = 120, m\angle Q = 110, m\overarc{PS} = 65,$ $\qquad m\overarc{PQ} = 55,$ $\qquad m\overarc{QR} = 85, m\overarc{SR} = 155$
20. Center O lies on diagonal $\overline{QS}$, $m\overarc{PQ} = 70$, and $\overline{PQ} \cong \overline{QR}$. See side column.

21. Center O lies on diagonal $\overline{QS}$, $m\overarc{PQ} = 70$, and $\overline{RS} \cong \overline{QR}$.

22. Center O lies on diagonal $\overline{QS}$, $m\overarc{PQ} = 20$ less than $m\overarc{PS}$, and $RS = 2 \cdot QR$.
    $m\angle P = m\angle R = 90, m\angle Q = 110, m\angle S = 70, m\overarc{PQ} = 80, m\overarc{PS} = 100, m\overarc{RS} = 120, m\overarc{QR} = 60$
23. Find the measure of each arc of an inscribed regular hexagon. 60

24. Find the measure of each arc of an inscribed regular octagon. 45

See Additional Answers, p. 702.
Prove each of these corollaries of Theorem 9.9.

25. Corollary 1   26. Corollary 2   27. Corollary 3   28. Corollary 4

C
29. **Prove:** If a parallelogram is inscribed in a circle, then the parallelogram must be a rectangle.

9.4 Inscribed Angles **371**

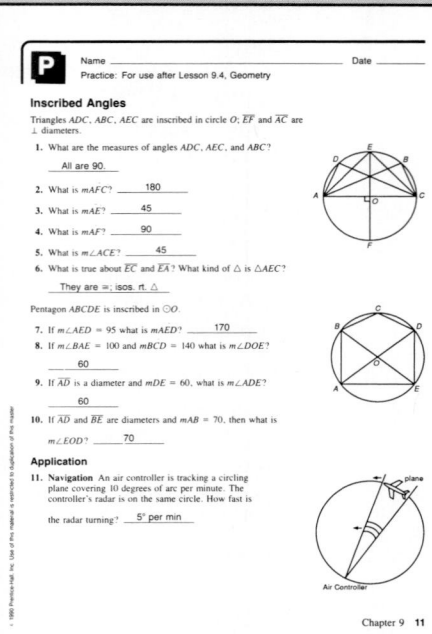

P Name _____ Date _____
Practice: For use after Lesson 9.4, Geometry

Inscribed Angles

Triangles ADC, ABC, AEC are inscribed in circle O; $\overline{EF}$ and $\overline{AC}$ are ⊥ diameters.

1. What are the measures of angles ADC, AEC, and ABC?
   All are 90.
2. What is mAFC? _____ 180 _____
3. What is mAE? _____ 45 _____
4. What is mAF? _____ 90 _____
5. What is m∠ACE? _____ 45 _____
6. What is true about $\overline{EC}$ and $\overline{EA}$? What kind of △ is △AEC?
   They are ≅; isos. rt. △

Pentagon ABCDE is inscribed in ⊙O.

7. If m∠AED = 95 what is m∠AED? _____ 170 _____
8. If m∠BAE = 100 and mBCD = 140 what is m∠DOE?
   _____ 60 _____
9. If $\overline{AD}$ is a diameter and mDE = 60, what is m∠ADE?
   _____ 60 _____
10. If $\overline{AD}$ and $\overline{BE}$ are diameters and mAB = 70, then what is
    m∠EOD? _____ 70 _____

Application

11. **Navigation** An air controller is tracking a circling plane covering 10 degrees of arc per minute. The controller's radar is on the same small circle. How fast is the radar turning? _____ 5° per min _____

Chapter 9   11

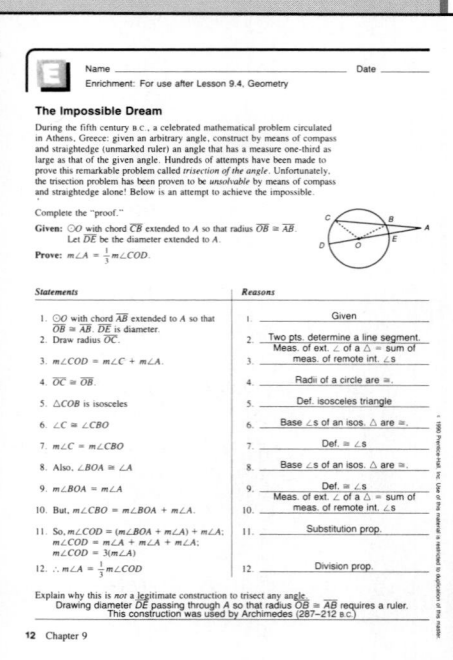

E Name _____ Date _____
Enrichment: For use after Lesson 9.4, Geometry

The Impossible Dream

During the fifth century B.C., a celebrated mathematical problem circulated in Athens, Greece: given an arbitrary angle, construct by means of compass and straightedge (unmarked ruler) an angle that has a measure one-third as large as that of the given angle. Hundreds of attempts have been made to prove this remarkable problem called *trisection of the angle*. Unfortunately, the trisection problem has been proven to be *unsolvable* by means of compass and straightedge alone! Below is an attempt to achieve the impossible.

Complete the "proof."

Given: ⊙O with chord $\overline{CB}$ extended to A so that radius $\overline{OB} ≅ \overline{AB}$.
Let $\overline{DE}$ be the diameter extended to A.

Prove: $m∠A = \frac{1}{3}m∠COD$.

Statements	Reasons
1. ⊙O with chord $\overline{AB}$ extended to A so that $\overline{OB} ≅ \overline{AB}$. $\overline{DE}$ is diameter.	1. _____ Given _____
2. Draw radius $\overline{OC}$.	2. Two pts. determine a line segment.
3. m∠COD = m∠C + m∠A.	3. Meas. of ext. ∠ of a △ = sum of meas. of remote int. ∠s
4. $\overline{OC} ≅ \overline{OB}$.	4. Radii of a circle are ≅.
5. △COB is isosceles	5. Def. isosceles triangle
6. ∠C ≅ ∠CBO	6. Base ∠s of an isos. △ are ≅.
7. m∠C = m∠CBO	7. Def. ≅ ∠s
8. Also, ∠BOA ≅ ∠A	8. Base ∠s of an isos. △ are ≅.
9. m∠BOA = m∠A	9. Def. ≅ ∠s
10. But, m∠CBO = m∠BOA + m∠A.	10. Meas. of ext. ∠ of a △ = sum of meas. of remote int. ∠s.
11. So, m∠COD = (m∠BOA + m∠A) + m∠A; m∠COD = m∠A + m∠A + m∠A; m∠COD = 3(m∠A)	11. Substitution prop.
12. ∴ m∠A = $\frac{1}{3}$ m∠COD	12. Division prop.

Explain why this is *not* a legitimate construction to trisect any angle.
Drawing diameter $\overline{DE}$ passing through A so that radius $\overline{OB} ≅ \overline{AB}$ requires a ruler.
This construction was used by Archimedes (287–212 B.C.)

12   Chapter 9

See Additional Answers, p. 702.

30. **Given:** $\overline{AD}$ and $\overline{AC}$ intersect ⊙O in points E, D, B, and C, as shown.
    Prove: $m∠4 = m∠C + m∠A$

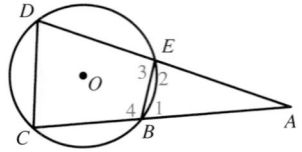

31. **Prove:** If two chords with a common endpoint on a circle are congruent, then the chord that bisects their included angle is a diameter of the circle.

32. **Prove:** A chord perpendicular to another chord at one endpoint is congruent to the chord perpendicular to the second chord's other endpoint.

Applications

33. **Design** An index card is placed on a small circle so that one corner lies on the circle and two adjacent sides intersect the circle. What happens if you connect those two points of intersection between the card and the circle? Explain.
The intercepted arc is a semi-⊙. The seg. is a diam of the ⊙.

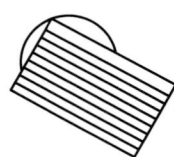

34. **Technology** Using Logo, inscribe a triangle, square, or hexagon in a circle. How would you change your procedure so that any regular *n*-gon could be inscribed? See Solutions Manual.

Developing Mathematical Power

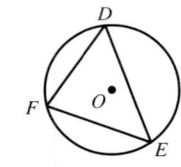

35. **Extension** △DEF is inscribed in ⊙O. Find a new method of proving that the sum of the measures of the angles of a triangle equals 180.
See Additional Answers, p. 702.

36. **Investigation** The *Moebius strip* is an unusual figure in mathematics. It was introduced by Ferdinand Moebius in the late eighteenth century. Give a one-half twist to a piece of paper 1 in. wide and at least 6 in. long, and tape the ends together. Without lifting your pencil, draw a line down the center of the strip until you return to your starting point.

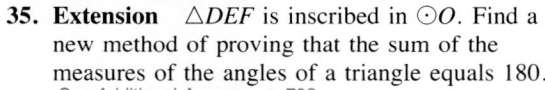

What do you observe? The line is continuous and closed. There is no "second side" to the strip.
Because of this result, the Moebius strip is said to have only one side. Now carefully cut along the line. What happens? The result is a strip with 2 twists and 2 sides.
Make another Moebius strip that is at least 8 in. long before taping, and 1 to $1\frac{1}{2}$ in. wide. Cut along a line, staying $\frac{1}{2}$ in. from the edge of the strip.
Do you get the same result as before? no; 2 interconnected strips, 1 one-sided and 1 two-sided

372   Chapter 9 Circles

9.5 Tangents, Secants, and Angles

Objective: To solve problems and prove statements involving angles formed by chords, secants, and tangents

Central angles and inscribed angles are measured in relation to their intercepted arcs. Several other types of angles are associated with circles and are also measured in terms of the arcs that they intercept.

Investigation—*Thinking Critically*

In circle O, $\angle AXD$ is neither a central angle nor an inscribed angle.

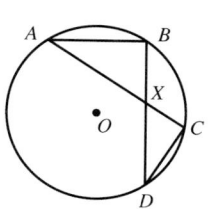

1. Relate $\angle AXD$ to the inscribed angles of $\triangle ABX$. Write an equation to show this relationship.
$m\angle AXD = m\angle A + m\angle B$
2. Rewrite the equation by using the relationship between the arc measures and the inscribed angle measures of $\triangle ABX$. $m\angle AXD = \frac{1}{2}m\widehat{BC} + \frac{1}{2}m\widehat{AD}$
3. Relate the inscribed angles to $\triangle DCX$. $m\angle AXD = m\angle C + m\angle D$
$= \frac{1}{2}m\widehat{AD} + \frac{1}{2}m\widehat{BC}$
4. What generalizations can you make? The meas. of an $\angle$ formed by 2 chords that intersect inside a $\odot$ is $\frac{1}{2}$ the sum of the meas. of the intercepted arcs.

Auxiliary lines are helpful in the proofs of the following theorems.

Theorem 9.10 If two chords intersect within a circle, then the measure of the angle formed is equal to one-half the sum of the measures of the intercepted arcs.

Given: Chords $\overline{AC}$ and $\overline{BD}$ intersecting within $\odot O$

Prove: $m\angle AXD = \frac{1}{2}(m\widehat{BC} + m\widehat{DA})$

Plan: Draw $\overline{AB}$ to form $\triangle ABX$. $m\angle A = \frac{1}{2}m\widehat{BC}$, and $m\angle B = \frac{1}{2}m\widehat{DA}$. Now use the fact that $\angle AXD$ is an exterior angle of $\triangle ABX$. Proved in Practice Exercise 14

The proofs of Theorems 9.11 and 9.12 involve more than one case. The plans are shown for two cases of Theorem 9.11. Only the first of three cases is planned for Theorem 9.12.

9.5 Tangents, Secants, and Angles   **373**

Developing Mathematical Power

Cooperative Learning Working in groups, students can complete the Critical Thinking activity, p. 9, in the *Teacher's Resource Book.* Allow time for groups to discuss ideas and illustrations. Elicit from students the criteria they used to determine all possible alternatives.

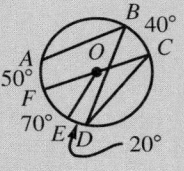
373

When applying Theorem 9.10, point out that when two chords of a circle intersect, the measure of an angle formed must be equal to its vertical angle. That would be impossible if one *subtracted* arc measures. When applying Theorem 9.12 to two tangents, students should see that *adding* the arc measures would always lead to a measure of 180 for the angle formed by the tangents, which is impossible.

CHALKBOARD EXAMPLES

• For the Example

$\overline{ET}$ and $\overline{EP}$ are tangent to $\odot O$ at T and P. $\overline{BA} \parallel \overline{EP}$, $m\widehat{BT} = 40$, and $m\angle BPE = 49$. Find $m\widehat{BP}$, $m\widehat{AP}$, $m\widehat{AT}$, $m\angle TCA$, $m\angle ABP$, and $m\angle E$.

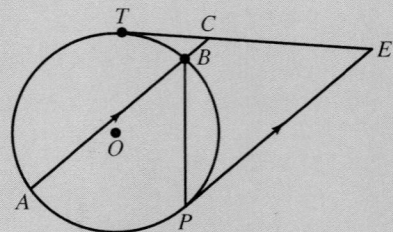

$m\widehat{BP} = m\widehat{AP} = 98$;
$m\widehat{AT} = 360 - (98 + 98 + 40) = 124$;
$m\angle TCA = 42$; $m\angle ABP = 49$; $m\angle E = 42$

Common Error

- Students may confuse Theorems 9.10 and 9.12, therefore not knowing whether to add or subtract arc measures. Have these students place any 2 points on a circle. From these points, draw 2 lines that intersect within the circle and 2 lines that intersect beyond the circle. In measuring the 2 angles, they should see that the angle on the exterior is smaller and thus is the one that is found by subtraction.
- See *Teacher's Resource Book* for additional remediation.

Theorem 9.11 If a tangent and a chord intersect in a point on the circle, then the measure of the angle they form is one-half the measure of the intercepted arc.

Given: $\odot O$ with chord $\overline{PR}$ and tangent $\overleftrightarrow{PT}$
Prove: $m\angle RPT = \frac{1}{2}m\widehat{RP}$

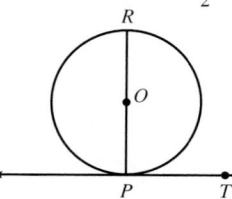 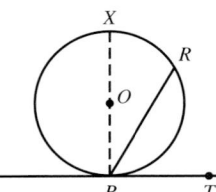 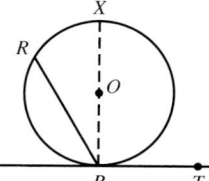

Plan (Case 1):
Since $\overline{RP}$ is a diameter, $\widehat{RP}$ is a semicircle and $m\widehat{RP} = 180$.
Since $\overline{RP} \perp \overleftrightarrow{PT}$, $m\angle RPT = 90$. The conclusion follows.

Plan (Case 2):
Draw diameter $\overline{XP}$. From Case 1, $m\angle XPT = \frac{1}{2}m\widehat{XRP}$. Use
Th. 9.9 to show that $m\angle RPT = \frac{1}{2}m\widehat{RP}$. (Proof of Case 3 is similar.)
Case 3 planned in Class Exercise 7 and Cases 1–3 proved in Practice Exercises 6, 7, and 13

Theorem 9.12 If a tangent and a secant, two secants, or two tangents intersect in a point in the exterior of a circle, then the measure of the angle formed is equal to one-half the difference of the measures of the intercepted arcs.

Given: $\odot O$ with tangent $\overrightarrow{PT}$ and secant $\overrightarrow{PB}$
Prove: $m\angle P = \frac{1}{2}(m\widehat{BT} - m\widehat{AT})$

Plan (Case 1):
Draw $\overline{AT}$. $m\angle BAT = \frac{1}{2}m\widehat{BT}$ and $m\angle ATP = \frac{1}{2}m\widehat{AT}$.
Now use the fact that $\angle BAT$ is an exterior angle of $\triangle ATP$ to reach the desired conclusion. Proved in Practice Exercises 15–17

EXAMPLE $\overrightarrow{ZY}$ is tangent to $\odot O$ at D.
$m\widehat{AD} = 90$, $m\widehat{DC} = 50$,
$m\widehat{CB} = 80$. Find $m\angle 1$,
$m\angle 2$, and $m\angle 3$.

374 Chapter 9 Circles

Developing Mathematical Power

Keeping a Portfolio Students should summarize the concepts in Lesson 9.1–Lesson 9.5. Have them identify the main ideas and organize the theorems in a way that will make them easy to remember.

$$m\angle 1 = \frac{1}{2}(m\widehat{AD} - m\widehat{DC})$$
$$= \frac{1}{2}(90 - 50)$$
$$= 20$$

$$m\angle 2 = \frac{1}{2}m\widehat{BD}$$
$$= \frac{1}{2}(m\widehat{DC} + m\widehat{CB})$$
$$= \frac{1}{2}(50 + 80) = 65$$

$$m\angle 3 = \frac{1}{2}(m\widehat{AB} + m\widehat{DC})$$
$$= \frac{1}{2}(140 + 50)$$
$$= 95$$

CLASS EXERCISES

Find the indicated measures, using the given chords, secants, and/or tangents.

1.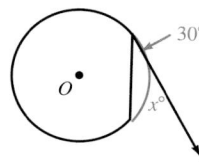

x = 60

2.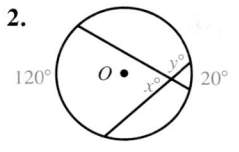

x = 70
y = 110

3.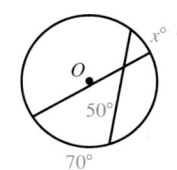

x = 30

4.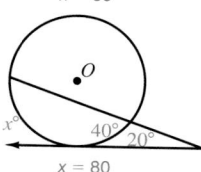

x = 80

5.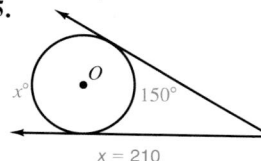

x = 210

6.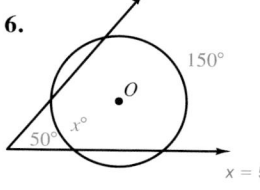

x = 50

7. Write a Plan for Case 3 of Theorem 9.11. See side column.

PRACTICE EXERCISES   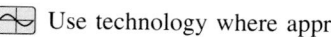 Use technology where appropriate.

Find the indicated measures, using the given chords, secants, and/or tangents.

A

1.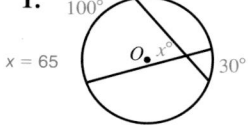

x = 65

2.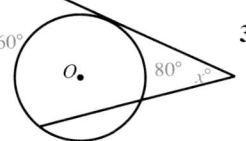

x = 40

3.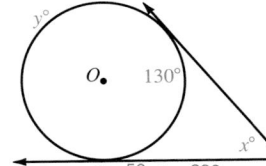

x = 50, y = 230

Find the measures of the indicated arcs and numbered angles.

4.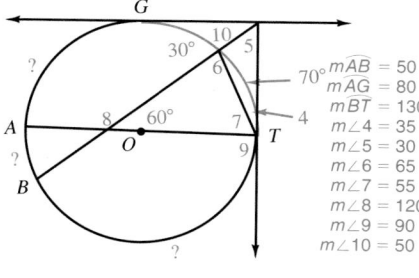

$m\widehat{AB} = 50$
$m\widehat{AG} = 80$
$m\widehat{BT} = 130$
$m\angle 4 = 35$
$m\angle 5 = 30$
$m\angle 6 = 65$
$m\angle 7 = 55$
$m\angle 8 = 120$
$m\angle 9 = 90$
$m\angle 10 = 50$

5.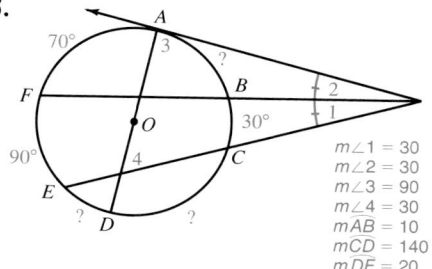

$m\angle 1 = 30$
$m\angle 2 = 30$
$m\angle 3 = 90$
$m\angle 4 = 30$
$m\widehat{AB} = 10$
$m\widehat{CD} = 140$
$m\widehat{DE} = 20$

9.5 Tangents, Secants, and Angles   **375**

LESSON FOLLOW-UP

Assignment Guide
See p. 350B for assignments.

Additional Answers

7. Plan (Case 3):
Draw diam. $\overline{YP}$. By Case 1, $m\angle YPT = \frac{1}{2}m\widehat{YP}$. Since $\angle YPR$ is inscribed, $m\angle YPR = \frac{1}{2}m\widehat{RY}$. Then use Th. 9.9 to show $m\angle RPT = \frac{1}{2}m\widehat{RYT}$.

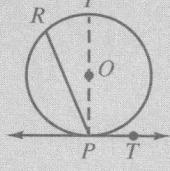

Additional Answers for p. 376

6. Proof:

Statements	Reasons
1. In $\odot O$, $\overline{RP}$ is a diam.; $\overleftrightarrow{PT}$ is a tan.	1. Given
2. $\overline{RP}$ is a semi-$\odot$	2. Def. of semi-$\odot$
3. $m\widehat{RP} = 180$	3. Meas. of a semi-$\odot$ = 180°.
4. $\frac{1}{2}m\widehat{RP} = 90$	4. Mult. prop.
5. $\overline{RP} \perp \overleftrightarrow{PT}$	5. Th 9.1
6. $\angle RPT$ is a rt. $\angle$.	6. Def. of $\perp$
7. $m\angle RPT = 90$	7. Def. of rt. $\angle$
8. $m\angle RPT = \frac{1}{2}m\widehat{RP}$	8. Trans. prop.

Conclusion: If a tan. and a diam. intersect, the meas. of the $\angle$ formed $= \frac{1}{2}$ the meas. of the intercepted arc.

1. If $m\overarc{AC} = 60$ and $m\overarc{ADB} = 2m\overarc{BC}$, find $m\overarc{ADB}$, $m\overarc{BC}$, and the measure of each numbered angle.

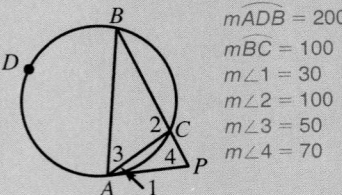

$m\overarc{ADB} = 200$
$m\overarc{BC} = 100$
$m\angle 1 = 30$
$m\angle 2 = 100$
$m\angle 3 = 50$
$m\angle 4 = 70$

2. $m\overarc{DR} = 50$, $m\overarc{HR} = 90$, and $m\angle HFG = 85$. Find $m\overarc{GH}$, $m\overarc{DG}$, $m\angle E$, and $m\angle ERG$.

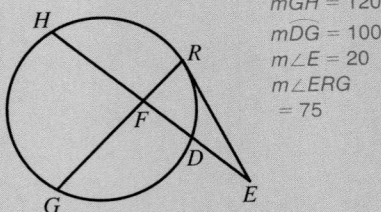

$m\overarc{GH} = 120$
$m\overarc{DG} = 100$
$m\angle E = 20$
$m\angle ERG = 75$

Enrichment

The measure of an angle formed by two tangents to a circle is x. In terms of x find the measures of the two intercepted arcs. Let y and $360 - y$ be the measures of the arcs. Then $x = \frac{1}{2}[(360 - y) - y] = 180 - y$, so $y = 180 - x$ and $360 - y = 180 + x$. The measures of the arcs are $180 - x$ and $180 + x$.

6. Prove Case 1 of Theorem 9.11 based on the given Plan. See side column page 375.

7. Prove Case 2 of Theorem 9.11 based on the given Plan. See Additional Answers, p. 702.

In Exercises 8–10, the secant to the circle contains the center.

8. Find the measure of the angle formed by the secant and a tangent if the smaller intercepted arc measures 30°. 60

9. Find the measure of the angle formed by the secant and a tangent if the larger intercepted arc measures 130°. 40

10. Find the measures of the intercepted arcs and the angle formed by the secant and a tangent if one intercepted arc is 30° more than the other. 75, 105; $m\angle = 15$

11. The measure of the angle formed by two tangents to a circle is 60. Find the measures of the intercepted arcs. 240, 120

12. One of the congruent sides of an isosceles trapezoid inscribed in a circle intercepts an 80° arc. What are the measures of the angles formed by the diagonals of the trapezoid? 80, 100

13. Prove Case 3 of Theorem 9.11. See Additional Answers, p. 702.

Use the figure, Given, Prove, and Plan to write a proof.

B **14.** Theorem 9.10   **15.** Case 1 of Theorem 9.12

Use the given figures to prove the following cases of Theorem 9.12.

16. Case 2 (two secants)

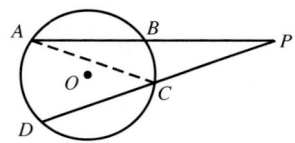

17. Case 3 (two tangents)

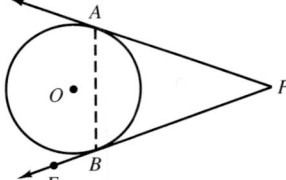

18. Prove that a trapezoid inscribed in a circle is isosceles.

19. Prove that if an equilateral triangle is inscribed in a circle, the tangents to the vertices of the triangle form an equilateral triangle.

C **20.** Theorem 9.10 can also be proven using an auxiliary segment parallel to one of the intersecting chords. Write that proof.

21. Prove that if an isosceles triangle is inscribed in a circle, the tangent to the circle at the vertex angle is parallel to the base of the triangle.

22. One of the parallel sides of an isosceles trapezoid inscribed in a circle intercepts an arc of 50°, while the other is a diameter. Find the measures of the angles formed by the trapezoid's diagonals. 65, 115

Applications

23. Technology Using Logo, circumscribe a circle with a triangle, square, or hexagon. Refine your procedure so that you can circumscribe a circle with any regular *n*-gon. See Solutions Manual.

24. Sports Apply the angle-measure theorems to the angles as seen by a point-after-touchdown kicker in a football game. See below.

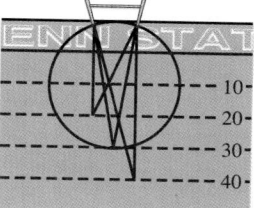

Algebra Review

Factor the polynomial.

25. $x^2 + 10x + 9$
$(x + 9)(x + 1)$

26. $x^2 + 6x + 8$
$(x + 4)(x + 2)$

27. $x^2 - 10x + 21$
$(x - 3)(x - 7)$

28. $x^2 - 11x + 24$
$(x - 3)(x - 8)$

29. $x^2 - 36$
$(x - 6)(x + 6)$

30. $x^2 + 8x + 16$
$(x + 4)(x + 4)$

31. $x^2 + 2x - 15$
$(x + 5)(x - 3)$

32. $x^2 - 3x - 18$
$(x - 6)(x + 3)$

33. $x^2 + x - 6$
$(x + 3)(x - 2)$

Solve. Check your solutions.

34. $x^2 = 81$
$x = 9, x = -9$

35. $x^2 - 11x = 12$
$x = -1, x = 12$

36. $x^2 - 5x = -4$
$x = 4, x = 1$

37. $x^2 - 20 = x$
$x = 5, x = -4$

38. $x^2 + x = 30$
$x = -6, x = 5$

39. $x^2 - 4x = 32$
$x = -4, x = 8$

CONSTRUCTIONS

Construct a tangent to a circle from a point not on the circle.

Given: ⊙O and point P not on ⊙O   *Construct:* A tangent from P to ⊙O

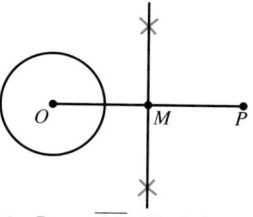

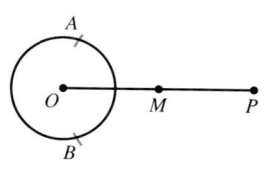

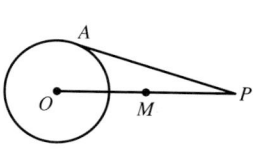

1. Draw $\overline{OP}$. Find the midpoint M of $\overline{OP}$.

2. With center M and radius OM, draw $\overline{AB}$. Label A and B.

3. Draw $\overline{PA}$. $\overline{PA}$ is tangent to ⊙O at point A.

EXERCISE: *Given:* ⊙Q and point R not on ⊙Q   *Construct:* A tangent from R to ⊙Q

Answers may vary but should reproduce the constr. shown.

9.5 Tangents, Secants, and Angles   **377**

24. Consider a circle containing points that are the bases of the goal posts. Consider the position of the football as the vertex of an angle that intercepts the arc whose endpoints are the posts. If the position of the football is inside the ⊙, the ∠ and intercepted arc formed are larger than any ∠ and intercepted arc formed by the football positioned outside the ⊙. The larger the ∠ and intercepted arc, the greater the chance of success.

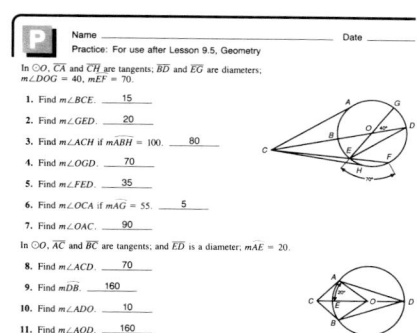
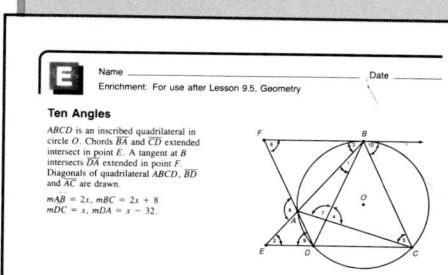

Materials/Manipulatives
Compasses and straightedges
*Teaching Transparencies 61 and
61A*

Technology
*Computer Test Bank, pp.
578–582*

LESSON FOCUS

Review
Remind students that proofs of many theorems are facilitated by using an auxiliary segment; this has been particularly true of the proofs involving circles and segments and angles associated with them. Briefly review segments that might be useful in proving theorems about circles (for example, radii, chords, tangents, secants, internal or external tangents) and also review theorems that highlight relationships among segments, angles, and arcs in circles.

Alternative Learning Styles
Some students may have difficulty visualizing the auxiliary figures needed to prove a statement. They should focus on what is given and what needs to be proved. Suggest that they use a different color for the auxiliary lines and figure(s).

Critical Thinking
Comprehension Ask students to explain the importance of auxiliary figures in proofs involving circles and related segments and angles.

9.6 Strategy: Use an Auxiliary Figure

Auxiliary figures can facilitate the solution of problems or proofs. The problem solving steps can aid in the selection and use of auxiliary figures.

EXAMPLE 1 A navigational map shows that there are unsafe waters within the 280° arc of $\odot O$. Lighthouses X and Y are at the endpoints of $\overarc{XWY}$. Using the boat as an angle vertex and a sextant to measure angles, a navigator can keep a boat in safe waters. What are the measures of angles in safe waters? in unsafe waters? on the border between safe and unsafe waters?

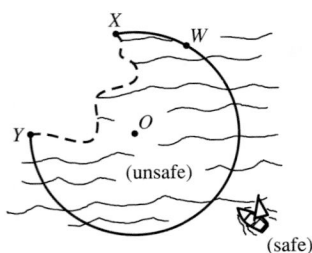

Understand the Problem
What are the given facts?
$m\overarc{XWY} = 280$. It is safe outside this arc and unsafe inside. A navigator can measure angles with the boat as vertex.
What is the question?
For which angle measures is the boat inside, on, or outside $\odot O$?

Plan Your Approach
Sketch a figure to explore angles and measures related to circles.
Draw auxiliary lines.
1. Inside $\odot O$, angles formed by intersecting chords:
$$m\angle XIY = \frac{1}{2}(m\overarc{XY} + m\overarc{CD})$$
2. On $\odot O$, inscribed angles:
$$m\angle XAY = \frac{1}{2}m\overarc{XY}$$
3. Outside $\odot O$, angles formed by intersecting tangents and/or secants: $m\angle XEY = \frac{1}{2}(m\overarc{XY} - m\overarc{FG})$

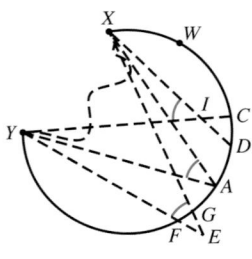

Implement the Plan
Use the given information to calculate each angle measure.
1. $m\angle XIY = \frac{1}{2}(80 + m\overarc{CD})$ 2. $m\angle XAY = \frac{1}{2}(80)$
3. $m\angle XEY = \frac{1}{2}(80 - m\overarc{FG})$

378   Chapter 9 Circles

Developing Mathematical Power
Cooperative Learning Assign groups of students to complete Practice Exercises 1–8. Each member of the group should draw the figure and auxiliary figure for Exercises 1–4. Then the group should discuss and agree on the best one to use before checking. Have the groups share with the class their proofs of Exercises 5–8.

Compare the angle measures.

1. $m\angle XIY$ is always > 40.   **2.** $m\angle XAY$ is always $= 40$.

3. $m\angle XEY$ is always < 40.

Interpret the Results

Draw a conclusion.
If the boat is the vertex of an angle greater than 40°, it is in unsafe waters; if the angle is less than 40°, it is in safe waters. If the angle is equal to 40°, the boat is on the border between safe and unsafe waters.

Generalize.
In the plane of a given circle, if the same arc is intercepted by an angle whose vertex is in the circle's interior, an inscribed angle, and an angle whose vertex is in the circle's exterior, then the interior angle is the largest and the exterior angle is the smallest.

Problem Solving Reminders

- The figure for a problem or proof may suggest the most appropriate auxiliary figure(s) to provide.
- When there is a choice of possible auxiliary figures, try each and decide which leads most readily to the conclusion or solution.

EXAMPLE 2   Two congruent circles are tangent externally at a point T. A secant to both circles passes through T. Prove that the chords created by the secant are congruent.

Understand the Problem

Draw a figure. State the *Given* and *Prove*.

Given: $\odot O \cong \odot Q$; $\overleftrightarrow{AB}$ is a secant through tangent point T.

Prove: $\overline{AT} \cong \overline{TB}$

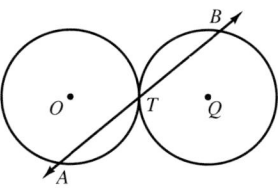

Plan Your Approach

Look Ahead.
The *Given* contains no information about arcs that might lead to congruent chords.

9.6 Strategy: Use an Auxiliary Figure   **379**

TEACHING SUGGESTION

TEACHING SUGGESTION

In Example 1, tell students that the angle at A ($\angle XAY$) is called the "horizontal danger angle." It is a tool used by ships' navigators to position ships close to dangerous shorelines.

- **For Example 1**
  A garden is bounded by four sidewalks as shown. How can a sidewalk having the shape of a circle be constructed to be tangent to $\overline{XY}$ at A and also tangent to $\overline{YZ}$?

  Const. the $\perp$ to $\overline{XY}$ at A and the bis. of $\angle Y$. Their intersection is the center O of the $\odot$, and OA is the radius length.

  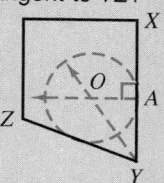

- **For Example 2**
  Given: $\overleftrightarrow{PQ}$ tan. $\odot O$ at M, the midpt. of $\overarc{AB}$.
  Prove: $\overleftrightarrow{PQ} \parallel \overline{AB}$

  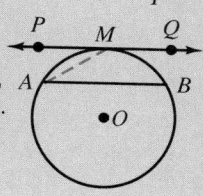

  Plan: Draw $\overline{AM}$. $m\angle PMA = (\tfrac{1}{2})m\overarc{AM} = (\tfrac{1}{2})m\overarc{MB} = m\angle MAB$. The conclusion follows.

Proof:

Statements	Reasons
1. $\overleftrightarrow{PQ}$ tan. $\odot O$ at M, the midpt. of $\overarc{AB}$.	1. Given
2. $\overarc{AM} \cong \overarc{MB}$	2. Def. of midpt. of an arc
3. $m\overarc{AM} = m\overarc{MB}$	3. Def. of $\cong$ arcs
4. $(\tfrac{1}{2})m\overarc{AM} = (\tfrac{1}{2})m\overarc{MB}$	4. Mult. prop. of $=$
5. Draw $\overline{AM}$.	5. Two pts. determine a line
6. $m\angle PMA = (\tfrac{1}{2})m\overarc{AM}$	6. $m\angle$ formed by a chord and a tan. $= \tfrac{1}{2}m$(int. arc)
7. $m\angle MAB = (\tfrac{1}{2})m\overarc{MB}$	7. m(inscribed $\angle$) $= \tfrac{1}{2}m$(int. arc)
8. $m\angle PMA = m\angle MAB$	8. Subst. prop.

9. $\angle PMA \cong \angle MAB$	9. Def. of $\cong \angle$s
10. $\overleftrightarrow{PQ} \parallel \overline{AB}$	10. If 2 lines have a trans. such that alt. int. $\angle$s are $\cong$, the lines are $\parallel$.

Conclusion: A line tan. to a $\odot$ at the midpt. of an arc is $\parallel$ to the chord of the arc.

Common Error

- Some students choose random auxiliary segments. Be sure that they plan the proof to check on the usefulness of the segment
- See *Teacher's Resource Book* for additional remediation.

LESSON FOLLOW-UP

Assignment Guide

See p. 350B for assignments.

Project

Students might benefit from working out this problem in pairs.

Lesson Quiz

Give a plan for proof.
Given: $\odot O$ and $\odot O'$ are ext. tan. at X; $\overline{YZ}$ is a common ext. tan.; $\overline{XY}$ and $\overline{ZX}$ are chords.
Prove: $\angle YXZ$ is a right angle.

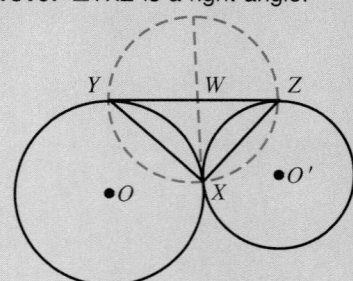

Plan: Draw $\overline{XW}$, the common int. tan., intersecting $\overline{YZ}$ at W. Afer showing that $WY = WX = WZ$, consider $\odot W$ with radius length WY. Since $\overline{YZ}$ is a diam. of this $\odot$, $\angle YXZ$ is inscribed in a semicircle and is thus a rt. $\angle$.

Look Back.

There are several theorems that conclude that two chords of congruent circles are congruent. If it could be shown that $\overset{\frown}{AT}$ and $\overset{\frown}{TB}$ are intercepted by congruent angles of the same type, then $\overset{\frown}{AT}$ and $\overset{\frown}{TB}$ wo be congruent and the conclusion would follow.

Plan: Draw $\overleftrightarrow{XY}$, a common internal tangent to $\odot O$ and $\odot Q$. Then vertical angles BTX and ATY are formed that intercept arcs AT and TB. Hence, $\overset{\frown}{AT} \cong \overset{\frown}{TB}$ and $\overline{AT} \cong \overline{TB}$.

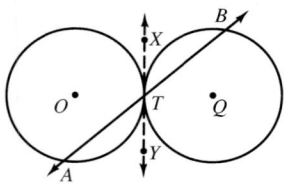

Implement the Plan

Proof:

Statements	Reasons
1. Draw $\overleftrightarrow{XT}$, a common internal tan. to $\odot O$ and $\odot Q$.	1. Def. of tan.
2. $\angle ATY \cong \angle BTX$	2. Vertical $\angle$s are $\cong$.
3. $m\angle ATY = m\angle BTX$	3. Def. of $\cong \angle$s
4. $m\angle ATY = \frac{1}{2}m\overset{\frown}{AT}$ $m\angle BTX = \frac{1}{2}m\overset{\frown}{BT}$	4. The measure of an $\angle$ forme by a chord and a tan. $= \frac{1}{2}$ tl measure of the intercepted a
5. $\frac{1}{2}m\overset{\frown}{AT} = \frac{1}{2}m\overset{\frown}{BT}$	5. Trans. prop.
6. $m\overset{\frown}{AT} = m\overset{\frown}{BT}$	6. Mult. prop.
7. $\overset{\frown}{AT} \cong \overset{\frown}{BT}$	7. Def. of $\cong$ arcs
8. $\overline{AT} \cong \overline{BT}$	8. In $\cong$ circles, $\cong$ arcs have $\cong$ chords.

Interpret the Results

Any secant that passes through the point of tangency of two congruent externally tangent circles creates congruent chords.

CLASS EXERCISES See page 758.

Sketch figures for these previously proven theorems from this chapter. Draw auxiliary figures needed to do the proofs. Check your work by looking up the figures used in the plans and/or proofs.

1. Two tangent segments from a common external point are congruent.

2. If a diameter is perpendicular to a chord, then it bisects the chord and its arc.

380   Chapter 9 Circles

Sketch figures for these theorems. Draw auxiliary figures. Check your work by looking up the figures used in the plans and/or proofs.

1. The measure of an inscribed angle is equal to one-half the measure of its intercepted arc.

2. If two arcs of a circle are included between parallel segments, then the arcs are congruent.

3. If a tangent and a chord intersect in a point on the circle, then the measure of the angle they form is one-half the measure of the intercepted arc.

4. The measure of an angle formed by two chords that intersect within a circle is equal to one-half of the sum of the measures of the intercepted arcs.

5. **Given:** $\odot O$ and $\odot Q$ are externally tangent at T; $\overline{AB}$ and $\overline{CD}$, are secants through T.
   Prove: $\overline{AC} \parallel \overline{DB}$

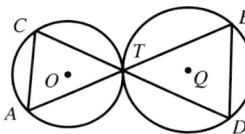

6. **Given:** any $\triangle ABC$ inscribed in $\odot O$; $\overline{OX} \perp \overline{AB}$
   Prove: $\angle BOX \cong \angle C$

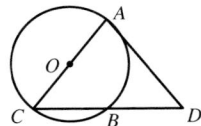

7. **Given:** $\triangle ACD$ is isosceles with base $\overline{CD}$; $\overline{AC}$ is a diameter of $\odot O$.
   Prove: $\overarc{BC}$ bisects $\overline{CD}$.

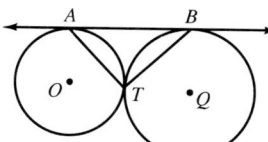

8. **Given:** $\odot O$ and $\odot Q$ are externally tangent at T; $\overleftrightarrow{AB}$ is their common external tangent.
   Prove: $\triangle ATB$ is a right triangle.

PROJECT

Rewrite Example 1, changing the boat to an airship and the circle to a sphere. Would the solution change? How? See Solutions Manual.

9.6 Strategy: Use an Auxiliary Figure **381**

Teacher's Resource Book

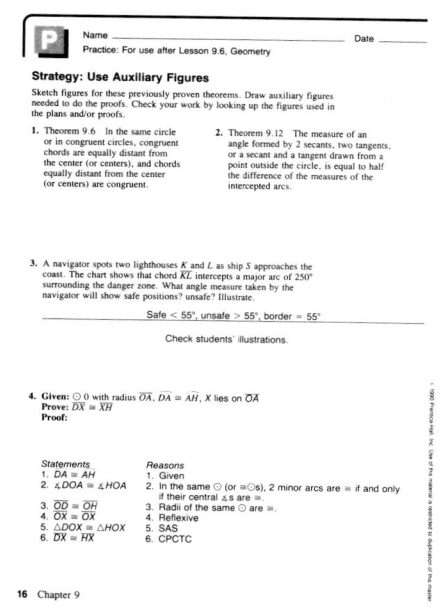

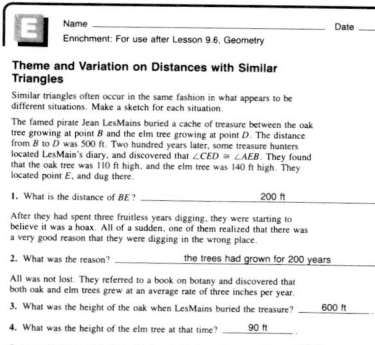

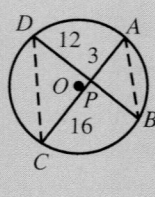
9.7 Circles and Segment Lengths

Objectives: To prove and apply theorems relating lengths of chords, secant segments, and tangent segments
To find ratios and products of lengths of segments related to a circle

The properties of similar triangles can be used to prove numerical relationships existing among the segment lengths formed by two intersecting chords, two intersecting secants, and an intersecting secant and tangent.

Investigation—*Visualizing the Concept*

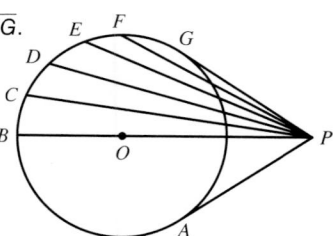

1. Measure $\overline{PA}$, $\overline{PB}$, $\overline{PC}$, $\overline{PD}$, $\overline{PE}$, $\overline{PF}$, and $\overline{PG}$.

2. Are any of these segments congruent? What kinds of segments are they?
   $\overline{PG} \cong \overline{PA}$; tan. seg.

3. Which secant is longest? Why?
   $\overline{PB}$; it contains the longest chord (the diam.).

4. Which secant is shortest? Why?
   $\overline{PF}$; it contains the chord farthest from the center.

5. Are there any segments shorter than the shortest secant? Why? Only the tan. seg.; the segs. are even farther from the center.

Theorem 9.13 If two chords intersect inside a circle, then the product of the lengths of the segments of one chord is equal to the product of the lengths of the segments of the other chord.

Given: Chords $\overline{AC}$ and $\overline{BD}$ intersect at P.

Prove: $AP \cdot PC = BP \cdot PD$

Plan: Draw $\overline{DC}$ and $\overline{AB}$. Show that $\triangle APB \sim \triangle DPC$.

Thus, $\dfrac{AP}{PD} = \dfrac{BP}{PC}$ and the conclusion follows.

Proved in Practice Exercise 15

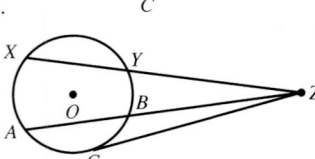

In the figure, $\overline{XZ}$ and $\overline{AZ}$ are *secant segments* and $\overline{CZ}$ is a *tangent segment*. $\overline{YZ}$ and $\overline{BZ}$ are the *external segments* of $\overline{XZ}$ and $\overline{AZ}$, respectively.

Developing Mathematical Power
Cooperative Learning   The Project, pp. 25 and 26, in *Connections* can be done with students working in small groups. Have them research R. Buckminster Fuller in addition to creating the various geodesic domes described.

Theorem 9.14 If two secants intersect in the exterior of a circle, then the product of the lengths of one secant segment and its external segment is equal to the product of the lengths of the other secant segment and its external segment.

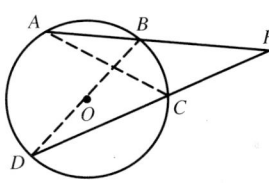

Given: Secants $\overline{AP}$ and $\overline{DP}$ with external segments $\overline{PB}$ and $\overline{PC}$

Prove: $AP \cdot PB = DP \cdot PC$

Plan: Draw $\overline{AC}$ and $\overline{BD}$. Show $\triangle APC \sim \triangle DPB$. Thus, $\dfrac{AP}{DP} = \dfrac{PC}{PB}$ and the conclusion follows.
Proved in Practice Exercise 16

Theorem 9.15 If a secant and a tangent intersect in the exterior of a circle, then the product of the lengths of the secant segment and its external segment is equal to the square of the length of the tangent segment.

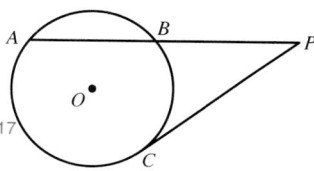

Given: Tangent $\overline{CP}$ and secant $\overline{AP}$ with external segment $\overline{BP}$

Prove: $AP \cdot BP = CP^2$
Planned in Class Exercise 7; proved in Practice Exercise 17

EXAMPLE 1 Find x to the nearest tenth.

a.
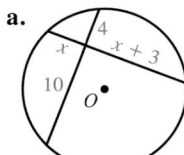

b.
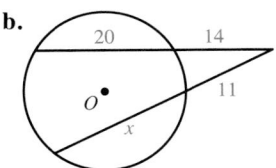

c.
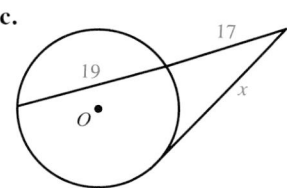

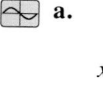

a. $\begin{aligned} x(x+3) &= 4 \cdot 10 \\ x^2 + 3x &= 40 \\ x^2 + 3x - 40 &= 0 \\ (x+8)(x-5) &= 0 \\ x &= 5 \end{aligned}$

b. $\begin{aligned} 11(x+11) &= 14(20+14) \\ 11x + 121 &= 476 \\ 11x &= 355 \\ x &\approx 32.3 \end{aligned}$

c. $\begin{aligned} x^2 &= 17(17+19) \\ x^2 &= 612 \\ x &\approx 24.7 \end{aligned}$

Developing Mathematical Power

Keeping a Portfolio Have students write a brief paragraph in which they describe what previously learned concepts they needed to understand this lesson and why. They should be specific in showing the correlation between these concepts and the new material.

TEACHING SUGGESTIONS

- Point out that Theorems 9.13 and 9.14 can be thought of as *one* statement: If A, B, C, and D are points of a circle, and $\overleftrightarrow{AC}$ and $\overleftrightarrow{BD}$ intersect at a point P that is in the interior or exterior of a circle, then $AP \cdot PC = BP \cdot PD$.
- Make sure that students understand why $x = -8$ is rejected in Example 1a.

CHALKBOARD EXAMPLES

- **For Example 1**
Find x and the lengths of each chord, secant segment, and tangent segment.

a.
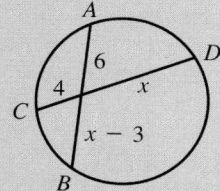

b.
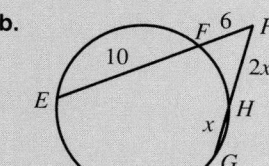

c.
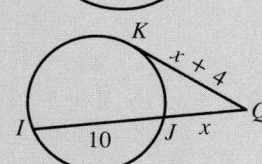

a. $4x = 6(x-3)$
   $x = 9$
   $AB = 12;\ CD = 13$

b. $6(10+6) = 2x(3x)$
   $x = 4$
   $EP = 16;\ GP = 12$

c. $x(x+10) = (x+4)^2$
   $x = 8$
   $KQ = 12;\ IQ = 18$

383

384

- **For Example 2**

Find *x*, *PT*, *LP*, and *MP* if:

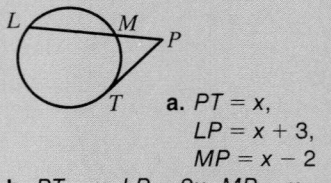

a. $PT = x$,
$LP = x + 3$,
$MP = x - 2$
b. $PT = x$, $LP = 2x$, $MP = x - 4$

a. $x^2 = (x + 3)(x - 2)$
$x = 6$
$PT = 6$; $LP = 9$; $MP = 4$
b. $x^2 = 2x(x - 4)$
$x = 8$ or $x = 0$ (reject)
$PT = 8$; $LP = 16$; $MP = 4$

Common Error

- Students might confuse Theorems 9.13, 9.14, and 9.15. Encourage them to draw diagrams in order to determine similar triangles, rather than trying to memorize theorems.
- See *Teacher's Resource Book* for additional remediation.

LESSON FOLLOW-UP

Discussion

When two secants to a sphere, such as $\overline{PR}$ and $\overline{PT}$, intersect outside the sphere, is it still true that $PR \cdot PQ = PT \cdot PS$?

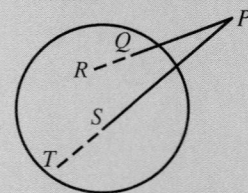

The ensuing discussion will review not only this lesson, but also the fact that two intersecting lines lie in exactly one plane. The intersection of that plane and the sphere is a circle.

EXAMPLE 2 In making this design, *PA* must be 16 and *PB* must be 6. *P*, *C*, and *D* can be located in either of two ways.

a. $PC = 8$ **b.** $PC = CD$

In both cases, find *PD* to the nearest hundredth.

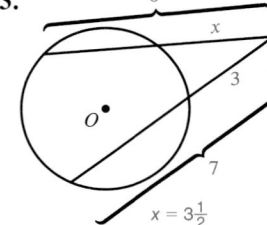

 a. $PA \cdot PB = PD \cdot PC$
$16 \cdot 6 = PD \cdot 8$
$PD = 12$

b. Since $PC = \frac{1}{2}PD$,
$PA \cdot PB = PD \cdot \frac{1}{2}PD$
$16 \cdot 6 = \frac{1}{2}PD^2$
$PD = 8\sqrt{3}$, or ≈ 13.86

Example 2 illustrates that these theorems can be useful in solving practical problems.

CLASS EXERCISES

In Exercises 1–6, find *x* using the given chords, secants, and tangents. Simplify fractions and radicals and round the answer to the nearest tenth.

1.

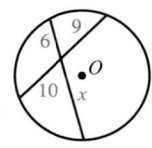

$x = 15$

2.

$x = 16$

3.

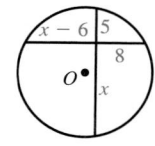

$x = 3\frac{1}{2}$

4.

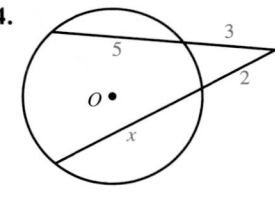

$x = 10$

5.

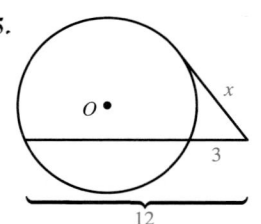

$x = 6$

6.

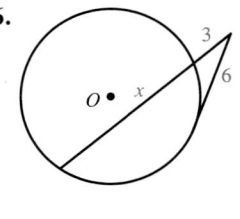

$x = 9$

7. Develop a Plan to prove Theorem 9.15. (*Hint:* Draw $\overline{AC}$ and $\overline{CB}$.)
Show $\triangle PAC \sim \triangle PCB$. Then $\frac{PA}{PC} = \frac{PC}{PB}$ and the concl. follows by the means-extremes prop.

PRACTICE EXERCISES

~~ Use technology where appropriate.

In Exercises 3–13, find *x* and *y* using the given chords, secants, and tangents. Simplify fractions and radicals and round the answer to the nearest tenth.

Critical Thinking

Comparing-Contrasting Have students examine the relationship between two-dimensional and three-dimensional situations.

Assignment Guide

See p. 350B for assignments.

A

1.
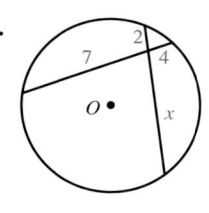

$x = 14$

2.
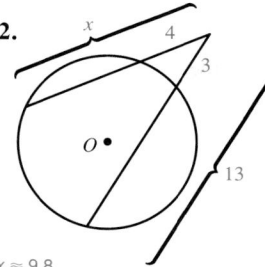

$x \approx 9.8$

3.
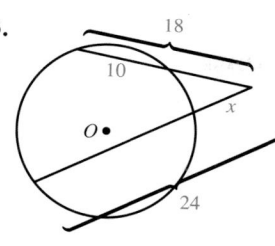

$x = 6$

4.
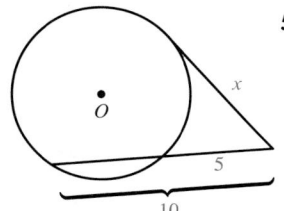

$x \approx 7.1$

5.
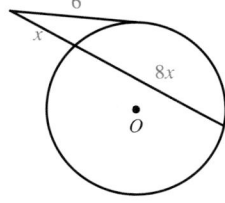

$x = 2$

6.
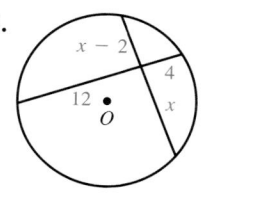

$x = 8$

7.
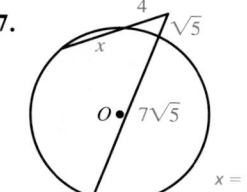

$x = 6$

8.
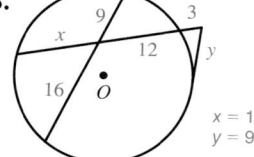

$x = 12$
$y = 9$

9.
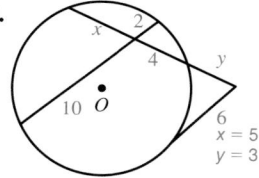

$x = 5$
$y = 3$

10.
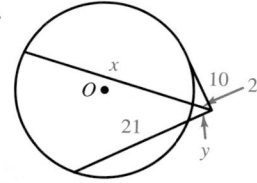

$x = 48$
$y = 4$

11.
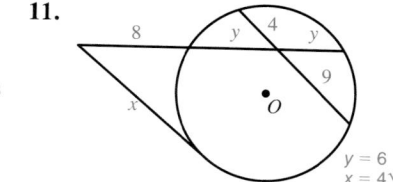

$y = 6$
$x = 4\sqrt{10} \approx 12.6$

B **12.** Two chords intersect in the interior of a circle. Two segments of one chord measure 21 and 28, respectively. The lengths of the two segments of the other chord are in the ratio of 3 to 1. Find those lengths. 42, 14

13. In a circle, $\overline{WP}$ and $\overline{ZP}$ are secant segments with external segments $\overline{XP}$ and $\overline{YP}$, respectively. If $PW = 16$, $WX = 10$, and $\overline{PY} \cong \overline{YZ}$, find PZ. $8\sqrt{3} \approx 13.9$

9.7 Circles and Segment Lengths   **385**

Lesson Quiz

Find *x*.

1.

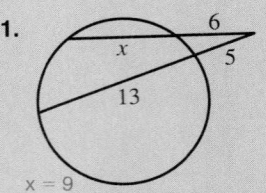
6
x
5
13

x = 9

2.

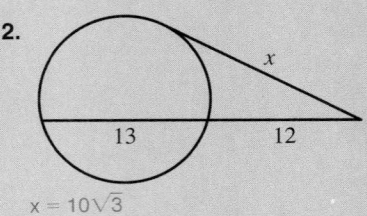
x
13   12

x = 10√3

3.

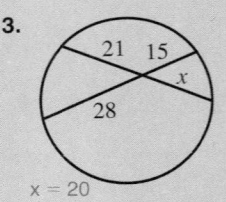
21 15
x
28

x = 20

4. A diameter 26 cm long intersects a chord 5 cm from the center of the circle, so that the chord is separated into segments whose lengths are in the ratio 2:1. Find the length of the chord. 18√2 cm

14. The length of a tangent segment from point *P* in the exterior of circle *O* is 24 mm. The length of a radius is 7 mm. Find the distance from *P* to *O*.
25 mm   See Additional Answers, p. 702.

Use the figure, Given, Prove, and Plan to prove the theorem.

15. Theorem 9.13.   **16.** Theorem 9.14.   **17.** Theorem 9.15.

18. The length of a chord is 48 cm. It is 7 cm from the center of the circle. Find the length of a radius. 25 cm

C   **19.** A diameter of a circle measures 26 cm. Find the length of a chord that is 5 cm from the center. 24 cm

20. The length of a tangent segment from a point *P* in the exterior of circle *O* is 12 cm. The length of a secant segment from *P* through center *O* is 36 cm. Find the length of a radius. 16 cm

21. Why is there no solution for *x* as shown in the figure? What might be changed so that there is a solution?
If 5*x* = 8(*x* + 6), then *x* = −16, which cannot be the length of a segment; change *x* + 6 to *x* − 6; then *x* = 16.

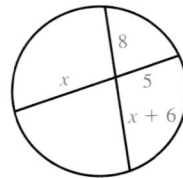
8
x
5
x + 6

Applications

22. Measurement Find the distance to a forest fire on the horizon from the top of a watchtower that is $\frac{1}{8}$ mi tall. (Assume that the earth is a sphere with a diameter of 8000 miles.)
31.6 mi

Architecture This geodesic dome approximates a half-sphere, or *hemisphere*, with a diameter of 50 feet. Poles extend to the ceiling for part of a garden display.

23. Suppose a pole is to be placed in the dome. What is the maximum height of such a pole? Explain. 25 ft; the radius is the longest ⊥ seg. from the diam. to the dome.

24. If the base of a pole is 20 ft from the intersection of the dome and the ground, about how tall is the pole?
10√6 ≈ 24.5 ft

25. Aeronautics How far away can you see the earth's surface from a glider plane 400 ft above the ocean? 24.6 mi

TEST YOURSELF

Find the measures of these arcs and angles.

1. $\overset{\frown}{AB}$ 60   2. $\angle C$ 30   3. $\overset{\frown}{CD}$ 80

4. $\angle A$ 40   5. $\overset{\frown}{BC}$ 100   6. $\angle BXC$ 110

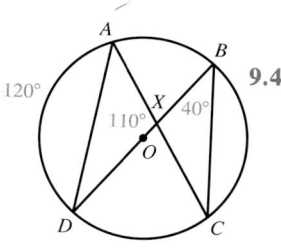
9.4

7. The angle measures for a triangle inscribed in a circle are in the ratio of $1:2:3$. Find the measures of the angles and their intercepted arcs.
30, 60, 90; 60, 120, 180

True or false? If false, explain.

8. The opposite angles of a quadrilateral inscribed in a circle are complementary. False; they are supplementary.

9. The measure of an angle formed by two chords that intersect inside a circle is equal to one-half the difference of the measures of the intercepted arcs. False; it is the sum, not the difference of the meas.

9.5

10. Find the measures of $\angle 1$, $\angle 2$, $\angle 3$, and $\overset{\frown}{RS}$.

$m\angle 1 = 5$
$m\angle 2 = 95$
$m\angle 3 = 90$
$m\overset{\frown}{RS} = 50$

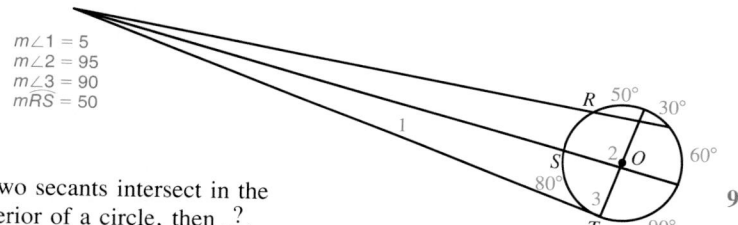

11. If two secants intersect in the exterior of a circle, then __?__

9.6, 9.7

12. If two chords intersect inside a circle, then __?__. the prod. of the lengths of the seg. of 1 chord = the prod. of the lengths of the seg. of the other chord

13. Draw a figure and add the auxiliary lines necessary to prove: Two tangent rays from a common external point determine an angle that is bisected by the ray from the external point to the center of the circle. See Ex. 23, p. 361.

Find x in Exercises 14–16.

14.
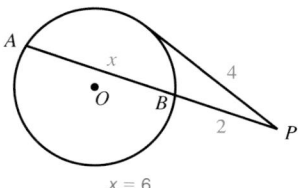
$x = 1$

15.
$x = 6$

16.
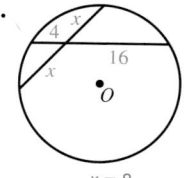
$x = 8$

9.7 Circles and Segment Lengths **387**

11. The product of the lengths of 1 secant seg. and its external seg. = prod. of the lengths of the other secant seg. and its external seg.

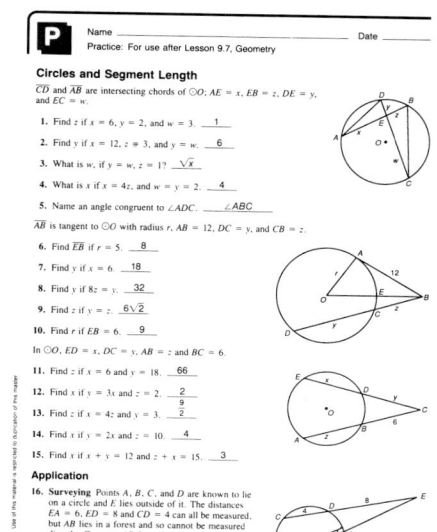
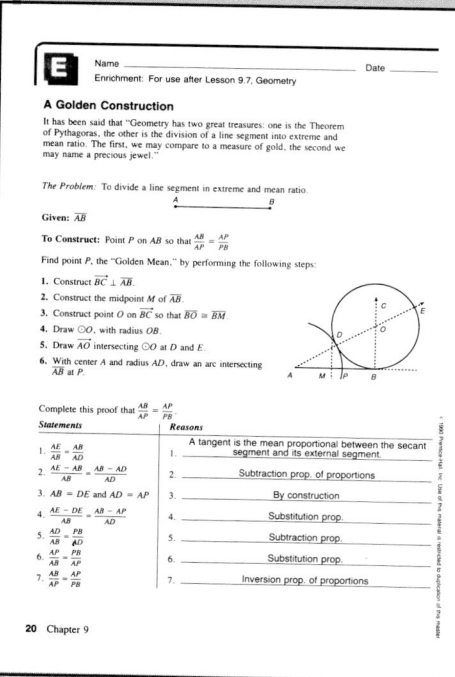

See *Teacher's Resource Book*, Follow-up *Technology*, pp. 11–12.

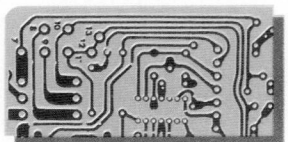

TECHNOLOGY:
Using Logo to Create Geometric Marks and Mandalas

Stone mason marks are the marks that builders left as signatures of their work on Gothic cathedrals. The dark lines are the actual lines that the builders left, and the light lines show the underlying design. To prove that you were a mason, you had to be able to draw the underlying structure which formed the basis of your mark.

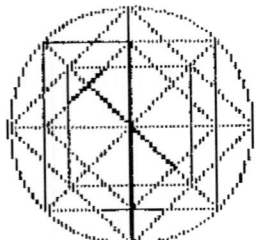

The mason mark on the right uses the following polygon procedure:

```
to concentric.poly :n :radius
pu fd :radius
rt (90+180/:n) pd
repeat :n [ fd (2*:radius*sin(180/:n) rt 360/:n]
lt (90+180/:n)
pu bk :radius pd
end
```

EXAMPLE   Write a procedure that generates the above mason mark. Use one color for the geometric base and another color for the actual mark.

```
to mason.mark
geometric.base
mark
end
```

```
to geometric.base
setc 2
concentric.poly 36 60
repeat 2[ concentric.poly 4 60 lt 4]
repeat 4[ lt 45 fd 60 bk 120 fd 60]
repeat 2[ concentric.poly 4 (30 * sqrt 2) lt 45]
end
```

388   Chapter 9 Circles

```
to mark
setc 1
fd 60 bk (60 + (30 * sqrt 2)
rt 90
fd (30 * sqrt 2) bk (30 * sqrt 2)
lt 90
fd (30 * sqrt 2)
lt 45 fd 30 bk 60 rt 90 fd (7.5 * sqrt 2) bk (15 * sqrt 2) fd (7.55 * sqrt 2)
lt 90 fd 30 rt 45 fd (30 * sqrt 2) rt 90 fd 15 bk 30
end
```

Note: The above procedure uses 60 as the radius of the circle, so all the calculations are based on that number. Actually, the turtle is drawing a 36-sided polygon, but the resolution on the screen makes it appear to be a circle.

Many Eastern religions use designs called *mandalas* to illustrate the structure of the universe and the place of the observer within it. Notice the geometric basis of this mandala.

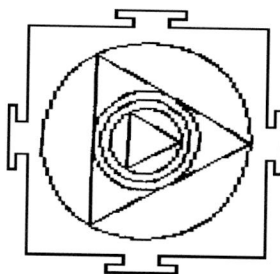

EXERCISES

1. Research the history of mason marks and design a series of mason marks.

2. Design your own mason mark.

3. Design a mason mark that is appropriate for a 20th-century building. How would it differ from the early mason marks?

4. Write the procedure which would generate the above mandala.

5. Many ceremonies involve people moving or dancing in different patterns within a circle. Generate a graphic that illustrates a textured pattern of movement.

6. Research Native American sand painting and generate your own sand painting.

7. Explain the relationships between the numbers used in the procedure to generate the mason mark on the previous page.

- See *Teacher's Resource Book, Spanish Chapter Summary and Review*, pp. 17–18.
- See Extra Practice, p. 651.

Vocabulary

adjacent nonoverlapping arcs (363)	diameter (353)	measure of semicircle (362)
center (352)	exterior (352)	minor arc (362)
central angle (362)	externally tangent circles (359)	point of tangency (357)
chord (353)	great circle (353)	polygon inscribed in a circle (353)
circle (352)	inscribed angle (368)	radius (352)
circumscribed (353)	intercepted arc (368)	secant (353)
circumscribed about a polygon (353)	interior (352)	secant segment (382)
common tangent (359)	internally tangent circles (359)	semicircle (362)
concentric circles (353)	major arc (362)	sphere (353)
congruent arcs (363)	measure of major arc (362)	tangent (357)
congruent chords (363)	measure of minor arc (362)	tangent segment (357)
congruent circles (353)		

Circles   A circle is a set of points in a plane with every point a given distance r from a given point O. A sphere is a set of points in space with every point a given distance r from a given point O.   **9.1**

Use the figure to name the following.

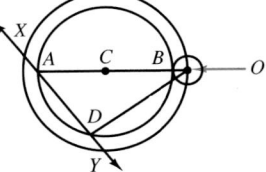

1. All concentric circles
  ⊙C with pt. B, ⊙C with pt. O
3. 3 chords $\overline{AB}$, $\overline{AD}$, $\overline{XY}$

2. 4 radii $\overline{AC}$, $\overline{BC}$, $\overline{BO}$, $\overline{OC}$
4. one secant $\overleftrightarrow{XY}$

5. If $CB = 6$ and $BO = 3$, what is the length of any diameter of the larger circle with center at C? 18

Properties of Tangents   A tangent to a circle is a line in the plane of the circle that intersects the circle in exactly one point. A line tangent to a circle is perpendicular to the radius at the point of tangency.   **9.2**

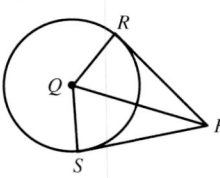

6. If $QS = 5$ mm and $PS = 12$ mm, find PQ, PR, and RQ. $PQ = 13$ mm; $PR = 12$ mm; $RQ = 5$ mm

7. Sketch two circles having one common internal tangent and two common external tangents.
See side column.

7.

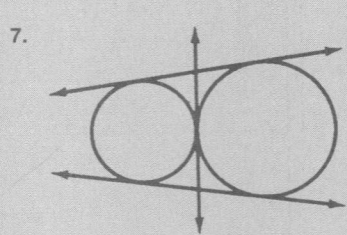

Arcs, Chords, and Central Angles   A central angle of a circle has its vertex at the center of the circle. The measure of an arc intercepted by a central angle is the measure of that angle.
9.3

8. In the figure above $m\angle RQP = 40$ and $\angle RQP \cong \angle SQP$. Find $m\overset{\frown}{RS}$. 80

Inscribed Angles   An inscribed angle has its vertex on a circle and sides that contain chords of the circle; its measure is one-half the measure of its intercepted arc.
9.4

In quadrilateral $ABCD$ **inscribed in a circle,** $m\angle A = 100$, $m\angle B = 75$, **and** $m\angle ADB = 50$. **Give the measures of the following.**

9. $m\angle C$ 80   **10.** $m\overset{\frown}{AB}$ 100   **11.** $m\overset{\frown}{BC}$ 110

Tangents, Secants, and Angles   There are formulas for finding the measures of angles formed by chords, tangents, and secants.
9.5

Find x and/or y.

12.
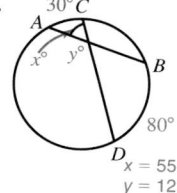
$x = 55$
$y = 125$

13.
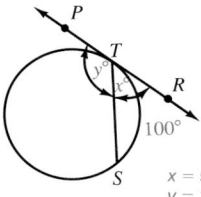
$x = 50$
$y = 130$

14.
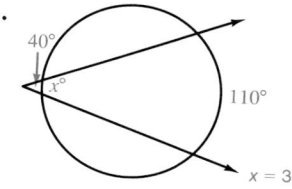
$x = 30$

15. Draw a figure and prove: In congruent circles, if two minor arcs are congruent, then their chords are congruent. See Exercise 33, p. 366.
9.6

Circles and Segment Lengths   There are methods for finding the segment lengths of chords that intersect within a circle and for finding segment lengths when two secants or a secant and a tangent intersect in the exterior of the circle.
9.7

Find x, the measure of a segment.

16.
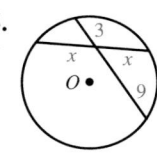
$x = 3\sqrt{3}$

17.
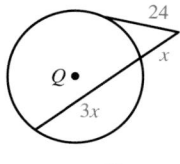
$x = 12$

18.
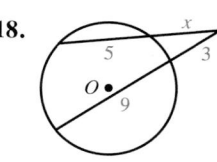
$x = 4$

Summary and Review   **391**

See Teacher's Resource Book, *Tests*, pp. 97–100.

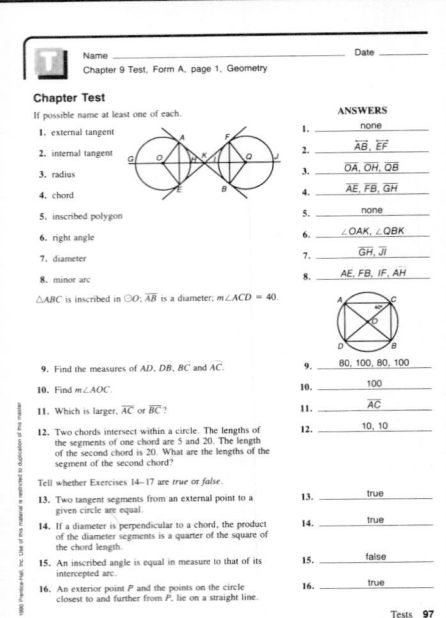

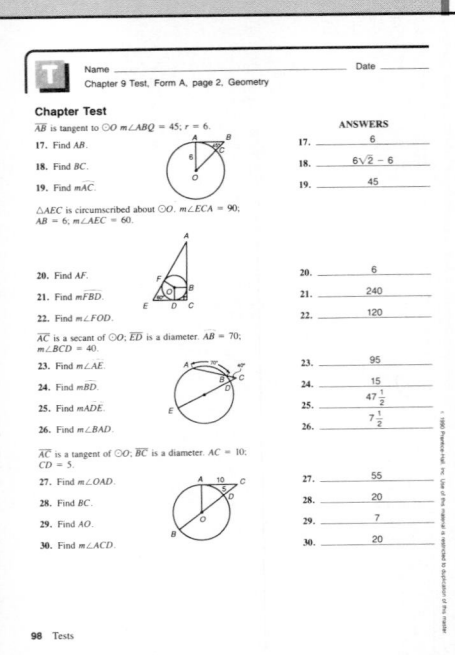

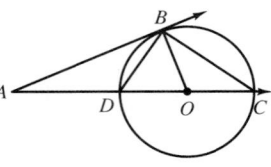

If possible, name at least one of each.

1. tangent
$\overline{AB}$

2. radius
$\overline{OB}, \overline{OC}, \overline{OD}$

3. diameter
$\overline{DC}$

4. chord
$\overline{DB}, \overline{DC}, \overline{BC}$

5. inscribed
polygon
$\triangle BDC$

6. right angle
rt. $\angle OBA$ or
rt. $\angle DBC$

If $\overline{EG} \parallel \overline{FH}$ and $m\widehat{EF} = 80$, find the following.

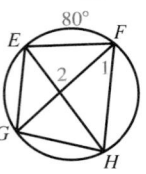

7. $m\angle 1$ 40

8. $m\angle 2$ 80

9. Is EF equal to, less than, or greater than GH? Justify.
$EF = GH$; in a $\odot$, $\cong$ arcs have $\cong$ chords.

The arcs intercepted by the sides of quadrilateral $ABCD$ inscribed in a circle are such that $m\widehat{AB} : m\widehat{BC} : m\widehat{DA} : m\widehat{CD}$ as $1:2:2:3$. Find the measures.

10. The arcs? $m\widehat{AB} = 45$; $m\widehat{BC} = m\widehat{DA} = 90$;
$m\widehat{CD} = 135$

11. The angle measures of $ABCD$? $m\angle A =$
$m\angle B = 112.5$; $m\angle C = m\angle D = 67.5$

Find x and/or y.

12.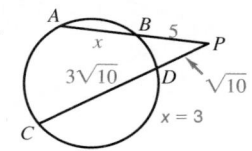

$x = 3$

13.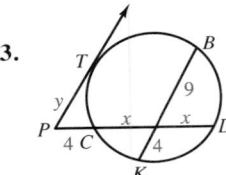

$x = 6$
$y = 8$

14. Two chords intersect within a circle. The lengths of the segments of one chord are 4 and 9. The length of the second chord is 15. What are the lengths of the segments of the second chord? 3, 12

Tell whether the statement is true or false. If false, correct it.

15. When a secant and a tangent intersect in the exterior of a circle, the product of the lengths of the secant segment and its external segment is equal to the length of the tangent segment. False; product = the square of the length of the tan. seg.

16. If a rhombus is inscribed in a circle, then the rhombus is a square. true

Challenge

A chord of a circle is 10 mm. It is parallel to a tangent and bisects the radius drawn to the point of tangency. Find the circumference of the circle. $\frac{20\sqrt{3}}{3}\pi$

Alternative Assessment   Students should complete the Reading and Writing in Geometry activity, p. 9, in the *Teacher's Resource Book*. In addition to writing definitions, they should draw a large circle and use it to illustrate all of the terms (except 4). They should also include any formulas that relate the parts drawn, and label, describe, and state how to measure the angles formed.

According to the College Entrance Examination Board and the Educational Testing Service, the 1994 revision of the SAT will include a section of problems that require students to produce and grid in their own answers.

See *Teacher's Resource Book*, Preparing for College Entrance Exams, for grids.

Solve. Grid in your responses on the answer sheet.

1. If $a - 2b = 17$ and $2a - b = 16$, then what does $a - b$ equal? 11

2. If $\overline{PA}$ and $\overline{PB}$ are tangent segments to $\odot O$, find $m\angle P$ when $m\angle P = \frac{2}{3} m\angle O$. 72

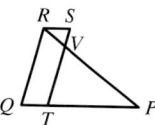

3. How many integers are there such that $7x + 2 \le 23$ and $3x - 5 \ge 1$? 2

4. In $\triangle PQR$, $\overline{TS}$ is drawn so that $QRST$ is a parallelogram. If $PT = 8$, $PV = 9$, $VR = 4.5$, and the perimeter of $\triangle PTV = 23$, find the perimeter of $QRST$. 26

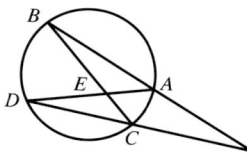

5. If $m\angle P = 26$ and $m\angle DEB = 42$, what is $m\angle D$? 8

6. If $AB = 14$, $CD = 16$, and $DE = 12$, find the positive difference between AE and EB. 2

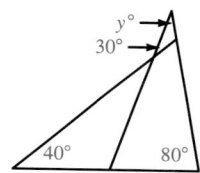

7. Written as a decimal, what is the value of $\frac{8}{100} + \frac{21}{1000} + \frac{3}{10}$? 0.401

8. This sequence starts with 2, 5, 9, and from the fourth term on, each term is found by adding the three preceding terms. What will be the seventh term? 101

2, 5, <u>9</u>, <u>?</u>, <u>?</u>, <u>?</u>, <u>?</u>, . . .

9. In a circle graph showing world production of copper, what is the measure in degrees of the central angle of the sector representing a country that produces $\frac{2}{15}$ of the total world production of copper? 48

10. A coin is tossed, and a die is rolled. What is the probability of getting heads and 6? $\frac{1}{12}$

Use this diagram for Exercise 11.

11. Find y. 30

12. Alvin has $50 to buy tickets to a basketball game, and the tickets cost $7.75 each. What is the greatest number of tickets he can buy? 6

13. The sum of the digits of a two-digit number is 12. If the digits are reversed, the new number is 54 more than the original number. What is the number? 39

The following skills and concepts are reviewed:
Evaluating algebraic
  expressions
Solving formulas
  for a given variable

ALGEBRA REVIEW

Evaluate each expression for the given values of the variables.

Example Area of a circle: $A = \pi r^2$; $r = 5$, $\pi \approx 3.14$
$$A \approx 3.14 \cdot 25$$
$$\approx 78.5$$

1. Area of a trapezoid: $A = \frac{1}{2}h(B + b)$; $h = 5$, $B = 7$, $b = 9$ 40

2. Interest: $I = PRT$; $P = \$1000$, $R = 5.3\%$, $T = \frac{1}{2}$ year $26.50

3. Power: $P = I^2R$; $I = 15$, $R = 25$ 5625

4. Length of hypotenuse of right triangle: $h = \sqrt{a^2 + b^2}$; $a = 6$, $b = 8$ 10

5. Area of a square: $A = s^2$; $s = 9.5$ 90.25

6. Distance: $D = RT$; $R = 500$, $T = 3$ 1500

7. Volume of a rectangular solid: $V = lwh$; $l = 4$, $w = 3$, $h = 3.5$ 42

8. Temperature: $C = \frac{5}{9}(F - 32)$; $F = 98.6$ 37

9. Temperature: $F = \frac{9}{5}C + 32$; $C = -40$ -40

10. Area of a triangle: $A = \frac{1}{2}bh$; $b = 11$, $h = 12$ 66

11. Volume of a cube: $V = e^3$; $e = 2.6$ 17.576

12. Area of a sector: $A = \frac{n}{360}\pi r^2$, in terms of π; $n = 90$, $r = 10$ 25π

13. The quadratic formula: $x = \dfrac{-b \pm \sqrt{b^2 - 4ac}}{2a}$; $a = 2$, $b = 3$, $c = -4$ $\frac{-3 \pm \sqrt{41}}{4}$

Solve for x.

Examples **a.**
$$y = mx + b$$
$$y - b = mx$$
$$\frac{y - b}{m} = x$$

b.
$$\frac{a}{bx} = c$$
$$a = bcx$$
$$\frac{a}{bc} = x$$

14. $ax + by = c$ $x = \frac{c - by}{a}$

15. $x^2 + y^2 = z^2$ $x = \pm\sqrt{z^2 - y^2}$

16. $\frac{x}{a} = \frac{b}{x}$ $x = \pm\sqrt{ab}$

17. $P = 2(x + y)$ $\frac{P}{2} - y = x$

18. $5 = \frac{y + 4}{x - 2}$ $x = \frac{y + 14}{5}$

19. $a^2 + x^2 = (a\sqrt{2})^2$ $x = \pm a$

SUMMARY

In Chapter 10, students learn methods of construction involving segments, midpoints, angles, angle bisectors, perpendicular and parallel lines, circles, and proportional segments. Following an introduction to theorems about concurrent lines, they study constructions for concurrent lines as well. All constructions are then applied in original construction exercises. The chapter ends with a discussion of loci and instructions on determining the loci of a given set of conditions. Note that the basic constructions have already been presented in concept-specific lessons throughout the text.

CHAPTER OBJECTIVES

- To perform constructions involving segments, midpoints, angles, angle bisectors, perpendicular and parallel lines, circles, and proportional segments

- To state and apply theorems about concurrent lines

- To perform basic concurrent line constructions

- To use the basic constructions in original construction exercises

- To describe and sketch the loci that satisfy one or more given conditions

- To use loci in solving construction problems

CHAPTER HIGHLIGHTS

DEVELOPING MATHEMATICAL POWER

Problem Solving

The strategy lesson incorporates the four problem solving steps for using loci to solve construction problems.

Communication

The side column suggests topics for writing such as comparing the incenter, circumcenter, orthocenter, and centroid in an equilateral triangle. Paper-folding is an alternative learning style. Students are asked to describe in their journals the method for a given construction. There is a Chapter Summary and Review in Spanish in the *Teacher's Resource Book*.

Reasoning

Students justify their constructions with theorems, definitions, postulates, and axioms. They are asked to describe an alternate method for constructing the sum of two angles of a triangle.

Connections

Real-world applications include such topics as drawing, architecture, and archaeology.

Technology

The technology feature at the end of the chapter involves using Logo in constructions. A calculator will be needed to find the approximate rational length of the side of a triangle before actually measuring its length and to investigate the Golden Ratio and its reciprocal.

STUDENT TEXT

Chapter Content	Basic	Average	Enriched	NCTM STANDARDS*
10.1 Beginning Constructions	D: 400/1-10, 13-16, 38, 46, 47, AR	D: 400/1-20 odd, 21-26, 38, 39, 46, 47, AR	D: 400/1-31 odd, 32-39, 46-48, AR	1, 3
10.2 Constructing Perpendiculars and Parallels	D: 405/1-11, 15, 28, 30 R: 400/11, 12, 17-20	D: 405/1-25 even, 28-33 R: 400/27-31	D: 405/1-27 even, 28-33 R: 400/23-31 even	1, 3, 4
10.3 Concurrent Lines	D: 410/1-16 odd, 31 R: 405/12-14, 16, 17	D: 410/1-22, 31, 32 R: 405/19-25 odd	D: 410/1-22, 28-32 R: 405/19-27 odd	1, 3, 8
10.4 Circles	D: 415/2-10, 23 R: 410/1-16 even	D: 415/1-14, 23-25 R: 410/23-27	D: 415/1-14, 21-25 R: 410/23-27	3, 4
10.5 Special Segments	D: 419/1-10, 27, 37, MR R: 415/11, 12	D: 419/1-23 odd, 27, 28, 36, 37, MR R: 415/15-18	D: 419/1-23 odd, 24-28, 36, 37, MR R: 415/15-20	2, 3, 4, 5, 12
10.6 Loci	D: 424/1-12, 34 R: 419/11-13	D: 424/1-10, 17-27 odd, 35 R: 419/14-23 even	D: 424/1-10, 17-33 odd, 36 R: 419/14-23 even	1, 3, 12
10.7 Strategy: Use Loci in Solving Construction Problems	D: 430/1-6, 11 R: 424/13-16	D: 430/2-11 R: 424/17-27 even	D: 430/1-6, 11-14 R: 424/20-33 even	1, 3, 12

D = Daily   R = Review   MR = Mixed Review   AR = Algebra Review

*For a complete list of NCTM Standards, see p. T7.

STUDENT TEXT

Review/Assessment

Mixed Review 421

Algebra Review 402

Summary and Review 434

College Ent. Exam Rev. 437

Cumulative Review 438

Extra Practice 652

Test Yourself 411, 431

Chapter Test 436

Chapter Project 395

Special Features

Career 426

Technology 402, 406, 411, 416, 421, 426, 432-433

Devel. Math. Power 400, 406, 416, 421

Applications 402, 406, 411, 416, 421, 426

RESOURCES

Teacher's Resource Book

Ch. 10: Investigation/Practice/ Enrichment 1-20

Spanish Sum. and Rev. 19-20

Quizzes 101-104

Chapter Tests 105-108

Cumulative Tests 109-112

Perf. Assessment Proj. Ch. 10

Critical Thinking 10

Reading and Writing in Geom. 10

Technology 13-14

Teaching Aid 10

Transparencies 15-18

Teaching Transparencies 63-69

Computer Test Bank 593-670

PH Graph. Utility

Overhead Manip. Kit

Constructions and Loci

A Ruler's Theorem?

MODELING

Mathematics provides the power to develop concepts logically. This project involves visualizing a construction and proving a theorem.

Cooperative Learning

This project is accomplished through a succession of tasks, each of which is well-suited to a cooperative learning situation. These tasks include:
1. Understanding the problem.
2. Planning an approach.
3. Constructing a figure to verify certain propositions.
4. Writing a proof.

Alternative Assessment

See the *Teacher's Resource Book,* Assessment, Chapter 10. This project and the TRB page may be used as an alternative form of assessment for selected topics in Chapter 10.

Developing Mathematical Power

Napoleon Bonaparte (1769–1821) came to power in 1799, and he ruled France for 15 years. Under Napoleon, the laws of France were revised into a system of laws known as the Code Napoleon, which remains the basis of French law today.

Napoleon also had a great aptitude for mathematics. The theorem below is attributed to Napoleon.

Project

Prove Napoleon's Theorem.

NAPOLEON'S THEOREM

If three equilateral triangles are constructed off the sides of any triangle, then the centers of the circles which circumscribe each equilateral triangle are vertices of another equilateral triangle.

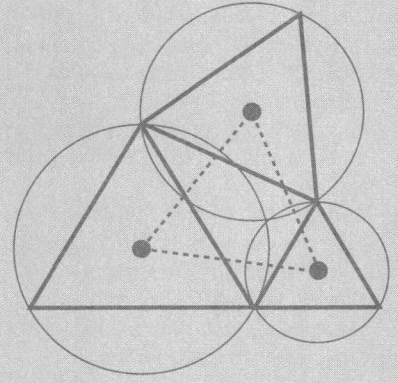

395

LESSON FOCUS

Review

- Review the concept of a bisector. Have students solve the following. *M* is the midpoint of $\overline{AB}$. $AM = 2x + 5$; $MB = 3x$. Find *AB*. 30
- The Algebra Review, Exercises 40–45, involves solving quadratic equations that are not given in standard form.

Alternative Learning Styles

- The paper-folding technique in the Investigation models the construction of a perpendicular bisector of a segment. Students can also use paper-folding for the construction of an angle bisector (see Ex. 46 and 47).
- Some students may need help with the constructions and may benefit from Teaching Transparency 63. Having them verbalize and then visualize the construction should improve their understanding.

10.1

Beginning Constructions

Objectives: To perform constructions involving segments, midpoints, angles, and angle bisectors
To use the basic constructions in original construction exercises

In previous lessons, you studied geometric constructions that were made using only a compass and straightedge. It can be proven or justified that proper construction techniques will yield the desired result.

Investigation—*Using Manipulatives*

Many geometric figures and relationships can be illustrated by folding paper. When performing paper-folding experiments, it is best to use a felt-tipped marker and transparent paper, such as waxed paper.

1. Draw $\overline{AB}$ on a piece of paper. Then fold the paper so that points *A* and *B* coincide. Unfold the paper and label the intersection of $\overline{AB}$ and the crease *M*.

2. How could you justify that *M* is the midpoint of $\overline{AB}$? Since $\overline{AM}$ and $\overline{MB}$ are made to coincide, $\overline{AM} \cong \overline{MB}$.

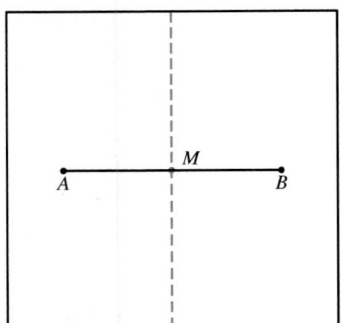

The only instruments used for **construction** in geometry are a *straightedge* and a *compass*. A straightedge is used to construct a line, ray, or segment when two points are given. The ruler's marks may not be used for measurement. A compass is used to construct an arc or a circle, given a center point and a radius length. Since all radii of a given circle are congruent, a compass can be used to construct congruent segments.

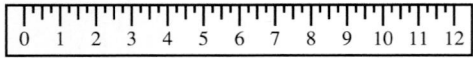

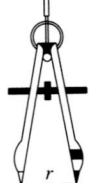

Every construction can be justified by applying definitions, postulates, and/or theorems. Usually the justifications are written in paragraph form.

396   Chapter 10 Constructions and Loci

Developing Mathematical Power

Cooperative Learning   Assign groups of students to complete the Investigation, p. 1, in the *Teacher's Resource Book.* You may want students to do the constructions independently and then, within a group, compare and discuss their results. When they unanimously agree on a figure, have them complete the exercises and share their results with the class.

Construction 1 To construct a segment congruent to a given segment

Given: $\overline{AB}$ A •————————• B

Construct: $\overline{XY}$ such that $\overline{XY} \cong \overline{AB}$

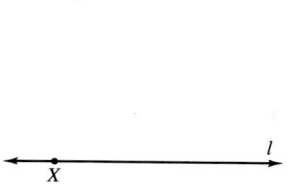

Use a straightedge to draw a line. Mark a point X on the line.

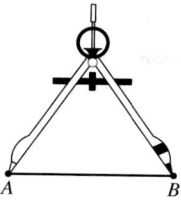

Fix the compass opening so that AB is its length.

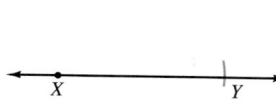

With X as center and AB as radius length, construct an arc intersecting l at Y.

Result: $\overline{XY} \cong \overline{AB}$

Justification: Since the compass opening was fixed, $\overline{AB}$ and $\overline{XY}$ are radii of the same circle. Thus $\overline{XY} \cong \overline{AB}$.

Construction 2 To construct the midpoint of a given segment

Given: $\overline{AB}$ A •————————• B

Construct: M, the midpoint of $\overline{AB}$

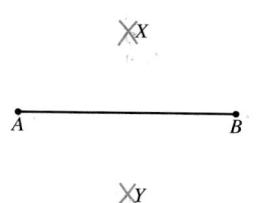

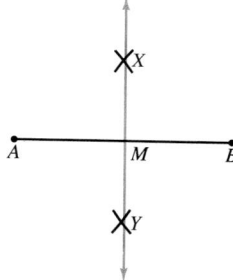

With A and B as centers, and with any radius length greater than $\frac{1}{2}AB$, draw arcs intersecting at X and Y.

Draw $\overleftrightarrow{XY}$. Mark and name its intersection with $\overline{AB}$ point M.

Result: M is the midpoint of $\overline{AB}$.

Justification: Since radii of congruent circles are congruent, $\overline{AX} \cong \overline{BX}$ and $\overline{AY} \cong \overline{BY}$. By the Reflexive property, $\overline{XY} \cong \overline{XY}$. Thus, $\triangle AXY \cong \triangle BXY$ by SSS, and so $\triangle AXM \cong \triangle BXM$ by SAS. Thus, $\overline{AM} \cong \overline{BM}$ and M is the midpoint of $\overline{AB}$.

TEACHING SUGGESTIONS

- Model the constructions on the chalkboard, having students carry them out at their desks. Describe each step, and ask students to explain the steps in their own words.
- Although students should be familiar with the use of construction tools, allow some time for practice with the tools, watching to make certain they are being used correctly.
- Emphasize the need for care and neatness in student work. Careless efforts will often produce misleading results.
- Review the methods for proving triangles congruent—SSS, SAS, ASA, and AAS. Have students construct congruent triangles using the first three methods. Ask how they would use the AAS method. As shown below, construct an angle congruent to the third angle of the triangle. Then use ASA.

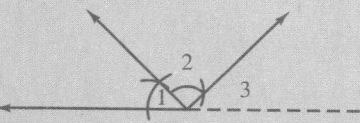

- Many of the exercises require that students combine the basic constructions in different ways. Point out the relationship between planning for such constructions and the problem solving process. Students should think their way through a plan for completing a construction before they begin, and should justify the plan upon its completion.

Critical Thinking

1. *Application* Ask students to construct triangles using SSS, SAS, ASA, and AAS methods.
2. *Analysis* Have students take a problem solving approach to doing construction exercises.

CHALKBOARD EXAMPLES

• **For Example 1**

Given: $\overline{AB}$ A ————————— B

a. Construct: equilateral $\triangle JKL$ where each side $= \frac{1}{2}AB$.

b. Use $\triangle JKL$ to construct a 90°$\angle$.

a. Const. the midpt. M of $\overline{AB}$. On line l const. $\overline{JK} \cong \overline{AM}$. With J and K as centers and radius length AM, const. arcs intersecting at L. $\triangle JKL$ is the required $\triangle$.

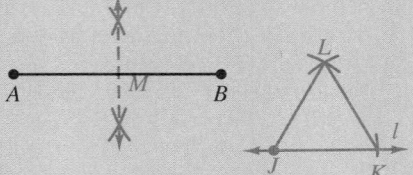

b. Bisect $\angle LJK$, forming $\angle LJX$ and $\angle XJK$. Copy $\angle LJK$ and $\angle LJX$ side by side. $\angle CDE$ is the required $\angle$.

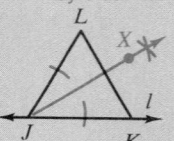 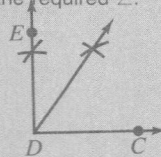

• **For Example 2**

Given: $\overline{MN}$ and $\angle O$

M ——•——— N   O

Construct: Isos. $\triangle RST$, having base $\overline{ST} \cong \overline{MN}$ and base $\angle$s S and $T \cong$ to $\angle O$. On line j const. $\overline{ST} \cong \overline{MN}$. Using S as vertex and $\overrightarrow{ST}$ as the initial side, const. $\angle S \cong \angle O$. Using T as vertex and $\overrightarrow{TS}$ as the initial side, const. $\angle T \cong \angle O$. Extend the sides of $\angle S$ and $\angle T$ until they intersect at R. $\triangle RST$ is the required $\triangle$.

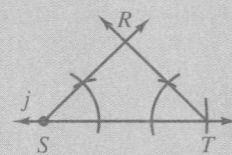

Construction 3   To construct an angle congruent to a given angle

Given: $\angle A$

Construct: $\angle W$ such that $\angle W \cong \angle A$

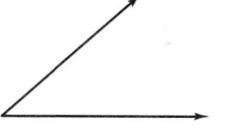

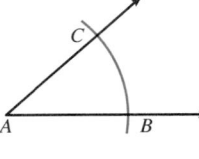

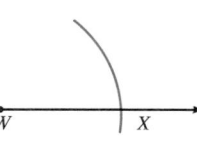

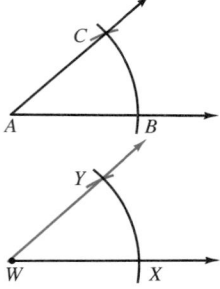

Use a straightedge to draw ray r. Mark W on r.

Using a compass at center A, draw any $\overparen{BC}$. Repeat with the same radius at center W. Draw an arc intersecting r at X.

Using BC as a radius length and with center at X, draw an arc intersecting at Y. Draw $\overrightarrow{WY}$.

Justified in Class Exercise 1

Result: $\angle W \cong \angle A$

Construction 4   To construct the bisector of a given angle

Given: $\angle A$

Construct: $\overrightarrow{AX}$ such that $\angle BAX \cong \angle XAC$

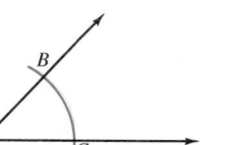

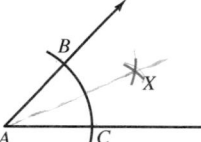

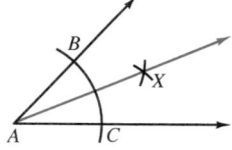

With A as center and any convenient radius length, draw $\overparen{BC}$.

With B and C as centers and radius length $> \frac{1}{2}BC$, draw arcs intersecting at X.

Draw $\overrightarrow{AX}$.

Result: $\overrightarrow{AX}$ bisects $\angle A$.

Justification: Since radii of congruent circles are congruent, $\overline{AB} \cong \overline{AC}$ and $\overline{BX} \cong \overline{CX}$. Since $\overline{AX} \cong \overline{AX}$, $\triangle ABX \cong \triangle ACX$ by SSS. By CPCTC, $\angle BAX \cong \angle CAX$ and $\overrightarrow{AX}$ bisects $\angle A$ by the definition of angle bisector.

---

398   Chapter 10 Constructions and Loci

EXAMPLE 1 Given: $\overline{AB}$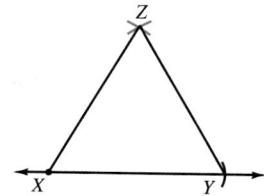

  a. Construct: Equilateral $\triangle XYZ$ with each side congruent to $\overline{AB}$.

  b. How could you use $\triangle XYZ$ to construct a 30° angle?

a.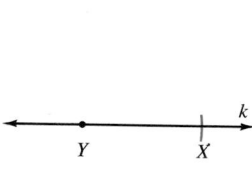

On line k, construct $\overline{XY} \cong \overline{AB}$.

With X and Y as centers, and AB as radius length, construct arcs intersecting at Z. $\triangle XYZ$ is equilateral.

  b. Construct the bisector of any angle of $\triangle XYZ$.

EXAMPLE 2 **Given:** $\overline{CD}$ and $\angle E$

       Construct: Isosceles $\triangle XYZ$ with $\overline{XY} \cong \overline{YZ} \cong \overline{CD}$, and $\angle Y \cong \angle E$.

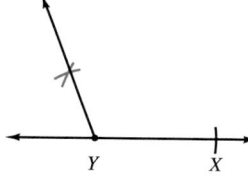

On k, construct $\overline{YX} \cong \overline{CD}$.

Construct $\angle Y \cong \angle E$.

Construct $\overline{YZ} \cong \overline{CD}$. Draw $\overline{ZX}$.

EXAMPLE 3 **Given:** $\triangle CNS$

  a. Construct a segment equal to $3CS - SN$.

  b. Construct an angle equal to $m\angle N + m\angle S$.

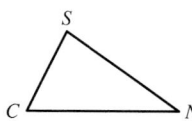

a. Beginning at X, mark the length of $\overline{CS}$ three times. From Z, mark the length of $\overline{SN}$. XP is $3CS - SN$.

    b. On line l, construct $\angle BYR \cong \angle N$. On $\overrightarrow{YR}$, construct $\angle RYT \cong \angle S$. $m\angle TYB$ is $m\angle N + m\angle S$.

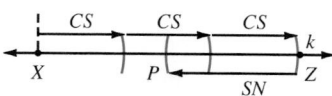

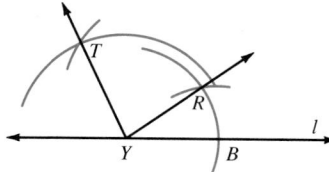

• **For Example 3**
  Given: $\triangle XYZ$
  a. Construct: a segment equal to $2XZ + XY$.
  b. Construct: an angle equal to $2m\angle X$.

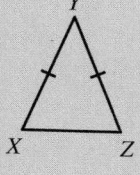

  a. Beginning at F, mark the length of XZ two times. From G mark the length of XY. FY is $2XZ + XY$.

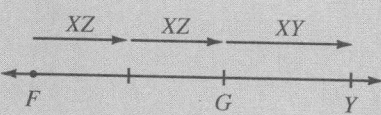

  b. On line m construct $\angle LMN \cong \angle X$. On $\overrightarrow{ML}$ construct $\angle PML \cong \angle X$. $m\angle PMN = 2m\angle X$.

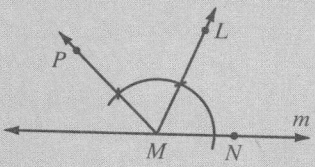

Common Errors

• Some students will be careless or will attempt to "fake" constructions. Insist on careful, neat work.
• Some students will be confused by the "drawing" versus "construction" distinction. Emphasize that constructions do not rely on measurements, whereas drawings do.
• See *Teacher's Resource Book* for additional remediation.

LESSON FOLLOW-UP

Discussion
Have students demonstrate the constructions on the chalkboard and explain the steps. Listen for the language used, and watch their techniques. Present a few problems in which the techniques must be combined in different ways.

Assignment Guide
See p. 394B for assignments.

Class Exercises

6.

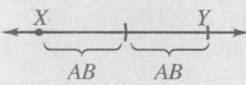

Practice Exercises

1.

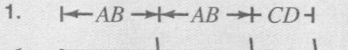

2.

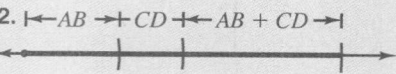

3.

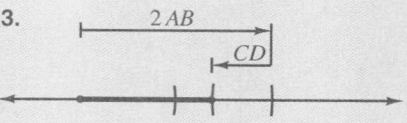

4.

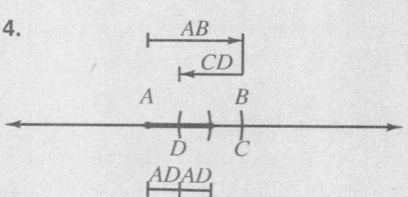

5.

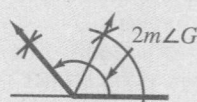

Developing Mathematical Power

- *Investigation* Students are asked to use paper-folding to bisect an angle.
- *Thinking Critically* Students are asked to find another way of constructing the sum of two angles of a triangle.

CLASS EXERCISES

Thinking Critically

1. Develop a justification for Construction 3. Radii of ≅ ⊙s are ≅, so $\overline{AB} \cong \overline{WX}$, $\overline{BC} \cong \overline{XY}$, and $\overline{AC} \cong \overline{WY}$. Thus, $\triangle ABC \cong \triangle WXY$ by SSS and $\angle W \cong \angle A$ by CPCTC.

If you are given $\overline{AB}$ and $\overline{CD}$, how can you use Construction 1 to construct $\overrightarrow{XY}$ such that 2. On line *l*, const. $\overline{XW} \cong \overline{AB}$. Then on $\overrightarrow{XW}$, const. $\overline{WY} \cong \overline{CD}$ with *W* between *X* and *Y*.
3. On line *l*, const. $\overline{XP} \cong \overline{AB}$. Then on $\overrightarrow{XP}$, const. $\overline{PQ} \cong \overline{AB}$ and $\overline{QY} \cong \overline{AB}$.

2. $XY = AB + CD$?   **3.** $XY = 3AB$?

4. If $\overline{AB}$, $\overline{CD}$, and $\overline{EF}$ are given, describe how to construct a $\triangle XYZ$ such that its sides are congruent to $\overline{AB}$, $\overline{CD}$, and $\overline{EF}$. Const. $\overline{XY} \cong \overline{AB}$. Using X and Y as centers, const. arcs with radius length *CD* for center *X* and *EF* for center *Y*. Label the intersection of the two arcs Z. Draw $\overline{XZ}$ and

In Exercises 5-8, unless otherwise instructed, use these figures as models in starting your constructions.

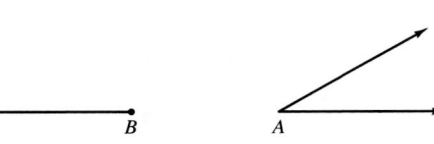
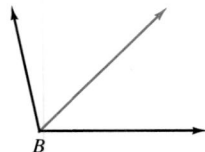

5. Bisect $\angle B$. Check your work by measuring $\angle B$ and the resulting angles to the nearest degree. Answers may vary. Check students' constructions. 102°; 51°; 51°

6. Construct a segment whose length is $2AB$.
See side column.

7. Here is the result of constructing an angle equal in measure to $m\angle A + m\angle B$. Explain how to do the construction. Copy $\angle A$; then use one side of $\angle A$ to construct adj. $\angle B$.

8. Construct an angle equal to $\frac{1}{2} m\angle A + m\angle B$.
Copy $\angle A$ and bis. it; then use the bis. as a side and constr. $\angle B$.

PRACTICE EXERCISES   Use technology where appropriate.

In Exercises 1–7, use these figures as models in starting your constructions.

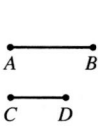
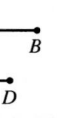

Construct segments having these measures. See side column.

A **1.** $2AB + CD$ **2.** $2(AB + CD)$ **3.** $2AB - CD$ **4.** $2(AB - CD)$

6.

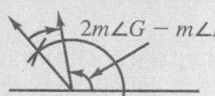

$2m\angle G - m\angle H$

7.

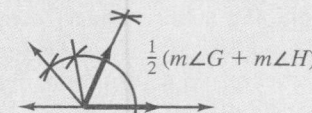

$\frac{1}{2}(m\angle G + m\angle H)$

Construct angles having these measures. See side column, p. 400.

5. $2m\angle G$ 6. $2m\angle G - m\angle H$ 7. $\frac{1}{2}(m\angle G + m\angle H)$

8. Draw any acute scalene $\triangle PQR$. Construct $\triangle XYZ \cong \triangle PQR$ based on the SSS Postulate. See side column.

9. Draw any obtuse scalene $\triangle STU$. Construct $\triangle XYZ \cong \triangle STU$ based on the SAS Postulate.

10. Draw any isosceles $\triangle JKL$. Construct $\triangle XYZ \cong \triangle JKL$ based on the ASA Postulate. See Additional Answers, p. 702.

11. Using isosceles $\triangle JKL$ drawn for Exercise 10, construct $\triangle STU \cong \triangle JKL$, based on the SSS Postulate.

12. Construct an equilateral $\triangle MNO$ whose sides are congruent to $\overline{AB}$ at the beginning of the Practice Exercises.

Given equilateral $\triangle MNO$, describe how to construct the following angles.

13. $30°$ 14. $15°$ 15. $45°$ 16. $120°$

17. $90°$ 18. $135°$ 19. $150°$ 20. $82.5°$

B   21. Construct $\triangle PQR$ with angles respectively congruent to $\angle 1$, $\angle 2$, and $\angle 3$. Why is it necessary to construct only two of these angles to get $\triangle PQR$? Will your $\triangle PQR$ necessarily be congruent to that of any other student? Explain.

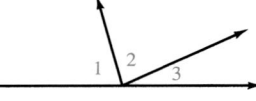

22. Draw $\triangle STU$. Construct an angle with measure $m\angle S + m\angle T + m\angle U$.

Use an equilateral triangle and the model segments at the beginning of the Practice Exercises to construct these polygons.

23. $\triangle JKL$, where $m\angle J = 30$, $m\angle K = 45$, and $\overline{JK} \cong \overline{AB}$.

24. $\triangle MNO$, where $m\angle M = 120$, $\overline{MN} \cong \overline{AB}$, and $\overline{MO} \cong \overline{CD}$.

25. Isosceles $\triangle PQR$, where $m\angle Q = 135$ and $\overline{QR} \cong \overline{AB}$.

26. $\triangle STU$, where $m\angle S = m\angle T = 45$ and $\overline{ST} \cong \overline{CD}$.

27. Parallelogram $WXYZ$, where $m\angle X = 60$, $\overline{XW} \cong \overline{AB}$, and $\overline{XY} \cong \overline{CD}$.

28. Square $STUV$, where $\overline{ST} \cong \overline{AB}$.

29. Rhombus $WXYZ$, where $m\angle W = 135$ and each side is congruent to $\overline{AB}$.

30. Is it possible to construct a $\triangle WXY$ where $WX = 2AB$, $XY = 3AB$, and $YW = 4AB$? If so, do so. If not, tell why.

Lesson Quiz

1. Construct right $\triangle GHI$ with H as the right $\angle$.

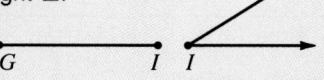

On line n construct $\angle I$. Mark off $\overline{GI}$ on the side of the angle. Then construct a perpendicular to n from G. $\triangle GHI$ is a right $\triangle$.

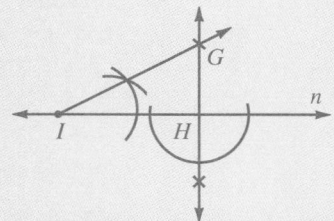

2. Construct a segment of length $2AB - \frac{1}{2}CD$.

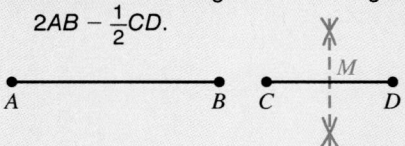

On line j construct $\overline{XY} \cong \overline{AB}$. Construct $\overline{YZ} \cong \overline{AB}$. Construct M, the midpoint of $\overline{CD}$. Then, construct $\overline{ZW} \cong \overline{CM}$, with W between X and Z. $\overline{XW}$ is the required segment, since $XW = 2AB - \frac{1}{2}CD$.

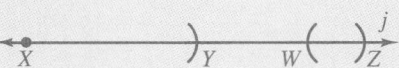

3. Construct an angle with measure $\frac{3}{2}m\angle IEJ$.

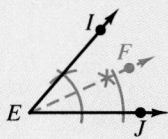

Bisect $\angle IEJ$, forming $\angle IEF$ and $\angle FEJ$. Construct $\angle XYZ \cong \angle IEJ$. With Y as vertex, $\overrightarrow{YX}$ as one side, and $\overrightarrow{YX}$ between $\overrightarrow{YZ}$ and $\overrightarrow{YW}$, construct $\angle WYZ \cong \angle FEJ$. Then $\angle ZYW$ is the required angle, since $m\angle ZYW = \frac{3}{2}m\angle IEJ$.

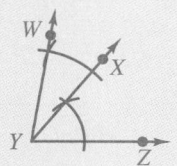

8.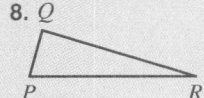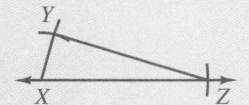

9.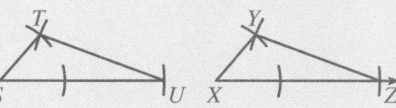

401

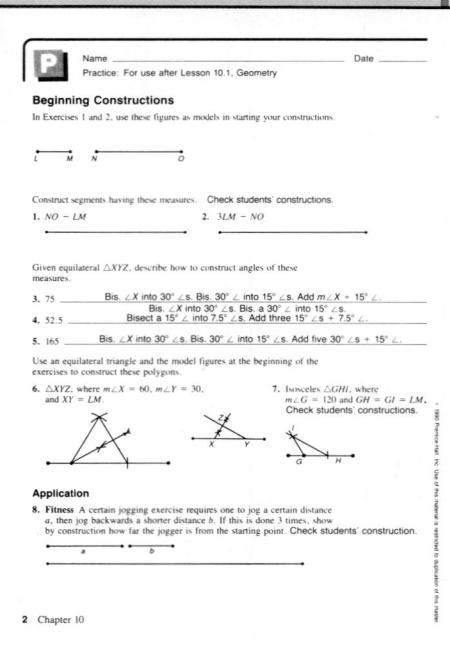

31. Is it possible to construct a $\triangle WXY$ where $WX = AB$, $XY = 2AB$, and $YW = 3AB$? If so, do so. If not, tell why. no; $WX + XY \not> YW$

C 32. Draw an acute scalene triangle. Bisect all three angles. What do you observe about the bisectors? They intersect at one point.

33. Draw any isosceles triangle. Bisect the vertex angle. Where does it seem to intersect the opposite side? Prove it. The ∠ bis. is the ⊥ bis. of opp. side. The ∠ bis. forms 2 ⚟ that are ≅ by SAS. Concl. follows by CPCTC.

34. Suppose $\angle A$ is the vertex angle of an isosceles triangle. Construct the base angles. See Additional Answers, p. 702.

35. Draw any $\triangle JKL$. Construct $\triangle XYZ \sim \triangle JKL$ such that $XY = 3JK$.

36. Using $\triangle JKL$ of Exercise 35, construct $\square WXYZ$ where JK is the length of one side, KL of a second side, and JL is the length of a diagonal.

37. Construct $\square JKLM$, where one side $\cong \overline{AB}$, one angle is $120°$, and a diagonal $\cong \overline{CD}$.

Applications

38. **Technology** If A, B, and C are collinear, use Logo to draw $\overline{AB}$ with length b and $\overline{BC}$ with length c. Use different colors to draw the line segment with length $2b - 2c$. See Solutions Manual.

39. **Architecture** A blueprint indicates that the rafters for the roof of a new house rise at a $15°$ angle. Another house requires an angle twice that measure. Show how to construct this second angle. See Additional Answers, p. 702.

Algebra Review

Solve.

40. $3x = \frac{1}{2}(5x + 2)$ 2

41. $8x = \frac{1}{5}(3x - 37)$ –1

42. $2x + 1 = \frac{1}{2}(3x - 5)$ –7

43. $4x - 3 = \frac{1}{3}(2x + 11)$ 2

44. $5(x - 1) = \frac{1}{4}(x^2 - x)$ 1; 20

45. $3(x + 5) = \frac{1}{2}(x^2 + 5x)$ –5; 6

Developing Mathematical Power

Investigation This figure shows the results of a paper-folding experiment to find the angle bisector of a given $\angle AVC$. Given $\angle AVC$, fold so that $\overrightarrow{VA}$ coincides with $\overrightarrow{VC}$. Unfold and label the crease $\overrightarrow{VX}$.

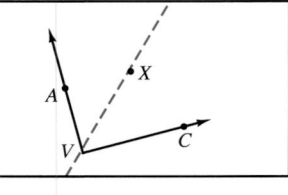

46. Describe how the experiment was done.

47. How can you justify that $\overrightarrow{VX}$ bisects $\angle AVC$? The fold creates $\angle AVX$, which coincides with $\angle CVX$. Hence $\angle AVX \cong \angle CVX$ and so $\overrightarrow{VX}$ is the bis. of $\angle AVC$.

48. **Thinking Critically** Explain another way to do Example 3a, constructing the sum of two angles of a triangle. Construct the third angle ($\angle C$), forming a linear pair. The other angle of the linear pair has a measure $= m\angle N + m\angle S$. (Sum of the measures of the ∠s of a △ = the sum of the measures of a linear pair.)

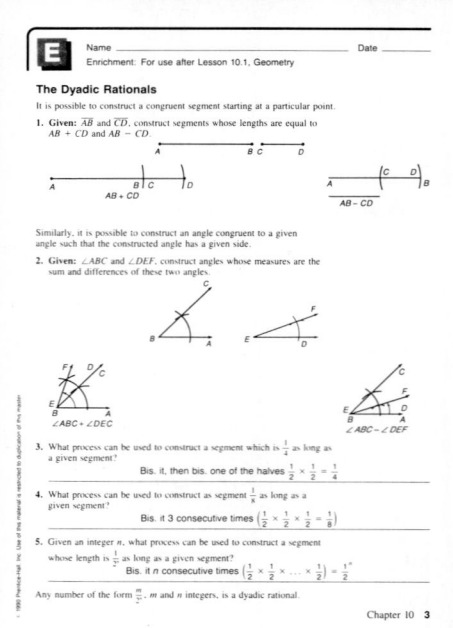

Constructing Perpendiculars and Parallels

Objectives: To perform constructions involving perpendicular and parallel lines
To use these basic constructions in original construction exercises

The theorems about perpendicular lines and parallelism can be used to justify constructions.

Investigation—*Using Manipulatives*

This paper-folding experiment can be used to construct a perpendicular to a line through a point on the line.

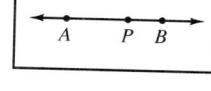

1. Draw $\overleftrightarrow{AB}$ with point P. Then fold through P such that $\overrightarrow{PB}$ lies on $\overrightarrow{PA}$. Unfold the paper, locate point X on the crease, and draw $\overrightarrow{PX}$.

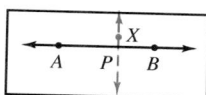

2. How can you justify that $\overrightarrow{PX} \perp \overleftrightarrow{AB}$? ∠APX and ∠BPX are a linear pair and therefore supp. ∠APX ≅ ∠BPX when folded,

so $m\angle APX = m\angle BPX = 90$ and $\overleftrightarrow{PX} \perp \overleftrightarrow{AB}$.

Construction 5 To construct the perpendicular bisector of a given segment

Given: $\overline{AB}$

Construct: $\overleftrightarrow{XY}$, the perpendicular bisector of $\overline{AB}$

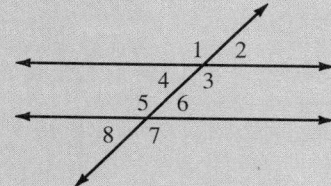

Use Construction 2 for finding the midpoint of a segment.

Result: $\overleftrightarrow{XY} \perp \overline{AB}$; $\overleftrightarrow{XY}$ bisects $\overline{AB}$.

Justification: The construction made $\overline{AX} \cong \overline{BX}$ and $\overline{AY} \cong \overline{BY}$, since radii of congruent circles are congruent. Hence $AX = BX$ and $AY = BY$, which means that X is equidistant from endpoints A and B, and Y is equidistant from endpoints A and B. Thus X and Y lie on the perpendicular bisector of $\overline{AB}$.

You will be asked to provide justifications of Constructions 6, 7, and 8 in Exercises 15–17.

Developing Mathematical Power

Cooperative Learning   Working in groups, students can complete the Investigation, p. 4, in the *Teacher's Resource Book*. Have them read through the directions, sketch what they think the resulting figure will be, and discuss why. Then have them do the construction, complete the exercises, and share their results.

LESSON PLAN

Materials/Manipulatives
Compasses and straightedges
Paper-folding materials
Teaching Transparency 64

Technology
Computer Test Bank, pp. 605–616

LESSON FOCUS

Review
Review the relationships that exist between the angles formed by parallel lines and a transversal. Draw the following on the chalkboard. Ask the students to identify and name the congruent angle pairs.

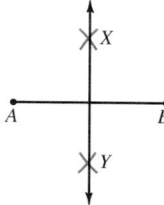

Alternative Learning Styles
Manipulatives can be particularly effective when introducing new constructions. The Investigation presents an alternative way of constructing the perpendicular bisector of a segment. Ask students how they could use paper-folding techniques to construct a perpendicular to a line from a point not on the line. Fold the paper so that the point lies on the crease and two rays of the line coincide.

Ask students how they could use paper-folding to construct a line parallel to a given line through a given point not on the line. Fold the paper to construct a perpendicular to the line through the point and then construct a perpendicular to that perpendicular.

TEACHING SUGGESTIONS

- Demonstrate the constructions on the board and have students model them at their desks. Be sure to use precise language, and to insist that students do the same when describing steps used in constructions.
- Review sufficient conditions for quadrilaterals to be parallelograms, rectangles, squares, and rhombuses.
- Make certain students are able to justify constructions.

Common Errors

- For Construction 7, students may try to use a radius length that is less than or equal to the distance to the line. Have students demonstrate how such radius lengths do not work.
- Some students may try to "fake" Construction 8 by drawing the parallel instead of constructing it. Have these students review and practice Construction 3.
- See *Teacher's Resource Book* for additional remediation.

LESSON FOLLOW-UP

Discussion

Suggest alternatives to Construction 8, based on alternate interior angles or on supplementary angles on the same side of the transversal.

Critical Thinking

Analysis Ask students to examine alternatives to Construction 8.

Assignment Guide

See p. 394B for assignments.

Construction 6 To construct the perpendicular to a given line at a given point on the line

Given: Point P on l
Construct: $\overleftrightarrow{PZ} \perp l$

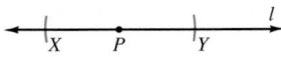
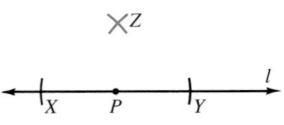
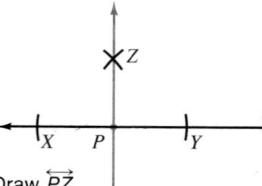

With P as center and with any radius, draw arcs on l at X and Y.

With centers X and Y and a radius greater than PX, draw arcs intersecting at Z.

Draw $\overleftrightarrow{PZ}$.

Result: $\overleftrightarrow{PZ} \perp l$ Justified in Practice Exercise 15

Construction 7 To construct the perpendicular to a given line from a given point not on the line

Given: Line l and point P not on l
Construct: $\overleftrightarrow{PZ} \perp l$

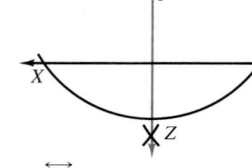

With center P and any radius > distance P to l, draw $\overset{\frown}{XY}$.

With centers X and Y and the same radius, locate Z.
Justified in Practice Exercise 16

Draw $\overleftrightarrow{PZ}$.

Result: $\overleftrightarrow{PZ} \perp l$

Construction 8 To construct a line parallel to a given line and through a given point not on the line

Given: Line l with point P not on l
Construct: Line k through P and parallel to l

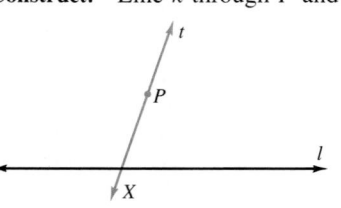
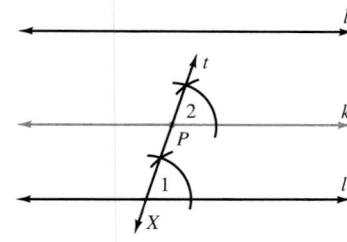

Through P, draw t intersecting l at X.

At P, construct $\angle 2$ corresponding and $\cong$ to $\angle 1$.

Result: $k \parallel l$
Justified in Practice Exercise 17

404   Chapter 10 Constructions and Loci

Developing Mathematical Power

Keeping a Portfolio Have students write a paragraph in which they explain how Construction 5 is used in Construction 6 and how Construction 3 is used in Construction 8. Have them record their responses to the Discussion suggestion in the Lesson Follow-Up (see side column).

CLASS EXERCISES

Thinking Critically

Describe how you would construct each angle.

1. 90° Use Const. 6.   **2.** 45° Bisect one of the rt. ∠s from Ex. 1.   **3.** 135° Add the ∠s from Exercises 1 and 2.   **4.** 22.5° Bisect the ∠ from Exercise 2.

Given any △ABC, explain how you would construct each segment.

5. any altitude Use Const. 7.   **6.** any median Use Const. 5, then draw the segment from midpt. to the opposite vertex.

7. Draw $\overline{AB}$ 3 cm long. Construct its perpendicular bisector $\overline{XY}$ intersecting $\overline{AB}$ at M. How would you check your construction? Measure the lengths of $\overline{AM}$ and $\overline{MB}$.

PRACTICE EXERCISES   Use technology where appropriate.

In Exercises 1–8, construct the indicated angles. See side column.

A   **1.** 45°   **2.** 150°   **3.** 75°   **4.** 112.5°

                                               See Additional Answers, p. 702.

5. 105°   **6.** 135°   **7.** 150°   **8.** 120°

9. Draw a scalene triangle. Through one vertex, construct a line parallel to the opposite side.

10. Draw an acute angle. Construct its bisector. From any point on the angle bisector, construct a perpendicular to each side. What is true of the resulting triangles? Justify your answer. Answers may vary. They are ≅ by LA, by ASA, and so on.

11. Draw any acute ∠AVB. Through A, construct a parallel to $\overrightarrow{VB}$. Through B, construct a parallel to $\overrightarrow{VA}$. What is the resulting figure? Justify. a parallelogram; both pairs of opposite sides are parallel

Repeat Exercise 11 and adjust it in order to construct the following.

12. a rhombus Make $\overline{VA} \cong \overline{VB}$.   **13.** a rectangle Make ∠AVB a rt. ∠.   **14.** a square Make ∠AVB a rt. ∠ and $\overline{VA} \cong \overline{VB}$.

Write a justification for the following constructions. See Additional Answers, p. 702.

15. Construction 6   **16.** Construction 7   **17.** Construction 8

Use these figures as models for the constructions in Exercises 18–22.
Constructions may vary.

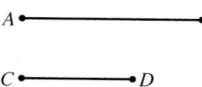
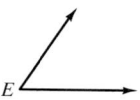
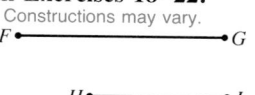

B   **18.** Construct a right triangle with legs congruent to $\overline{AB}$ and $\overline{CD}$. Const. $\overline{XY} \cong \overline{AB}$; then const. $\overline{XZ} \cong \overline{CD}$ and ⊥ $\overline{XY}$; draw $\overline{ZY}$.

19. Construct a right triangle with one leg congruent to $\overline{CD}$ and the hypotenuse congruent to $\overline{AB}$. Const. $\overline{XY} \cong \overline{CD}$; at X, const. the ⊥; with center Y and radius AB, draw an arc intersecting the ⊥; label the intersection Z. Draw $\overline{YZ}$.

10.2 Constructing Perpendiculars and Parallels   **405**

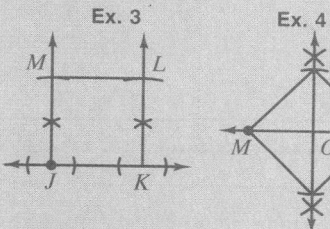
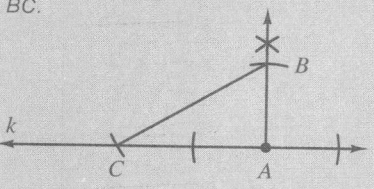
405

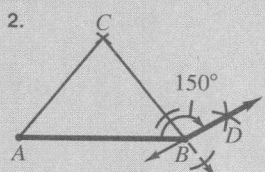

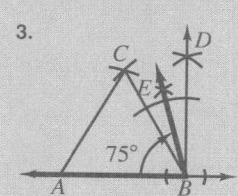

Teacher's Resource Book

Follow-Up Investigation, *Chapter 10,*
p. 4.

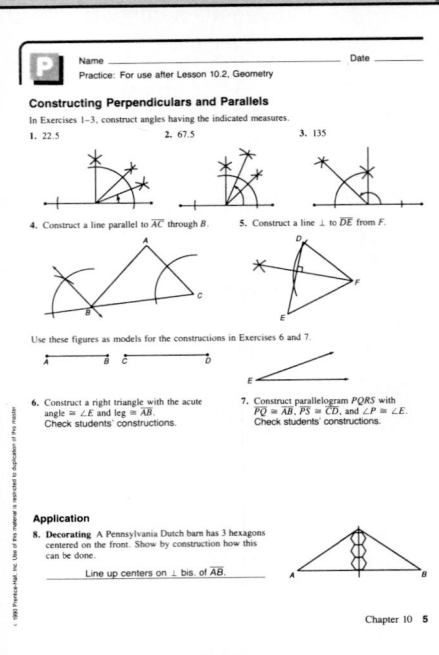

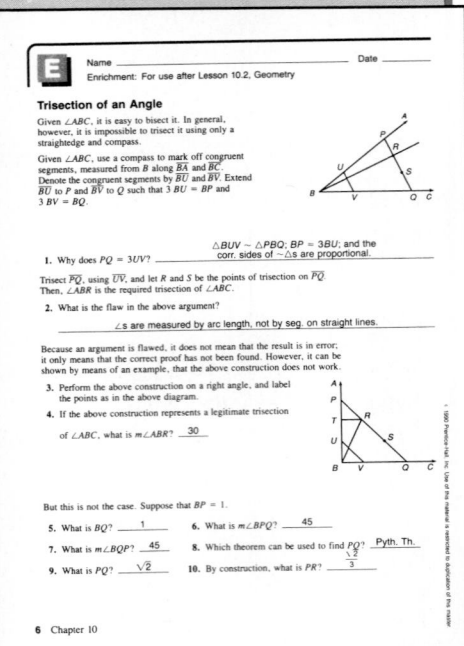

See Additional Answers, p. 702.

20. Construct a right triangle having one leg congruent to $\overline{AB}$ and one acute angle congruent to $\angle E$. Const. $\overline{XY} \cong \overline{AB}$; const. $\perp$ at X; const. $\angle Y \cong \angle E$; extend side of $\angle Y$ to intersect the $\perp$ at Z.

21. Construct a quadrilateral with one angle congruent to $\angle E$ and sides congruent to $\overline{AB}$, $\overline{CD}$, $\overline{FG}$, and $\overline{HI}$. Const. $\angle X \cong \angle E$; then const. remaining sides.

22. Construct a square having sides congruent to $\overline{HI}$. Use Const. 5 for a rt. angle, then four sides $\cong \overline{HI}$.

23. Draw any acute scalene triangle. Construct the three altitudes. What seems to be true of their intersection(s)? It's a pt. in the interior of the △.

24. Draw any obtuse scalene triangle. Construct the three altitudes. Compare the result with the result in Exercise 23. The intersection is in the exterior of the △.

25. Draw any scalene triangle. Construct midpoints M and N of two sides. Draw $\overline{MN}$. What seems to be true of $\overline{MN}$ and the third side? Justify. $\overline{MN} \parallel \overline{BC}$. The segment joining the midpts. is ∥ to third side.

C **26.** Draw any △ABC. Construct midpoints M, N, and O of the three sides. Draw △MNO. What is its relationship to △ABC? Justify your answer. The △s are ~. SSS Th.

27. Draw any two segments. Construct a parallelogram with diagonals congruent to the two segments. Is this parallelogram unique? Explain. No; the segments may intersect to form an $\angle$ of any size.

Applications

28. Architecture How could you check by construction whether or not the peak of the Eiffel Tower is equidistant from the four bases of its support braces? Find the intersection of the diagonals; then construct the $\perp$ from that intersection.

29. Technology A shopkeeper wants to display nine clocks on a wall in three rows of three. Use Logo to generate the design that shows how she can do this. See Solutions Manual.

Developing Mathematical Power

Extension Construct a right triangle whose legs have lengths in the ratio 2 to 1.

30. Why is the ratio of the hypotenuse length to the shorter leg length $\sqrt{5}$? by the Pyth. Th., $(2x)^2 + (x)^2 = h^2$; $h = x\sqrt{5}$; $\frac{x\sqrt{5}}{x} = \sqrt{5}$

31. Use a calculator to find $\sqrt{5}$ and check your construction by measuring the hypotenuse and the shorter leg to the nearest millimeter. $\sqrt{5} \approx 2.24$; $\frac{\text{length of hyp.}}{\text{length of shorter leg}} \approx 2.2$

32. Draw any segment $\overline{AB}$. Construct a segment whose length is $\sqrt{2} \cdot AB$. See Additional Answers, p. 702.

33. Draw any segment $\overline{AB}$. Construct a segment whose length is $\sqrt{3} \cdot AB$.

406 Chapter 10 Constructions and Loci

Concurrent Lines

Objectives: To state and apply theorems about concurrent lines
To perform basic concurrent line constructions and use them in original construction exercises

In mathematical applications to navigation, astronomy, and other sciences, it is important to know when three or more light or radio beams meet in the same point. Such applications use the geometric concept *concurrency*.

Investigation—*Constructions*

1. Draw an acute triangle and construct its three altitudes.
2. Which construction did you use? Const. 7
3. What seems to be true about the lines that contain the altitudes? They intersect at a single pt.
4. Repeat Step 1 with a right triangle and an obtuse triangle.
5. Does your conclusion in Step 3 still hold true? yes

Three or more lines are **concurrent** if and only if they intersect in the same point. Several kinds of lines associated with triangles are concurrent and each intersection point has a special name.

> **Theorem 10.1** The bisectors of the angles of a triangle intersect in a point that is equidistant from the three sides of the triangle.

Given: $\triangle ABC$ with angle bisectors $\overrightarrow{AO}$, $\overrightarrow{BO}$, and $\overrightarrow{CX}$

Prove: $\overrightarrow{CX}$ is concurrent at O with $\overrightarrow{AO}$ and $\overrightarrow{BO}$, and $OP = OQ = OR$.

Plan: Consider $\overline{OP}$, $\overline{OQ}$, and $\overline{OR}$ perpendicular to the sides of the triangle. Since O must be equidistant from the sides of $\angle A$ and $\angle B$, it follows that $OP = OR$ and $OP = OQ$. By the transitive property, $OR = OQ$ so O must lie on the bisector of $\angle C$.
Proved in Practice Exercise 22

The point of concurrency of the angle bisectors of a triangle is called the **incenter**.

10.3 Concurrent Lines **407**

Developing Mathematical Power

Cooperative Learning Assign groups of students to complete the Critical Thinking activity, p. 10, in the *Teacher's Resource Book*. Stress the importance of following directions and being precise in constructions. Each group should reach a consensus on its results. Allow time for the reporter from each group to present the group's findings to the class.

LESSON PLAN

Vocabulary

Centroid   Incenter
Circumcenter   Orthocenter
Concurrent

Materials/Manipulatives

Compasses and straightedges
Waxed-paper triangles
Teacher's Resource Book,
Transparency 15
Teaching Transparency 65

Technology

Computer
Computer Test Bank, pp.
616–627
The Geometric Supposer:
Triangles
Geometry Problems and
Projects: Triangles, Worksheet
T41, T45–47

LESSON FOCUS

Review

Review medians, altitudes, and bisectors of triangles.

Alternative Learning Styles

Some students may benefit from a kinesthetic approach. Give students large triangles (acute, obtuse, and right) drawn on waxed paper. Ask them to fold angle bisectors, perpendicular bisectors of sides, and medians, and to form conclusions based on their observations.

- Use paper folding to demonstrate and enhance the theorems of the lesson.
- Emphasize that in a scalene triangle the points of concurrency of the special segments are distinct (although they are collinear), and that in an equilateral triangle the points of concurrency coincide.
- Tell students that Theorems 10.3 and 10.4 will be proven in Chapter 13, using *coordinate geometry*.

Common Error

- Some students will be confused by the terms *circumcenter*, *incenter*, *orthocenter*, and *centroid*. Having students define these terms in their own words should help them remember the distinctions.
- See *Teacher's Resource Book* for additional remediation.

Theorem 10.2 The perpendicular bisectors of the sides of a triangle intersect in a point that is equidistant from the vertices of the triangle.

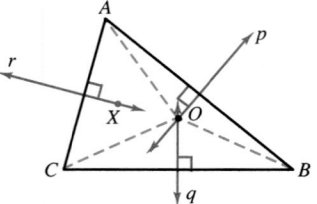

Given: $\triangle ABC$ with perpendicular bisectors p, q, and r of its three sides

Prove: r is concurrent with p and q at O, and $OA = OB = OC$.

Plan: Prove that O is equidistant from A and B and from C and B. Hence O must also lie on the perpendicular bisector of $\overline{AC}$.
Proved in Practice Exercise 23

The point of concurrency of the perpendicular bisectors of the sides of a triangle is called the **circumcenter.**

Theorem 10.3 The lines that contain the altitudes of a triangle intersect in one point. Proved in Exercise 29, page 576 (Chapter 13)

The point of concurrency of the altitudes is called the **orthocenter.**

Construction 9 To construct the orthocenter of a given triangle

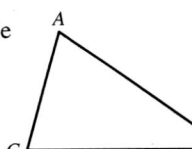

Given: $\triangle ABC$

Construct: Orthocenter X of $\triangle ABC$

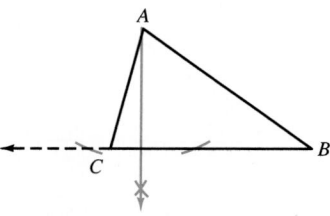

Construct the perpendicular from vertex A to opposite side $\overline{BC}$.

Construct the perpendicular from vertex B to opposite side $\overline{AC}$.

Result: X is the orthocenter.
Justified in Practice Exercise 26.

Developing Mathematical Power

Keeping a Portfolio To help students keep the terminology straight, have them write a definition for each term in their own words and sketch an illustration of each. Encourage them to create mneumonics to help remember what intersects for what "center," for example; mc—medians intersect for centroid.

> **Theorem 10.4** The medians of a triangle are concurrent. The length of the segment of a median from the vertex to the point of concurrency is $\frac{2}{3}$ the length of the entire median. Proved in Exercise 30, page 576 (Chapter 13)

The point of concurrency of the medians of any triangle is called the **centroid.**

Construction 10 To construct the centroid of a given triangle

Given: △ABC

Construct: Centroid X of △ABC

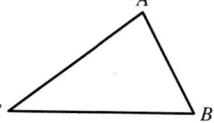

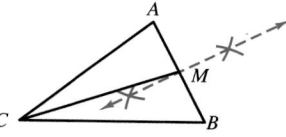

Construct midpoint *M* and median $\overline{CM}$.

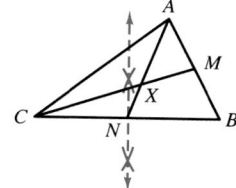

Construct median $\overline{AN}$.

Result: Their intersection *X* is the centroid.
Justified in Practice Exercise 27

CLASS EXERCISES

Name each of the following from this figure.

1. altitude $\overline{AT}$ **2.** ∠ bisector $\overline{RC}$

3. median $\overline{SB}$ **4.** ⊥ bisector $\overline{AT}$

5. Draw an obtuse triangle and construct its orthocenter. See side column.

6. Draw an obtuse triangle and construct its centroid.

$\overline{AQ}$, $\overline{BR}$, and $\overline{CP}$ **are the medians of △ABC.**
△BCP is isosceles, with $\overline{CP} \cong \overline{CB}$, **BR = 12 and**
CO = 22. Find these lengths.

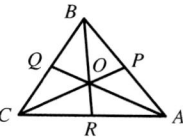

7. CP 33   **8.** OR 4   **9.** BC 33   **10.** OP 11

LESSON FOLLOW-UP

Assignment Guide
See p. 394B for assignments.

Additional Answers

5.

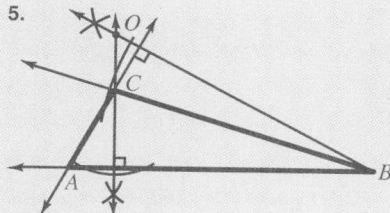

6.

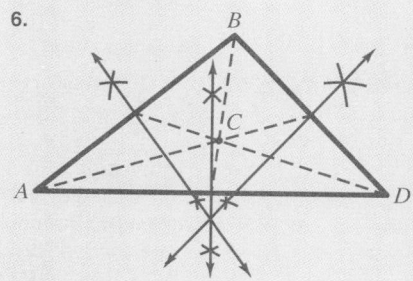

Additional Answers for p. 410

3.

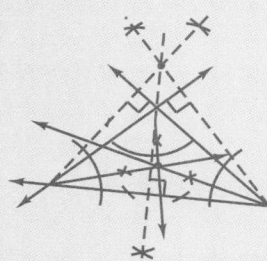

4.

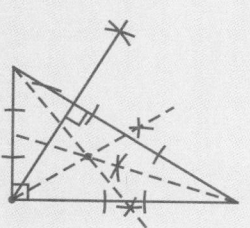

Test Yourself

See *Teacher's Resource Book, Tests,*
pp. 101–102.

Lesson Quiz

Describe a triangle that satisfies the
given conditions.

1. The orthocenter is at a vertex of the
   triangle.
2. The circumcenter, incenter, centroid, and orthocenter are the same
   point.

$\overline{AN}$ and $\overline{CM}$ are medians of $\triangle ABC$
that intersect in point O.

3. If $AO = 12$ cm, then $AN = \underline{?}$.
4. If $CO = x^2 - 2x$ and $MO = 8 - x$,
   then $x = \underline{?}$ or $\underline{?}$ and $CM = \underline{?}$ or
   $\underline{?}$.

1. a rt. $\triangle$ 2. equilateral $\triangle$
3. 18 cm   4. 4 or −4; 12 or 36

Enrichment

A *cevian* is a segment that joins a vertex of a triangle to a point on the opposite side. In 1678, an Italian mathematician named Ceva proved Ceva's The-
orem: Three cevians, $\overline{JM}$, $\overline{KN}$, and $\overline{LO}$
of $\triangle JKL$, are con-
current if and only
if $\dfrac{JN}{NL} \cdot \dfrac{LM}{MK} \cdot$
$\dfrac{KO}{OJ} = 1$.

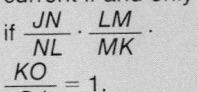

Use Ceva's Theorem to show that the
angle bisectors of a triangle are concurrent.

Given: $\triangle ABC$ with an-
gle-bisectors $\overrightarrow{AD}$, $\overrightarrow{BE}$,
and $\overrightarrow{CF}$

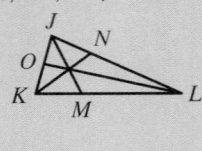

Prove: $\overline{AD}$, $\overline{BE}$, and $\overline{CF}$
are concurrent.

Proof: By the $\triangle$ Angle-Bisector Th.,
since AD bisects $\angle BAC$, $\dfrac{BD}{DC} = \dfrac{AB}{AC}$;

Similarly, $\dfrac{AF}{FB} = \dfrac{CA}{CB}$ and $\dfrac{CE}{EA} = \dfrac{BC}{BA}$;

thus $\dfrac{BD}{DC} \cdot \dfrac{AF}{FB} \cdot \dfrac{CE}{EA} = \dfrac{AB}{AC} \cdot \dfrac{CA}{CB} \cdot \dfrac{BC}{BA} = 1$.

By Ceva's Th., $\overline{AD}$, $\overline{BE}$, and $\overline{CF}$ are concurrent.

PRACTICE EXERCISES   Use technology where appropriate.

A   **1. Writing in Geometry** Construct a large equilateral triangle. Then
construct the triangle's circumcenter, incenter, centroid, and orthocenter.
Describe the result. All four are the same pt; see side column.

**Draw an example of each type of triangle. Estimate the location of the
incenter and the orthocenter. Then check by construction.** Answers may vary.
See side column pages 409–410.

2. Acute triangle   3. Obtuse triangle   4. Right triangle

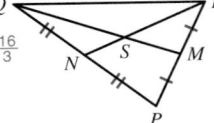

5. If $RN = 24$, find RS and SN. 16; 8
6. If $QM = 16$, find SQ and SM. $\frac{32}{3}$, $\frac{16}{3}$
7. If $SQ = 6$, find SM and MQ. 3; 9
8. If $SN = 12$, find RS and RN. 24; 36
9. $SM:SN = 4:3$ and $SM = 12$. Find SQ, MQ, SN, RS, and RN. 24; 36; 9; 18; 27
10. $SM:SN = 4:3$ and $SQ = 6$. Find SM, MQ, SN, RS, and RN. 3; 9; $\frac{9}{4}$; $\frac{9}{2}$; $\frac{27}{4}$
11. In what kind of triangle are the medians also angle bisectors? equilateral
12. In what kind of triangle is at least one median an angle bisector? isos.
13. In what kind of triangle is the orthocenter at a vertex? rt. $\triangle$
14. In what kind of triangle is the orthocenter also the incenter? equilateral
15. In what kind of a triangle is the circumcenter outside the triangle? obtuse $\triangle$
16. In what kind of a triangle is the circumcenter on one of the sides? right $\triangle$

$\triangle JKL$ has medians $\overline{OJ}$, $\overline{NL}$, and $\overline{MK}$.

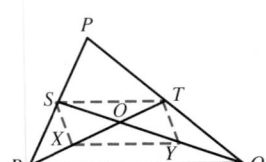

B   17. If $LP = 6n$ and $PN = n^2$, then $n = \underline{?}$. 3
18. If $MP = 2x - 3$ and $MK = 5x + 7$, then $x = \underline{?}$ and
   $PK = \underline{?}$. 16; 58
19. If $JP = x^2 - 2x$ and $PO = 2(x + 4)$, then $x = \underline{?}$ or
   $\underline{?}$ and $OJ = \underline{?}$. 8; −2; 12 or 72
20. If $JK = LK$, $NP = x^2 + 3x + 1$, and $PL = 3x^2 - 5$, then $OJ = \underline{?}$. 213

21. $\overline{QS}$ and $\overline{RT}$ are medians of $\triangle PQR$. X and Y are
   midpoints of $\overline{RO}$ and $\overline{QO}$, respectively. Explain
   why $STYX$ is a parallelogram.
   See Additional Answers, p. 702.

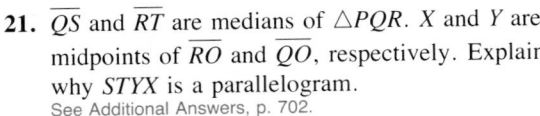

22. Prove Theorem 10.1.
23. Prove Theorem 10.2.

1.

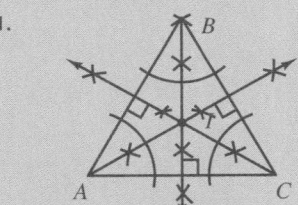

2.

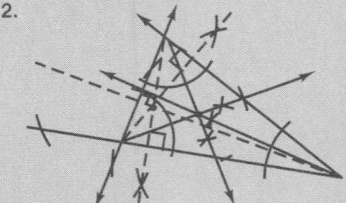

24. Prove: The median of an isosceles triangle from its vertex angle is also the altitude from that vertex. See Additional Answers, p. 702.

25. Prove: The altitude from the vertex angle of an isosceles triangle is also the median from that vertex.

26. Justify Construction 9.   **27.** Justify Construction 10.

C **28.** The length of each side of equilateral $\triangle ABC$ is 24. Find the radius of the circumscribed circle. $8\sqrt{3}$

29. The length of each side of equilateral $\triangle ABC$ is 24. Find the radius of the inscribed circle. $4\sqrt{3}$

30. Prove: If a triangle has two congruent medians, then it is isosceles.

Applications

31. Architecture A decoration over the entrance to a shopping center is to consist of a circle inscribed in an isosceles triangle. Describe how an architect might draw it on a blueprint. Draw an isos. △. Use Const. 4 to find the incenter. Using the distance from the incenter to one side as a radius, draw the ⊙ with center at the incenter.

32. Technology Use Logo to design the solution to this planning problem: Town B is 20 km due East of Town A, and Town C is 15 km due North of Town A. Locate a shopping center that is equidistant from all three towns. See Solutions Manual.

TEST YOURSELF

1. Construct $\overline{ER} \cong \overline{AB}$.

2. Construct $\overline{GH}$ so that $GH = 2 \cdot CD + \frac{1}{2}AB$. See side column.

3. Based upon the SAS Postulate, construct $\triangle IJK$ such that $\overline{IJ} \cong \overline{AB}$, $\overline{JK} \cong \overline{CD}$, and $\angle J \cong \angle Z$. See Additional Answers, p. 702.

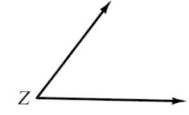

10.1

4. By constructing an equilateral triangle, construct a 30° angle.

For Exercises 5–8, draw any $\triangle VXY$ with an obtuse angle at V.

5. Construct the altitude from vertex V.

10.2

6. Construct the median to side $\overline{VX}$.

7. Construct the perpendicular bisector of $\overline{VY}$.

8. Construct its orthocenter.

10.3

9. Draw a right triangle. Construct its centroid.

10. One of the medians of a triangle is 18 cm long. Where will a second median of the triangle intersect the given median? If AM in △ABC is 18 cm, the 2nd median will intersect it 12 cm from A to M.

10.3 Concurrent Lines **411**

2.

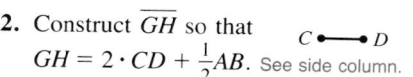

3.

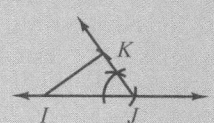

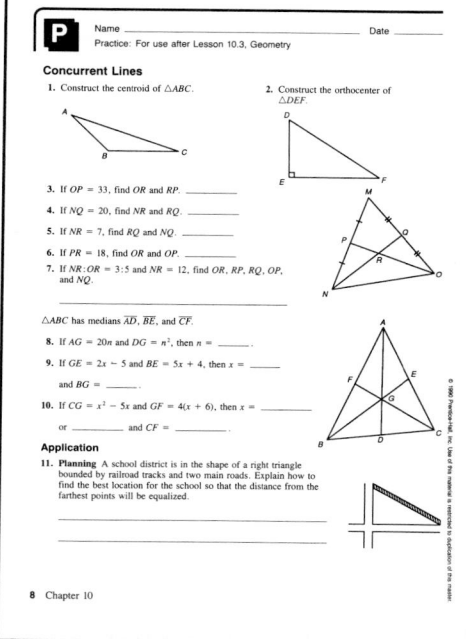
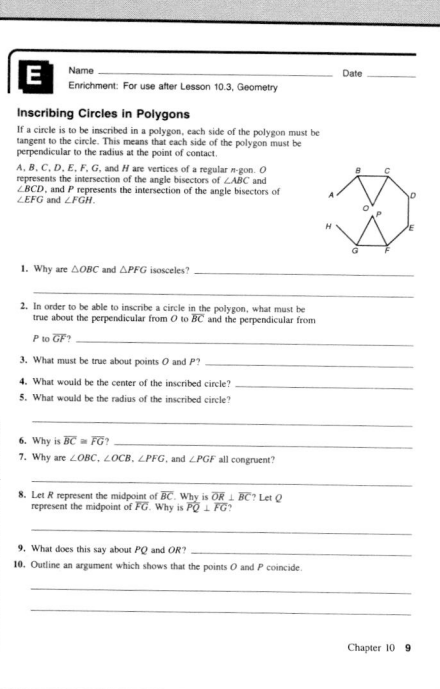

Materials/Manipulatives

Compasses and straightedges
Paper-folding materials
Cardboard
Teacher's Resource Book,
  Transparency 16
Teaching Transparency 66

Technology

Computer
Computer Test Bank, pp.
  627–636
The Geometric Supposer:
  Triangles, p. 91

LESSON FOCUS

Review

As a review, ask students how tangents are related to radii of circles. A line is a tangent iff it is ⊥ to a radius at a point on the circle.

Alternative Learning Styles

• The Investigation provides a concrete approach to the construction of a tangent to a circle at a point on the circle. Challenge students to demonstrate how they would use paper-folding to locate the center of a given circle. Fold the paper so that two halves of the circle coincide. Unfold. Fold in another way so that two halves of the circle coincide. The point of the intersection of the folds (diameters) is the center.

• Students may trace the steps to the constructions in the text. Then they should repeat the procedure by going over their tracing using a compass and a straightedge.

10.4

Circles

Objectives: To perform constructions involving circles
To use these basic constructions in original construction exercises

The constructions presented thus far can be used in performing constructions involving circles and their related lines, rays, and segments.

Investigation—*Using Manipulatives*

You can use paper folding to construct a tangent to a given ⊙*O* through a given point *P* on the circle.

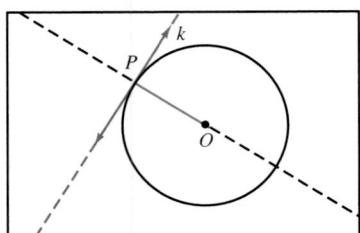

1. Fold and make a crease along $\overleftrightarrow{OP}$ and mark $\overline{OP}$.

2. At *P*, fold and crease line *k* ⊥ $\overline{OP}$.

3. Why is *k* tangent to ⊙*O*? Th. 9.2 states that a line ⊥ to a radius at its endpt. on the circle is tan. to the ⊙.

Construction 11 To construct a tangent to a circle at a point on the circle

Given: Point *P* on ⊙*O*

Construct: Line *t* tangent to ⊙*O* at *P*

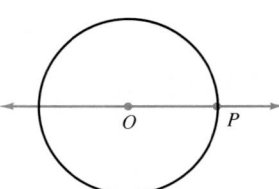

Draw $\overleftrightarrow{OP}$.
Justified in Practice Exercise 13

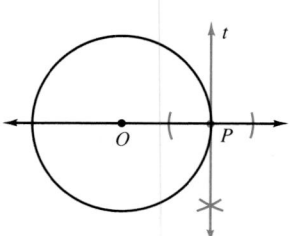

Construct *t* ⊥ $\overleftrightarrow{OP}$ at *P*.

Result: *t* is tangent to ⊙*O* at *P*.

Developing Mathematical Power

Keeping a Portfolio Have students record the steps they used to do Exercises 11, 12, 15, and 16. Then have them write a brief description of the correlation between Exercises 11 and 15 and 12 and 16. Have them discuss if any of those exercises would be helpful for Exercise 20 and explain why or why not.

Construction 12   To construct a tangent to a circle through a point in the exterior of the circle

Given: Point P in the exterior of $\odot O$

Construct: $\overleftrightarrow{PT}$ tangent to $\odot O$

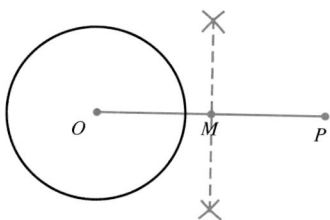

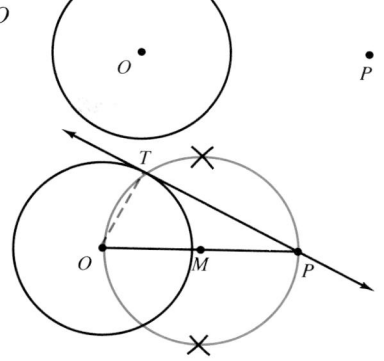

Draw $\overline{PO}$. Construct the midpoint M of $\overline{PO}$.

With M as center and with $\overline{MO}$ as radius, draw $\odot M$ intersecting $\odot O$ at T.

Result: $\overleftrightarrow{PT} \perp \overline{OT}$; so $\overleftrightarrow{PT}$ is tangent to $\odot O$.

Justification: Since M is a midpt., it is the center of a $\odot$ with diam. $\overline{OP}$. T on $\odot O$ is also the vertex of an inscribed $\angle$ of $\odot M$. The intercepted arc is a semicircle. Thus $\angle T$ is a rt. $\angle$. Hence $\overline{OT} \perp \overleftrightarrow{PT}$, so $\overleftrightarrow{PT}$ is tan. to $\odot O$ at T.

Construction 13   To locate the center of a given circle

Given: $\odot O$ with unknown location of center O

Construct: The location of center point O

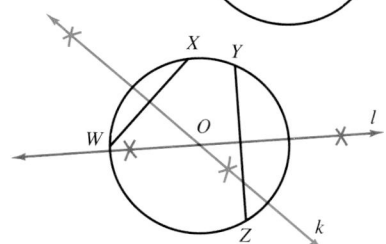

Draw any two nonparallel chords $\overline{WX}$ and $\overline{YZ}$.
Justified in Practice Exercise 16

Construct k and l, the perpendicular bisectors of $\overline{WX}$ and $\overline{YZ}$, respectively.

Result: Their intersection is center O.

10.4 Circles   **413**

- Before beginning the lesson, review important theorems about tangents. This will make the constructions more reasonable to students.
- Continue the lesson format in which the constructions are demonstrated on the chalkboard, while students do the same steps at their desks. Make certain students can describe the steps.
- Continue to emphasize the justifications of the constructions, making certain that students can provide appropriate justifications when asked.
- Provide several examples in which constructions must be combined in original ways. This aids in problem solving.
- Point out that the circumcenter of a triangle is the center of its circumscribed circle, and that the incenter of a triangle is the center of its inscribed circle.
- Use the Class Exercises to provide closure to the lesson, since they emphasize many of the important points related to justifications and mechanics of constructions.

Common Error

- Constructions involving tangents require a great deal of accuracy in order to produce the desired results. Some students may be careless in carrying out steps, so continue to emphasize the need for appropriate techniques in completing constructions.
- See *Teacher's Resource Book* for additional remediation.

Discussion

Ask students a series of questions designed to help them work *backwards* to answer the first question.

1. How would you inscribe an equilateral triangle in a given circle?
2. How would you inscribe a regular hexagon in a given triangle?
3. How could you divide a circle into six congruent arcs?
4. How could you mark a 60° arc of a circle?

4. Mark point A on ⊙O. With A as center and radius length AO, draw an arc intersecting the ⊙ at a point B. Then △ABO is an equil. △, so m∠AOB = 60, and m$\overarc{AB}$ = 60.
3. Continue the process described above; with the same radius length and center B, determine C so that m$\overarc{BC}$ = 60, and so on.
2. Draw $\overline{AB}$, $\overline{BC}$, $\overline{CD}$, $\overline{DE}$, $\overline{EF}$, and $\overline{FA}$ for points A, B, . . ., F determined above. Since each chord has length equal to the radius length of the ⊙, the chords are ≅.
1. Draw $\overline{AC}$, $\overline{CE}$, and $\overline{EA}$. Since each chord intercepts a 120° arc, △ACE is an equil. △.

Critical Thinking

Analysis Ask students to reason backward to solve a problem.

Assignment Guide

See p. 394B for assignments.

Construction 14 To circumscribe a circle about a given triangle

Given: △ABC

Construct: ⊙X circumscribed about △ABC

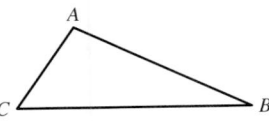

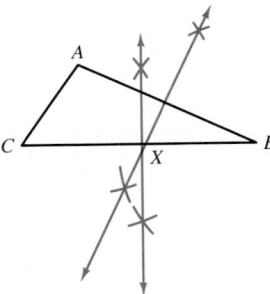

Construct perpendicular bisectors of any two sides of △ABC, intersecting at X.

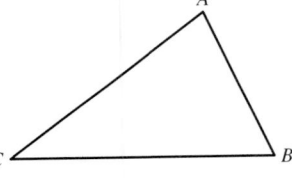

With center X, draw ⊙X with radius $\overline{XA}$.

Result: ⊙X passes through A, B, and C.

Justified in Class Exercise 3

Construction 15 To inscribe a circle in a given triangle

Given: △ABC

Construct: ⊙X inscribed in △ABC

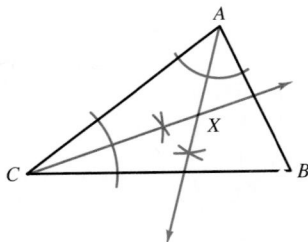

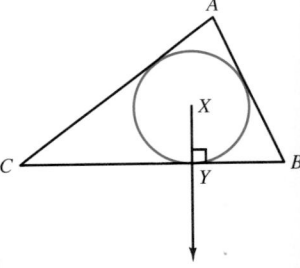

Construct the angle bisectors of any two angles of △ABC, intersecting at X.

Construct the perpendicular from X to any side of △ABC. Call the intersection Y.

Justified in Class Exercise 4

Construct a circle with center X and radius $\overline{XY}$.

Result: ⊙X is inscribed.

Class Exercises

3a.

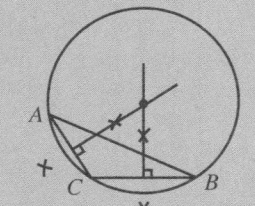

3b.

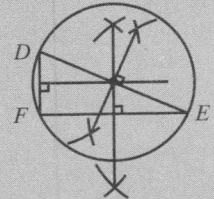

CLASS EXERCISES

Thinking Critically

1. In doing Construction 14, why is it necessary to construct only two perpendicular bisectors? The 3rd ⊥ bis. will intersect the other 2 at the circumcenter.

2. In doing Construction 15, why is it necessary to construct only two angle bisectors? The 3rd ∠ bis. will intersect the other 2 at the incenter.

Draw an obtuse scalene triangle, △ABC, and a right triangle, △DEF.

3. Estimate where the circumcenters are. Then use Construction 14 to circumscribe a circle about each triangle. Justify. The ⊥ bisectors of the sides of a △ intersect in a pt. equidist. from the vertices.

4. Estimate where the incenters are. Then use Construction 15 to inscribe a circle in each triangle. Justify. The bis. of the ∠s of a △ intersect in a pt. that is equidist. from the 3 sides.

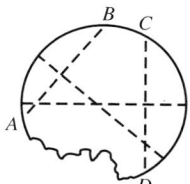

PRACTICE EXERCISES

Use technology where appropriate.

A

1. Writing in Geometry A circular piece of paper has been torn. The figure suggests how to find the circle's center by paper folding. Describe the procedure. Fold non∥ chords $\overline{AB}$ and $\overline{CD}$. Then fold along the ⊥ bis. of each chord. The intersection of the ⊥ bis. is the center.

See Additional Answers, p. 702.

2. Draw a ⊙O. Select any point P on it. Construct a tangent to ⊙O at P.

3. Draw a ⊙Q. Draw any diameter. Construct tangents to ⊙Q at the endpoints of the diameter. Describe how the tangents are related. Tangents are ∥.

4. Draw a ⊙R. Select any point E in the circle's exterior. Construct two tangents from E to ⊙R.

Draw a large example of each triangle. Estimate the location of the circumcenter. Then check your estimate by using construction methods.

5. Acute scalene   **6.** Obtuse scalene   **7.** Right

Draw a large example of each triangle. Estimate the location of the incenter. Then check your estimate by using construction methods.

8. Acute scalene   **9.** Obtuse scalene

10. Draw a ⊙R. Using the radius length on your compass, make consecutive arcs around the circle. Draw segments between consecutive arcs. What kind of figure does this appear to be? Justify your answer. regular hexagon; each arc mark creates an equilateral △, 6 ⩰ altogether.

10.4 Circles   **415**

Developing Mathematical Power

Cooperative Learning Select teams of students to compete in the Centroid Challenge. Since the centroid is the center of gravity of a triangle, challenge each team to cut out three triangles (one acute, one right, and one obtuse), construct the centroid of each, and successfully balance the triangle on a pencil point.

Developing Mathematical Power

Thinking Critically Students are asked to predict where the center of gravity is for a circular disk and a rectangular piece.

Lesson Quiz

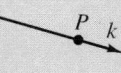

1. Construct a tangent to ⊙O from P.

2. Construct a line tangent to ⊙O that is perpendicular to k.

3. Given any three noncollinear points, A, B, and C, explain how to construct a circle passing through the points.

1. Use Construction 12.

2. Through O, construct line j ∥ k. Let X be one of the 2 points in which j intersects ⊙O. Const. a ⊥ to j at X. This ⊥ is also ⊥ to k, since a line ⊥ to one of 2 ∥ lines is ⊥ to the other.

3. Const. $\overline{AB}$, $\overline{BC}$, and $\overline{CA}$ and use Construction 14.

Enrichment

The ancient Greeks found at least three construction problems they were unable to solve using only a compass and straightedge. These problems are:

1. Trisecting an angle
2. "Doubling a cube," in which a cube is to be constructed that has a volume exactly twice that of another cube
3. "Squaring the circle," in which a square is to be constructed that has area equal to the area of a given circle

Research these problems.

Class Exercises

4a.
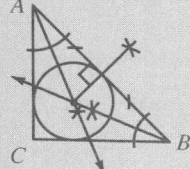

Teacher's Resource Book

Follow-Up Investigation, *Chapter 10*, p. 10.

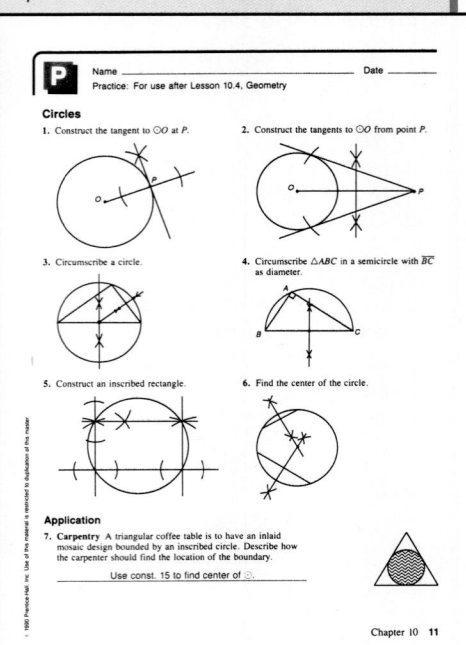

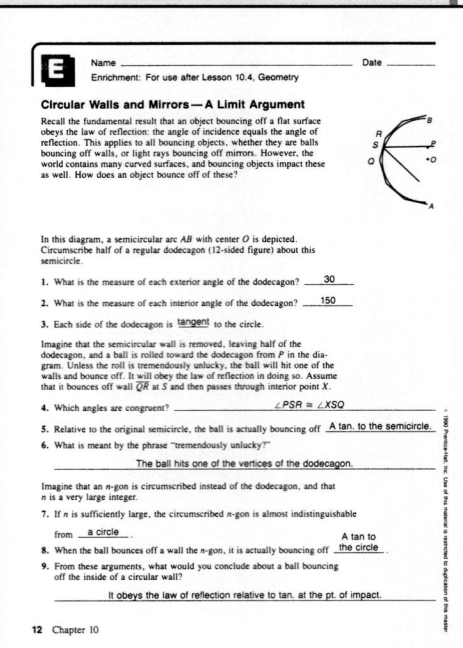

11. Draw a circle. Construct a square circumscribed around the circle.

12. Draw a circle. Construct a square inscribed in the circle.

B **13.** Write a justification of Construction 11. *t was constructed ⊥ radius $\overline{OP}$ of ⊙O. A line ⊥ to a radius at its endpt. on the ⊙ is tan. to the ⊙.*

14. Examine an alternative method of constructing a perpendicular to $\overline{AB}$ at *P*. Use any point *O* not on $\overline{AB}$ as center and $\overline{OP}$ as radius to construct ⊙O intersecting $\overline{AB}$ at *D* and *P*. Draw diameter $\overline{DC}$. Draw $\overleftrightarrow{PC}$. Justify. *∠CPD is an inscribed ∠ that intercepts a semicircle; hence m∠CPD = 90, and $\overleftrightarrow{CP}$ ⊥ $\overline{AB}$ at P.*

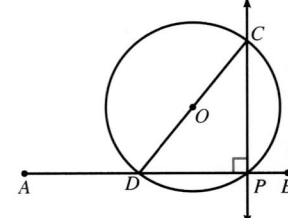

15. Draw a square. Construct a circle circumscribed around the square.

16. Draw a square. Construct a circle inscribed in the square.

17. Justify Construction 13. Explain why the chords must not be ‖ . *The ⊥ bis. of a chord contains a diameter; if the chords were ‖, the ⊥ bis. would coincide and there*

18. Inscribe a 12-sided regular polygon in a circle. *would be no one pt. of intersection.*

C **19. Given:** ⊙O and line *k*, which are nonintersecting
Construct: line *l* such that *l*‖*k*, and *l* tangent to ⊙O

20. Given: $\overline{AB}$
Construct: a square having $\overline{AB}$ as its diagonal

21. Given: $\overline{AB}$ and acute ∠*C*
Construct: ⊙O with a segment congruent to $\overline{AB}$ as a chord and with an inscribed angle congruent to ∠*C*

22. Given: Two nonintersecting ⊙s with radius lengths in the ratio 1:2
Construct: A common external tangent to the circles

Applications

23. Archaeology This fragment of a circular metal disk is used to reconstruct the complete disk. How can this be done? *Const. 13*

24. Technology Use Logo to generate a circle with tangents at six equidistant points on the circle. What polygon is generated by the tangents? Use your procedure to generate any *n*-sided polygon. *See Solutions Manual.*

Developing Mathematical Power

25. Logical Reasoning The center of gravity of a triangular piece of an evenly distributed material is the centroid. The centroid is a balancing point. Where would you expect to find the center of gravity for a circular disk? for a rectangular piece?
center of the ⊙; intersection of diag.

416 Chapter 10 Constructions and Loci

Special Segments

Objectives: To perform constructions involving proportional segments
To use the basic special-segment constructions in original construction exercises

Once a segment length has been chosen as a unit, it is possible to construct a segment of length n, where n is any positive integer. Here is an example for $n = 3$.

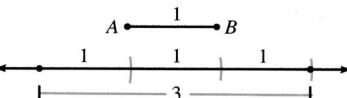

Investigation—*Visualizing the Concept*

This figure shows how to construct a segment of length $m \cdot n$, where $m = 3$ and $n = 2$.

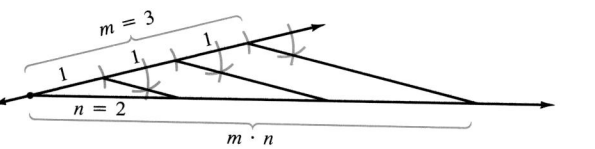

1. Describe the segments between the lines labeled $m = 3$ and $m \cdot n$. ‖

2. Letting $m = 3$ and $n = 1.5$, construct $m \cdot n$. See Additional Answers, page 702.

Construction 16 To divide a given segment into a specified number of congruent segments

Given: $\overline{AB}$

$A \bullet\!\!-\!\!\!-\!\!\!-\!\!\!-\!\!\!-\!\!\!-\!\!\!\bullet B$

Construct: Points C and D such that $\overline{AC} \cong \overline{CD} \cong \overline{DB}$

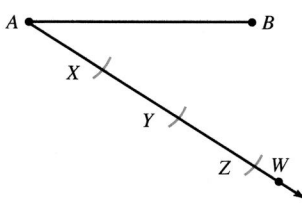

Draw $\overrightarrow{AW}$, where W is any point not on $\overleftrightarrow{AB}$. Use any convenient radius to construct three congruent segments: $\overline{AX}$, $\overline{XY}$, and $\overline{YZ}$.

Draw $\overline{ZB}$. Through X and Y, construct lines parallel to $\overline{ZB}$ and intersecting $\overline{AB}$ at C and D.

Result: $\overline{AC} \cong \overline{CD} \cong \overline{DB}$

Justification: $\overline{AX} \cong \overline{XY} \cong \overline{YZ}$. Constructing $\angle 2$ and $\angle 3$, each congruent to $\angle 1$, created corresponding angles with $\overline{ZB} \parallel \overline{YD} \parallel \overline{XC}$. Hence, the segments cut off on $\overline{AB}$ are also congruent.

10.5 Special Segments **417**

Developing Mathematical Power

Cooperative Learning Working in groups, students can read through the Reading and Writing in Geometry activity, p. 10, in the *Teacher's Resource Book*. They should research one of the three mathematicians mentioned. Each group should prepare a report that is biographical, historical, and visual. Their presentations should include bulletin-board material.

LESSON PLAN

Materials/Manipulatives
Compasses and straightedges
Centimeter rulers
Teacher's Resource Book,
Transparency 17
Teaching Transparency 67

Technology
Calculator
Computer Test Bank, pp.
637–652

LESSON FOCUS

Review
- Solve.

  1. $\dfrac{5}{9} = \dfrac{x}{63}$ **2.** $\dfrac{3}{7} = \dfrac{9}{x}$

  3. $\dfrac{x}{5} = \dfrac{20}{25}$ **4.** $\dfrac{8}{x} = \dfrac{16}{26}$

  1. 35   2. 21   3. 4   4. 13
- Find the geometric mean of:

  5. 3 and 12   **6.** 4 and 18
  7. 5 and 7   **8.** 10 and 12

  5. 6 6. $6\sqrt{2}$ 7. $\sqrt{35}$ 8. $2\sqrt{30}$
- The Mixed Review, Exercises 29–35, involves tangents, secants, and special right triangles.

Alternative Learning Styles
- The Investigation provides the opportunity for students to use a multiplicative method rather than an additive method to construct a segment of a specified unit length.
- The linguistic learner will benefit from verbally explaining the method and the product of each of the constructions on Teaching Transparency 67.

Multicultural Opportunity
See Developing Mathematical Power, p. 417.

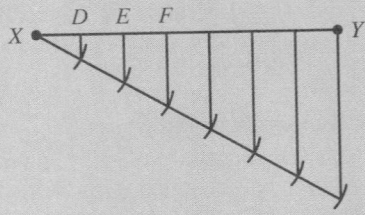
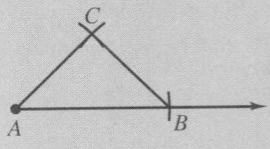
418

Construction 17 To construct a fourth segment in proportion with three given segments

Given: $\overline{AB}$, $\overline{CD}$, and $\overline{EF}$, having lengths a, c, and e, respectively

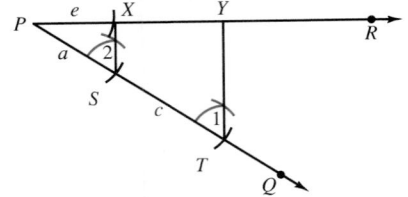

Construct: $\overline{XY}$ such that $a:c = e:XY$

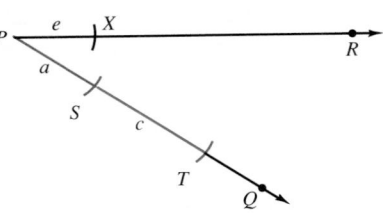

Draw $\angle RPQ$. On $\overrightarrow{PQ}$, construct $\overline{PS}$ and $\overline{ST}$ with lengths a and c, respectively. On $\overrightarrow{PR}$, construct $\overline{PX}$ with length e.

Draw $\overline{SX}$. At T, construct $\angle 1 \cong \angle 2$ at S. Draw $\overline{TY}$.

Result: $a:c = e:XY$

Justification: The construction created $\triangle PTY$ with $\overline{SX} \parallel \overline{YT}$. Thus, sides $\overline{PY}$ and $\overline{PT}$ are divided proportionally, so $a:c = e:XY$.

Construction 18 To construct a segment whose length is the geometric mean between the lengths of two given segments

Given: $\overline{AB}$ and $\overline{CD}$ of lengths a and c

Construct: A segment of length b such that $a:b = b:c$

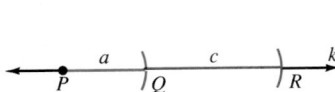

Draw line k. On k, construct $\overline{PQ}$ and $\overline{QR}$ so that $PQ = a$ and $QR = c$.

Construct M, the midpoint of $\overline{PR}$. Draw semi-$\odot M$ with radius $\overline{MP}$. Construct $\overline{YQ} \perp k$.

Result: in right $\triangle PYR$, QY is the geometric mean between a and c.

Justified in Class Exercise 4

1.
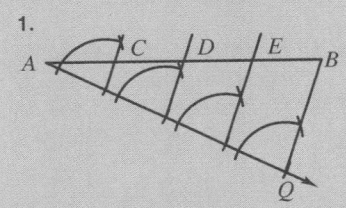

2.
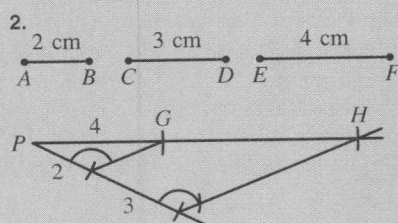

EXAMPLE   **Construct a segment of length $\sqrt{6}$.**

Since $6 = 3 \cdot 2$, $\sqrt{6}$ is the geometric mean between 2 and 3.
Use Construction 18 with $a = 3$ and $c = 2$.

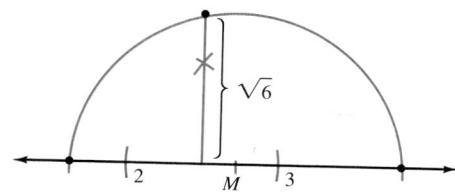

How could a segment of length $\sqrt{6}$ be constructed without using 3 and 2?
Use lengths of 1 and 6.

CLASS EXERCISES   See side column.

1. Draw $\overline{AB}$ such that $AB = 8$ cm. Use Construction 16 to divide $\overline{AB}$ into four congruent segments. Use a ruler to check your work.

2. Use a ruler to draw $\overline{AB}$, $\overline{CD}$, and $\overline{EF}$ such that $AB = 2$ cm, $CD = 3$ cm, and $EF = 4$ cm. Use Construction 17 to construct $\overline{GH}$ such that $AB:CD = EF:GH$. How long should $\overline{GH}$ be? 6 cm

3. State three different ways to use Construction 18 to find $\sqrt{12}$. Do the construction using any one of them. Discuss how a ruler and a calculator can be used to check your work. Use lengths 1,12; 2,6; 4,3. $\sqrt{12} \approx 3.5$ Meas. $\sqrt{12}$ length to see if it is close to 3.5.

Complete this justification of Construction 18.

4. $\overline{PR}$ is a $\underline{}$ of $\odot M$. The perpendicular through Q intersects $\odot M$ at Y. $\angle PYR$ is a $\underline{}$ because it is inscribed in a $\underline{}$. Thus $\triangle PYR$ is a $\underline{}$ with hypotenuse $\underline{}$; $\underline{}$ is the altitude to the $\underline{}$; hence YQ or b is the $\underline{}$ between $\underline{}$ and $\underline{}$. diameter; rt. $\angle$; semicircle; rt. $\triangle$; $\overline{PR}$; $\overline{QY}$; hyp.; geom.-mean; a; c

PRACTICE EXERCISES   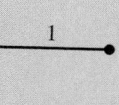 Use technology where appropriate.

For each exercise, draw a 12-cm segment. Divide it into the given number of congruent parts. Check your accuracy with a ruler.

A   1. 3   2. 4   3. 6   4. 8
Check students' drawings. See Additional Answers, page 702.

Draw three segments having lengths of 2 cm, 3 cm, and 5 cm, respectively. Use them to construct a segment of length x. Check your accuracy with a ruler. See side column, p. 420.

5. $\dfrac{2}{3} = \dfrac{5}{x}$ 6. $\dfrac{3}{5} = \dfrac{2}{x}$

10.5 Special Segments   **419**

3.

Developing Mathematical Power

- *Extension* Students devise a construction to find a segment with length $\frac{2}{3}$.
- *Investigation* Students use calculators to determine the decimal for the Golden Ratio and its reciprocal to eight decimal places.

Lesson Quiz

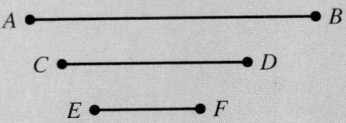

1. Construct $\overline{XY}$ such that $AB : EF = CD : XY$.
2. Find a point Z on $\overline{AB}$ such that $AZ : ZB = 2 : 3$.
3. Using EF as 1 unit, construct a segment with length $\sqrt{12}$.

1. Use Construction 17.
2. Use Construction 16 to divide $\overline{AB}$ into 5
   $\cong$ segments such that $\overline{AG} \cong \overline{GZ} \cong$
   $\overline{ZH} \cong \overline{HK} \cong \overline{KB}$; then Z is the required point.
3. Construct segments having lengths 3 and 4, for example, and use Construction 18 with $a = 3$ and $c = 4$.

Additional Answers

24. Use the lengths from Ex. 19 to copy the given construction. Then const. a ⊙ with radius length 1 cm. Choose a pt. of the ⊙ and use x to mark off 10 $\cong$ arcs. Connect the pts. to form a decagon.

26. From the figure.
$$\frac{1}{x} = \frac{x}{1-x}$$
$$x^2 = 1 - x$$
$$x^2 + x - 1 = 0$$
$$x = \frac{-1 \pm \sqrt{5}}{2}$$
$$x = \frac{\sqrt{5} - 1}{2}$$

Use the three segments of Exercises 5 and 6 to construct the geometric mean of each pair of numbers. Check your accuracy with a ruler and a calculator.

7. 2 and 5   8. 3 and 5   9. 2 and 3   10. 2 and 8

11. Draw any $\overline{AB}$. Separate it into 5 congruent segments $\overline{AW}$, $\overline{WX}$, $\overline{XY}$, $\overline{YZ}$, and $\overline{ZB}$.

12. Use $\overline{AW}$, $\overline{WX}$, and $\overline{XY}$ of Exercise 11 to construct a segment with a length that is to AB as $3 : 5$. $\overline{AY}$ in Ex. 11 is a segment such that $AY : AB = 3 : 5$.

13. Use result of Exercise 11 to construct a triangle with sides having lengths in the ratio $3 : 4 : 5$. The result should look like a right triangle. Is it? Justify your answer. yes, by the Pyth. Th.

B 14. Use the result of Exercise 11 to construct a triangle with sides having lengths in the ratio $3 : 3 : 5$. What kind of triangle is it? isos.

15. Draw any segment $\overline{CD}$. Construct an equilateral triangle with a perimeter CD.

16. Draw any segment $\overline{EF}$. Construct an isosceles triangle with a perimeter EF and with the length of a leg twice as long as the base length.

17. Construct a segment with a length of $\sqrt{14}$ cm. Check your accuracy with a ruler and a calculator.

18. Construct a segment with a length of $\sqrt{5}$ cm. Check your accuracy with a ruler and a calculator.

19. Use segment lengths 1 cm and 10 cm to construct a segment with length $\sqrt{10}$ cm. Compare the result with Exercise 7.

20. Prove that Construction 16 separates a segment into n congruent segments. (Let $n = 3$.)

21. Prove that, given three segments, Construction 17 produces a fourth segment such that the lengths of the four segments are in proportion.

22. Prove that, given two segments, Construction 17 constructs a segment whose length is the geometric mean of the lengths of the given segments.

23. Draw any two segments. Construct a segment whose length is the geometric mean of the lengths of the drawn segments. Use a ruler and a calculator to check your accuracy. See side column and Additional Answers, p. 702.

C 24. The side length of a regular decagon inscribed in a unit circle is $\frac{\sqrt{5} - 1}{2}$, which is also known as the Golden Ratio. Construct a regular decagon with $\frac{\sqrt{5} - 1}{2}$ as a side length.

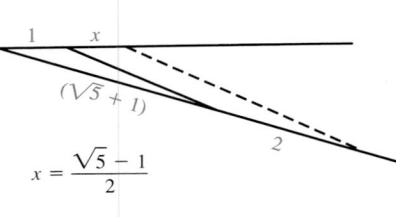

5.
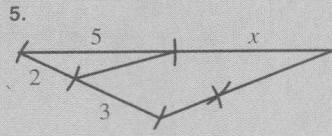

6.
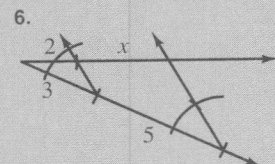

25. Use the construction in Exercise 24 to inscribe a regular pentagon in a unit circle. Repeat Ex. 24, but connect alt. pts. on the ⊙.

26. Prove that the side length of an inscribed regular decagon is the Golden Ratio by using the angle bisector of $\angle B$ as an auxiliary line and using similar triangles to solve for x.

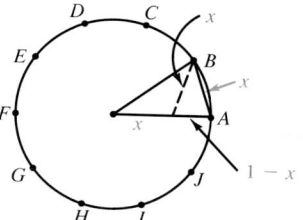

Applications

27. Drawing   Describe how a compass and straightedge can be used to divide a piece of unlined paper into three columns of equal width.
Let the edge of the paper be the given seg. and apply Const. 16.

28. Technology   Use Logo to generate a rectangle with sides in the Golden Ratio. Generate another rectangle with sides in the ratio of the reciprocal of the Golden Ratio. What is the difference between your rectangles?
See Solutions Manual.

Mixed Review

29. Trace $\odot O$ and P. Construct a tangent to $\odot O$ through point P. Label the tangent $\overline{AP}$. See Additional Answers, p. 702.

30. Draw a secant $\overline{BP}$. Label the points that intersect the circle point B and point C.

31. If $AP = 6$ and $CP = 3$, find BP. 12

Given that $\triangle JKL$ is a right triangle with $m\angle L = 90$.

32. If $m\angle K = 30$ and $JL = 5$, find KL. $5\sqrt{3}$

33. If $m\angle J = 45$ and $JK = 8$, find JL. $4\sqrt{2}$

34. If $JL = 13$ and $KL = 5$, find JK. 13

35. If $m\angle J = 60$ and $JL = 2.5$, find JK. 5

Developing Mathematical Power

36. Extension   The construction presented in the Investigation gave the product $m \cdot n$. Devise a construction to find the quotient $\frac{m}{n}$. Use it to find a segment with length $\frac{2}{3}$. See Additional Answers, page 702.

37. Investigation   Use a calculator to show that the Golden Ratio is 0.61803399 to the nearest eight decimal places. Show that the reciprocal, also called the Golden Ratio, is 1.61803399 to the nearest eight decimal places. Find the reciprocal in simplest radical form.

$$\frac{2}{\sqrt{5}-1} \cdot \left(\frac{\sqrt{5}+1}{\sqrt{5}+1}\right) = \frac{2\sqrt{5}+2}{4} = \frac{\sqrt{5}+1}{2}$$

10.5 Special Segments   **421**

Teacher's Resource Book
Follow-Up Investigation, *Chapter 10,* p. 13.

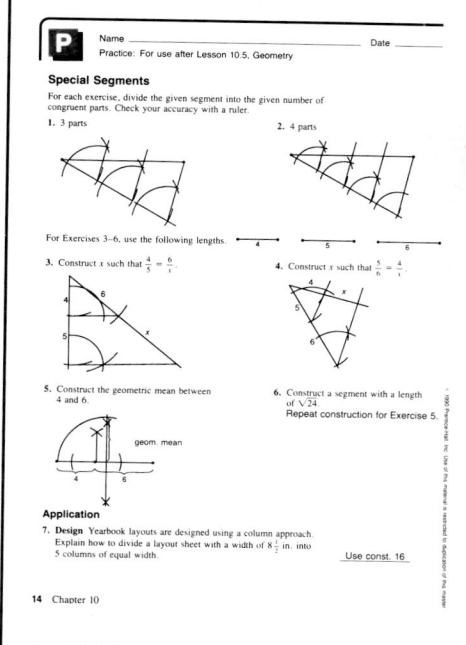

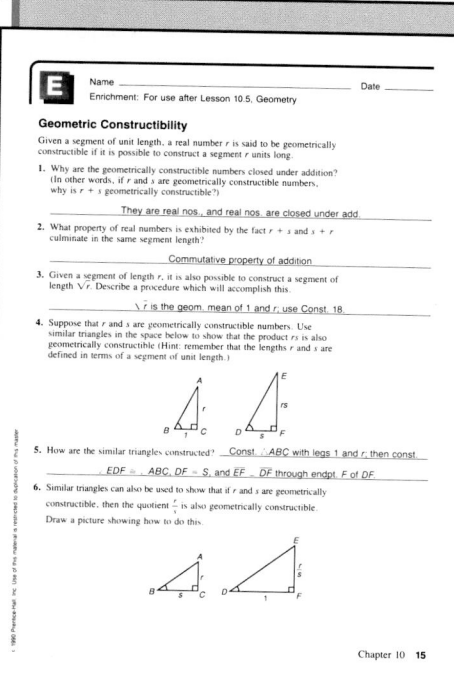

Vocabulary
Locus (loci)

Materials/Manipulatives
Compasses and straightedges
Overhead transparencies
Teacher's Resource Book,
 Transparency 18
Teaching Transparency 68
Connections, p. 23

Technology
Computer Test Bank, pp.
 652–662

LESSON FOCUS

Review
- Review the definitions of *perpendicular bisector* and *circle.* Each definition describes a locus of points.
- The Chapter Summary and Review, pp. 434–435, gives vocabulary and concepts and review exercises by lesson.
- The end of chapter features a Cumulative Review on p. 438.

Alternative Learning Styles
- Using an overhead transparency of the drawing in the Investigation to illustrate how the center of the light fixture is located will help students visualize the concept of locus.
- Some students may benefit from the use of overlays and a colored pen to sketch a locus that satisfies more than one condition. Students can sketch each condition on a separate sheet of tracing paper and then superimpose the sheets over the original figure to help them describe the result.

10.6 Loci

Objective: To describe and sketch the locus that satisfies one or more given conditions

When a pilot flies a plane at a certain speed, direction, and altitude, the plane is satisfying a specified set of conditions. In mathematics, any set of points satisfying a set of conditions is called a *locus*.

Investigation—*Visualizing the Concept*

A round light fixture with a 12 in. diameter is to be hung on a wall that is 8 ft high by 12 ft wide. The light is to be centered between the furniture at 2.5 ft from the ceiling.

Describe the possible spots to locate the fixture. Its center will be $5\frac{1}{2}$ ft up from the floor, $6\frac{1}{2}$ ft from the left end, and $5\frac{1}{2}$ ft from the right end.

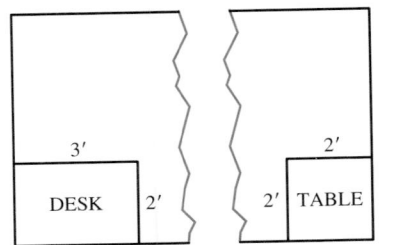

A set of points is a **locus** (plural: *loci*) if and only if it consists of the set of all points and only the points that satisfy one or more given conditions.

An example of a locus is the set of coplanar points that are 3 cm from point P in the plane. This locus is a circle with center point P and radius length 3 cm. Two steps are helpful for finding loci.

1. Make a drawing and locate enough points satisfying the given condition(s) to help you decide how to describe the locus. Include three dimensions unless restricted to a plane.

2. Describe the locus. Then check: Is every point satisfying the condition(s) in your set and does every point in your set satisfy the condition?

EXAMPLE 1 **Describe the locus of points in a plane 3 cm from line k.**
Draw a picture. Locate some points.

The locus is two lines, each parallel to k and 3 cm from k.

422 Chapter 10 Constructions and Loci

Developing Mathematical Power
Cooperative Learning Assign students to work in small groups to do the Practice Exercises. As students gain confidence, encourage them to write their own locus problems for others to solve. Each group should choose a postulate or theorem in the lesson to illustrate for a bulletin-board display.

Three loci are obvious and can be stated as postulates.

> **Postulate 19** In a plane, the locus of points at a given distance d from a given point P is a circle with center P and with d the length of a radius.
>
> **Postulate 20** In a plane, the locus of points a given distance d from a given line l is a pair of lines each parallel to l and at the distance d from l.
>
> **Postulate 21** In a plane, the locus of points equidistant from two given parallel lines is a line midway between and parallel to each of the given lines.

How would you illustrate Postulate 21?

Locus theorems are biconditionals and require a two-part proof showing that every point of the locus satisfies the condition(s) and that every point that satisfies the condition(s) is a point of the locus.

> **Theorem 10.5** In a plane, the locus of points equidistant from two given points is the perpendicular bisector of the segment joining the points.
> Proved in Practice Exercise 25
>
> **Theorem 10.6** In a plane, the locus of points equidistant from the sides of an angle is the angle bisector. Proved in Practice Exercise 31

When a locus must satisfy more than one condition, it will consist of the intersection of the sets of points in each condition.

EXAMPLE 2 **In a plane, what is the locus of points at a given distance d from given point P and also equidistant from two parallel lines?**

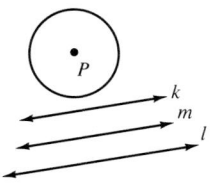

The locus of points at a given distance d from P is a circle with center P and radius length d.
The locus of points equidistant from lines k and l is a line m midway between k and l.

These figures suggest the three possibilities for the locus.

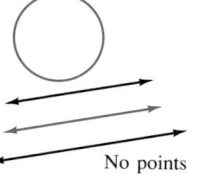
No points

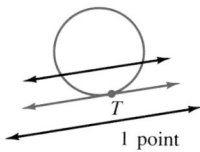
1 point

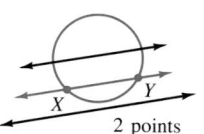
2 points

10.6 Loci **423**

** Developing Mathematical Power **

Keeping a Portfolio Have students complete the Critical Thinking activity, p. 23, in *Connections.* This provides a look at curves of constant width. Have students construct curves of constant width for a regular pentagon and a regular nonagon.

TEACHING SUGGESTIONS

- Emphasize repeatedly the biconditional nature of locus problems—that all points described as belonging to the locus satisfy the given conditions, and that *only* those points satisfy the conditions.
- Provide many examples in which the arrangement of points, lines, or circles can result in more than one solution to a locus problem. Students often have difficulty identifying various ways in which figures may, or may not be related.
- Emphasize the importance of sketching a locus by identifying a few points that satisfy the given conditions, before attempting to describe it. Tell students that only in a few situations will they be able to instantly identify the desired locus. Most of the time, several points will have to be identified before a pattern becomes apparent.
- Be sure to discuss with students the concept of *distance from a point to a circle,* relating distance to radius.

CHALKBOARD EXAMPLES

- **For Example 1**
  Describe the locus of points in a plane that could be vertex A of isosceles triangle ABC with a given base $\overline{BC}$. The locus is all points of the $\perp$ bis. of $\overline{BC}$, except the midpt. of $\overline{BC}$.

- **For Example 2**
  Describe the locus of points in a plane that are equidistant from A and B and also from C and D. The set of pts. equidistant from A and B is the $\perp$ bis. of $\overline{AB}$. The set of pts. equidistant from C and D is the $\perp$ bis. of $\overline{CD}$ (continued on p. 424).

423

There are 3 possibilities for the locus:

1.

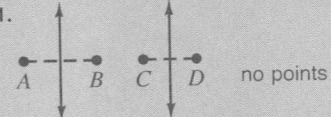

no points

2.

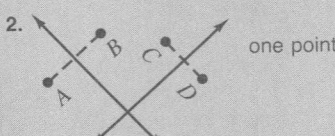

one point

3.

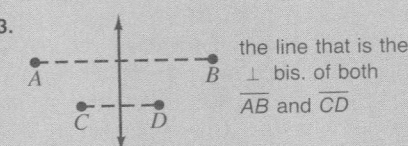

the line that is the ⊥ bis. of both $\overline{AB}$ and $\overline{CD}$

Common Error

- Some students will have difficulty recognizing alternatives that may exist as solutions in locus problems. Use many examples to help alleviate this difficulty.
- See *Teacher's Resource Book* for additional remediation.

LESSON FOLLOW-UP

Discussion

Use the Class Exercises as group discussion.

Assignment Guide

See p. 394B for assignments.

Class Exercises
3.

CLASS EXERCISES

Sketch and describe each locus. See side column.

1.  In a plane, the locus of points 3 cm from circle *P* with radius length 5 cm a ⊙ with radius 2 cm and center *P*, and a ⊙ with radius 8 and center *P*

2. In a plane, the locus of points equidistant from two intersecting lines the bisectors of the 4∠s formed by the given lines

3. In space, the locus of points 4 cm from sphere *P* with radius length of 10 cm 2 spheres with center *P*, one of radius 6 cm and one of radius 14 cm

4. In a plane, the locus of points equidistant from two parallel lines *k* and *l* that are 10 cm apart a line parallel to the 2 given lines 5 cm from both

5. In the same plane, the locus of points 6 cm from a point *P* on line *k* a circle with center *P* and radius 6 cm

6. In the same plane, the locus of points satisfying conditions of Exercise 4 and Exercise 5 the 2 points at which the ⊙ intersects the line of Ex. 4

7. State the two conditionals implied in Theorem 10.5. If, in a plane, the locus of pts. is equidistant from 2 given pts., then the locus is the ⊥ bis. of the seg. joining the pts.; if, in a plane, the locus of pts. is the ⊥ bis. of a seg., then the locus is equidistant from the endpts. of the seg.

8. State the two conditionals implied in Theorem 10.6. If, in a plane, the locus of pts. is the ∠ bis., then the locus is equidistant from the sides of an ∠, then the locus is the ∠ bis.; if, in a plane, the locus of pts. is equidistant from the sides of the ∠

9. State the previously proven theorem(s) that can be used in the proof of Theorem 10.5. Th. 4.2, 4.3

10. State the previously proven theorem(s) that can be used in the proof of Theorem 10.6. Th. 4.4, 4.5

2.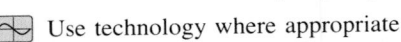

PRACTICE EXERCISES   Use technology where appropriate.

Sketch and describe each locus. See Additional Answers, p. 702.

A

1. In a plane, points in the interior of a square that are equidistant from two opposite sides of the square the line segment joining the midpts. of the remaining 2 sides but excluding the endpts. See side column.

2. In a plane, points in the interior of a square that are equidistant from two adjacent sides of the square the diag. of the square excluding the endpts. which passes through the intersection of the given sides. See Additional Answers, p. 702.

3. In space, points in the interior of a cube that are equidistant from two opposite faces of the cube all int. pts. of the square that is ∥ to and midway between the given faces

4. In space, points in the interior of a cube that are equidistant from two faces of the cube that share an edge all int. pts. of the cube that are also on the plane that bisects the dihedral ∠ formed by the 2 given faces

5. In a plane, points equidistant from the centers of two given nonconcentric, nonoverlapping circles the ⊥ bis. of the segment joining the centers of the two ⊙s

6. In a plane, points 10 cm from a circle with a 5 cm radius length a ⊙ with the same center and radius length 15 cm

7. In a plane, points equidistant from a pair of opposite sides of a rectangle the line joining the midpts. of the other pair of sides of a rectangle

8. In a plane, points equidistant from both pairs of opposite sides of a rectangle the intersection of the 2 lines that join the midpts. of the opposite sides of a rectangle

4.

See Additional Answers, p. 702.

9. In space, all points equidistant from the endpoints of a segment the plane ⊥ to the given segment at its endpt.

10. In a plane, points equidistant from the vertices of a triangle the circumcenter; the intersection of the ⊥ bis. of each side of the △

11. In a plane, points equidistant from the three sides of a given triangle the incenter; the intersection of the ∠ bis. of the △

12. In a plane, points that are the vertices of the right angles in the right triangles whose hypotenuses are a common given segment all pts. on ⊙ whose center is the midpt. of the hyp. except those on hyp.

13. In space, points equidistant from two given parallel planes the plane ∥ to each of the given planes and midway between them

14. In a plane, points that are equidistant from two parallel lines k and l that are 6 cm apart and 4 cm from a fixed point of k 2 pts: the intersection of a line ∥ to each of the given lines and midway between them; and the ⊙ with center P and radius of 4 cm

15. In a plane, all points that are equidistant from the sides of a given angle and also a given distance from the vertex of the angle the pt. on the ∠ bis. that is also the given dist from the vertex

16. In a plane, all points that are equidistant from two intersecting lines and at a given distance from the intersection of the two lines 4 pts. that are the intersection of given lines and the ⊙ with center at the intersection of the given lines and a radius length of the given distance the bis. of the ∠s formed by the

B 17. In a plane, all points that are centers of circles tangent to a given line k at a given point P of k the line ⊥ k at P but excluding pt. P

18. In a plane, points equidistant from two parallel lines k and l and equidistant from A and B, where $\overleftrightarrow{AB}$ intersects k at a 60° angle the pt. of intersection of the line ∥ to and halfway between k and l and the ⊥ bis. of $\overline{AB}$

19. In a plane, all points that are the midpoints of chords from a fixed point on a given circle a ⊙, excluding the fixed pt. on the given ⊙, with center at the midpt. of the line from the circle's center to the fixed pt., with a radius = to half the given radius

20. In a plane, all points that are the centers of circles tangent to a given line and to a given point a curve consisting of pts. equidistant from the given line and the given pt.

21. In a plane, points that are the centers of all congruent circles with radius length d and that are tangent to a given line k 2 lines, each ∥ to k and at distance d from k

22. In space, points that are equidistant from two intersecting planes 2 planes ⊥ to each other and bisecting the dihedral ∠s formed by the given planes

23. In a plane, points equidistant from two parallel lines k and l and a given distance d from a fixed point of k the intersection (0, 1, or 2 pts.) of the line ∥ to and halfway between k and l, and the ⊙ centered on the fixed point with radius d

24. In a plane, points that are equidistant from the sides of a given angle and also a given distance d from a given point P of the plane the intersection (0, 1, or 2 pts.) of the ⊙ at a given distance d and the ∠ bis.

25. Prove Theorem 10.5.

26. In a plane, all points that are midpoints of chords parallel to the diameter of a given circle O the diam. of ⊙O that is ⊥ to the given diam., excluding pt. O.

27. In a plane, all points that are the points of tangency of concentric circles with center O and the tangent lines from external point P semicircular arc with center at the midpt. of $\overline{OP}$ and radius = to half OP

C 28. In a plane, all points equidistant from two parallel lines k and l and equidistant from two given points A and B

29. In space, all points equidistant from two parallel planes M and R, and a given distance d from a fixed point P the intersection (0, 1, or 2 pts.) of the plane ∥ to and halfway between the two given planes, and the sphere centered at pt. P with radius length d

Lesson Quiz

Sketch and describe the locus.

1. In a plane, the points at a given distance from a fixed point and equidistant from the sides of a given angle

2. In a plane, the points that are vertices of right triangles with a given hypotenuse $\overline{AB}$

3. The points that are vertices C of right triangles ABC with a given hypotenuse $\overline{AB}$

1. There are 3 possibilities.
  (1) No points if the ∠ bis. does not intersect the ⊙.
  (2) 1 point if the ∠ bis. is tangent to the ⊙.
  (3) 2 points

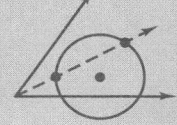

2. The ⊙ with diameter $\overline{AB}$ excluding A and B

3. The sphere with diameter $\overline{AB}$ except for pts, A and B.

6.

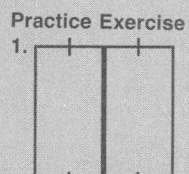

6 cm

5 cm

5 cm

k

l

Practice Exercise

1.

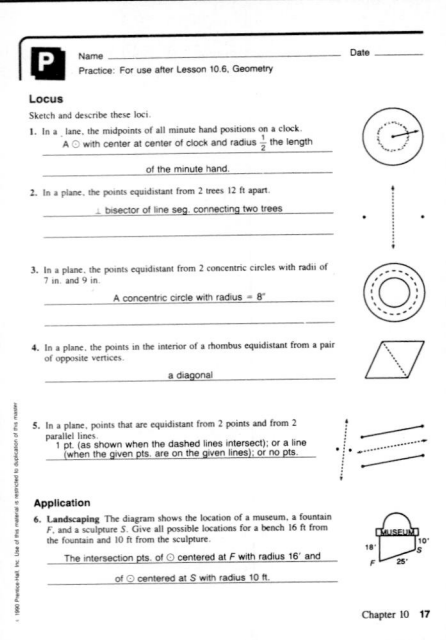

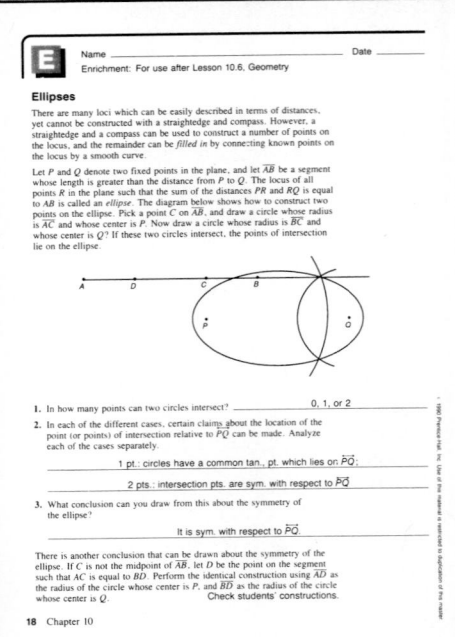

30. In space, all points a distance d from plane P and equidistant from a given sphere See Additional Answers, p. 702.

31. Prove Theorem 10.6.

32. Prove that the locus of the midpoints of all chords parallel to the diameter of a given circle O is another diameter of O (excluding its endpoints) that is perpendicular to the given diameter.

Applications

33. **Landscaping** The diagram shows the locations of a school, statue S, and fountain F. Give all possible location(s) of a flagpole to be 8 ft from the statue and 10 ft from the fountain. at either of the two pts. of intersection of a circle centered at S with radius 8 ft and ⊙ centered at F with radius 10 ft

34. **Technology** Use Logo to draw the design for the possible locations(s) of the flagpole if it is to be equidistant from the statue and the fountain and 9 ft east of the school. See Solutions Manual.

35. **Navigation** Describe some of the conditions a navigator must take into account in order to safely guide a ship's course. How do these conditions relate to the concept *locus*?

CAREERS

Selma Maria Gomez credits the many enrichment programs at her public junior and senior high schools in Florida with nurturing her enthusiasm for mathematics and science. By her third year at Harvard University in Massachusetts, Selma had enough credits to earn a bachelor's degree in applied mathematics. In her fourth year, she took graduate courses and earned a master's degree in applied mathematics. Selma remained at Harvard to earn another master's degree in engineering sciences, a master's of business administration, and a Ph.D. in decision sciences. In her graduate program, she enjoyed learning quantitative skills for interdisciplinary decision-making. In her doctoral research, Selma used a new mathematical technique for solving problems in water-resources planning.

Selma plans to continue conducting research and to teach. Eventually, she hopes to work in government, making technology policy. Selma notes that her role model has been her mother, a dedicated teacher who is committed to advanced education.

426 Chapter 10 Constructions and Loci

10.7 Strategy: Use Loci in Solving Construction Problems

Many construction problems consist of finding loci that satisfy one or more given conditions. The locus postulates and theorems and the problem-solving steps can be applied when solving construction problems.

EXAMPLE 1   Construct a $\square ABCD$, given its diagonals $\overline{AC}$ and $\overline{BD}$ and altitude length, h.

  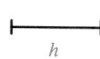

Understand the Problem

Sketch a figure that indicates the final result.

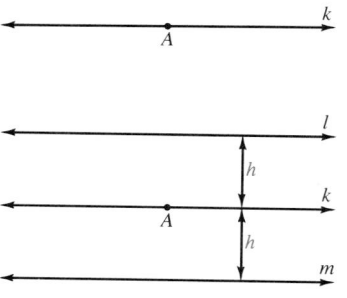

What properties of a parallelogram might be involved?
The diagonals bisect each other.
The altitude is the distance between the bases.

Which locus postulates or theorems might be involved?
The locus of points a given distance d from a given point P is a circle with center P and with d the length of the radius. (Postulate 19)

The locus of points a given distance d from a given line l is a pair of lines each parallel to l and at the distance d from l. (Postulate 20)

Plan Your Approach

Start with a line k that will contain one of the sides, $\overline{AB}$.
Since AB is not given, only one endpoint of $\overline{AB}$ can be located.

The locus of points a distance h from k will be the line containing the side opposite $\overline{AB}$, or $\overline{DC}$. However, a locus postulate states that there are two such lines. This indicates that there may be more than one solution.

Choose one of the lines l as the line containing $\overline{DC}$ opposite $\overline{AB}$.

10.7 Strategy: Use Loci in Solving Construction Problems   **427**

Developing Mathematical Power
Cooperative Learning   The Class Exercises can be done by students working in small groups. Stress that there may be more than one way to do the construction. Encourage students to exchange ideas and to help each other to develop skills. Challenge them to complete the Enrichment activity, p. 20, in the *Teacher's Resource Book.*

LESSON PLAN

Materials/Manipulatives
Compasses and straightedges
Teaching Transparency 69

Technology
Computer Test Bank, pp. 663–670

LESSON FOCUS

Review
Pose the following problem and ask students to suggest a way to do the construction.

Construct $\triangle ABC$ so that $AB = x$, $AC = y$, and the length of the altitude from A is z.

x	y	z

Draw any line l. At any pt. *D* on *l*, const. a ⊥ to *l*. On the ⊥, const. $DA = z$. With *A* as center and radius lengths x and y, draw arcs that intersect *l* at *B* and *C*. Draw $\overline{AB}$ and $\overline{AC}$.

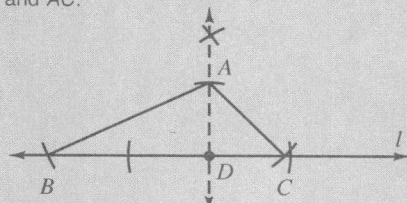

Alternative Learning Styles
Some students need help in understanding and applying the important details provided by a diagram for a construction problem. By studying the diagram and verbalizing what they know, they should be able to determine what loci theorems and postulates they can use. This will help them to gain confidence in solving construction problems.

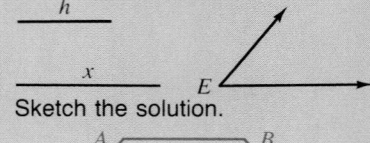
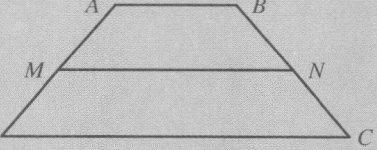
Endpoint C of $\overline{AC}$ will be the locus of points a distance AC from A and lying on l. There are two possibilities for C. Choose one (C_1) and draw $\overline{AC}$.

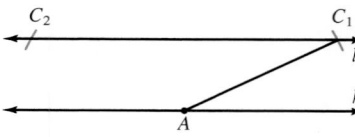

Since the diagonals of a parallelogram bisect each other, construct the midpoint M of $\overline{AC}$. Since M is also the midpoint of $\overline{BD}$, B and D must be on the locus of all points distance $\frac{BD}{2}$ from M and on lines l and k.

☐ **Implement the Plan** Construct any line k to contain $\overline{AB}$. Then construct one of the two lines parallel to k and at a distance h from k. Do this by choosing a point on k and constructing the perpendicular. Then use h to construct a segment on the perpendicular. Through endpoint E construct the line parallel to k.

Construct $\odot A$ with center A and radius length AC. Choose one of the two intersections with l to be C.

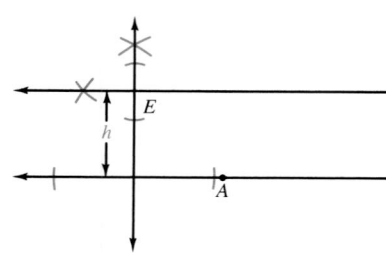

Bisect $\overline{AC}$ and label the midpoint M. Construct $\odot M$ with center M and radius length $\frac{1}{2}BD$. Draw $\overline{BD}$, $\overline{AD}$, and $\overline{CB}$.

☐ **Interpret the Results** Given only the diagonals and the altitude length, the parallelogram can be constructed. Since there were two possibilities for the line parallel to k and hence four possibilities for the location of point C, there are three other possible solutions.

Additional Answers for p. 430

1.

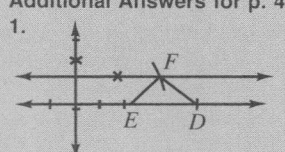

2.

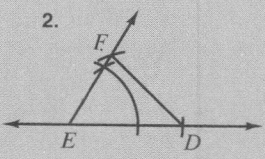

Problem Solving Reminders

- The locus postulates and theorems may be helpful in planning the solution to a construction problem.
- Sometimes there is more than one possible solution.

EXAMPLE 2   Construct $\triangle ADE$, given $\angle A$, x the length of base $\overline{AD}$, and y the length of the altitude from E to $\overline{AD}$.

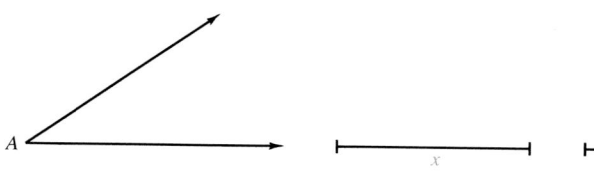

Understand the Problem   **Sketch a figure that indicates the final result.**
Use it to decide what properties of a triangle and what locus postulates or theorems might apply.

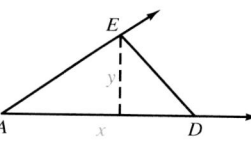

Plan Your Approach   Starting with $\angle A$, vertex D will be the intersection of one side of $\angle A$ with the locus of all points a distance x from A. Vertex E will be the intersection of the other side of $\angle A$ with the locus of all points a distance y from $\overline{AD}$.

Implement the Plan   **Use the length x to construct $\overline{AD}$ along one side of $\angle A$.**
Construct the parallel that is distance y from $\overline{AD}$ and intersects the other side of $\angle A$. Draw $\overline{DE}$.

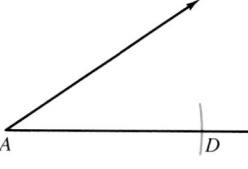

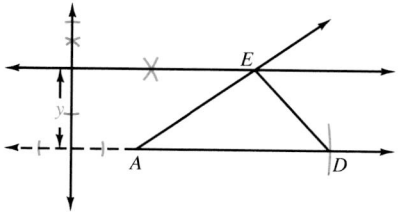

10.7 Strategy: Use Loci in Solving Construction Problems   **429**

3.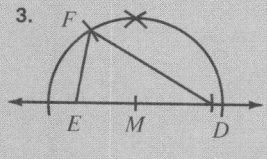

4.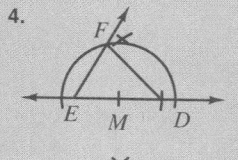

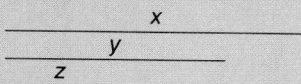
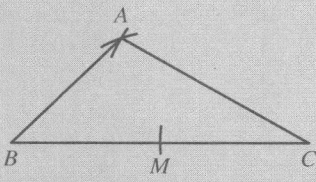

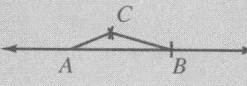
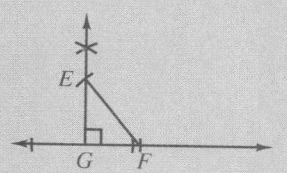
429

Lesson Quiz

Construct $\triangle ABC$ with given $\angle A$, so that the alt. to $\overline{AC} = x$ and median to $AC = y$.

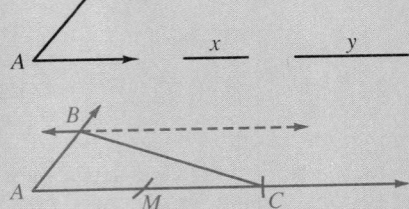

Begin with $\angle A$. Const. the line $\parallel$ to one side of the $\angle$ and x units from it. Let B be the pt. where the $\parallel$ intersects the other side of $\angle A$. With B as center and y as radius length, draw an arc intersecting the other side of $\angle A$ at M. On $\overrightarrow{AM}$, const. C so that $AC = 2 \cdot AM$. Draw $\overline{BC}$.

□ **Interpret the Results**   Given an angle, a base length, and an altitude length to that base, a triangle can be constructed.

The locus of points equidistant from $\overleftrightarrow{AD}$ consists of two parallel lines. However, there is only one solution because only one of the parallel lines intersects the other side of $\angle A$.

CLASS EXERCISES

In Exercises 1–4, solve the construction problems. Tell what locus postulates or theorems are involved. Use $\angle W$ and lengths x, y, and z, as specified.

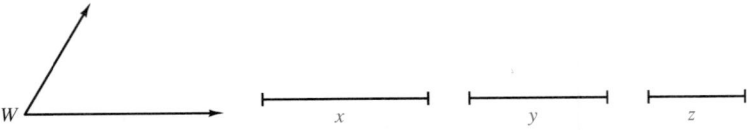

1. Construct $\triangle DEF$, given x and y as the lengths of $\overline{ED}$ and $\overline{EF}$, respectively, and z as the altitude from F to $\overline{ED}$. Post. 19, 20

2. Construct $\triangle DEF$, given $\angle E \cong \angle W$ and x as the length $\overline{ED}$ and $\overline{FD}$. Post. 19

3. Construct $\triangle DEF$, given x as the length $\overline{ED}$ y as the length of the median from F to $\overline{ED}$, and z as the length of $\overline{EF}$. Post. 19

4. Construct $\triangle DEF$, given $\angle E \cong \angle W$, x as the length of $\overline{ED}$, and y as the length of the median from F to $\overline{ED}$. Post. 19

PRACTICE EXERCISES See side column pages 429–430.

A   **In each exercise, construct only one solution, even though there may be more than one. Use the angle and segments given in the Class Exercises.**

1. Construct $\triangle ABC$, given x, y, and z the lengths of sides $\overline{AB}$, $\overline{BC}$, and $\overline{CA}$, respectively. What conditions must x, y, and z satisfy in order that there be a solution? $x + y > z$, $y + z > x$, and $x + z > y$.

2. Construct right $\triangle EFG$ with right $\angle G$, $GF = y$, and $EF = x$.

3. Construct $\triangle WFG$, given $\angle W$, x the length of side $\overline{WF}$, and $\angle G$ a right angle.

4. Construct right $\triangle PQR$, given x the length of hypotenuse $\overline{QR}$ and z the length of the altitude to the hypotenuse. many possible answers

3.
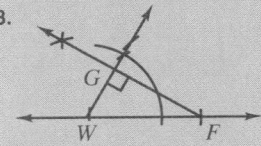

4.
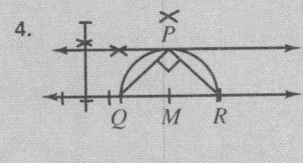

5. Construct isosceles $\triangle STU$, given x the length of base $\overline{TU}$ and y the length of the altitude to $\overline{TU}$. See side column.

6. Construct $\triangle PQR$ such that x is the length of $\overline{PQ}$, y is the length of the median from R, and z is the length of the altitude from R.

7. Sketch any other possible solution for Exercise 2. Answers may vary; See page 767.

8. Sketch any other possible solution for Exercise 4. Answers may vary.

9. Construct $\triangle ABC$, given x the length of side $\overline{AC}$, y the length of the median from A, and z the length of the altitude from A.

10. Construct $\triangle WPQ$, given $\angle W$, z one-half the length of side $\overline{WQ}$, and y the length of the altitude from P.

11. Construct $\square EFGH$, given y and z as the lengths of two sides and x as the length of the longer diagonal.

12. Construct $\triangle DEF$, given y the length of side $\overline{ED}$, z the length of the altitude from F to $\overline{ED}$, and x the length of the median from D to $\overline{EF}$.

13. Construct $\triangle ABC$, given y the length of side $\overline{BC}$, z the length of the altitude to side $\overline{AC}$, and x the radius length of the circumscribed circle. See Solutions Manual.

14. Construct $\triangle ABC$, given x and y the lengths of sides $\overline{BC}$ and $\overline{AC}$, respectively, and z the length of the median from A to $\overline{BC}$.

ST YOURSELF See pages 767–768.

1. Draw any acute triangle. Construct its circumscribed circle.   10.4

2. Draw a segment. Use a compass and a straightedge to separate it into three congruent segments.   10.5

3. Draw three segments having lengths of 2 cm, 5 cm, and 6 cm. Construct a segment of length x such that $5:6 = 2:x$.

4. Construct a segment whose length is equal to $\sqrt{8}$ cm.

For Exercises 5–7, sketch and describe the locus.   10.6, 10.7

5. What is the locus of all points 10 cm from a given plane? two planes ‖ to the given plane, 10 cm above and below the given plane

6. In a plane, what is the locus of all points equidistant from two intersecting lines and 5 cm from the intersection of the lines? the intersection of the two ∠ bis. of the two intersecting lines and the ⊙ centered at the intersection of the two lines with radius length 5 cm

7. In a plane, what is the locus of the centers of all circles that are tangent to two intersecting lines? the two ∠ bis. of the 4 ∠s created by the two intersecting lines, excluding the intersection of the given lines

5.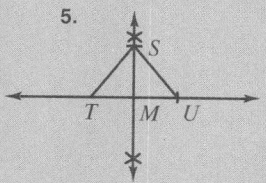

6.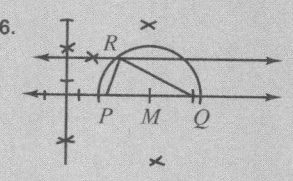

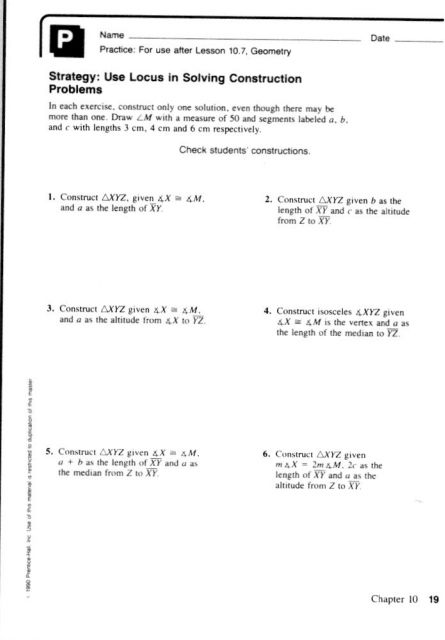

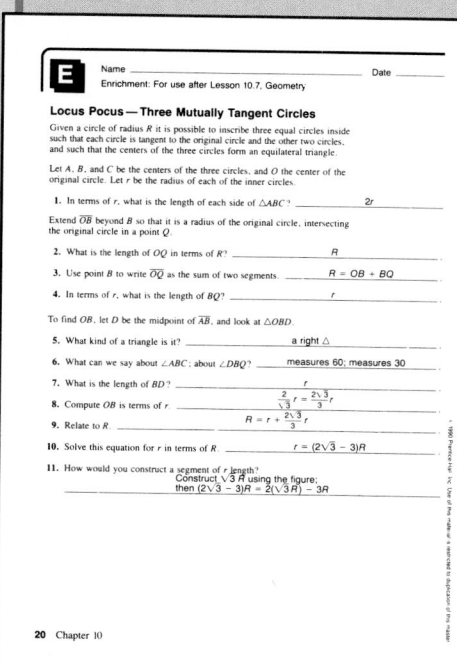

See *Teacher's Resource Book*,
Follow-Up *Technology*, pp. 13–14.

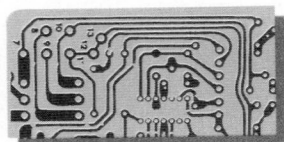

TECHNOLOGY:
Using Logo in Constructions

Constructions done with compass and straightedge and that use no angle
measurement are not readily transferable to the Logo screen. However, loci
can be expanded with Logo to give remarkable and sometimes unpredictable
results.

EXAMPLE **Find the locus of points from the center of a set of concentric triangles
when these triangles are rotated about**

    a. the center   **b.** a vertex

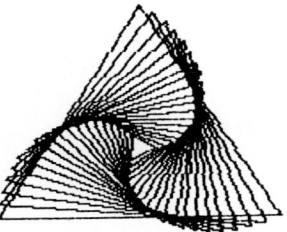
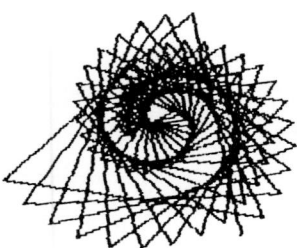

    a. three distinct spirals   **b.** three spirals that appear as
                                                             almost one spiral

Consider the locus of all points equidistant from two endpoints of a segment.
In Logo, the locus could be generated by a set of isosceles triangles with the
line segment as the base of all of the triangles, using the trigonometric ratio
sin. The procedure is:

```
to isostri :length :angle :inc :limit
if :angle > :limit [stop]
forward :length right (180 − :angle)
forward (:length / sin (:angle + 90))
right (2 * :angle)
forward (:length / sin (:angle + 90))
right (180 − :angle)
forward :length
isostri :length (:angle + :inc) :inc :limit
end
```

isostri 60 10 5 30

The **cardiod** can be constructed as the locus of two sets of increasing circles rotating about a point.

The one below shows one set of circles rotated to the left and the other to the right.

This cardiod can be generated using other polygons. The one below is based on two sets of squares.

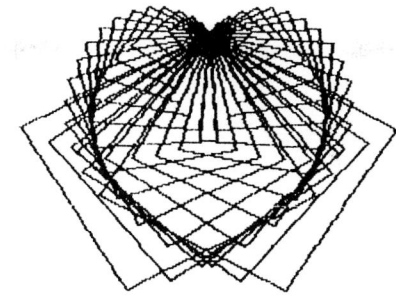

The above examples all use loci with polygons or circles whose sides or radii increase. However, if the side stays the same and the angle increases, the turtle will spiral inwards; once it reaches 180°, the turtle starts spiraling outwards, drawing a very different type of path. The simplest procedure for this is:

```
to inspi :length :angle :inc
forward :length right :angle
inspi :length (:angle + :inc) :inc
end
```

inspi 20 0 10

EXERCISES

1. Find the locus of points that are equidistant from the center of a set of concentric squares when the squares are rotated about
   a. the center   **b.** the vertex

2. Experiment with the *isostri* procedure to draw a set of triangles that you like. Try reflecting the triangles outwards, and rotate your set of triangles only three times. What polygon is formed?

3. Use the *isostri* procedure with a repeat command to form a square.

4. Write the procedures that draw a cardoid.

5. Try the following values in the *inspi* procedure.
   a. inspi 5 0 11   **b.** inspi 20 2 10   **c.** inspi 20 2 20

6. Experiment with other *inspi* procedures. Which values generate a path that repeats itself? Which values generate a path that never repeats?

- See *Teacher's Resource Book, Spanish Chapter Summary and Review,* pp. 19–20.
- See Extra Practice, p. 652.

1.

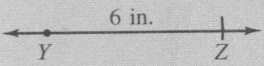

2.

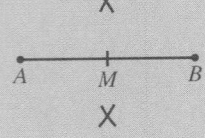

3.

Vocabulary

centroid (409)   concurrent (407)   locus (422)
circumcenter (408)   construction (396)   orthocenter (408)
compass (396)   incenter (407)   straightedge (396)

Beginning Constructions   Using only a compass and a straightedge, it is possible to construct a segment congruent to a given segment, the midpoint of a given segment, an angle congruent to a given angle, and the angle bisector of a given angle.   **10.1**

Draw $\overline{AB}$ **such that** $AB = 6$ **in. and** $\angle C$ **such that** $m\angle C = 56$. See side column.

1. Construct $\overline{YZ} \cong \overline{AB}$.

2. Construct midpoint M of $\overline{AB}$.

3. Construct $\angle X \cong \angle C$.

4. Construct the bisector of $\angle C$.

Constructing Perpendiculars and Parallels   Using only a compass and a straightedge, it is possible to construct the perpendicular bisector of a segment, the perpendicular to a line at a point on the line or from a point not on the line, and the parallel to a line through a point not on that line.   **10.2**

Draw $\overline{AB}$ **such that** $AB = 8$ **in., with point** P **on** $\overline{AB}$ **and 3 in. from** A.

5. Construct the perpendicular bisector of $\overline{AB}$.

6. At P, construct a perpendicular to $\overline{AB}$.

7. At a point Q not on $\overline{AB}$, construct a perpendicular to $\overline{AB}$.

8. Through a point R not on $\overline{AB}$, construct a line $k \parallel \overline{AB}$.

Concurrent Lines   In any triangle, the lines in each of these four sets are concurrent: the angle bisectors, in the center of the triangle's inscribed circle; the perpendicular bisectors of the sides, in the center of the triangle's circumscribed circle; the altitudes, in a point called the *orthocenter*; and the medians, in a point called the *centroid*.   **10.3**

9. Draw any obtuse scalene triangle. Construct its orthocenter.

10. Draw any acute scalene triangle. Construct its centroid.

Circles   It is possible to construct a tangent to a circle at a point on the circle, a tangent to circle from a point outside the circle, the center of a circle, and the circumscribed circle and the inscribed circle of a triangle.   **10.4**

434   Chapter 10 Constructions and Loci

4.

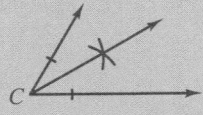

5.

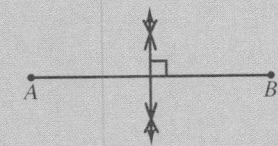

11. Draw a circle. Select any point P on the circle. Construct a tangent to the circle at P. See page 768.

12. Draw a circle. Select any point Q in the circle's exterior. Construct a tangent to the circle from Q.

13. The location of the center of a circular disk is unknown. Describe how you would use a construction to locate the center. Draw any 2 non‖ chords and construct the ⊥ bis. of each. The pt. of intersection is the center of the disk.

14. Draw an obtuse scalene triangle. Construct its circumscribed circle.

15. Draw an acute scalene triangle. Construct its inscribed circle.

Special Segments   Using only a compass and a straightedge, it is possible   10.5
to construct the following: points that will separate a segment into n congruent segments; a fourth segment whose length is in proportion with three given segment lengths; and a segment whose length is the geometric mean between the lengths of two given segments.

16. Draw any segment and divide it into five congruent segments.

17. Draw three segments measuring 3 cm, 4 cm, and 5 cm, respectively. Construct a fourth segment of length x such that $3:4 = 5:x$.

18. Construct the geometric mean between the first two segments of Ex. 17.

Loci   A set of points is a locus if and only if it consists of all points and   10.6
only the points that satisfy one or more geometric conditions.

Describe and sketch each locus.

19. All points in a plane a given distance from a given point
a ⊙ with radius length = to the given dist. and centered at the given pt.
20. All points in a plane a given distance from a given line
two ‖ lines at the given distance above and below the given line
21. In a plane, all points equidistant from two parallel lines k and l, and equidistant from two points A and B located so that $\overline{AB} \perp k$ Let m be the locus of pts. equidist. from k and l: If the ⊥ bis. of $\overline{AB}$ is m, then m is the locus; if the ⊥ bis. of $\overline{AB}$ is not m, there are no pts. in the locus.
22. In space, all points equidistant from two intersecting lines
the two ⊥ planes that bisect the ∠s formed by the two lines and intersect where the lines intersect, excluding the pt. of intersection of the lines

Strategy: Constructing Loci   Recall the problem solving steps.   10.7

| Understand the Problem | Plan Your Approach | Implement the Plan | Interpret the Results |

23. Construct $\triangle DEF$, given 3 cm and 2 cm as the lengths of $\overline{ED}$ and $\overline{EF}$, respectively. Then construct a different triangle that satisfies the same conditions. How many triangles satisfy those conditions? What locus properties are involved in the construction? Infinitely many. Post. 19

6.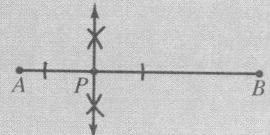

7.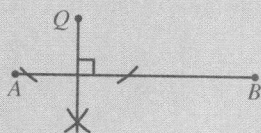

8.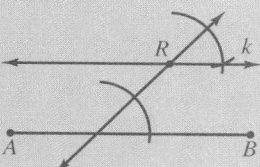

9.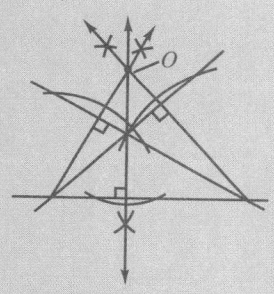

21. Let m be the locus of pts. equidist. from k and l; If the ⊥ bis. of $\overline{AB}$ is m, then m is the locus; if the ⊥ bis. of $\overline{AB}$ is not m, there are no pts. in the locus.

10.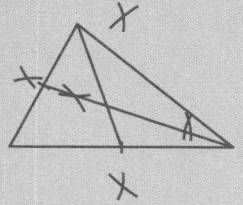

11.

See *Teacher's Resource Book*, Tests, pp. 105–108.

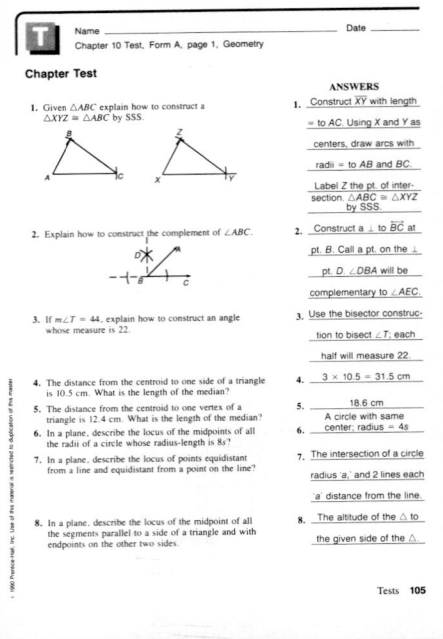

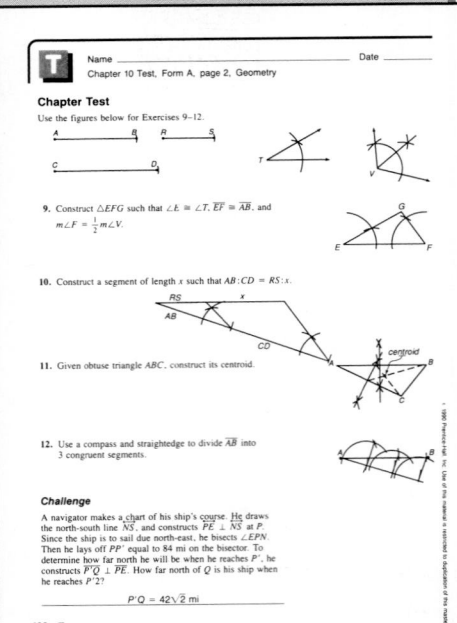

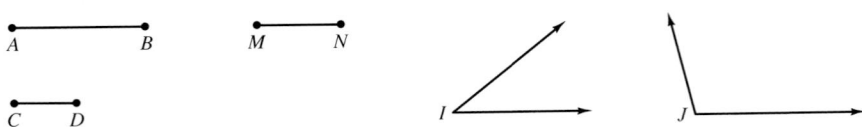

Draw figures that look like these figures. Use them for Exercises 1–6.

1. Construct $\overline{EF}$ such that $EF = AB + CD$. See side column

2. Construct $\overline{GH}$ such that $GH = 3 \cdot CD - \frac{1}{2}AB$.

3. Construct $\triangle PQR$ such that $\angle P \cong \angle I$, $\overline{PR} \cong \overline{AB}$, and $\angle R \cong \angle J$. See page 768.

4. Construct a segment of length x such that $AB:CD = MN:x$.

5. Use a compass and a straightedge to divide $\overline{AB}$ into 5 congruent segments.

6. Construct a segment whose length is the geometric mean of AB and CD.

7. Construct a 45° angle.

8. Draw any $\triangle STU$ with an obtuse angle at T. Construct the orthocenter.

9. Draw any circle. Mark its center O and any exterior point P. Construct a tangent from P to $\odot O$. See page 769.

10. The distance from the centroid to one side of a triangle is 12 cm. What is the length of the median to that side? 36 cm

For Exercises 11 and 12, sketch and describe the locus.

11. In a plane, what is the locus of the midpoints of all the radii of a circle whose radius length is d? a concentric circle with radius $\frac{d}{2}$

12. In a plane, what is the locus of all points distance d ($d <$ radius of $\odot O$) from a given $\odot O$ and equidistant from the endpoints of chord $\overline{AB}$ of $\odot O$? 4 pts. that are the intersection of ⊥ bis. of $\overline{AB}$ and the 2 concentric⊙s

Challenge

Suppose x is the length of any side of a regular polygon inscribed in a unit circle. Then the length y of the side of the inscribed regular polygon having twice as many sides is given by

$$y = \sqrt{2 - \sqrt{4 - x}}.$$

Use this formula to find the perimeter of a 12-sided polygon inscribed in a circle. Is the perimeter greater than, equal to, or less than the circle's circumference? Find the difference between the two lengths in terms of pi. (*Recall:* $C = 2\pi r$.) P = $12\sqrt{2 - \sqrt{4 - r^2}}$; less than; $2\pi r - 12\sqrt{2 - \sqrt{4 - r^2}}$

Alternative Assessment Draw a triangle. Ask students to: **1.** Copy a side and an angle. **2.** Construct a median, an altitude, and an angle bisector of the triangle. **3.** Construct a line parallel to the base. **4.** Circumscribe a circle about the triangle. **5.** Construct a tangent to the circle.

Directions: In each item, compare a quantity in Column 1 with a quantity in Column 2. Write the letter of the correct answer from these choices:

A. The quantity in Column 1 is greater then the quantity in Column 2.
B. The quantity in Column 2 is greater than the quantity in Column 1.
C. The quantity in Column 1 is equal to the quantity in Column 2.
D. The relationship cannot be determined from the given information.

Notes: A symbol that appears in both columns has the same meaning in each column. All variables represent real numbers. Most figures are not drawn to scale.

Column 1	Column 2
1. 3^5	$2 \cdot 11^2$

A

$$n = 123.456$$

2. n rounded to nearest 10th n rounded to nearest 100th

A

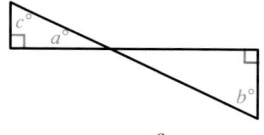

3. b c
C
4. a c
D

k is a positive number and $(0.01k)^2 = 2.25$.

5. k 15
A

$$ab > 0, \ a < -1$$

6. b 0
B

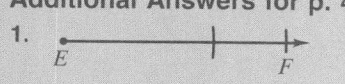

7. a c
A
8. a $b + c$
A

Column 1	Column 2
9. $\sqrt{\dfrac{25}{16}}$	$(1.3)^2$

B

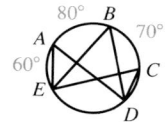

10. $m\angle BEC$ $m\angle BDA$
B
11. $m\angle EAD$ $m\angle ECD$
C

$\overline{PQ}$ is the $\perp$ bisector of $\overline{XY}$.

12. PX PY
C
13. PQ XY
D

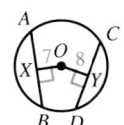

14. AX CY
A

$\square ABCD$, $AB > BC$, $\overline{DE}$ bis. $\angle ADC$.

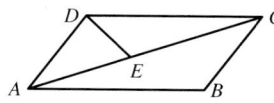

15. AE EC
B

The individual comments provided for certain problems may help the students in solving them.

5. In this problem the multiplication could be done instead of taking the square root. Then, $0.0001k^2 = 2.25$, and $k = 150$.
6. Students need frequent practice with problems of this type to help them understand that a variable such as x can represent negative values as well as positive ones, even though it is written as $+x$.
8. This is an example of the special cases of inequalities of the sides of triangles based on the Pythagorean Theorem and is often useful in problem solving.
15. Since both multiplication and division are involved in working with the inequalities of the problem, remind students that distances are positive.

See *Teacher's Resource Book* for *Preparing for College Entrance Exams*.

Additional Answers for p. 436

1.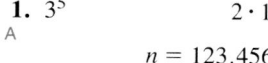

2.

X

See *Teacher's Resource Book*, Tests, pp. 109–112.

27. Given: trap. *ABCD* inscribed in ⊙*O*; bases $\overline{AB}$ and $\overline{CD}$

Prove: *ABCD* is isos.

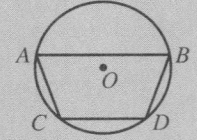

Plan: Since $\overline{AB} \parallel \overline{CD}$, $\overparen{AC} \cong \overparen{BD}$. Thus $\overline{AC} \cong \overline{BD}$ and the concl. follows.

Proof:

Statements	Reasons
1. Trap. *ABCD* inscribed in ⊙*O*; bases $\overline{AB}$ and $\overline{CD}$	1. Given
2. $\overline{AB} \parallel \overline{CD}$	2. Bases of a trap. are ∥.
3. $\overparen{AC} \cong \overparen{BD}$	3. If 2 arcs of a ⊙ are included between ∥ chords, then the arcs are ≅.
4. $\overline{AC} \cong \overline{BD}$	4. In the same ⊙, ≅ arcs have ≅ chords.
5. Trap. *ABCD* is isos.	5. If the legs of a trap. are ≅, then the trap. is isos.

Concl.: If a trap. is inscribed in a ⊙, then the trap. is isos.

23.

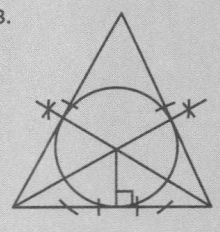

X

Complete.

1. In plane *P*, *l* ⊥ *k* and *k* ⊥ *j*, therefore *l* ⁢ ? *j*. ∥   3.3

2. There are ? ways to prove triangles congruent, namely ?.   4.2, 4.7
8; SSS, SAS, ASA, AAS, HL, HA, LA, LL

3. There are ? ways to prove quadrilaterals congruent, namely ?.   6.6
2; SASAS, ASASA

4. There are ? ways to prove triangles similar, namely ?.   7.4, 7.5
3; AA, SAS Th., SSS Th.

5. If the lengths of two sides of a triangle are 4 and 7, then the third side must be longer than ? and shorter than ?. 3; 11   5.6

6. If the hypotenuse of a 30°-60°-90° triangle has length 12, then the longer leg has length ?. $6\sqrt{3}$ 8.4

7. The centroid of a triangle is the intersection of the ?. medians   10.5

8. The intersection of the angle bisectors of a triangle is the ?. incenter   10.5

Find the indicated measures.   9.4, 9.5

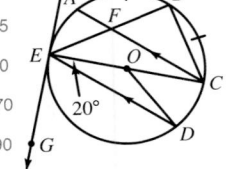

9. $m\overparen{AB}$ = ? 70

10. $m\angle ACB$ = ? 35

11. $m\angle AFE$ = ? 55

12. $m\angle EBC$ = ? 90

13. $m\overparen{EBD}$ = ? 220

14. $m\angle GED$ = ? 70

15. $m\angle COD$ = ? 40

16. $m\angle GEC$ = ? 90

Given right triangle *ABC*:

17. sin ∠*C* = ? $\frac{5}{13}$

18. tan ∠*A* = ? $\frac{12}{5}$ 8.6

19. cos ∠*A* = ? $\frac{5}{13}$

20. sin ∠*A* = ? $\frac{12}{13}$

Given ⊙*O* with secants $\overline{FA}$ and $\overline{DA}$ and tangent segment $\overline{BA}$:   9.7

21. If *AB* = 10 and *EA* = 8, then *FE* = ?. 4.5

22. If *AC* = 4, *DC* = 5, and *AE* = 3, then *AF* = ?. 12

23. Draw any acute triangle. Construct its inscribed circle.   10.3

24. Draw any obtuse triangle. Construct its circumscribed circle. See side column.   10.3

25. Construct a ▱ with the side length ratio 1:2, and a 120° angle.   10.2

26. What is the locus of points in a plane 6 cm from point *P*? What is the locus in space? a circle with center *P* and *r* = 6; a sphere with center *P* and *r* = 6   10.6

27. Prove that a trapezoid inscribed in a circle is isosceles.   9.4

24.

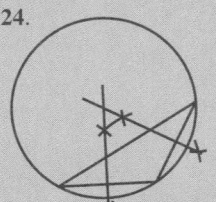

25.

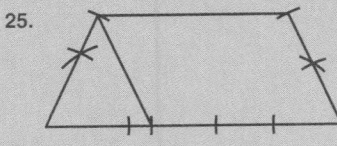

SUMMARY

In Chapter 11, students explore applications of area. They study and use formulas for the area of squares, rectangles, parallelograms, and triangles. Formulas for areas of trapezoids and regular polygons are developed and applied. Students then learn to compute circumferences and arc lengths in circles and use area formulas to compute area of circles, sectors, and segments of circles. Concepts of similarity are combined with the formulas studied to calculate perimeters and areas of similar figures.

CHAPTER OBJECTIVES

- To state and apply the formulas for the areas of squares, rectangles, parallelograms, triangles, trapezoids, regular polygons

- To relate the perimeter and area formulas for regular polygons to the circumference and area formulas of a circle

- To compute the area of circles, sectors, and segments of circles

- To state and apply the relationships among scale factors, perimeters, and the areas of similar figures

- To understand formulas for the circumference and area of circles as an outgrowth of related formulas for polygons through *finding limits*

CHAPTER HIGHLIGHTS

DEVELOPING MATHEMATICAL POWER

Problem Solving

Lesson 11.5 uses the four problem solving steps to find mathematical limits. This will help students to see the relationship between the perimeter of a regular polygon and the circumference of a circle as presented in Lesson 11.6.

Communication

In the side column, methods for alternative learning styles and cooperative learning activities include creating tessellations and counting unit squares to find area. The *Teacher's Resource Book* offers a Chapter Summary and Review in Spanish. The side column mentions topics for students' portfolios such as describing how the area of a polygon will change by changing its dimensions.

Reasoning

Thinking critically topics ask for numerical comparisons of the area and perimeter of a polygon and of the diameter and circumference of a circle. Students write proofs to show equal areas of polygons.

Connections

Real-world applications include such topics as traffic engineering, manufacturing, and landscaping. The never-ending story of pi provides an example of the variety of cultural influences on mathematics. The Integrating Geometry feature shows how to approximate areas of figures.

Technology

Logo exercises appear throughout the chapter. Students are encouraged to use calculators for finding some areas, for investigating limits, and when using Heron's formula for finding the area of a triangle using side lengths.

STUDENT TEXT

Chapter Content	Basic	Average	Enriched	NCTM STANDARDS*
11.1 Area of Squares and Rectangles	D: 442/1-14, 30	D: 442/1-19, 24-26, 30-31	D: 442/1-19, 24-31	1, 3, 5, 7, 12
11.2 Area of Parallelograms and Triangles	D: 447/1-14, 35 R: 442/15-17	D: 447/1-18, 23-29, 35-38 R: 442/20-23	D: 447/1-18, 23-32, 35-38 R: 442/20-23	3, 4, 5, 7, 8
11.3 Area of Trapezoids	D: 452/2-11, 28, MR R: 447/15-18	D: 452/1-15, 20-23, 28, MR R: 447/19-22, 30	D: 452/1-15, 24-29, MR R: 447/19-22, 33, 34	3, 4, 5, 8
11.4 Area of Regular Polygons	D: 457/1-10, 34, 35, 37 R: 452/12-15	D: 457/1-18, 25-27, 34-38 R: 452/16-19	D: 457/1-18, 26-38 R: 452/16-21	5, 8, 12, 13
11.5 Strategy: Find Limits	D: 464/1-8 R: 457/11-13	D: 464/1-10 R: 457/19-24	D: 464/1-10, 13 R: 457/19-25	1, 3, 12, 13
11.6 Circumference and Arc Length	D: 468/2-5, 10-19, 36 R: 464/9	D: 468/1-25, 35-37 R: 464/11, 12	D: 468/1-25, 30-37 R: 464/11, 12, 14	3, 5, 12, 13
11.7 Area of Circles, Sectors, and Segments	D: 474/1-9, 22, AR R: 468/6-9	D: 474/1-9, 12-17, 22, 24, AR R: 468/26-29	D: 474/1-15, 20-23, AR R: 468/26-29	2, 4, 5
11.8 Areas of Similar Figures	D: 478/1-20, 35 R: 474/10, 11	D: 478/1-28, 34, 35 R: 474/10, 11, 18	D: 478/1-29 odd, 30-35 R: 474/16-19	3, 5, 8, 12

D = Daily   R = Review   MR = Mixed Review   AR = Algebra Review

*For a complete list of NCTM Standards, see p. T7.

STUDENT TEXT

Review/Assessment

Mixed Review 454

Algebra Review 475, 488

Summary and Review 484

College Ent. Exam Rev. 487

Extra Practice 653

Test Yourself 460, 481

Chapter Test 486

Chapter Project 439

Special Features

Construction 444

Historical Note 475

Technology 444, 449, 460, 470, 481

Devel. Math. Power 449, 460, 470

Applications 444, 449, 454, 460, 470, 475, 481, 482-483

Project 465

RESOURCES

Teacher's Resource Book

Ch. 11: Investigation/Practice/ Enrichment 1-23

Spanish Sum. and Rev. 21-22

Quizzes 113-116

Chapter Tests 117-120

Perf. Assessment Proj. Ch. 11

Critical Thinking 11

Reading and Writing in Geom. 11

Applications—Ch. 11, 24

Teaching Aid 11

Transparencies 19-21

Teaching Transparencies 70-77

Computer Test Bank 671-748

Connections 25-26, 33-34

PH Graph. Utility

Overhead Manip. Kit

Area

A puzzling problem?

Developing Mathematical Power

This Tethered Goat puzzle was created by an English mathematician and puzzle inventor, Henry Dudeney (1847–1930).

A goat is enclosed in a 2π-acre pen in the shape of an equilateral triangle. The goat is tethered to a post at a vertex of the triangle. To the nearest foot, determine the length of rope which will allow the goat to eat only one half the grass in the pen.

Project

Solve the Tethered Goat puzzle. Then create your own geometric puzzle and provide the solution.

BACKGROUND

Henry Dudeney (1847–1930) was an English mathematician and a well-known inventor of puzzles. For twenty years, Dudeney's puzzle page, "Perplexities," appeared in *The Strand Magazine*, in England. He also published six books of puzzles. The solution to this puzzle involves a knowledge of areas of polygons and circles.

MODELING

This project involves designing a mathematical model to solve a problem. The model is developed by drawing a diagram, applying concepts of area, and using logical reasoning.

Cooperative Learning

This project is accomplished through a succession of tasks, each of which is well-suited to a cooperative learning situation. These tasks include:
1. Drawing a diagram.
2. Planning a procedure to solve a puzzle.
3. Applying formulas for the areas of polygons and circles.
4. Solving a puzzle.

Alternative Assessment

See the *Teacher's Resource Book*, Assessment, Chapter 11. This project and the TRB page may be used as an alternative form of assessment for selected topics in Chapter 11.

Picture a hexagon composed of six congruent equilateral triangles, each with an area of 2π acres. The area of the hexagon is 12π acres. The goat can graze in a π-acre area that is one sixth of a circle. The circle's area is half the hexagon's area, so the area of the circle is 6π acres or 261,360π square feet. The radius of the circle is the length of the goat's rope.

$$\pi r^2 = 261{,}360\pi \text{ sq ft}$$
$$r^2 = 261{,}360 \text{ sq ft}$$
$$r = 511.2338 \text{ ft}$$

439

Vocabulary
Altitude
Area
Base
Height
Square unit

Materials/Manipulatives
Geoboards
Graph paper
Teaching Transparencies 70 and 70A
Connections, pp. 35 and 36

Technology
Calculator
Computer Test Bank, pp. 671–677

LESSON FOCUS

Review
Review the characteristics of a square, a rectangle, a parallelogram, a triangle, and a trapezoid.

Alternative Learning Styles
- The Investigation introduces students to the concept of area through a kinesthetic approach. They count unit squares and estimate parts of units to approximate the area of a triangle. Students may arrive at slightly different answers, depending on how they approximate pieces of units.
- Distribute graph paper and ask each student to draw a rectangle and a triangle. Have students exchange papers. Ask them to approximate the number of square units enclosed in each figure.
- Encourage students to verbalize a relationship between a rectangle's base and height and its area.

Area of Squares and Rectangles

11.1

Objectives: To state and apply the area postulates
To state and apply the formulas for the areas of squares and rectangles

This polygon encloses a portion of the plane indicated by the shaded region. The size of the region enclosed is the *area* of the figure.

Investigation—*Visualizing the Concept*

Determine the approximate area of the triangle by using the indicated unit: ☐ 24 units

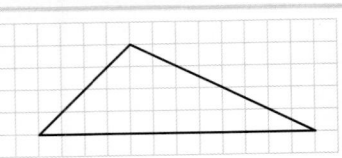

Postulate 22   **Area Postulate**   Every polygonal region corresponds to a unique positive number, called the **area** of the region.

The area of a polygonal region depends on its shape and size. Postulate 23 follows from the fact that congruent figures have the same shape and size.

Postulate 23   **Area Congruence Postulate**   If two polygons are congruent, then the polygonal regions determined by them have the same area.

$\overline{RT}$ divides rectangle *RSTU* into two congruent triangles, $\triangle RST$ and $\triangle TUR$, which are nonoverlapping; thus they have no interior points in common. If each has area *A*, then it appears that the area of rectangle *RSTU* is $A + A$.

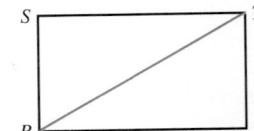

Postulate 24   **Area Addition Postulate**   If a region can be subdivided into nonoverlapping parts, the area of the region is the sum of the areas of those nonoverlapping parts.

Although area is actually the area of the polygonal region enclosed by a polygon, it is common to speak of the ''area of the polygon.''

Postulate 25   The area of a square is the square of the length of its side, or $A = s^2$.

Developing Mathematical Power
Cooperative Learning   The applications of the Golden Rectangle are especially evident in art, architecture, and nature. Working in groups, students can complete p. 36 in *Connections* and use the Golden Rectangle to construct a spiral, which should be a close approximation of the shell of the chambered nautilus. Have each group research other applications.

Area is measured in *square units*. A **square unit** is a square region having sides that measure one unit in length.

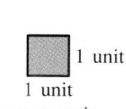

Area = 1 square unit = 1 unit^2

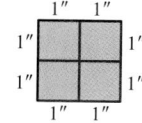

Area = 4 square inches = 4 in.^{2}

Formulas for finding the area of parallelograms require the identification of the *base* and *altitude*. Any side can be considered the **base** of the figure and its length will be denoted by b. An **altitude** is a segment perpendicular to the base and joining the base to the opposite side. The length of an altitude is called the **height**, h. All altitudes drawn to a single base have equal lengths.

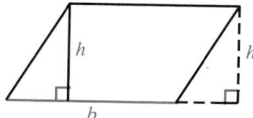 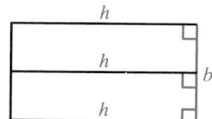 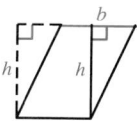

Theorem 11.1 The area of a rectangle equals the product of its base and height, or $A = bh$.

Given: Rectangle $RSTV$ with base b and height h

Prove: $A = bh$

Plan: Extend $\overrightarrow{RS}$ to E such that $SE = h$. Extend $\overrightarrow{RV}$ to G such that $VG = b$. Through G construct $\overline{GF} \parallel \overline{RE}$, with length $b + h$. Construct $\overline{EF} \parallel \overline{RG}$. EF also has length $b + h$; the area of square $REFG$ = Area (I) + Area (II) + Area (III) + Area (IV) = $(b + h)^2$. Now use the properties of algebra to show $A = bh$.
Proved in Practice Exercise 18

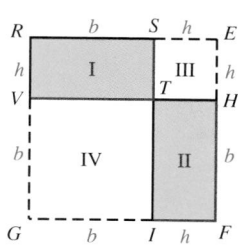

EXAMPLE Rectangle *DBIR* has base b and height h.

a. If $b = 12$ ft and $h = 4$ ft, what is the area of *DBIR*?

b. If *DBIR* has area 100 cm^2 and $h = 5$ cm, what is b?

c. If *DBIR* has area 24 in.^{2}, name the sets of possible whole number values for b and h. How many sets of possible values are there?

a. 48 ft^2　　b. 20 cm　　c. 1 and 24, 2 and 12, 3 and 8, 4 and 6; infinitely many

11.1 Area of Squares and Rectangles **441**

- Emphasize the *square unit,* and how appropriate units for measuring area are chosen.
- Help students to distinguish between linear and square units, and between perimeter and area.
- Stress the "why" behind the formulas; otherwise students try to memorize formulas without understanding why they are appropriate or what purposes they serve.
- Familiarize students with the terms "base" and "height," instead of "length" and "width." Point out that since a rectangle is a parallelogram, the formula for its area is a special case of the formula for area of a parallelogram that students will study in the next section.

CHALKBOARD EXAMPLES

- **For the Example**
  Rectangle *ABCD* has base b and height h. The length of a side of square *EFGH* is s.

  a. If $b = 6$ in. and $h = 8$ in., what is the area of *ABCD*?　48 in.^{2}
  b. If the area of *ABCD* is 96 cm^2 and $b = 4$ cm, find h.　24 cm
  c. If $s = 7$ cm, what is the area of *EFGH*?　49 cm^2
  d. If the area of *EFGH* is 64 in.^{2}, what is the length of a side of *EFGH*?　8 in.

Common Error

- Students might confuse linear and square units, and/or attach the wrong unit to an area computation. Emphasize that area is always measured in *square* units.
- See *Teacher's Resource Book* for additional remediation.

LESSON FOLLOW-UP

Discussion

Ask students to construct the following figures on their geoboards. If a figure is impossible, have them explain why.

Rectangle with perimeter of 16 units and area of:

1. 7 square units 1 × 7
2. 10 square units There are no integers whose sum is 8 and whose product is 10.
3. 12 square units 6 × 2
4. 16 square units 4 × 4
5. As many rectangles as possible with perimeter 12 units. 1 × 5; 2 × 4; 3 × 3
6. A square with area 2 square units.

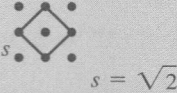

$s = \sqrt{2}$

7. For a fixed perimeter, which rectangle has the largest area? a square

Assignment Guide

See p. 438B for assignments.

Thinking Critically

1. Is it possible for a rectangle to have the same numerical perimeter and area measure? If so, give an example of such a figure. If not, tell why not.
   Yes; if it is a square with each side 4 units long (or, if $b = \frac{2h}{h-2}$ where $h > 2$).

True or false? Justify your answer.

2. The area of a square is equal to the product of its base and height.
   True; a square is a rectangle, so $A = bh$.
3. The Area Postulate guarantees that every plane figure has an area.
   False; a segment has no area and is a plane figure; every polygonal region has an area.
4. If two polygonal figures have the same area, they are congruent.
   False; 2×2 square and a 1×4 rectangle have equal areas but aren't congruent.
5. A square and a rectangle can have the same area.
   True; 2×2 square and a 1×4 rectangle have the same area.
6. If two triangles are congruent, they have the same area.
   True; by the Area Congruence Postulate

MOPT is a rectangle; MNQT and NOPQ are squares.

7. If a square having sides 1 in. is contained in MOPT exactly 18 times, what is the area of MOPT? 18 in.²
8. If MNQT is a square unit, what is the area of MOPT? 2 sq units
9. If MO = 8 cm, find the areas of rectangle MOPT and square MNQT. 32 cm²; 16 cm²
10. If NP = $\sqrt{8}$ cm, find the area of square NOPQ. 4 cm²
11. If m∠OTP = 30 and if OP = 6 cm, find the area of rectangle MOPT. 36√3 cm²
12. If TO = 13 in. and TP = 12 in., find the area of rectangle MOPT. 60 in.²
13. Is a figure that measures "4 inches square" the same as a figure whose area is "4 square inches"? Explain. No; the first figure will have an area of 16 sq in.

PRACTICE EXERCISES 🔁 Use technology where appropriate.

Writing in Mathematics

A shop produces 10,000 flat metal plates like the one shown. The top of each plate is covered with a thin plastic coating.

A 1. Give a strategy for determining how much plastic is required to cover each one.
   Add the areas: 5·35, 5·20, 5·40, 20·20, and 10·35

2. Determine the total area (for all plates) in mm² to be coated.
   12,250,000 mm²

Complete the table. The figures in Exercises 3–6 are rectangles.

	Base	Height	Area	Perimeter
3.	3 cm	? 5 cm	15 cm²	? 16 cm
4.	8 in.	2.5 in.	? 20 in.²	? 21 in.
5.	? 4 in.	5 in.	? 20 in.²	18 in.
6.	7 cm	? 2.5 cm	? 17.5 cm²	19 cm

Classify ▭USHB as a rectangle and/or square. Find its area.

7. $\overline{BU} \perp \overline{US}$, $BH = 14$ in., $SH = 6$ in.
rectangle, 84 in.²

8. $\overline{BU} \perp \overline{US}$, $\overline{BU} \cong \overline{US}$, $SH = 11$ cm.
both; 121 cm²

9. $\overline{BS} \cong \overline{UH}$, $\overline{BS} \perp \overline{UH}$, the perimeter of USHB is 20 in. both; 25 in.²

10. $\overline{BS} \cong \overline{UH}$, $\overline{BS} \perp \overline{UH}$, and $US = 2.5$ in.
both; 6.25 in.²

Rectangle ANGL has base b and height h.

11. If $LG = 10$ cm, $AL = (2n - 3)$ cm and the area of ANGL is 50 cm², find AL.
n = 4; AL = 5 cm

12. If $b = (7x - 2)$ mm, $h = 6$ mm and the perimeter of ANGL is $(6x + 32)$ mm, find b, the area, and the perimeter of ANGL.
b = 19 mm; A = 114 mm²; P = 50 mm

13. If $b = (x + 3)$ cm, $h = (x - 3)$ cm and the area is 72 cm², find x, b, and h. x = 9, b = 12 cm, h = 6 cm

14. If $h = (x - 1)$ ft, $b = (x + 1)$ ft and the area of ANGL is 35 ft², find x, h, and b.
x = 6, h = 5 ft, b = 7 ft

Square TUVN has sides of length s.

15. If $s = (2a + 3)$ dm, find the area of square TUVN in terms of a.
A = (4a² + 12a + 9) dm²

16. If the area of square TUVN is $16n^2$ cm², find s in terms of n. s = 4n cm

17. If its perimeter is $(4y - 12)$ cm, find the area of square TUVN in terms of y.
s = y - 3, A = (y - 3)² = (y² - 6y + 9) cm²

18. Write and solve the equation that completes the proof of Theorem 11.1.
(b + h)² = A + A + h² + b²; b² + 2bh + h² = 2A + h² + b²; 2bh = 2A; A = bh

19. Find the area of rectangle ABCD if $\overline{AC}$ bisects $\angle A$ and $AC = \sqrt{50}$ in. 25 in.²

Square RBED is circumscribed about ⊙O.

20. If the radius of ⊙O is 6 cm, find the area of square RBED. 144 cm²

21. If the radius of ⊙O is 3 cm, find the perimeter of RBED. 24 cm

22. Find the area of a square circumscribed about a circle of radius r. A = 4r²

23. Find the area of a square inscribed in a circle of radius r. A = 2r²

Determine the area of the new rectangle (in relation to the original rectangle) when the dimensions are altered as follows.

24. The base of a rectangle of area A is doubled. new area = 2A

B
b + h)² = A + A + h² + b²; b² + 2bh + h² = 2A + h² + b²; 2bh = 2A; A = bh

---

Construction

Students should be reminded that the Golden Ratio is approximately equal to 1.62. When they complete the construction, they should measure for accuracy.

Lesson Quiz

1. If rectangle IJKL has $IL = 8$ cm, $IJ = (6n + 2)$ cm, and the area of IJKL is 160 cm², find n and IJ. n = 3; IJ = 20 cm

2. If a rectangle has $h = (2n + 1)$ cm, $b = 4$ cm, and perimeter $(3n + 20)$ cm, find h, the perimeter, and the area of the rectangle. h = 21 cm; P = 50 cm; A = 84 cm²

3. If the perimeter of a square is $(4y + 16)$ cm, find its area in terms of y. (y² + 8y + 16) cm²

4. A rectangle has a diagonal 20 cm that makes a 30° angle with one side of the rectangle. Find the area of the rectangle. $100\sqrt{3}$ cm²

Additional Answer for p. 444

29. Plan: Use the props. of ▭s and isos. traps. to show ▭JLOQ ≅ ▭MKPN by SASAS. The concl. follows by the Area Cong. Post.

Proof:

Statements	Reasons
1. ▭JLOQ; ▭MKPN	1. Given
2. $\overline{OQ} \cong \overline{JL}$; $\overline{PN} \cong \overline{MK}$	2. Opp. sides of a ▭ are ≅.
3. $\overline{OQ} \cong \overline{PN}$	3. Given
4. $\overline{JL} \cong \overline{MK}$	4. Subst. prop.
5. Isos. trap. KLOP	5. Given
6. $\angle KLO \cong \angle LKP$; $\angle LOP \cong \angle KPO$	6. Base ∠s of an isos. trap. are ≅.
7. $\overline{KP} \cong \overline{LO}$	7. Def. of isos. trap.
8. ▭JLOQ ≅ ▭MKPN	8. SASAS
9. Area of ▭JLOQ = area of ▭MKPN	9. Area Congruence Post.

Concl.: In the given figure, if JLOQ and MKPN are▭s and KLOP is an isos. trap., then the area of ▭JLOQ = area of ▭MKPN.

25. The base and height of a rectangle of area A are both doubled.
new area = $4A$

26. The base of a rectangle of area A is doubled and the height is halved.
new area = A

C **27.** If the ratio of the base to the height in a rectangle is $2:3$, what is the area of the rectangle in terms of the height? of the base? $\frac{2}{3}h^2; \frac{3}{2}b^2$

28. Suppose a square and a nonsquare rectangle whose base and height are whole numbers each have a perimeter of 20 in. Which figure has the larger area? How do you know? Repeat, using a perimeter of 64 inches. Generalize your results. The square; of all rectangles with the same perimeter, the square has the greatest area.

29. Given: $\square JLOQ$; $\square MKPN$;
$\overline{OQ} \cong \overline{PN}$, isosceles
trapezoid $KLOP$

Prove: Area of $\square JLOQ$ = area of $\square MKPN$ See side column page 443.

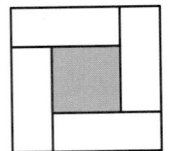

Applications

30. Design The tiles for a kitchen floor look like the diagram on the right. Each is a square 1 ft on a side with the middle green tile a 6-in. by 6-in. square. How many square feet of white tile will there be in a kitchen that is 8 ft by 11 ft? 66 ft²

31. Technology Use Logo to draw the Golden Rectangle as described below. In your procedure, use the necessary information from the Construction. See Solutions Manual.

CONSTRUCTION

In a Golden Rectangle the ratio of length to width is the Golden Ratio (see Exercise 32, p. 270). Construct a Golden Rectangle.

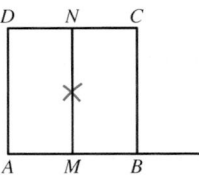

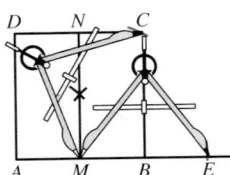

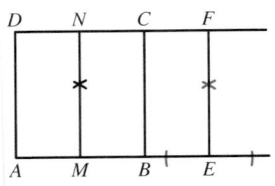

1. Construct square ABCD. Extend $\overrightarrow{AB}$. Construct the perpendicular bisector of $\overline{AB}$. Label it $\overleftrightarrow{MN}$.

2. Place the point of a compass on M. With radius MC draw an arc intersecting the extension of $\overrightarrow{AB}$ at E.

3. Construct a perpendicular through E. Extend $\overrightarrow{DC}$ to intersect this perpendicular at F. ADFE is a Golden Rectangle.

Developing Mathematical Power

Keeping a Portfolio Have students define, in their own words, the vocabulary in this lesson. Then have them record their responses to Class Exercises 2–6. They should include an illustration of the true statements and an example that shows how the others are false. Have them generalize about what happens to the area of a rectangle as its dimensions are changed.

Reproduced Worksheet (Practice)

Name _____ Date _____
Practice: For use after Lesson 11.1, Geometry

Area of Squares and Rectangles
Complete the table. The figures in Exercises 1–3 are rectangles.

	Base	Height	Area	Perimeter
1.	7 cm	3 cm	21 cm²	20 cm
2.	9 in.	3.5 in.	31.5 in.²	25 in.
3.	5 in.	8 in.	40 in.²	26 in.

In Exercises 4–6, classify $\square DCBA$ as a rectangle or square and find its area.

4. $\overline{DA} \perp \overline{AB}, \overline{DA} \cong \overline{AB}, DA = 7$ in. Square; 49 in.²
5. $\overline{DA} \perp \overline{AB}, DA = 15$ cm, $AB = 12$ cm Rectangle; 180 cm²
6. $\overline{DB} \cong \overline{AC}, \overline{DA} \perp \overline{AC}, DC = 8.5$ in. Square; 72.25 in.²

Rectangle $BYXA$ has base b and height h.

7. If $YX = 25, YB = 3n - 5$, and the area is 100 cm², find n and YB. $n = 3; YB = 4$
8. If $b = (8x - 4)$ mm, $h = 5$, and the perimeter of $BYXA$ is $(5x + 46)$ mm, find b, the area, and the perimeter of $BYXA$. $b = 28$ mm; $A = 140$ mm²; $p = 66$ mm
9. If $h = (x - 2)$ ft, $b = (x + 2)$ ft, and the area of $BYXA$ is 60 ft² find x, h, and b. $x = 8$ ft; $h = 6$ ft; $b = 10$ ft

Square $TSRW$ has sides of length s.

10. If $s = (3n + 4)$ mm, find the area of square $TSRW$ in terms of n. $A = 9n^2 + 24n + 16$ mm²
11. If the area of square $TSRW$ is $49x^2$ in.², find s in terms of x. $s = 7x$ in.
12. If its perimeter is $(8y - 20)$ cm, find the area of square $TSRW$ in terms of y. $A = 4y^2 - 20y + 25$ cm²

Application
13. **Construction** A cement walkway 3 ft wide is to be constructed around a swimming pool 18 ft by 40 ft. How many square feet of cement walkway will there be? 384 ft²

2 Chapter 11

Reproduced Worksheet (Enrichment)

Name _____ Date _____
Enrichment: For use after Lesson 11.1, Geometry

Area Maximization Problems
Suppose that you have 100 yd of fencing with which to enclose a rectangular pasture.

1. You could enclose a field 40 yd by 10 yd. What is the enclosed area? 400 yd²
2. What is the enclosed area of a field 30 yd by 20 yd? 600 yd²

What is the enclosed area of a field:

3. 28 by 22 yd? 616 yd²   4. 27 by 23 yd? 621 yd²
5. 26 by 24 yd? 624 yd²   6. 25 by 25 yd? 625 yd²
7. Formulate a conjecture based on the information you have acquired so far. The area of the largest area using 100 yd of fencing is 625 yd².

8. Why isn't it possible to verify the conjecture that the 25 by 25 fence encloses the maximum area simply by trying different sizes for the pasture? There are infinite numbers of possibilities.

It is possible to use algebra to establish this conjecture. Expand the binomial $(s + a)^2: s^2 + 2as + a^2$.

9. What is the coefficient of s^2? 1   10. Of s^2? 2a

Notice that the remaining term a^2, is the square of half the coefficient of s. This insight enables us to maximize the area of a rectangle with a given perimeter through the procedure completing the square.

Suppose that you have 100 yd of fencing, and decide to enclose a rectangle of length l. In terms of l:

11. What is the width of the rectangle? 50 – l
12. What is the area of the rectangle? $l(50 - l)$, or $50l - l^2$
13. Why did the area remain unchanged? added and subtracted the same number (625)
14. Can the square of an expression ever be positive? yes
zero? yes   negative? no
15. What is the smallest possible value for the square of an expression? 0
16. In the expression for A in terms of l, what is the largest possible value for A? 625

Chapter 11 3

Area of Parallelograms and Triangles

Objective: To state and apply the formulas for the areas of parallelograms and triangles

The area postulates and the formula for the area of a rectangle can be used to derive the formulas for the area of other simple polygons.

Investigation—*Thinking Critically*

Four adjoining cattle pens were made from two existing fences that intersect.

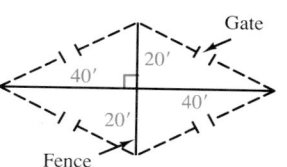

1. What is the area enclosed by the four pens?
   1600 ft²
2. What geometric principles are involved?
   Area Con. Post.; Area Add. Post.; Th. 11.1
3. What geometric figure is formed by these four pens?
   parallelogram; rhombus

> **Theorem 11.2** The area of a parallelogram equals the product of the length of a base and its corresponding height, or $A = bh$.

Given: $\square GRAM$ with base b, altitudes $\overline{RN}$ and $\overline{AO}$, and height h

Prove: Area of $\square GRAM = bh$

Plan: Show that $\triangle RNG \cong \triangle AOM$, so they have the same area.
Since the area of rectangle $NRAO$ equals the sum of the areas of quad. $NRAM$ and $\triangle AOM$, you can now show that rectangle $NRAO$ and $\square GRAM$ have the same area. Using the transitive property will lead to the desired conclusion.
Proved in Practice Exercise 25

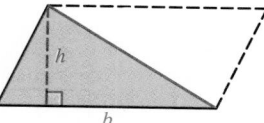
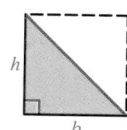
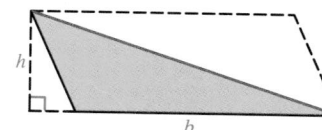

The diagonal separates each parallelogram into two congruent triangles. In both the parallelograms and the shaded triangles, b and h represent a base and a corresponding height. This leads to Theorem 11.3 and its corollaries.

Developing Mathematical Power

Cooperative Learning Assign each group of students a different figure, such as a parallelogram, a triangle, a rhombus, or an equilateral triangle. Each group should prepare a presentation to show how the specific area formula for that figure was derived from the formula for the area of a square or a rectangle. They should include in their presentations how manipulatives (such as cutouts) can be used to illustrate their derivations.

LESSON PLAN

Vocabulary
Semiperimeter

Materials/Manipulatives
Models of parallelograms cut from construction paper
Scissors   Geoboards
Teacher's Resource Book, Transparency 19
Teaching Transparency 71

Technology
Calculator
Computer
Computer Test Bank, pp. 678–689
The Geometric Supposer: Triangles
Geometry Problems and Projects: Triangles, Worksheets T14, T18, T22-T24

LESSON FOCUS

Review

Complete the table. The figures in Exercises 1–3 are rectangles.

	Base	Height	Area
1.	8 cm	9 cm	?
2.	5 cm	?	125 cm²
3.	?	8 cm	128 cm²

1. 72 cm²   2. 25 cm   3. 16 cm

Alternative Learning Styles

The figure in the Investigation may provide students with an opportunity to derive the formula for the area of a rhombus by using manipulatives. If students trace the figure to make a model, cut it apart, and reassemble it as a square, they can see that the vertical diagonal forms one side of the square, and $\frac{1}{2}$ the horizontal diagonal forms the other side of the square. Thus $A = s^2$ becomes $A = \frac{1}{2}d_1 \cdot d_2$.

- Make use of physical models wherever possible. This helps students understand the derivation of the formulas and contributes to retention.
- Emphasize how all the formulas in this lesson are derived from the formula for the area of a rectangle.
- Provide many examples of parallelograms and triangles in which students must determine the "base" and "height." Give some examples with more information than necessary to assist students in determining what is required and what is not.
- Assign Practice Exercises 17 and 18 together.
- Use grids to show students several examples of parallelograms that have congruent corresponding sides but unequal areas.

CHALKBOARD EXAMPLES

- **For the Example**
  Given: Isos. trap. *ABCD* with $m\angle CDA = 60$, $CD = 12$ cm, and $BC = 10$ cm; $m\angle DEC = 60$; $ED = CF$

  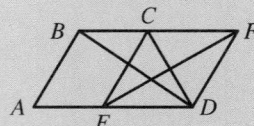

  Find:
  a. Area of $\triangle CDE$
  b. Area of $\triangle ABD$
  c. Area of $\square ABFD$
  d. Area of $\square ABCE$
  e. EF
  f. Area of rhombus $ECFD$

  a. $A = \frac{12^2\sqrt{3}}{4} = 36\sqrt{3}$ cm^2
  b. $A = \frac{1}{2}(22)(6\sqrt{3}) = 66\sqrt{3}$ cm^2
  c. $A = 22(6\sqrt{3}) = 132\sqrt{3}$ cm^2
  d. $A = 10(6\sqrt{3}) = 60\sqrt{3}$ cm^2
  e. $72\sqrt{3} = \frac{1}{2}(12)EF$; $EF = 12\sqrt{3}$ cm
  f. $A = \frac{1}{2}(12)(12\sqrt{3}) = 72\sqrt{3}$ cm^2

Theorem 11.3 The area of a triangle is equal to one-half the product of the length of a base and its corresponding height, or $A = \frac{1}{2}bh$.
Proved in Practice Exercise 28

Corollary 1 The area of a rhombus equals one-half the product of the lengths of its diagonals, or $A = \frac{1}{2}d_1 \cdot d_2$. Proved in Practice Exercise 29

Corollary 2 The area of an equilateral triangle equals one-fourth the product of $\sqrt{3}$ and the square of the length of the side, or $A = \frac{s^2\sqrt{3}}{4}$. Proved in Practice Exercise 30

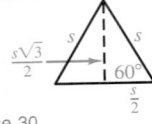

EXAMPLE Find the area of each figure using the given information. $l_1 \parallel l_2 \parallel l_3$; $t_1 \parallel t_2 \parallel t_3$; $\overline{AG} \cong \overline{GF}$

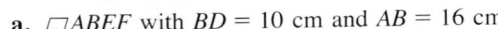

a. $\square ABEF$ with $BD = 10$ cm and $AB = 16$ cm

b. $\triangle BDF$ with $BD = 7$ cm and $FB = 25$ cm

c. Rhombus $BCIE$ with $EC = 10$ cm and $BI = 9$ cm

d. $\triangle FBI$ with $BF = 12$ cm and $m\angle BFI = m\angle BIF = 60$

a. $A = bh$
$= 10 \cdot 16$
$= 160$ cm^2

b. $A = \frac{1}{2}bh$
$= \frac{1}{2} \cdot 24 \cdot 7$
$= 84$ cm^2

c. $A = \frac{1}{2}d_1 \cdot d_2$
$= \frac{1}{2} \cdot 10 \cdot 9$
$= 45$ cm^2

d. $A = \frac{s^2\sqrt{3}}{4}$
$= \frac{12^2\sqrt{3}}{4}$
$= 36\sqrt{3}$ cm^2

CLASS EXERCISES

True or false? Justify your answers.

1. If a parallelogram has a right angle, its area is the product of the lengths of a pair of consecutive sides. True; the parallelogram is a rectangle; thus by Theorem 11.1, $A = bh$ where b and h are consecutive sides.
2. If a rhombus has a right angle, its area is the length of a side squared. True; the rhombus is a square, therefore $A = s^2$.
3. The area of a square is one half the product of the lengths of the diagonals. true; Theorem 11.3, Corollary 1
4. The area of a parallelogram is the square of the length of its base. False; the measure of the base may not be equal to the measure of the height.
5. The area of a right triangle is the product of the lengths of its legs. False; $A = \frac{1}{2}$ product of the length of its legs.
6. If *ABCD* is a parallelogram, *ADGH* is a rectangle, *AEFH* is a trapezoid, and $\overline{BI} \cong \overline{AH}$, find the area of figure *ABCDEFH*. $1200 + 200\sqrt{3}$ mm^2

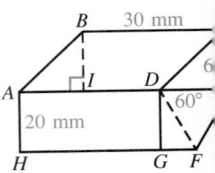

PRACTICE EXERCISES 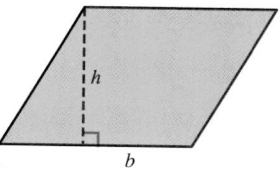 Use technology where appropriate.

Thinking Critically A parallelogram has base b and height h.

A **1.** If the base is doubled and the height remains unchanged, how does the area of the new parallelogram compare to the area of the original? new area = 2A

2. If the base is doubled, how must the height be changed to produce a parallelogram having the same area as the original? The height must be halved.

Find the area of each figure. All quadrilaterals are parallelograms.

3.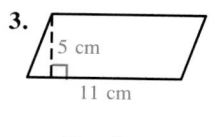
5 cm
11 cm
55 cm²

4.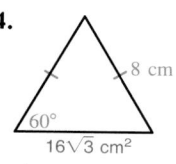
8 cm
60°
16√3 cm²

5.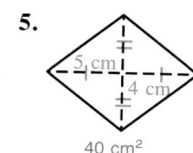
5 cm
4 cm
40 cm²

6.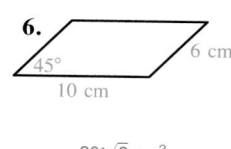
6 cm
45°
10 cm
30√2 cm²

Find the missing dimensions of □ONYT.

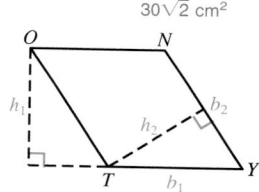

	b_1	b_2	h_1	h_2	Area (□ONYT)
7.	? / 21 in.	12 in.	8 in.	? / 14 in.	168 in.²
8.	15 cm	? / 5 cm	? / 4 cm	12 cm	60 cm²

FARM is a rhombus with diagonals $\overline{AM}$ and $\overline{FR}$.

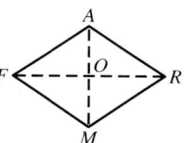

9. If $FO = 3.5$ cm and $AO = 3$ cm, the area of $FARM =$? . 21 cm²

10. If $FA = 13$ cm and $AO = 5$ cm, the area of $FARM =$? . 120 cm²

11. If the area of $FARM = 160$ cm² and $AM = 8$ cm, find FR. 40 cm

△TAK is a right triangle and $\overline{AY} \perp \overline{TK}$.

12. If $TA = 10$ in. and $AK = 24$ in., find the area of $△TAK$. 120 in.²

13. If $AY = 15$ in. and $AK = 25$ in., find the area of $△AYK$. 150 in.²

14. If $m\angle ATK = 60$ and $AT = 6$ cm, find the area of $△TAK$. 18√3 cm²

15. An equilateral $△$ has area $16\sqrt{3}$ cm². Find the side length and the height. $16\sqrt{3} = \frac{s^2\sqrt{3}}{4}$; s = 8 cm, h = 4√3 cm

16. Find the area of an equilateral triangle whose perimeter is 12 in.
4√3 in.²

17. Find the areas of $△ANY$ and $△AND$. 9√3 and 18√3

18. Find the length of the altitude to $\overline{ND}$ in $△NYD$. 3

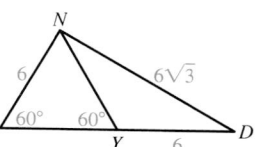
N
6
6√3
60°
60°
A
Y
6
D

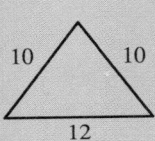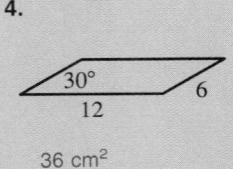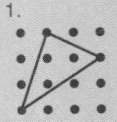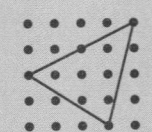
448

Find the area of each figure.

B

19.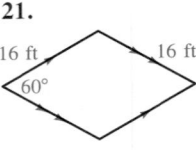
$75\sqrt{2}$ cm^2

20.
$18\sqrt{5}$ in.^{2}

21.
$128\sqrt{3}$ ft^2

22.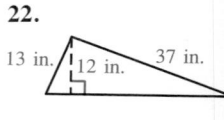
240 in.^{2}

23. If the diameter of $\odot O$ is 45 cm, *PE* = 53 cm, and $\overline{EK}$ is tangent to $\odot O$ at *K*, find the area of $\triangle PEK$. $A = \frac{1}{2} \cdot 45 \cdot 28 = 630$ cm^2

24. If isosceles $\triangle PYK$ is inscribed in $\odot O$ of diameter 15 cm, find the area of $\triangle PYK$. $YO = h = \frac{15}{2}; A = \frac{1}{2}(15 \times \frac{15}{2}) = 56\frac{1}{4}$ cm^2

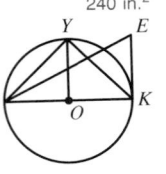

25. Complete the proof of Theorem 11.2. See page 769.

26. Compare the bases of a triangle and a parallelogram that have equal areas and equal heights. base of △ = 2 times base of ▱

27. Compare the areas of a triangle and a parallelogram that have equal heights and equal bases. area of ▱ = 2 times area of △

Prove each of the following. See pages 769–771.

28. Th. 11.3   **29.** Cor. 1 of Th. 11.3   **30.** Cor. 2 of Th. 11.3

C   **31. Given:** $\overline{KM}$ is a median of $\triangle JKL$.
   Prove: Area of $\triangle JKM$ = area of $\triangle KML$

32. Given: Quad. *QUAD*; $\overline{UD}$ bisects $\overline{QA}$.
   Prove: Area of $\triangle DQU$ = area of $\triangle DAU$

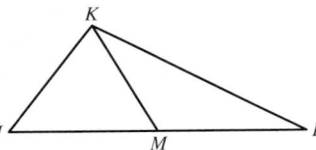

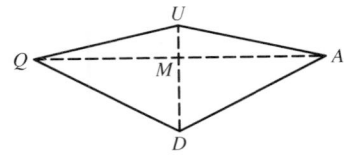

33. Given: ▱*ABLE*; *C* and *D* are midpoints of $\overline{AB}$ and $\overline{LE}$, respectively.
   Prove: Area of *BDEC* = $\frac{1}{2}$ · area of ▱*ABLE*

34. Given: ▱*ABCD* and $\triangle FDA$; *E* is the midpoint of $\overline{BC}$.
   Prove: Area of ▱*ABCD* = area of $\triangle FDA$

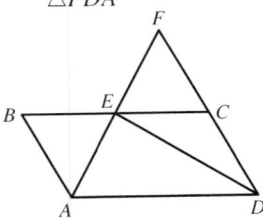

448   Chapter 11 Area

Applications

35. Quilting A quiltmaker uses the "baby's blocks" pattern shown on the right. If the graph paper is in 1-in. units, how many square inches is each white panel of the pattern? 12 in.²

36. Technology In Logo, generate a quilt of red and white squares. Calculate the total area for each color. See Solutions Manual.

37. City Planning How many parallel parking spaces can a city planner fit in an area 15 ft × 105 ft if the spaces must be arranged at a 45° angle and are 10 ft wide? How much space is wasted? Illustrate your answer with a drawing. 6 spaces; $15 \cdot 105 - 6(10 \cdot 15\sqrt{2})$ or $1575 - 900\sqrt{2} \approx 302.2$ ft²

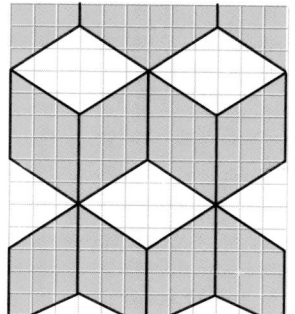

Teacher's Resource Book
Follow-Up Investigation, Chapter 11, p. 4

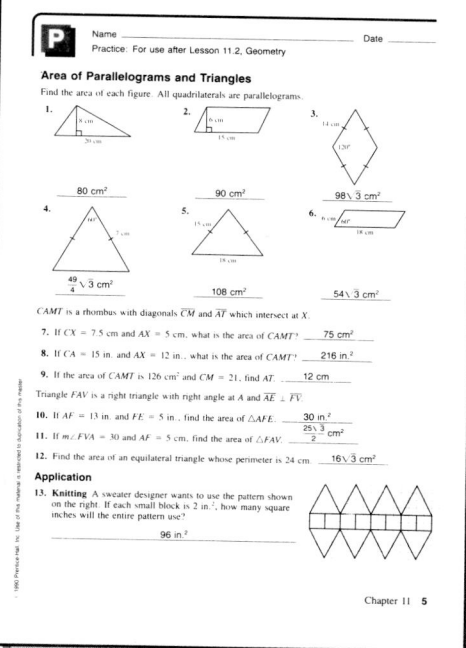

Developing Mathematical Power

38. Extension You can compute the area of a triangle by using the length of its sides. The Greek mathematician Heron proved this by developing a formula that involved the *semiperimeter* of a triangle. The **semiperimeter** of a triangle is one-half the perimeter.

Heron's Formula If a triangle has sides of lengths a, b, and c, and if s is the semiperimeter of the triangle, then the area A of the triangle is:

$$A = \sqrt{s(s-a)(s-b)(s-c)}$$

EXAMPLE A triangular lot has the dimensions shown. Find the area of the lot.

Use Heron's Formula:
$A = \sqrt{s(s-a)(s-b)(s-c)}$
    where $a = 10.3$, $b = 17.1$, and $c = 21.4$.

a. Calculate. $s = \dfrac{a+b+c}{2} = \dfrac{10.3 + 17.1 + 21.4}{2} = 24.4$

b. $A = \sqrt{24.4(24.4 - 10.3)(24.4 - 17.1)(24.4 - 21.4)}$
    $= \sqrt{24.4(14.1)(7.3)(3)}$ *This is now calculation-ready.*
    $= \sqrt{7534.476}$
    $= 86.8$ The area is approximately 86.8 m².

Use Heron's formula to find the area of a right triangle whose sides are 5, 12, and 13. Check your answer by using $A = \frac{1}{2}bh$. $A = \sqrt{15 \cdot 10 \cdot 3 \cdot 2} = 30$; $A = \frac{1}{2} \cdot 5 \cdot 12 = 30$

11.2 Area of Parallelograms and Triangles   **449**

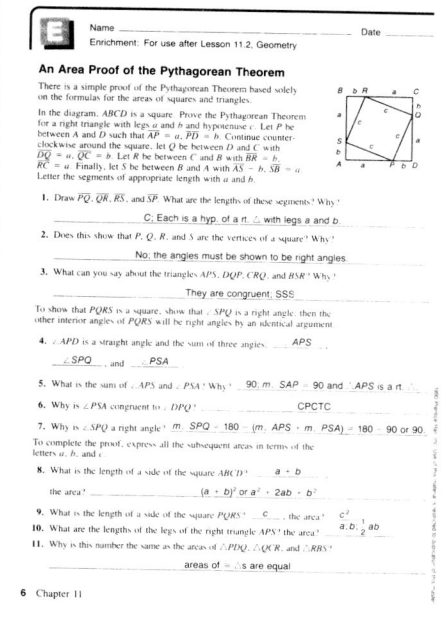

37.

Vocabulary

Altitude
Height

Materials/Manipulatives

Several different trapezoids for
use in the activity described in
the Investigation
Tracing paper
*Teacher's Resource Book,
Teaching Aid 11,
Transparency 19
Teaching Transparency 72*

Technology

Computer
Computer Test Bank, pp.
690–699
*The Geometric Supposer:
Quadrilaterals,* p. 90

LESSON FOCUS

Review

• Find the area.

1. 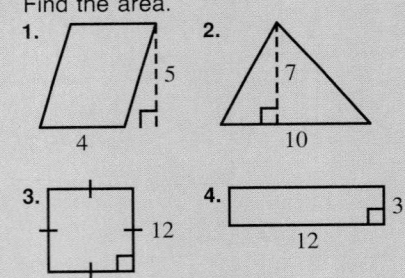   2.

5

4

7

10

3.

12

4.

3

12

1. 20   2. 35   3. 144   4. 36

• Exercises 30–43 provide a Mixed
Review.

Alternative Learning Styles

• The Investigation provides a kinesthetic approach to finding the formula for the area of a trapezoid.

11.3

Area of Trapezoids

Objective: To state and apply the formula for the area of trapezoids

Recall that a trapezoid is a quadrilateral that has exactly one pair of parallel
sides. The formula for the area of a trapezoid is based on the area formulas
that have already been developed in this chapter.

Investigation—*Using Manipulatives*

Trace the trapezoid on the right and cut it out.
Label its bases b_1 and b_2.
Fold it so that the bases meet.
Cut along the fold (the median of the trapezoid).
Label the height of each piece $\frac{h}{2}$.

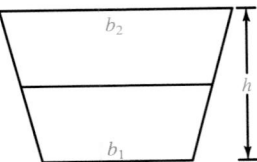

Rotate the top piece clockwise
until b_1 and b_2 are collinear.

1. What figure has been formed?
   parallelogram
2. What is its base? Its height?
   $b_1 + b_2$; $\frac{h}{2}$
3. Develop a formula for its area. $A = \frac{h}{2}(b_1 + b_2)$

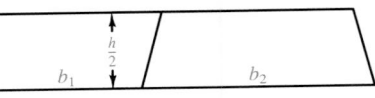

An **altitude of a trapezoid** is a segment that is
perpendicular to, and has its endpoints on, the bases
of the trapezoid. The base lengths and the length of
the altitude, called the *height*, are used to find the
area of the trapezoid.

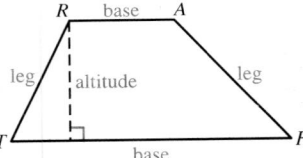

> **Theorem 11.4** The area of a trapezoid equals one-half the product of the
> height and the sum of the lengths of the bases, or $A = \frac{h}{2}(b_1 + b_2)$.

Given: Trapezoid *RANF* with bases of
length b_1 and b_2 and height h

Prove: Area of $RANF = \frac{h}{2}(b_1 + b_2)$

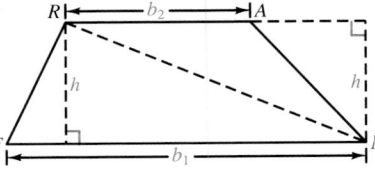

Developing Mathematical Power

Cooperative Learning Select teams of students to "decompose" triangles into
exactly three trapezoids and derive the formula for the area of a triangle from the
area of a trapezoid by completing the Enrichment activity, p. 9, in the *Teacher's
Resource Book* (see side column, p. 454). Challenge students to "decompose"
other triangles.

Plan: Draw $\overline{RN}$ to form $\triangle FRN$ and RAN that have the same height, h. Find the areas of $\triangle FRN$ and RAN. Use the Area Addition Postulate and the substitution property to reach the desired conclusion.
Proved in Practice Exercise 24

EXAMPLE Use trapezoid *VANE* to find the missing quantities. All length measures are in centimeters.

a. If $AN = 8$, $VA = 10$, and $EN = 14$, find the area of *VANE*.

b. If $VA = 12$, $EV = 10$, and $ET = 6$, find the area of *VANE*.

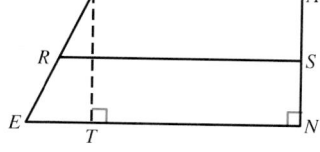

c. If $\overline{RS}$ is the median of *VANE*, $SN = 5$, $EN = 15$, and $VA = 11$, find the area of *VANE*.

d. If $VA = 14$, $EN = 18$, and the area of *VANE* = 128 cm², find VT.

e. If $VT = 6$, $EN = 9$, and the area of *VANE* = 48 cm², find VA.

a. $A = \frac{8}{2}(10 + 14) = 96$ cm²

b. $h^2 = 10^2 - 6^2$ and $h = 8$ cm; $A = \frac{8}{2}(12 + 18) = 120$ cm²

c. Since $AN = 10$, $A = \frac{10}{2}(11 + 15) = 130$ cm².

d. 128 cm² $= \frac{VT}{2}(14 + 18)$; $VT = 8$ cm

e. 48 cm² $= \frac{6}{2}(VA + 9)$; $VA = 7$ cm

CLASS EXERCISES

1. In this trapezoid, if $l_1 = l_2$ and you are given b_1, b_2, and l_1, can the area be determined? If so, how? If not, why not? Yes; by the Pyth. Th., $h^2 + \left(\frac{b_1 - b_2}{2}\right)^2 = l_1^2$ determines h; then $A = \frac{h}{2}(b_1 + b_2)$.

2. If b_1, b_2, and A are given, how could the height be determined? $h = \frac{2A}{b_1 + b_2}$

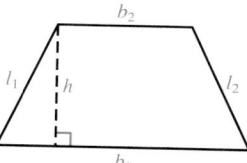

Trapezoid *TCKM* has area A. All length measures are in inches.

3. If $MK = 17$, $TC = 12$, and $TY = 8$, find A. 116 in.²

4. If $TY = 8$, $MK = 20$, and $A = 120$ in.², find TC. 10 in.

5. If $MT = CK = 10$, $TC = 14$, and $MK = 26$, find A. 160 in.²

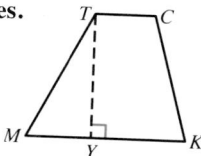

11.3 Area of Trapezoids   **451**

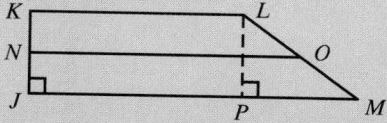

Additional Answers for p. 453.

24. Proof:

Statements	Reasons
1. Draw $\overline{RN}$ to form $\triangle FRN$ and $\triangle RAN$.	1. Two pts. determine a line.
2. Area of $\triangle FRN =$ $\frac{1}{2}b_1 \cdot h$	2. Area of $\triangle = \frac{1}{2}bh$
3. Extend $\overrightarrow{RA}$ through A.	3. Two pts. determine a line.
4. Draw a line $\perp \overrightarrow{RA}$ from pt. N.	4. From a pt. not on a line, exactly one $\perp$ can be drawn.
5. $\triangle RAN$ has height h.	5. Def. of height
6. Area of $\triangle RAN =$ $\frac{1}{2}b_2h$	6. Area of $\triangle = \frac{1}{2}bh$
7. Area of $RANF =$ area of $\triangle FRN +$ area of $\triangle RAN$	7. Area Add. Post.
8. Area of $RANF =$ $\frac{1}{2}b_1h + \frac{1}{2}b_2h$	8. Subst. prop.
9. Area of $RANF =$ $\frac{1}{2}h(b_1 + b_2)$	9. Distrib. prop.

Conclusion: If trap. $RANF$ has bases of length b_1 and b_2 and height h, then the area of $RANF = \frac{1}{2}h(b_1 + b_2)$.

PRACTICE EXERCISES   Use technology where appropriate.

A   1. **Thinking Critically** Rewrite the formula for the area of a trapezoid so that the height can be found using only the area and the median. Use a calculator to find the height to the nearest hundredth of a foot when the area of a trapezoid is 192.56 ft² and the median is 11.49 ft. $A = hm$; $h = \frac{A}{m}$; $h = 16.76$ ft

Find the area of each trapezoid. All length measures are in centimeters.

2. 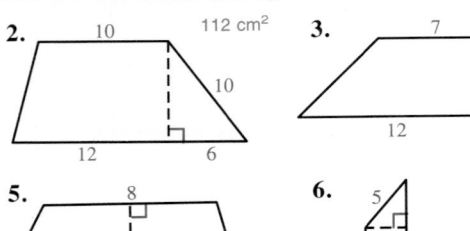 112 cm²

3. 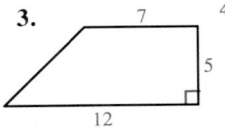 47.5 cm²

4. 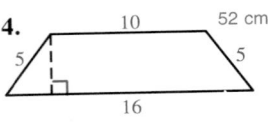 52 cm²

5. 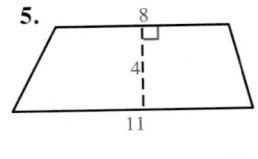 38 cm²

6. 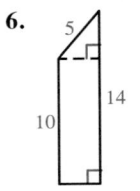 36 cm²

7. 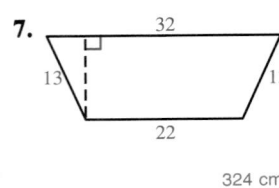 324 cm²

Trapezoid $CERI$ has area A. All length measures are in feet.

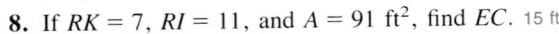

8. If $RK = 7$, $RI = 11$, and $A = 91$ ft², find EC. 15 ft

9. If EC is three times as long as RI, $RK = 6$, and $A = 48$ ft², find RI and EC. 4 ft; 12 ft

10. If RI is 6 feet shorter than EC, $RK = 5$, and $A = 75$ ft², find RI and EC. 12 ft; 18 ft

11. If $RI = 2x$, $EC = 3x + 1$, $RK = 9$, and $A = 117$ ft², find x, RI, and EC. 5 ft; 10 ft; 16 ft

$KBCD$ is an isosceles trapezoid with legs $\overline{KD}$ and $\overline{BC}$ and area A. All length measures are in inches.

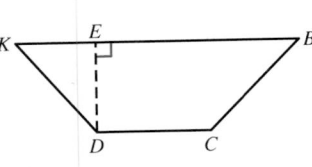

12. If $KD = 10$, $DE = 6$, and $A = 246$ in.², find KB and DC. 49 in.; 33 in.

13. If the perimeter of $KBCD$ is 50, $KB = 24$, $ED = 3$, and $KD = 5$, find A. $A = 60$ in.²

14. If the perimeter of $KBCD$ is 56, $BC = 13$, and $DC = 10$, find ED and A. 12 in.; 180 in.²

15. If $m\angle K = 45$, and $ED = DC = 8$, find the perimeter and the area. $P = (32 + 16\sqrt{2})$ in.; $A = 128$ in.²

Developing Mathematical Power

Keeping a Portfolio Have students write, in their own words, the definition of *the median of a trapezoid* and give a general formula for its length. Then have them rewrite the formula for the area of a trapezoid in terms of its median. They should provide a labeled illustration of the trapezoid.

Find the area of each trapezoid. All length measures are in centimeters.

B 16.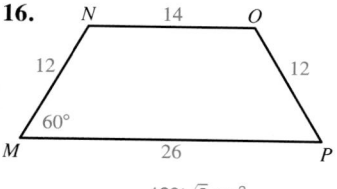

$120\sqrt{3}$ cm²

17.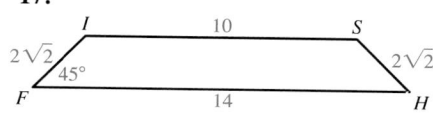

24 cm²

Isosceles trapezoid MINE is inscribed in ⊙O, which has radius r. All length measures are in millimeters.

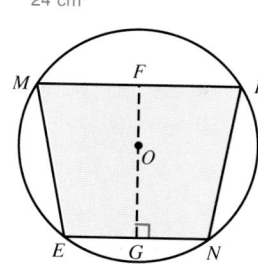

18. If $r = 29$, $OF = 20$, and $OG = 21$, find MI, EN, and the area of *MINE*. 42 mm; 40 mm; A = 1681 mm²

19. If $r = 65$, $MI = 112$, and $EN = 66$, find the area of *MINE*. A = 7921 mm²

20. Find the area of *MNOPR*. A = 124

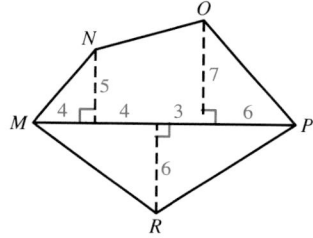

21. Find the area of *TRAP*. A = 144

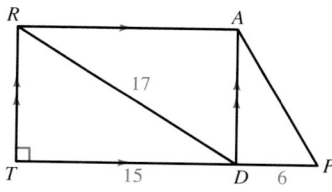

A trapezoid has area A, bases c and d, and height h.

22. **a.** Express A in terms of c, d, and h. $A = \frac{h}{2}(c + d)$
   b. If c and d are each doubled, how does the area of the resulting trapezoid compare to A? New area is double area A.

23. **a.** If c is increased by one unit and d is decreased by one unit, how does the area of the resulting trapezoid compare to A? It is equal to A.
   b. If c and d remain the same, but h is increased by one unit, how does the area of the resulting trapezoid compare to A? new area = $\frac{1}{2}(h + 1)(c + d) = A + \frac{1}{2}(c + d)$

C 24. Complete the proof of Theorem 11.4. See side column page 452.

25. If a trapezoid has height 15 in. and a median of length 21 in., find the area of the trapezoid. 315 in.²

26. Find the area of a trapezoid with height 30 cm and median 25 cm. 750 cm²

 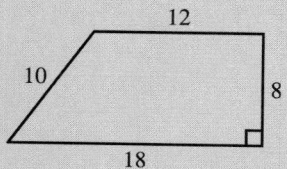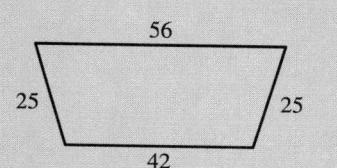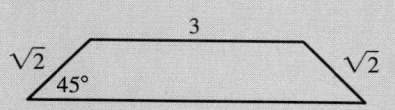
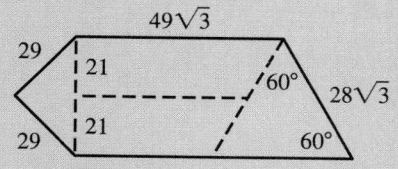
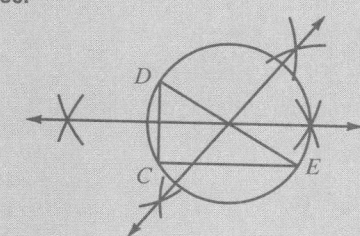

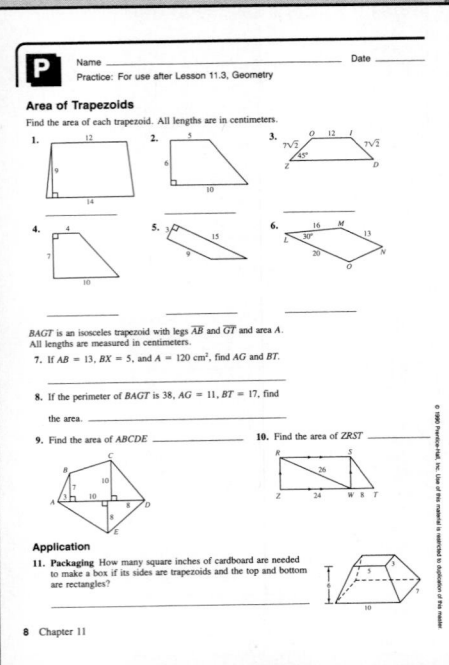

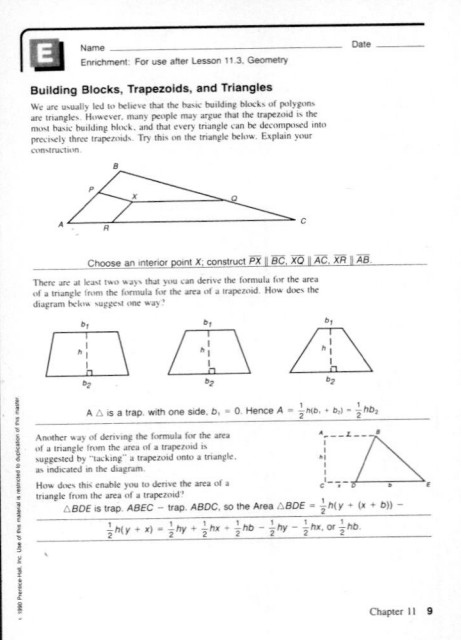

27. Trapezoid *ACDF* has the indicated
dimensions and median $\overline{BE}$. Are the areas of
trapezoids *BCDE* and *ABEF* equal? Justify
your answer.

No; $A(BCDE) = \dfrac{h(b_2 + m)}{4}$, $A(ABEF) = \dfrac{h(b_1 + m)}{4}$, and $b_1 \neq b_2$.

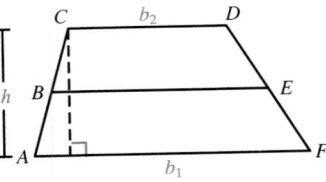

Applications

28. **Carpentry** Find the area of each section of the
wooden frame if the picture itself is $16'' \times 8''$ and
the overall dimensions are $20'' \times 12''$. upper and lower:
36 in.²; sides: 20 in.²

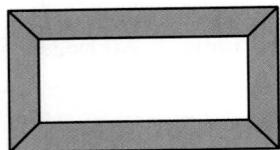

29. **Landscaping** How many square inches of
plywood are needed to build a planter for
flowers if its sides are trapezoids with height
$4.29''$ and its base is rectangular?
$A = 2[\frac{1}{2}(4.29)(10.4 + 12.48) + \frac{1}{2}(4.29)(8.32 + 6.24)] +$
$(10.4)(6.24) = 160.6176 + 64.896 = 225.5136 \approx 226$ in.²

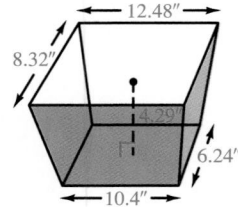

Mixed Review

$\overline{DE} \parallel \overline{AB}$. **Find the indicated measure.**

30. $CE = \underline{\ ?\ }$ $4\sqrt{3}$ 31. $EB = \underline{\ ?\ }$ $8\sqrt{3}$

32. $AC = \underline{\ ?\ }$ 12   33. $m\angle A = \underline{\ ?\ }$ 60

34. $\cos \angle B = \underline{\ ?\ }$ $\dfrac{\sqrt{3}}{2}$ 35. $\tan \angle D = \underline{\ ?\ }$ $\sqrt{3}$

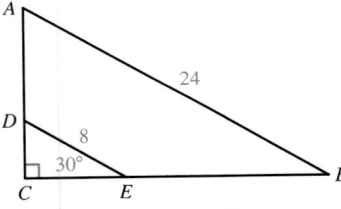

36. Copy $\triangle DEC$. Circumscribe a circle about $\triangle DEC$. See side column, p. 453.

37. $m\widehat{CE} = \underline{\ ?\ }$ 120 38. $m\widehat{DE} = \underline{\ ?\ }$ 180

39. Describe the locus of points equidistant from points *M* and *N*. the
perpendicular bisector of $\overline{MN}$

Is the triangle with the given side lengths right, obtuse, or acute?

40. 5, 9, 12   41. 5, 12, 13   42. 8, 9, 12   43. $\sqrt{3}$, 5, $2\sqrt{7}$
obtuse   right   acute   right

Area of Regular Polygons

Objective: To state and apply the formula for the area of regular
polygons

No simple method exists for finding the area of general nonregular polygons.
If a polygon is regular, however, a formula for its area can be determined.

Investigation—*Coordinate Geometry*

Have you ever wondered why bees
build the cells of their honeycombs in
hexagonal shapes rather than in
simpler ones, such as squares? One
aspect of this question can be
explored by comparing the
approximate area enclosed by
squares and hexagons.

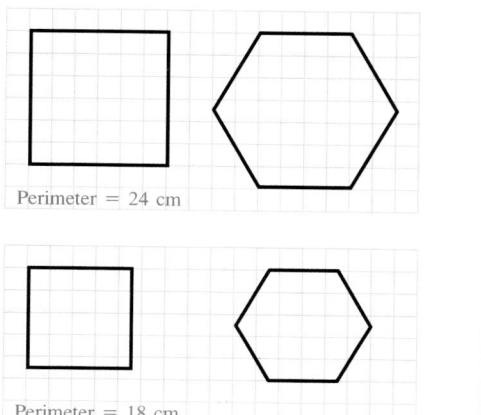

Perimeter = 24 cm

1. In both cases pictured, which
   figure encloses the larger area?
   hexagon
2. How can this help explain why a
   bee builds its hive as it does?

A larger area suggests that more honey can be stored.

3. Would a triangular cell enclose a
   larger area than a hexagonal cell
   of equal perimeter? no

Perimeter = 18 cm

Any regular polygon can be inscribed in a circle, and a circle can be
circumscribed about any regular polygon. The following terms related to
regular polygons refer to either a segment or its length.

A point is the **center of a regular polygon** if it is the
center of the circle circumscribed about the polygon.
Here the center is O. A **radius r of a regular polygon**
joins the center to a vertex of the polygon. Thus a
radius of a regular polygon is a radius of the
circumscribed circle. An **apothem a of a regular
polygon** is the distance from the center to a side of the
polygon. An angle is a **central angle of a regular
polygon** if its vertex is the center of the polygon and
its sides are two consecutive radii.

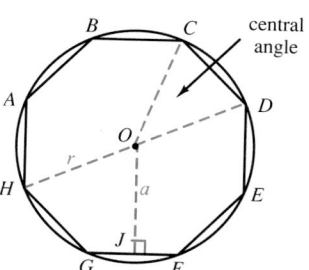

central
angle

Developing Mathematical Power

Keeping a Portfolio   Have students complete the Critical Thinking activity in *Connections*, pp. 33 and 34. It extends the Investigation above to reinforce earlier work
that showed that among regular polygons (with a fixed radius) that will tessellate
the plane, the hexagon has the largest area. Have them create a tessellation and
color it.

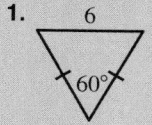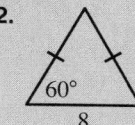

- Use many models to illustrate the parts of regular polygons and essential relationships among those parts.
- Students might find it useful to make a chart that summarizes important relationships among sides, radii, and apothems of equilateral triangles, squares, and regular hexagons, since these are frequent examples.
- Point out the occurrences of 30°-60°-90° and 45°-45°-90° triangles within regular polygons, and how the known relationships of sides of those triangles can aid in working with those figures.

CHALKBOARD EXAMPLES

- **For Example 1**

  Find the radius and apothem of an equilateral triangle whose sides have length 6 in.   *a*, 3 in., and *r* are the respective lengths of sides opposite 30°, 60°, and 90° ∠s of a △.

  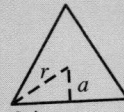

  $a = \frac{3}{\sqrt{3}} = \sqrt{3}$ in.

  $r = 2\sqrt{3}$ in.

  3 in.

- **For Example 2**

  Find the area of a regular pentagon whose side has length 10 cm and whose apothem is 6.9 cm.

  $A = \frac{1}{2}(6.9)(50) = 172.5$ cm²

EXAMPLE 1   Regular hexagon *LUTEFG* is inscribed in ⊙*O*. Each side of the hexagon is 16 cm. ⊙*O* has a radius of 16 cm. Find the following.

a. Apothem of *LUTEFG*   **b.** Perimeter of *LUTEFG*
c. Measure of central ∠*LOU*   **d.** Area of △*LOU*

a. Using the Pyth. Th., $OY = 8\sqrt{3}$ cm.   **b.** $P = 6 \cdot 16 = 96$ cm
c. $\frac{360}{6} = 60$ **d.** $A = \frac{1}{2} \cdot 8\sqrt{3} \cdot 16 = 64\sqrt{3}$ cm²

In Example 1, since 6 central angles could have been formed at center *O*, the central angle was found using $\frac{360}{6}$. The following formula generalizes this fact.

For any regular *n*-gon, the measure of each central angle is $\frac{360}{n}$.

Any regular polygon of *n* sides can be partitioned into *n* nonoverlapping congruent triangles. This observation leads to the next theorem.

> **Theorem 11.5**   The area of a regular polygon is equal to one-half the product of the apothem and the perimeter, or $A = \frac{1}{2}aP$.

Given: A regular *n*-gon with side *s*, apothem *a*, and perimeter *P*

Prove: Area $= \frac{1}{2}aP$

Plan: Each central angle and a side of the *n*-gon determine a triangle with area $\frac{1}{2}as$. Since the polygon contains *n* triangles, the area of the *n*-gon is $n\left(\frac{1}{2}as\right)$ or $\frac{1}{2}a(ns)$. Since *ns* is the perimeter of the *n*-gon, the conclusion follows.
Proved in Practice Exercise 29

EXAMPLE 2   Find the area *A* of each regular polygon.

a.

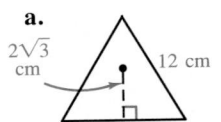

2√3 cm   12 cm

b.

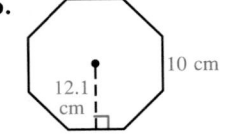

12.1 cm   10 cm

c.

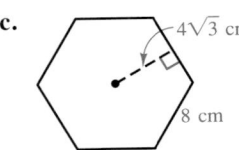

4√3 cm   8 cm

a. $A = \frac{1}{2}(2\sqrt{3})(36)$
      $= 36\sqrt{3}$ cm²

b. $A = \frac{1}{2}(12.1)(80)$
      $= 484$ cm²

c. $A = \frac{1}{2}(4\sqrt{3})(48)$
      $= 96\sqrt{3}$ cm²

Developing Mathematical Power

Cooperative Learning   Working in groups, students can explore relationships among radius, perimeter, apothem, and area of a square by completing the Investigation activity, p. 10, in the *Teacher's Resource Book*. Challenge them to use this hands-on approach for a 30°-60°-90° right triangle in which the shorter leg is 4 cm and the hypotenuse is 8 cm.

EXAMPLE 3 Find the apothem, radius, and area of these regular figures.

a.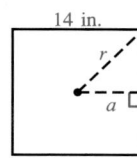
14 in.

b.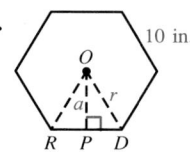
10 in.

a. Using 45°-45°-90° △ relationships, $a = 7$, $r = 7\sqrt{2}$, $A = \frac{1}{2}(7)(56) =$ 196 in.^{2} A can also be found by $(14 \text{ in.})^2 = 196 \text{ in.}^2$

b. Use $\frac{360}{6}$ to find that $m\angle ROD = 60$, and $\triangle ROP \cong \triangle DOP$ to show that $\triangle POD$ is a 30°-60°-90° triangle with $PD = 5$, $OD = 10$, $OP = 5\sqrt{3}$, and $A = \frac{1}{2}(5\sqrt{3})(60) = 150\sqrt{3}$ in.^{2}

In part (b) of Example 3, observe that the radius and the length of the side of a regular hexagon are equal. What conclusion can you draw about each of the triangles formed when a regular hexagon is partitioned? Each △ is equilateral.

CLASS EXERCISES

Write *always*, *sometimes*, or *never* to complete each statement for a regular polygon. Justify your answer.

1. A radius ⎯?⎯ bisects the vertex angle to which it is drawn. Always; the △s formed are isosceles and congruent.
2. The apothem is ⎯?⎯ less than the radius of the polygon. Always; the hypotenuse is the longest side of a rt. △.
3. The radius is ⎯?⎯ equal to the length of the side of the polygon. Sometimes; it is true only for regular hexagons.
4. The segment that represents the apothem ⎯?⎯ bisects the side to which it is drawn. Always; a diameter perpendicular to a chord bisects the chord.

5. Find the area of a regular hexagon whose side is 6 cm. $54\sqrt{3}$ cm^2

6. Find the area of an equilateral triangle whose apothem is 12 cm. $432\sqrt{3}$ cm^2

PRACTICE EXERCISES   Use technology where appropriate.

The regular polygons are inscribed in circles. Find the measure of each numbered angle.

A   1.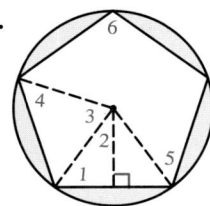

$m\angle 1 = 54$,
$m\angle 2 = 36$,
$m\angle 3 = 72$,
$m\angle 4 = 54$,
$m\angle 5 = 54$,
$m\angle 6 = 108$

2.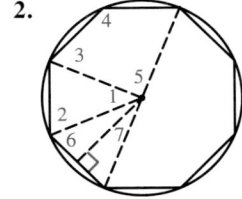

$m\angle 1 = 45$,
$m\angle 2 = 67.5$,
$m\angle 3 = 67.5$,
$m\angle 4 = 135$,
$m\angle 5 = 90$,
$m\angle 6 = 67.5$,
$m\angle 7 = 22.5$

11.4 Area of Regular Polygons   **457**

- **For Example 3**
  Find the apothem, radius, and area of a regular hexagon whose sides have length 6 cm. $r = 6$ cm, $a = 3\sqrt{3}$ cm
  $A = \frac{1}{2}(3\sqrt{3})(36) = 54\sqrt{3}$ cm^2

Common Errors
- Some students might confuse the parts of regular polygons; e.g., confuse apothem with radius. Have students make a list of parts with definitions.
- Students may attempt to apply the area formula from insufficient information, or with information used inappropriately. Make sure that students write formulas for each problem, filling in necessary information.
- Students could attempt to apply the area formula to irregular figures. Remind students that formulas apply only to regular figures.
- See *Teacher's Resource Book* for additional remediation.

LESSON FOLLOW-UP

Assignment Guide
See p. 438B for assignments.

Find the area of each regular polygon. All length measures are in inches.

3. $s = 12$;
   $r = 10.2$
   $A \approx 247.5$ in.^{2}

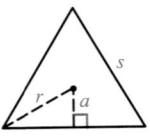

4. $a = 7$;
   $r = 14$
   $A = 147\sqrt{3}$ in.^{2}

Regular hexagon ABCDEF has been inscribed in ⊙O having radius 12 cm. It is also circumscribed about another circle also having O as its center. Find the following.

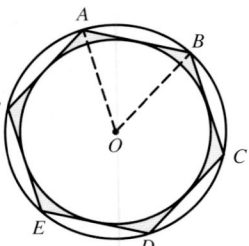

5. The radius of *ABCDEF* 12 cm

6. The apothem of *ABCDEF* $6\sqrt{3}$ cm

7. The radius of the inscribed circle $6\sqrt{3}$ cm

8. The measure of central ∠*AOB* 60

9. The perimeter of *ABCDEF* 72 cm

10. The area of *ABCDEF* $216\sqrt{3}$ cm^2

Find the missing information for each regular polygon in Exercises 11–13. All length measures are in centimeters.

11. $r = \sqrt{6}$. Find a, s, P, and A.

   $a = \sqrt{3}$ cm
   $s = 2\sqrt{3}$ cm
   $P = 8\sqrt{3}$ cm
   $A = 12$ cm^2

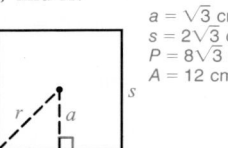

12. $a = 4$. Find s, A, and r.

   $s = 8\sqrt{3}$ cm
   $r = 8$ cm
   $A = 48\sqrt{3}$ cm^2

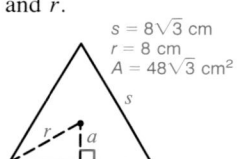

13. $s = 4$. Find a, r, and A.

   $a = 2\sqrt{3}$ cm
   $r = 4$ cm
   $A = 24\sqrt{3}$ cm^2

B 14. If the length of the sides of a regular hexagon is doubled, how does the new area compare to the original area of the hexagon? new area = 4 times original area

15. Find the area of a regular hexagon whose radius is 24 in. $864\sqrt{3}$ in.^{2}

16. Find the area of an equilateral triangle whose apothem is $\sqrt{12}$ in. $36\sqrt{3}$ in.^{2}

17. A regular hexagon is inscribed in a circle of radius 10 in. Find the area of the hexagon. $150\sqrt{3}$ in.^{2}

18. An equilateral triangle has sides of length s. Find the height and the apothem of this triangle. What is the ratio of the height to the apothem? $h = \frac{s}{2}\sqrt{3}$; $a = \frac{s}{6}\sqrt{3}$; 3 : 1

A regular decagon is inscribed in a circle with radius 10.

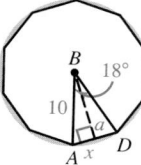

19. The measure of central angle $\angle ABD$ is 36. Why? $\frac{360}{10 \text{ sides}} = 36$

20. Using $\cos 18° = \frac{a}{10}$, find the apothem to the nearest tenth. 9.5

21. Using $\sin 18° = \frac{x}{10}$, find the side to the nearest tenth. 6.2

22. Find the area of this decagon. 294.5

23. If a regular hexagon has area $54\sqrt{3}$ cm², find the apothem and perimeter of the hexagon. $a = 3\sqrt{3}$ cm; $P = 36$ cm

24. Find the area of an equilateral triangle circumscribed about a circle of radius $\sqrt{3}$. $9\sqrt{3}$

A regular hexagon is circumscribed about an equilateral triangle.

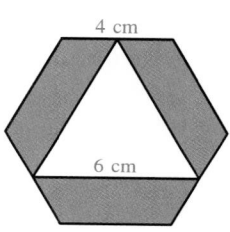

25. Find the area of the shaded region by finding the difference between the areas of the hexagon and the triangle. $A_\triangle = 9\sqrt{3}$ cm²; $A_{\text{hex}} = 24\sqrt{3}$ cm²; $24\sqrt{3} - 9\sqrt{3} = 15\sqrt{3}$ cm²

26. Show that an alternative formula for the area of a regular hexagon in terms of length s of a side is $\frac{3}{2}\sqrt{3}s^2$. $a = \frac{s}{2}\sqrt{3}$; $P = 6s$; $A = \frac{1}{2}aP = \frac{3}{2}\sqrt{3}s^2$

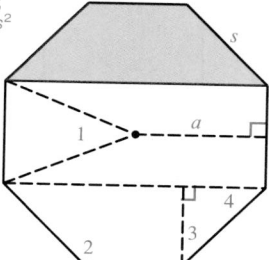

27. Find the measure of each numbered angle of this regular octagon. Find the length of the apothem. $m\angle 1 = 45$, $m\angle 2 = 135$, $m\angle 3 = 45$, $m\angle 4 = 45$; $a = \frac{s}{2}(1 + \sqrt{2})$

C 28. Find the area of the shaded region. $A = 2s^2(1 + \sqrt{2})$

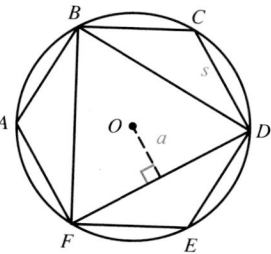

29. Use the figure, *Given*, *Prove*, and *Plan* to prove Theorem 11.5.
See Solutions Manual.

Regular hexagon *ABCDEF* of side length s and equilateral $\triangle BDF$ are inscribed in $\odot O$.

30. Show that $s = 2a$, where a is the apothem of $\triangle BDF$. $s = r$, $a = \frac{1}{2}r$, $r = 2a$; $s = 2a$

31. Find the length of the side of $\triangle BDF$. $h = 3a$, $h = \frac{s}{2}\sqrt{3}$, $3a = \frac{s}{2}\sqrt{3}$; $s = 2a\sqrt{3}$

32. How do the perimeters of the equilateral triangle and the hexagon compare? $P_\triangle : P_{\text{hex}} = \sqrt{3} : 2$

33. How does the area of the hexagon compare to the area of the triangle? $A_{\text{hex}} = 6a^2\sqrt{3}$, $A_\triangle = 3a^2\sqrt{3}$, $A_{\text{hex}} = 2A_\triangle$

Developing Mathematical Power

Investigation Students are given the opportunity to explore tessellations of the pentagon, the hexagon, and the octagon.

Test Yourself

See *Teacher's Resource Book, Tests,* pp. 113–114.

Lesson Quiz

Find the area of each regular polygon. All lengths are in inches.

1.   2.

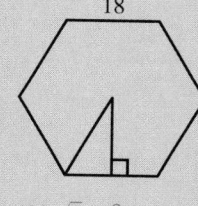

18

144 in.² $486\sqrt{3}$ in.²

3. An equilateral triangle is circumscribed about a circle of radius 8 cm. Find the apothem and area of the triangle. 8 cm; $192\sqrt{3}$ cm²

Enrichment

Use trigonometry to find the area of:

a. a regular pentagon whose sides have length 2.

b. a regular octagon whose sides have length 2.

a. $\tan 54° = \frac{a}{1}$; $a \approx 1.38$
$A \approx \frac{1}{2}(1.38)(10) \approx 6.9$ square units

b. $\tan 67.5° = \frac{a}{1}$; $a \approx 2.3655$
$A \approx \frac{1}{2}(2.3655)16 \approx 18.9$ square units

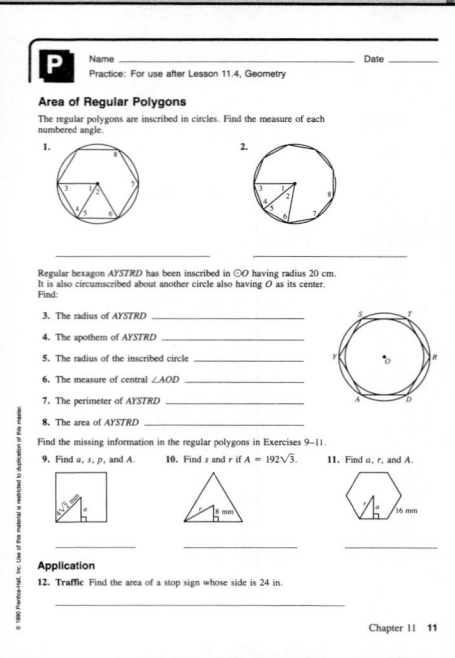

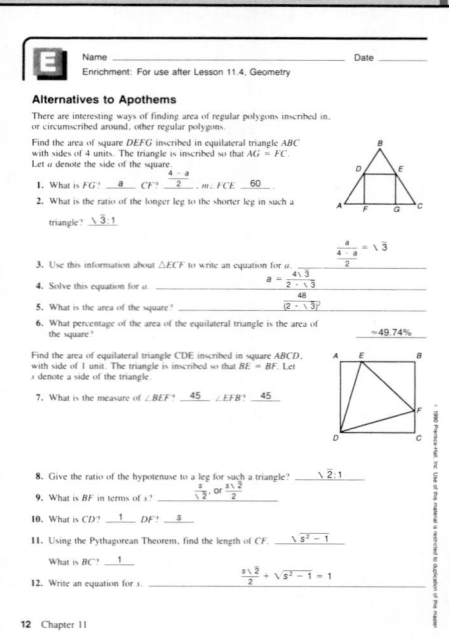

Applications

34. Traffic Engineering   Find the area of an octagonal stop sign with a 10-in. side and a 12-in. apothem. 480 in.²

35. Architecture   What is the approximate square footage enclosed at ground level of the Pentagon building in Washington, D.C., if its sides are about 280 m and its apothem is about 193 m? approx. 135,100 m²

36. Technology   Using Logo, draw a regular polygon, find its center, and connect the center to each vertex. Can you find the apothem? See Solutions Manual.

Developing Mathematical Power

Investigation   Trace these polygons and cut out copies of each one. Try to cover a sheet of paper using the pentagon, then the hexagon, and so on.

37. Which figure best covers the paper? Explain.
Hexagon; the sides can be matched so that the entire paper is covered.

38. This activity is an example of *tessellations*. Research tessellations.

TEST YOURSELF

Find the area of each figure. All length measures are in centimeters.   11.1–11.4

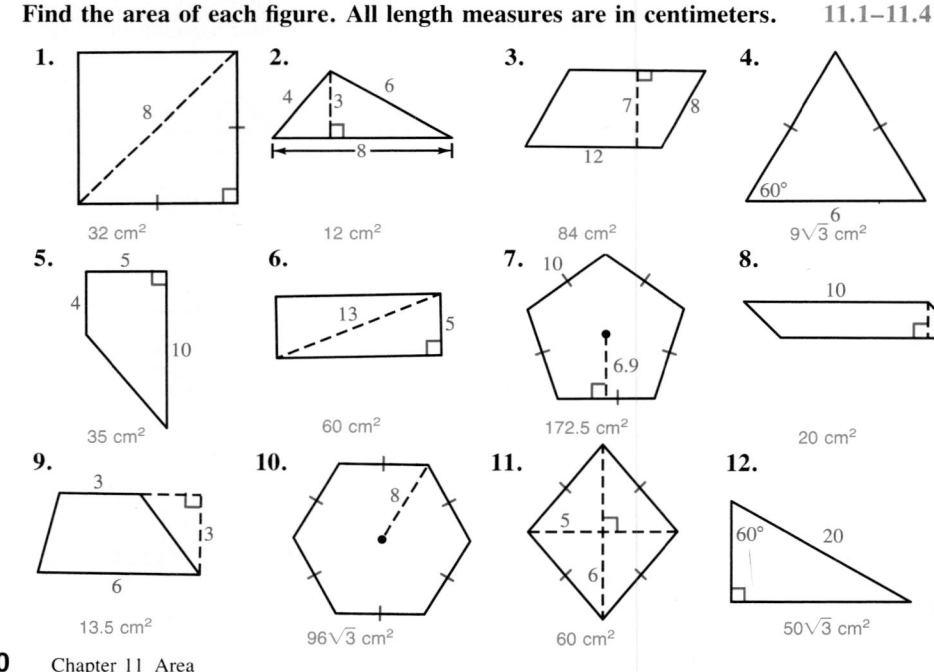

11.5 Strategy: Find Limits

An ordered arrangement of numbers such as 2, 4, 6, 8, . . . , or 0.5, 0.05, 0.005, . . . , is called a **sequence.** The numbers that make up a sequence are called its *terms;* the first term in a sequence is represented as a_1, the second term as a_2, and so on, with the nth term represented as a_n. In the first sequence above, $a_1 = 2 \cdot 1$, $a_2 = 2 \cdot 2$, . . . , and $a_n = 2 \cdot n$, ...

Note that as n increases, the terms of the sequence 2, 4, 6, 8, . . . , $2n$, . . . increase in size with no bounds; but the terms of the sequence $\frac{1}{2}$, $\frac{2}{3}$, $\frac{3}{4}$, $\frac{4}{5}$, . . . , $\frac{n}{(n+1)}$, . . . , while increasing in size, appear to approach 1 but never exceed 1. When the terms of a sequence get close to some fixed number, that number is called the *limit* of the sequence. If the terms approach the number L as a limit as n increases in size, write $a_n \rightarrow L$ to represent that fact.

EXAMPLE 1 Find the next three terms of each sequence. Does the sequence appear to have a limit? If so, what is it?

a. 0.1, 0.01, 0.001, . . .   **b.** 2, $1\frac{1}{2}$, $1\frac{1}{4}$, $1\frac{1}{8}$, . . .

c. −3, 0, 3, 6, . . .   **d.** 2, 2, 2, . . .

a. 0.0001, 0.00001, 0.000001; $a_n \rightarrow 0$

b. $1\frac{1}{16}$, $1\frac{1}{32}$, $1\frac{1}{64}$; $a_n \rightarrow 1$

c. 9, 12, 15; the terms can be made as large as desired; no limit.

d. 2, 2, 2; $a_n \rightarrow 2$

EXAMPLE 2 A computer program created this design. The midpoints of the sides of the largest equilateral triangle were joined to form the large shaded triangle; the midpoints of the sides of the remaining triangles were joined to form the smaller shaded triangles; and so on. Find the first four terms of a sequence that represents the portion of the area of the original triangle that is shaded at each step. Find an expression for the nth term. Does this sequence have a limit? If so, what is it?

Developing Mathematical Power

Cooperative Learning Select teams of students to create sequences. They can then challenge the other teams to write the next three terms of the sequence and find its limit, if it exists. A special challenge can be presented by having each team write the nth term of the sequence.

- Encourage students to generate examples of sequences with and without limits, making certain they can express the nth term of each sequence.
- Point out the importance of considering at least four or five terms of a sequence before attempting to express the nth term.
- Most students will be familiar with π from earlier mathematics courses and may recognize how π relates to some of the examples and exercises of this lesson.

CHALKBOARD EXAMPLES

- **For Example 1**

  Find the next three terms of each sequence. Does the sequence appear to have a limit? If so, what is it?

  a. $2, \dfrac{3}{2}, \dfrac{4}{3}, \dfrac{5}{4}, \ldots$

  b. $-\dfrac{1}{2}, \dfrac{1}{2}, -\dfrac{1}{2}, \dfrac{1}{2}, \ldots$

  c. $-\dfrac{1}{2}, \dfrac{1}{2}, -\dfrac{1}{3}, \dfrac{1}{3}, -\dfrac{1}{4}, \dfrac{1}{4}, \ldots$

  a. $\dfrac{6}{5}, \dfrac{7}{6}, \dfrac{8}{7}$; limit is 1

  b. $-\dfrac{1}{2}, \dfrac{1}{2}, -\dfrac{1}{2}$; no limit

  c. $-\dfrac{1}{5}, \dfrac{1}{5}, -\dfrac{1}{6}$; limit is 0

- **For Example 2**

  Regular hexagon H_1 has sides of length 1. Regular hexagon H_2 is constructed by joining the midpoints of the sides of H_1; the midpoints of the sides of H_2 are joined to form H_3, and so on.

  a. Write a sequence whose terms represent the areas of H_1, H_2, H_3, ... What is the nth term of this sequence?

  b. Does this sequence have a limit? If so, what is it?

Understand the Problem

What is given?

An equilateral triangle of area 1 has been partitioned into smaller equilateral triangles by joining the midpoints of the sides of the triangle. This process can be repeated infinitely many times.

What is to be determined?

A sequence of numbers that represents the portion of the original triangle that is covered by the shaded triangles as the process continues.
The nth term of the sequence;
The limit of the sequence, if it exists.

Plan Your Approach

Create a simpler problem.

If only one partition is made, the area of the shaded triangle is $\dfrac{1}{4}$ of the total area. Since $DE = \dfrac{1}{2}AC$, the area of $\triangle DEF = \dfrac{1}{4}$ area of $\triangle ABC$. Hence, $\dfrac{3}{4}$ area of $\triangle ABC$ is unshaded.

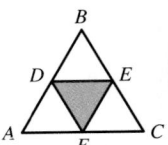

Look for a pattern.

If another partition is made, an additional $\dfrac{1}{4}$ of the unshaded area, or $\dfrac{1}{4} \cdot \dfrac{3}{4} = \dfrac{3}{16}$, will then be shaded. The total shaded area will be $\dfrac{1}{4} + \dfrac{3}{16}$, or $\dfrac{7}{16}$ of the area of $\triangle ABC$.

Generalize.

If A_1 and A_2 represent the total shaded area after the first and second partitions, then $A_2 = \dfrac{1}{4}(1 - A_1) + A_1$, or

$$A_2 = \dfrac{1}{4}(1 + 3A_1) = \dfrac{1}{4}(1 + 3(\tfrac{1}{4})) = \dfrac{7}{16}.$$

Implement the Plan

Use the general pattern to find the first four terms and A_n.

$$A_1 = \dfrac{1}{4}$$

$$A_2 = \dfrac{1}{4}(1 + 3A_1) = \dfrac{7}{16}$$

$$A_3 = \dfrac{1}{4}(1 + 3A_2) = \dfrac{1}{4}(1 + 3 \cdot \dfrac{7}{16}) = \dfrac{37}{64}$$

$$A_4 = \dfrac{1}{4}(1 + 3A_3) = \dfrac{1}{4}(1 + 3 \cdot \dfrac{37}{64}) = \dfrac{175}{256}$$

$$A_n = \dfrac{1}{4}(1 - A_{n-1}) + A_{n-1} = \dfrac{1}{4}(1 + 3A_{n-1})$$

462   Chapter 11 Area

So the first four terms of the wanted sequence are:

$$\frac{1}{4}, \frac{7}{16}, \frac{37}{64}, \frac{175}{256}, \ldots$$

As n gets larger, A_n gets larger and approaches but never exceeds 1. Thus, $A_n \to 1$.

Interpret the Results

Draw a conclusion.

As the partitioning process is continued, more and more of the area of the original triangle is covered. However, the shaded area will never exceed the total area of 1.

Problem Solving Reminders

- Some problems can be solved by writing a sequence and determining its limit.
- A sequence may or may not have a limit.

AMPLE 3 If a regular n-gon has radius r, its perimeter is given by the formula

$$P = 2r\left(n \sin \frac{180}{n}\right)$$

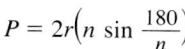

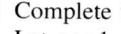 Complete the table.
Let $r = 1$.

n	6	10	18	30	60
P	6	6.18	?	?	?
s	1	0.618	?	?	?
a	0.866	0.951	?	?	?

Find the limit of the sequence $a_1, a_2, a_3, \ldots$, where the a's are the respective apothems of the n-gons in the table.

Understand the Problem

What is given?

The number of sides of a set of regular n-gons of radius 1.

What is to be determined?

The perimeters, side lengths, and apothem lengths of the n-gons; the limit of the sequence of apothems.

11.5 Strategy: Find Limits **463**

---

a. $A_n = \frac{1}{2}a_n P$, where $a_n = \frac{s_n \sqrt{3}}{2}$.

$s_1 = 1$; $A_1 = \frac{1}{2}(\frac{\sqrt{3}}{2})6 = \frac{3\sqrt{3}}{2}$

$s_2 = \frac{\sqrt{3}}{2}$; $A_2 = \frac{1}{2}(\frac{3}{4})(3\sqrt{3}) = \frac{9\sqrt{3}}{8}$

$s_3 = \frac{3}{4}$; $A_3 = \frac{1}{2}(\frac{3\sqrt{3}}{8})(\frac{9}{2}) = \frac{27\sqrt{3}}{32}$

$s_4 = \frac{3\sqrt{3}}{8}$; $A_4 = \frac{1}{2}(\frac{9}{16})(\frac{9\sqrt{3}}{4}) = $

$\frac{81\sqrt{3}}{128}$

$s_n = (\frac{\sqrt{3}}{2})^{n-1}$; $A_n = \frac{1}{2}(\frac{\sqrt{3}}{2})^n(6)$

$(\frac{\sqrt{3}}{2})^{n-1} = 3(\frac{\sqrt{3}}{2})^{2n-1}$,

$= $ or $2\sqrt{3}(\frac{3}{4})^n$

b. $A_n \longrightarrow 0$

Assignment Guide
See p. 438B for assignments.

Project
Point out that while the Fibonacci sequence involves addition of neighboring numbers, other functions of these pairs produce other sequences. You might want to have students research geometric applications as well as examples in nature.

Lesson Quiz
Consider rectangle F_1, having length 2 and width 1. F_2 is the rhombus formed by joining the midpoints of the sides of rectangle F_1. F_3 is the rectangle formed by joining the midpoints of the sides of F_2, and so on.

1. Write the first five terms of a sequence representing the areas of F_1, F_2, F_3, ... What is the nth term?
2. Does this sequence appear to have a limit? If so, what is it?
3. Consider the sequence whose nth term is the sum of the areas of F_1 through F_n. What is the limit of this sequence?

1. $2, 1, \frac{1}{2}, \frac{1}{4}, \frac{1}{8}, \ldots, \frac{4}{2^n}, \ldots$ (Other forms of $\frac{4}{2^n}$ may be given.)
2. The limit is 0.
3. Since $(\frac{1}{2} + \frac{1}{4} + \frac{1}{8} + \frac{1}{16} + \ldots + \frac{1}{2^n})$
$\longrightarrow 1, (2 + 1 + (\frac{1}{2} + \frac{1}{4} + \ldots +$
$\frac{1}{2^n} \longrightarrow 4.$

CLASS EXERCISES
1. a. $-4, -5, -6$ 2. a. $\frac{1}{81}, \frac{1}{243}, \frac{1}{729}$
   b. $a_n = -(n - 1)$ b. $a_n = \frac{1}{3^{n-1}}$
   c. no limit   c. 0
3. a. $0.1000, 0.10000, 0.100000$
   b. $a_n = \frac{10^n}{10^{n+1}} = 0.1$
   c. 0.1

- ☐ **Plan Your Approach**
  Complete the table.
  Use a calculator to find P, s, and a. Use the Pythagorean Theorem to find a.

- ☐ **Implement the Plan**
  The completed table is:

n	6	10	18	30	60
P	6	6.18	6.25	6.27	6.28
s	1	0.618	0.347	0.209	0.105
a	0.866	0.951	0.985	0.995	0.999

As n increases, $a_n \to 1$, the radius of the n-gon.

- ☐ **Interpret the Results**
  It appears that as the number of sides in a regular n-gon of radius r increases, the apothems of the n-gons approach the radius as a limit.

CLASS EXERCISES See side column.

For each sequence, find the next three terms, an expression for the nth term, and the limit, if it exists.

1. $0, -1, -2, -3, \ldots$
2. $1, \frac{1}{3}, \frac{1}{9}, \frac{1}{27}, \ldots$
3. $0.1, 0.10, 0.100, \ldots$
4. $0.3, 0.33, 0.333, \ldots$
5. $-1, 1, -1, 1, \ldots$
6. $0.4, 0.44, 0.444, \ldots$

PRACTICE EXERCISES ⟿ Use technology where appropriate.

A **Find a_n for each sequence, and find the limit if it exists.**

1. $5, \frac{5}{2}, \frac{5}{4}, \frac{5}{8}, \frac{5}{16}, \ldots$ $\frac{5}{2^{n-1}}$; 0
2. $\frac{1}{5}, \frac{2}{5}, \frac{4}{5}, \frac{8}{5}, \frac{16}{5}, \ldots$ $\frac{2^{n-1}}{5}$; no limit
3. $1, 3, 5, 7, 9, \ldots$ $2n - 1$; no limit
4. $1.9, 1.99, 1.999, \ldots$ $a_n = 1.\underline{9 \ldots 9}$; 2 n places

Consider the sequence $3.1, 3.01, 3.001, \ldots$.

5. Write the first 10 terms of this sequence. 3.1, 3.01, 3.001, 3.0001, 3.00001, 3.000001, 3.0000001, 3.00000001, 3.000000001, 3.0000000001
6. What is the first term, a_n, such that $|3 - a_n| < 0.00001$? 3.000001
7. What is the first term, a_n, such that $|3 - a_n| < 0.0000001$? 3.00000001
8. What is the limit of the given sequence? 3

4. a. $0.3333, 0.33333, 0.333333$
   b. $a_n = 0.33 \ldots$ (number of decimal places corresponds to term number)
   c. $\frac{1}{3}$
5. a. $-1, 1, -1$
   b. $a_n = (-1)^n$
   c. no limit
6. a. $0.4444, 0.44444, 0.444444$
   b. $a_n = 0.444 \ldots$ (number of places corresponds to term number)
   c. $\frac{4}{9}$

B Square S_2 has been constructed by joining the midpoints of the sides of square S_1. The midpoints of the sides of S_2 have been joined to form S_3, and so on.

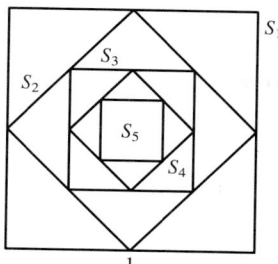

9. Write a sequence whose terms represent the area of S_1, area of S_2, area of S_3, ... Include the first four terms of the sequence and an expression for the nth term. $1, \frac{1}{2}, \frac{1}{4}, \frac{1}{8}, \ldots, \frac{1}{2^{n-1}}$

10. Consider the sequence whose nth term is the sum of the areas of S_1 through S_n; that is, $a_1 =$ area of S_1; $a_2 =$ area of $S_1 +$ area of S_2, and so on. What is the limit of this sequence? Justify your answer. sum $= 1 + \frac{1}{2} + \frac{1}{4} + \frac{1}{8} + \cdots + \frac{1}{2^{n-1}} = 1 + 1 = 2$

An expression for the nth term of a sequence is given. Use your calculator to complete each table, rounding results to four decimal places. For each sequence, what appears to be the limit?

11. $a_n = n \sin\left(\frac{180}{n}\right)$

n	10	20	30	40	50	60
a_n	?	?	?	?	?	?

3.0902, 3.1287, 3.1359, 3.1384, 3.1395, 3.1402
Limit appears to be π.

12. $a_n = \left(1 + \frac{1}{n}\right)^n$

n	10	30	50	100	500	1000
a_n	?	?	?	?	?	?

2.5937, 2.6743, 2.6916, 2.7048, 2.7156, 2.7169
Limit appears to be e, the natural log base.

The area of any regular n-gon of radius r can be found by using the formula: $A = \left(n \sin \frac{180}{n}\right)\left(\cos \frac{180}{n}\right)r^2$.

13. Complete this table for a sequence of regular n-gons of radius r. Express results to four decimal places.

n	6	12	20	30	60	90
A	?	?	?	?	?	?

$2.5981r^2$ $3.0000r^2$ $3.0902r^2$ $3.1187r^2$ $3.1359r^2$ $3.1390r^2$

14. Let A_n represent the area of a polygon of n sides and radius r, where $n \geq 3$. As n increases, does the sequence $A_1, A_2, A_3, \ldots$ appear to have a limit? If so, what is it? Yes; it appears that πr^2 is the limit.

PROJECT

Research some of the applications of the Fibonacci sequence. Include a verification that $\frac{a_{n+1}}{a_n} \to \phi$, the Golden Ratio.

11.5 Strategy: Find Limits **465**

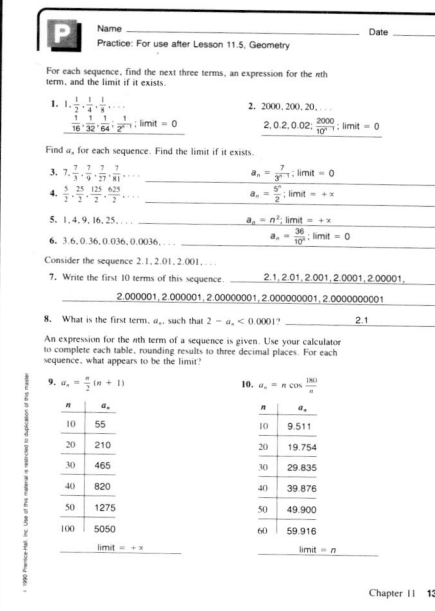

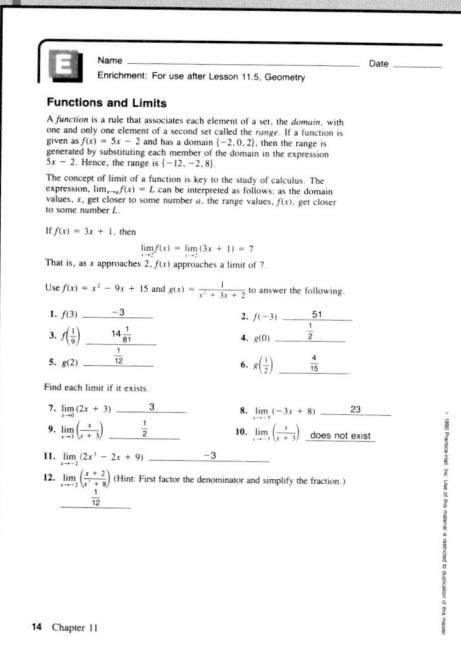

Vocabulary
Arc length
Circumference
π (pi)

Materials/Manipulatives
Several circular objects whose
circumferences and diameters
can be easily measured
Teaching Transparency 75

Technology
Calculator
Computer Test Bank, pp.
714–724

LESSON FOCUS

Review
Find the perimeter.

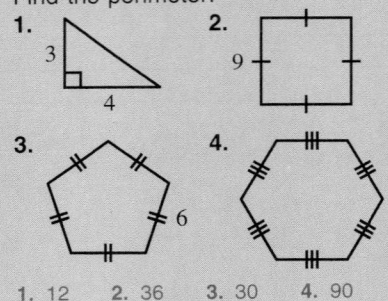

1. 12   2. 36   3. 30   4. 90

Alternative Learning Styles

• Students who learn by finding patterns can use the Investigation to discover that the circumference and diameter of a circle vary directly; that is, that their quotient is a constant.

• Kinesthetic learners may benefit from using manipulatives. Students should use a string to measure the circumference and diameter of several circular objects. They should record their results in a table similar to the one in the Investigation and find $\frac{C}{d}$ for each object.

466

11.6 Circumference and Arc Length

Objectives: To state the circumference formula for a circle and relate it to the perimeter formula for regular polygons
To compute circumferences and arc lengths for circles

The concept of perimeter can be applied to circles. There are methods for finding the distance all or part of the way around a circle.

Investigation—*Thinking Critically*

A chemistry teacher asked the class to find the circumference and diameter of 3 circular beakers, and then to compute the ratio $\frac{C}{d}$.

Beaker	Circumference (distance around)	Diameter (distance across)	$\frac{C}{d}$
1	24 cm	7.6 cm	?
2	33 cm	10.5 cm	?
3	48 cm	15.3 cm	?

1. Find $\frac{C}{d}$ in each case.   2. Describe the pattern in the answers. $\frac{C}{d} \approx 3.1$ in each case.

3. Compute the ratio $\frac{C}{d}$ for a circular container that measures 60.5 in. around and 19.5 in. across. Do your findings agree with those above? 3.1026; yes

These regular polygons are inscribed in congruent circles.

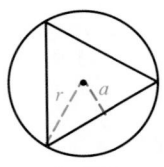 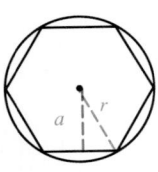 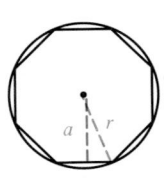 

3 sides   6 sides   8 sides   10 sides

As the number of sides increases, the polygon begins to look more like a circle, and the apothem and radius get closer in size. Also, the perimeter of the polygon becomes a closer approximation of the distance around the circle, or the **circumference** of the circle.

As the number of sides increases, the perimeter P of the inscribed regular polygons approaches the circumference C of the circle. This is denoted by $P \rightarrow C$. Thus, the circumference of a circle is said to be the *limit* of the perimeters of the regular polygons inscribed in the circle.

466   Chapter 11 Area

Developing Mathematical Power

Keeping a Portfolio   Have students write a paragraph in which they discuss the historical development of π. Encourage them to use illustrations where appropriate. The illustrated reports can be used for a bulletin-board display.

Theorem 11.6 For all circles, the ratio of the circumference to the length of the diameter is the same.

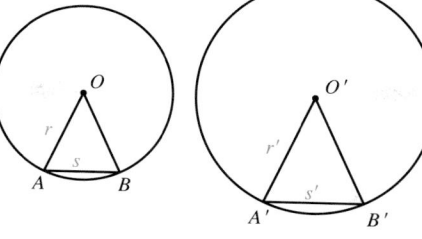

Given: Circles O and O' with radii r and r', diameters d and d', and circumferences C and C', respectively

Prove: $\dfrac{C}{d} = \dfrac{C'}{d'}$

Plan: In each circle, inscribe a regular n-gon and consider one of the isosceles triangles formed,

such as $\triangle AOB$ and $\triangle A'O'B'$. Since $\triangle AOB \sim \triangle A'O'B'$, $\dfrac{s}{r} = \dfrac{s'}{r'}$.

Now use the properties of proportions, substitution, and the fact that the circumference of a circle is the limit of the perimeters of n-sided regular polygons. Proved in Practice Exercise 23

The ratio $\dfrac{C}{d}$, denoted by the Greek letter **pi (π)**, is an irrational number, and is represented by a nonterminating, nonrepeating decimal: $\pi = 3.14159\ldots$. Rational approximations of π that are often used are 3.14 and $\dfrac{22}{7}$. Answers can be left in terms of π unless otherwise specified. Notice that the distance around any circle C, no matter how large or how small, is always a little more than three times as large as the distance d across it. Notice that the circumference varies directly with the diameter, or the radius.

Corollary 1 The circumferences of any two circles have the same ratio as their radii. Proved in Practice Exercise 29

Corollary 2 If C is the circumference of a circle with a diameter of length d and a radius of length r, then $C = \pi d$, or $C = 2\pi r$. Proved in Practice Exercise 28

EXAMPLE 1 $\odot O$ has radius r, diameter d, and circumference C.

a. If $r = 5$ cm, find d and C.

b. If $d = 10$ in., find C. Use 3.14 for π.

c. If $r = 14$ in., find C. Use $\dfrac{22}{7}$ for π.

d. If $C = 28\pi$ cm, find r.

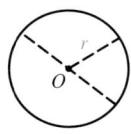

a. $d = 10$ cm; $C = 2\pi(5) = 10\pi$ cm   b. $C = 3.14(10) = 31.4$ in.

c. $C = 2\left(\dfrac{22}{7}\right)(14) = 88$ in.   d. 28π cm $= 2\pi r$; 14 cm $= r$

11.6 Circumference and Arc Length **467**

- The use of physical models helps build understanding of formulas.
- The "limit" approach to circumference should not be belabored. Students have an intuitive notion for what is meant by saying that the perimeters of the inscribed regular polygons approach the circumference.
- Emphasize the proportion behind the method used to determine the length of an arc. Remind students that the entire circle can be viewed as an arc of measure 360.
- If any of Practice Exercises 31–33 are assigned, they should all be assigned as a group.

CHALKBOARD EXAMPLES

- **For Example 1**
  $\odot O$ has radius r, diameter d, and circumference C.

  a. If $r = 7$ in., find d and C. $d = 14$ in.; $C = 14\pi$ in.
  b. If $d = 15$ cm, find C. Use $\pi \approx 3.14$. 47.1 cm
  c. If $r = 35$ in., find C. Use $\pi \approx \dfrac{22}{7}$. 220 in.
  d. If $C = 36\pi$ cm, find r. 18 cm

An **arc length** is a portion of the circumference of the circle; the ratio $\dfrac{\text{degree measure of arc}}{360}$ gives the fractional part of the circle that the arc represents.

> **Corollary 3**   In a circle, the ratio of the length l of an arc to the circumference C equals the ratio of the degree measure m of the arc to 360:
> $$\frac{l}{C} = \frac{m}{360}; \quad l = \frac{m}{360}(2\pi r).$$ Proved in Practice Exercise 34

EXAMPLE 2   Circle T with radius r has arc $\overset{\frown}{AB}$ with length l. If the diameter of $\odot T$ is 24 in. and $m\overset{\frown}{AB} = 60$, find l.

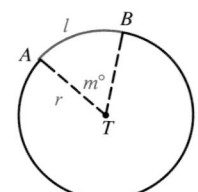

$$l = \frac{60}{360}(24\pi) = 4\pi \text{ in.}$$

CLASS EXERCISES

1. **Thinking Critically**   Is it possible to have a circle of circumference exactly 6 in. and a diameter exactly 2 in.? Explain. No; the ratio of circumference to diameter must be π.

Complete the table.

	r	d	C
2.	6 cm	$\underset{12 \text{ cm}}{?}$	$\underset{12\pi \text{ cm}}{?}$
3.	$\underset{4 \text{ cm}}{?}$	8 cm	$\underset{8\pi \text{ cm}}{?}$
4.	$\underset{\frac{5}{2\pi} \text{ cm}}{?}$	$\underset{\frac{5}{\pi} \text{ cm}}{?}$	5 cm

A circle has radius r, circumference C, and arc $\overset{\frown}{MN}$ of length l. Complete.

	r	C	$m\overset{\frown}{MN}$	l
5.	$\underset{1.5 \text{ cm}}{?}$	3π cm	30	$\underset{\frac{\pi}{4} \text{ cm}}{?}$
6.	$\underset{27 \text{ cm}}{?}$	$\underset{54\pi \text{ cm}}{?}$	80	12π cm

PRACTICE EXERCISES   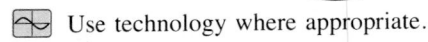 Use technology where appropriate.

A   1. On an old 10-in. phonograph record revolving at a rate of 78 revolutions per minute, how far does a point on the outer rim travel in 10 minutes? How far does a point 3 in. from the center travel? How far does a point on the edge of the label travel? (Labels for 78s are $2\frac{7}{8}$ in. in diameter.)
24,492 in.; 14,695.2 in.; 7041.45 in.

468   Chapter 11 Area

Complete the table. Use $\frac{22}{7}$ for π in Exercises 6–9.

	r	d	C
2.	4	? 8	? 8π
3.	? 3	6	? 6π
4.	? $\frac{7}{2\pi}$	? $\frac{7}{\pi}$	7
5.	? $\frac{5}{\pi}$	? $\frac{10}{\pi}$	10

	r	d	C
6.	? 7	14	? 44
7.	35	? 70	? 220
8.	? 3.5	? 7	22
9.	? $\frac{49}{11}$	? $\frac{98}{11}$	28

A circle has a circumference of 72π cm. Find the length of the arc with each given degree measure.

10. 30 6π cm   **11.** 45 9π cm   **12.** 120 24π cm   **13.** 180 36π cm

A circle has radius r, circumference C, and arc $\overset{\frown}{MN}$ of length l. Complete the table.

	r	C	$m\overset{\frown}{MN}$	l
14.	? 1 cm	2π cm	30	? $\frac{\pi}{6}$ cm
15.	3 cm	? 6π cm	72	? $\frac{6\pi}{5}$ cm
16.	? 30 cm	? 60π cm	60	10π cm
17.	? 72 cm	? 144π cm	50	20π cm
18.	6 cm	? 12π cm	? 90	3 π cm

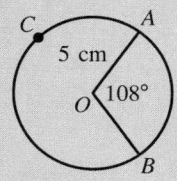

19. Two circles have circumferences in the ratio of 4:3. If the radius of the smaller circle is 12 cm less than the radius of the larger circle, find the circumference of each. 96π cm; 72π cm

B **20.** The diameters of two circles are in the ratio of 3:1. If the circumference of the larger circle is 18π in. more than the circumference of the smaller circle, find the diameter of each circle. 27 in.; 9 in.

21. If a square has sides of length 8 in., find the ratio of the radius of the circumscribed circle to the radius of the inscribed circle. √2:1

22. If the length of a side of the square is s in., find the ratio of the circumference of the circumscribed circle to the circumference of the inscribed circle. √2:1

23. Write a paragraph proof for Theorem 11.6. See side column.

24. The minute hand of a courthouse clock measures 12 ft. How far does the tip of the hand travel in 25 minutes? in one hour? 10π ft; 24π ft

25. A wheelbarrow has a front wheel 1 ft in diameter. How far does the wheelbarrow travel in one complete revolution of the front wheel? Use 3.14 for π. 3.14 ft

23. Inscribe a regular n-gon in each circle and consider one pair of △s, such as △AOY and △A'O'Y'. $m\angle O = \frac{360}{n}$ and $m\angle O' = \frac{360}{n}$; since n is the same in each regular n-gon, $m\angle O = m\angle O'$ and $\angle O \cong \angle O'$. Since the △s are isos., the leg lengths are in proportion, so △AOY ~ △A'O'Y' by the SAS Th. Thus, $r:r' = s:s'$ and $P:P' = s:s'$. Since $P \to C$ and $P' \to C'$, $C:C' = r:r'$ and $C:C' = d:d'$. By propor. prop., $C \cdot d' = C' \cdot d$ and $C:d = C':d'$.

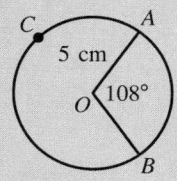
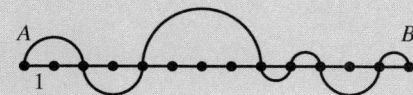
469

Regular hexagon *HEXGON* is inscribed in ⊙A.

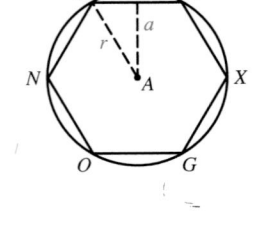

26. If ⊙A has radius 8 in., find the degree measure and length of $\overset{\frown}{EX}$. 60, $\frac{8\pi}{3}$ in.

27. If the apothem of *HEXGON* is 6 cm, find the circumference of ⊙A. $8\pi\sqrt{3}$ cm

28. Prove Corollary 2 of Theorem 11.6. See side column.

29. Prove Corollary 1 of Theorem 11.6.

A belt is stretched tightly over two wheels. Wheel O′ has radius 4 cm, wheel O has radius 1 cm, and the centers are 6 cm apart.

C   30. Find $m\angle A'O'O$.
    (*Hint:* Draw $\overline{OD'}$ such that $\overline{OD'} \parallel \overline{AA'}$.) 60

31. How long is the portion of the belt represented by $\overline{AA'}$? $3\sqrt{3}$ cm

32. What is the length of the belt represented by $\overset{\frown}{ABC}$? by $\overset{\frown}{A'B'C'}$? $\frac{2\pi}{3}$ cm; $\frac{16\pi}{3}$ cm

33. What is the total length of the belt? $6\pi + 6\sqrt{3}$ cm

34. Prove Corollary 3 of Theorem 11.6.
    See side column.

Applications

35. **Technology**   Using Logo, demonstrate the relationship between perimeter of polygons and circumference of a circle by generating a sequence of *n*-gons. For what value of *n* does an *n*-gon appear to be a circle? Similarly, approximate the area of a circle using polygons. How would you use these procedures to estimate the value of pi (π)? See Solutions Manual.

36. **Computer Graphics**   If the radius is 15.3 mm, what is the distance around PACMAN when his mouth is open 160°? when his mouth is open 40°? Remember to include his mouth in your calculations.
83.98 mm; 116.008 mm

Developing Mathematical Power

37. **Thinking Critically**   Suppose a rope is stretched around the equator of the Earth. If the length of the rope is increased by 1 mi, how far above the Earth's surface is the rope now positioned? Assume that the Earth is a sphere with a diameter of 8000 mi.
$8000\pi + 1 = \pi d_2$; $25{,}121 = 3.14d_2$, $d_2 = 8000.3185$; diam. diff. = 0.3185, $\frac{0.3185}{2} = 0.159$ mi above Earth

28. Since $\frac{C}{d} = \pi$ by def. of π, $C = \pi d$. Since $d = 2r$, $C = \pi \cdot 2r = 2\pi r$.

29. From Th. 11.6, $C:d = C':d'$; then $C \cdot d' = C' \cdot d$ and $C:C' = d:d'$.

34. $l = r\frac{\pi}{180}m$, where m is the degree measure of the central angle.
   Since $C = 2\pi r$, $\frac{l}{C} = \frac{r\frac{\pi}{180}m}{2\pi r} = \frac{m}{360}$, or $l = \frac{m}{360}C$.

Area of Circles, Sectors, and Segments

Objectives: To relate the area formula for regular polygons to the area formula for circles

To compute the areas of circles, sectors, and segments of circles

Imagine that a sequence of regular polygons with an increasing number of sides is inscribed in a circle. The areas of these inscribed regular polygons can be used to find the area of the circle.

Investigation—*Visualizing the Concept*

The circle is divided into eight parts and rearranged as follows:

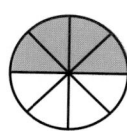 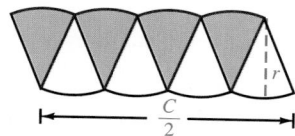

If the radius is r and the figure on the right approximates a parallelogram, what are its base and height? What is its area? $\frac{C}{2}$; r (approx.); $\frac{r \cdot C}{2}$ (approx.)

These figures show regular polygons inscribed in congruent circles.

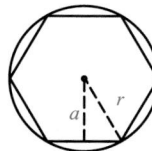 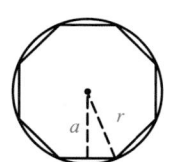 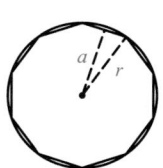

As the number of sides increases, the areas of the inscribed regular polygons become closer approximations of the area of the circle. In symbols, write $A_n \rightarrow A$ to show that the area of the regular n-gon approaches the area A of the circle as n increases.

As n increases, $a \rightarrow r$, $P \rightarrow C$. Since A_n is $\frac{1}{2}aP$, $A_n \rightarrow \frac{1}{2}rC$.

Thus, since $A_n \rightarrow A$, $A = \frac{1}{2}rC = \frac{1}{2}(r)(2\pi r) = \pi r^2$.

11.7 Area of Circles, Sectors, and Segments **471**

Developing Mathematical Power

Keeping a Portfolio   Have students write explanations for the derivation of the area formulas in Chapter 11 by completing the Critical Thinking activity, p. 11, in the *Teacher's Resource Book*. This will help them understand the relationships among the formulas. Allow time for them to share their responses.

- Use physical models to develop understanding of the basis for the formulas of this lesson.
- Compare the statement of Corollary 1 of Theorem 11.7, which shows how the areas of two circles are related to their radii, with Corollary 1 of Theorem 11.6, which shows how the circumferences of two circles are related to their radii.

CHALKBOARD EXAMPLES

- **For Example 1**

  Square *PQRS* is inscribed in $\odot T$ having radius 2 in. Find the area of the shaded region.

  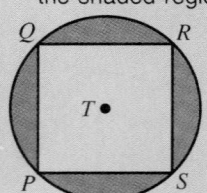

  A of $\odot T = 4\pi$ in.²; side of square = $2\sqrt{2}$ in., so A of square = 8 in.²; A of shaded region = $(4\pi - 8)$ in.²

- **For Example 2**

  a. If $m\widehat{JL} = 120$ and $KL = 6$ cm, what is the area of sector *JKL*?

  b. If $m\angle JKL = 135$ and $KJ = 2$ cm, what is the area of sector *JKL*?

  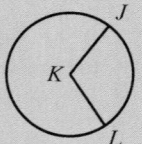

  c. If $KL = 4$ cm and $m\widehat{JL} = 140$, find the ratio of the areas of the sector to the circle.

  a. $A = \frac{120}{360}(36\pi) = 12\pi$ cm²

  b. $A = \frac{135}{360}(4\pi) = \frac{3}{8}(4\pi) = \frac{3\pi}{2}$ cm²

  c. $\frac{A}{16\pi} = \frac{140}{360} = \frac{7}{18}$

Theorem 11.7 summarizes this result.

> **Theorem 11.7** The area A of a circle with radius of length r is given by the formula $A = \pi r^2$. Proved in Practice Exercise 18

EXAMPLE 1 $\odot Q$ is inscribed in square *RSTU* having sides of 10 in. Find the area of the shaded region.

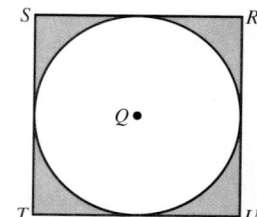

Since $s = 10$ in., $r = 5$ in.

A of $\odot Q = \pi(5^2)$ A of $RSTU = 10^2$
$\quad\quad\quad = 25\pi$ in.² $\quad\quad\quad = 100$ in.²

Thus the area of the shaded region = $(100 - 25\pi)$ in.²

These figures show that if the radius of a circle is multiplied by three, the area of the circle is multiplied by the square of three, or nine. Corollary 1 of Theorem 11.7 confirms the relationship $\dfrac{A \text{ of } O_1}{A \text{ of } O_2} = \dfrac{r^2 \text{ of } O_1}{r^2 \text{ of } O_2}$.

$A = \pi r^2 \quad A = 9\pi r^2$

> **Corollary 1** The areas of two circles have the same ratio as the squares of their radii. Proved in Practice Exercise 16

A **sector of a circle** is the region bounded by two radii of the circle and their intercepted arc. Sector *AOB* is bounded by $\overline{OA}$, $\overline{OB}$, and $\widehat{AB}$.

The ratio $\dfrac{\text{degree measure of arc}}{360}$ tells what fractional part of the circle is in the sector; this fraction multiplied by the area of the circle gives the area of the sector.

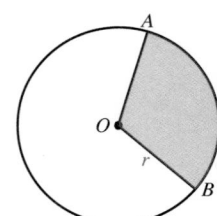

> **Corollary 2** In a circle with radius r, the ratio of the area A of a sector to the area of the circle (πr^2) equals the ratio of the degree measure m of the arc of the sector to 360. Proved in Practice Exercise 17

$$\frac{A}{\pi r^2} = \frac{m}{360} \quad \text{or} \quad A = \frac{m}{360}(\pi r^2).$$

EXAMPLE 2   **a.** If $m\widehat{JN} = 60$ and $ON = 5$ cm, what is the area of sector JON?

b. If $m\angle JON = 72$, and $JO = 1$ in., what is the area of sector JON?

c. Find the ratio of the area of the sector to the area of the circle if $ON = 2$ cm and $m\widehat{JN} = 84$.

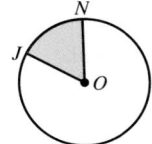

a. $A = \dfrac{60}{360}(25\pi) = \dfrac{25}{6}\pi$ cm^2

b. $m\widehat{JN} = 72$; thus $A = \dfrac{72}{360}(\pi) = \dfrac{\pi}{5}$ in.^{2}.   **c.** $\dfrac{A}{4\pi} = \dfrac{84}{360} = \dfrac{7}{30}$

A **segment of a circle** is a region bounded by an arc and the chord of the arc.

The area of this segment of $\odot P$ is found by subtracting the area of $\triangle MPN$ from the area of sector MPN.

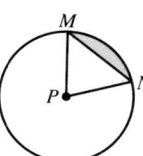

EXAMPLE 3   In $\odot R$, $LR = 10$ cm and $m\angle LRS = 60$.

a. Find the area of sector LRS.

b. Find the area of $\triangle LRS$.

c. Find the area of the shaded segment.

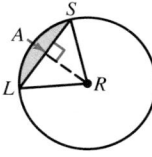

a. $A = \dfrac{60}{360}(100\pi) = \dfrac{50}{3}\pi$ cm^2

b. Draw $\overline{RA} \perp \overline{LS}$ at A. Then $\triangle LRA$ is a 30°-60°-90° $\triangle$, so $LA = 5$ cm and $RA = 5\sqrt{3}$ cm. Hence, the area of $\triangle LRS = \dfrac{1}{2}(10)(5\sqrt{3}) = 25\sqrt{3}$ cm^2.

c. $A = \left(\dfrac{50}{3}\pi - 25\sqrt{3}\right)$cm^2

CLASS EXERCISES

1. Which has a greater area: 5 circles of diameter 1 in. each, or 1 circle of diameter 5 in.? Justify your answer. 1 circle of diameter 5 in.; $5\pi\left(\frac{1}{2}\right)^2 < \pi\left(\frac{5}{2}\right)^2$

Use $\odot O$ to answer Exercises 2–5.

2. What is the area of circle O? of sector BOC? 64π cm^2; $\frac{64\pi}{3}$ cm^2

3. What is the length of $\widehat{AD}$? $\frac{4}{3}\pi$ cm

4. What is the area of sector AOD? $\frac{16}{3}\pi$ cm^2

5. What is the area of the shaded segment? $\left(\frac{32\pi}{3} - 16\sqrt{3}\right)$cm^2

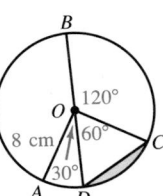

11.7 Area of Circles, Sectors, and Segments   **473**

- **For Example 3**

In $\odot O$, $AO = 8$ in. and $m\angle AOB = 90$.

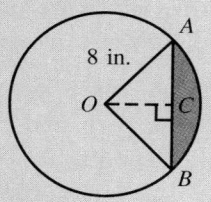

a. Find the area of sector AOB.
b. Find the area of $\triangle AOB$.
c. Find the area of the shaded segment.

a. $A = \left(\dfrac{90}{360}\right)64\pi = 16\pi$ in.^{2}
b. $\triangle AOB$ is a 45°-45°-90° rt. $\triangle$; $AC = OC = 4\sqrt{2}$ in., and A of $\triangle AOB = \frac{1}{2}(8\sqrt{2})(4\sqrt{2}) = 32$ in.^{2}
c. $A = (16\pi - 32)$ in.^{2}

Common Errors

- Some students will apply area formulas for circles and sectors incorrectly, or in inappropriate ways. Insist that formulas be written and checked for all problems.
- Some students will confuse squaring the radius with doubling the radius to find area of circles. Remind students that squares multiply numbers by themselves.
- See *Teacher's Resource Book* for additional remediation.

LESSON FOLLOW-UP

Discussion

Ask students to justify in their own words, the formula for the area of a circle. Make sure they understand the use of the idea of limits in this context, although their understanding may still be intuitive.

Assignment Guide

See p. 438B for assignments.

473

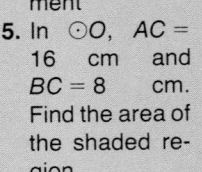
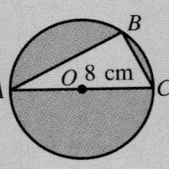
PRACTICE EXERCISES   Use technology where appropriate.

A   1. If you like pizza, which would you choose, and why?

A 16-in. pizza to share equally with 7 of your friends

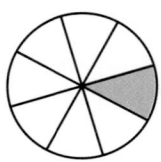

A 14-in. pizza to share equally with 5 of your friends

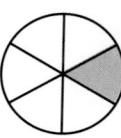

the 14 in. pizza; 49π/6 > 64π/8

Circle O has radius r and sector DOE of area A. Complete the table.

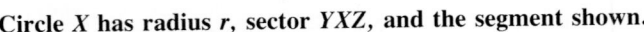

	r	d	m∠DOE	DE͡	C	A
2.	4	? 8	72	? 8π/5	? 8π	? 16π/5
3.	1	? 2	? 45	π/4	? 2π	? π/8
4.	? 3√7	6√7	120	? 2√7π	6√7π	? 21π
5.	6	? 12	36	? 6/5 π	? 12π	? 3.6π

Circle X has radius r, sector YXZ, and the segment shown.

6. If r = √2, find the area of the segment. π/2 − 1

7. If r = 1, find the area of sector YXZ. π/4   3/2 π² − 3π

8. If the area of △YXZ is 3π, find the area of the segment.

9. If YZ = 8, find the area of ⊙X. 32π

10. A circle of radius r has a sector whose arc length is l. Find a formula for the area of the sector in terms of r and l. A = rl/2

11. If a circle has radius r, what is the maximum value of the area of a segment of the circle? Explain your answer. πr²/2; this is the limit of a segment whose chord approaches a diameter and whose cental angle approaches 180°.

In Exercises 12–15, find the area of the shaded region.

B   12.
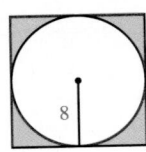

13.
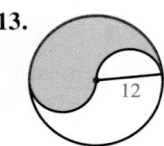

14.
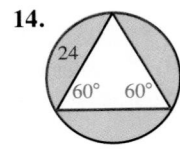

15.
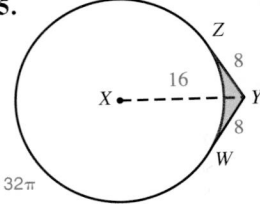

64(4 − π)   72π   192π − 144√3   64√3 − 32π

Use algebra to justify each of the following corollaries. See Additional Answers, p. 702.

16. Corollary 1 of Theorem 11.7   17. Corollary 2 of Theorem 11.7

18. Write a paragraph proof to justify Theorem 11.7.

Developing Mathematical Power

Cooperative Learning   The Enrichment activity, p. 20, in the *Teacher's Resource Book* (see side column, p. 475) provides a visual approach to the concepts of the lesson. Challenge groups of students to design a "still life" with circles and polygons and write questions to accompany it.

C

19. Circles O and P, each having radius r, intersect as shown. Determine the area of the shaded region. (*Hint:* Draw $\overline{RO}$ and $\overline{RP}$ and consider $\triangle ROP$.)

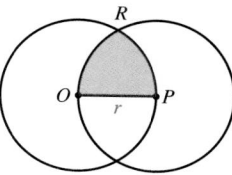

20. A circle of radius r has area A. If the radius is increased by 1 unit, how does the area of the resulting circle compare to A?

21. In this equilateral triangle having sides of length 6 in., M, N, and O are the midpoints of the sides. $\overset{\frown}{MN}$, $\overset{\frown}{NO}$, and $\overset{\frown}{MO}$ have the vertices of the triangle as their centers. Find the area of the shaded region. $9\left(\sqrt{3} - \frac{\pi}{2}\right)$in.²

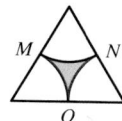

Applications

22. Automobiles Suppose the arm of a windshield wiper is 16 in. long, with a blade 12 in. long. If the wiper moves through an angle of 90°, how much of the windshield is cleaned in one pass of the wiper? 60π in.²

23. Manufacturing Lids for tin cans are stamped out of a solid sheet of tin as shown. How much of the tin is wasted in this process? $6(15) - 10\left(\frac{3}{2}\right)^2\pi = (90 - 22.5\pi)$ in.²

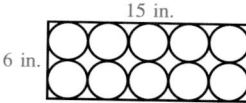

15 in.

6 in.

Algebra Review

Multiply and simplify.

24. $\sqrt{3} \cdot \sqrt{8}$ $2\sqrt{6}$

25. $-2\sqrt{5} \cdot 3\sqrt{8}$ $-12\sqrt{10}$

26. $\sqrt{6}\left(3\sqrt{2} - 5\sqrt{6}\right)$ $6\sqrt{3} - 30$

HISTORICAL NOTE

Pi—The Never-ending Story

The Greek mathematician Archimedes placed the value of pi between two limits: $3\frac{10}{71} <$ pi $< 3\frac{1}{7}$. By the latter part of the fifth century, T'su Ch'ung-chih had found $3.1415926 <$ pi < 3.1415927. By the beginning of the seventeenth century, 35 decimal places had been calculated. By the end of the eighteenth century, Georg Vega presented 136 correct places. In 1949, a new era of pi research was launched when a computer ground out 2037 decimal digits in just seventy hours. By 1966, 500,000 decimal digits had been recorded. Professor Yasumasa Kaneda of the University of Tokyo obtained 201,326,000 decimal digits in 1988 in a shade under six hours. The value of pi is now used to test the programs used on the new supercomputers and also to determine the performance quality of the supercomputer.

11.7 Area of Circles, Sectors, and Segments   **475**

Teacher's Resource Book

Follow-Up Investigation, Chapter 11, p. 18

P   Name _____ Date _____
Practice: For use after Lesson 11.7, Geometry

Areas of Circles, Sectors, and Segments

⊙O has a radius r and sector JOL of area A. Complete the table.

	r	d	$m\angle JOL$	$m\overset{\frown}{JL}$	C of ⊙O	A of sector JOL
1.	5		18			
2.	7			15		
3.			150			5π
4.			36		18π	

Circle M has radius r, sector AMT, and the segment shown.

5. If $r = \sqrt{5}$, find the area of the segment. _____

6. If $r = 9$, find the area of sector AMT. _____

7. If $AT = 10$, find the area of ⊙M. _____

8. If $AT = 4\sqrt{2}$, find the area of ⊙M. _____

9. If $AT = 3\sqrt{2}$, find the area of sector AMT. _____

In Exercises 10–12, find the area of the shaded region.

10.   **11.**   **12.**

Applications

13. Automotives The headlight of a car shines in 120° arc for a distance of 20 ft. How many square feet does it illuminate?

14. Manufacturing Chips are stamped out of a piece of cardboard as shown. How much cardboard is wasted? (Use 3.14 for π.)

Chapter 11   **19**

E   Name _____ Date _____
Enrichment: For use after Lesson 11.7, Geometry

Still Life With Circles and Polygons

All figures that appear to be tangent to each other in the diagram below are, and all polygons are regular.

1. The radius of the outer circle is 1. What is the area? _____ π

2. Find the length of a side of the inscribed equilateral triangle. _____ $\sqrt{3}$

3. What is its area? _____ $\frac{3\sqrt{3}}{4}$

4. What is the shaded area? _____ $\pi - \frac{3\sqrt{3}}{4}$

5. Find the radius of the inner circle. _____ $\frac{1}{2}$

6. What is its area? _____ $\frac{\pi}{4}$

7. Each side of the outside square is 2. What is its area? _____ 4

8. Find the radius of the circle. _____ 1

9. What is its area? _____ π

10. Find the length of a side of the inner square. _____ $\sqrt{2}$

11. What is its area? _____ 2

12. Find the area of the shaded portion. _____ $\pi - 2$

20 Chapter 11

Materials/Manipulatives
Geoboards
Teacher's Resource Book,
 Teaching Aid 11
Teaching Transparency 77

Technology
Computer Test Bank, pp.
 737–747

LESSON FOCUS

Review

- These polygons are similar. Give a
 similarity statement, the scale factor, and the missing lengths.

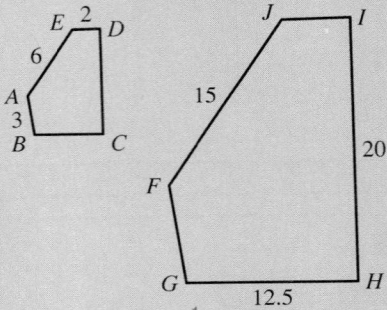

$ABCDE \sim FGHIJ$; $2\frac{1}{2}$; $FG = 7.5$, $JI = 5$,
$CD = 8$, $BC = 5$

- The Chapter Summary and Review, pp. 484 and 485, gives vocabulary and concepts and review
 exercises by lesson.
- The end of the chapter features an
 Algebra Review on p. 488.

Alternative Learning Styles

The kinesthetic learner will benefit
from using the geoboard to study the
characteristics of similar polygons.
Students can construct several pairs
of similar rectangles on their geoboards and record the scale factor of
the similarity, and the perimeter and
area of each figure in a table. Ask for
observations about relationships between the scale factor and the ratios of
the perimeters and areas of a pair of
similar figures.

476

Areas of Similar Figures

Objective: To state and apply the relationships between scale factors,
perimeters, and areas of similar figures

If two polygons are congruent, their respective perimeters and areas are equal.
This lesson relates the perimeters and areas of similar polygons.

Investigation—*Thinking Critically*

A mill produces sheets of metal in two sizes.

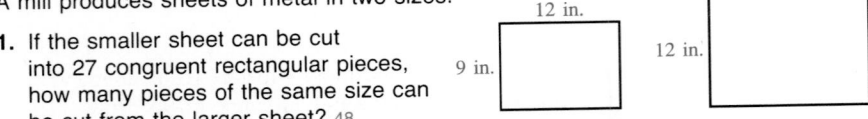

1. If the smaller sheet can be cut
   into 27 congruent rectangular pieces,
   how many pieces of the same size can
   be cut from the larger sheet? 48

2. How does the ratio of the lengths of the corresponding sides of the sheets
   compare with the ratio of their areas? $\frac{l_1}{l_2} = \frac{3}{4}$, $\frac{A_1}{A_2} = \frac{9}{16}$, $\frac{A_1}{A_2} = \frac{l_1^2}{l_2^2}$

3. How does the ratio of the number of cut rectangles compare to the ratio of
   the lengths of the corresponding sides of the sheets? $\frac{n_1}{n_2} = \frac{l_1^2}{l_2^2}$

Study this table of pairs of similar figures.

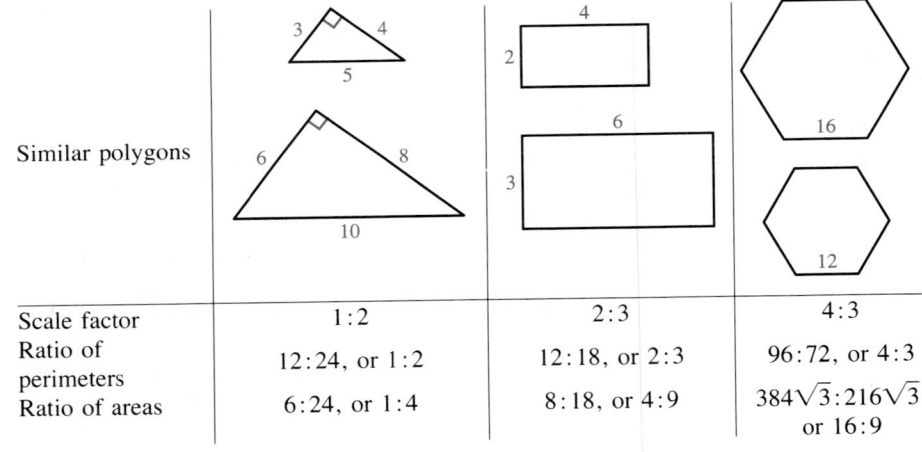

Similar polygons			
Scale factor	1:2	2:3	4:3
Ratio of perimeters	12:24, or 1:2	12:18, or 2:3	96:72, or 4:3
Ratio of areas	6:24, or 1:4	8:18, or 4:9	$384\sqrt{3}:216\sqrt{3}$, or 16:9

Note that the perimeters have the same ratio as the scale factor, but the ratio
of the areas is the square of the scale factor.

Developing Mathematical Power

Cooperative Learning Assign groups of students to complete the Reading and
Writing in Geometry activity, p. 11, in the *Teacher's Resource Book*. In addition to
justifying that each statement is true or false, have them further refine their answers
to *always, sometimes,* or *never* and provide an illustration.

Theorem 11.8 If the scale factor of two similar figures is $a:b$, then the ratio of corresponding perimeters is $a:b$ and the ratio of corresponding areas is $a^2:b^2$. Proved in Practice Exercise 29

EXAMPLE 1 $\triangle DEF \sim \triangle HJK$

a. What is the scale factor?

b. What is the ratio of the perimeters?

c. What is the ratio of the areas?

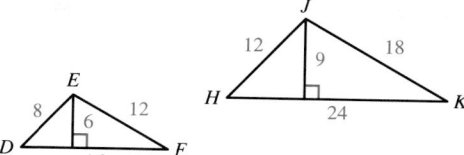

a. $2:3$　b. $2:3$　c. $2^2:3^2$, or $4:9$

EXAMPLE 2 Regular hexagon $H_1 \sim$ regular hexagon H_2

a. What is $s_1:s_2$?

b. What is the ratio of the perimeters?

c. What is the ratio of the areas?
(Use the formula $A = \frac{3}{2}s^2\sqrt{3}$.)

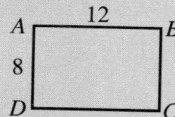
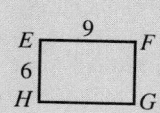

d. Find the apothem of each hexagon.　e. What is the ratio of the apothems?

a. $s_1:s_2 = 10:15 = 2:3$　b. $2:3$　c. $2^2:3^2$, or $4:9$

d. a_1 and a_2 are the longer legs of 30°-60°-90° triangles; $a_1 = 5\sqrt{3}$ and $a_2 = \frac{15}{2}\sqrt{3}$

e. $a_1:a_2 = 5\sqrt{3}:\frac{15}{2}\sqrt{3} = 2:3$

Observe from this last example that the ratio of the apothems of two regular hexagons is the same as the ratio of the lengths of the corresponding sides. Will this be true for all pairs of similar regular polygons? yes

In summary, these are the formulas for area of polygons and the circle formulas that have been presented in this chapter:

Square: $A = s^2$

Rectangle: $A = bh$

Parallelogram: $A = bh$

Triangle: $A = \frac{1}{2}bh$

Rhombus: $A = \frac{1}{2}d_1 \cdot d_2$

Trapezoid: $A = \frac{h}{2}(b_1 + b_2)$

Regular polygon: $A = \frac{1}{2}aP$

Circumference: $C = 2\pi r$

Arc length: $l = \frac{m}{360}(2\pi r)$

Area of circle: $A = \pi r^2$

Area of sector: $A = \frac{m}{360}(\pi r^2)$

11.8 Areas of Similar Figures　**477**

For Example 2

Regular pentagon P_1 has sides of length 12. Regular pentagon P_2 has sides of length 18.

a. What is $s_1:s_2$? 2:3
b. What is ratio of the perimeters? 2:3
c. Use the relationship $\frac{s}{2}$ tan $54° = a$ to find the apothem of each pentagon. $a_1 \approx 8.26$; $a_2 \approx 12.39$
d. What is the ratio of the apothems? 2:3
e. What is the area of each pentagon?
f. What is the ratio of the areas? 4:9

e. $A_1 \approx 247.8$ square units; $A_2 \approx 557.55$ square units

Common Error

• Some students might confuse the relationship of the scale factor of similar figures with the ratio of areas and of perimeters. Point out that since perimeter is a linear measure the ratio of the perimeters is the same as the scale factor. Since area is in square units, its ratio is the square of the scale factor.
• See *Teacher's Resource Book* for additional remediation.

LESSON FOLLOW-UP

Discussion

• Ask students to determine the area of an equilateral triangle, a square, and a regular hexagon, each of side length 1 cm. $\frac{\sqrt{3}}{4}$ cm², 1 cm², $\frac{3\sqrt{3}}{2}$ cm²

CLASS EXERCISES

Drawing in Geometry

True or false? If false, sketch a counterexample.

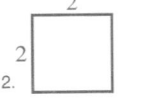 

2.

1. If the length and width of a rectangle are doubled, its perimeter is doubled. true

2. If the sides of a square are halved, the area of the square is also halved. false; $2 \cdot 2 = 4$, $1 \cdot 1 = 1$; not halved, quartered

3. If two triangles have equal perimeters, they must also have equal areas. false; See side column.

4. If two rectangles have the same area, they must be similar. false

5. The ratio of any two corresponding sides in similar polygons is equal to the square root of the ratio of the areas. true

In Exercises 6–9, ANDYC ~ TORES.

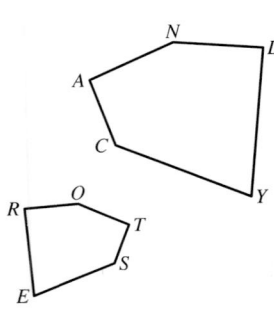

6. If $AN:TO = 5:3$, and if the perimeter of $TORES = 24$ cm, find the perimeter of $ANDYC$. 40 cm

7. If the area of $ANDYC = 448$ cm², the area of $TORES = 175$ cm², and $DY = 16$ cm, find RE. 10 cm

8. If the ratio of the perimeter of $ANDYC$ to the perimeter of $TORES$ is $7:4$, then find the ratio of the area of $ANDYC$ to the area of $TORES$. 49:16

9. If $CA = 4$ cm, $ST = 2$ cm, and the area of $TORES$ is 18 cm² less than the area of $ANDYC$, find the area of $ANDYC$. $\frac{A}{A-18} = \frac{4^2}{2^2}$; $A = 24$ cm²

PRACTICE EXERCISES   Use technology where appropriate.

A 1. **Thinking Critically**   Harry is going to help his neighbor build a patio similar in shape to Harry's, but having twice the area. Harry and his neighbor decide that the way to do this is to double the lengths of all sides of Harry's patio.

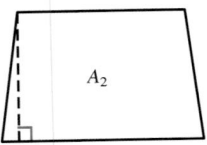

Explain whether or not their method will work. If not, what dimensions should they use in order to double the area? No; they should multiply the dimensions by $\sqrt{2}$.

3.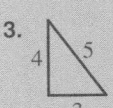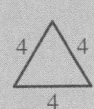

4.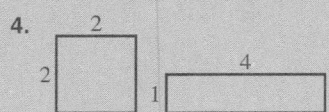

Each pair of figures is similar. Give the scale factor, the ratio of the perimeters, and the ratio of the areas.

2.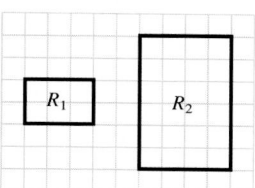

1:2, 1:2, 1:4

3.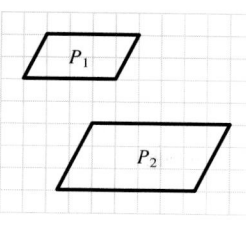

2:3, 2:3; 4:9

4.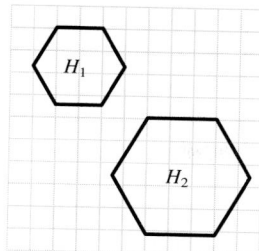

2:3, 2:3, 4:9

• By what amount would the side length of each figure have to be multiplied to produce a similar figure whose area is twice that area? Whose area is three times the area? Generalize. $\sqrt{2}$; $\sqrt{3}$; a regular polygon of side length $\sqrt{n}$ cm would have area n times the area of the polygon of side length 1 cm.

Critical Thinking

1. *Application* Have students apply area concepts to calculate areas.
2. *Reasoning* Lead students to deduce the relationship of linear measures, given the relationship of areas, and generalize.

Assignment Guide

See p. 438B for assignments.

Polygon $X_1 \sim$ polygon X_2. Complete the ratios in the table.

	Side lengths $s_1 : s_2$	Perimeter $P_1 : P_2$	Area $A_1 : A_2$
5.	5:1	? : ? 5; 1	? : ? 25; 1
6.	? : ? 6; 1	6:1	? : ? 36; 1
7.	1:2	? : ? 1; 2	? : ? 1; 4
8.	? : ? a; 2	? : ? a; 2	a^2:4
9.	? : ? 4; 3	? : ? 4; 3	16:9
10.	3:2	? : ? 3; 2	? : ? 9; 4

In $\triangle ABC$, $\overline{DE} \parallel \overline{AC}$.

11. If D and E are midpoints, find the ratio of the area of $\triangle DBE$ to the area of $\triangle ABC$. 1:4

12. If $AB = 6$ cm and $DB = 2$ cm, find the ratio of the area of $\triangle DBE$ to the area of $\triangle ABC$. 1:9

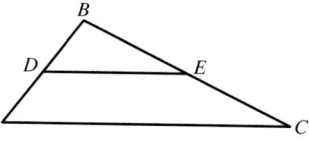

13. If $\dfrac{\text{perimeter of } \triangle ABC}{\text{perimeter of } \triangle DBE} = \dfrac{3}{2}$, find $\dfrac{AC}{DE}$. $\frac{3}{2}$

14. If $\dfrac{\text{perimeter of } \triangle ABC}{\text{perimeter of } \triangle DBE} = \dfrac{4}{1}$, find $\dfrac{\text{area of } \triangle ABC}{\text{area of } \triangle DBE}$. $\frac{16}{1}$

In this figure, $\overline{AB} \parallel \overline{CD}$.

15. If $\dfrac{\text{perimeter of } \triangle CED}{\text{perimeter of } \triangle BEA} = \dfrac{5}{2}$ and $BA = 6$ in., find CD. 15 in.

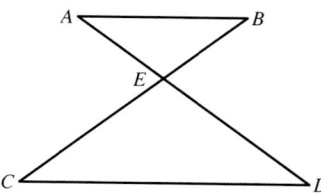

16. If $ED : EA = 14 : 9$ and the perimeter of $\triangle BEA = 27$ in., find the perimeter of $\triangle CED$. 42 in.

11.8 Areas of Similar Figures   **479**

Lesson Quiz

$\triangle BCD \sim \triangle EFG$

1. If $BC:EF = 7:21$, find the ratios of the perimeters and of the areas. 1:3; 1:9
2. If $CD:FG = 3:4$ and the area of $\triangle BCD$ is 54 cm^2, find the area of $\triangle EFG$. 96 cm^2
3. If the ratio of the perimeters is 2:3 and the sum of the perimeters is 175 in., find the perimeter of each triangle. 70 in.; 105 in.

Additional Answers

29. Since the two given figures are similar, the ratio of a pair of corr. sides is equal to a constant $\left(K = \frac{a}{b}\right)$. The ratio of the sum of the lengths of the sides of one figure to the sum of the lengths of the sides of the other figure is also equal to the same constant K by the proportion prop.: $\frac{a}{b} = \frac{c}{d} = \frac{e}{f} = \frac{a+c+e}{b+d+f}$. The ratio of the corr. apothems and altitudes of similar figures is the same as the ratio of corr. sides.

Since the area of a $\triangle$ is equal to half the product of the base and height $\left(A = \frac{1}{2}bh\right)$, and the area of a reg. polygon is equal to half the product of the apothem and the perimeter $\left(A = \frac{1}{2}aP\right)$, it follows that the ratio of corr. areas of similar figures is equal to the following:

$$\frac{\text{area of one similar figure}}{\text{area of the other similar figure}}$$
$$= \frac{\frac{1}{2}a_1 P_1}{\frac{1}{2}a_2 P_2} = \frac{a_1 \cdot P_1}{a_2 \cdot P_2}. \text{ However,}$$

$\frac{a_1}{a_2} = K \left(\text{or } \frac{a}{b}\right)$ and $\frac{P_1}{P_2} = K \left(\text{or } \frac{a}{b}\right)$.

By the subst. prop.,

$$\frac{\text{area}_1}{\text{area}_2} = \frac{a_1}{a_2} \cdot \frac{P_1}{P_2} = K \cdot K \left(\text{or } \frac{a}{b} \cdot \frac{a}{b}\right)$$
$$= K^2 \text{ or } \frac{a^2}{b^2}$$

Recall that in this figure, $\overline{AB} \parallel \overline{CD}$.

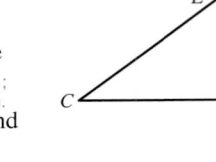

17. If $\dfrac{\text{perimeter of } \triangle CED}{\text{perimeter of } \triangle BEA} = \dfrac{3}{2}$ and the sum of the perimeters is 110 in., find the perimeter of each triangle. $P(\triangle CED) = 66$ in.; $P(\triangle BEA) = 44$ in.

18. If the ratio of the perimeters of $\triangle BEA$ and $\triangle CED$ is 3:5 and the sum of the perimeters is 320 in., find the perimeter of each triangle. 120 in.; 200 in.

19. If $CD:BA = 6:5$ and the area of $\triangle CDE = 288$ in.^{2}, find the area of $\triangle BEA$. 200 in.^{2}

B 20. If the area of $\triangle CED = 425$ in.^{2}, the area of $\triangle BEA = 68$ in.^{2}, and $BE = 10$ in., find CE. 25 in.

Square S_1 has sides of length s_1. Square S_2, having sides of length s_2, is formed by joining in order the midpoints of the sides of S_1.

21. If $s_1 = 2$, find $s_1:s_2$. $\sqrt{2}:1$

22. If $s_1 = n$, find $s_1:s_2$. $\sqrt{2}:1$

23. If $s_1 = 2$, find $\dfrac{\text{perimeter of } S_1}{\text{perimeter of } S_2}$. $\frac{\sqrt{2}}{1}$

24. If $s_1 = n$, find $\dfrac{\text{perimeter of } S_1}{\text{perimeter of } S_2}$. $\frac{\sqrt{2}}{1}$

25. If $s_1 = 2$, find $\dfrac{\text{area of } S_1}{\text{area of } S_2}$. $\frac{2}{1}$

26. If $s_1 = n$, find $\dfrac{\text{area of } S_1}{\text{area of } S_2}$. $\frac{2}{1}$

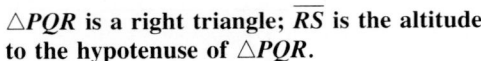

$\triangle PQR$ is a right triangle; $\overline{RS}$ is the altitude to the hypotenuse of $\triangle PQR$.

27. If the area of $\triangle PQR$ is 4 times the area of $\triangle PRS$ and PQ is 6 more than PR, find PR and PQ. PR = 6; PQ = 12

28. Consider $\triangle PRS$ and $\triangle QRS$. If $\dfrac{\text{perimeter of } \triangle QRS}{\text{perimeter of } \triangle PRS} = \dfrac{3}{2}$ and PR is 4 less than QR, find QR and PR. PR = 8; QR = 12

C 29. Write an inductive argument to justify Theorem 11.8. (*Hint:* The ratio of a pair of corresponding sides of similar figures can be represented by a constant.) See side column.

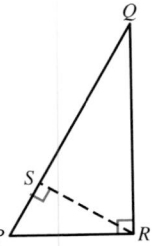

H_1 and H_2 are regular hexagons and $H_1 \sim H_2$.

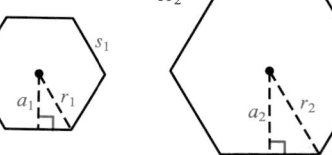

30. How does $\dfrac{\text{area of } H_1}{\text{area of } H_2}$ compare

to $\dfrac{a_1}{a_2}$? to $\dfrac{r_1}{r_2}$? $\dfrac{A(H_1)}{A(H_2)} = \dfrac{a_1^2}{a_2^2} = \dfrac{r_1^2}{r_2^2}$

31. How does $\dfrac{\text{perimeter of } H_1}{\text{perimeter of } H_2}$ compare to $\dfrac{a_1}{a_2}$? to $\dfrac{r_1}{r_2}$? $\dfrac{P(H_1)}{P(H_2)} = \dfrac{a_1}{a_2} = \dfrac{r_1}{r_2}$

32. Generalize the results of Exercise 30 for pairs of regular polygons.
See side column.
33. Generalize the results of Exercise 31 for pairs of regular polygons.

Applications

34. Technology Computer graphics can be created by generating a closed region of one color and then superimposing another region in black, leaving only parts of the original color showing. Use Logo to generate a computer graphic using this technique. See Solutions Manual.

35. Hobbies If the length ratio of John's miniature house to the original structure is $2:35$ and the miniature requires 4 ft^2 of flooring, how much flooring exists in the larger house? 1225 ft²

TEST YOURSELF

1. The circumference of $\odot O$ is ___?___. 8π cm

2. The area of $\odot O$ is ___?___. 16π cm²

3. The length of $\overparen{AB}$ is ___?___. 2π cm

4. The area of sector AOB is ___?___ 4π cm²

5. The area of the shaded segment is ___?___.
$(4\pi - 8)$cm²

11.6, 11.7

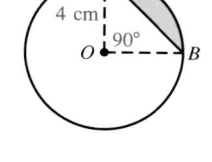

Circles A and B are inscribed in squares S_1 and S_2.

11.6–11.8

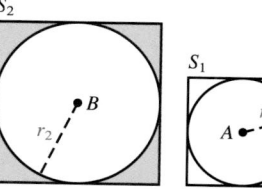

6. If $r_2 = 2 \cdot r_1$, how does the circumference of $\odot A$ compare to the circumference of $\odot B$? $C_A = \frac{1}{2}C_B$

7. If $\dfrac{\text{area of } \odot B}{\text{area of } \odot A} = \dfrac{25}{16}$, what is $\dfrac{r_2}{r_1}$? $\frac{5}{4}$

8. If $r_1 = 2$ cm and $r_2 = 3$ cm,

find $\dfrac{\text{perimeter of } S_1}{\text{perimeter of } S_2}$ and $\dfrac{\text{area of } S_1}{\text{area of } S_2}$. $\frac{P_1}{P_2} = \frac{2}{3}, \frac{A_1}{A_2} = \frac{4}{9}$

9. If $r_2 = 5$ cm, find the area of the shaded region in S_2. $(100 - 25\pi)$ cm²

11.8 Areas of Similar Figures **481**

32. The areas of two regular polygons having the same number of sides have the same ratio as the squares of the corresponding linear parts.
33. The perimeters of two regular polygons having the same number of sides have the same ratio as the corr. linear parts.

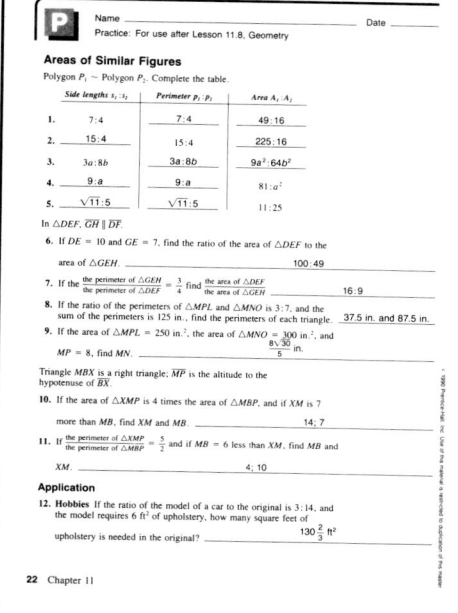
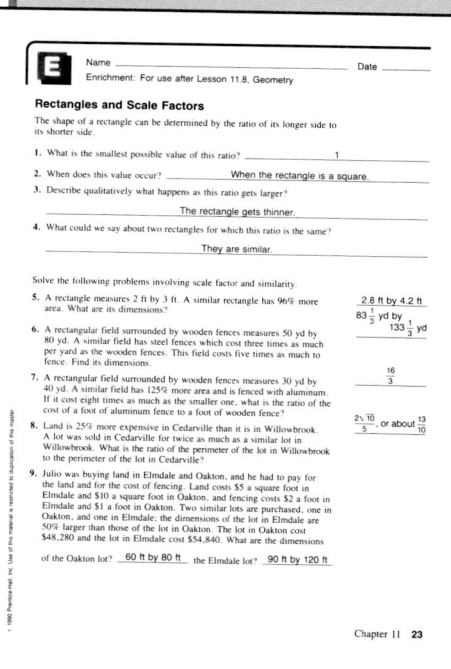

See *Teacher's Resource Book*, Follow-up Application, *Chapter 11*, p. 24.

INTEGRATING GEOMETRY
Approximations of Area

The ancient Greek mathematician Archimedes devised a method for calculating the area of a region that led to the development of the modern technique called *integral calculus*. This method uses limits to compute the exact value of the area of a region that has a curve as part of its boundary.

To approximate the area of region bounded by the *y*-axis, the *x*-axis, and the line whose equation is $x + y = 1$, divide the region into rectangles of equal width. (Note that the unit is equal to 8 grid units.) This can be accomplished with rectangles that fit entirely inside the boundaries (a lower estimate) or with those that overlap the boundaries (an upper estimate). The actual area of the region lies between the estimates, each of which is obtained by summing the areas of the individual rectangles. Note that if the region is subdivided into 8 rectangles, the approximation seems to be closer. Subdividing into 16 rectangles gives an approximation that is still closer. In fact, the greater the number of subdivisions, the more accurate the computed area measure; the lower and upper estimates will approach each other and thus approach the exact value of the area.

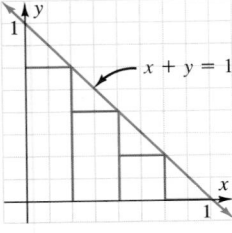

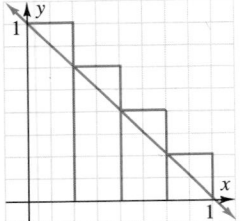

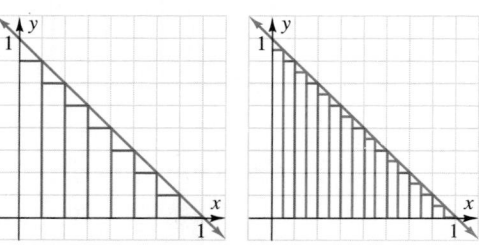

Since the area of a rectangle equals the product of its length and width, the lower estimate A_L for the first figure is:

$$A_L = \left(\frac{1}{4}\right)\left(\frac{3}{4}\right) + \frac{1}{4}\left(\frac{2}{4}\right) + \left(\frac{1}{4}\right)\left(\frac{1}{4}\right) + \left(\frac{1}{4}\right)\left(\frac{0}{4}\right) = \frac{6}{16}, \text{ or } 0.375$$

The upper estimate A_U for the second figure is:

$$A_U = \frac{1}{4}(1) + \frac{1}{4}\left(\frac{3}{4}\right) + \frac{1}{4}\left(\frac{2}{4}\right) + \frac{1}{4}\left(\frac{1}{4}\right) = \frac{10}{16}, \text{ or } 0.625$$

The closer estimate, using 8 rectangles, yields

$$A_L = \frac{1}{8}\left(\frac{7}{8}\right) + \frac{1}{8}\left(\frac{6}{8}\right) + \frac{1}{8}\left(\frac{5}{8}\right) + \cdots + \frac{1}{8}\left(\frac{1}{8}\right) + \frac{1}{8}\left(\frac{0}{8}\right) = \frac{28}{64}, \text{ or } 0.438$$

$$A_U = \frac{1}{8}\left(\frac{8}{8}\right) + \frac{1}{8}\left(\frac{7}{8}\right) + \frac{1}{8}\left(\frac{6}{8}\right) + \cdots + \frac{1}{8}\left(\frac{2}{8}\right) + \frac{1}{8}\left(\frac{1}{8}\right) = \frac{36}{64}, \text{ or } 0.562$$

Sixteen subdivisions result in a lower estimate of 0.469 and an upper estimate of 0.531; 32 subdivisions yield $A_L = 0.484$ and $A_U = 0.516$. The region under consideration has the shape of a triangle, so the exact area can be calculated using the formula

$$A = \frac{1}{2} \cdot 1 \cdot 1, \text{ or } 0.5$$

Note how the sequences of estimated values approach the exact value as the number of rectangles increases.

Sequence of lower values: 0.375, 0.438, 0.469, 0.484
Sequence of upper values: 0.625, 0.562, 0.531, 0.516

By the techniques of calculus, the exact value can be obtained as a limit.

EXERCISES

In Exercises 1–4, graph the region described and compute A_L and A_U for the given number of subdivisions. Let 16 squares on the graph paper equal 1 unit.

1. The region bounded by the x-axis, the y-axis, and the line $y = -x + 2$ for 4 subdivisions $A_L = 1.5, A_U = 2.5$

2. The region in Exercise 1 for 8 subdivisions $A_L = 1.75, A_U = 2.25$

3. The region bounded by the x-axis, the y-axis, and the line $y = -2x + 4$ for 4 subdivisions $A_L = 3, A_U = 5$

4. The region in Exercise 3 for 8 subdivisions $A_L = 3.5, A_U = 4.5$

5. Using the formula for area of a triangle, compute the areas of the triangular regions in Exercises 1 and 3. How do they compare to your estimates? Ex. 1: $A = 2$; Ex. 2: $A = 4$; in each case, the area is the mean of A_L and A_U.

- See *Teacher's Resource Book, Spanish Chapter Summary and Review*, pp. 21–22.
- See Extra Practice, p. 653.

CHAPTER 11   SUMMARY AND REVIEW

Vocabulary

altitude and base of a parallelogram (441)	height of a parallelogram (441)
altitude of a trapezoid (450)	height of a trapezoid (450)
apothem of a regular polygon (455)	pi (π) (467)
arc length (468)	radius of a regular polygon (455)
area of a circle (472)	sector of a circle (472)
area of a polygonal region (440)	segment of a circle (473)
center of a regular polygon (455)	semiperimeter of a triangle (449)
central angle of a regular polygon (455)	square unit (441)
circumference of a circle (466)	

Area of Squares and Rectangles   The area of a polygonal region is the measure of the region enclosed by the figure.   **11.1**

Area of a rectangle $= b \cdot h$ Area of a square $= s^2$

1. If $AD = (x + 6)$cm, $AB = 5$ cm and the perimeter of $ABCD$ is 26 cm, find the area of rectangle $ABCD$.
   40 cm²

2. If $AB = (4n + 1)$cm, $AD = (n - 5)$cm, and the area of rectangle $ABCD$ is 25 cm², find AB and AD.
   $n = 6$, $AB = 25$ cm, $AD = 1$ cm

Area of Parallelograms and Triangles   The area of a parallelogram is equal to the product of the length of a base and its corresponding height. The area of a triangle with a base of length b and corresponding height h is $\frac{1}{2}bh$. The area of a rhombus is equal to one-half the product of the lengths of its diagonals. The area of an equilateral triangle having sides of length s is $\frac{s^2\sqrt{3}}{4}$.   **11.2**

ITEK is a parallelogram and IS = 3 cm.

3. If $KE = 8$ cm, the area of $ITEK = \underline{?}$. 24 cm²
4. If $IT = 6.5$ in., the area of $\triangle ITE = \underline{?}$. 9.75 cm²
5. If $IE = 5$ cm and $KS = 2$ cm, the area of $ITEK = \underline{?}$. 18 cm²

Area of Trapezoids   The area of a trapezoid is equal to one-half the product of the height and the sum of the lengths of the bases.   **11.3**

6. If $ET = 7$ cm, $TP = 9$ cm, and $RA = 15$ cm, the area of trapezoid $RAPT = \underline{?}$. 84 cm²
7. If $m\angle R = 60$, $RT = 6$ in., $TP = 10$ in., and $EA = 12$ in., the area of trap. $RAPT = \underline{?}$. $\frac{75\sqrt{3}}{2}$ in.²

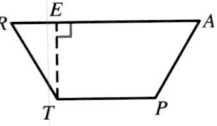

484   Chapter 11 Area

Area of Regular Polygons The area of a regular polygon is equal to
one-half the product of the apothem and the perimeter.   11.4

Find the area of each regular polygon.

8.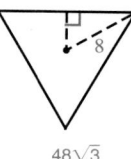

9.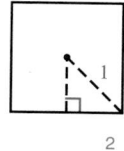

10.

48√3   2   294√3

Find a_n for each sequence. Find the limit if it exists.   11.5

11. $10, 1, \dfrac{1}{10}, \dfrac{1}{100}, \ldots$
   $a_n = \dfrac{10}{10^n}$; limit = 0

12. $-2, 4, -8, 16, -32, \ldots$
   $a_n = -2a_{n-1}$; no limit

Circumference and Arc Length The ratio of the circumference to the   11.6
diameter of any circle is a constant, pi (π). The length of an arc of a circle
is $l = \dfrac{m}{360}(2\pi r)$, with m the degree measure of the arc.

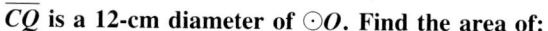

13. If $PL = 5$ in., $C = \underline{\ ?\ }$. 10π in.   14. If $C = 14\pi$ in., $d = \underline{\ ?\ }$. 14 in.

15. If $m\angle LPQ = 72$ and $PL = 6$ in., the length of $\overset{\frown}{LQ} = \underline{\ ?\ }$. $\frac{12\pi}{5}$ in.

16. If the length of $\overset{\frown}{LQ}$ is 6π cm and $PQ = 16$ cm, $m\overset{\frown}{LQ} = \underline{\ ?\ }$. 67.5

Area of Circles, Sectors, and Segments The area of a circle of radius r 11.7
is πr^2; the area of a sector of a circle of radius r and intercepted arc of degree
measure m is $\dfrac{m}{360}(\pi r^2)$. To find the area of a segment of a circle, subtract
the area of the triangle of the corresponding sector from the area of the sector.

$\overline{CQ}$ **is a 12-cm diameter of $\odot O$. Find the area of:**

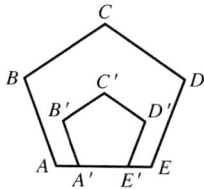

17. $\odot O$ 36π cm²

18. Sector COL 6π cm²

19. Sector LOQ 12π cm²

20. Segment LQ $(12\pi - 9\sqrt{3})$ cm²

Areas of Similar Figures If two figures are similar, their perimeters have   11.8
the same ratio as the scale factor and the ratio of their areas is the square of
the scale factor.

21. The pentagons are similar. If $AE = 6$ cm and
   $A'E' = 4$ cm, what is the scale factor? the
   ratio of the perimeters? the ratio of the
   areas? 3:2; 3:2; 9:4

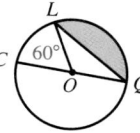

See *Teacher's Resource Book, Tests,* pp. 117–120.

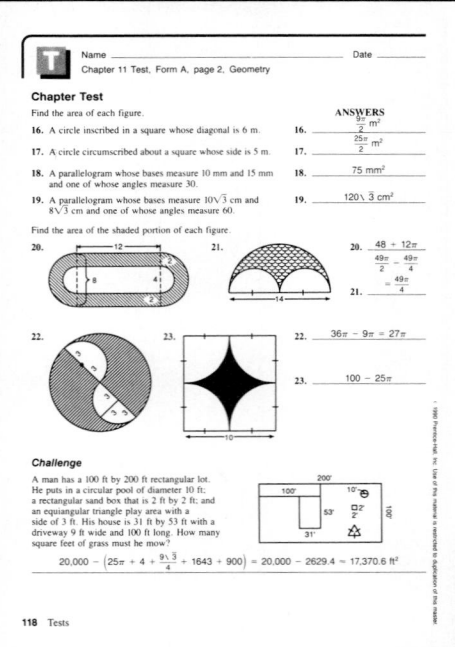

Choose the best answer.

1. If the length of each side of a rectangle is divided by 3, the area of the rectangle is divided by: d
   (a) $\frac{1}{9}$ (b) $\frac{1}{3}$ (c) 3   (d) 9

2. Two similar hexagons have a scale factor of 2:5. The ratio of their areas is: c
   (a) 4:10   (b) 2:5   (c) 4:25   (d) $\sqrt{2}:\sqrt{5}$

3. If a circle has radius r, the ratio of the area of the inscribed square to the area of the circumscribed square is: a
   (a) 1:2   (b) $\sqrt{2}:1$ (c) $\sqrt{2}:2$ (d) $\sqrt{2}:4$

Find the area of each figure.

4. A parallelogram whose bases measure 5 cm and 6 cm and whose corresponding heights are 4.8 cm and 4 cm, respectively $A = 24$ cm^2

5. An equilateral triangle circumscribed about a circle of radius 4 cm $48\sqrt{3}$ cm^2

6. A square of radius length 3 in. 18 in.^{2}

7. A triangle whose sides have lengths 8 m, 15 m, and 17 m 60 m^2

8. A rhombus whose sides and one diagonal have length 10 in. $50\sqrt{3}$ in.^{2}

9. A circle inscribed in a square whose diagonal is 4 cm long 2π cm^2

10. A parallelogram with bases of 6 cm and 12 cm and one angle of 30°
    36 cm^2

Find the area of the shaded regions.

11.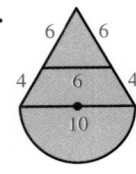
    $\frac{25\pi}{2} + 25\sqrt{3}$

12. $\pi - \frac{3\sqrt{3}}{4}$

13. $\frac{3d^2}{4}$

Challenge

Find the area of the shaded portion of this figure. $\odot O$ has a diameter of 10 cm and $\triangle ABC$ is equilateral. $\frac{25}{6}(2\pi - 3\sqrt{3})$ cm^2

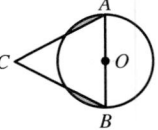

Alternative Assessment Have students draw and label each type of quadrilateral, a triangle, a regular pentagon, and a circle and write the formulas for finding the area in terms of the labeled parts. They should then explain how they would find an arc length and the area of a sector.

Select the best choice for each question.

1. In square
   B ABCD, DX:
   XC = 5:2
   and BY:YC =
   3:4. What is
   the ratio of
   the area of △AXC to the area of
   △ABY?

   A. 2:7 **B.** 2:3 **C.** 3:4
   D. 4:9 **E.** 9:16

2. If $\overleftrightarrow{AB}$ intersects $\overleftrightarrow{CD}$ at E, which
   word(s) can be used to describe
   D ∠AEC and ∠BEC?

       I. supplementary
       II. congruent
      III. adjacent

   A. I only   **B.** I, II only
   C. II, III only   **D.** I, III only
   E. I, II, III

3. The sum of the squares of five
   consecutive positive integers is 510.
   B Find the largest integer.

   A. 11   **B.** 12   **C.** 13
   D. 14   **E.** 15

4. In East Park School, 20% of the
   students taking math also take
   computer science and 70% of those
   taking computer science also take
   math. If 28 students take both of
   these courses, how many students
   D take only one of the two?

   A. 180   **B.** 166   **C.** 152   **D.** 124
   E. It cannot be determined from the
   information given.

5. What is the sum of the reciprocal and
   A the square root of 0.25?

   A. 4.5   **B.** 4.05   **C.** 2.5
   D. 2.0   **E.** 0.45

6. Isosceles trapezoid ABCD has bases
   AB = 37 and CD = 13. If AD = 17,
   the area of XYCD is what per cent of
   B the area of ABCD?

   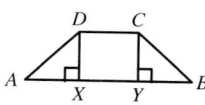

   A. 39   **B.** 52   **C.** 60
   D. 68   **E.** 72

7. The side of a square is the same
   length as the altitude of an equilateral
   triangle. Find k if the area of the
   square is k times the area of the
   B triangle.

   A. $\sqrt{2}$ **B.** $\sqrt{3}$ **C.** $2\sqrt{2}$
   D. $2\sqrt{3}$ **E.** $3\sqrt{2}$

8. Find the shaded area formed by the
   A tangents and circle.

   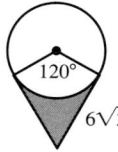

   A. $36\sqrt{3} - 12\pi$ **B.** $18\sqrt{3} - 12\pi$
   C. $36\sqrt{3} - 18\pi$ **D.** $18\sqrt{3} - 6\pi$
   E. $12\sqrt{3} - 6\pi$

The individual comments provided for
certain problems may help the students in solving them.

1. When discussing this problem and
   its solution, perhaps an example in
   which the sides are divided into a
   different number of equal parts, say
   5:2 and 2:3, would help students
   realize the importance of this in the
   solution.

3. An alternate solution could be to
   use x, x + 1, x + 2, x + 3, and x + 4
   as the 5 integers. Then, the equation to be solved would be:

   $5x^2 + 20x + 30 = 510$ or
      $x^2 + 4x - 96 = 0$
   $(x + 12)(x - 8) = 0$
   $x = -12$ or $x = 8$

4. If a student adds the 140 math students to the 40 computer science
   students, then the 28 must be subtracted twice in order to answer the
   question.

7. Since the required answer is a ratio, the problem could also be
   worked using sample numbers. For
   example: Isos. △ABC with side =
   2, and square ABCD with side =
   $\sqrt{3}$. Then, area sq. = $\sqrt{3}$ area △
   and k = $\sqrt{3}$.

   See *Teacher's Resource Book* for
   *Preparing for College Entrance Ex-
   ams.*

The following skills and concepts are reviewed:

Rewriting linear equations
Solving systems of equations

Write each linear equation in standard form; $ax + by = c$.

Example $10 - 3y = 5x$
$-5x - 3y = -10$
$5x + 3y = 10$

1. $x = y$ $x - y = 0$

2. $y = 2x + 3$ $2x - y = -3$

3. $x + 5 = 0$ $x = -5$

4. $\dfrac{x - y}{2} = \dfrac{x + 4}{4}$ $x - 2y = 4$

5. $\dfrac{x}{2} = \dfrac{y}{3}$ $3x - 2y = 0$

6. $y = 5x - 2$ $5x - y = 2$

Write each linear equation in slope-intercept form: $y = mx + b$.

Example $4x + 3y = 36$
$3y = -4x + 36$
$y = \dfrac{-4}{3}x + 12$

7. $2x + y = 4$ $y = -2x + 4$

8. $x - y = 7$ $y = x - 7$

9. $2x + 3y = 6$ $y = -\frac{2}{3}x + 2$

10. $3x = 2y$ $y = \frac{3}{2}x$

11. $x - 3y = 9$ $y = \frac{1}{3}x - 3$

12. $\dfrac{y}{4} - \dfrac{x}{3} = \dfrac{1}{2}$ $y = \frac{4}{3}x + 2$

Solve each system of equations.

Example $x - 5y = 6$
$3x - 2y = 5$

Substitution Method

Solve $x - 5y = 6$ for x: $x = 5y + 6$

Substitute: $3(5y + 6) - 2y = 5$
$15y + 18 - 2y = 5$
$13y = -13$
$y = -1$

Substitute: $x - 5(-1) = 6$
$x + 5 = 6$
$x = 1$

Addition Method

Multiply the first equation by -3:

$-3(x - 5y) = (6)(-3)$
Add: $-3x + 15y = -18$
$\underline{3x - 2y = 5}$
$13y = -13$
$y = -1$

Substitute: $x - 5(-1) = 6$
$x = 1$

13. $4x - 8y = 8$
$x + 6y = 2$ $x = 2, y = 0$

14. $c - 2d = 7$
$c + 3d = 2$ $c = 5, d = -1$

15. $x - 5y = 2$
$2x + y = 4$ $x = 2, y = 0$

16. $x = 4y$
$3x + 2y = 28$ $x = 8, y = 2$

17. $y - 2x = -17$
$x + y = 16$ $x = 11, y = 5$

18. $3y - x = 13$
$2x + 3y = 16$ $x = 1, y = \frac{14}{3}$

OVERVIEW • Chapter 12

SUMMARY

In Chapter 12, students identify and sketch each of the basic solid figures: prisms, pyramids, cylinders, cones, and spheres. The formulas for lateral and total area of these figures are introduced and applied. Students then compute the volumes of these solids. They learn the properties of similar solids and use these properties to find ratios of side lengths, areas, and volumes.

CHAPTER OBJECTIVES

- To identify and sketch the parts of prisms, pyramids, cylinders, and cones

- To find the lateral area and total area of a right prism, regular pyramid, right circular cylinder, and right circular cone

- To find the volume of a prism, pyramid, cylinder, cone, and sphere

- To find the area and volume of a sphere

- To state and apply the properties of similar solids

- To prove theorems about figures by *analyzing cross sections*

CHAPTER HIGHLIGHTS

DEVELOPING MATHEMATICAL POWER

Problem Solving

The strategy lesson incorporates the four problem solving steps for analyzing cross sections of solid figures.

Communication

The side column suggests using manipulatives as an alternative learning style. Students are asked to compare and contrast in their journals the several kinds of polyhedra discussed in the chapter. There is a Chapter Summary and Review in Spanish in the *Teacher's Resource Book*.

Reasoning

In a thinking critically exercise students are asked to devise the formulas for inscribed and circumscribed spheres of a cube of side length *e*.

Connections

Real-world applications include such topics as ranching, water management, and metallurgy. The investigation of Cavalieri's Principle provides students with an example of the variety of cultural influences on mathematics.

Technology

Logo exercises appear throughout the chapter. The technology feature at the end of the chapter looks at the coordinate system in Logo. Where appropriate, students are encouraged to use calculators for finding areas and volumes.

STUDENT TEXT

Chapter Content	Basic	Average	Enriched	NCTM STANDARDS*
12.1 Prisms	D: 493/1-13, 27, 30	D: 493/1-13, 17-20, 27-30	D: 493/1-13, 21-30	4, 5, 7, 12
12.2 Pyramids	D: 498/1-9, 28, 30 R: 493/14,15	D: 498/1-17, 28-30 R: 493/14-16, 21, 22	D: 498/1-17, 24-30 R: 493/14-20	4, 5, 7
12.3 Cylinders	D: 504/1-7, 11-14, 25 R: 498/10-15	D: 504/1-7, 13-20, 25-27 R: 498/18-23	D: 504/1-12 odd, 17-27 R: 498/18-23	3, 4, 5, 7, 12
12.4 Strategy: Analyze Cross Sections of Solids	D: 510/1-4 R: 504/8-9	D: 510/1-4 R: 504/8-12	D: 510/1-4 R: 504/13-16	1, 3, 7, 8
12.5 Cones	D: 513/1-8, 10, 27, MR R: 510/5	D: 513/1-18, 27-29, MR R: 510/5	D: 513/1-18, 24-29, MR R: 510/5, 6	5, 7, 8
12.6 Spheres	D: 518/3-7, 22, AR R: 513/9, 11-15	D: 518/1-13, 22, 23, AR R: 513/19-23	D: 518/1-13, 20-23, AR R: 513/19-23	3, 7, 13
12.7 Areas and Volumes of Similar Solids	D: 523/4-20, 24 R: 518/8-12	D: 523/1-29, 34, 35 R: 518/14-19, 27	D: 523/1-7, 12-35 R: 518/14-19, 27	5, 7, 8

D = Daily   R = Review   MR = Mixed Review   AR = Algebra Review

*For a complete list of NCTM Standards, see p. T7.

STUDENT TEXT

Review/Assessment

Mixed Review 515

Algebra Review 520

Summary and Review 528

College Ent. Exam Rev. 531

Cumulative Review 532

Extra Practice 654

Test Yourself 506, 525

Chapter Test 530

Chapter Project 489

Special Features

Technology 494, 506, 515, 520, 525, 526-527

Devel. Math. Power 494, 501, 520

Applications 494, 501, 506, 515, 520, 525

Project 510

RESOURCES

Teacher's Resource Book

Ch. 12: Investigation/Practice/ Enrichment 1-20

Spanish Sum. and Rev. 23-24

Quizzes 121-124

Chapter Tests 125-128

Cumulative Tests 129-136

Perf. Assessment Proj. Ch. 12

Critical Thinking 12

Reading and Writing in Geom. 12

Technology 15-16

Teaching Aid 12

Transparencies 22-23

Teaching Transparencies 78-84

Computer Test Bank 749-812

Connections 18-26

PH Graph. Utility

Overhead Manip. Kit

Area and Volume of Solids

Searching for another dimension?

■ ■ ■ ■ ■ ■ ■ ■ ■

Developing Mathematical Power

Many factors are considered when the packaging for a product is designed. The packaging must protect the product during shipping. The cost of the materials and the amount of materials needed must be taken into account. The shape will affect how much the package holds. The package should be a convenient size for storage, and, of course, it should be attractive.

Project

Your job is to design the new Super Start cereal package. Many people in the company favor the traditional cereal box; others want something different. What other factors will you consider? Prepare a presentation for the board of directors. Include a model or a diagram of the new package.

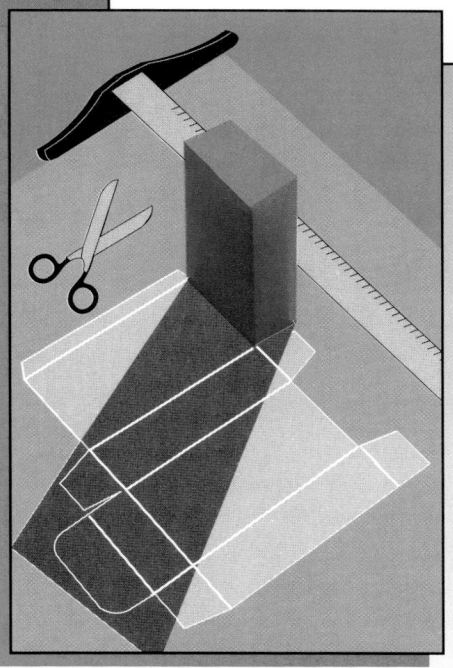

489

Vocabulary
Altitude of a prism
Bases of a prism
Edges of a polyhedron
Faces of a polyhedron
Height of a prism
Lateral area
Lateral edges
Lateral faces
Oblique prism
Polyhedron
Prism
Regular prism
Right prism
Total area
Vertices
Volume

Materials/Manipulatives
Models of several types of
  prisms, pyramids, cones,
  cylinders, and spheres
Box filled with number cubes
Index cards
*Teacher's Resource Book,
  Transparency 22
Teaching Transparency 78*

Technology
*Computer Test Bank, pp.
  749–758
Connections, p. 24*

LESSON FOCUS

Review
Review areas of regular polygons.

Alternative Learning Styles
• Kinesthetic learners will benefit
  from the use of a variety of models
  of prisms. They can use the models
  to identify all the parts of a prism.
• The Investigation provides an opportunity for visual learners to relate prisms and plane figures.

490

12.1

Prisms

Objectives: To identify and sketch the parts of prisms
To find the lateral area and total area of a right prism
To find the volume of a prism

Most of the geometric figures studied up until now have been two-dimensional, or *plane figures*. Measures of common three-dimensional or solid figures, called *polyhedra,* are introduced in this chapter.

Investigation—*Visualizing the Concept*

A *net* is a pattern that can be used to create a model of a three-dimensional figure.

1. Which of these nets could be folded to make a cube? *b, d*

2. Sketch another net that can form a cube. Answers may vary.

a. 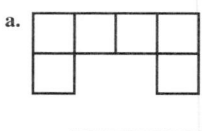 **b.**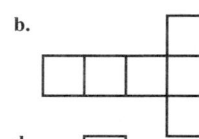

c. 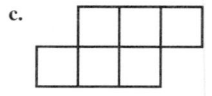 **d.**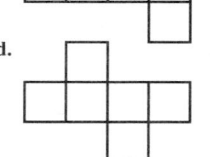

A **polyhedron** is a geometric figure made up of a finite number of polygons that are joined by pairs along their sides and that enclose a finite portion of space. The polygons that make up a polyhedron are called the **faces,** the common sides are called the **edges,** and the points where the edges intersect are called the **vertices.**

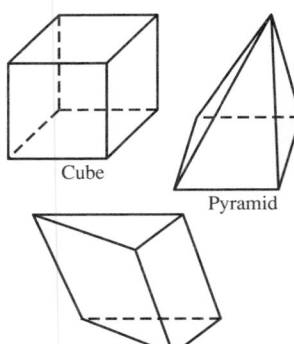

Cube

Pyramid

Triangular Prism

A polyhedron is a **prism** if and only if it has two congruent faces that are contained in parallel planes, and its other faces are parallelograms.

The two congruent faces are the **bases;** the other faces are the **lateral faces.** Lateral faces intersect in the **lateral edges,** all of which are parallel and congruent.

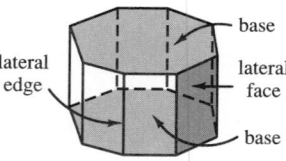

base
lateral edge
lateral face
base

490 Chapter 12 Area and Volume of Solids

Developing Mathematical Power
Cooperative Learning Working in groups, students can draw nets of a triangular prism, a pyramid, a rectangular prism, and a pentagonal prism. They should create challenging problems in spatial relations by drawing nets and asking if they represent a specific prism. Groups can exchange, cut out, and fold the nets to verify the results.

If the lateral edges are perpendicular to the planes of the bases, the prism is called **right**; if the lateral edges are not perpendicular to the bases, the prism is called **oblique**. A **regular prism** is one whose bases are regular polygons. How would you name a regular right prism all of whose faces are square? square prism or cube

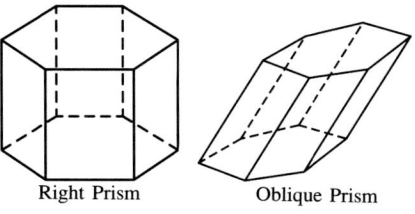

Right Prism   Oblique Prism

A segment is an **altitude of a prism** if and only if it is perpendicular to the planes of both bases of the prism. The length of the altitude of a prism is called the *height* of the prism. In a right prism, the height is the same as the length of any lateral edge. What is the relationship between the height and the length of a lateral edge in an oblique prism? The length of the lateral edge is greater than that of the height.

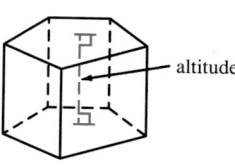

altitude

The **lateral area** of a prism is the sum of the areas of the lateral faces, and the **total area** of a prism is the sum of the lateral area plus the area of the two bases. If a prism is a right prism, its lateral faces are rectangles, and formulas exist for finding the lateral and total area.

Theorem 12.1   The lateral area L of a right prism equals the perimeter of a base P times the height h of the prism, or $L = Ph$.
Proved in Practice Exercise 19

Theorem 12.2   The total area T of a right prism is the sum of the lateral area L and the area of the two bases $2B$, or $T = L + 2B$.
Proved in Practice Exercise 20

The **volume** of a figure is the amount of space occupied by the figure. Determining the volume of a figure means determining the number of cubic units that can be placed inside the figure. Since the box holds 3 layers of 8 unit cubes, the volume of the box is 24 cubic units. This reasoning leads to the following theorem.

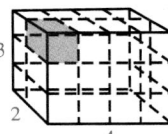

Theorem 12.3   The volume V of a prism equals the area of a base B times the height h of the prism, or $V = Bh$. Proved in Practice Exercise 21

Corollary   The volume of a cube with edge e is the cube of e, or $V = e^3$.
Proved in Practice Exercise 22

TEACHING SUGGESTIONS

- The use of models is strongly encouraged. Students must learn to recognize various polyhedra in order to be able to understand correct approaches to measuring those figures.
- Use a box filled with uniformly-sized number cubes to introduce the concept of volume and cubic unit.
- Insist that students attach the correct units to area and volume measures.
- Emphasize that the lateral and total areas of a *right* prism and the volume of *any* prism can be determined with the formulas in this lesson. With a pack of index cards, illustrate Cavalieri's Principle (the volumes of two noncongruent solids are equal if each pair of cross sections, at equal distances from their bases, have equal areas).

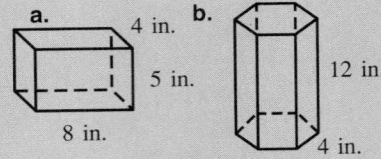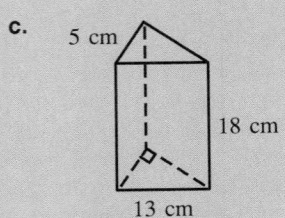
EXAMPLE   Find the lateral area, the total area, and the volume of each right prism.

a.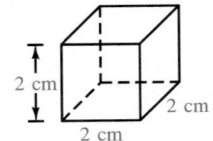
2 cm
2 cm
2 cm

b.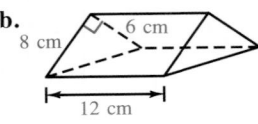
6 cm
8 cm
12 cm

c.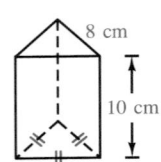
8 cm
10 cm

a. $L = Ph = (2 + 2 + 2 + 2)2 = 16$ cm²; $T = L + 2B = 16 + 2(2 \cdot 2) = 24$ cm²; $V = Bh = (2 \cdot 2) \cdot 2 = 8$ cm³

b. Using the Pythagorean Theorem, the third side of the base is 10 cm. The area of the base B is $\frac{1}{2}h \cdot b = \frac{1}{2}(6)(8) = 24$ cm².
$L = Ph = (6 + 8 + 10)(12) = 288$ cm²; $T = L + 2B = 288 + 2(24) = 336$ cm²; $V = Bh = 24 \cdot 12 = 288$ cm³.

c. The perimeter of the base $= 24$ cm. The area of the base B is
$\frac{s^2\sqrt{3}}{4} = \frac{64\sqrt{3}}{4} = 16\sqrt{3}$ cm². $L = Ph = 24 \cdot 10 = 240$ cm²; $T = L + 2B = 240 + 2(16\sqrt{3}) = 240 + 32\sqrt{3}$ cm²; $V = Bh = 16\sqrt{3}(10) = 160\sqrt{3}$ cm³.

CLASS EXERCISES   Check students' drawings.

Copy each prism and add dashed lines to show the hidden edges.

1. 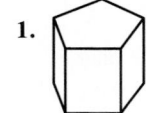   2.    3. 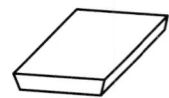   4.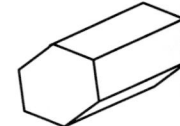

5. Name the lateral face opposite *DEKJ*. *ABHG*

6. Name all the edges parallel to $\overline{CI}$. $\overline{AG}$, $\overline{BH}$, $\overline{FL}$, $\overline{EK}$, $\overline{DJ}$

7. Name the bases of the prism. *ABCDEF, GHIJKL*

8. What do faces *ABHG* and *BCIH* have in common? $\overline{BH}$

9. How many vertices in this prism? edges? faces? 12; 18; 8

10. What is the ratio of the number of lateral edges to base edges? 1:2

B C
A D
F H I E
G J
L K

Each edge of this cube is 6 in. long.

11. What is the length of diagonal $\overline{JK}$? $6\sqrt{2}$ in.

12. What is the length of diagonal $\overline{HN}$? $6\sqrt{3}$ in.

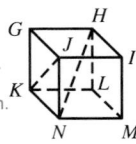
G H
J I
K L
N M

PRACTICE EXERCISES   ⊿ Use technology where appropriate.

A   A cube has each edge length *e*. Sketch it.

1. Find the total area if $e = 12$ in.
864 in.²

2. Find *e* if the total area is 294 in.².
7 in.

3. Find the volume if $e = 7.5$ cm.
421.875 cm³

4. Find *e* if the volume is 1728 in.³.
12 in.

5. Find the total area if the diagonal of a face has length 10 in. 300 in.²

Find the lateral area, total area, and volume of each right prism.

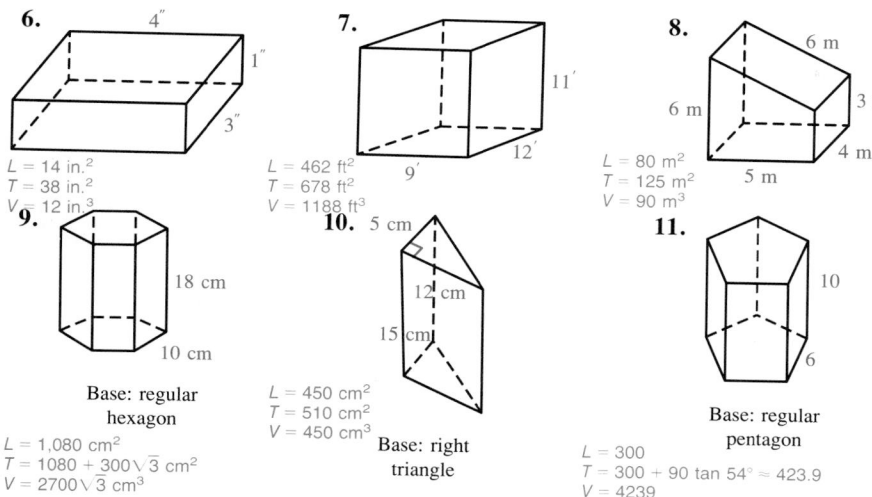

6.
4″   1″   3″
$L = 14$ in.²
$T = 38$ in.²
$V = 12$ in.³

7.
11′   12′   9′
$L = 462$ ft²
$T = 678$ ft²
$V = 1188$ ft³

8.
6 m   6 m   3 m   4 m   5 m
$L = 80$ m²
$T = 125$ m²
$V = 90$ m³

9.
18 cm   10 cm
Base: regular hexagon
$L = 1{,}080$ cm²
$T = 1080 + 300\sqrt{3}$ cm²
$V = 2700\sqrt{3}$ cm³

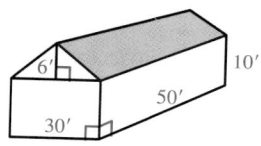

10. 5 cm
12 cm   15 cm
$L = 450$ cm²
$T = 510$ cm²
$V = 450$ cm³
Base: right triangle

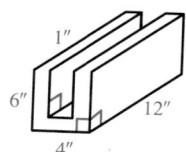

11.
10   6
Base: regular pentagon
$L = 300$
$T = 300 + 90 \tan 54° \approx 423.9$
$V = 4239$

Sketch each right prism. Find its lateral area, total area, and volume.

12. Bases are regular hexagons with 4 cm sides; $h = 6$ cm. $L = 144$ cm²;
$T = 144 + 48\sqrt{3}$ cm²; $V = 144\sqrt{3}$ cm³

13. Bases are equilateral triangles with 8 cm sides; $h = 12$ cm. $L = 288$ cm²;
$T = 288 + 32\sqrt{3}$ cm²; $V = 192\sqrt{3}$ cm³

B   14. Find the total area and volume.
6′   10′   50′   30′
$T \approx 4896$ ft²
$V = 19{,}500$ ft³

15. Find the total area.
$T = 388$ in.²
1″   6″   12″   4″

16. Find the edge of a cube that has the same total area as a rectangular solid measuring 4 ft by 6 ft by 9 ft high. $e = \sqrt{38} \approx 6.2$ ft

17. Find the volume of a regular triangular prism whose height is 6 cm and whose lateral area is 36 cm². $6\sqrt{3}$ cm³

18. Thinking Critically Is there a cube having the same number of cubic inches in its volume as square inches in its total area? Justify your answer.
yes; if an edge is 6 in. long

12.1 Prisms   **493**

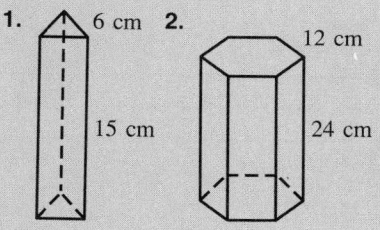
493

Prisms

A cube has edge length *e*.

1. Find the total area if *e* = 8 cm. _____ 384 cm²
2. Find the volume if *e* = 8.5 cm. _____ 614.125 cm
3. Find *e* if the total area is 216 in.² _____ 6 in.
4. Find *e* if the volume is 9261 cm³. _____ 21 cm
5. Find the total area if the diagonal of a face is 16″. _____ 768 in.²

Find the lateral area, total area, and volume of each prism. All the measurements are cm and the bases are as indicated.

6.	7.	8.	9.
Rectangle	Right △	Square	Regular Hexagon
LA 224 cm²	LA 300 cm²	LA 192 cm²	LA 360 cm²
TA 344 cm²	TA 360 cm²	TA 224 cm²	TA 108√3 cm² + 360
V 420 cm³	V 300 cm³	V 192 cm³	V 540√3 cm³

10. Find the lateral area, total area, and volume of a right prism whose bases are equilateral triangles with 6 in. sides and *h* = 15 in.

LA = 270 in.², TA = 270 + 18√3 in.², V = 135√3 in.³

Application

11. **Painting** The stadium is a prism with a regular hexagonal floor. If the walls must be painted inside and out, how many square feet of paint are needed to paint the walls and the floor. Approximate to the nearest 100 ft².

148, 500 ft²

2   Chapter 12

Constructing Rectangular Boxes

Given a rectangular sheet of material, such as paper or metal, it is possible to cut out squares and rectangles and reassemble the result into a right rectangular prism. For example, the piece of metal pictured in the diagram below is 8 in. by 12 in.

1. What is the area of the rectangle? _____ 96 in.²
2. Suppose that two two-inch squares are cut out as indicated along the dotted lines. What is the total area of the two squares? _____ 8 in.²
3. These squares are to be used as the top and bottom of a right rectangular prism, and the remaining material is to be used to construct the sides. After the top and bottom have been cut out from the sheet, how much area remains? _____ 88 in.²
4. How many lateral faces will the rectangular prism have? _____ 4
5. What must be the area of each face? _____ 22 in.²
7. What must be the height of the prism? _____ 11 in.
8. What is the volume of the prism? _____ 44 in.³

Suppose that each side of the square is *s*.

9. What is the total area of the top and bottom? _____ 2*s*²
10. How much area remains? _____ 96 − 2*s*²
11. How many lateral faces will the rectangular prism have? _____ 4
12. What must be the area of each face? _____ 24 − 0.5*s*²
13. One side of each face is known, since it is also the side of either the top or bottom; its length is _____ *s*
14. What must be the height of the prism? _____ $\frac{24}{s}$ − 0.5*s*
15. What is the volume of the rectangular prism? _____ 24*s* − 0.5*s*³
16. By trial and error, see if you can determine the maximum volume of a prism that can be constructed using this method. _____ When *s* = 4, volume = 64 in.³

Chapter 12   **3**

Use this figure to write a justification for each.

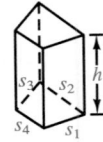

19. Theorem 12.1   20. Theorem 12.2
21. Theorem 12.3   22. Cor. of Theorem 12.3

C   23. Allowing 5 percent of the area for seams and waste, how much material is used in making the tent, including the floor? 977 ft² ≈ 980 ft²

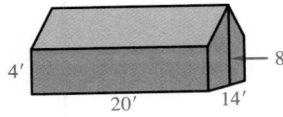

24. Express the length of *d*, the diagonal of a rectangular solid, in terms of width *w*, length *l*, and height *h*. $d = \sqrt{w^2 + l^2 + h^2}$

25. *Prove:* The height of an oblique prism is less than the length of a lateral edge.
See Additional Answers, p. 702.

26. This decorative building block is 12″ square and 3″ thick, with two holes cut through it, each measuring 4″ by 8″. What is the total area of the block? 448 in.²

Applications

27. **Package Design** Parcel-post packages cannot exceed 70 lb and the length plus the total distance around the package cannot exceed 102 in. Assuming that the box has a square base, what is the volume of the largest package that can be sent by parcel post? If base is 17×17 and length of box is 34 in., volume = 9826 in.³

28. **Ranching** If the water tank on a rancher's truck holds 250 gal, can this trough be completely filled in one trip? If not, how many trips must be made? (1 ft³ = 7.48 gal)

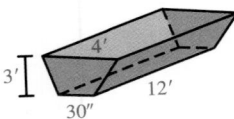

29. **Technology** Using Logo, draw a cube. Use the FILL command to create a three-dimensional effect. Which sides should be *filled*? See Solutions Manual.

28. no; 4 trips; 117 ft³ ≈ 875.16 gal; $\frac{875.16}{250}$ ≈ 3.5 → 4 trips

Developing Mathematical Power

30. **Investigation** There are only five regular convex polyhedra, called *Platonic solids*.

 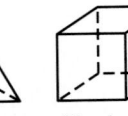  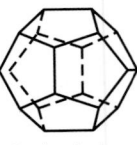 

Tetrahedron   Hexahedron   Octahedron   Dodecahedron   Icosahedron

Wire straws together to build a model of each. Then write a description of each.

12.2 Pyramids

Objectives: To identify and sketch the parts of pyramids
To find the lateral area and total area of a regular pyramid
To find the volume of a pyramid

The *pyramid* is a familiar geometric shape. Its mathematical properties were known to those who constructed the pyramids of ancient Egypt and Mexico.

Investigation—*Using Manipulatives*

Construct a tetrahedron, a special type of pyramid, from a rectangular piece of paper. Follow these steps:

1. Construct equilateral △MON by locating vertex O.

2. Through O, construct $\overline{M'N'} \parallel \overline{MN}$, and cut along $\overline{M'N'}$. Let O' be the point on the opposite side corresponding to O.

3. Fold along $\overline{MO}$ and then along $\overline{NO}$.

4. Now fold along $\overline{M'N'}$, $\overline{M'O'}$, $\overline{N'O'}$.

5. Bring points M, N, and O together to form the model. Tape along the cut sides.

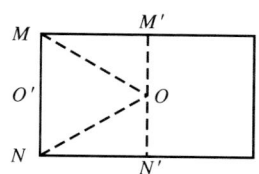

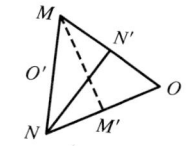

A polyhedron is a **pyramid** if and only if all the faces except one have a vertex in common. This common vertex is called the **vertex** of the pyramid. The face that does not contain the vertex is called the **base;** the other faces are called the **lateral faces.** Lateral faces are joined by **lateral edges;** the edges of the base are called **base edges.**

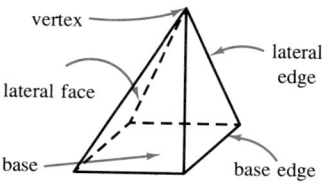

A pyramid is **regular** if its base is a regular polygon and its lateral edges are congruent. Pyramids are named by the type of polygon in the base.

The **slant height** of a regular pyramid is the distance from the vertex of the pyramid to a base edge. The *height* (altitude) of a pyramid is the distance from the vertex to the base. How does the slant height compare in size to the height of a regular pyramid? slant height is greater

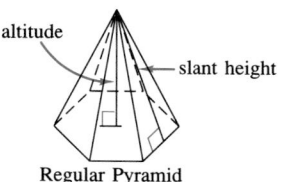

Regular Pyramid

12.2 Pyramids **495**

Developing Mathematical Power

Cooperative Learning   Assign groups of students to complete *Writing in Geometry: Projections* in *Connections*, p. 22. Clear plastic models of the solids will help students visualize the projection from various viewpoints. Encourage students to color the projections on p. 22 and the ones they create. Their drawings can be used in a bulletin-board display.

LESSON PLAN

Vocabulary

Base	Pyramid
Base edges	Regular
Height	pyramid
Lateral edges	Slant height
Lateral faces	Tetrahedron
	Vertex

Materials/Manipulatives

Model of a triangular prism that can be partitioned into three pyramids of equal volume
Several models of pyramids, some of which are regular
Paper, tape, compasses, and straightedges
Teaching Transparency 79
Connections, p. 22

Technology

Computer Test Bank, pp. 758–768

LESSON FOCUS

Review

Find the lateral area, total area, and volume of each right prism.

1. 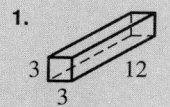   **2.**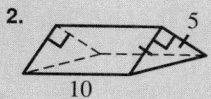

1. 90; 162; 108   2. $100 + 50\sqrt{2}$; $125 + 50\sqrt{2}$; 125

Alternative Learning Styles

Some students have difficulty recognizing the important details of a figure. Help students to observe that the faces of a regular pyramid are congruent isosceles triangles. Use models of pyramids to illustrate their parts.

495

TEACHING SUGGESTIONS

- Make certain that students understand the justification of the formula for the lateral area of a pyramid, and can explain the basis for the formula in their own words.
- Use a model of a triangular prism, partitioned into three pyramids of equal volume, to help students understand the justification for the volume formula.
- Provide many examples of regular pyramids in which students have to determine a missing dimension, such as height or slant height. Point out that the Pythagorean Theorem must be satisfied by the apothem of the base, the height, and slant height of the pyramid ($a^2 + h^2 = l^2$).
- Some examples involve the use of 45°-45°-90°, or 30°-60°-90° triangle relationships. This provides a good review for students.
- Point out that the formula for the lateral area of a regular pyramid depends on the fact that the faces of a regular pyramid are congruent isosceles triangles. There is no formula for lateral area of a nonregular pyramid because there is no constant slant height.
- Remind students that the volume of *any* pyramid (regular or nonregular) can be found by the formula in this lesson.
- Continue to insist that students attach the correct units to the results of an area or volume computation.

EXAMPLE 1   Complete the table for these two regular pyramids.

	Vertex	Base	Lateral Faces	Lateral Edges
a.	?	?	?	?
b.	?	?	?	?

a. A; $BCDE$; $\triangle ABC$, ABE, AED, and ADC; $\overline{AB}$, $\overline{AC}$, $\overline{AD}$, and $\overline{AE}$

b. G; $PENTA$; $\triangle GEP$, GPA, GAT, GTN, and GNE; $\overline{GE}$, $\overline{GN}$, $\overline{GT}$, $\overline{GA}$, and $\overline{GP}$

The lateral area of this regular pyramid is the sum of the areas of its four triangular lateral faces represented by A_1, A_2, A_3, and A_4. The height of each triangle is slant height l.

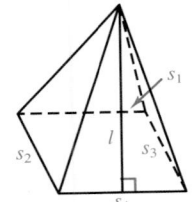

$$\text{Lateral area} = A_1 + A_2 + A_3 + A_4$$
$$= \frac{1}{2}s_1 l + \frac{1}{2}s_2 l + \frac{1}{2}s_3 l + \frac{1}{2}s_4 l$$
$$= \frac{1}{2}l(s_1 + s_2 + s_3 + s_4)$$
$$= \frac{1}{2}lP, \text{ where } P = s_1 + s_2 + s_3 + s_4$$
$$\text{is the perimeter of the base.}$$

This argument is used to justify the next two theorems. Note that Theorem 12.5 is dependent on Theorem 12.4.

> **Theorem 12.4**   The lateral area L of a regular pyramid equals one-half the product of the slant height l and the perimeter P of the base, or $L = \left(\frac{1}{2}\right)lP$.
>
> **Theorem 12.5**   The total area T of a regular pyramid equals the lateral area L plus the area of the base B, or $T = L + B$.

496   Chapter 12 Area and Volume of Solids

EXAMPLE 2 Find the lateral area and the total area of each regular pyramid.

a.

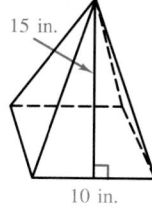
15 in.

10 in.

b.

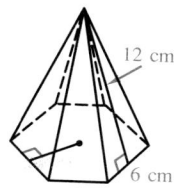
12 cm

6 cm

a. $L = \frac{1}{2}(15)(40) = 300$ in.^{2}

$B = 10^2 = 100$ in.^{2}

$T = 300 + 100 = 400$ in.^{2}

b. $L = \frac{1}{2}(12)(36) = 216$ cm^2

$B = \frac{1}{2}(3\sqrt{3})36 = 54\sqrt{3}$ cm^2

$T = 216 + 54\sqrt{3}$ cm^2

The volume of a pyramid can be determined from the volume of a related prism. This triangular prism is partitioned into three pyramids, each with the same volume; the volume of each is one-third the volume of the prism.

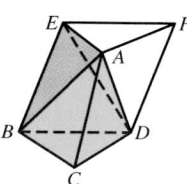

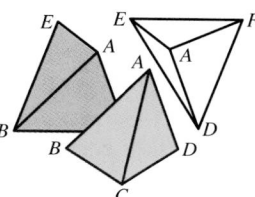

> **Theorem 12.6** The volume V of a pyramid is one-third the product of its height h and the area of its base B, or $V = \frac{1}{3}Bh$.

EXAMPLE 3 Find the volume of each pyramid.

a.

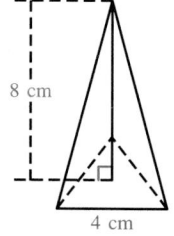
8 cm

4 cm

Equilateral Triangular Pyramid

b.

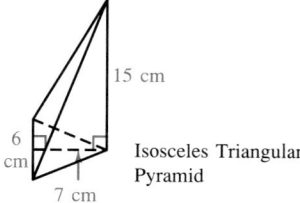
15 cm

6 cm

7 cm

Isosceles Triangular Pyramid

a. $B = \frac{16\sqrt{3}}{4} = 4\sqrt{3}$ cm^2

$V = \frac{1}{3}(4\sqrt{3})8 = \frac{32\sqrt{3}}{3}$ cm^3

b. $B = \frac{1}{2}(6)(7) = 21$ cm^2

$V = \frac{1}{3}(21)(15) = 105$ cm^3

• **For Example 1**

Name the vertex, base, lateral faces, and lateral edges of the regular pyramid.

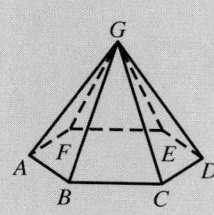
G

F   E

A   D

B   C

Vertex: G
Base: $ABCDEF$
Lateral faces: $\triangle AGB$, $\triangle BGC$, $\triangle CGD$, $\triangle DGE$, $\triangle EGF$, $\triangle FGA$
Lateral edges: $\overline{AG}$, $\overline{BG}$, $\overline{CG}$, $\overline{DG}$, $\overline{EG}$, $\overline{FG}$

• **For Example 2**

The lateral area of a regular hexagonal pyramid is 48 cm^2 and the slant height is 4 cm. Find the length of a side of the base, the area of the base, the total area, and the height of the pyramid.

$L = (\frac{1}{2})lP$ $B = (\frac{1}{2})aP$

$48 = \frac{1}{2}(4)P$ $= \frac{1}{2}(2\sqrt{3})(24) = 24\sqrt{3}$

$s = 4$ cm $T = (48 + 24\sqrt{3})$ cm^2

$a^2 + h^2 = l^2$

$(2\sqrt{3})^2 + h^2 = 4^2$

$h = 2$ cm

• **For Example 3**

A regular hexagonal pyramid has volume $648\sqrt{3}$ cm^3, base area $162\sqrt{3}$ cm^2, and slant height 15 cm. Find h, s, L, and T.

$V = (\frac{1}{3})Bh$

$648\sqrt{3} = \frac{1}{3}(162\sqrt{3})h$

$h = 12$ cm

$a^2 + h^2 = l^2$

$a^2 + 12^2 = 15^2$

$a^2 = 225 - 144 = 81, a = 9$

$s = \frac{2a}{\sqrt{3}} = \frac{18}{\sqrt{3}} = 6\sqrt{3}$ cm

$L = \frac{1}{2}(15)(36\sqrt{3}) = 270\sqrt{3}$ cm^2

$T = 270\sqrt{3} + 162\sqrt{3} = 432\sqrt{3}$ cm^2

Common Errors

- Students may confuse the height and slant height of a regular pyramid. Emphasize that the height is the perpendicular distance from the base to the vertex.
- Some students may have difficulty determining missing dimensions of pyramids. Make certain that they can equate the shape of the base with the number of faces and edges in the figure.
- See *Teacher's Resource Book* for additional remediation.

LESSON FOLLOW-UP

Discussion

Ask students to explain in their own words the basis for the formulas in this lesson. Make certain they understand and can express these justifications, and are not relying on rote memorization. Point out that the exercises often require manipulations of the formulas in some way, so that understanding is essential.

Assignment Guide

See p. 488B for assignments.

CLASS EXERCISES

Sketch a pyramid that satisfies the indicated conditions. (*Hint:* First sketch the base, then draw the altitude from the center of the base to the vertex.) See side column page 499.

1. Regular with triangular base

The shortest distance from a point to a line is the perpendicular.

2. Nonregular with hexagonal base

3. If the height h of a pyramid is 12 cm, is the slant height l greater than, less than, or equal to h? Justify your answer. segment; $l > h$.

4. If the lateral faces make an angle of 60° with the base of a pyramid and if the height of the pyramid is $5\sqrt{3}$ in., find the slant height of the pyramid. 10 in.

True or false? Justify your answers.

5. The base edges of a pyramid are always congruent. False; base may have noncongruent edges.

6. The vertex of a regular pyramid is equidistant from the endpoints of the base edges of the pyramid. True; the lateral edges of a regular pyramid are congruent.

7. The height of a pyramid may be equal to the length of a lateral edge of the pyramid. true; if one of the faces contains the altitude

8. If the bases of two pyramids of equal height have the same area, the pyramids have congruent bases. False; the bases may have different shapes and still have equal areas.

9. If two pyramids have congruent bases and the height of the second is twice the height of the first, then the volume of the second is twice the volume of the first. true; $V = \frac{1}{3}Bh$, $\dfrac{V_1}{V_2} = \dfrac{\frac{1}{3}Bh}{\frac{1}{3}B(2h)} = \frac{1}{2}$

10. The lateral faces of a regular pyramid are isosceles triangles. True; by def., the lateral edges are congruent.

PRACTICE EXERCISES 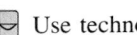 Use technology where appropriate.

Find the lateral area, total area, and volume of each regular pyramid.

A 1.
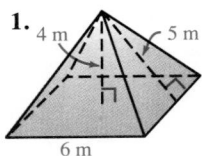
4 m   5 m
6 m

$L = 60 m^2$
$T = 96 m^2$
$V = 48 m^3$

2.
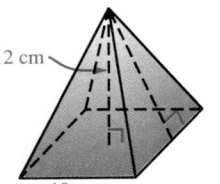
12 cm
10 cm

$L = 260 cm^2$
$T = 360 cm^2$
$V = 400 cm^3$

3.
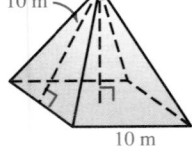
10 m
10 m

$L = 200 m^2$
$T = 300 m^2$
$V = \frac{500\sqrt{3}}{3} m^3$

498   Chapter 12 Area and Volume of Solids

Use this regular hexagonal pyramid in Exercises 4–9.

	Units			Square Units			Cubic Units
	h	l	s	B	L	T	V
4.	? (4)	5	? ($2\sqrt{3}$)	$18\sqrt{3}$	? ($30\sqrt{3}$)	? ($48\sqrt{3}$)	$24\sqrt{3}$
5.	7	? (25)	$16\sqrt{3}$	? ($1152\sqrt{3}$)	$1200\sqrt{3}$	? ($2352\sqrt{3}$)	? ($2688\sqrt{3}$)
6.	? ($\sqrt{3}$)	$\sqrt{6}$	? (2)	? ($6\sqrt{3}$)	$6\sqrt{6}$	? $6(\sqrt{3}+\sqrt{6})$	? (6)
7.	14	$4\sqrt{19}$	? (12)	? ($216\sqrt{3}$)	$144\sqrt{19}$	$216\sqrt{3}+144\sqrt{19}$	$1008\sqrt{3}$
8.	20	29	? ($14\sqrt{3}$)	$882\sqrt{3}$	? ($1218\sqrt{3}$)	? ($2100\sqrt{3}$)	? ($5880\sqrt{3}$)
9.	? (5)	? (13)	? ($8\sqrt{3}$)	? ($288\sqrt{3}$)	$312\sqrt{3}$	$600\sqrt{3}$	? ($480\sqrt{3}$)

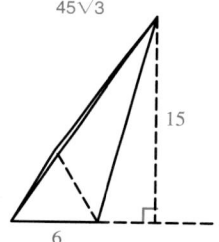

Area of base $= \frac{3s^2}{2}\sqrt{3}$

Additional Answers for p. 498

1.

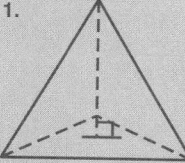

2.

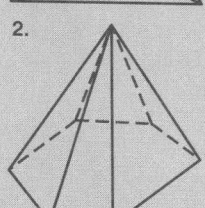

Find the volume of each pyramid.

10. Regular square

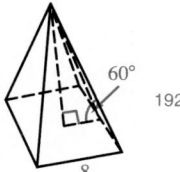

400

12

10

11. Regular hexagonal

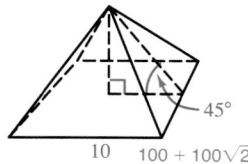

$175\sqrt{3}$

14

5

12. Oblique triangular

72

9

6

8

13. Oblique equilateral triangular

$45\sqrt{3}$

15

6

This regular pyramid has a square base and a lateral area 144 in.²

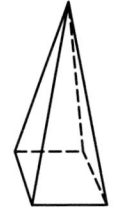

14. If the slant height is twice the length of a base edge, find the length of the base edge, the slant height, and the total area.
$s = 6$ in.; $l = 12$ in.; $T = 180$ in.²

15. Find the height of the pyramid. $h = 3\sqrt{15}$ in.

Find the total area of each regular square pyramid.

16.

60°

192

8

17.

45°

10

$100 + 100\sqrt{2}$

A tetrahedron is a pyramid having faces that are congruent equilateral triangles. This tetrahedron is 12 cm on an edge.

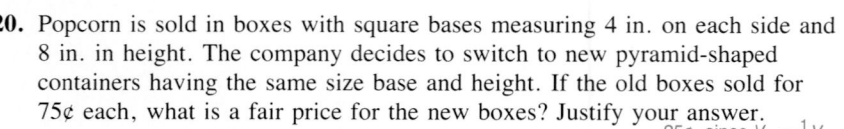

18. Find the lateral and total area. $L = 108\sqrt{3}$ cm^2; $T = 144\sqrt{3}$ cm^2

19. Find the volume. $V = 144\sqrt{2}$ cm^3

20. Popcorn is sold in boxes with square bases measuring 4 in. on each side and 8 in. in height. The company decides to switch to new pyramid-shaped containers having the same size base and height. If the old boxes sold for 75¢ each, what is a fair price for the new boxes? Justify your answer. 25¢, since $V_p = \frac{1}{3}V_b$

21. A packager is investigating containers shaped like regular pyramids. If the perimeter of the base is to be 20 in. and the height 5 in., will a square-based or a pentagonal-based container hold more? How much more? pentagonal base; $V_p - V_s = \frac{1}{3}$ $5(\frac{1}{2} \cdot 20 \cdot 2 \tan 54°) - \frac{1}{3} \cdot 5 \cdot 5^2 = 4.213$ in.^{3}

Find the total area and volume of each.

22.
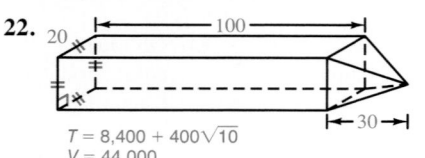
$T = 8{,}400 + 400\sqrt{10}$
$V = 44{,}000$

23.
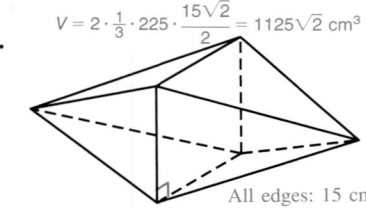
$T = \frac{1}{2} \cdot \frac{15}{2}\sqrt{3} \cdot 60 = 450\sqrt{3}$ cm^2
$V = 2 \cdot \frac{1}{3} \cdot 225 \cdot \frac{15\sqrt{2}}{2} = 1125\sqrt{2}$ cm^3
All edges: 15 cm

A pyramid has been inscribed in a rectangular prism having a square base, 12-cm-long sides, and an 18-cm height.

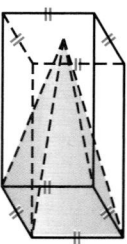

C 24. Find the total area and volume of the pyramid. $144(1 + \sqrt{10})$ cm^2; 864 cm^3

25. Find the volume of the region outside the pyramid and inside the prism. Explain your answer. $V_{region} = V_{prism} - V_{pyramid} = 2592 - 864 = 1728$ cm^3, Vol. of pyr. $= \frac{1}{3}$ vol. of prism.

If a plane parallel to the base of a pyramid is passed through it and the top section removed, a figure called a *frustum* of a pyramid is formed.

This figure has two bases having areas A_1 and A_2. The perpendicular segment joining the top base to the bottom base is the altitude of the frustum; its length is the height.

26. Explain why the lateral faces of the frustum of a pyramid are trapezoids. If the pyramid is regular, why are the faces isosceles trapezoids? See side column.

27. The lateral area of the frustum of a regular pyramid is equal to one-half the product of the sum of the perimeters of the bases times the slant height, or $L = \frac{1}{2}(P_1 + P_2)l$. Explain why this formula is correct.

$L = \frac{1}{2}(a_1 + b_1)l + \frac{1}{2}(a_2 + b_2)l + \cdots + \frac{1}{2}(a_n + b_n)l = \frac{1}{2}[(a_1 + a_2 + a_2 + \cdots + a_n) + (b_1 + b_2 + \cdots + b_n)]l = \frac{1}{2}(P_1 + P_2)l$

500   Chapter 12 Area and Volume of Solids

Applications

28. Archaeology When it was built, the Great Pyramid of Cheops was 480.75 ft high and the sides of its square base measured 764 ft. An outside coating of stone has now been removed, leaving the dimensions 460 ft and 720 ft, respectively. What was the weight of the stone removed, if 1 cubic foot of stone weighs 100 lb? $W = 1,404,928,400$ lb

29. Packing What is the largest number of these regular pyramids having square bases that measure 4 in. on a side and 6 in. high that can be packed into a box 12 in. × 8 in. × 8 in.? Explain how to pack them most efficiently.
20; 1st layer: 2 rows of 3 each pointing "up"; 2nd layer: 4 with "points" down between pyramids of first row; repeat the layers

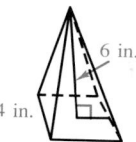

6 in.

4 in.

Developing Mathematical Power

30. Thinking Critically Archimedean solids are polyhedra with faces that are regular polygons of more than one type. Which regular polygons make up each of the following solids?

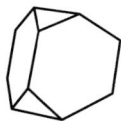

Truncated Tetrahedron
hexagon, triangle

Truncated Dodecahedron
decagon, triangle

Truncated Octahedron
hexagon, square

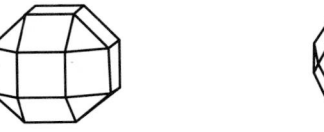

Rhombicuboctahedron
square, triangle

Rhombicosidodecahedron
pentagon, triangle, square

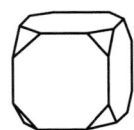

Truncated Hexahedron
octagon, triangle

Truncated Icosidodecahedron
decagon, hexagon, square

Truncated Cuboctahedron
octagon, hexagon, square

Truncated Icosahedron
pentagon, hexagon

There are 13 Archimedean solids in all. Research the remaining ones.

Teacher's Resource Book
Follow-Up Investigation, *Chapter 12,*
p. 4

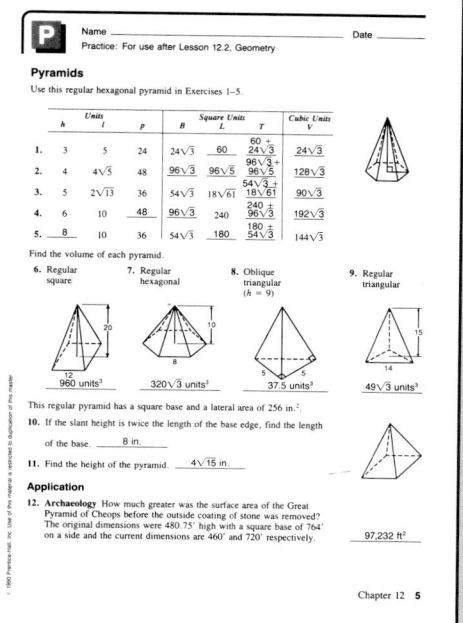

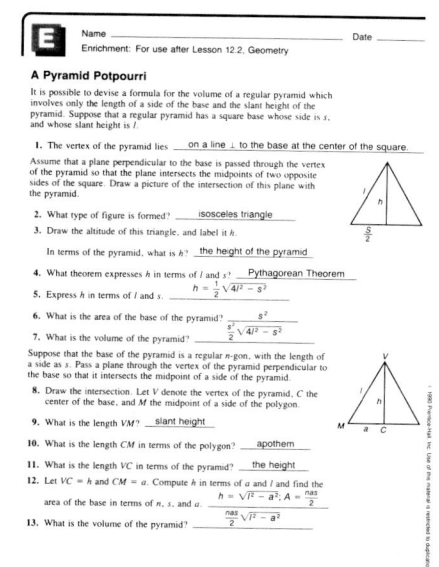

LESSON FOCUS

Review

Find the circumference and area of
each to the nearest tenth.

1. 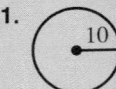   **2.**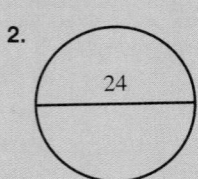

1. 62.8; 314.2
2. 75.4; 452.4

Alternative Learning Styles

A standard tin can with a label can be
used to model the idea of lateral area.
Remove the label to show that it is a
rectangle with base $2\pi r$ and height h
(the height of the can). The two ends
of the can represent the area of the
bases, which makes the formula for
total area reasonable. Elicit a discussion of how the volume (contents) may
be determined.

502

12.3

Cylinders

Objectives: To identify and sketch the parts of cylinders
To find the lateral area and the total area of a right
circular cylinder
To find the volume of a cylinder

Many everyday objects are shaped as cylinders. The methods for finding the
lateral area, total area, and volume of cylinders are similar to those used when
working with prisms.

Investigation—*Using Manipulatives*

Take two sheets of 8.5 × 11 in. paper. Using the first
sheet, form a right cylinder whose height is 11 in. and
tape the edges together. Use the second sheet to form
a right cylinder 8.5 in. in height.

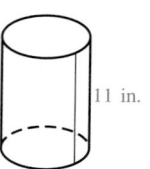
11 in.

1. What is the circumference of each cylinder? 8.5 in.;
11 in.
2. Which cylinder, if either, has the greater lateral
area? How do you know? neither; they are formed from
congruent rectangles
3. Which cylinder, if either, has the greater volume?
the shorter
4. Devise a method for determining the volume of
each cylinder. *Bh* or $\pi r^2 h$

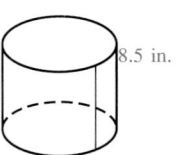
8.5 in.

A **cylinder** may be thought of as a prism whose base
is a polygon having infinitely many sides. Its bases
are congruent circles contained in parallel planes.

The *lateral surface* of a cylinder corresponds to
the lateral faces of a prism, and the *circumference*
of the bases corresponds to the perimeter of the
base of the prism.

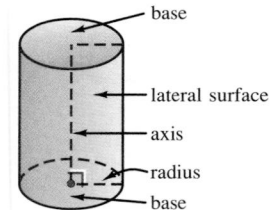
base
lateral surface
axis
radius
base

Right Circular Cylinder

The **axis** is the segment that joins the centers of the
bases of a cylinder. If the axis is perpendicular to the
bases, the cylinder is called a **right circular cylinder**
or a **right cylinder;** if the axis is not perpendicular to
the bases, the cylinder is called an **oblique circular**
cylinder, or simply **oblique.**

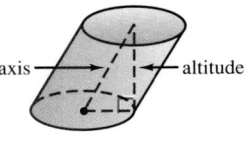
axis
altitude

Oblique Cylinder

502   Chapter 12 Area and Volume of Solids

Developing Mathematical Power

Cooperative Learning   The Enrichment activity, p. 9, in the *Teacher's Resource
Book* provides an economic approach to the design of cans for liquids. Working in
groups, students can complete the worksheet. Challenge them to design a can and
label for a product. Designing the most creative and most economical packaging is
the goal.

The **altitude** of a cylinder is the perpendicular segment that joins its bases. The length of the altitude is called the **height** of the cylinder. In what type of cylinder will the altitude correspond to the axis? The lateral area of a right circular cylinder depends on the circumference of the base and the height of the cylinder. Why? The total area depends on the lateral area and on the area of the circles that are the bases. right cylinder; just as lateral area of prism depends on
perimeter of base and height

> **Theorem 12.7** The lateral area L of a right circular cylinder equals the product of the circumference C of the base and the height h of the cylinder, or $L = C \cdot h = 2\pi rh$.
>
> **Theorem 12.8** The total area T of a right circular cylinder equals the sum of the lateral area L and the area of the two bases $2B$, or $T = L + 2B = 2\pi rh + 2\pi r^2 = 2\pi r(h + r)$.

EXAMPLE 1 **Find the lateral area and the total area of each right cylinder.**

a.

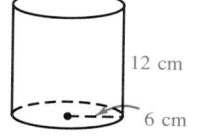
12 cm

6 cm

b.
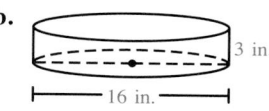
3 in.

16 in.

a. $L = 2\pi(6)(12) = 144\pi$ cm^2
$T = 2\pi(6)(12 + 6) = 216\pi$ cm^2

b. $L = 2\pi(8)(3) = 48\pi$ in.^{2}
$T = 2\pi(8)(3 + 8) = 176\pi$ in.^{2}

Finding the volume of a cylinder is similar to finding the volume of a prism.

> **Theorem 12.9** The volume V of a cylinder equals the product of the area of the base B and the height of the cylinder, or $V = B \cdot h = \pi r^2 h$.

EXAMPLE 2 **Find the volume of each cylinder.**

a.

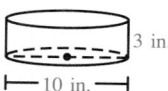
3 in.

10 in.

b.
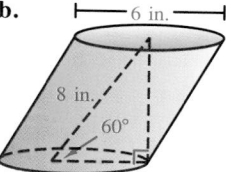
6 in.

8 in.

60°

a. $V = \pi(5^2)3 = 75\pi$ in.^{3}

b. $V = \pi(3^2)4\sqrt{3} = 36\sqrt{3}\pi$ in.^{3}

12.3 Cylinders **503**

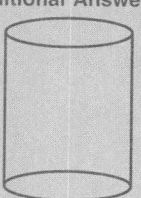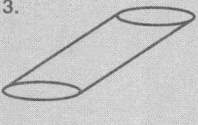
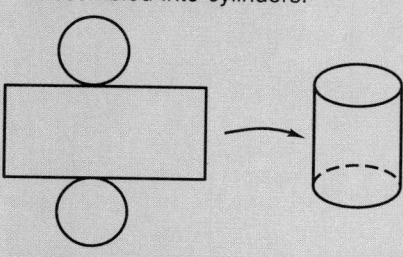
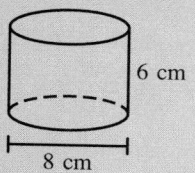
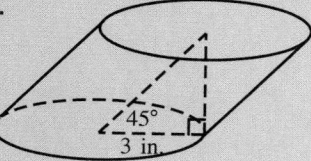
503

Common Errors

- Some students may have difficulty using π correctly, or may be careless about including π in answers where appropriate. Have these students write π with its value in parenthesis throughout their work. Let them use either π, or its approximate value in their final answers.
- Some students may confuse radius and diameter, and use the values interchangeably. Encourage these students to *always* label both parts and to *always* write the required formula in order to determine which measurement is needed.
- See *Teacher's Resource Book* for additional remediation.

LESSON FOLLOW-UP

Discussion

Have students describe the analogies that exist between cylinders and prisms. This should help them make appropriate generalizations about these three-dimensional figures. Point out that the methods for determining area and volume of cylinders and prisms are based on the same ideas.

Critical Thinking

Comparing-Contrasting Have students compare and contrast cylinders and prisms.

Assignment Guide

See p. 488B for assignments.

504

CLASS EXERCISES

Thinking Critically

1. There is a right cylinder whose volume in cubic units equals its total area in square units. Describe this cylinder. $r = \frac{2h}{h-2}$ with $h > 2$, or $h = \frac{2r}{r-2}$ with $r > 2$

Give a plan for drawing each figure. Then draw it. See side column page 503.

2. A right circular cylinder Draw two congruent ovals, one directly above the other, then connect.

3. An oblique cylinder Draw two congruent ovals not directly above each other, and connect the edges.

The radius of the smaller of the concentric circles is 1 and the radius of the larger is 2.

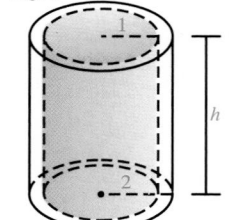

4. Find the ratio of the total area of the larger cylinder to the total area of the smaller. $\frac{2(2+h)}{1+h}$

5. Find the ratio of the volume of the larger to the smaller cylinder. $\frac{4}{1}$

6. What is the volume of the space between the cylinders? $V = 3\pi h$

7. If a cylinder has lateral area of 88π m² and volume of 176π m³, what is its total area? $T = 120\pi$ m²

PRACTICE EXERCISES   Use technology where appropriate.

A   1. **Thinking Critically**   A right circular cylinder can be thought of as the figure formed by rotating a rectangle in space about one of its sides. When viewed in this manner, what determines the height and radius of the cylinder? the height and base of the rectangle

Complete this table for a right circular cylinder.

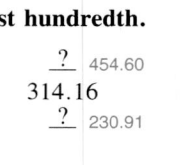

	Units		**Square Units**		**Cubic Units**
	h	r	L	T	V
2.	6	2	? 24π	? 32π	? 24π
3.	5	4	? 40π	? 72π	? 80π
4.	? 4	8	64π	? 192π	? 256π
5.	? 3.5	1	7π	? 9π	? $\frac{7}{2}\pi$
6.	? 6	? 6	72π	? 144π	216π
7.	? 14	? 10	280π	? 480π	1400π

In Exercises 8–10, express answers to the nearest hundredth.

8.	5.25	5.25	? 173.18	? 346.36	? 454.60
9.	4	? 5	? 125.66	? 282.74	314.16
10.	? 6	3.5	131.95	? 208.92	? 230.91

504   Chapter 12 Area and Volume of Solids

Find the volume of each oblique cylinder.

11.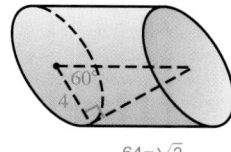

$64\pi\sqrt{3}$

12.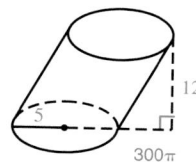

300π

Consider two right circular cylinders, cylinder A having $r = 2$ and $h = 1$, and cylinder B having $r = 1$ and $h = 2$.

B

13. Compare the lateral and total areas of these figures. equal; $T_A = 2T_B$

14. Compare the volumes of cylinder A and cylinder B. $V_A = 2V_B$

This cylinder is inscribed in a rectangular solid of dimensions $l = 10$ in., $w = 10$ in., and $h = 16$ in.

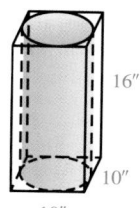

15. Find the total area and volume of the cylinder.
$T = 210\pi$ in.²; $V = 400\pi$ in.³

16. Find the volume of the region between the cylinder and the prism. $V_{region} = 1600 - 400\pi$ in.³

This rectangular solid is inscribed in a right circular cylinder of height 12 cm and radius 6 cm.

17. Find the total area and volume of the prism.
$T = 144 + 288\sqrt{2}$ cm²; $V = 864$ cm³

18. Find the volume of the region between the cylinder and the prism.
$432\pi - 864$ cm³

19. Suppose the volume in cubic in. of a right circular cylinder of height h equals twice the number of square inches in its total area. What is the radius r of the cylinder in terms of h? $r = \frac{4h}{h-4}$; $h > 4$

20. Suppose the height of a right circular cylinder is doubled and the radius is halved. How do the lateral area and volume of the new cylinder compare to the lateral area and volume of the old? $L_{NEW} = L_{OLD}$ because
$L_{OLD} = 2\pi rh$ and $L_{NEW} = 2\pi\left(\frac{r}{2}\right)(2h) = 2\pi rh$; $V_{new} = \frac{1}{2}V_{old}$

In Exercises 21–24, express answers to the nearest tenth.

C

21. If 10 percent of the total surface area of this aluminum tank is to be allowed for waste and seams, how many square inches of aluminum will be required for its construction?
$T + 10\% \approx 4665.3$ in.²

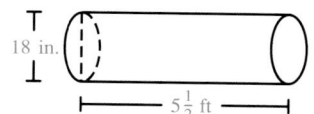

22. How many gallons will the tank hold if 1 gal = 231 in.³? 72.7 gal

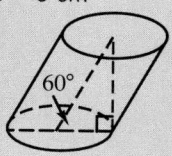

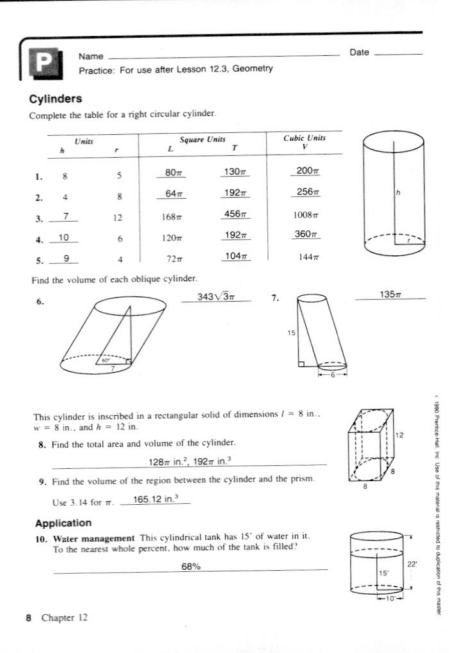

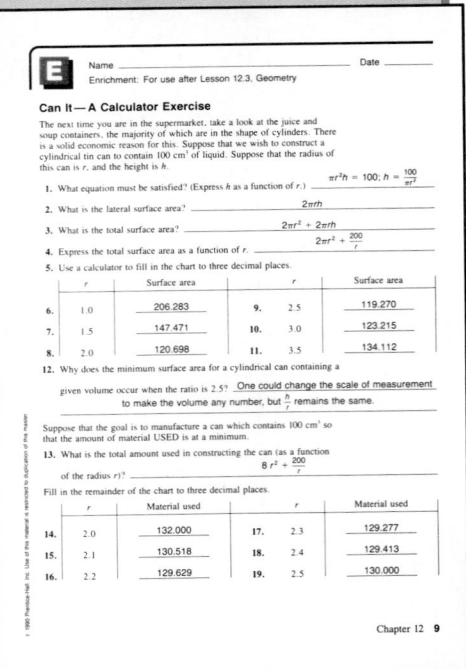

Teacher's Resource Book
Follow-Up Investigation, Chapter 12,
p. 7

---

23. Under certain conditions, the most economical proportions for a tin can are for the height to equal the diameter of the base. What dimensions would produce a can of volume 96.5 in.^{3}? $96.5 = \pi r^2(2r)$; $\pi r^3 = 48.25$, $r = \sqrt[3]{(48.25/\pi)} \approx 2.5$ in., $h \approx 5$ in.

24. If a tunnel is to have a semicircular shape and is to be 25 ft high and 0.75 mi long, how many cubic yards of dirt must be removed? $143{,}989.7$ yd^3

Applications

25. Water Management This tank has 10 in. of water in it. How much of the tank is filled? Half is filled.

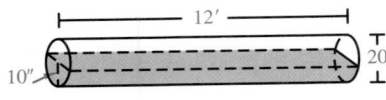

26. Metallurgy A metallurgist drops a piece of ore into a graduated right circular cylinder having a base 10 cm in diameter. If the level of the water in the cylinder rises 15 cm, what is the weight in grams of the ore if it weighs 25 g per cubic centimeter? $V = \pi\left(\frac{10}{2}\right)^2 15 = 1177.5$ cm^3; therefore, $W = 25(1177.5) = 29{,}437.5$ g

27. Technology Use Logo to write a procedure to generate the area and volume of a given cylinder. Use recursion to generate a table of areas and volumes of a sequence of cylinders. See Solutions Manual.

TEST YOURSELF

Find the lateral area, total area, and volume of each solid. 12.1–12.3

1. Right triangular prism

$L = 156 + 12\sqrt{41}$;
$T = 188 + 12\sqrt{41}$;
$V = 192$

2. Right cylinder

$C = 5\pi$ $L = 75\pi$;
$T = 87.5\pi$;
$V = 93.75\pi$

3. Square pyramid

$L = 28\sqrt{305}$
$T = 196 + 28$
$V = 1045\frac{1}{3}$

4. Rectangular solid

$L = 676$;
$T = 756$;
$V = 1040$

5. Regular equilateral pyramid

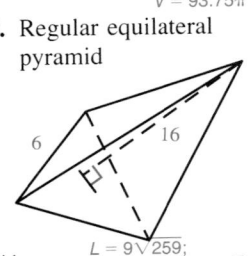

$L = 9\sqrt{259}$;
$T = 9\sqrt{259} + 3\sqrt{3}$;
$V = 48\sqrt{3}$

6. Right cylinder

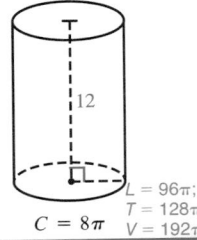

$L = 96\pi$;
$T = 128\pi$;
$C = 8\pi$ $V = 192\pi$

506   Chapter 12 Area and Volume of Solids

506

12.4 Strategy: Analyze Cross Sections of Solids

A **cross section** of a geometric solid is the plane figure formed by the intersection of the solid and a plane. If the plane of a section is perpendicular to the lateral edges of the figure (or to the surface in the case of a cylinder), the cross section is called a **right section.** Here are two different cross sections of a cube.

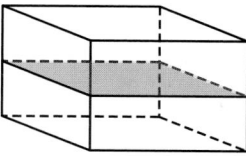

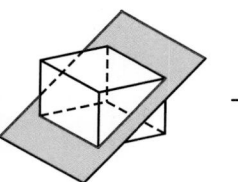  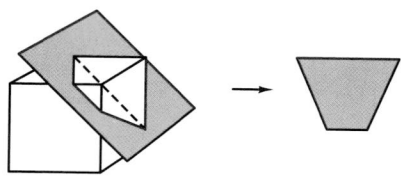

EXAMPLE 1 **Prove:** If two parallel planes intersect a prism, the cross sections formed are congruent.

Understand the Problem

Draw a figure.

State the Given and Prove.

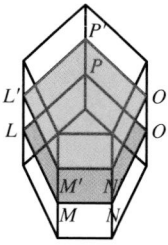

Given: Prism with parallel planes intersecting the prism, forming cross sections $LMNOP$ and $L'M'N'O'P'$

Prove: $LMNOP \cong L'M'N'O'P'$

Plan Your Approach

Look Ahead.

To show that two polygons are congruent, show that their corresponding sides and angles are congruent.

Look Back.

Since the given figure is a prism, its lateral faces are parallelograms. Recall the theorem about what happens when two parallel planes are intersected by a third plane.

Developing Mathematical Power

Cooperative Learning Assign groups of students to complete the Practice activity, p. 10, in the *Teacher's Resource Book* (see side column, p. 510). Each member of the group should complete Exercises 1–3 and 6 independently and then discuss results to get a group answer. Challenge them to sketch as many cross sections of a square pyramid as possible (point, line, triangle, square, trapezoid).

Vocabulary
Cross section
Right section

Materials/Manipulatives
Materials that can be easily shaped and sliced, such as large potatoes
Knife
Teaching Transparency 81

Technology
Computer Test Bank, pp. 781–786

LESSON FOCUS

Review
Review the characteristics of prisms, pyramids, and cylinders.

Alternative Learning Styles
- Kinesthetic learners will benefit from a hands-on demonstration of the cross sections of a solid. Large potatoes can be shaped into cubes, rectangular prisms, and pyramids, and then sliced to show different possible cross sections. Ask students to predict the shape of the cross section before actually slicing to verify.
- All students should benefit from Teaching Transparency 81, which provides visual presentation of possible cross sections of a cube.

TEACHING SUGGESTION

Since visualization and drawing skills will be poorly developed in some students, use many models and examples to enhance these skills as they relate to cross sections of solids.

CHALKBOARD EXAMPLES

- **For Example 1**

  Prove that a cross section of a rectangular solid made by passing a plane through all four parallel edges is a parallelogram. Under what circumstances will such a section be a rectangle?

  Given: The rectangular solid with cross section $ABCD$ that intersects the 4 ∥ edges.
  Prove: $ABCD$ is a ▱
  Plan: Opp. lateral faces represent ∥ planes. Recall the th. about 2 ∥ planes intersected by a third plane. Then use the def. of a ▱.

  Proof:

Statements	Reasons
1. Cross section $ABCD$ intersects all ∥ edges of the rect. solid.	1. Given
2. Plane $ADE \parallel BCF$; plane $ABE \parallel DCF$	2. Def. of rect. solid
3. $\overline{AD} \parallel \overline{BC}$; $\overline{AB} \parallel \overline{DC}$	3. If 2 ∥ planes are intersected by a by a third plane, lines of intersection are ∥.
4. $ABCD$ is a ▱.	4. Def. of a ▱

  Conclusion: A cross section of a rectangular solid made by passing a plane through 4 ∥ edges is a ▱. The section will be a rectangle if the intersecting plane is ∥ to a base.

Plan.

An intermediate goal is to show that $LMM'L'$ and $MNN'M'$ are ▱s. Doing so will show that $\overline{LM} \cong \overline{L'M'}$ and $\overline{MN} \cong \overline{M'N'}$. Then show that $\angle LMN \cong \angle L'M'N'$. This follows if segments $\overline{LN}$ and $\overline{L'N'}$ are drawn and $\triangle LMN$ is shown congruent to $\triangle L'M'N'$ (by SSS). Since $\overline{LM} \cong \overline{L'M'}$, $\overline{MN} \cong \overline{M'N'}$ and $\angle LMN \cong \angle L'M'N'$, and since similar arguments could be used to demonstrate that all pairs of corresponding sides and angles are congruent, it follows that $LMNOP \cong L'M'N'O'$

■ **Implement the Plan**

Proof:

Statements	Reasons
1. ∥ planes intersect the prism forming cross sections $LMNOP$ and $L'M'N'O'P'$.	1. Given
2. The faces of the prism are ▱.	2. Def. of prism
3. $\overline{LL'} \parallel \overline{MM'}$; $\overline{MM'} \parallel \overline{NN'}$, . . .	3. Def. of ▱
4. $\overline{LM} \parallel \overline{L'M'}$; $\overline{MN} \parallel \overline{M'N'}$, . . .	4. If 2 ∥ planes are intersected by a 3rd plane, the line intersection are ∥.
5. $LMM'L'$ and $MNN'M'$ are ▱.	5. Def. of ▱
6. $\overline{LM} \cong \overline{L'M'}$; $\overline{MN} \cong \overline{M'N'}$; $\overline{LL'} \cong \overline{MM'}$; $\overline{MM'} \cong \overline{NN'}$	6. Opp. sides of a ▱ are
7. Draw $\overline{LN}$ and $\overline{L'N'}$.	7. Two pts. determine 1 a only 1 line seg.
8. $\overline{LL'} \parallel \overline{NN'}$	8. Two lines ∥ to the same are ∥ to each other.
9. $\overline{LL'} \cong \overline{NN'}$	9. Trans. prop. of ≅
10. $LNN'L'$ is a ▱.	10. If a quad. has 1 pair of sides ∥ and ≅, it is a ▱
11. $\overline{LN} \cong \overline{L'N'}$	11. Opp. sides of a ▱ are
12. $\triangle LMN \cong \triangle L'M'N'$	12. SSS Post.
13. $\angle LMN \cong \angle L'M'N'$	13. CPCTC
14. $LMNOP \cong L'M'N'O'P'$	14. Def. of ≅ polygons

■ **Interpret the Results**

The cross sections formed when two parallel planes intersect a are congruent.

Also, you could observe that if a plane parallel to the base of a pri intersects the prism, the cross section formed is congruent to the ba the prism.

Problem Solving Reminder

- Cross sections can provide useful information about solid figures and can aid in proving theorems about the figures.

This theorem is useful in problems involving cross sections of pyramids.

If a pyramid is intersected by a plane that is parallel to its base, then the lateral edges and altitude are divided proportionally and the cross section is similar to the base.

MPLE 2   The area of the base of a pyramid is 98 in.², and the height is 8 in. How far from the vertex must a plane parallel to the base be passed so that the area of the cross section is half the area of the base?

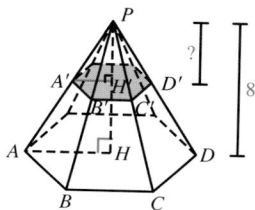

Understand the Problem   A cross section of area 49 in.² has been formed by a plane parallel to the base. Find the distance from the vertex to the plane forming the cross section; or, the height of the top pyramid.

Plan Your Approach

$$\frac{\text{area of } A'B'C'D' \ldots}{\text{area of } ABCD \ldots} = \frac{(A'B')^2}{(AB)^2}$$
   The areas of ~ polygons are proportional to the squares of the lengths of the corr. sides.

$$\frac{PA'}{PA} = \frac{PB'}{PB}$$
   From the theorem above

$$\triangle PA'B' \sim \triangle PAB$$
   SAS Theorem

$$\frac{PA'}{PA} = \frac{A'B'}{AB} = \frac{PH'}{PH}$$
   Corr. side lengths of ~ polygons are in proportion and theorem above.

The last two fractions provide the needed relationship.

Implement the Plan

$$\frac{(A'B')^2}{(AB)^2} = \frac{(PH')^2}{(PH)^2} \text{ or } \frac{49}{98} = \frac{(PH')^2}{64}, \text{ or } PH' = 4\sqrt{2}$$

Interpret the Results   In general, if a pyramid has base area A and height h, then a plane parallel to the base at a distance of $\frac{h\sqrt{2}}{2}$ from the vertex produces a cross section of area $\frac{1}{2}A$.

12.4 Strategy: Analyze Cross Sections of Solids   **509**

For Example 2

The area of the base of a pyramid is 784 in.² The area of a cross section of the pyramid, parallel to the base and 6 in. from it, is 484 in.² What is the height of the pyramid?

$$\frac{(h-6)^2}{h^2} = \frac{484}{784}; \text{ since } \frac{484}{784} = \frac{121}{196} = \frac{11^2}{14^2},$$
$$\frac{h-6}{h} = \frac{11}{14}.$$
$$h = 28 \text{ in.}$$

Common Error

- Because of poor visualization and drawing skills, some students will have a great deal of difficulty with problems of this lesson. Provide many practice exercises and opportunities to improve visualization and drawing skills to remedy these difficulties.
- See *Teacher's Resource Book* for additional remediation.

LESSON FOLLOW-UP

Assignment Guide

See p. 488B for assignments.

Project

You might want to discuss materials that would be appropriate for these models. This might be another good project for students to work on in pairs.

Lesson Quiz

1. Which could *not* be a cross section of a rectangular solid?
   a. square   b. parallelogram
   c. hexagon   d. octagon
2. A plane parallel to the square base of a pyramid and 8 cm above it forms a cross section having an area of 100 cm². If the pyramid has a height of 12 cm, find the length of each side of its base.   1. *d*
   2. 30 cm

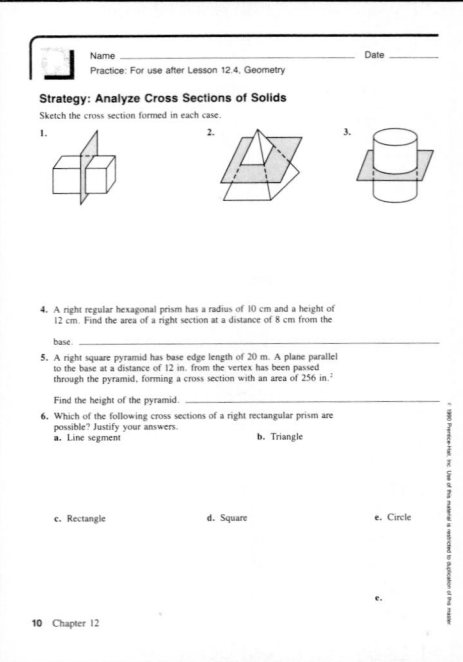

Name _____ Date _____
Practice: For use after Lesson 12.4, Geometry

Strategy: Analyze Cross Sections of Solids
Sketch the cross section formed in each case.
1.   2.   3.

4. A right regular hexagonal prism has a radius of 10 cm and a height of 12 cm. Find the area of a right section at a distance of 8 cm from the

base. _____

5. A right square pyramid has base edge length of 20 m. A plane parallel to the base at a distance of 12 in. from the vertex has been passed through the pyramid, forming a cross section with an area of 256 in.²

Find the height of the pyramid. _____

6. Which of the following cross sections of a right rectangular prism are possible? Justify your answers.
   a. Line segment   b. Triangle

   c. Rectangle   d. Square   e. Circle

   e.

10   Chapter 12

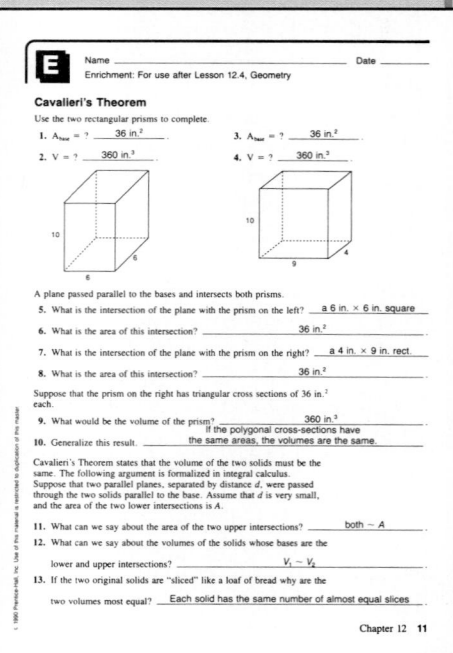

E   Name _____ Date _____
Enrichment: For use after Lesson 12.4, Geometry

Cavalieri's Theorem
Use the two rectangular prisms to complete.
1. A_base = ?   36 in.²   3. A_base = ?   36 in.²
2. V = ?   360 in.³   4. V = ?   360 in.³

A plane passed parallel to the bases and intersects both prisms.
5. What is the intersection of the plane with the prism on the left?   a 6 in. × 6 in. square
6. What is the area of this intersection?   36 in.²
7. What is the intersection of the plane with the prism on the right?   a 4 in. × 9 in. rect.
8. What is the area of this intersection?   36 in.²

Suppose that the prism on the right has triangular cross sections of 36 in.² each.
9. What would be the volume of the prism?   360 in.³
10. Generalize this result.   If the polygonal cross-sections have the same areas, the volumes are the same.

Cavalieri's Theorem states that the volume of the two solids must be the same. The following argument is formalized in integral calculus. Suppose that two parallel planes, separated by distance d, were passed through two solids parallel to the base. Assume that d is very small, and the area of the two lower intersections is A.

11. What can we say about the area of the two upper intersections?   both ~ A
12. What can we say about the volumes of the solids whose bases are the

   lower and upper intersections?   V₁ ~ V₂
13. If the two original solids are "sliced" like a loaf of bread why are the

   two volumes most equal?   Each solid has the same number of almost equal slices

Chapter 12   **11**

CLASS EXERCISES

1. Select the cross section that results. **b**; **c** if the plane is not ∥ to the base.

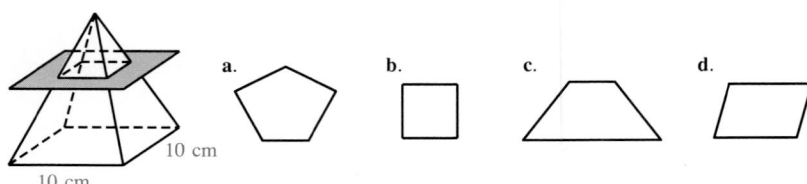
a.   b.   c.   d.

2. A right regular hexagonal prism has a radius of 12 cm and height 15 cm. Find the area of a right section 10 cm from the base. 216√3 cm²

PRACTICE EXERCISES

A   **1.** Select the cross section that results. **d**

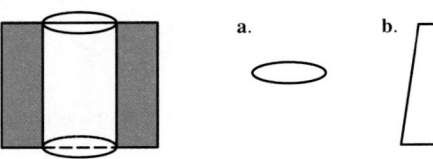 a.   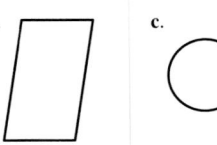 b.   c.   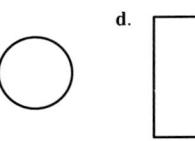 d.

2. A right square pyramid has base edge length of 12 in. A plane parallel to the ba 5 in. from the vertex has been passed through the pyramid, forming a cross section with an area of 36 in.². Find the height of the pyramid. 10 in.

B   **3.** Which cross sections of a cube are possible? Justify. See page 772.
   a. triangle   **b.** trapezoid   **c.** pentagon   **d.** hexagon

4. Which cross sections of a cylinder are possible? Justify.
   a. line segment   **b.** parallelogram   **c.** rectangle   **d.** circle

C   **5.** Prove: A cross section of a prism made by a plane passing through two nonconsecutive lateral edges is a parallelogram.

6. Prove: A cross section of a rectangular solid made by passing a plane through a pair of nonconsecutive lateral edges is a rectangle.

PROJECT

Choose one of the Platonic solids and investigate the different kinds of polygons formed by cross sections. Make a model to help you visualize the cross sections.

Cones

Objectives: To identify and sketch the parts of cones
To find the lateral area and total area of a right circular cone
To find the volume of a cone

The formulas for surface area and volume of *cones* are related to formulas for pyramids.

Investigation—*Using Manipulatives*

Construct the lateral surface of a right circular cone from a sector of a circle. Copy the sector using the dimensions shown.

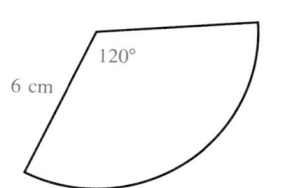

6 cm

120°

1. What is the radius of the base of the cone made from this sector? 2 cm

Construct a cone from a sector that is a semicircle.

2. What is the slant height of the cone constructed? r

3. What is the radius of the base of the cone? $\frac{1}{2}r$

A **cone** has a circular *base* and a *vertex* that is not coplanar with the base. Its **lateral surface** is the set of all points of the cone not in the base. The **axis** of a cone joins the vertex to the center of the base. If the axis is perpendicular to the base, the cone is a **right circular cone;** if the axis is not perpendicular to the base, the cone is **oblique.**

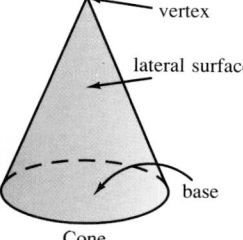

vertex

lateral surface

base

Cone

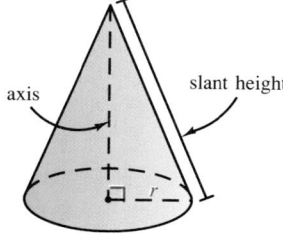

axis

slant height

Right Circular Cone

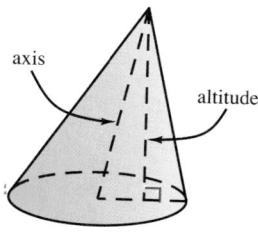

axis

altitude

Oblique Cone

The perpendicular segment joining the vertex of a cone to the plane of the base is called the **altitude** of the cone; its length is the cone's **height.** The **slant height** of a right circular cone is the distance from the vertex to any point of the circle that forms the base of the cone.

12.5 Cones   **511**

Developing Mathematical Power

Cooperative Learning Working in groups, students can complete the Critical Thinking activity, p. 12, in the *Teacher's Resource Book.* For Exercise 3, you may want to provide each group with some salt or sand, and a conical container and a cylindrical container that have congruent bases and equal heights. Allow time for sharing.

> **Theorem 12.10** The lateral area L of a right circular cone having slant height l and base circumference $C = 2\pi r$, where r is the radius of the base, is one-half the product of the circumference and the slant height, or
>
> $L = \frac{1}{2}Cl = \frac{1}{2}(2\pi r)l = \pi rl$. Proved in Practice Exercise 21
>
> **Theorem 12.11** The total area T of a right circular cone is the sum of the lateral area L and the area of the base B, or
>
> $T = L + B = \pi rl + \pi r^2 = \pi r(l + r)$. Proved in Practice Exercise 22

EXAMPLE 1 Find the lateral area and the total area of each right circular cone.

a. 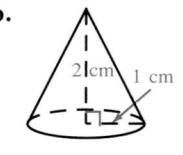 10 cm 5 cm

b. 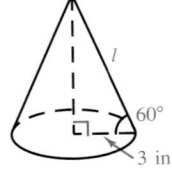 2 cm 1 cm

c. l 60° 3 in.

a. $L = \pi(5)(10) = 50\pi$ cm²; $T = 5\pi(15) = 75\pi$ cm²

b. $l = \sqrt{5}$ cm, so $L = \pi\sqrt{5}$ cm²; $T = \pi(1 + \sqrt{5})$ cm²

c. $l = 6$ in., so $L = 18\pi$ in.²; $T = 3\pi(9) = 27\pi$ in.²

The formula for the volume of a cone is similar to the formula for the volume of a pyramid.

> **Theorem 12.12** The volume V of a cone is one-third the product of the area of the base B and the height h, or $V = \frac{1}{3}Bh = \frac{1}{3}\pi r^2 h$.
> Proved in Practice Exercise 23

EXAMPLE 2 Find the volume of each cone.

a. 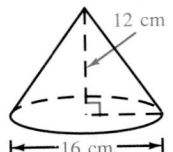 12 cm 16 cm

b.  h 10 cm 6 cm

a. $V = \frac{1}{3}(64\pi)(12) = 256\pi$ cm³

b. $h = 8$ cm, so $V = \frac{1}{3}(36\pi)(8) = 96\pi$ cm³

CLASS EXERCISES

Give a strategy for sketching each cone, then sketch each one.

1. A right circular cone with axis length 8 cm and radius length 6 cm draw an oval with "radius" 6 cm, connect lines from edge of oval to point above oval's center 8 cm

2. An oblique cone with axis length 13 cm, height 12 cm, and radius 5 cm draw oval with "radius" 5 cm, vertical line from one edge and slanted line from other, dotted line from center of oval to top labeled 13 cm, vertical segment labeled 12 cm

Use this cone to find the measure of each of the following:

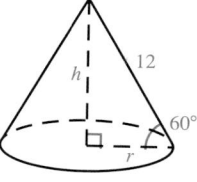

3. Radius 6   4. Circumference of the base 12π

5. Diameter 12   6. Area of the base 36π

7. Height $6\sqrt{3}$ 8. Lateral area 72π

9. Total area 108π 10. Volume $72\pi\sqrt{3}$

11. If a right circular cone has lateral area of 3660π ft^2 and total area of 7260π ft^2, what is its volume? $V = 13{,}200\pi$ ft^3

PRACTICE EXERCISES   Use technology where appropriate.

Thinking Critically   Plane R passes through a right circular cone of radius r_1 and height h_1 and is parallel to the base, at a distance of h_2 from the vertex of the cone.

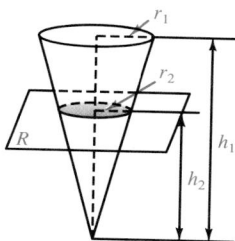

A   1. What is the relationship between r_1, r_2, h_1, and h_2? Justify your answer. $\frac{r_1}{r_2} = \frac{h_1}{h_2}$; lengths of corr. sides of similar $\triangle$s are proportional

2. If $h_1 = 10$, $h_2 = 8$, and $r_1 = 5$, find r_2. 4

Complete the table for this right circular cone. Leave π in your answers.

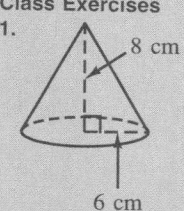

	Units			Square Units		Cubic Units
	h	r	l	L	T	V
3.	? 24	7	25	? 175π	? 224π	? 392π
4.	20	21	? 29	? 609π	? 1050π	? 2940π
5.	? 5	? 12	13	? 156π	300π	? 240π
6.	? 8	? 15	? 17	255π	480π	? 600π

If $l = 10$ and α has the given measure, find the lateral area, total area, and volume of this right circular cone.

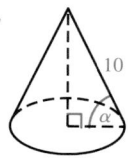
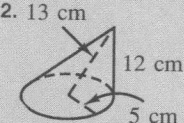

7. $\alpha = 45$
$h = 5\sqrt{2}$;
$r = 5\sqrt{2}$
$L = 50\pi\sqrt{2}$;
$T = 50\pi(\sqrt{2} + 1)$;
$V = \dfrac{250\pi\sqrt{2}}{3}$

8. $\alpha = 30$
$h = 5$; $r = 5\sqrt{3}$
$L = 50\pi\sqrt{3}$;
$T = 25\pi(2\sqrt{3} + 3)$;
$V = 125\pi$

9. $\alpha = 60$
$h = 5\sqrt{3}$; $r = 5$
$L = 50\pi$;
$T = 75\pi$;
$V = \dfrac{125\pi\sqrt{3}}{3}$

12.5 Cones   **513**

513

Lesson Quiz

1. Find the lateral area, total area, and volume of a right circular cone with radius 7 cm and slant height 14 cm.
$L = 98\pi$ cm²; $T = 147$ cm²; $V = \frac{343\pi\sqrt{3}}{3}$ cm³

2. A cone and a right circular cylinder have congruent radii and altitudes. If the volume of the cone is 30π cm³, what is the volume of the cylinder? 90π cm³

Find the volume of each cone.

10.

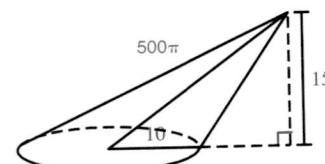

11.

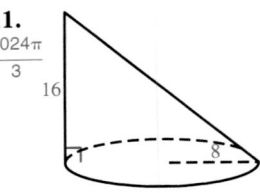

Suppose a 30°-60°-90° triangle is revolved about its longer leg to form a right circular cone. Express each as a function of the longer leg, a.

12. Total area $T = a^2\pi$

13. Volume $V = \frac{a^3\pi}{9}$

Suppose an equilateral triangle of side length s is revolved about its altitude to generate a right circular cone. Find each.

B **14.** Total area $T = \frac{3\pi s^2}{4}$

15. Volume $V = \frac{s^3\pi\sqrt{3}}{24}$

A right circular cone is inscribed in a cube having side lengths that are 10 cm.

16. Find the total area of the cone. $25\pi(1 + \sqrt{5})$ cm²

17. Find the volume of the cone. $\frac{250\pi}{3}$ cm³

18. Find the volume of the region between the cone and the cube.
$V = V_{cube} - V_{cone} = \frac{3000 - 250\pi}{3}$ cm³

19. If the height of this cone remains constant, by what should the radius be multiplied to produce a cone with twice the volume of the original? $\sqrt{2}$

20. If the radius remains constant, by what should the height be multiplied to produce a cone having triple the volume of the original? 3

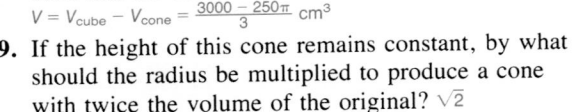

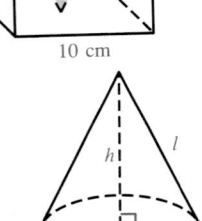

Write a paragraph proof to justify each theorem. See side column.

21. Theorem 12.10   **22.** Theorem 12.11   **23.** Theorem 12.12

A regular hexagonal pyramid with base edges s is inscribed in a right circular cone of radius r and height h.

C **24.** Find the volume of the region between the cone and the pyramid in terms of r and h.
$V_R = V_C - V_P = \frac{r^2 h}{6}(2\pi - 3\sqrt{3})$

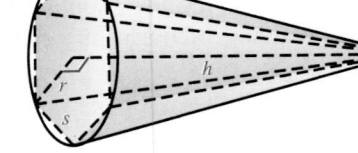

514   Chapter 12 Area and Volume of Solids

Developing Mathematical Power

Keeping a Portfolio Have students complete the Reading and Writing in Geometry activity, p. 12, in the *Teacher's Resource Book*. It provides students with an opportunity to summarize their understanding of the vocabulary in the chapter. They should provide a labeled diagram wherever appropriate.

This figure shows a frustum of a right circular cone. It was formed by slicing the cone with a plane parallel to the base.

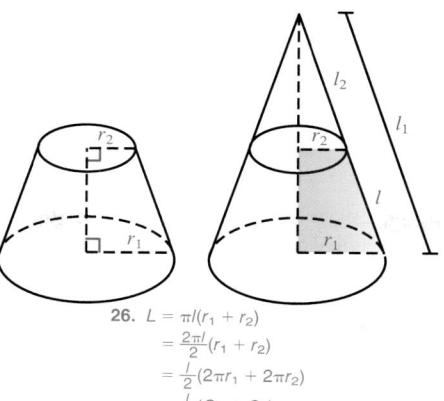

25. Show that the lateral area of the frustum is given by the formula $L = \pi l(r_1 + r_2)$. (*Hint:* Use the fact that $l_1 : r_1 = l_2 : r_2$.)
See side column page 514.

26. Show how the formula in Exercise 25 can be written in the form $L = \frac{1}{2}l(C_1 + C_2)$, where C_1 and C_2 are the respective circumferences.

26. $L = \pi l(r_1 + r_2)$
$= \frac{2\pi l}{2}(r_1 + r_2)$
$= \frac{l}{2}(2\pi r_1 + 2\pi r_2)$
$= \frac{l}{2}(C_1 + C_2)$

Applications

27. **Agriculture** Find the volume of this grain holding tank if it is 15 ft high and 6 ft in diameter, and the height of the funnel is 4 ft.
$V = \pi r^2 h_1 + \frac{1}{3}\pi r^2 h_2 = 147\pi \ \text{ft}^3$

28. **Technology** Using Logo generate the volume of a right circular cone. Use recursion to generate a table of volumes for a sequence of right circular cones. See Solutions Manual.

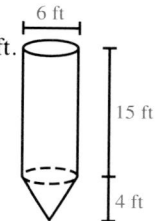
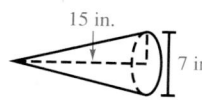

6 ft

15 ft

4 ft

29. **Sewing** How much material would be required to cover this cone-shaped hat if the hat is 15 in. high and the base is 7 in. in diameter? Allow 20 in.^{2} for waste and seams.
$A = \pi r l + 20, \ l \approx 15.4; \ A = 189.246 \ \text{in.}^2$

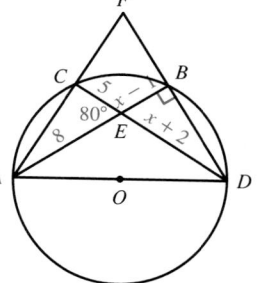

15 in.

7 in.

Mixed Review

Find the following.

30. $ED = \underline{\ ?\ }$ 8

31. $m\widehat{AD} = \underline{\ ?\ }$ 180

32. $m\angle BED = \underline{\ ?\ }$ 80

33. $m\widehat{CB} = \underline{\ ?\ }$ 20

34. $m\angle AED = \underline{\ ?\ }$ 100

35. $AB = \underline{\ ?\ }$ 13

36. $m\angle F = \underline{\ ?\ }$ 80

37. $BD = \underline{\ ?\ }$ $\sqrt{39}$

38. Area $\triangle ABD = \underline{\ ?\ }$ $\frac{13\sqrt{39}}{2}$

39. $m\angle A = \underline{\ ?\ }$ 50

40. What is the locus of points in a plane that are equidistant from two points that are 4 cm apart? the ⊥ bisector of the segment joining the two points

12.5 Cones **515**

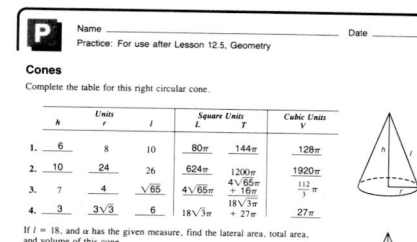

Cones

Complete the table for this right circular cone.

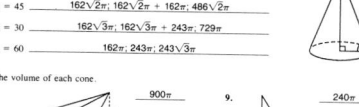

| | Units | | | Square Units | | Cubic Units |
	h	r	l	L	T	V
1.	6	8	10	80π	144π	128π
2.	10	24	26	624π	1200π	1920π
3.	7	4	$\sqrt{65}$	$4\sqrt{65}\pi$	$4\sqrt{65}\pi + 16\pi$	$\frac{112}{3}\pi$
4.	3	$3\sqrt{3}$	6	$18\sqrt{3}\pi$	$18\sqrt{3}\pi + 27\pi$	27π

If $l = 18$, and α has the given measure, find the lateral area, total area, and volume of this cone.

5. $\alpha = 45$ $\quad 162\sqrt{2}\pi; 162\sqrt{2}\pi + 162\pi; 486\sqrt{2}\pi$

6. $\alpha = 30$ $\quad 162\sqrt{3}\pi; 162\sqrt{3}\pi + 243\pi; 729\pi$

7. $\alpha = 60$ $\quad 162\pi; 243\pi; 243\sqrt{3}\pi$

Find the volume of each cone.

8. $\qquad\qquad 900\pi$

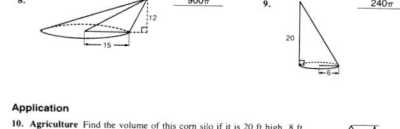

9. $\qquad 240\pi$

Application

10. **Agriculture** Find the volume of this corn silo if it is 20 ft high, 8 ft in diameter, and the length of the funnel is 6 ft. $\quad 352 \ \text{ft}^3$

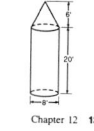

Chapter 12 **13**

Inscribing Cubes in Cones

A cone with radius r and height h is given. We wish to inscribe a cube in the cone. The base of the cube will lie on the base of the cone, and the vertices of the top of the cube will lie on the lateral surface of the cone, as indicated in the diagram. Let s denote a side of the cube. We wish to find the value of s in terms of r and h.

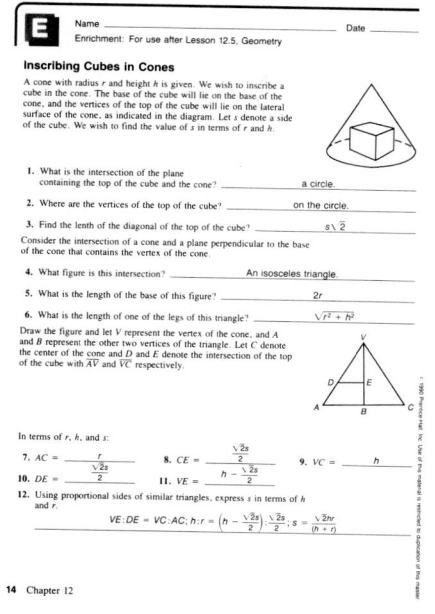

1. What is the intersection of the plane containing the top of the cube and the cone? a circle.

2. Where are the vertices of the top of the cube? on the circle.

3. Find the length of the diagonal of the top of the cube? $s\sqrt{2}$

Consider the intersection of a cone and a plane perpendicular to the base of the cone that contains the vertex of the cone.

4. What figure is this intersection? An isosceles triangle.

5. What is the length of the base of this figure? $2r$

6. What is the length of one of the legs of this triangle? $\sqrt{r^2 + h^2}$

Draw the figure and let V represent the vertex of the cone, and A and B represent the other two vertices of the triangle. Let C denote the center of the cone and D and E denote the intersection of the top of the cube with $\overline{AV}$ and $\overline{VC}$ respectively.

In terms of r, h, and s:

7. $AC = \dfrac{r}{\quad}$

8. $CE = \dfrac{\frac{\sqrt{2}s}{2}}{\quad}$

9. $VC = h$

10. $DE = \dfrac{\sqrt{2}s}{2}$

11. $VE = h - \dfrac{\sqrt{2}s}{2}$

12. Using proportional sides of similar triangles, express s in terms of h and r.

$VE : DE = VC : AC; h : r = \left(h - \dfrac{\sqrt{2}s}{2}\right) : \dfrac{\sqrt{2}s}{2}; s = \dfrac{\sqrt{2}hr}{(h + r)}$

14 Chapter 12

Vocabulary
Hemisphere
Quadrant

Materials/Manipulatives
Models of spheres
Compasses, paper, rulers,
  scissors, and tape
Teaching Transparency 83

Technology
*Computer Test Bank, pp.
797–804*

LESSON FOCUS

Review
• Draw a circle on the chalkboard
  and review the terms *radius, diameter,* and *pi* (π), and the formulas
  for circumference and area of a circle.
• The Algebra Review, Exercises
  24–26, involves solving simulta-
  neous equations.

Alternative Learning Styles
Kinesthetic learners will benefit from
the use of manipulatives. Students
can make their own by using flash
cards of the formulas for the area and
volume of solids. Students can make a
sketch of the solid on the unlined side
of an index card and label the drawing.
On the lined side of the card, students
should write the formulas. They can
use the cards as study aids.

Multicultural Opportunity
See Developing Mathematical Power,
p. 520.

12.6 Spheres

Objective: To find the area and volume of a sphere

Imagine rotating a circle in space about one of its diameters. The three-dimensional figure formed is called a *sphere.* Recall these facts about spheres. A sphere is a set of points in space equidistant from a given point, called the *center.* When a plane intersects a sphere in more than one point, the intersection is a *circle* and if the plane passes through the center of the sphere, the intersection is a *great circle.*

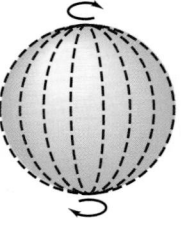

Investigation—*Using Manipulatives*

Using a compass, draw 2 circles, each with a radius of 3 in. Cut out each circular shape and set one aside. Fold the other one in half three successive times. Number its central angles 1 through 8. Cut the sectors and tape them together to model as closely as possible the arrangement shown. Now take the one you had set aside, fold it in half, and tape it to the rearranged circle so that together they form a quadrant of a sphere. Since the area of one great circle has covered one quadrant of a sphere, how many great circles would you expect to cover an entire sphere? 4

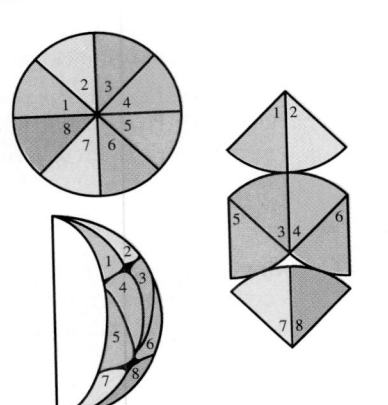

The area of a sphere is equal to the sum of the areas of the four quadrants of the sphere. The surface area of each quadrant is equal to the area of a great circle, or πr^2.

This leads to the next theorem.

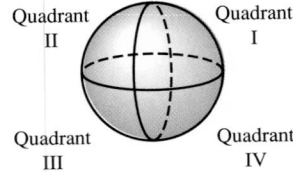

Quadrant II Quadrant I
Quadrant III Quadrant IV

> **Theorem 12.13** The area A of a sphere of radius r is four times the area of a great circle, or $A = 4\pi r^2$.

516   Chapter 12 Area and Volume of Solids

Developing Mathematical Power
Cooperative Learning   Select teams of students to complete the Investigation activity, p. 15, in the *Teacher's Resource Book.* For the toys they design, challenge them to develop an ad campaign (magazine ads and commercials), an economic study (efficient and maximum use of materials), and a name.

EXAMPLE 1   Complete the table for the sphere shown.

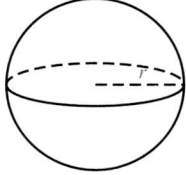

	Radius of Sphere	Area of Great Circle	Area of Sphere
a.	6 cm	?	?
b.	?	16π cm^2	?
c.	?	?	196π in.^{2}

a. 36π cm^2; 144π cm^2 **b.** 4 cm; 64π cm^2 **c.** 7 in.; 49π in.^{2}

The formula for the volume of a sphere can be found by using the formula for the volume of a pyramid. Think of dividing the surface of a sphere into n "polygons," and then joining the vertices of each polygon to the center of the sphere, forming pyramids of height r, the radius of the sphere.

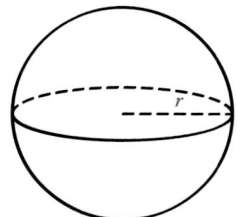 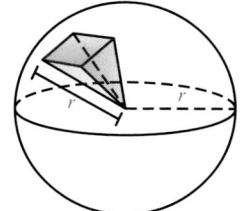

The volume of each pyramid is $\frac{1}{3}Br$, where B is the area of the base. Then

$$V_{sphere} = \text{Sum}(V_{pyramids}) = \frac{1}{3}B_1r + \frac{1}{3}B_2r + \cdots + \frac{1}{3}B_nr$$

$$= \frac{1}{3}(B_1 + B_2 + \cdots + B_n)r$$

Since $(B_1 + B_2 + \cdots + B_n)$ is the area of the sphere, we have

$$V_{sphere} = \frac{1}{3}(4\pi r^2)r, \text{ or } = \frac{4}{3}\pi r^3.$$

Theorem 12.14   The volume V of a sphere of radius r is $\frac{4}{3}\pi r^3$, or $V = \frac{4}{3}\pi r^3$.

EXAMPLE 2   If r has the given value, find the volume of the sphere.

a. $r = 4$ cm   **b.** $r = 6\pi$ in.

c. $r = 1$ in.

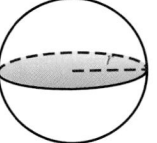

a.  $\frac{256}{3}\pi$ cm^3 **b.** $288\pi^4$ in.^{3} **c.** 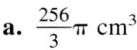 $\frac{4}{3}\pi$ in.^{3}

Developing Mathematical Power

Keeping a Portfolio   Have students describe what they found most difficult in this lesson, whether it was a visualization or computational difficulty, and what was most helpful in overcoming the difficulty. They should also write a brief comment on the correlation of spheres to geography (great circle, hemisphere).

Common Error

- Some students will confuse the volume with the area of a sphere. Emphasize the relationship between the *area* of a sphere and the *area* of its four great circles.
- See *Teacher's Resource Book* for additional remediation.

LESSON FOLLOW-UP

Assignment Guide

See p. 488B for assignments.

EXAMPLE 3 If the diameter of a sphere is 20 m, and if a plane is passed through the sphere at a distance of 8 m from the center, what is the area of the circle of intersection?

Since $r^2 = \sqrt{10^2 - 8^2}$, the radius of the circle of intersection is 6 m. Thus, the area of the circle is πr^2, or 36π m².

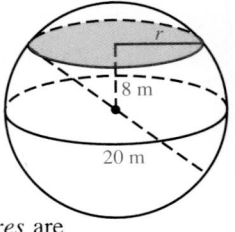

If a plane is passed through the center of a sphere, two *hemispheres* are formed.

CLASS EXERCISES

1. Name all radii shown. $\overline{PJ}, \overline{PL}, \overline{PM}, \overline{PN}$

2. What name is given to $\overline{LM}$? diameter

3. If $PN = 4$ cm, what is the area of $\odot P$? 16π cm²

4. Find the area of $\odot P$: the area of the sphere. 1 : 4

5. If $LM = 12$ in., what is the volume of the sphere? 288π in.³

6. If $\overline{JP} \perp \overline{PM}$, what kind of triangle is $\triangle JPM$? Find JM. isos. rt. △; $PM\sqrt{2}$

7. If the volume of the sphere is $\frac{9}{16}\pi$ in.³, what is the radius? $\frac{3}{4}$ in.

8. If the radius of the sphere is 8 cm, and if a plane is passed through the sphere at a distance of 5 cm from the center, what is the area of the circle of intersection? $r^2 + 5^2 = 8^2$; $r^2 = 39$; $A = \pi r^2 = 39\pi$ cm²

A plane is passed through the center of a sphere.

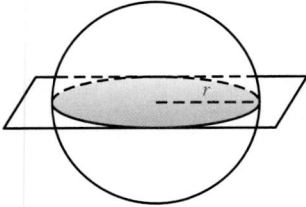

9. What is the surface area of each hemisphere? $2\pi r^2$

10. What figure forms the base of each hemisphere? What is its area? a great circle; πr^2

11. What is the volume of each hemisphere? $\frac{2}{3}\pi r^3$

PRACTICE EXERCISES ⌇ Use technology where appropriate.

A 1. If the area of a sphere is 144π in.², what is its volume? 288π m³

2. If the area of a sphere in square units equals its volume in cubic units, what is the radius? $r = 3$

518   Chapter 12 Area and Volume of Solids

Complete this table.

	Units Radius	Square Units Area of Great Circle	Area of Sphere	Cubic Units Volume
3.	1	? π	? 4π	? $\frac{4}{3}$π
4.	11	? 121π	? 484π	? $\frac{5324}{3}$π
5.	? 7	49π	? 196π	? $\frac{1372}{3}$π
6.	0.75	? 0.5625π	? 2.25π	? 0.5625π
7.	? 4	? 16π	? 64π	$\frac{256}{3}$π
8.	? 3√2	? 18π	72π	? 72π√2
9.	? 2√6	24π	? 96π	? 64π√6
10.	? 5	? 25π	100π	? $\frac{500\pi}{3}$

A sphere of radius 8 in. is inscribed in a right circular cylinder.

11. Find the area of the sphere. 256π in.²

12. Find the lateral area of the cylinder. 256π in.²

B   **13.** How do the area of the sphere and the lateral area of the cylinder compare? Generalize the results. They are equal. The area of a sphere inscribed in a right circular cylinder equals the lateral area of the cylinder.

A sphere of radius r is inscribed in a cube of edge length e.

14. The longest diagonal of the cube is $6\sqrt{3}$ in. Find the volume of the sphere. 36π in.³

15. The area of the sphere is 192π cm². Find the edge of the cube. $e = 8\sqrt{3}$ cm

16. What is the ratio of the volume of the sphere to the volume of the cube? $\frac{\pi}{6}$

17. What percentage of the volume of the cube is outside the sphere? $100\left(1 - \frac{\pi}{6}\right) \approx 47.6\%$

Find the area and volume of each figure.

18.

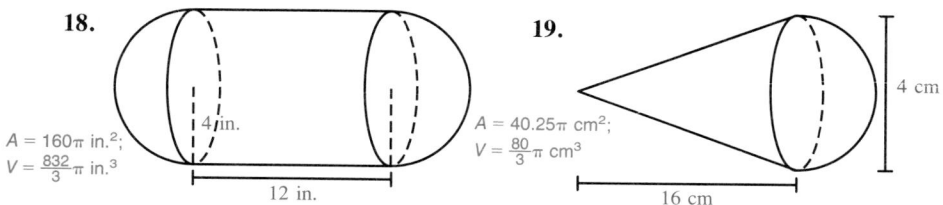

$A = 160\pi$ in.²;
$V = \frac{832}{3}\pi$ in.³
4 in., 12 in.

19. $A = 40.25\pi$ cm²;
$V = \frac{80}{3}\pi$ cm³
4 cm, 16 cm

C   **20.** Suppose the lateral area of a right circular cone and the area of a sphere equal 64π in.² If the radius of the sphere and the radius of the base of the cone are equal, what is the height of the cone? $4\sqrt{15}$ in.

12.6 Spheres   **519**

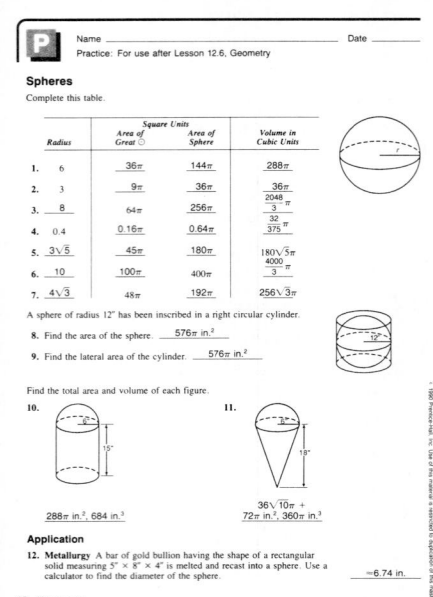

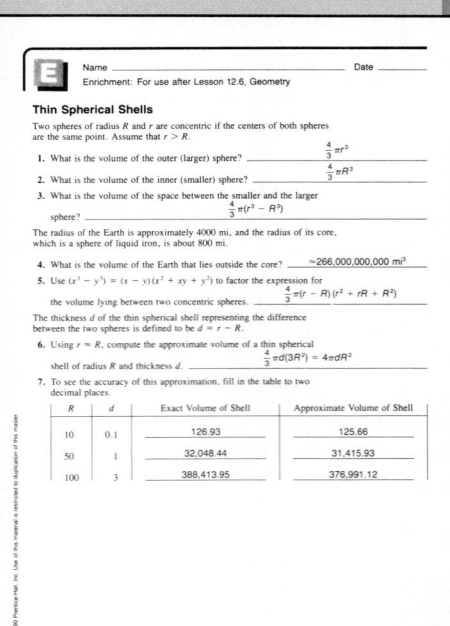

21. Is there a sphere for which the ratio of area to volume = 1:3? If so, describe the sphere; if not, tell why not. yes; $r = 9$

Applications

22. Technology Using Logo, generate in tabular form the volume of a sequence of spheres. What value for r gives the error message number too big in (procedure name)? See Solutions Manual.

23. Metallurgy A $4'' \times 6'' \times 2''$ rectangular bar of silver is melted and recast into a sphere. Use a calculator to find the radius of the sphere. $\frac{4}{3}\pi r^3 = 4 \cdot 6 \cdot 2$, $r^3 = \frac{36}{\pi}$; $r \approx 2.25$

Algebra Review

Solve each system of equations.

24. $2x - y = 7$
$x + y = 11$ (6, 5)

25. $x + 3y = 16$
$2x + y = 2$ (−2, 6)

26. $2x + 3y = 42$
$3x + 2y = 13$ (−9, 20)

Developing Mathematical Power

Investigation The Italian mathematician Bonaventura Cavalieri (1598–1647) demonstrated that the volumes of two noncongruent solids are equal if each pair of cross sections at equal distances from their bases have equal areas.

Consider a hemisphere and a right circular cylinder, each having radius r. The height of the cylinder is also r. Inscribe a cone in the cylinder. Pass a plane through the hemisphere and the cylinder parallel to plane P at distance x from the plane. See side column.

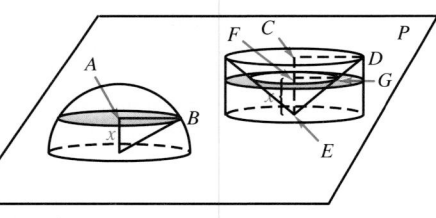

27. Show that the area of circle A is $\pi(r^2 - x^2)$.

28. Prove $\triangle CDE \sim \triangle FGE$, and that $FG:r = x:r$. Solve for FG.

29. Show that the area of the circular ring is $\pi(r^2 - x^2)$.
$A = \pi r^2 - \pi(FG)^2 = \pi r^2 - \pi x^2$; $A = \pi(r^2 - x^2)$
Since the cross sections of the hemisphere and the portion of the cylinder outside the cone have the same area, the hemisphere and the portion of the cylinder outside the cone have the same volume (Cavalieri's Principle).

30. Find the volume of the portion of the cylinder outside the cone. Multiply this answer by 2 to get the volume of the entire sphere.

520 Chapter 12 Area and Volume of Solids

27. $A = \pi(AB)^2$, $x^2 + (AB)^2 = r^2$, $(AB)^2 = r^2 - x^2$; $A = \pi(r^2 - x^2)$

28. Since $\overline{CD} \parallel \overline{FG}$, $\angle CDE \cong \angle FGE$. Also, $\angle DEC \cong \angle GEF$. Thus, $\triangle CDE \sim \triangle FGE$ by AA. Since the $\triangle$ are $\sim$, $FG:CD = EF:EC$. But, $EF = x$, $EC = r$, and $CD = r$. Thus, $FG:r = x:r$ and $FG = x$.

30. $V = \pi r^2 h - \frac{\pi r^2 h}{3} = \frac{2}{3}\pi r^2 h$; $h = r$, $V = \frac{2}{3}\pi r^3$; $V = \frac{4}{3}\pi r^3$

<table>
<tr><td>12.7</td><td colspan="2"></td></tr>
</table>

Areas and Volumes of Similar Solids

Objective: To state and apply the properties of similar solids

Similar solids have the same shape. How do corresponding measures of similar solids compare? How do their lateral areas and volumes compare?

Investigation—*Visualizing the Concept*

Country *B* consumed twice the number of barrels of oil as country *A*. An artist graphed this comparison as shown.

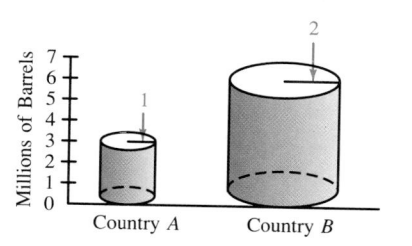

1. Assuming that the two barrels are similar in shape, has the artist conveyed the message she intended? no; volume of 2nd barrel is 8 × volume of 1st.
2. Find the ratio of the radii of the two cylinders and of their volumes. radii 1:2 volumes 1:8

Generally speaking, two solids are **similar** if their bases are similar and corresponding lengths are proportional. The ratio of corresponding lengths of similar solids is called the **scale factor** of the pair of figures.

EXAMPLE 1 **Each pair is similar. Determine the scale factor, ratio of heights, and ratio of base perimeters or circumferences of the first figure to the second.**

a. 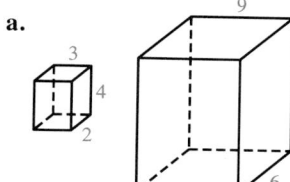 b. 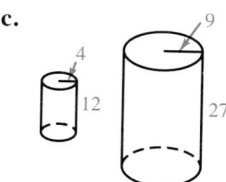 c.

	Scale Factor	$h_1 : h_2$	$P_1 : P_2$
a.	1:3	4:12 = 1:3	10:30 = 1:3
b.	4:3	8: 6 = 4:3	48:36 = 4:3
c.	4:9	12:27 = 4:9	$8\pi : 18\pi = 4:9$

Observe that the ratios of corresponding heights and base perimeters of these pairs of similar figures are the same as the scale factors.

12.7 Areas and Volumes of Similar Solids **521**

Developing Mathematical Power

Cooperative Learning   The Application activity, pp. 20 and 21, in *Connections* can be done by students working in cooperative groups. It provides a hands-on investigation of the relationship of the volume of a cone to its slant height. Allow time for students to explore and exchange ideas and conclusions.

LESSON PLAN

Vocabulary
Similar solids
Scale factor

Materials/Manipulatives
Models of pairs of similar and nonsimilar solids
Teacher's Resource Book, Teaching Aid 12
Transparency 23
Teaching Transparency 84
Connections, pp. 20–21

Technology
Computer Test Bank, pp. 804–812

LESSON FOCUS

Review
- The Chapter Summary and Review, pp. 528–529, gives vocabulary and concepts and review exercises by lesson.
- The end of the chapter features a Cumulative Review on pp. 532–534.

Alternative Learning Styles
- Some students read more slowly than others and cannot visualize information quickly. Others read so fast that they do not internalize the facts. Use the Investigation to help those students visualize the effects of misleading information as well as to emphasize the importance of reading for understanding. Have them locate other graphs that misrepresent data in newspapers or magazines.
- Students may benefit from a kinesthetic approach by using models of pairs of similar solids. Have students measure corresponding lengths to determine scale factors, and then have them compute and compare the volumes of each pair.

521

TEACHING SUGGESTIONS

- Use several examples in which students have to determine corresponding lengths for pairs of similar figures, in which one has volume or area that is twice the volume or area of the other. Repeat for three times the volume or area, and so on.
- Have students verbalize the results of Theorem 12.15. Watch for misconceptions such as "doubling the lengths of the sides doubles the volume."

CHALKBOARD EXAMPLES

- **For Example 1**

Two right circular cones have heights 15 cm and 9 cm, and radius-lengths 10 cm and 6 cm, respectively. Determine the scale factor, ratio of heights, and ratio of base circumferences.

Scale factor 5:3
$h_1:h_2$ 15:9, or 5:3
$C_1:C_2$ $20\pi:12\pi$, or 5:3

- **For Example 2**

Two right circular cylinders have radius-lengths 8 cm and 6 cm, and heights 16 cm and 12 cm, respectively. Find the scale factor, ratio of base circumferences, ratio of lateral areas, and ratio of volumes.

Scale factor 4:3
$C_1:C_2$ $16\pi:12\pi$, or 4:3
$L_1:L_2$ $256\pi:144\pi$, or 16:9
$V_1:V_2$ $1024\pi:432\pi$, or 64:27

EXAMPLE 2 Find the scale factor, ratio of base perimeters, ratio of lateral areas, and ratio of volumes for these pairs of similar figures.

a.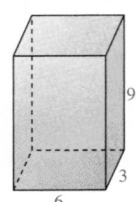

b.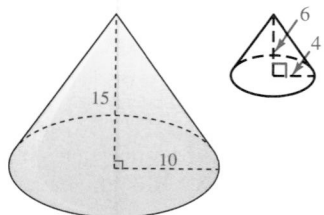

Ratios	a.	b.
Scale factor	2:3	5:2
Perimeter/Circumference	$12:18 = 2:3$	$20\pi:8\pi = 5:2$
Lateral area	$72:162 = 4:9$	$50\pi\sqrt{13}:8\pi\sqrt{13} = 25:4$
Volume	$48:162 = 8:27$	$500\pi:32\pi = 125:8$

Note that the ratio of the lateral areas of the two figures is the square of the ratio of the scale factor, and the ratio of the two volumes is the cube of the scale factor.

Theorem 12.15 If the scale factor of two similar solids is $a:b$, then

1. the ratio of corresponding perimeters or circumferences of the bases is $a:b$;
2. the ratios of base areas, lateral areas, and total areas are $a^2:b^2$; and
3. the ratio of volumes is $a^3:b^3$.

CLASS EXERCISES

Are these right circular cylinders similar? Justify.

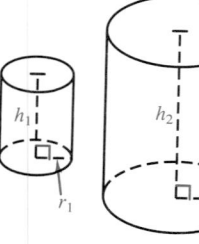

	Radii		Heights	
	r_1	r_2	h_1	h_2
1.	3	5	6	10 yes; $\frac{h_1}{h_2} = \frac{r_1}{r_2}$
2.	4	1	12	8 no; $\frac{h_1}{h_2} \neq \frac{r_1}{r_2}$
3.	7	4	14	10 no; $\frac{h_1}{h_2} \neq \frac{r_1}{r_2}$
4.	5	12	15	36 yes; $\frac{h_1}{h_2} = \frac{r_1}{r_2}$

522   Chapter 12 Area and Volume of Solids

Developing Mathematical Power

Keeping a Portfolio Have students compare and contrast the area and volume of similar plane figures to the area and volume of similar solid figures. They should explain why they think the similarities occur and why there is no ratio of volumes of similiar plane figures. Have them illustrate their work.

True or false? Justify your answers.

5. All spheres are similar. true; r is the only variable, scale factor $r_1:r_2$

6. All cubes are similar. true; e is only variable, scale factor $e_1:e_2$

7. All regular pyramids with square bases are similar. false; heights may be different

8. All right prisms having equilateral triangles as bases are similar. false; heights may be different

9. Since all circles are similar, all right circular cyclinders are similar. false; heights may be different

10. Two right circular cones are similar if their radii have the same ratio as their slant heights. true; $\frac{r_1}{r_2} = \frac{l_1}{l_2}$ and bases are similar

11. Two regular square pyramids are similar if their heights are proportional to their perimeters. true; $\frac{h_1}{h_2} = \frac{p_1}{p_2}$ and bases are similar

12. If the ratio of the volumes of two right prisms is $8:1$, the prisms are similar. false; bases may be different

PRACTICE EXERCISES   Use technology where appropriate.

Thinking Critically   A cube having edge length e has an inscribed and circumscribed sphere.

A   1. What is the radius of the inscribed sphere? the circumscribed sphere? $\frac{e}{2}$; $\frac{e}{2}\sqrt{3}$

2. Find the ratio of the areas of the inscribed and circumscribed spheres. 1:3

3. Find the ratio of the volumes of the inscribed and circumscribed spheres. $\sqrt{3}:9$

These two hexagonal right prisms are similar. Complete the table.

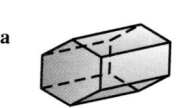 a   b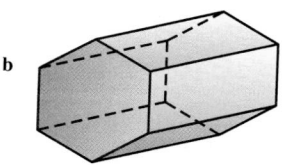

	Scale Factor $s_a:s_b$	Perimeter of Bases $P_a:P_b$	Area of Bases $B_a:B_b$	Lateral Area $L_a:L_b$	Total Area $T_a:T_b$	Volume $V_a:V_b$
4.	1:2	? 1:2	? 1:4	? 1:4	? 1:4	? 1:8
5.	? 5:6	5:6	? 25:36	? 25:36	? 25:36	? 125:216
6.	? 3:4	3:4	? 9:16	? 9:16	? 9:16	? 27:64
7.	? 3:4	? 3:4	9:16	? 9:16	? 9:16	? 27:64
8.	? 1:2	? 1:2	? 1:4	1:4	? 1:4	? 1:8
9.	? 3:7	? 3:7	? 9:49	? 9:49	9:49	? 27:343
10.	? 7:11	? 7:11	? 49:121	? 49:121	? 49:121	343:1331
11.	? 3:4	? 3:4	? 9:16	? 9:16	? 9:16	27:64

If two similar right circular cones have lateral areas 108π cm^2 and 192π cm^2, respectively, find the ratio of their

12. total areas 9:16   13. volumes 27:64   14. circumferences 3:4

12.7 Areas and Volumes of Similar Solids   **523**

Lesson Quiz

1. A right circular cone has radius 4 cm and total area 36π cm². A similar cone has radius 6 cm. Find the total area of the larger cone. 81π cm²

A square pyramid has slant height 13 cm and lateral area 312 cm². A similar pyramid has lateral area 1248 cm².

2. Find the slant height of the larger pyramid 26 cm

3. Find the ratio of the volumes of the smaller to the larger pyramid. 1:8

Enrichment

The volumes of similar solids are given. Find each scale factor.

1. 5103 in.³ and 7000 in.³
2. 288π cm³ and $864\sqrt{3}\pi$ cm³
3. 120π cm³ and 75π cm³

1. $5103:7000 = 729:1000 = 9^3:10^3$; scale factor is 9:10.
2. $288\pi:864\sqrt{3}\pi = 1:3\sqrt{3} = 1^3:(\sqrt{3})^3$; scale factor is $1:\sqrt{3}$.
3. $120\pi:75\pi = 8:5 = 2^3:(\sqrt[3]{5})^3$; scale factor is $2:\sqrt[3]{5}$.

Two similar square-based regular pyramids have lateral areas 588 in.² and 1452 in.², respectively. Find the ratio of their

15. base perimeters 7:11

16. slant heights 7:11

These two regular square-based pyramids are similar. If the volumes are 800 cm³ and 12,500 cm³, respectively, and if $l_2 = 65$ cm, find each of the following.

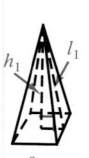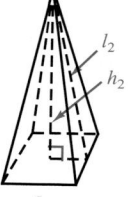

17. $s_1:s_2$ 2:5

18. l_1 26

19. $T_1:T_2$ 4:25

20. $L_1:L_2$ 4:25

If the lateral areas of the figures are 320 cm² and 720 cm², respectively, and if $h_1 = 6$ cm, find each of the following.

B **21.** s_1 and s_2
16 cm; 24 cm

22. l_1 and l_2
10 cm; 15 cm

23. V_1 and V_2
512 cm³; 1728 cm³

24. $V_1:V_2$ 8:27

Consider this rectangular solid having dimensions l, w, and h. If the given transformation is applied, describe the result.

Transformation	Result on:
25. Halve l, w, and h	Total area multiplied by $\frac{1}{4}$
26. Halve l, w, and h	Volume multiplied by $\frac{1}{8}$
27. Halve l, double w and l	Volume doubled
28. Double l, halve h	Volume no change

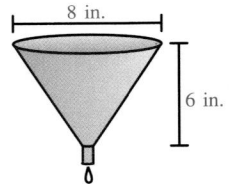

29. If a sphere has radius 1 and volume V, by what amount must the radius be increased to produce a sphere of volume $2V$? $\sqrt[3]{2}$

C **30.** Water is dripping out of this conical funnel at the rate of 8 in.³ per minute. At this rate, how long will it take for a full funnel to become half-full? Where will the water level be at that time? 6.28 min.; $h_1 = 4.76$ in. from bottom vertex

31. Prove Part 2 of Theorem 12.15 for similar right circular cones. See page 773.

Given: Right circular cones C_1 and C_2 with $C_1 \sim C_2$

Prove: $\dfrac{\text{Total area } C_1}{\text{Total area } C_2} = \dfrac{r_1^2}{r_2^2} = \dfrac{h_1^2}{h_2^2} = \dfrac{l_1^2}{l_2^2}$

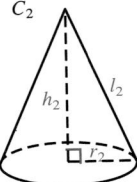

32. If the upper pyramid is similar to the entire pyramid, a formula for the volume of the frustum of the original pyramid is $V = \frac{1}{3}h_1 (B + B_u + \sqrt{B_u B})$, where B_u is the area of the upper base and B is the area of the lower base. Derive this formula.
See Additional Answers, p. 702.

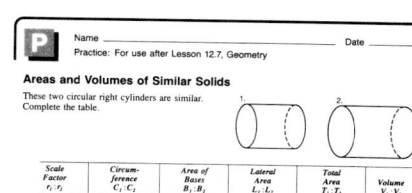

33. Derive a formula for the volume of the frustum of a right circular cone using an approach similar to that of Exercise 32.

Applications

no; scale factor is $\frac{3}{2}$; $\frac{V_L}{V_S} = \frac{27}{8} = 3.375$ and $\frac{\text{price}_L}{\text{price}_S} = \frac{1.29}{.39} = 3.308$

34. Consumer Math A small can of soup is 4 in. tall and 2 in. in diameter and sells for 39 cents; the large size is 6 in. tall and 3 in. in diameter and sells for $1.29. Is the large size comparably priced with the small?

35. Technology Use Logo to draw two similar polyhedra and print out the ratios of their perimeters, lateral areas, and volumes.
See Solutions Manual.

TEST YOURSELF

1. Find the lateral area, total area, and volume of this cone.

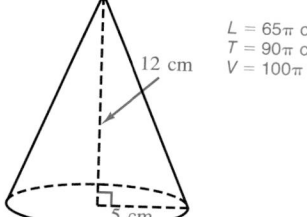

$L = 65\pi$ cm^2
$T = 90\pi$ cm^2
$V = 100\pi$ cm^3

12 cm

5 cm

2. Find the area of the shaded cross section.

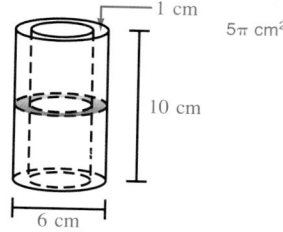

1 cm

5π cm^2

10 cm

6 cm

12.4, 12.5

12.6

3. Find the volume of a sphere having radius 3 cm. 36π cm^3

4. Find the radius of a sphere if its hemisphere has an area of 100π in.^{2} $5\sqrt{2}$ in.

5. If the area of a sphere is 324π in.^{2}, find the volume of the sphere. 972π in.^{3}

6. If the radius of a sphere is increased by 1 cm, by what amount is the area of the sphere increased? $8\pi r + 4\pi$ cm^2

7. If the edge of a cube is increased by 2 in., what is the ratio of the volume of the new cube to that of the original? $\frac{(e+2)^3}{e^3}$

12.7

8. If the total areas of two similar right circular cylinders are 180π cm^2 and 320π cm^2, respectively, find the ratio of their volumes. $27:64$

12.7 Areas and Volumes of Similar Solids **525**

Teacher's Resource Book
Follow-Up Investigation, Chapter 12, p. 18

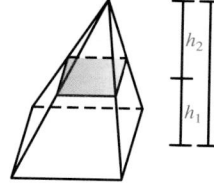

P Name _____ Date _____
Practice: For use after Lesson 12.7, Geometry

Areas and Volumes of Similar Solids
These two circular right cylinders are similar.
Complete the table.

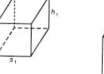

	Scale Factor $r_1 : r_2$	Circumference $C_1 : C_2$	Area of Bases $B_1 : B_2$	Lateral Area $L_1 : L_2$	Total Area $T_1 : T_2$	Volume $V_1 : V_2$
1.	1:4	1:4	1:16	1:16	1:16	1:64
2.	3:7	3:7	9:49	9:49	9:49	27:343
3.	2:5	2:5	4:25	4:25	4:25	8:125
4.	5:6	5:6	25:36	25:36	25:36	125:216
5.	2:9	2:9	4:81	4:81	4:81	8:729
6.	3:8	3:8	9:64	9:64	9:64	27:512

Two similar rectangular-based pyramids have lateral areas 375 in.^{2} and 2160 in.^{2} respectively. Find the ratio of their:

7. perimeters ___5:12___ **8.** slant heights ___5:12___

If the volume of these regular square prisms are in the ratio of 8:27, and if $s_1 = 13$, find:

9. s_2 ___19.5___

10. $T_1:T_2$ ___4:9___

11. $h_1:h_2$ ___2:3___

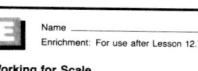

Application

12. Consumer goods A small box of detergent 1″ × 5″ × 7″ sells for $1.25; the large size is 2″ × 6″ × 9″ and sells for $3.50. Is the large size comparably priced with the small size?
___Large size more economical___

Chapter 12 **19**

E Name _____ Date _____
Enrichment: For use after Lesson 12.7, Geometry

Working for Scale

Costs are proportional to the number of units purchased or used. Two storage bins are built in the form of rectangular prisms, and the two storage bins are similar. One is storing wheat at a cost of 15 cents per bushel, and the other is storing corn at a cost of 20 cents per bushel. The silo storing the wheat has a square base 80 ft on a side, and 120 ft tall.

1. If the cost of storing the wheat is $8000, and the cost of storing the corn is $36,000, find the height and the length of a side of the silo storing corn. ___180 ft; 120 ft___

A sphere with a 4-in. radius is being plated with silver, for a cost of $30.

2. If gold plating costs 75% more than silver plating, how much will it cost to gold-plate a sphere of radius 6 in.? ___$118.13___

3. To two decimal places, what is the radius of a sphere which is plated with silver for a cost of $80? ___6.53 in.___

4. To two decimal places, what is the radius of a sphere which is plated with gold at a cost of $100? ___5.52 in.___

Two similar cylinders contain juice. The first cylinder has a radius of 6-in. and a height of 10-in., contains orange juice, and sells for $2.40.

5. If grapefruit juice costs two-thirds of the price of an equal volume of orange juice, what is the cost of a container of grapefruit juice that has a radius of 9 in. and a height of 15 in.? ___$5.40___

6. To two decimal places, what is the radius of a container holding $4.00 worth of grapefruit juice? ___8.14 in.___

7. To two decimal places, what is its height? ___13.57 in.___

Two similar cones have a combined volume of 400 cubic inches, and the larger cone holds 80 cubic inches more than the smaller cone, which has a radius of 3 inches.

8. To two decimal places, what is the height of the smaller cone? ___16.98 in.___

9. What is the radius of the larger cone? ___3.43 in.___

10. What is the height of the larger cone? ___19.44 in.___

20 Chapter 12

525

See *Teacher's Resource Book,* Follow-up *Technology,* pp. 15–16.

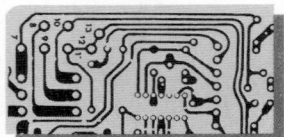

TECHNOLOGY:
The Coordinate System in Logo

LogoWriter has a built-in coordinate system with the turtle in the center at the position of (0, 0). The dimensions of the screen with this coordinate system are as follows:

$$90$$

$$-140 \qquad\qquad 0 \qquad\qquad 139$$

$$-89$$

To move the turtle to any position on the screen, the command is:

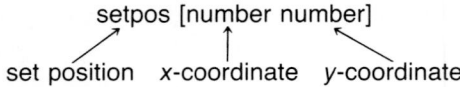

setpos [number number]

set position   *x*-coordinate   *y*-coordinate

EXAMPLE   **Given that the turtle is in the center of the screen, predict each output.**

   a. setpos [−90 90]   **b.** setpos [0 90]

   a. A line from the center of the screen to the upper left corner
   b. A line straight up the screen

The following procedure uses the **setpos** command to draw a square.

```
to square
setpos [0 50]
setpos [50 50]
setpos [50 0]
setpos [0 0]
end
```

(0,50)   (50,50)

(0,0)   (50,0)

In order to use variables with the **setpos** commands, the **sentence (se)** primitive is used. The **sentence (se)** command is used when you want to (1) put together variables and statements, as in:

print (se [the area of this cube is:] :area)

(2) put together more than one variable, as in:

setpos (se :x :y)   *Note that parentheses are placed before the se command and after the last item in the list.*

The following procedure draws a line from a point with an *x*-coordinate less than 80 to a point with *x*-coordinate equal to 80 using the **se** command.

```
to draw.a.line :x :y
if :x > 80[stop]
setpos (se :x :y)
draw.a.line (:x + 1) (:y + 1)
end
```

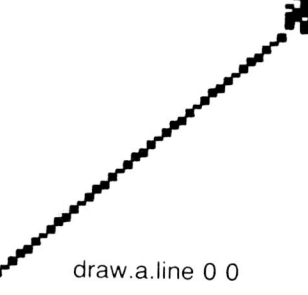

draw.a.line 0 0

Logo has other coordinate commands that help in drawing graphics.

Input	Ouput
seth number	Turns the turtle that "number" of degrees
print pos (or pr pos)	Prints out both coordinates of the turtle's position
print heading (or pr heading)	Prints out the angle turn of the turtle
heading	Outputs a number *n,* where $0 \leq n \leq 360$, and represents the direction the turtle is facing

EXERCISES   See Solutions Manual.

1. Change the *square* procedure shown above to draw a square which is symmetric about the origin. How would you describe symmetry about the origin in terms of the *x*- and *y*-coordinates?

2. Draw a cube using the **setpos** commands. Since Logo has only a two-dimensional coordinate system, what relationships exist between the *x*- and *y*-coordinates?

3. Draw a pyramid and a prism using the **setpos** commands. Which did you find more challenging?

4. Use **setpos** commands in your polyhedra procedure from page 525. Discuss the difference in your thinking for each procedure.

5. Try different **:x** and **:y** with the *line* procedure shown above. What happens if your line starts at some point other than the origin?

6. Write a short procedure to place the turtle at the beginning of the line you wish to draw.

7. Use the **heading** command to change the turtle's direction, then move the turtle with a **setpos** command. What happens to the **heading**?

8. How could you incorporate **setpos** commands with a variable into a *tessellation* procedure?

Technology: The Coordinate System in Logo   **527**

- See *Teacher's Resource Book, Spanish Chapter Summary and Review,* pp. 23–24.
- See Extra Practice, p. 654.

Vocabulary

altitude (491, 503, 511)
axis (502, 511)
base (490, 495)
base edge (495)
cone (511)
cylinder (502)
edge (490)
face (490)
lateral area (491, 496, 503, 512)
lateral edge (490, 495)

lateral face (490, 495)
lateral surface (511)
oblique circular cylinder (502)
oblique cone (511)
oblique prism (491)
polyhedron (490)
prism (490)
pyramid (495)
right circular cone (511)

right circular cylinder (502)
scale factor (521)
similar solids (521)
slant height (495, 511)
total area (491, 503, 512)
vertex (490, 495)
volume (491, 497, 503, 512, 517)

Prisms Prisms are polyhedra having a pair of congruent bases contained in parallel planes. Formulas for finding the lateral and total area of right prisms and the volume of any prism are: $L = Ph;\ T = L + 2B;\ V = Bh.$

This figure is a regular right prism.

1. Name the bases.   2. Name the face opposite *ELMF*.
   CDEFGH; JKLMNO   *CHOJ*
3. Find the lateral area, total area, and volume. 768;
   $768 + 192\sqrt{3};\ 1536\sqrt{3}$

12.1

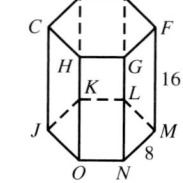

Pyramids A pyramid is a polyhedron all of whose faces except one have a vertex in common. A regular pyramid has a regular polygon as its base. The lateral and total areas of a regular pyramid and the volume of any pyramid are found by these formulas: $L = \frac{1}{2}lP;\ T = L + B;\ V = \frac{1}{3}Bh.$

12.2

This figure is a square-based right pyramid.

4. If $s = 10$ and $h = 12$, find l, the lateral area, the total area, and the volume. 13; 260; 360; 400

5. If the lateral area is 80 in.^{2} and the slant height, l, is 5 in., find the volume. 64 in.^{3}

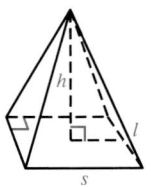

Cylinders A cylinder is a solid figure with a pair of bases that are congruent circles in parallel planes. The lateral area and total area of right circular cylinders are found with these formulas: $L = Ch = 2\pi rh$ and $T = L + 2B = 2\pi r(h + r)$. For any cylinder, the volume formula is $V = Bh = \pi r^2 h$.

12.3

6. If $r = 5$ cm and $h = 9$ cm, find the lateral area, total area, and volume of this right circular cylinder.
90π cm²; 140π cm²; 225π cm³

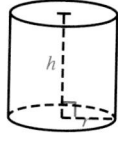

7. If the lateral area is 180π in.², and the total area is 252π in.², find the volume. $V = 540\pi$ in.³

8. A right regular hexagonal pyramid has a radius of 8 cm and height 8 cm. Find the area of a right section at a distance of 6 cm from the base. 6√3 cm²

12.4

Cones A cone is a figure having a circular base and a vertex that is not in the plane of the base. For right circular cones, the formula for lateral area is $L = \frac{1}{2}Cl = \pi r l$, and the formula for total area is $T = L + B = \pi r(l + r)$. For any cone, the volume formula is $V = \frac{1}{3}Bh = \frac{1}{3}\pi r^2 h$.

12.5

9. If $r = 4$ in. and $h = 10$ in., find the lateral area, total area, and volume of this right circular cone. $8\pi\sqrt{29}$ in.²; $16\pi + 8\pi\sqrt{29}$ in.²; $\frac{160\pi}{3}$ in.³

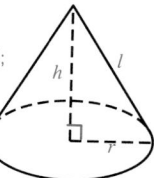

10. If $r = 7$ cm, and if the slant height is 1 cm longer than the height, find the lateral area and volume.
175π cm²; 392π cm³

Spheres A sphere is the set of all points in space that are equidistant from a given point, the center. The area and volume formulas for a sphere are $A = 4\pi r^2$ and $V = \frac{4}{3}\pi r^3$.

12.6

11. If a sphere has radius 7 in., find its area and volume. 196π in.²; $\frac{1372\pi}{3}$ in.³

Areas and Volumes of Similar Solids Two solids are similar if their bases are similar and corresponding length measures are proportional. If the scale factor of two similar solids is $a:b$, the ratio of base perimeters or circumferences is also $a:b$; the ratio of areas associated with the solids is $a^2:b^2$ and the ratio of their volumes is $a^3:b^3$.

12.7

12. Are these solids similar? If so, give the ratio of their perimeters, lateral areas, and volumes. If not, explain.
no; corr. length measures are not necessarily in proportion

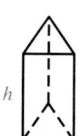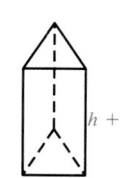

13. A rectangular solid has length 15 cm, width 12 cm, and height 9 cm. If each dimension is divided by 3, give the scale factor and the ratios of the base perimeters, total areas, and volumes of the original figure to the second figure. scale factor = 3:1; $P_1:P_2 = 3:1$; $T_1:T_2 = 9:1$; $V_1:V_2 = 27:1$

See *Teacher's Resource Book*, Tests, pp. 125–128.

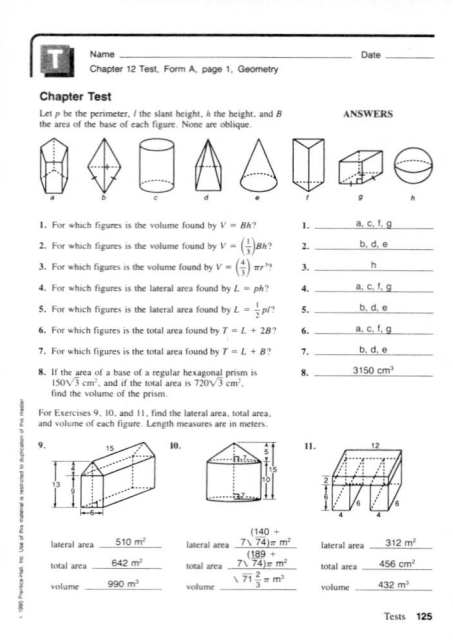

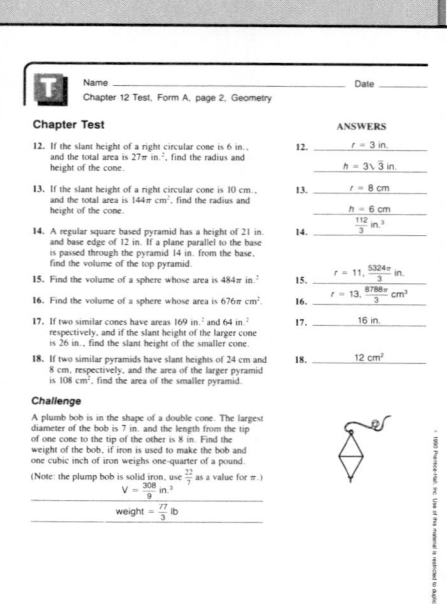

---

a 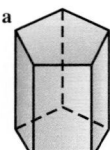 b 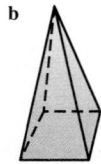 c 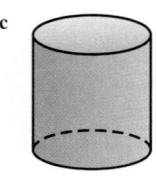 d 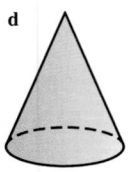 e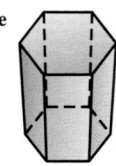

For which of the above nonoblique figures is the statement true?

1. The volume is found by $V = Bh$.
a; c; e

2. The volume is found by $V = \frac{1}{3}Bh$.
b; d

3. The lateral area is given by $L = Ph$.
a; c; e

4. The lateral area is given by $L = \frac{1}{2}Pl$.
b; d

For Exercises 5 and 6, find the total area and volume of each figure.

5.

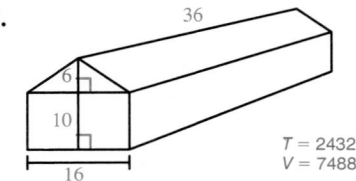

36

6

10

16

$T = 2432$;
$V = 7488$

6.

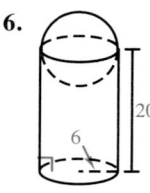

20

6

$T = 348\pi$;
$V = 864\pi$

7. If the area of a base of a regular hexagonal prism is $\frac{3\sqrt{3}}{2}$ in.^{2} and the total area is $45\sqrt{3}$ in.^{2}, find the volume of the prism. $\frac{63}{2}$ in.^{3}

8. If the slant height of a right circular cone is 13 in. and the total area is 90π in.^{2}, find the radius and the height of the cone. 5 in.; 12 in.

9. A regular square-based pyramid has a height of 16 in. and base edge of 10 in. If a plane parallel to the base is passed through the pyramid 12 in. from the base, find the volume of the top pyramid. $\frac{25}{3}$ in.^{3}

10. Find the volume of a sphere whose area is 324π in.^{2} 972π in.^{3}

11. If two similar cones have lateral areas 121 in.^{2} and 49 in.^{2} and the slant height of the larger cone is 22 in., find the slant height of the smaller one. 14 in.

Challenge

A spherical ball of radius 4 cm is dropped into a cone. A cross section of the cone through its axis is an isosceles triangle having a 60° vertex angle.
What is the circumference of the intersection of the sphere and the cone?
$4\sqrt{3}\,\pi$ cm

Alternative Assessment   Have students write eight questions that they think cover the concepts of the chapter. They may use the text as a reference for ideas, but numbers must be changed. For each question, they should describe the concept being tested and provide an illustrated, detailed answer.

Solve. Grid in your response on the answer sheet.

1. A circle with radius 12 and a rectangle with width 16 have equal areas. Find the length of the rectangle to the nearest tenth. 28.3

2. How many integers between 1400 and 1500 contain at least one digit 3? 19

3. Mr. Fuller paid $12.50 for a new tire and tube for his son's old bicycle and had it serviced for $35. He then advertised it for sale at $120. When it hadn't sold after a few days, he reduced the sales price by 15% and sold it then. How much in dollars and cents did Mr. Fuller actually make on the sale? $54.50

4. The circle is inscribed in the equilateral triangle. The shaded area can be written as $p\sqrt{3} - q\pi$. Find the value of $p + q$. 64

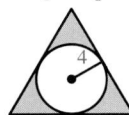

5. A rectangular prism has width 6, height 3, and length 12. Its volume is equal to the volume of a cube with diagonal k. Find k to the nearest tenth. 10.4

6. Simplify: $\dfrac{2^3 + 2^3 + 2^3}{3^2 + 3^2 + 3^2}$. $\frac{8}{9}$

Use this information for 7–8.

The River Rafting Co. offers a 1-day trip for groups. They charge $50 per person but have a minimum charge of $900 and a maximum charge of $1350 for one raft for the day. Each raft can hold 33 passengers.

7. A boating club of 15 members took the 1-day trip and were the only ones on the raft. In dollars, how much did each member pay for the trip? $60

8. If each member of a hiking club paid $45 for the 1-day trip using one raft, how many went rafting? 30

9. Noreen ran 4 mi farther than Susan. Together they ran a distance of 20 mi. How many miles did Noreen run? 12

Use this diagram for 10.

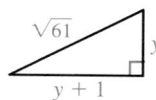

10. Find the value of y. 5

11. In the figure below, the length of the minor arc DF is $\frac{1}{9}$ of the circumference of the circle with center O. What is the measure of $\angle DOF$ in degrees? 40

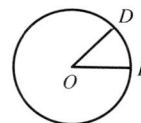

College Entrance Exam Review **531**

According to the College Entrance Examination Board and the Educational Testing Service, the 1994 revision of the SAT will include a section of problems that require students to produce and grid in their own answers.

See *Teacher's Resource Book*, Preparing for College Entrance Exams, for grids.

True or false? Justify each answer.

1. If $\angle 1 \cong \angle 2$ and $m\angle RST = m\angle 1 + m\angle 4$, then $m\angle RST = m\angle 2 + m\angle 4$. — 2.3
   true; subst. prop.
2. Each interior angle of a regular hexagon has a measure of 60. false; 120 — 3.8
3. If $\triangle MAP \cong \triangle TIN$, then $\overline{MP} \cong \overline{NT}$. true; CPCTC — 4.1
4. The median to the base of an isosceles triangle is perpendicular to the base. true; median to the base forms $\cong$ adj. $\angle$s — 4.5
5. In $\triangle RAP$, if $\angle A \cong \angle P$, then $\overline{AP} \cong \overline{AR}$. false; $\overline{RP} \cong \overline{AR}$ — 5.1
6. In any proportion, the product of the extremes equals the product of the means. true; proportion prop. — 7.1
7. The geometric mean between 5 and 20 is 12.5. false; geom. mean is 10 — 7.2
8. The tangent of a 45° angle is 1. true; def. of tan — 8.6
9. The products of the segment lengths of two intersecting chords in a circle are equal. true; Theorem 9.13 — 9.7
10. Concentric circles have the same radii. false; have the same center — 9.1
11. The locus of points in space equidistant from two parallel planes is a point. false; a plane — 10.6
12. If two circles have radii of 5 and 9, then the ratio of their areas is 10:27. false; ratio is 25:81 — 11.7
13. The formula for finding the area of an equilateral triangle is $A = \dfrac{s^2\sqrt{3}}{4}$. true; Corollary 2 of Theorem 11.3 — 11.2

Is each statement true *sometimes*, *always*, or *never*? Justify each answer.

14. Two planes ___?___ intersect at one point. never; one line — 1.2
15. The supplement of an acute angle is ___?___ an acute angle. never; obtuse — 1.5
16. If two lines have a transversal and interior angles on the same side of the transversal complementary, then the lines are ___?___ parallel. never; $\angle$s must be supp. — 3.3
17. If quad. $ABCD \cong$ quad. $MNPQ$, then $\overline{AD}$ is ___?___ congruent to $\overline{MN}$. sometimes; when $\overline{AD} \cong \overline{AB}$ and $\overline{MN} \cong \overline{MQ}$ — 6.6
18. The altitude to the base of an isosceles triangle ___?___ bisects the base. always — 4.5
19. The lengths of the sides of a triangle can ___?___ be 1, $\sqrt{2}$, and 3. never; $1 + \sqrt{2} \not> 3$ — 5.6
20. A trapezoid is ___?___ a rhombus. never; a trap. has only one pair of $\parallel$ sides — 6.5
21. The sum of the acute angle measures of a right triangle is ___?___ equal to 90. always — 3.4

Is each statement true *sometimes*, *always*, or *never*? Justify each answer.

22. If the legs of a right triangle measure 6 and 9, then the hypotenuse ?_ measures $3\sqrt{13}$. always; $6^2 + 9^2 = (3\sqrt{13})^2$ 8.2

23. A radius and a secant are ?_ perpendicular. sometimes   9.1

24. The opposite angles of an inscribed quadrilateral are ?_ congruent.   9.4
 sometimes; when it is a rect.

25. The intersection of the three medians of a triangle is ?_ the   10.5
 circumcenter. sometimes; when the △ is equilateral

26. The area of a triangle is ?_ the product of the base and the height.   11.2

27. Regular septagons are ?_ similar. always   7.3

                                                                      never; $A = \frac{1}{2}bh$

Complete.

28. The sum of the exterior angles of a dodecagon is ?_. 360   3.8

29. Given the statement *All right angles are congruent*, write the   2.1, 2.2
 conditional statement, converse, inverse, and contrapositive. State
 the truth value of each. See side column.

30. If M is the midpoint of $\overline{DE}$ with $DM = 3x - 7$ and $DE = 4x + 2$, then   1.3
 $x = $?_. 8

Given △*QRN* and △*BPT*.

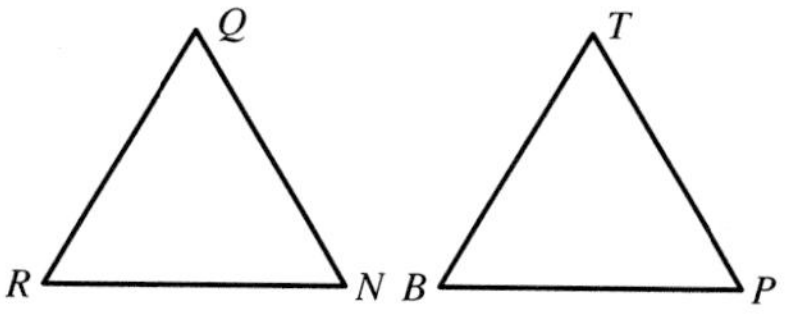

31. If $QR > QN$, then $m\angle R$?_   5.5
 $m\angle N$. <

32. If $\overline{QR} \cong \overline{BP}$, $\overline{RN} \cong \overline{TB}$, and   5.6
 $m\angle B < m\angle R$, then QN ?_ TP. >

33. If $\angle Q \cong \angle T$, $\angle R \cong \angle P$, and $\overline{QN} \cong \overline{TB}$,   4.2
 then $\overline{RN}$?_ $\overline{BP}$ because ?_. ≅ CPCTC

34. In this figure, $x = $?_. 8.5   6.5

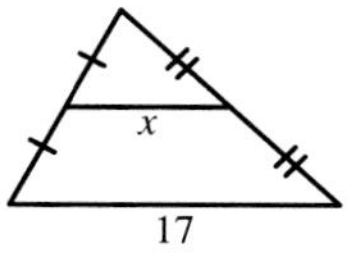

35. The measures of the angles of a triangle are in the ratio $4:4:7$. Find   3.4, 7.1
 the three measures. 48, 48, 84

36. If $\overline{BE} \parallel \overline{CD}$, then $x = $?_   7.7
 and $y = $?_. 16, 3

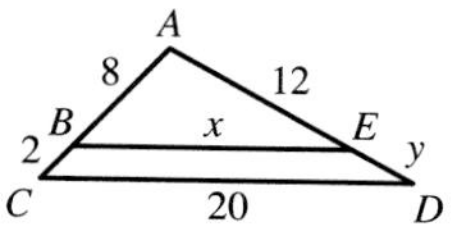

29. Cond.: If 2 ∠s are rt. ∠s, then they
 are ≅. (true)
 Conv.: If 2 ∠s are ≅, then they are rt.
 ∠s. (false)
 Inv.: If 2 ∠s are not rt. ∠s, then they are
 not ≅. (false)
 Ctpos.: If 2 ∠s are not ≅, then they are
 not rt. ∠s. (true)

46. Plan: Use the postulate for adding adj. nonoverlapping arcs to show $\overarc{AC} \cong \overarc{BD}$. Then $\overline{CA} \cong \overline{BD}$ because their arcs are $\cong$.

Proof:

Statements	Reasons
1. $\overarc{AB} \cong \overarc{CD}$	1. Given
2. $m\overarc{AB} = m\overarc{CD}$	2. Def. of $\cong$ arcs
3. $\overarc{BC} \cong \overarc{BC}$	3. Refl. prop.
4. $m\overarc{BC} = m\overarc{BC}$	4. Def. of $\cong$ arcs
5. $m\overarc{AB} + m\overarc{BC} =$ $m\overarc{CD} + m\overarc{BC}$	5. Add. prop.
6. $m\overarc{AC} = m\overarc{BD}$	6. Meas. of the arc formed by 2 adj. nonoverlapping arcs is the sum of the meas. of the two arcs.
7. $\overarc{CA} \cong \overarc{BD}$	7. Def. of $\cong$ arcs
8. $\overline{CA} \cong \overline{BD}$	8. If 2 minor arcs are $\cong$, their chords are $\cong$.

Concl.: In the given figure, if $\overarc{AB} \cong \overarc{CD}$, then $\overline{CA} \cong \overline{BD}$.

47. Plan: Assume the negation of $\overline{BT} \not\cong \overline{CT}$ and show that this leads to a contradiction.

Proof:
Assume:

$\overline{BT} \cong \overline{CT}$	Neg. of the concl.
$\overline{AB} \cong \overline{AC}$	Given
$\overline{AT} \cong \overline{AT}$	Refl. prop.
$\triangle ABT \cong \triangle ACT$	SSS
$\angle 1 \cong \angle 2$	CPCTC

Contradiction: $\angle 1 \not\cong \angle 2$
Concl.: Since the assumption that $\overline{BT} \cong \overline{CT}$ leads to a contradiction, $\overline{BT} \cong \overline{CT}$ is false. Therefore, $\overline{BT} \not\cong \overline{CT}$.

Complete.

37. In this figure, $x = \underline{\ ?\ }$ and $y = \underline{\ ?\ }$. 5, 12   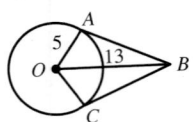   8.2

38. If an inscribed angle measures $30°$, then its intercepted arc measures $\underline{\ ?\ }$. 60   9.4

39. If $\overline{AB}$ and $\overline{BC}$ are tangent segments, then the perimeter of the quadrilateral is $\underline{\ ?\ }$. 34   9.2

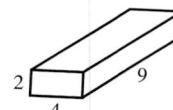

40. If the diagonals of a rhombus have measures of 12 and 16, then the perimeter is $\underline{\ ?\ }$. 40   6.4, 8.2

41. The area of this trapezoid is $\underline{\ ?\ }$. $14\sqrt{3}$ 11.3, 8.4

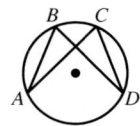

42. If the perimeter of a regular hexagon is 24, then the apothem is $\underline{\ ?\ }$, the radius is $\underline{\ ?\ }$, and the area is $\underline{\ ?\ }$. $2\sqrt{3}$ 4 $24\sqrt{3}$ 11.4

43. If two similar pyramids have a scale factor of $7:4$, then the ratio of slant heights is $\underline{\ ?\ }$, the ratio of base areas is $\underline{\ ?\ }$, the ratio of volumes is $\underline{\ ?\ }$, and the ratio of total areas is $\underline{\ ?\ }$. $7:4$ $49:16$ $343:64$ $49:16$ 12.7

44. If two similar polygons have a scale factor of $6:5$ and the area of the larger is 108, then the area of the smaller is $\underline{\ ?\ }$. 75   11.8

45. In this rectangular solid, $L = \underline{\ ?\ }$, $T = \underline{\ ?\ }$, and $V = \underline{\ ?\ }$. 52 124 72   12.1

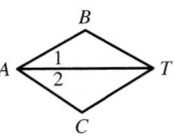

46. Given: $\overarc{AB} \cong \overarc{CD}$
Prove: $\overline{CA} \cong \overline{BD}$

See side column.

47. Write an indirect proof.
Given: $\overline{AB} \cong \overline{AC}$, $\angle 1 \not\cong \angle 2$
Prove: $\overline{BT} \not\cong \overline{CT}$

OVERVIEW   Chapter 13

SUMMARY

In Chapter 13, students learn to use coordinates to specify points on the plane. Guidelines are established for writing the equation of a line given a point and its slope or given two points on the line. Students also learn to determine points of intersection between two lines and to determine whether lines are parallel or perpendicular.

CHAPTER OBJECTIVES

- To specify points in the coordinate plane by means of their coordinates

- To state and apply the Distance Formula, the general equation of a circle and the Midpoint Formula

- To find the slope of a line, given two points on the line

- To draw the graph of a line specified by a given equation

- To write the equation of a line, given either one point and the slope of the line, or two points on the line

- To determine the point of intersection of two lines

- To determine whether two lines are parallel, perpendicular, or neither

- To write an equation of a line parallel or perpendicular to a given line

- To *use coordinate geometry in proofs* by choosing a convenient placement of the coordinate axes and assigning appropriate coordinates for proving statements

CHAPTER HIGHLIGHTS

Problem Solving

Lesson 13.7 presents the four problem solving steps as a means for analyzing and writing coordinate geometry proofs.

Communication

The side column suggests using manipulatives and the coordinate plane as an alternative learning style. Students are asked to compare and contrast in their journals the equations of lines that are parallel and perpendicular. There is a Chapter Summary and Review in Spanish in the *Teacher's Resource Book.*

Reasoning

Students will write coordinate proofs of previous theorems. In a thinking critically exercise students are asked to find the equations for the midpoint and distance of a line in three dimensional space.

Connections

Real-world applications include such topics as interior decorating, recreation, and science. The biographical sketches of three mathematicians provide students with an example of the variety of cultural influences on mathematics.

Technology

Logo exercises appear throughout the chapter. Embedded recursion and dragon curves of Logo comprise the technology feature at the end of the chapter.

STUDENT TEXT

Chapter Content	Basic	Average	Enriched	NCTM STANDARDS*
13.1 The Distance Formula	D: 538/1-29, 56	D: 538/1-33, 38-49 even, 56-58	D: 538/10-25, 38-49 even, 50-58	3, 5, 8, 14
13.2 The Equation of a Circle	D: 543/1-18, 40 R: 538/34-39	D: 543/1-26, 40-43 R: 538/38-49 odd	D: 543/1-32 odd, 37-43 R: 538/38-49 odd	3, 5, 8
13.3 The Midpoint Formula	D: 548/1-14, 35, MR R: 543/19-22	D: 548/1-24, 35, 45, MR R: 543/27-32	D: 548/1-29 odd, 30-36, 45, MR R: 543/33-36	1, 4, 8, 14
13.4 Slope of a Line	D: 555/1-22, 46-48, MR R: 548/17-20	D: 555/1-20, 21-39 odd, 45-48, MR R: 548/25-29	D: 555/1-39 odd, 40-48, MR R: 548/21-29 even	3, 5, 8, 12
13.5 Equations of a Line	D: 561/1-28, 56 R: 555/23, 24, 26, 28	D: 561/1-24, 25-36 odd, 37-48, 56-58 R: 555/21-39 even	D: 561/1-24, 25-48 odd, 49-58 R: 555/20-31 even	1, 5, 8
13.6 Slopes of Parallel and Perpendicular Lines	D: 567/1-20, 41, AR R: 561/29, 31, 33	D: 567/1-24, 29-34, 41, 42, AR R: 561/25-36 even	D: 567/1-14, 15-34 odd, 35-42, AR R: 561/33-44, even	1, 3, 5, 8
13.7 Strategy: Use Coordinate Geometry in Proofs	D: 574/1-16 R: 567/21-24	D: 574/1-16 odd, 17-26 R: 567/25-28	D: 574/10-26 even, 27-32 R: 567/31-34 even	1, 7, 8, 12, 14

D = Daily   R = Review   MR = Mixed Review   AR = Algebra Review

*For a complete list of NCTM Standards, see p. T7.

STUDENT TEXT

Review/Assessment

Mixed Review 550, 557

Algebra Review 569, 584

Summary and Review 580

College Ent. Exam Rev. 583

Extra Practice 655

Test Yourself 551, 577

Chapter Test 582

Chapter Project 535

Special Features

Technology 540, 545, 550 557, 564, 569, 578-579

Devel. Math. Power 540, 545, 550

Applications 540, 545, 550, 557, 564, 569

Project 577

Biography 545, 564

RESOURCES

Teacher's Resource Book

Ch. 13: Investigation/Practice/ Enrichment 1-20

Spanish Sum. and Rev. 25-26

Quizzes 137-140

Chapter Tests 141-144

Perf. Assessment Proj. Ch. 13

Critical Thinking 13

Reading and Writing in Geom. 13

Technology 17-18

Teaching Aid 13

Transparency 24-25

Teaching Transparencies 85-91

Computer Test Bank 813-864

PH Graph. Utility

Overhead Manip. Kit

534B

3 Coordinate Geometry

A spiraling effect?

Developing Mathematical Power

[spi]ral is a curve generated [by] a point moving around [and] away from a fixed point. [The] nautilus shell is a logarithmic spiral in which the distance between loops increases as the point moves away from the fixed point.

In Archimedean spirals, the distance between loops is constant. A phonograph needle tracks an Archimedean spiral path as a record is played.

Project

Construct an Archimedean spiral using a coordinate grid. Then adapt your method to construct different Archimedean spirals. Analyze the spirals. Which properties are the same for all Archimedean spirals? Which are different?

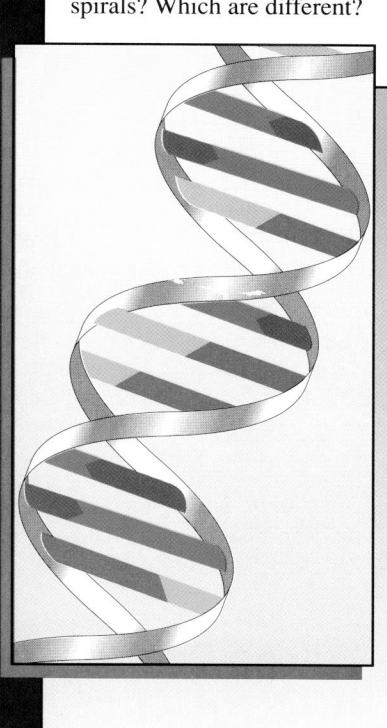

535

Alternative Assessment
See *Teacher's Resource Book,* Assessment, Chapter 13. This project and the TRB page may be used as an alternative form of assessment for selected topics in Chapter 13.

BACKGROUND

- As a chambered nautilus grows, its shell grows in the shape of a logarithmic spiral. The nautilus always lives in the outermost chamber. When that chamber becomes too small, the nautilus moves ahead inside the shell and builds a wall behind itself to form a new chamber.
- A real-life example of an Archimedean spiral is a person walking at a constant speed from the center of a merry-go-round toward a fixed point on the merry-go-round while the merry-go-round rotates at a constant speed.

MODELING

Mathematics provides the power to model physical situations. This project involves constructing a model of an Archimedean spiral—a point moving along a ray, away from its origin at a constant speed, while the ray itself rotates around the origin at a constant speed.

Cooperative Learning

This project is accomplished through a succession of tasks, each of which is well-suited to a cooperative learning situation. These tasks include:
1. Deciding on the parameters for a mathematical model.
2. Drawing the model.
3. Drawing variations of the model.
4. Analyzing the models.
5. Drawing conclusions.

Students' drawings should resemble this spiral:

Vocabulary

Coordinate	Vertical line
plane	*x*-axis
Horizontal line	*x*-coordinate
Ordered pair	*y*-axis
Origin	*y*-coordinate
Quadrants	

Materials/Manipulatives

Graph paper
Teacher's Resource Book,
Teaching Aid 13,
Transparency 24
Teaching Transparencies 85 and
85A

Technology

Computer Test Bank, pp.
813–821

LESSON FOCUS

Review

Refer to the number line. Find

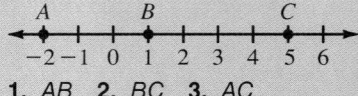

1. *AB* **2.** *BC* **3.** *AC*
1. 3 2. 4 3. 7

Alternative Learning Styles

- Using a map will help students with a real-life application of coordinate geometry in the Investigation. Point out that points on a map aren't located as precisely as points on a coordinate plane. On the map, B3 represents a square in which Alamo is located.
- The logical learner may benefit from relating the Distance Formula to the Pythagorean Theorem to find the distance between two points on a line.

Multicultural Opportunity

See Biography, p. 540.

13.1

The Distance Formula

Objectives: To specify points in the coordinate plane by means of their coordinates
To state and apply the Distance Formula

By imposing a coordinate system on a plane, you can locate points in the plane, find distances between them, and solve geometric problems using algebra.

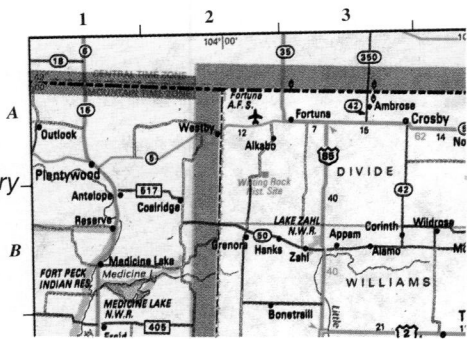

Investigation—*Coordinate Geometry*

The index of a road atlas indicates that the town of Alamo can be found on the map at *B*3. Describe how to use *B*3 to locate Alamo.

To create the **coordinate plane:**

1. Draw a pair of perpendicular number lines intersecting at their zero points.
2. Name the horizontal number line the **x-axis.**
3. Name the vertical number line the **y-axis.**
4. Call the point of intersection the **origin.**

For any **ordered pair** of real numbers, (x, y), there exists a unique point on the coordinate plane.
Point $P(-3, 4)$ has **x-coordinate** -3 and **y-coordinate** 4.
To locate P: draw a perpendicular at -3 on the *x*-axis, then draw a perpendicular at 4 on the *y*-axis.
Point P is the intersection of these perpendiculars.

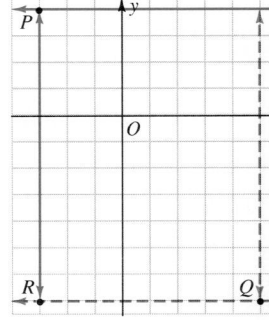

Conversely, with any point of the plane, there is associated a unique ordered pair. To find the coordinates for point Q, draw the perpendiculars to the *x*-axis and the *y*-axis. Write $Q(5, -7)$.

Note that $P(-3, 4)$ and $R(-3, -7)$ have the same *x*-coordinate. They determine vertical line $\overleftrightarrow{PR}$. The equation of $\overleftrightarrow{PR}$ is $x = -3$. The distance from R to P is $|4-(-7)|$, or $RP = 11$. Note also that $R(-3, -7)$ and $Q(5, -7)$ have the same *y*-coordinate. They determine horizontal line $\overleftrightarrow{RQ}$, whose equation is $y = -7$. The distance from Q to R is $|-3-5|$, or $QR = 8$.

536 Chapter 13 Coordinate Geometry

Developing Mathematical Power

Cooperative Learning Working in groups, students can create dot pictures on the coordinate plane. They should identify the coordinates of the points to be connected. When they have completed the picture, have them calculate the total distance from dot to dot from the beginning to the end. They should create a copy of their picture for a bulletin-board display.

The axes separate the coordinate plane into 4 **quadrants**.
$N(1, 2)$ is in *Quadrant 1*. $P(-1, 2)$ is in *Quadrant 2*.
$R(-1, -2)$ is in *Quadrant 3*. $Q(1, -2)$ is in *Quadrant 4*.

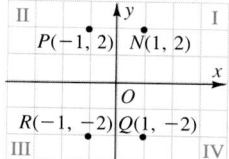

- Make sure that students understand that points on the axes do not lie in any quadrant.
- Practice Exercise 53 should be an interesting challenge for your best students.
- Indicate to students that squares on a graph sometimes represent units other than one. In the graph for Practice Exercises 1–21 and 30–33, each square is 2 units in length.

EXAMPLE 1   **a.** Name the coordinates of D; of B.

b. Which point has coordinates $(-4, -2)$?

c. What is the distance from C to B?

d. What is the equation of $\overleftrightarrow{BC}$? $\overleftrightarrow{CD}$?

e. Which line has equation $y = 4$? $x = 1$?

f. What subset of the plane is $y \le -2$?

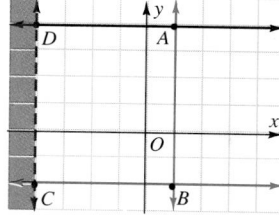

g. What algebraic sentence represents the shaded half-plane?

a. $(-4, 4)$; $(1, -2)$ **b.** C **c.** $BC = |1 - (-4)| = 5$;

d. $y = -2$; $x = -4$ **e.** $\overleftrightarrow{AD}$; $\overleftrightarrow{AB}$

f. $y \le -2$ is $\overleftrightarrow{BC}$ and the half-plane below $\overleftrightarrow{BC}$.   **g.** $x < -4$

EXAMPLE 2   **△ABC is a right triangle with right ∠B. What is the distance from C(-6, -4) to A(2, 6)?**

$AC = \sqrt{(BC)^2 + (BA)^2}$ *Use the Pythagorean theorem with △ABC.*
$= \sqrt{|2 - (-6)|^2 + |6 - (-4)|^2}$
$= \sqrt{8^2 + 10^2} = \sqrt{64 + 100} = \sqrt{164}$, or $2\sqrt{41}$

CHALKBOARD EXAMPLES

- **For Example 1**

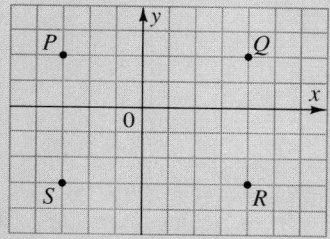

Theorem 13.1   The Distance Formula   The distance d between any two points (x_1, y_1) and (x_2, y_2) is $d = \sqrt{|x_2 - x_1|^2 + |y_2 - y_1|^2}$.

---

a. Name the coordinates of P, Q, R, and S.

b. What is the distance from P to Q? from Q to R?

c. What is the equation of $\overleftrightarrow{PQ}$? of $\overleftrightarrow{PS}$?

d. What line has equation $x = 4$? $y = -3$?

e. What algebraic sentence represents $\overleftrightarrow{SR}$ and the half-plane above $\overleftrightarrow{SR}$?

Given: Point A (x_2, y_2); point C (x_1, y_1)
$\overline{AC}$ is neither vertical nor horizontal.

Prove: $AC = \sqrt{|x_2 - x_1|^2 + |y_2 - y_1|^2}$

Plan: Locate B such that $\overline{AC}$ is the hypotenuse of right $\triangle ABC$. Apply the Pythagorean theorem to the coordinates of A, B, and C.
Proved in Practice Exercise 50

Since the square of any real number is positive or zero, the Distance Formula is usually written as $d = \sqrt{(x_2 - x_1)^2 + (y_2 - y_1)^2}$.

a. $(-3, 2)$, $(4, 2)$, $(4, -3)$, $(-3, -3)$
b. 7; 5 **c.** $y = 2$; $x = -3$
d. $\overleftrightarrow{QR}$; $\overleftrightarrow{SR}$ **e.** $y \ge -3$

13.1 The Distance Formula   **537**

- **For Example 2**

  What is the distance from $A(4, -2)$ to $C(-4, 4)$?

  Locate B so that AC is the hypotenuse of right $\triangle ABC$. There are two choices, with coordinates $(4, 4)$ and $(-4, -2)$. Use $(4, 4)$.

  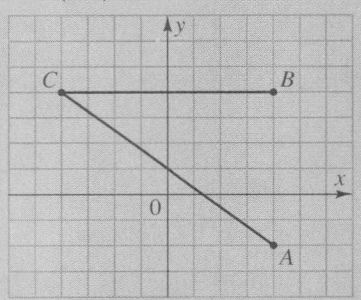

  Apply the Pythagorean Theorem.
  $$AC = \sqrt{(BC)^2 + (BA)^2}$$
  $$= \sqrt{|4 - (-4)|^2 + |4 - (-2)|^2}$$
  $$= \sqrt{8^2 + 6^2} = \sqrt{100}$$
  $$AC = 10$$

Common Errors

- Students may have trouble applying the Distance Formula correctly, especially when subtracting a negative coordinate. Review rules for subtraction of integers and have students verify their answers on graphs.
- Students may not simplify radicals correctly. Provide a short review on simplifying radicals.
- See *Teacher's Resource Book* for additional remediation.

LESSON FOLLOW-UP

Assignment Guide

See p. 534B for assignments.

Developing Mathematical Power

Extension Exercise 58 expands the concepts of the lesson to three dimensions by asking students to find the formula for distance in space.

CLASS EXERCISES

1. Name the given points in each quadrant.
   I: *B, D, V*; II: *A, C*; III: *E, G, W*; IV: *F, H*

Find the distances between these points.

2. C and D 7
3. A and E 6
4. F and H $\sqrt{5}$
5. G and F $\sqrt{29}$

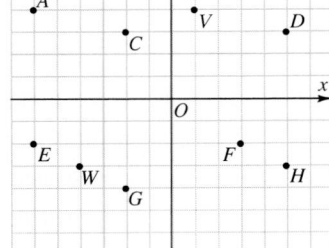

Give the equations of these lines.

6. $\overleftrightarrow{BF}$ $x = 3$
7. $\overleftrightarrow{EF}$ $y = -2$
8. $\overleftrightarrow{CD}$ $y = 3$
9. $\overleftrightarrow{AE}$ $x = -6$

Which lines have these equations?

10. $y = 4$ $\overleftrightarrow{AV}$
11. $x = -2$ $\overleftrightarrow{CG}$
12. $x = 5$ $\overleftrightarrow{DH}$
13. $y = -3$ $\overleftrightarrow{WH}$

Which subsets of the coordinate plane are given by these inequalities?

14. $y > 0$ the half-plane above $y = 0$
15. $y < 5$ the half-plane below $y = 5$
16. $x < 0$ the half-plane to the left of $x = 0$
17. $x > -3$ the half-p to the right of $x = -$

PRACTICE EXERCISES ⌇ Use technology where appropriate.

Use this figure for Exercises 1–21 and 30–33. In Exercises 1–4 give the coordinates of these points.

A 1. A $(-6, 8)$
2. F $(-6, -4)$
3. D $(-2, 0)$
4. G $(6, -8)$

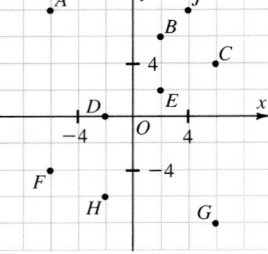

Name the points having these coordinates.

5. $(2, 6)$ B
6. $(6, 4)$ C
7. $(2, 2)$ E
8. $(-2, -6)$ H

9. Name all the given points in each quadrant.
   I: *B, C, E, J*; II: *A*; III: *F, H*; IV: *G*

Find the distances.

10. AF 12
11. CE $2\sqrt{5}$
12. FG $4\sqrt{10}$
13. EG $2\sqrt{29}$

Give the equations of these lines.

14. $\overleftrightarrow{AJ}$ $y = 8$
15. $\overleftrightarrow{DH}$ $x = -2$
16. $\overleftrightarrow{CG}$ $x = 6$
17. x-axis $y = 0$

Which lines have these equations?

18. $x = -6$ $\overleftrightarrow{AF}$
19. $x = 2$ $\overleftrightarrow{BE}$
20. $x = 0$ y-axis
21. $y = 8$ $\overleftrightarrow{AJ}$

Which subsets of the coordinate plane are given by these inequalities?

22. $x > -1$ the half-plane to the right of $x = -1$

23. $x \le -6$ $x = -6$ and the half-plane to the left

24. $y > 1$ the half-plane above $y = 1$

25. $y \le -5$ $y = -5$ and the half-plane below

Use graph paper to locate and mark these points. See side column.

26. $S(-8, -7)$

27. $J(-7, 8)$

28. $W(-7, 0)$

29. $P(0, -1.5)$

Give the inequalities for these subsets of the coordinate plane.

B

30. all points above the x-axis $y > 0$

31. all points to the right of $\overleftrightarrow{AF}$ $x > -6$

32. all points below and on $\overleftrightarrow{AJ}$ $y \le 8$

33. all points to the left of and on $\overleftrightarrow{BE}$ $x \le 2$

In which quadrant do all points have each type of coordinate?

34. negative x and positive y II

35. positive x and negative y IV

36. negative x and negative y III

37. positive x and positive y I

Graph each exercise on separate coordinate axes. Connect the points in the order given. Identify the figure. See Additional Answers, p. 702.

38. $A(0, 0)$, $B(-4, 0)$, $C(-2, 4)$ $CB = CA$; isos. $\triangle$

39. $D(-1, 2)$, $E(-1, 8)$, $F(3, 5)$ $DF = EF$; Isos. $\triangle$

40. $G(0, -1)$, $H(5, -1)$, $I(5, 11)$ $m\angle H = 90$; rt. $\triangle$

41. $J(-3, 3)$, $K(3, 3)$, $L(3, 9)$ $JK = KL$ and $m\angle K = 90$; rt. isos. $\triangle$

42. $A(-1, -3)$, $B(3, 0)$, $C(0, 3)$, $D(-5, 0)$ Quad.

43. $E(-6, -3)$, $F(-3, -3)$, $G(3, 5)$, $H(0, 5)$ $\square$; $EF = HG$ and $EH = FG$

44. $I(0, 0)$ $J(3, 3)$, $K(0, 6)$, $L(-3, 3)$ square; all $\angle$s are 90° and all sides are =

45. $M(0, 0)$, $N(2, 2)$, $O(0, 6)$, $P(-2, 2)$ kite; $OP = ON$ and $MP = MN$

46. The vertices of $\triangle RST$ are $R(-2, 1)$, $S(0, -1)$, and $T(2, 5)$. Find the ratio of the longest side length to the shortest. $\sqrt{5}:1$

47. The vertices of $\triangle PQR$ are $P(-1, 1)$, $Q(1, 0)$, and $R(3, 3)$. Find the ratio of the longest side length to the shortest. $2:1$

48. Graph $A(-3, 3)$, $B(0, 0)$, and $C(3, -3)$. Join A to B, B to C, and C to A with segments. What kind of figure is formed? a line segment

49. Are points $D(1, 1)$, $E(5, 5)$, and $F(9, 9)$ collinear? If the x-coordinate of G is -3, what must its y-coordinate be to be collinear with D and E? yes; -3

C **50.** Complete the proof of Theorem 13.1. See Additional Answers, p. 702.

51. Find the perimeter of $\triangle GHI$, with vertices $G(8, 5)$, $H(-1, -4)$, and $I(-4, 0)$. Write the answer as a simplified radical and then estimate to the nearest tenth. $18 + 9\sqrt{2}$; 30.7

52. Find the length of median $\overline{CM}$ if the vertices of $\triangle CBA$ are $C(-4, 3)$, $B(-1, 3)$, and $A(-4, 7)$. $\frac{5}{2}$

13.1 The Distance Formula   **539**

Biography: René Descartes

Students might be interested in learning more about Descartes' unusual lifestyle. For those students, you may wish to assign a research project on Descartes.

Lesson Quiz

1. Give the equation of the line that contains $A(-3, 2)$ and $B(1, 2)$.

Find the distance between the points.

2. $A(-3, 2)$ and $B(1, 2)$

3. $C(-2, 4)$ and $D(3, -8)$

4. $E(7, -1)$ and $F(2, -3)$

5. $G(-4, 2)$ and $H(-1, -4)$

1. $y = 2$ 2. 4
3. 13   4. $\sqrt{29}$ 5. $3\sqrt{5}$

Enrichment

a. Quadrilateral $ABCD$ has vertices $A(-1, 1)$, $B(1, 4)$, $C(0, 1)$, and $D(-2, -2)$. Is $ABCD$ a parallelogram? Explain.

b. Three vertices of a parallelogram have coordinates $(-1, -1)$, $(0, 1)$, and $(2, -1)$. Find all possible coordinates of the fourth vertex of the parallelogram.

a. Yes; $AB = \sqrt{13} = DC$ and $DA = \sqrt{10} = CB$. Since both pairs of opposite sides are $\cong$, $ABCD$ is a $\square$.

b. $(3, 1)$, $(-3, 1)$, and $(1, -3)$

For Exercises 26–29, check student graphs. From the origin, the point is:
26. 8 units left, 7 units down   **27.** 7 units left, 8 units up   **28.** 7 units left
29. 1.5 units down

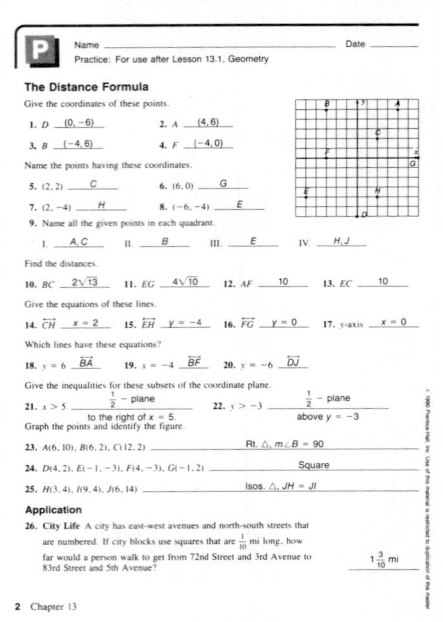

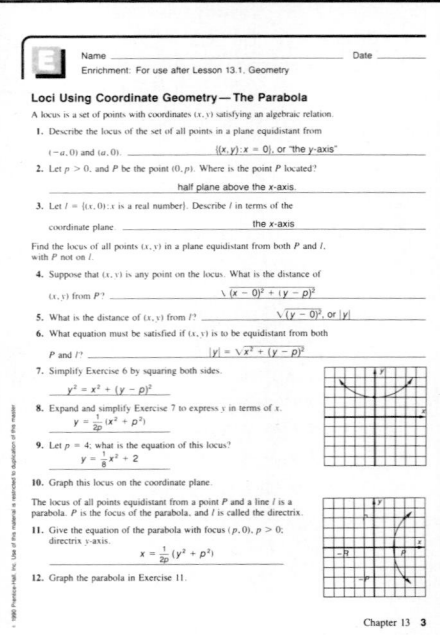

In Exercises 53–56, given: $A(-5,-1)$ **and** $B(1,-1)$.

53. Select coordinates for C such that $\triangle ABC$ is a right isosceles triangle. Is there more than one answer? How many? yes; 6; (1,5), (1,−7), (−5,5), (−5, −7), (−2, 2), or (−2, −4)

54. Select coordinates for C such that $\triangle ABC$ is a right scalene triangle. Is there more than one answer? How many? yes; infinitely many

55. Select coordinates for C such that $\triangle ABC$ is an isosceles triangle with vertex angle at C and the congruent sides 5 units long. Is there more than one answer? How many? yes; 2: (−2,3) and (−2,−5)

Applications

56. Interior Design   This designer's diagram shows how a table is to be placed in a six-foot square portion of a room. Find the table's dimensions.
$4\sqrt{2}$ ft by $2\sqrt{2}$ ft, or approx. 5.6 ft by 2.8 ft

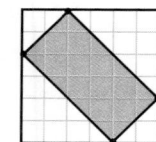

57. Technology   Logo can be used to simulate curves from straight lines using the SETPOS command. Generate the illustrated graphic and then create a series of string art graphics. Answers may vary. See Solutions Manual.

Developing Mathematical Power

58. Extension   By drawing a z-axis that is perpendicular to both the x-axis and the y-axis, points can be located in space with ordered triples of the form (x, y, z). Find a formula for the distance from $A(x_1, y_1, z_1)$ to $B(x_2, y_2, z_2)$ in three dimensions. (*Hint:* Think of a rectangular solid.)
$d = \sqrt{(x_1 - x_2)^2 + (y_1 - y_2)^2 + (z_1 - z_2)^2}$

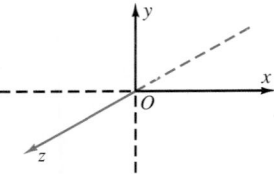

BIOGRAPHY: René Descartes (1596–1650)

René Descartes was a French mathematician and philosopher. He developed the present system of graphing sets of points and writing algebraic equations to represent the sets. This blending of algebraic and geometric approaches to problems is the foundation of modern geometry. The Cartesian coordinate system is named for this great thinker.

540   Chapter 13 Coordinate Geometry

The Equation of a Circle

Objective: To state and apply the general equation of a circle

There are two general equations that correspond to circles on the coordinate plane: one for circles whose centers are at the origin and one for circles whose centers are not.

Investigation—*Visualizing the Concept*

When a circle is drawn on a coordinate plane, the plane is partitioned into three sets of points.

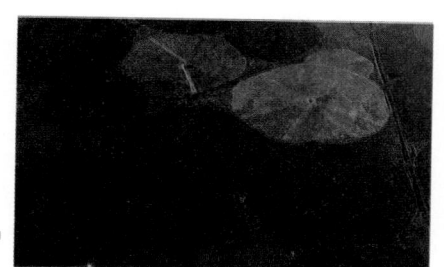

1. Describe each set of points. the ⊙; its interior; its exterior
2. If two concentric circles are drawn on the coordinate plane, describe the sets of points determined. the inner ⊙; the outer ⊙; exterior of outer ⊙; interior of inner ⊙; pts. in interior of outer ⊙ and in exterior of inner ⊙

Recall that a set of points in a plane is a *circle* if and only if it consists of every point in the plane a specified distance r from a specified point O.

If the center of a circle is the origin of the coordinate plane and the radius length is known, the equation of the circle can be found by applying the Distance Formula.

EXAMPLE 1 Find the equation of ⊙O with center at the origin and a radius length 3.

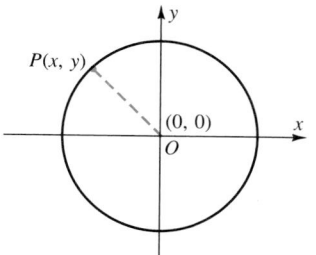

$P(x, y)$

$(0, 0)$

O

Let $P(x, y)$ be any point of ⊙O.
The distance from O to P is given by:

$$\sqrt{(x - 0)^2 + (y - 0)^2} = 3$$
$$(x - 0)^2 + (y - 0)^2 = 3^2$$
$$x^2 + y^2 = 3^2$$

Use the same method to find the equation of a circle whose center is *not* at the origin.

13.2 The Equation of a Circle **541**

Developing Mathematical Power

Cooperative Learning Assign groups of students to complete the Enrichment activity, p. 6, in the *Teacher's Resource Book* (see side column, p. 545). It provides an extension into the various symmetries associated with a circle. Challenge each group to create a design using circles and symmetry for a bulletin-board display.

EXAMPLE 2 Find the equation of $\odot Q$ with center $(4, -2)$ and radius length 5.

Let $P(x, y)$ be any point of $\odot Q$.
The distance from Q to P is given by:

$$\sqrt{(x - 4)^2 + (y - (-2))^2} = 5$$
$$(x - 4)^2 + (y + 2)^2 = 5^2$$

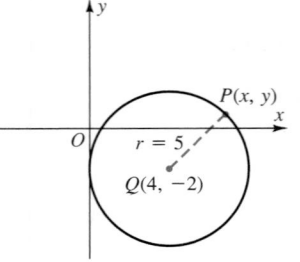

The solution for Example 2 can be generalized as a theorem.

Theorem 13.2 An equation of the circle with center (h, k) and radius length r is $(x - h)^2 + (y - k)^2 = r^2$.

Given: $\odot Q$ with center (h, k) and P a point of $\odot Q$ with coordinates (x, y)

Prove: The equation of $\odot Q$ is $(x - h)^2 + (y - k)^2 = r^2$.

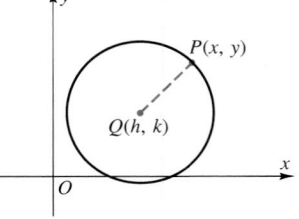

The equation $(x - h)^2 + (y - k)^2 = r^2$ is the *standard form* of the **equation of a circle.**

EXAMPLE 3 **Give the equation of the circle with center $(-3, 2)$ and radius length 6. Sketch its graph.**

Use the standard form. Replace h with -3, k with 2, and r with 6.
$(x - (-3))^2 + (y - 2)^2 = 6^2$
$(x + 3)^2 + (y - 2)^2 = 36$

Use the distance 6 from center $(-3, 2)$ to find some points of the circle:
$(3, 2)$ $(-3, 8)$ $(-9, 2)$ $(-3, -4)$
Use a compass to draw the graph.

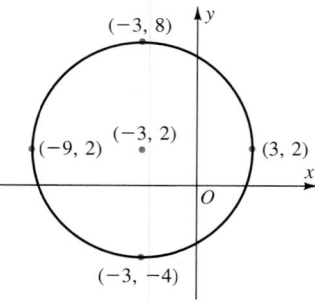

Developing Mathematical Power

Keeping a Portfolio Students may notice that for every point on a circle, there are three related points. For example, in the circle $x^2 + y^2 = 3^2$, four such points are $(3, 0), (0, 3), (-3, 0)$, and $(0, -3)$. Have students draw a circle, name several such sets of points, and then write a description of the relationship among the points.

EXAMPLE 4 Give the center and the radius length of the circle whose equation is $(x - 5)^2 + (y + 3)^2 = 16$. Sketch its graph.

Write the equation in standard form:
$(x - 5)^2 + (y - (-3))^2 = 4^2$
The center is $(5, -3)$;
the radius length is 4.

Use the radius length to graph
some points of the circle:
$(9, -3)$, $(5, 1)$, $(1, -3)$, and $(5, -7)$
Use a compass to graph the circle.

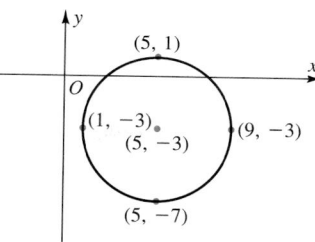

CLASS EXERCISES

1. **Thinking Critically** Formulate an inequality that describes the interior points of a circle with center $(-4, 6)$ and radius length 5. Explain your answer with a sketch.
$(x + 4)^2 + (y - 6)^2 < 5^2$; see Solutions Manual for sketch.

Give the center and radius length of each circle.

2. $(x - 0)^2 + (y - 0)^2 = 100$ (0,0); 10

3. $x^2 + y^2 = 4$ (0,0); 2

4. $(x - 5)^2 + y^2 = 9$ (5,0); 3

5. $(x + 1)^2 + (y + 2)^2 = 1$ (−1,−2); 1

6. $(x - 2)^2 + (y - 4)^2 = 36$ (2, 4); 6

7. $(x + 7)^2 + (y - 8)^2 = 80$ (−7, 8); 4√5

On separate coordinate axes, sketch the graph of each circle.

8. $x^2 + y^2 = 16$
See side column.

9. $(x - 1)^2 + (y + 2)^2 = 25$

Write an equation of a circle that has the given center and radius length.

10. $(2, 3)$; $r = 4$ (x − 2)² + (y − 3)² = 16

11. $(-2, -3)$; $r = 7$ (x + 2)² + (y + 3)² = 49

12. Graph the circle for Exercise 10.
See side column.

13. Graph the circle for Exercise 11.

PRACTICE EXERCISES   Use technology where appropriate.

Give the center and radius length of each circle. In Exercises 1–4, sketch the graph. See Solutions Manual for graphs of Ex. 1–4.

1. $(x - 1)^2 + (y - 2)^2 = 25$ (1,2); 5

2. $(x + 1)^2 + (y - 2)^2 = 36$ (−1,2); 6

3. $(x + 1)^2 + y^2 = 1$ (−1,0); 1

4. $x^2 + y^2 = 49$ (0,0); 7

5. $x^2 + y^2 = 64$ (0,0); 8

6. $(x - 4)^2 + y^2 = 2$ (4,0); √2

7. $(x - 3)^2 + (y - 2)^2 = 2.25$ (3,2); 1.5

8. $(x - 0)^2 + (y - 0)^2 = 6.25$ (0,0); 2.5

9. $(x - a)^2 + (y + b)^2 = 18$ (a,−b); 3√2

10. $(x + a)^2 + (y + b)^2 = 12$ (−a,−b); 2√3

Give the center and the radius length of the circle whose equation is $(x + 2)^2 + (y - 4)^2 = 4$. Sketch its graph.
$(x - (-2))^2 + (y - 4)^2 = 2^2$

Center is $(-2, 4)$; radius length is 2. Points of the ⊙ include $(0, 4)$, $(-4, 4)$, $(-2, 6)$, and $(-2, 2)$.

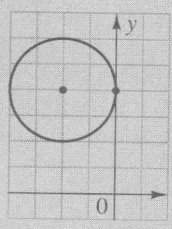

Common Errors
• Some students may have trouble finding the square root of a decimal such as 2.25 without using a calculator. Suggest that they convert 2.25 to the equivalent fraction, $\frac{9}{4}$, whose square root, $\frac{3}{2}$, may be recognizable to them.
• Students may forget to square the radius length when they write the equation of a circle, or may forget to find the square root when they use the equation to find the radius length.
• See *Teacher's Resource Book* for additional remediation.

LESSON FOLLOW-UP

Assignment Guide
See p. 534B for assignments.

Developing Mathematical Power
Extension Exercise 43 provides students with an opportunity to extend the Investigation by writing an inequality that describes the set of points between two concentric circles.

Additional Answers
8. A circle with center $(0, 0)$, and $r = 4$
9. A circle with center $(1, -2)$, and $r = 5$

12.
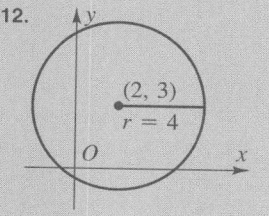

13.
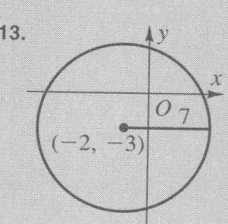

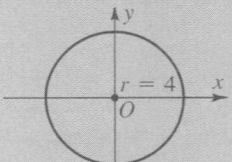
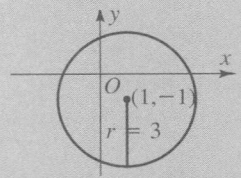
Find an equation of a circle that has the given center and radius length.

11. $(0, 0); r = 6$ $x^2 + y^2 = 36$
12. $(-2, 4); r = 4$ $(x + 2)^2 + (y - 4)^2 = 16$
13. $(4, -3); r = 2.5$ $(x - 4)^2 + (y + 3)^2 = 6.25$
14. $(0, 0); r = 1.5$ $x^2 + y^2 = 2.25$
15. $(-3, -3); r = 9$ $(x + 3)^2 + (y + 3)^2 = 81$
16. $(4, 0); r = \sqrt{3}$ $(x - 4)^2 + y^2 = 3$
17. $(7, k); r = 2\sqrt{5}$ $(x - 7)^2 + (y - k)^2 = 20$
18. $(d, -4); r = 1.5\sqrt{2}$ $(x - d)^2 + (y + 4)^2 = 4$

In Exercises 19–22, on separate coordinate axes, graph these subsets of the coordinate plane. Use shading to show regions. See side column.

B
19. $x^2 + y^2 = 16$
20. $(x - 1)^2 + (y + 1)^2 = 9$
21. $x^2 + y^2 < 16$
22. $(x - 1)^2 + (y + 1)^2 \geq 9$

23. On the coordinate axes for Exercise 19, graph $x = 4$ and $y \geq 4$.

24. On the coordinate axes for Exercise 20, graph $y = -4$ and $x \leq -2$.

For Exercises 25–26, write the inequality that describes the set of points.

25. The circle with center at the origin and radius length 3 and the interior of the circle $x^2 + y^2 \leq 9$

26. The circle with center at $(-3, 0)$ and radius length 5 and the exterior of the circle $(x + 3)^2 + y^2 \geq 25$

27. There are two horizontal lines tangent to the circle in Exercise 25. Write their equations. $y = 3; y = -3$

28. There are two vertical lines tangent to the circle in Exercise 26. Write their equations. $x = 2; x = -8$

Which equations describe circles? (*Hint:* Complete the squares in order to write each equation in standard form.)

29. $x^2 + y^2 - 10y = 0$ $x^2 + (y - 5)^2 = 25$; yes
30. $x^2 + 6x + y^2 + 4y + 9 = 0$ $(x + 3)^2 + (y + 2)^2 = 4$; yes
31. $x^2 - 4x + y^2 + 6y + 14 = 0$ $(x - 2)^2 + (y + 3)^2 = -1$; no
32. $x^2 + y^2 + 4y + 10x = -4$ $(x + 5)^2 + (y + 2)^2 = 25$; yes

C
33. Find the equation(s) of the locus of all points equidistant from these circles: $x^2 + y^2 = 4$ and $x^2 + y^2 = 64$. $x^2 + y^2 = 25$

34. Find the equation(s) of the locus of all points at a distance of one unit from the circle whose equation is $x^2 + y^2 = 25$. $x^2 + y^2 = 16$ and $x^2 + y^2 = 36$

35. Find the equation of the circle with center at $(3, -4)$ and passing through $(-1, -4)$. $(x - 3)^2 + (y + 4)^2 = 16$

36. Find the equation of the circle with diameter $\overline{PQ}$, where P and Q are $(-2, 5)$ and $(-2, 11)$, respectively. $(x + 2)^2 + (y - 8)^2 = 9$

544   Chapter 13 Coordinate Geometry

21.

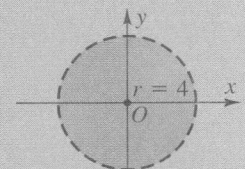

22.

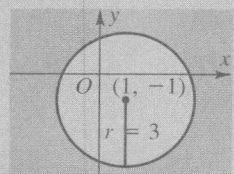

37. Find the equation of the locus of all points X such that $\angle PXR$ is a right angle and where $P(-5, 3)$ and $R(1, 3)$ are also in the locus. $(x + 2)^2 + (y - 3)^2 = 9$

38. Find the equation of a circle tangent to the line $x = 6$ and with center at $(2, -3)$. $(x - 2)^2 + (y + 3)^2 = 16$

39. Find the equation of a circle tangent to the circle $x^2 + y^2 = 4$ and with center at $(0, 5)$. $x^2 + (y - 5)^2 = 9$

Applications

40. **Recreation** A dartboard is drawn on graph paper so that its center is at the origin and its rings are each two units thick. If the target has seven rings, what are their equations? $x^2 + y^2 = 4$, $x^2 + y^2 = 16$, $x^2 + y^2 = 36$, $x^2 + y^2 = 64$, $x^2 + y^2 = 100$, $x^2 + y^2 = 144$, $x^2 + y^2 = 196$

41. **Sports** Sketch the following circles on one graph. Describe the resulting picture.

$$(x + 12)^2 + (y - 4)^2 = 25 \qquad x^2 + (y - 4)^2 = 25$$
$$(x - 12)^2 + (y - 4)^2 = 25 \qquad (x + 6)^2 + (y + 2)^2 = 25$$
$$(x - 6)^2 + (y + 2)^2 = 25$$

See Solutions Manual.

42. **Technology** Using the result from Exercise 41, generate the design in Logo. Compare the methods used in Exercises 41 and 42.

Developing Mathematical Power

43. **Extension** The circles shown are concentric. Explain how to formulate an inequality that describes the points that are in the exterior of the smaller circle and in the interior of the larger circle.
By the def. of a ⊙ and the Pyth. Th., any pt. $P(x, y)$ in the region described satisfies this ineq.: $r_s^2 < (x - h)^2 + (y - k)^2 < r_e^2$, where r_s and r_e are the respective radius lengths of the smaller ⊙ and the larger ⊙.

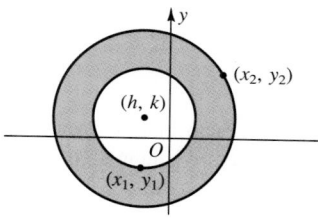

BIOGRAPHY: Leonhard Euler (1707–1783)

Leonhard Euler, the great mathematician whose life spanned most of the eighteenth century, spent his productive years in Russia and Germany. He began working at the Academy of Sciences at St. Petersburg in 1722. He left there for Berlin, where he worked from 1741 to 1766, and then returned to Russia.

Often referred to as one of history's most prolific mathematicians, Euler wrote over 500 books and papers in his lifetime. He is noted especially for his ability to develop procedures for solving problems. These procedures are called *algorithms*.

13.2 The Equation of a Circle **545**

23.

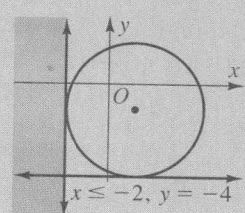

24.

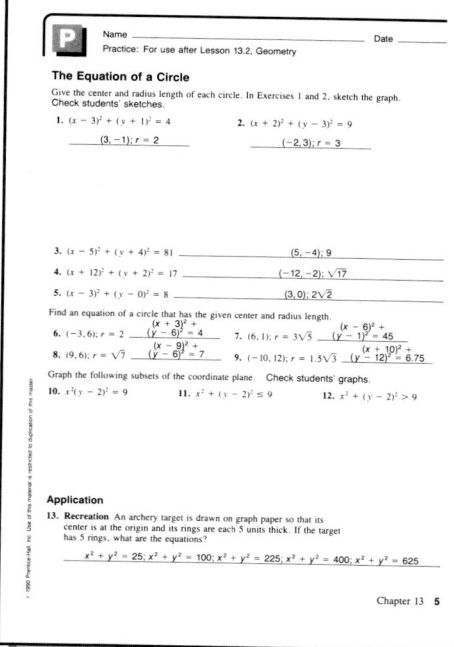
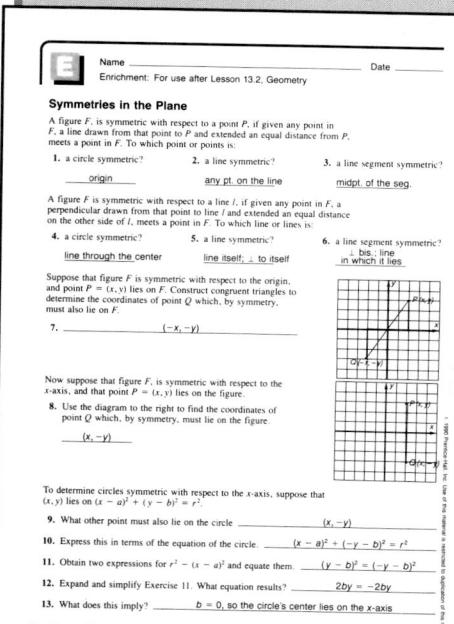

Materials/Manipulatives

A coordinate plane on the
chalkboard or overhead projector
Graph paper
Teaching Transparency 87

Technology

*Computer Test Bank, pp.
828–834*

LESSON FOCUS

Review

• On a coordinate plane, draw several vertical and horizontal segments
whose endpoints have integral coordinates. Ask students to find the
coordinates of each midpoint.

• Exercises 37–44 provide a Mixed
Review.

Alternative Learning Styles

• Students use visualization and critical thinking in the Investigation to
formulate a method for finding the
coordinates of the midpoint of a line
segment.

• The visual learner can also benefit
from seeing these concepts as presented on Teaching Transparency
87. If they recall that a line that
joins the midpoints of two sides of a
triangle is parallel to the third side,
they can easily determine the coordinates of *M*. First use the actual
numerical coordinates for *P, Q,*
and *R* to determine the numerical
coordinates of *X* and *Y*. Because
$\overline{YM}$ is vertical, *M* and *Y* have the
same *x*-coordinate. Similarly, be-
cause $\overline{XM}$ is horizontal, *M* and
X have the same *y*-coordinate.
These coordinates are the same as
the averages of the *x*- and *y*-coor-
dinates of *R* and *T*.

13.3

The Midpoint Formula

Objective: To state and apply the Midpoint Formula

The concepts of distance and the Midpoint Formula can be applied to the
coordinate plane to find the coordinates of the midpoint of any segment.

Investigation—*Thinking Critically*

In right $\triangle RST$, M_1, M_2, and M_3 are the
midpoints of sides $\overline{RS}$, $\overline{ST}$, and $\overline{TR}$,
respectively.

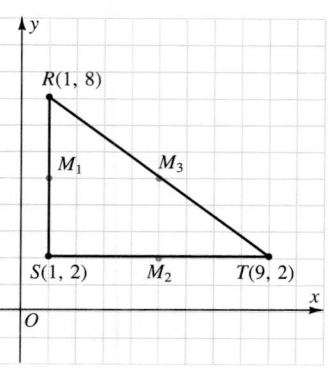

1. Give the coordinates of M_1 and M_2. (1,5)
   (5,2)

2. How do the coordinates of M_1 compare
   with those of *R* and *S*? the coordinates of
   M_2 with those of *S* and *T*? same *x*-coordinate;
   $y = \frac{y_2 + y_1}{2}$ (average); same *y*-coordinate; $x = \frac{x_2 + x_1}{2}$
   (average)

3. The answers to Question 2 suggest a way
   to find the coordinates of M_3. Explain the
   method. Find the average of the *x*-coords. and the
   average of the *y*-coords. for pts. *R* and *T*.

The coordinates of midpoints of horizontal or
vertical segments can often be found by
inspection. For $\overline{AB}$, with endpoints $(-7, -2)$ and
$(1, -2)$, the coordinates of midpoint *M* are
$(-3, -2)$. Note that the *y*-coordinate is the same
for all points on $\overline{AB}$. The *x*-coordinate of *M* is
found by adding $\frac{1}{2}AB$, or 4, to the smaller
x-coordinate.

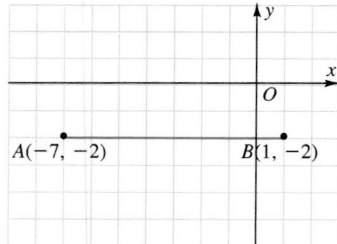

In general, to find the *x*-coordinate of the midpoint of x_1 and x_2:

Choose the smaller coordinate: x_1.

Find the distance: since $x_2 > x_1$, $|x_2 - x_1| = x_2 - x_1$.

Find $\frac{1}{2}$ the distance: $\frac{x_2 - x_1}{2}$.

Add $\frac{1}{2}$ the distance to the smaller coordinate: $x_1 + \frac{x_2 - x_1}{2}$.

546   Chapter 13 Coordinate Geometry

Developing Mathematical Power

Cooperative Learning The Enrichment activity, p. 9, in the *Teacher's Resource
Book* (see side column, p. 551) can be done with students working in groups. It
provides an opportunity to observe a pattern and make a generalization. You may
want to suggest that they let four grids equal one unit and that they use different
colors.

Since $x_1 + \frac{x_2 - x_1}{2} = \frac{x_1 + x_2}{2}$, the x-coordinate for the midpoint of any horizontal segment is $\frac{x_1 + x_2}{2}$. By similar reasoning, the y-coordinate for the midpoint of any vertical segment is $\frac{y_1 + y_2}{2}$.

These results can be combined and applied to any segment in the plane.

Theorem 13.3 The Midpoint Formula The midpoint of the segment with endpoint coordinates (x_1, y_1) and (x_2, y_2) is the point with coordinates $\left(\frac{x_1 + x_2}{2}, \frac{y_1 + y_2}{2}\right)$.

Given: $P(x_1, y_1)$ and $R(x_2, y_2)$;
M the midpoint of $\overline{PR}$

Prove: M has coordinates $\left(\frac{x_1 + x_2}{2}, \frac{y_1 + y_2}{2}\right)$.

Plan: Draw $\overline{QR} \parallel x$-axis and $\overline{PQ} \parallel y$-axis to form $\triangle PQR$. Draw $\overline{MX} \parallel \overline{QR}$ and $\overline{MY} \parallel \overline{PQ}$. Use the Triangle Proportionality Th. to find the coordinates of X and Y. Then use these coordinates to find the coordinates of M.
Proved in Practice Exercise 31

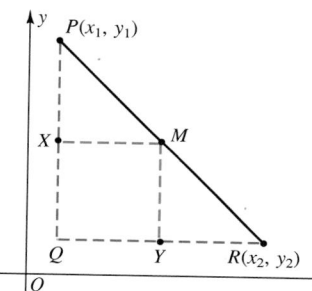

EXAMPLE 1   Find coordinates of the midpoints of these segments.

a. $\overline{GH}$, with $G(-7, 3)$ and $H(-1, -1)$

b. $\overline{IJ}$, with $I(5, -6)$ and $J(9, 5)$

a. $\left(\frac{-7 + -1}{2}, \frac{3 + -1}{2}\right) = (-4, 1)$ **b.** $\left(\frac{5 + 9}{2}, \frac{-6 + 5}{2}\right) = \left(7, -\frac{1}{2}\right)$

EXAMPLE 2 M is the midpoint of $\overline{AB}$. If M has coordinates $(3, -5)$ and A has coordinates $(-7, 2)$, find the coordinates of B.

Let the coordinates of A be (x_1, y_1). Then the coordinates of B are (x_2, y_2).
Thus:

$\frac{-7 + x_2}{2} = 3$ and $\frac{2 + y_2}{2} = -5$ B has coordinates $(13, -12)$.

$x_2 = 13$ $y_2 = -12$

Developing Mathematical Power

Keeping a Portfolio Have students describe how to find the coordinates of an endpoint of a segment when the coordinates of the other endpoint and the midpoint are given. They should illustrate their description with a drawing of the segment and label the coordinates of the given endpoint and midpoint.

- Better students may find Practice Exercises 33 and 34 interesting, since they require more abstract thinking.
- Stress the difference between locating a midpoint and locating one of the endpoints when a midpoint is given.

CHALKBOARD EXAMPLES

- **For Example 1**
  Find the coordinates of the midpoint of the given segment.

  a. $\overline{CD}$, with $C(-2, -5)$ and $D(-8, 3)$
  b. $\overline{EF}$, with $E(1, 4)$ and $F(7, -1)$

  a. $\left(\frac{-2 + (-8)}{2}, \frac{-5 + 3}{2}\right) = (-5, -1)$
  b. $\left(\frac{1 + 7}{2}, \frac{4 + (-1)}{2}\right) = (4, 1.5)$

- **For Example 2**
  M is the midpoint of $\overline{AB}$. If M has coordinates $(-2, 4)$ and A has coordinates $(-5, 9)$, find the coordinates of B.
  Let the coordinates of B be (x_2, y_2).
  $\frac{-5 + x_2}{2} = -2$ and $\frac{9 + y_2}{2} = 4$
  $-5 + x_2 = -4$ $9 + y_2 = 8$
  $x_2 = 1$ $y_2 = -1$
  B has coordinates $(1, -1)$.

Common Error
- For Example 2, some students will use the Midpoint Formula and get the midpoint of $\overline{AM}$ instead of the coordinates of B. Have these students graph A, M, and B to justify their answers.
- See *Teacher's Resource Book* for additional remediation.

LESSON FOLLOW-UP

Discussion

To help students prepare for Lesson 13.7, draw the following diagram on the chalkboard and tell students that M is the midpoint of $\overline{AB}$ and N is the midpoint of $\overline{AC}$.

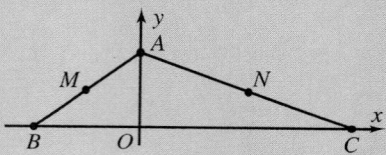

Ask students which coordinates of A, B, C, M, and N are known. The x-coordinate of A is 0. The y-coordinates of B and C are 0. Is it easier to find the coordinates of M and N if the coordinates of A, B, and C are (0, a), (b, 0), and (c, 0), respectively, or (0, 2a), (2b, 0), and (2c, 0), respectively? (0, 2a), (2b, 0) and (2c, 0); then M and N have coordinates (b, a) and (c, a), respectively.

CLASS EXERCISES

Find the coordinates of the midpoints of each segment with the given endpoints.

1. $A(-3, 2)$, $B(-3, 10)$ (−3,6)

2. $C(-3, -5)$, $D(9, -5)$ (3,−5)

3. $E(-3, 3)$, $F(5, -5)$ (1,−1)

4. $F(-4, -4)$, $G(-8, -2)$ (−6,−3)

5. $G(7, -1)$, $H(2, -1)$ (4.5,−1)

6. $I(6, 5)$, $J(7, -5)$ (6.5,0)

7. $R(a, 4)$, $N(c, 6)$ ($\frac{a+c}{2}$, 5)

8. $T(6b, 8)$, $S(3, 4d)$ ($\frac{6b+3}{2}$,4 + 2d)

M is the midpoint of $\overline{AB}$. Find the coordinates of A or B.

9. $M(5, -3)$, $A(3, -8)$ B(7,2)

10. $M(4, -4)$, $B(-2, -5)$ A(10,−3)

11. $M\left(-5, -4\frac{1}{2}\right)$, $B(-8, 7)$ A(−2, −16)

12. $M\left(0, 6\frac{1}{2}\right)$, $A(4, -9)$ B(−4, 22)

PRACTICE EXERCISES   Use technology where appropriate.

Find the coordinates of the midpoint of each $\overline{AB}$.

A

1. $A(-1, 3)$, $B(-5, 9)$ (−3,6)

2. $A(-1, -4)$, $B(7, -4)$ (3,−4)

3. $A(-5, 4)$, $B(5, -6)$ (0,−1)

4. $A(-2, -3)$, $B(-12, -5)$ (−7,−4)

5. $A(7, -3)$, $B(7, -4)$ (7,−3.5)

6. $A(4, 3)$, $B(7, -5)$ (5.5,−1)

7. $A(2.5, 7)$, $B(3.5, -11)$ (3,−2)

8. $A(-4, 1.3)$, $B(4, -1.3)$ (0,0)

9. $A(m, n)$, $B(p, q)$ $\left(\frac{m+p}{2}, \frac{n+q}{2}\right)$

10. $A(5, c + 3)$, $B(2, c - 1)$ (3.5,c + 1)

M is the midpoint of $\overline{AB}$. Find the coordinates of A or B.

11. $M(5, -3)$, $A(3, -10)$ B(7,4)

12. $M(4, -4)$, $B(-2, -7)$ A(10,−1)

13. $M(0, 0)$, $B(8, -5)$ A(−8,5)

14. $M(0, -5)$, $A(7, -5)$ B(−7,−5)

M is the midpoint of $\overline{AB}$. Find the coordinates of A or B.

15. $M(k, l)$, $A(m, n)$ B(2k − m,2l − n)

16. $M(-2, c)$, $B(-9, 4)$ A(5,2c − 4)

Find the coordinates of the midpoint of each side of the polygons with these vertices.

B

17. Triangle *ABC*: $A(-8, 11)$, $B(8, 5)$, $C(2, 5)$ M_{AB}(0,8); M_{BC}(5,5); M_{AC}(−3,8)

18. Triangle *DEF*: $D(3, 4)$, $E(-3, -4)$, $F(7, -2)$ M_{DE}(0,0); M_{EF}(2,−3); M_{DF}(5,1)

19. Quadrilateral *GHIJ*: $G(-3, 3)$, $H(9, 7)$, $I(5, -3)$, $J(-3, -3)$ M_{GH}(3,5); M_{HI}(7,2); M_{IJ}(1,−3); M_{GJ}(−3,0)

20. Quadrilateral *KLMN*: $K(0, 8)$, $L(8, 2)$, $M(2, -6)$, $N(-6, 0)$ M_{KL}(4,5); M_{LM}(5,−2); M_{MN}(−2,−3); M_{NK}(−3,4)

548   Chapter 13 Coordinate Geometry

Find the coordinates of the midpoints of the diagonals.

21. Quadrilateral $OPQR$: $O(-4, 5)$, $P(6, 7)$, $Q(4, 3)$, $R(-5, 1)$ $M_{OQ}(0,4)$; $M_{PR}(\frac{1}{2},4)$

22. Quadrilateral $STUV$: $S(-1, 1)$, $T(7, 3)$, $U(5, -1)$, $V(-3, -3)$ $M_{SU}(2,0)$; $M_{TV}(2,0)$

23. Find the length of median $\overline{AM}$ of $\triangle ABC$ for $A(-2, 0)$, $B(6, 5)$, and $C(2, 11)$. 10

24. Find the length of median $\overline{DM}$ of $\triangle DEF$ for $D(1, -6)$, $E(-7, -9)$, and $F(1, 5)$. $4\sqrt{2}$

Find the coordinates of the endpoints of the medians of the trapezoids with these vertices.

25. $A(-2, 4)$, $B(4, 4)$, $C(5, 2)$, $D(-4, 2)$ $M_{AD}(-3,3)$; $M_{BC}(\frac{9}{2},3)$

26. $E(-1, 5)$, $F(5, -3)$, $G(-2, -3)$, $H(-5, 1)$ $M_{EH}(-3,3)$; $M_{GF}(\frac{3}{2},-3)$

27. M_1 and M_2 are the respective midpoints of nonparallel sides $\overline{AB}$ and $\overline{CD}$ of trapezoid $ABCD$: $A(-3, -2)$, $B(-1, 4)$, $C(3, 4)$, $D(7, -2)$. Find the lengths of $\overline{M_1M_2}$, $\overline{BC}$, and $\overline{AD}$. Which theorem could you use to check your answers? Theorem 6.19 and Theorem 13.1 $M_1M_2 = 7$, $BC = 4$, $AD = 10$

Are these quadrilaterals parallelograms? Use the Midpoint Formula to justify your answer.

no; midpoints of diagonals do not coincide; $M_{BD}(\frac{11}{2},\frac{10}{2})$; $M_{AC}(\frac{11}{2},\frac{11}{2})$

28. Quadrilateral $ABCD$, with $A(1, 1)$, $B(9, 3)$, $C(10, 10)$, $D(2, 7)$

29. Quadrilateral $EFGH$, with $E(-4, 3)$, $F(2, 1)$, $G(4, 7)$, $H(-2, 9)$
yes; midpoints of diagonals coincide at $(0,5)$

C **30.** What is the relationship of the lengths of the hypotenuse and the median to the hypotenuse of any right triangle? Show that this is true for $\triangle PQR$, with $P(-3, -2)$, $Q(3, -2)$, and $R(3, 6)$. length of median $= \frac{1}{2}$ the length of hyp.; $PR = 10$, $QM = 5$

31. Prove Theorem 13.3.
See side column.
Suppose point $P(x, y)$ on $\overline{AB}$ separates $\overline{AB}$ such that AP and PB are in the ratio of r_1 to r_2. If A has coordinates (x_1, y_1) and B has coordinates (x_2, y_2), then the coordinates of P are given by these formulas:

$$x = \frac{r_2 x_1 + r_1 x_2}{r_1 + r_2} \qquad y = \frac{r_2 y_1 + r_1 y_2}{r_1 + r_2}$$

32. Find the coordinates of P on $\overline{AB}$, for $A(-8, 4)$, $B(-13, -6)$, and $r_1 : r_2 = 3:2$. Then graph A, B, and P to decide if your answer is reasonable. $P(-11,-2)$

33. Use the formulas to find the coordinates of a point $P(x, y)$ that is $\frac{2}{3}$ of the distance from $P_1(-3, -5)$ to $P_2(6, 7)$. $(3,3)$

34. Find the coordinates of the centroid of $\triangle ABC$ for $A(-3, -2)$, $B(7, -1)$, and $C(5, 9)$. $(3,2)$

13.3 The Midpoint Formula **549**

Analysis Ask students to determine the most convenient general coordinates to use in a given situation.

Assignment Guide
See p. 534B for assignments.

Developing Mathematical Power
Extension Exercise 45 provides students with an opportunity to extend the lesson concept by asking them to find the coordinates of the midpoint of a line in space.

Additional Answers
31. Proof:

Statements	Reasons
1. Draw $\overline{QR} \parallel$ x-axis and $\overline{PQ} \parallel$ y-axis.	1. Through a pt. not on a line exactly 1 $\parallel$ can be drawn.
2. Draw $\overline{MX} \parallel \overline{QR}$ and $\overline{MY} \parallel \overline{PQ}$.	2. Same as 1.
3. $\dfrac{PX}{XQ} = \dfrac{PM}{MR}$	3. If a line $\parallel$ to one side of a $\triangle$ intersects the other two sides, then it divides those sides proportionally.
4. M is midpt. of $\overline{PR}$.	4. Given
5. $\overline{PM} \cong \overline{MR}$	5. Def. of midpt.
6. $PM = MR$	6. Def. of $\cong$ seg.
7. $\dfrac{PX}{XQ} = \dfrac{PM}{PM}$	7. Subst. prop. (Step 3)
8. $PX = XQ$	8. Alg. props.
9. $QY = YR$	9. Similar reasoning (Steps 3, 7, 8)
10. $\overline{PX} \cong \overline{XQ}$; $\overline{QY} \cong \overline{YR}$	10. Def. of $\cong$ seg.
11. X is midpt. of $\overline{PQ}$; Y is midpt. of $\overline{QR}$.	11. Def. of midpt.
12. X has coords: $(x_1, \dfrac{y_1 + y_2}{2})$; Y has coords: $(\dfrac{x_1 + x_2}{2}, y_1)$	12. Coords. of midpts. for vertical and horizontal segments
13. M has coords: $(\dfrac{x_1 + x_2}{2}, \dfrac{y_1 + y_2}{2})$	13. M has x-coord. of Y and y-coord. of X.

Concl.: The coords. of the midpt. of a line seg. are the average of the coords. of the endpts. of the seg.

Lesson Quiz

Find the coordinates of the midpoint of each given segment.

1. $\overline{AB}$, with $A(-7, 3)$ and $B(-1, -5)$
2. $\overline{CD}$, with $C(2, -4)$ and $D(5, 6)$
3. If $M(2, -3)$ is the midpoint of $\overline{EF}$, with endpoint $F(4, 1)$, what are the coordinates of E?

1. $(-4, -1)$ 2. $(3.5, 1)$ 3. $(0, -7)$

Enrichment

The endpoints of one base of trapezoid $ABCD$ are $A(-4, -5)$ and $B(2, -2)$. The endpoints of the median of the trapezoid are $P(0, -\frac{1}{2})$ and $Q(-5, -3)$. Find the coordinates of C and D. Graphing A, B, P, and Q shows that Q is the midpoint of $\overline{AD}$ and P is the midpoint of $\overline{BC}$. Then C has coordinates $(-2, 1)$ and D has coordinates $(-6, -1)$.

35. Interior Decorating A designer plots a scale drawing of a rectangular room on the coordinate axes. He assigns the vertices the coordinates $A(0, 0)$, $B(10, 0)$, $C(10, 6)$, and $D(0, 6)$. How can he locate the center of the ceiling to place a light fixture? What will the coordinates be? Find the midpt. of either diagonal; (5,3).

36. Technology Study the following Logo procedure.

```
to midpoint :x1 :y1 :x2 :y2
pu setpos (se :x1 :y1)
pd setpos (se :x2 :y2)
make "xm (:x2+:x1)/2
make "ym (:y2+:y1)/2
pr [The midpoint is:]
setpos (se :xm :ym)
label (se [(] :xm [,] :ym [)])
end
```

a. Use the procedure to find the midpoint of $(7,3)$ and $(9,4)$.

b. Draw an isosceles trapezoid and join the midpoints of the consecutive sides. What polygon is formed? Why? See Solutions Manual.

Mixed Review

ABCD is a trapezoid inscribed in $\odot E$. Find the following.

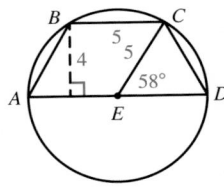

37. Circumference of $\odot E = \underline{\ ?\ }$ 38. Area of $ABCE = \underline{\ ?\ }$
    31.4 or 10π 20

39. $m\angle BCE = \underline{\ ?\ }$ 58   40. Area of $\odot E = \underline{\ ?\ }$
                                                                          78.5 or 25π

41. Area of $ABCD = \underline{\ ?\ }$ 30   42. Area of $\triangle CDE = \underline{\ ?\ }$
                                                                          10

43. $m\angle BCD = \underline{\ ?\ }$ 119   44. $m\ \overset{\frown}{BAD} = \underline{\ ?\ }$
                                                                           238

Developing Mathematical Power

45. Extension If $\overline{P_1P_2}$ is a segment in space with $P_1(x_1, y_1, z_1)$ and $P_2(x_2, y_2, z_2)$, then the formula for the coordinates of the midpoint is:

$$\left(\frac{x_1 + x_2}{2}, \frac{y_1 + y_2}{2}, \frac{z_1 + z_2}{2}\right)$$

Find the midpoint of $\overline{P_1P_2}$ with $P_1(3, -4, -3)$ and $P_2(-4, 5, 2)$.
$(-\frac{1}{2}, \frac{1}{2}, -\frac{1}{2})$

$P_2(-4, 5, 2)$

$P_1(3, -4, -3)$

Give the coordinates of these points.

1. A $(-4, 3)$ **2.** G $(1, -3)$

3. D $(-2, -2)$ **4.** F $(0, 3)$

Name the points having these coordinates.

5. $(2, 2)$ B **6.** $(4, 3)$ J

7. $(3, 0)$ E **8.** $(-2, 2)$ C

9. Name all the given points in each quadrant. I: B,J; II: A,C; III: H,D; IV: G

True or false? Justify all answers.

10. All coordinates in Quadrant I are positive numbers. True; x- and y-coordinates must be pos. to be in Quad. I.

11. All coordinates in Quadrant IV are negative numbers. False; x-coordinates are pos.

12. In Quadrant II, the x-coordinates are positive and the y-coordinates are negative. False; x-coordinates are neg., y-coordinates are pos.

13. $y = -10$ is the equation of a vertical line. false; horizontal

14. $x = 7.5$ is the equation of a line that intersects the x-axis at $(7.5, 0)$. true; vertical line with all values of x = 7.5

Find the distance between the two given points.

15. $A(-5, 5)$, $B(0, -7)$ 13

16. $C(-3, -1)$, $D(-9, 11)$ $6\sqrt{5}$

Give the center and the length of the radius of each circle.

17. $(x - 2)^2 + (y + 5)^2 = 4$ (2,-5); 2

18. $x^2 + y^2 = 16$ (0,0); 4

Give the equation of the circle with the given center and radius length.

19. $(5, 0)$, 3 $(x - 5)^2 + y^2 = 9$

20. $(-4, 3)$, $\sqrt{5}$ $(x + 4)^2 + (y - 3)^2 = 5$

Find the coordinates of the midpoint of the given segment.

21. $A(3, -4)$, $B(7, -12)$ (5,-8)

22. $C(-5, 7)$, $D(11, -7)$ (3,0)

For Exercises 23–24, apply the Midpoint Formula.

23. What are the coordinates of endpoint A of $\overline{AB}$ with $B(-1, -6)$ and midpoint $M(1, -1)$? A(3,4)

24. Find the length of the median $\overline{DM}$ of $\triangle DEF$ for $D(-1, -5)$, $E(-9, -8)$, and $F(-1, 4)$ 5

13.1

13.2

13.3

13.3 The Midpoint Formula **551**

Teacher's Resource Book
Follow-Up Investigation, *Chapter 13*, p. 7.

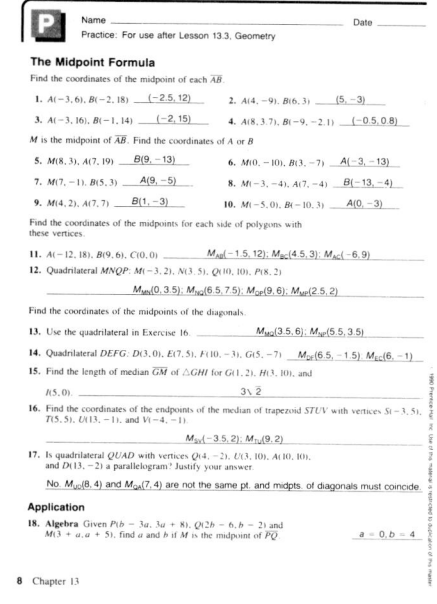

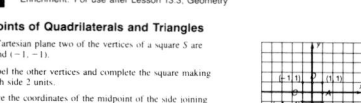

LESSON FOCUS

- Review subtraction of integers.

  1. $5 - (-3)$ **2.** $-8 - (-5)$
  3. $17 - 8$ **4.** $-6 - 7$
  1. 8   2. −3   3. 9   4. −13
- Review division of integers.

  5. $\dfrac{-8}{2}$ **6.** $\dfrac{-9}{-6}$

  7. $\dfrac{15}{-10}$ **8.** $\dfrac{12}{16}$

  5. −4   6. $\frac{3}{2}$ 7. $-\frac{3}{2}$ 8. $\frac{3}{4}$
- Exercises 49–52 provide a Mixed Review.

Alternative Learning Styles

- The Investigation provides an opportunity for students to visualize the concept of a slope as it is applied to a real-life situation.
- The linguistic learner may benefit from verbalizing an explanation of different slopes, while the visual learner may benefit from seeing different slopes. Teaching Transparency 88 provides an opportunity for both learners: The linguistic learner can gain confidence by explaining why the slope is what it is; the visual learner can easily make a visual comparison of why the slope is what it is.

Slope of a Line

Objective: To find the slope of a line, given two points on the line

One way to describe a line on the coordinate plane is to consider how the line rises or falls from left to right. The rise or fall of a line can be represented by a number called the *slope* of the line.

Investigation—*Visualizing the Concept*

An access ramp is placed over three steps. Each tread is 12 in. wide and each riser is 4 in.

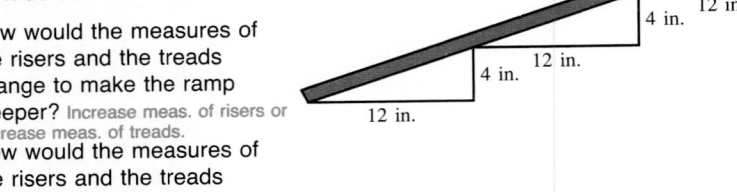

1. How would the measures of the risers and the treads change to make the ramp steeper? Increase meas. of risers or decrease meas. of treads.
2. How would the measures of the risers and the treads change to make the ramp less steep? Decrease meas. of risers or increase meas. of treads.
3. Generalize your answers to Questions 1 and 2. Steepness depends on ratio of meas. of riser to meas. of tread.

Note how these lines slope.
$\overleftrightarrow{AB}$ slopes "upward to the right"; the y-coordinates increase as the x-coordinates increase.

$\overleftrightarrow{CD}$ slopes "downward to the right"; the y-coordinates decrease as the x-coordinates increase.

The following definition restates these ideas algebraically.

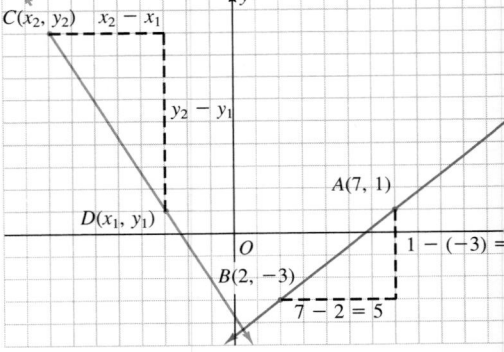

Definition   Given any two points with coordinates (x_1, y_1) and (x_2, y_2) on a line, the **slope *m*** of the line is given by $m = \dfrac{y_2 - y_1}{x_2 - x_1}$, provided that $x_2 \neq x_1$.

552   Chapter 13 Coordinate Geometry

Developing Mathematical Power

Cooperative Learning   Assign groups of students to complete the Investigation activity, p. 10, in the *Teacher's Resource Book*. Have them design a slide and a seesaw for the Recreation Area and determine the best slope for their slide. When they present their designs to the class, they should discuss the range of values for the slope of the seesaw.

EXAMPLE 1 Find the slope of the line that contains each pair of points. Check your work by graphing each line.

a. $E(-2, -5)$ and $F(8, 3)$

b. $G(-3, 11)$ and $H(2, 6)$

c. $G(-3, 11)$ and $I(7, 11)$

d. $G(-3, 11)$ and $J(-3, 6)$

e. Compute the slope of $\overleftrightarrow{EF}$ using the midpoint, M, of $\overline{EF}$ and E.

a. $\dfrac{y_2 - y_1}{x_2 - x_1} = \dfrac{3 - (-5)}{8 - (-2)} = \dfrac{8}{10}$ or $\dfrac{4}{5}$

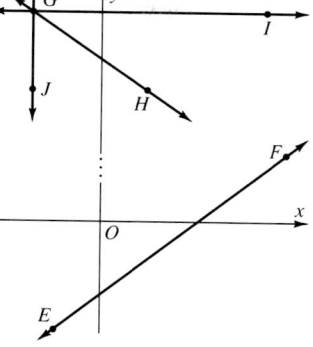

b. $\dfrac{6 - 11}{2 - (-3)} = \dfrac{-5}{5}$ or -1

c. $\dfrac{11 - 11}{7 - (-3)} = 0$

d. $\dfrac{6 - 11}{-3 - (-3)} = \dfrac{-5}{0}$, undefined

e. Midpoint $M(3, -1)$;

$\dfrac{y_2 - y_1}{x_2 - x_1} = \dfrac{-1 - (-5)}{3 - (-2)} = \dfrac{4}{5}$

The solutions to Example 1 suggest these properties:

1. Any line sloping upward to the right has a *positive slope*.

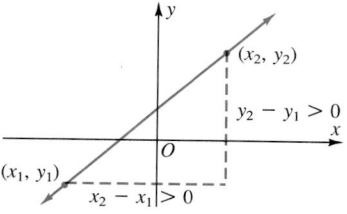

2. Any line sloping down to the right has a *negative slope*.

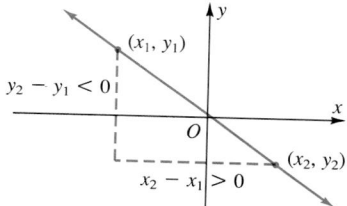

3. Any horizontal line has a *slope of 0*.

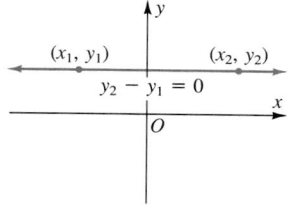

4. The slope of any vertical line is *undefined*.

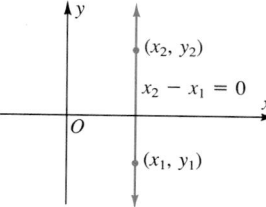

5. For any given line, the slope can be computed by using any two points on the line.

TEACHING SUGGESTIONS

- To give students a feeling for the meaning of "slope," have them *count* the change in coordinates.
- Make sure that students understand that if they want to find the slope of $\overleftrightarrow{AB}$, they can subtract the coordinates of A from B or vice versa, as long as they do the same for both the x- and y-coordinates.
- Since students are used to using m for the measure of an angle, they may wonder why it is being used here for the slope of a line. As they will see in the next lesson, m is traditionally used for the slope of a line when one writes the general equation for the line. To help prepare students for the discussion of the equation of a line, use "slope m" frequently when discussing the slope of a line.
- Practice Exercises 38–40 foreshadow Lesson 13.6.

CHALKBOARD EXAMPLES

- **For Example 1**
  Find the slope of the line that contains each pair of points.

  a. $A(-4, 5)$ and $B(-2, 3)$
  b. $C(-5, 4)$ and $D(4, -2)$
  c. $E(3, -4)$ and $F(-2, -4)$
  d. $G(2, 5)$ and $H(2, -1)$

  a. $\dfrac{y_2 - y_1}{x_2 - x_1} = \dfrac{3 - 5}{-2 - (-4)} = \dfrac{-2}{2}$, or -1
  b. $\dfrac{-2 - 4}{4 - (-5)} = \dfrac{-6}{9}$, or $-\dfrac{2}{3}$
  c. $\dfrac{-4 - (-4)}{-2 - 3} = 0$
  d. $\dfrac{-1 - 5}{2 - 2} = \dfrac{-6}{0}$; undefined

Developing Mathematical Power

Keeping a Portfolio Have students write in their own words the definition of *slope*. They should then relate their definitions to the concept of rise over run and also to the concept of the change in y compared to the change in x. Have them make a collage of pictures illustrating natural and artificial examples of slope.

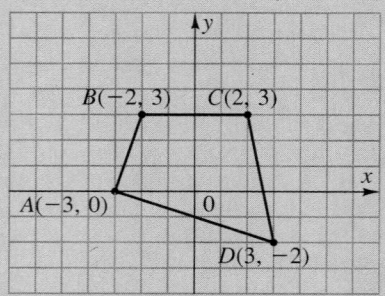
EXAMPLE 2   **Study this graph of a trapezoid.**

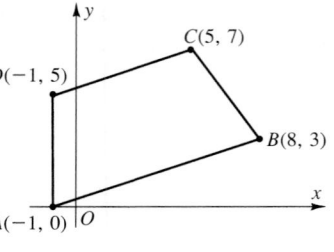

a. For each side, predict whether the slope is positive, negative, 0, or undefined.

b. Predict which side has the steepest slope.

c. Predict which two sides, if any, have the same slope.

d. Check your predictions by computing the slopes.

a. Slopes of $\overleftrightarrow{AB}$ and $\overleftrightarrow{CD}$ are positive; $\overleftrightarrow{BC}$, negative; $\overleftrightarrow{DA}$, undefined.

b. $\overleftrightarrow{DA}$ has an undefined slope. $\overleftrightarrow{BC}$ has a steeper incline than $\overleftrightarrow{AB}$ or $\overleftrightarrow{CD}$.

c. $\overleftrightarrow{AB}$ and $\overleftrightarrow{CD}$ have equal slopes.

d. $\overline{AB}$: $m = \frac{1}{3}$ $\overline{BC}$: $m = -\frac{4}{3}$

   $\overline{CD}$: $m = \frac{1}{3}$ $\overline{DA}$: m is undefined

   Slopes of $\overleftrightarrow{AB}$ and $\overleftrightarrow{CD}$ are equal.

   $\overleftrightarrow{BC}$ is steepest, since $|-\frac{4}{3}| > |\frac{1}{3}|$.

CLASS EXERCISES

Thinking Critically

1. How can the steepness of two lines be compared if one has a negative slope and the other has a positive slope? Compare absolute values.

2. If the coordinates of three points are given, how can it be determined, without graphing, whether or not they are collinear? Compute and compare slopes, between any 2 pairs of pts.

Find the slope of each line.

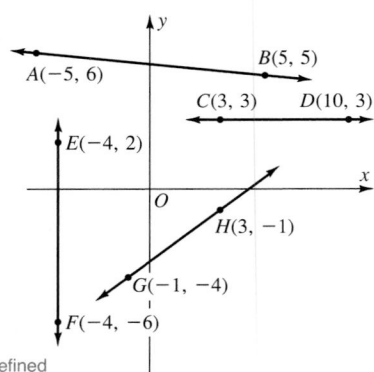

3. $\overleftrightarrow{AB}$ $-\frac{1}{10}$ 4. $\overleftrightarrow{CD}$ 0

5. $\overleftrightarrow{EF}$ undefined   6. $\overleftrightarrow{GH}$ $\frac{3}{4}$

7. If two points have the same y-coordinates, the slope of the line that contains them is ?. 0

8. If two points have the same x-coordinate, the slope of the line that contains them is ?. undefined

554   Chapter 13 Coordinate Geometry

Class Exercises
9.
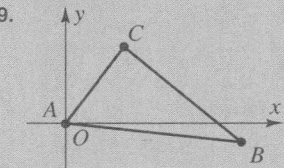

10.
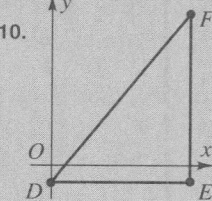

Graph the triangles. Predict which sides have positive, negative, zero, or undefined slopes. Then compute to verify your prediction.

9. $\triangle ABC$: $A(0, 0)$, $B(9, -1)$, $C(3, 4)$ $\overline{AC}$: $m = \frac{4}{3}$; $\overline{BC}$: $m = -\frac{5}{6}$; $\overline{AB}$: $m = -\frac{1}{9}$

10. $\triangle DEF$: $D(0, -1)$, $E(8, -1)$, $F(8, 9)$ $\overline{DE}$: $m = 0$; $\overline{EF}$: m is undefined; $\overline{DF}$: $m = \frac{5}{4}$
    See side column page 554.

PRACTICE EXERCISES   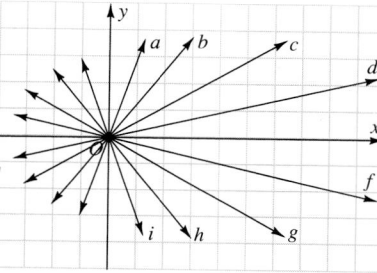 Use technology where appropriate.

Thinking Critically

Consider the slopes of lines labeled $a-i$.

1. What happens to the slope as the lines become steeper? less steep? Slope increases in abs. val.; slope decreases in abs. val.

2. What happens to the slope as the lines become closer to the y-axis? to the x-axis? They increase in absolute value and approach being undefined; they approach O.

3. Which lines have a positive slope? a, b, c, d a negative slope? f, g, h, i

   What patterns do you see? Answers may vary.

Which of these lines have

4. a positive slope? $\overleftrightarrow{AB}$, $\overleftrightarrow{EF}$
5. a negative slope? $\overleftrightarrow{CD}$, $\overleftrightarrow{KL}$
6. a slope of 0? $\overleftrightarrow{GH}$
7. an undefined slope? $\overleftrightarrow{IJ}$

Compute the slope of each line.

8. $\overleftrightarrow{AB}$ $\frac{-10}{3}$
9. $\overleftrightarrow{CD}$ $\frac{2}{3}$
10. $\overleftrightarrow{EF}$ $\frac{-3}{2}$
11. $\overleftrightarrow{GH}$ 0
12. $\overleftrightarrow{IJ}$ undefined
13. $\overleftrightarrow{KL}$ 2

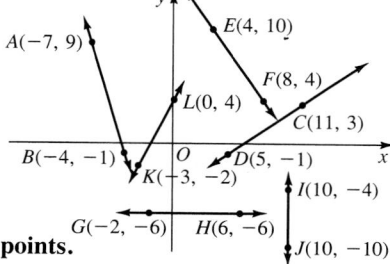
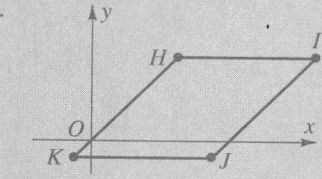

Find the slope of the line determined by the given points.

14. $(0, 0)$, $(4, 4)$ 1
15. $(0, 0)$, $(3, -3)$ −1
16. $(0, 5)$, $(5, 0)$ −1
17. $(-4, 0)$, $(4, 4)$ $\frac{1}{2}$
18. $(0, -5)$, $(7, -5)$ 0
19. $(-3, -2)$, $(-3, 2)$ undefined

Find the slopes of all sides of each polygon. Graph the polygon.
See side column.

20. $\triangle ABC$: $A(-5, 4)$, $B(3, 6)$, $C(7, -2)$ $\overline{AB}$: $m = \frac{1}{4}$; $\overline{BC}$: $m = -2$; $\overline{AC}$: $m = -\frac{1}{2}$

21. Quadrilateral $DEFG$: $D(-3, 8)$, $E(7, 6)$, $F(7, -1)$, $G(-1, -1)$ $\overline{DE}$: $m = -\frac{1}{5}$; $\overline{EF}$: m is undefined; $\overline{FG}$: $m = 0$; $\overline{DG}$: $m = -\frac{9}{2}$

22. Quadrilateral $HIJK$: $H(5, 5)$, $I(13, 5)$, $J(7, -1)$, $K(-1, -1)$ $\overline{HI}$: $m = 0$; $\overline{IJ}$: $m = 1$; $\overline{JK}$: $m = 0$; $\overline{HK}$: $m = 1$

23. Quadrilateral $LMNO$: $L(1, 1)$, $M(5, 5)$, $N(9, 1)$, $O(5, -3)$ $\overline{LM}$: $m = 1$; $\overline{MN}$: $m = -1$; $\overline{NO}$: $m = 1$; $\overline{LO}$: $m = -1$

13.4 Slope of a Line   **555**

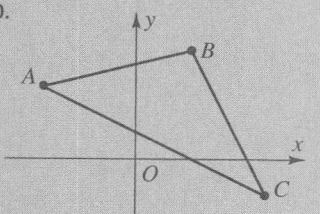
20.

21.

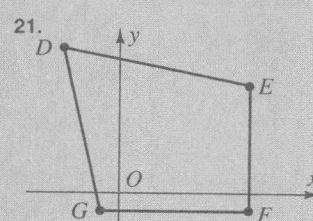

23.

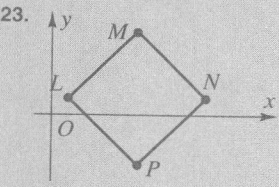

555

B 24. $\triangle PQR$ has vertices $P(3, 7)$, $Q(7, -1)$, and $R(-3, 5)$. Show that the segment joining the midpoints of $\overline{PQ}$ and $\overline{PR}$ has the same slope as $\overline{QR}$.
mdpt. of $\overline{PQ}$: $M_1(5,3)$; midpt. of $\overline{PR}$: $M_2(0,6)$; $\overline{QR}$: $m = -\frac{3}{5}$; M_1M_2: $M = -\frac{3}{5}$

25. $\triangle STU$ has vertices $S(3, 14)$, $T(-1, 2)$, and $U(-3, 6)$. Show that the segment joining the midpoints of $\overline{SU}$ and $\overline{TU}$ has the same slope as $\overline{ST}$.
midpt. of $\overline{SU}$: $M_1(0,10)$; midpt. of $\overline{TU}$: $M_2(-2,4)$; $\overline{ST}$: $m = 3$; M_1M_2: $m = 3$

26. Find the slopes of the medians of $\triangle WXY$ for $W(-6, 0)$, $X(0, 6)$, and $Y(6, 2)$. median from W: $m = \frac{4}{9}$; median from X: m is undefined; median from Y: $m = -\frac{1}{9}$

27. Find the slopes of the medians of $\triangle ABC$ for $A(-2, -2)$, $B(-2, 6)$, and $C(4, -2)$. median from A: $m = \frac{4}{3}$; median from B: $m = -\frac{8}{3}$; median from C: $m = -\frac{2}{3}$

Three points—A, B, and C—are collinear if and only if the slopes of $\overline{AB}$ and $\overline{BC}$ are equal. Are the following points collinear? Explain.

28. $D(-1, -6)$, $E(2, -4)$, $F(8, 0)$ Yes; slope of $\overline{DE}$ = slope of $\overline{EF}$ = $\frac{2}{3}$

29. $G(2, -3)$, $H(-4, 5)$, $I(-7, 9)$ Yes; slope of $\overline{GH}$ = slope of $\overline{HI}$ = $-\frac{4}{3}$

30. $J(1, -3)$, $K(-3, 1)$, $L(-9, 6)$ No; slope of $\overline{JK}$ = -1; slope of $\overline{KL}$ = $-\frac{5}{6}$

31. $M(-3, -3)$, $N(2, 1)$, $P(7, 6)$ No; slope of $\overline{MN}$ = $\frac{4}{5}$; slope of $\overline{NP}$ = 1

32. A line intersecting the x-axis at $(-5, 0)$ has a slope 2. Find the coordinates of the point where it intersects the y-axis. (0,10)

33. A line intersecting the x-axis at $(4, 0)$ has a slope $-\frac{3}{2}$. Find the coordinates of the point where it intersects the y-axis. (0,6)

34. Line k has a slope -3. It contains $A(1, 7)$ and $B(4, y_1)$. Find the y-coordinate of B. $y_1 = -2$

35. Line l has a slope $-\frac{4}{3}$. It contains $A(1, 7)$ and $B(7, y_1)$. Find the y-coordinate of B. -1

36. Line k intersects the y-axis where $y = 5$ and the x-axis where $x = -4$. What is the slope of k? $\frac{5}{4}$

37. Find the slope of any line that intersects the y-axis at $(0, b)$ and the x-axis at $(a, 0)$. $\frac{-b}{a}$

Show that these triangles are right triangles. Compare the slopes of the legs in each triangle.

38. $\triangle ABC$: $A(-2, -1)$, $B(-6, 7)$, $C(4, 2)$ $AB = \sqrt{80}$, $AC = \sqrt{45}$, $BC = \sqrt{125}$; by Pyth. Th., slope of $\overline{AB}$ = -2, slope of $\overline{AC}$ = $\frac{1}{2}$

39. $\triangle DEF$: $D(-1, 1)$, $E(3, 4)$, $F(9, -4)$ $ED = 5$, $EF = 10$, $DF = \sqrt{125}$; by Pyth. Th., slope of $\overline{ED}$ = $\frac{3}{4}$, slope of $\overline{EF}$ = $-\frac{4}{3}$

C 40. What do the results of Exercises 38–39 suggest about the product of the slopes of perpendicular lines? Their product is -1.

41. Line k passes through $(-3\frac{1}{2}, 2)$. Its slope is 2. Find the coordinates of two other points on k. Answers may vary; $(-2\frac{1}{2}, 4)$, $(-4\frac{1}{2}, 0)$

556   Chapter 13 Coordinate Geometry

42. Prove that all segments of any nonvertical line have the same slope. (Let $P_1(x_1, y_1)$ and $P_2(x_2, y_2)$ be two points on a nonvertical line k, and $P(x, y)$ be any other point on k.) See Additional Answers, p. 702.

It is true that for any line k with a positive slope, m = tangent A, where A is the measure of $\angle BAC$ formed by k and the x-axis.

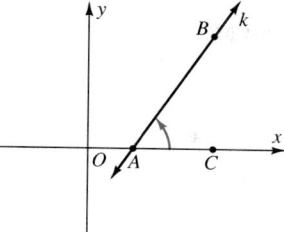

Use that fact to find A to the nearest degree for a line containing the given points.

43. $P_1(0, -3)$ and $P_2(3, 1)$ $\tan A = \frac{4}{3}, \angle A = 53°$

44. $P_1(-3, -3)$ and $P_2(5, 5)$ $\tan A = 1, \angle A = 45°$

Applications

45. Technology Using Logo and the SETH command, write a procedure with the variables :slope and :point to draw any line you wish.
See Solutions Manual.

46. Construction The pitch of a roof is defined as the rise divided by the span. Compare the slope of the roof to its pitch. slope = rise ÷ run = 2 · pitch

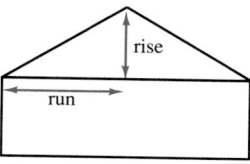

47. Construction Describe a situation in which the slope and the pitch of a roof will be the same.
The rise is 0, or the roof is flat.

48. Construction: One end of an access ramp is attached to the top of a 6-in. step. If the slope of the ramp is $\frac{1}{8}$, how many feet from the base of the step is the other end of the ramp? 4 ft

---

Mixed Review

Solve. Draw a figure when necessary.

49. On level ground, a 6-ft-tall person and a flagpole cast shadows of 15 ft and 120 ft respectively. What is the height of the flagpole? 48 ft

50. An 8-ft ladder makes an angle of $42°$ with the side of a building. How far up the side of the building is the ladder? 5.9 ft

51. $ABCDE \sim FGHIJ$. The area of $ABCDE$ is 525 cm^2, and the area of $FGHIJ$ is 175 cm^2. If $GH = 9$ cm, find BC. 27 cm

52. A diameter of a circle measures 50 cm. Find the length of a chord that is 7 cm from the center. 48 cm

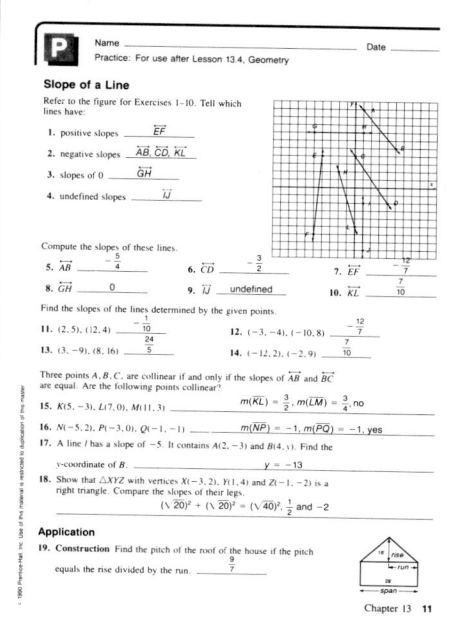

Vocabulary

Linear   Standard form
  equation   *x*-intercept
Point-slope   *y*-intercept
  form
Slope-intercept
  form

Materials/Manipulatives

Graph paper
Thread
Teaching Transparency 89

Technology

Graphing utility
Computer Test Bank, pp.
  842–852

LESSON FOCUS

Review

Use graph paper to locate, mark, and connect these points.

1. (1, 5)
2. (0, 2)
3. $(-\frac{2}{3}, 0)$
4. (−1, −1)
5. (−2, −4)

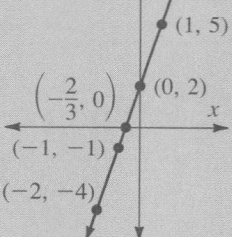

Alternative Learning Styles

- The Investigation provides students with an opportunity to use critical thinking to graph the function $F = \frac{9}{5}C + 32$.
- The kinesthetic learner may benefit from using colored thread taped on grid paper to illustrate the graphs of two lines.

Multicultural Opportunity

See the Biography, p. 564.

558

13.5 Equations of a Line

Objectives: To draw the graph of a line specified by a given equation
To write an equation of a line given either one point and the slope of the line or two points on the line
To determine the point of intersection of two lines

You have studied the equations of horizontal and vertical lines on the coordinate plane. All other lines can also be described with equations.

Investigation—*Thinking Critically*

Recall that the formula for converting Celsius temperature to Fahrenheit is $F = \frac{9}{5}C + 32$. This relationship can be described on the coordinate plane.

1. Copy the *C* and *F* axes and use the formula to complete the table.

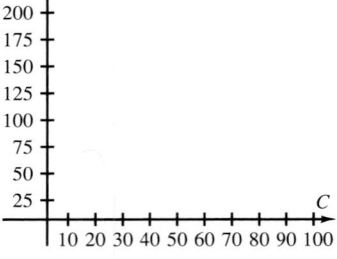

C	0	10	50	80	100
F	?	?	?	?	?
	32	50	122	176	212

2. Graph each point (*C*, *F*).

3. What figure is formed if they are connected? a line

4. How many possible points (*C*, *F*) are there? infinite

5. Draw a conclusion about the graph of $F = \frac{9}{5}C + 32$. It is a line.

Theorem 13.4 The graph of an equation that can be written in the form $ax + by = c$, with *a* and *b* not both zero, is a line.
Justified in Practice Exercise 55

The type of equation described in Theorem 13.4 is called **linear,** and $ax + by = c$ is called the **standard form** of a linear equation.

By Theorem 13.4, $2x - y = 4$ is a linear equation in standard form with $a = 2$, $b = -1$, and $c = 4$. One way to graph this equation is to find at least two ordered pairs (*x*, *y*) that satisfy the equation and then draw the line determined by them. Every ordered pair that is associated with a point of the line is a solution of $2x - y = 4$. How many solutions does a linear equation have? infinitely many

558 Chapter 13 Coordinate Geometry

Developing Mathematical Power

Cooperative Learning Select teams of students to investigate lines by comparing their slopes and *y*-intercepts. Give each group a set of equations to graph such as $y = 2x + 5$, $y = -\frac{1}{2}x - 3$, $y = 2x - 3$, $2y = 4x + 10$, and $y = 3x + 2$. They should graph each in a different color and summarize results in a chart.

EXAMPLE 1   **Graph $2x - y = 4$ and determine its slope.**

It is convenient to find the point with y-coordinate 0. The x-coordinate of this point is called the **x-intercept.**

$2x - 0 = 4$ *Substitute 0 for y.*
$\quad x = 2$ *Solve.*

$(2, 0)$ is a point of the line.

Find the point with x-coordinate 0. The y-coordinate of this point is the **y-intercept.**

$2 \cdot 0 - y = 4$ *Substitute 0 for x.*
$\quad\quad y = -4$ *Solve.*

$(0, -4)$ is a point of the line.

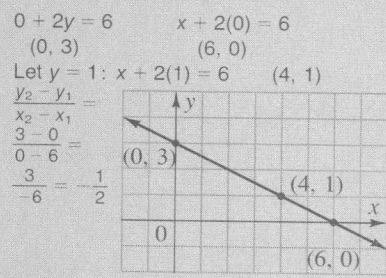

By the definition of slope:

$$\frac{y_2 - y_1}{x_2 - x_1} = \frac{0 - (-4)}{2 - 0} = 2$$

Check by finding a third point. Select a value for x and solve for y.
For example, for $x = 6$, $y = 8$.
The coordinates $(0, -4)$ and $(6, 8)$ also show that

$$m = \frac{-4 - 8}{0 - 6} = 2.$$

EXAMPLE 2   **Find an equation of the line containing $(6, 8)$ and having slope -3.**

Let (x, y) be any point of the line other than $(6, 8)$.

By definition of slope: $\dfrac{y - 8}{x - 6} = -3$ $\quad (y - 8) = -3(x - 6)$
In standard form: $\quad\quad 3x + y = 26$

The form $(y - 8) = -3(x - 6)$, is called the **point-slope** form of this equation.

Theorem 13.5   An equation of a line containing point (x_1, y_1) and having slope m is $(y - y_1) = m(x - x_1)$.
Proved in Practice Exercise 53

When the given point $P(x_1, y_1)$ of Theorem 13.5 is the y-intercept b, then the **slope-intercept** form can be developed.

Theorem 13.6   An equation of a line that has y-intercept b and slope m is $y = mx + b$.
Proved in Practice Exercise 54

CHALKBOARD EXAMPLES

• **For Example 1**

Graph $x + 2y = 6$ and find its slope. Find the coordinates of 3 points, including the point with x-coordinate 0 and with y-coordinate 0.

$0 + 2y = 6$ $x + 2(0) = 6$
$\quad (0, 3)$ $\quad\quad (6, 0)$
Let $y = 1$: $x + 2(1) = 6$ $(4, 1)$
$\dfrac{y_2 - y_1}{x_2 - x_1} =$
$\dfrac{3 - 0}{0 - 6} =$
$\dfrac{3}{-6} = -\dfrac{1}{2}$

• **For Example 2**

Find an equation of the line containing $(-1, 2)$ with slope $\dfrac{2}{3}$.
$\dfrac{2}{3} = \dfrac{y - 2}{x - (-1)}$
$2(x + 1) = 3(y - 2)$
$2x - 3y = -8$

560

- **For Example 3**

  Use the given information to write each equation in standard form.

  a. slope: $-\frac{2}{5}$; y-intercept: 2
  b. $P(-2, 3)$, $Q(4, -6)$

  a. $y = -\frac{2}{5}x + 2$
  $2x + 5y = 10$
  b. $m = \frac{-6 - 3}{4 - (-2)} = \frac{-9}{6} = -\frac{3}{2}$
  $(y - 3) = -\frac{3}{2}(x + 2)$
  $3x + 2y = 0$

- **For Example 4**

  Identify the form of each linear equation. Then graph by finding each slope and a point of the line.

  a. $y = -x + 2$
  b. $(y + 2) = \frac{1}{2}(x + 3)$
  c. $3x + 4y = 6$

  a. slope-intercept form
  slope: -1
  point: $(0, 2)$

  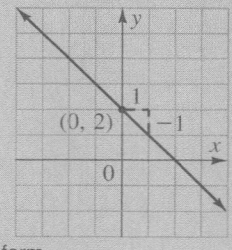

  b. point-slope form
  slope: $\frac{1}{2}$
  point: $(-3, -2)$

  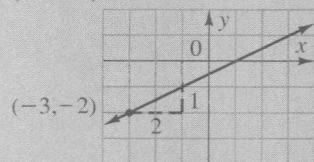

  c. standard form
  $3x + 4y = 6$
  $y = -\frac{3}{4}x + \frac{3}{2}$
  slope: $-\frac{3}{4}$
  point: $(2, 0)$

  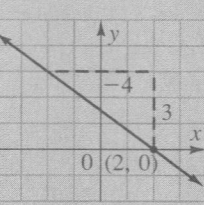

EXAMPLE 3   Use the given information to write each equation in standard form.

a. $m = \frac{3}{2}$; y-intercept: -4 **b.** $A(-2, 10)$; $B(5, -4)$

a. Use the slope-intercept form.

$$y = mx + b$$
$$y = \frac{3}{2}x - 4$$
$$-\frac{3}{2}x + y = 4$$
or $3x - 2y = 8$

b. First find the slope:

$$m = \frac{y_2 - y_1}{x_2 - x_1} = \frac{-4 - 10}{5 - (-2)} = -2$$

Use the point-slope form with A.

$$(y - y_1) = m(x - x_1)$$
$$y - 10 = -2(x + 2)$$
$$2x + y = 6$$

Would the solution to Example 3b be different if point B had been used instead of A? Explain. no; both points are on the same line and satisfy the same equation

EXAMPLE 4   Identify the form of each linear equation. Then graph.

a. $y = \frac{2}{3}x - 4$

b. $(y - 3) = 2(x + 1)$

c. $2x - 5y = -4$

a. slope-intercept
slope: $\frac{2}{3}$
y-intercept: -4

b. point-slope
slope: 2 or $\frac{2}{1}$
point: $(-1, 3)$

c. standard form
$y = \frac{2}{5}x + \frac{4}{5}$
slope: $\frac{2}{5}$
y-intercept: $\frac{4}{5}$

a.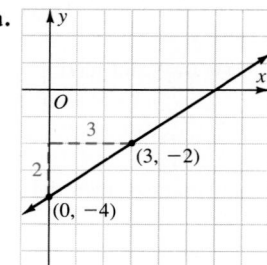

b.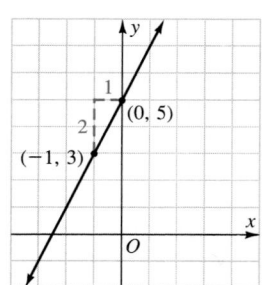

c.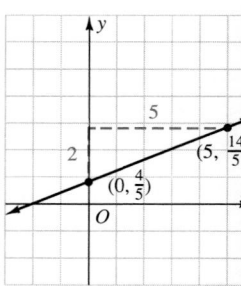

Algebraic properties can be applied to two linear equations to find the point of intersection, if any, of their graphs.

EXAMPLE 5 **Find the intersection point of lines given by**

1. $2x - y = 4$ 2. $x - 2y = -4$
Then check by graphing.

Multiply equation 2 by -2.
$$2x - y = 4$$
$$-2x + 4y = 8$$
Add to eliminate terms in x.
$$3y = 12$$
$$y = 4$$
In Equation 1, substitute 4 for y.
$$2x - 4 = 4$$
$$2x = 8$$
$$x = 4$$
Thus, $(4, 4)$ is the point of intersection.

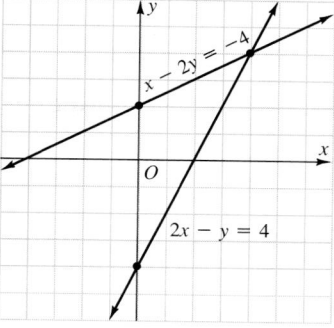

• **For Example 5**
Find the intersection point of the lines given by the following equations.

$$x - 2y = 0$$
$$2x + 3y = -7$$

Multiply the first equation by -2 and add (or multiply by 2 and subtract):
$$-2x + 4y = 0$$
$$2x + 3y = -7$$
Add: $7y = -7$
$$y = -1$$

Substitute: $2x + 3(-1) = -7$
$$2x = -4$$
$$x = -2$$
$$(-2, -1)$$

CLASS EXERCISES

Thinking Critically

Identify the form of each linear equation. Then, if necessary, rewrite each in slope-intercept form and identify the slope and y-intercept. See below.

1. $y = -5x - 7$

2. $(y - 6) = 4(x - 3)$

3. $2x + 3y = 9$

4. $6x - 3y = 7$

5. $(y + 2) = \frac{2}{3}(x - 6)$

6. $y = \sqrt{2}x + 5$

7. Solve this system of linear equations: $2x - y = 5$
$3x + 2y = 11$ (3,1)

8. Check your solution to Exercise 7 by graphing. See Additional Answers, p. 702.

9. Write the slope-intercept and standard form for the line with slope $\frac{3}{2}$ and y-intercept 4. $y = \frac{3}{2}x + 4; 3x - 2y = -8$

10. Write the point-slope and standard form for the line containing $Q(3, 4)$ and $R(2, 9)$. $y - 4 = -5(x - 3); 5x + y = 19$

11. Write the point-slope and standard form of the equation of the line containing $A(-4, 3)$ and $B(2, -1)$. $y - 3 = -\frac{2}{3}(x + 4); 2x + 3y = 1$

PRACTICE EXERCISES

A 1. **Thinking Critically** Show that the equation $2x^2 - y = 3$ is not linear by graphing it on the same plane as the graph of the linear equation $2x - y = 3$. Compare the graphs. The graph of $2x^2 - y = 3$ is a curve. The graphs intersect at $(0, -3)$ and $(1, -1)$. See Additional Answers, p. 702.

13.5 Equations of a Line   **561**

Common Error
• Some students may make computational errors if they try to use only two points to graph a line. Encourage them to use at least three points. If their three points are not collinear, they should graph a fourth point to determine which of the original points was incorrect, and then try to find and correct the computational error.
• See *Teacher's Resource Book* for additional remediation.

LESSON FOLLOW-UP

Discussion
Ask students which forms of equations are most useful when determining the point of intersection of two lines.   Either the standard form or the slope-intercept form

Critical Thinking
Analysis Ask students to determine which forms of equations are most convenient in certain situations.

1. slope-intercept; $m = -5$, $b = -7$

2. point-slope; $m = 4$, $b = -6$

3. standard; $m = \frac{-2}{3}$, $b = 3$

4. standard; $m = 2$, $b = \frac{-7}{3}$

5. point-slope; $m = \frac{2}{3}$, $b = -6$

6. slope-intercept; $m = \sqrt{2}$, $b = 5$

27.

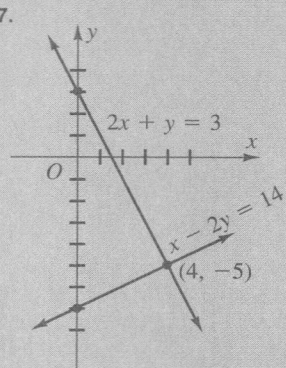

28.

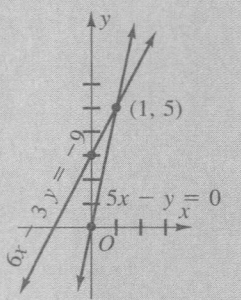

22.

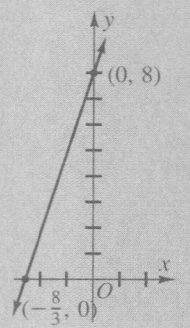

562

Find the slope-intercept form of each equation.

2. $3x + 2y = 6$ $y = \frac{-3}{2}x + 3$

3. $8x - 4y = 9$ $y = 2x - \frac{9}{4}$

4. $(y + 3) = \frac{5}{3}(x - 3)$ $y = \frac{5}{3}x - 8$

5. $-y = -2x + 5$ $y = 2x - 5$

Find the coordinates of one point and the slope.

6. $(y + 2) = 4(x - 5)$ $(5, -2); m = 4$

7. $(y - 4) = -\frac{2}{3}(x + 3)$ $(-3,4); m = -\frac{2}{3}$

Find the slope and y-intercept.

8. $y = -5x + 7.5$ $m = -5; 7.5$

9. $y = 0.5x - 3$ $m = 0.5; -3$

Write equations in slope-intercept form for lines with y-intercept b and slope m.

10. $b = -3, m = -\frac{5}{2}$ $y = -\frac{5}{2}x - 3$

11. $b = \frac{1}{2}, m = -8$ $y = -8x + \frac{1}{2}$

12. $b = 1.1, m = -0.5$ $y = -0.5x + 1.1$

13. $b = 0.5, m = \sqrt{3}$ $y = \sqrt{3}x + 0.5$

Write equations in point-slope form for lines containing point A and having slope m.

14. $A(-7, 0), m = -4$
$y = -4(x + 7)$

15. $A(-5, -6), m = \frac{2}{5}$
$y + 6 = \frac{2}{5}(x + 5)$

16. $A(1, -3), m = 3\sqrt{2}$
$(y + 3) = 3\sqrt{2}(x - 1)$

Write equations in point-slope and standard forms for the line containing

17. $C(1, -1), D(-1, -3)$.
$(y + 1) = 1(x - 1); x - y = 2$

18. $G(3, 0), H(0, 2)$.
$(y - 0) = -\frac{2}{3}(x - 3); 2x + 3y = 6$

19. $I(-3, 2), J(2, 17)$.
$(y - 2) = 3(x + 3); -3x + y = 11$

Graph these equations by finding the y-intercept and the x-intercept.

20. $2x - 3y = 6$ line through
x-intercept 3, y-intercept -2

21. $3x + 15y = -15$ line through
x-intercept -5, y-intercept -1

Graph these equations. See side column.

22. $y = 3x + 8$

23. $(y - 2) = -2(x + 4)$

24. $6x + 2y = 5$

Algebraically solve each system of linear equations.

25. $2x + y = 3$
$x - 2y = 14$ $(4, -5)$

26. $5x - y = 0$
$6x - 3y = -9$ $(1, 5)$

27. Solve the system of linear equations in Exercise 25 by graphing.

28. Solve the system of linear equations in Exercise 26 by graphing.

Solve each system algebraically.

B

29. $5x - 2y = -20$
$x - 2y = -25$ $(\frac{5}{4}, \frac{105}{8})$

30. $3x - 2y = 12$
$2x + 3y = 9$ $(\frac{54}{13}, \frac{3}{13})$

23.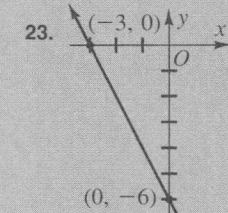

24.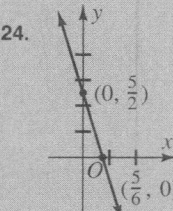

31. Solve Exercise 29 by graphing. What are the advantages of solving algebraically? Solving algebraically gives precise answers. With fractional coords. it can be hard to determine coord. of intersect. pt. See side column.

32. Solve Exercise 30 by graphing. What are the advantages of solving algebraically? Same as Ex. 31.

33. The x- and y-intercepts of a line are -2 and 5, respectively. Write the equation in standard form. $5x - 2y = -10$

34. The x- and y-intercepts of a line are 5 and -2, respectively. Write the equation in standard form. $2x - 5y = 10$

35. A line passes through the origin and has slope -2. Write the equation in standard form. $2x + y = 0$

36. A line passes through the origin and has slope $-\frac{5}{3}$. Write the equation in standard form. $5x + 3y = 0$

37. Find the point of intersection of the line $3x + y = 5$ and the line containing $(8, 1)$ and having slope $\frac{1}{3}$. $(2, -1)$

38. Find the point of intersection of the line $y = x + 9$ and the line having slope -2 and y-intercept 3. $(-2, 7)$

39. What is the equation in standard form of the line containing median $\overline{AM}$ of $\triangle ABC$ with $A(3, -4)$, $B(5, 3)$, and $C(-7, 1)$? $3x + 2y = 1$

40. What is the equation in standard form of the line through the midpoints of sides $\overline{DE}$ and $\overline{DF}$ of $\triangle DEF$ with $D(-3, 5)$, $E(3, -1)$, and $F(9, 9)$? Mdpts. are $(0,2)$ and $(3,7)$; $5x - 3y = -6$

41. Write the standard form of the equations of lines that contain the sides of $\triangle ABC$, with $A(0, 1)$, $B(2, -1)$, and $C(-2, 0)$. $\overleftrightarrow{AB}$: $x + y = 1$; $\overleftrightarrow{BC}$: $x + 4y = -2$; $\overleftrightarrow{CA}$: $x - 2y = -2$

42. Write the standard form of the equations of lines determined by the midpoints of the sides of $\triangle DEF$ with $D(0, 0)$, $E(4, 6)$, and $F(6, -4)$. Mdpts. are $(2,3)$, $(5,1)$, and $(3,-2)$; $2x + 3y = 13$; $3x - 2y = 13$; $5x + y = 13$

43. $\square ABCD$ has vertices $A(0, 0)$, $B(3, 4)$, $C(13, 4)$, and $D(10, 0)$. Find the equations in standard form of the lines containing the diagonals of $ABCD$. $\overleftrightarrow{BD}$: $4x + 7y = 40$; $\overleftrightarrow{AC}$: $4x - 13y = 0$

44. Rhombus $EFGH$ has vertices $E(0, 0)$, $F(3, 4)$, $G(8, 4)$, and $H(5, 0)$. Find the point of intersection of the diagonals. $(4, 2)$

Given a linear equation $ax + by = c$, the slope is always equal to $\frac{-a}{b}$ and the y-intercept is $\frac{c}{b}$, provided that $b \neq 0$.

Use these facts to find the slope and y-intercept for the equations.

45. $4x + 3y = 12$ 46. $3x + 4y = 12$ 47. $3x - 4y = 12$ 48. $-4y = 12$
$m = -\frac{4}{3}, b = 4$ $m = -\frac{3}{4}, b = 3$ $m = \frac{3}{4}, b = -3$ $m = 0, b = -3$

C 49. Prove that, given a linear equation $ax + by = c$, the slope is always equal to $\frac{-a}{b}$ and the y-intercept is $\frac{c}{b}$, provided that $b \neq 0$.
$ax + by = c$; $by = -ax + c$; $y = -\frac{a}{b}x + \frac{c}{b}$;
thus, $m = -\frac{a}{b}$; y-intercept $= \frac{c}{b}$.

13.5 Equations of a Line   **563**

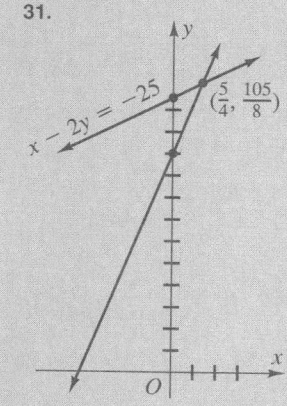
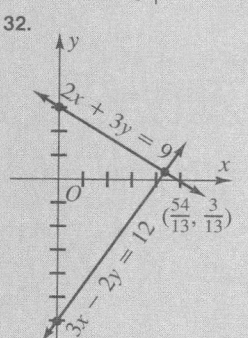

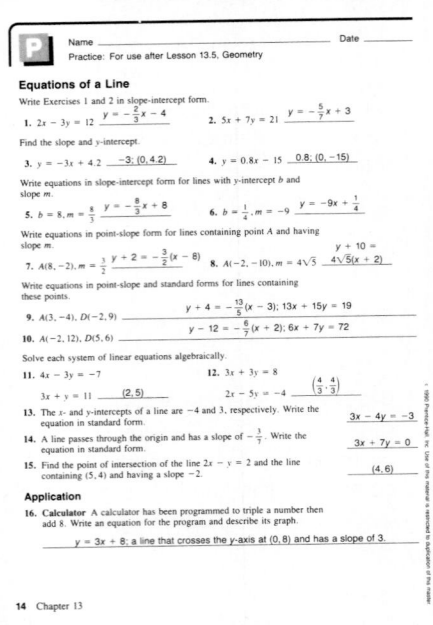

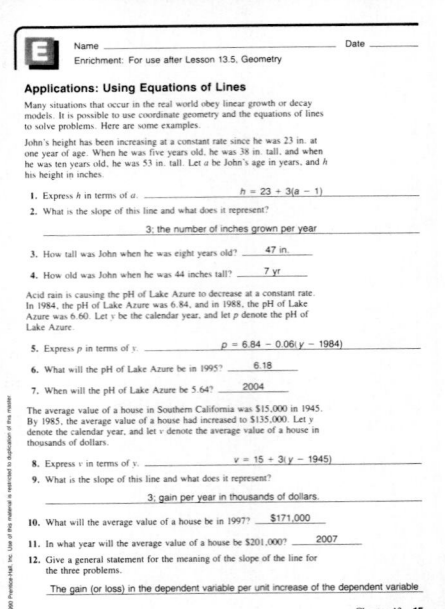

50. Find equations of the lines containing the medians of $\triangle PQR$ with $P(2, 2)$, $Q(6, 10)$, and $R(10, 6)$. Use them to find the coordinates of the centroid. Check your answer by using the Distance Formula. See Solutions Manual.

51. Find the general form of any equation of a line containing two points with the same y-coordinate. $y = b$ or $y = \frac{c}{b}$

52. Find the general form of any equation of a line containing two points with the same x-coordinate. $x = k$ or $x = \frac{c}{a}$

53. Prove Theorem 13.5.
See Additional Answers, p. 702.

54. Prove Theorem 13.6.
See Solutions Manual.

55. Write a justification of Theorem 13.4.

Applications

56. Science Solve the formula $F = \frac{9}{5}C + 32$ for C. If it is linear, give the slope and the y-intercept. Sketch the graph. $C = \frac{5}{9}F - \frac{160}{9}$; $m = \frac{5}{9}$, $b = -\frac{160}{9}$

57. Number Theory A calculator has been programmed to double a number, then subtract 5. Write an equation for the program and describe its graph. $y = 2x - 5$ The graph is a line that crosses the y-axis at -5 and has a slope of $\frac{2}{1}$, or 2.

58. Technology Use Logo to create a graphing utility that will draw any line using either the variables :slope and :yintercept or the variables :slope and :point. See Solutions Manual.

BIOGRAPHY: George Pólya (1885–1985)

George Pólya was born in Budapest, Hungary and received his doctoral degree from the University of Budapest. He began his work in philosophy and turned to the study of mathematics and physics for a deeper understanding. This drew him to do further work in mathematics. Pólya made significant contributions to several areas of mathematics, including probability, analysis, and studies of symmetry, but he is most famous for his work in the field of problem solving. After studying the work of other mathematicians and their methods of attacking problems, he developed basic principles that can be used for problem solving in general. These principles and techniques—such as seeking a related problem, breaking the problem into simpler parts, working backwards from the results, and generalizing the results—have been so widely accepted that they are quoted in most texts without reference to their source.

Pólya taught at universities for about 38 years. After he retired, he continued to spread his ideas to mathematics teachers through summer institutes. In 1944, Pólya wrote a book called *How to Solve It*, which discusses his understanding of the problem solving process. This book has sold over a million copies in 16 languages and is considered a classic in the field of problem solving.

564 Chapter 13 Coordinate Geometry

Slopes of Parallel and Perpendicular Lines

Objectives: To determine whether two lines are parallel, perpendicular, or neither

To write an equation of a line parallel or perpendicular to a given line

When the slopes of two lines are known, it is possible to determine whether or not the lines are parallel and whether or not they are perpendicular.

Investigation—*Coordinate Geometry*

Graph these equations on the same coordinate plane:

$$y = 2x + 1 \qquad y = 2x + 3 \qquad y = 2x - 1 \qquad y = 2x$$

What do you notice? Explain and make a generalization. They are ‖. If slopes are =, lines are ‖.

The relationship between two lines with equal slopes is suggested by a study of these equations and their graphs.

$$y = \sqrt{3}x + \sqrt{3} \qquad\qquad y = \sqrt{3}x - \sqrt{3}$$

slope: $= \sqrt{3}$

slope: $= \sqrt{3}$

y-intercept: $\sqrt{3}$

y-intercept: $-\sqrt{3}$

x-intercept: -1

x-intercept: 1

Note that two right triangles with leg lengths 1 and $\sqrt{3}$ are formed. Thus, the angles at $(-1, 0)$ and $(1, 0)$ each have measures of 60. Why? Since those angles are also alternate interior angles, the lines must be parallel. $\tan 60° = \frac{\sqrt{3}}{1}$

This example is generalized as the next theorem.

> **Theorem 13.7** Two nonvertical lines are parallel if and only if their slopes are equal.

Why are vertical lines excluded from the theorem? Their slopes are undefined.

Developing Mathematical Power

Cooperative Learning Working in groups, students can complete the Enrichment activity, p. 15, in the *Teacher's Resource Book* (see side column, p. 564). It provides real-life applications of using equations of lines. It also requires students to think about the meaning of slope and thus helps to prepare them for content of this lesson. Students may enjoy creating a graph for themselves similar to the one for Exercises 1–4 to predict how tall they will grow.

LESSON PLAN

Materials/Manipulatives
Graph paper
Teaching Transparency 90

Technology
Graphing utility
Computer Test Bank, pp. 852–858

LESSON FOCUS

Review

- Review the term *multiplicative inverse* or *reciprocal* and the term *negative reciprocal*. Have students find the following products.

  1. $3(-\frac{1}{3})$ **2.** $\frac{1}{5}(5)$ **3.** $(-\frac{2}{3})(\frac{3}{2})$

  1. -1 2. 1 3. -1

- Point out that $-\frac{1}{3}$ is the negative reciprocal of 3, and that 3 is the negative reciprocal of $-\frac{1}{3}$.
- The Algebra Review, Exercises 43–51, reviews solving radical equations.
- The Chapter Summary and Review, pp. 580–581, gives vocabulary and concepts and review exercises by lesson.
- The end of the chapter features a Algebra Review on p. 584.

Alternative Learning Styles

- The Investigation provides students with an opportunity to use coordinate geometry to determine the characteristics of the slopes of parallel lines.
- The visual learner may benefit from Teaching Transparency 90. It provides visual representation of a series of parallel lines. By calculating the slopes the student can easily see the relationship.

It will aid students' understanding of Theorems 13.7 and 13.8 if they graph parallel and perpendicular lines. For example, ask students to graph the following:

1. The line with equation $y = 2$, the line through $(-2, -1)$ parallel to it, and the line through $(4, 3)$ perpendicular to it.
2. The line with equation $x - 2y = -1$, the line through $(1, -2)$ parallel to it, and the line through $(3, 2)$ perpendicular to it.

Critical Thinking

Application Ask students to apply the concepts of parallel and perpendicular to the coordinate plane.

CHALKBOARD EXAMPLES

• **For the Example**
  Line k has equation $2x + 3y = -6$. Find the standard form of the equations of lines j and l containing $(-1, 3)$ if: **a.** $j \parallel k$ **b.** $l \perp k$
  a. $2x + 3y = -6$
  $y = -\frac{2}{3}x - 2$
  slope of $j = -\frac{2}{3}$
  $y - 3 = -\frac{2}{3}(x - (-1))$
  $2x + 3y = 7$
  b. slope of $l = \frac{3}{2}$
  $y - 3 = \frac{3}{2}(x - (-1))$
  $-3x + 2y = 9$

Common Errors

• Students may confuse the slopes of parallel and perpendicular lines. Stress the fact that parallel lines have the *same* slope.
• Students may use the reciprocal instead of the negative reciprocal for the slope of a line perpendicular to a given line. Have them graph each to see the difference.
• See *Teacher's Resource Book* for additional remediation.

This circle has its center at the origin and a radius length of 5. Thus, its equation is $x^2 + y^2 = 25$. It can be verified by substitution that $(3, 4)$ is a point of this circle.

Since $\angle RQP$ is inscribed in a semicircle, $\angle Q$ is a right angle, and so $\overleftrightarrow{RQ} \perp \overleftrightarrow{QP}$. Each slope can be computed:

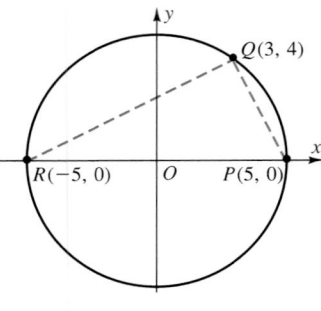

$$\text{slope of } \overleftrightarrow{PQ} = \frac{4 - 0}{3 - 5} \qquad \text{slope of } \overleftrightarrow{QR} = \frac{0 - 4}{-5 - 3}$$
$$= -2 \qquad\qquad\qquad = \frac{1}{2}$$

The product of these slopes is -1. In fact, -1 will always be the product of the slopes of perpendicular lines. The generalization follows.

> **Theorem 13.8**   Two nonvertical lines are perpendicular if and only if the product of their slopes is -1.

Any horizontal line is perpendicular to any vertical line. Why are vertical lines excluded from the theorem? They have an undefined slope.

EXAMPLE   Line k has equation $y = \frac{3}{4}x + 2$. Find the point-slope equations of lines l and j containing $(2, -1)$ if

a. $l \parallel k$.

b. $j \perp k$.

a. slope of l = slope of
$k = \frac{3}{4}$
$(y - y_1) = m(x - x_1)$
$(y - (-1)) = \frac{3}{4}(x - 2)$
$(y + 1) = \frac{3}{4}(x - 2)$

b. slope of m = negative reciprocal of slope of k
slope of $j = -\frac{4}{3}$
$(y - y_1) = m(x - x_1)$
$(y - (-1)) = -\frac{4}{3}(x - 2)$
$(y + 1) = -\frac{4}{3}(x - 2)$

CLASS EXERCISES

In each set of linear equations, pick out a pair whose graphs are parallel lines, and a pair whose graphs are perpendicular lines. Tell why.

1. a. $y = 3x + 7$ $a \parallel c$; same slopes

  b. $y = -3x + 7$ $b \perp d$; slopes are neg. reciprocals

  c. $y = 3x - 7$

  d. $y = \left(\frac{1}{3}\right)x - 7$

2. a. $(y - 2) = \frac{3}{5}(x - 3)$ $a \parallel b$; same slopes

  b. $(y - 2) = \frac{3}{5}(x - 2)$

  c. $(y - 2) = -\frac{3}{5}(x - 3)$

  d. $(y - 2) = \frac{5}{3}(x - 3)$ $c \perp d$; slopes are neg. reciprocals

Find the slope of any line perpendicular to the indicated line.

3. $y = 7x - 7$ $m = -\frac{1}{7}$

4. $(y - 5) = 5(x + 2)$ $m = -\frac{1}{5}$

5. $10x - 5y = 7$ $m = -\frac{1}{2}$

6. $5x - 10y = 7$ $m = -2$

7. $y = -\frac{3}{4}x + 5$ $m = \frac{4}{3}$

8. $(y + 3) = 4(x - 1)$ $m = -\frac{1}{4}$

In each Exercise, two points of $\overleftrightarrow{AB}$ and $\overleftrightarrow{CD}$ are given. Are the lines parallel, perpendicular, or neither?

9. $A(1, 3)$, $B(5, 9)$; $C(-3, 1)$, $D(-1, 4)$ ∥

10. $A(-2, -5)$, $B(3, -1)$; $C(-8, 1)$, $D(-13, 5)$ neither

11. $A(-5, -4)$, $B(-3, -10)$; $C(-2, 3)$, $D(-3, 0)$ neither

12. $A(7, 5)$, $B(5, 6)$; $C(4, -3)$, $D(6, 1)$ ⊥

13. $A(3, 9)$, $B(7, 5)$, $C(3, -3)$, $D(-1, 1)$ ∥

PRACTICE EXERCISES

A   **1.** Given the line $ax + by = c$, write the equation of
a. the line parallel to $ax + by = c$ and containing $(0, 0)$. $ax + by = 0$
b. the line perpendicular to $ax + by = c$ and containing $(0, 0)$. $bx - ay = 0$

2. Thinking Critically How do the answers to Exercise 1 suggest ways of finding slopes? $\frac{-a}{b}$ = slope of ∥ line; $\frac{b}{a}$ = slope of ⊥ line.

In each set of linear equations, pick out a pair whose graphs are parallel lines and a pair whose graphs are perpendicular lines.

3. a. $y = -4x + 7$ $b \parallel c$; $b \perp d$, $c \perp d$

b. $y = 4x + 7$

c. $y = 4x - 7$

d. $y = \left(-\frac{1}{4}\right)x - 7$

4. a. $(y - 3) = \frac{2}{3}(x - 3)$ $a \perp c$; $b \parallel d$

b. $(y - 2) = \frac{3}{2}(x - 2)$

c. $(y - 3) = -\frac{3}{2}(x - 3)$

d. $(y - 3) = \frac{3}{2}(x - 3)$

5. a. $2x + 4y = 5$ $b \parallel d$
b. $x + y = -5$
c. $x = -1$
d. $x + y = -1$

6. a. $2x + 4y = 5$ $a \parallel d$; $b \perp c$
b. $2x - 4y = 5$
c. $4x + 2y = 5$
d. $2x + 4y = 7$

Find the slope of $\overleftrightarrow{AB}$, the slope of any line parallel to $\overleftrightarrow{AB}$, and the slope of any line perpendicular to $\overleftrightarrow{AB}$.

7. $A(2, 3)$, $B(-5, 0)$ $\frac{3}{7}$; $\frac{3}{7}$; $-\frac{7}{3}$

8. $A(-3, 4)$, $B(-1, -4)$ -4; -4; $\frac{1}{4}$

9. $A(5, -2)$, $B(1, -1)$ $-\frac{1}{4}$; $-\frac{1}{4}$; 4

10. $A(-6, -2)$, $B(-1, 8)$ 2; 2; $-\frac{1}{2}$

13.6 Slopes of Parallel and Perpendicular Lines   **567**

LESSON FOLLOW-UP

Discussion

For △ABC with vertices $A(-1, 5)$, $B(-3, -3)$, and $C(5, 1)$, ask students to find equations in standard form of the median from A, the altitude from A, and the perpendicular bisector of $\overline{BC}$. $3x + y = 2$; $2x + y = 3$; $2x + y = 1$
Ask students how they could find the coordinates of the point where the three altitudes of △ABC intersect. Find the equations of the other two altitudes. Find the point of intersection of two of the altitudes, and substitute in the equation of the third altitude to check that the point lies on the third altitude.

altitude from B: $3x - 2y = -3$
altitude from C: $x + 4y = 9$
point of intersection: $\left(\frac{3}{7}, \frac{15}{7}\right)$

Critical Thinking
1. *Analysis* Ask students to compare and contrast ways of finding equations of medians, altitudes, and perpendicular bisectors.
2. *Synthesis* Have students develop a plan for finding the point of intersection of the altitudes of a triangle.

Assignment Guide
See p. 534B for assignments.

Lesson Quiz

Are $\overleftrightarrow{AB}$ and $\overleftrightarrow{CD}$ parallel, perpendicular, or neither?

1. $A(1, 1)$, $B(4, -1)$, $C(-3, 4)$, $D(-1, 1)$
2. $A(2, 0)$, $B(-1, -4)$, $C(-4, 2)$, $D(4, -4)$
3. $A(-3, 2)$, $B(1, 1)$, $C(3, -3)$, $D(-5, -1)$
4. Write the equation (in standard form) of the line through $(-2, 1)$ that is perpendicular to the line with equation $y = \frac{1}{3}x - 1$.
5. Write the equation (in standard form) of the line through $(-1, 1)$ that is parallel to $3x + 2y = 7$.

1. Neither   2. $\perp$ 3. $\parallel$
4. $3x + y = -5$ 5. $3x + 2y = -1$

Enrichment

Consider the following definition:

Lines j and k are *parallel* if and only if the slope of j equals the slope of k, or both j and k are vertical.

With this definition, is the relation of parallelism reflexive, symmetric, and transitive? How does the definition of parallelism in this chapter differ from the definition of parallel in Chapter 3? Yes, with this definition parallelism is reflexive, symmetric, and transitive. The definition of parallel in Chapter 3 does not allow a line to be parallel to itself; thus, with that definition parallelism is not reflexive.

Find the slope of any line perpendicular to the line with the given equation.

11. $y = 5x + 4$ $-\frac{1}{5}$
12. $(y + 1) = \frac{4}{5}(x - 2)$ $-\frac{5}{4}$
13. $12x - 4y = 7$ $-\frac{1}{3}$
14. $4x - 12y = 9$ -3

Are $\overleftrightarrow{AB}$ and $\overleftrightarrow{CD}$ parallel, perpendicular, or neither?

15. $A(2, 5)$, $B(5, 11)$; $C(3, 1)$, $D(4, 3)$ $\parallel$
16. $A(-2, -5)$, $B(3, -2)$; $C(-10, 0)$, $D(-13, 5)$ $\perp$
17. $A(-4, -3)$, $B(-2, -9)$; $C(-4, 1)$, $D(-7, 0)$ $\perp$
18. $A(5, 5)$, $B(4, 6)$; $C(4, -3)$, $D(6, 1)$ neither
19. $A(-4, 5)$, $B(-5, 12)$; $C(3, -5)$, $D(-1, -6)$ neither
20. $A(-7, 0)$, $B(0, 7)$; $C(-2, -3)$, $D(-4, -1)$ $\perp$

Write the equation of the line parallel to the given line through the given point; the equation of the perpendicular line through the given point.

B

21. $y = -5x + 8$; $(-4, 2)$ $(y - 2) = -5(x + 4)$; $(y - 2) = \frac{1}{5}(x + 4)$
22. $y = \frac{3}{7}x - 5$; $(4, -3)$ $(y + 3) = \frac{3}{7}(x - 4)$; $(y + 3) = -\frac{7}{3}(x - 4)$
23. $2x + 4y = -7$; $(-3, -2)$ $(y + 2) = -\frac{1}{2}(x + 3)$; $(y + 2) = 2(x + 3)$
24. $3x - 8y = 5$; $(7, 4)$ $(y - 4) = \frac{3}{8}(x - 7)$; $(y - 4) = -\frac{8}{3}(x - 7)$

$\triangle ABC$ has vertices $A(4, 1)$, $B(-2, 3)$, and $C(-4, -3)$.

25. Find the standard form equation of the line through A and parallel to $\overleftrightarrow{BC}$. $3x - y = 11$
26. Find the standard form equation of the line through A and perpendicular to $\overleftrightarrow{BC}$. $x + 3y = 7$
27. Find the standard form equation of the perpendicular bisector of $\overline{BC}$. Does it contain A? $x + 3y = -3$; since $4 + 3 \cdot 1 \neq -3$, it does not contain A.
28. Show that the line through the midpoint of $\overline{AB}$ and parallel to $\overleftrightarrow{BC}$ contains the midpoint of $\overline{AC}$.   See page 775.

Determine whether quadrilateral $ABCD$ is a trapezoid, a parallelogram, a rectangle, or a square. Justify your answer. Reasons may vary.

29. $A(1, 0)$, $B(2, -2)$, $C(4, -1)$, $D(7, 3)$ trapezoid; $\overline{BC} \parallel \overline{AD}$, $\overline{AB} \not\parallel \overline{CD}$
30. $A(1, 1)$, $B(3, -1)$, $C(5, 1)$, $D(3, 3)$ square; $\overline{AB} \perp \overline{BC}$, $AB = BC = CD = DA$
31. $A(1, 1)$, $B(6, 1)$, $C(6, 4)$, $D(1, 4)$ rectangle; $\overline{BC} \parallel \overline{AD}$, $\overline{AB} \parallel \overline{CD}$, $\overline{AB} \perp \overline{BC}$
32. $A(0, 0)$, $B(0, -3)$, $C(4, -1)$, $D(2, 1)$ trapezoid; $\overline{BC} \parallel \overline{AD}$, $\overline{AB} \not\parallel \overline{CD}$
33. State the two conditionals implied in Theorem 13.7. If 2 nonvert. lines are $\parallel$, then their slopes are =. If 2 nonvert. lines have = slopes, then they are $\parallel$.
34. State the two conditionals implied in Theorem 13.8. If 2 nonvert. lines are $\perp$, then the prod. of their slopes is -1. If the prod. of the slopes of 2 nonvert. lines is -1, then the lines are $\perp$.

568   Chapter 13 Coordinate Geometry

Developing Mathematical Power

Keeping a Portfolio Have students explain how they would find the equation of the perpendicular bisector of a given segment in the coordinate plane. They should then illustrate their responses for a specific segment and show each step of their work. Have them compare the slopes of each to verify.

C **35.** Coordinates of three vertices $\square IJKL$ are $I(5, 0)$, $J(0, 0)$, and $K(-3, 4)$. Show that it is a rhombus. Find the coordinates of L. $L(2, 4)$; length of consecutive sides is 5.

36. Find the equation in standard form of the line containing altitude $\overline{AP}$ of $\triangle ABC$, with $A(-1, 7)$, $B(-2, 3)$, and $C(4, 5)$. $3x + y = 4$

37. Find the equation in standard form of the line containing median $\overline{AM}$ of $\triangle ABC$ with $A(-1, 7)$, $B(-2, 3)$, and $C(4, 5)$. $3x + 2y = 11$

38. The center of $\odot O$ has coordinates $(1, 3)$. $4x + 7y = -3$ is the equation of a line tangent to the circle. Find the equation of the line perpendicular to the tangent and passing through the center of $\odot O$. $(y - 3) = \frac{7}{4}(x - 1)$, or $7x - 4y = -5$

39. If line k with slope m is perpendicular to line l with slope n, prove $m \cdot n = -1$. [*Hint for a plan:* Place coordinate axes on k and l as shown. Why, for k and l, are the equations $y = mx$ and $y = nx$? What must be the y-coordinates of P and Q? Use the Pythagorean Theorem on $\triangle POQ$.] See Additional Answers, p. 702.

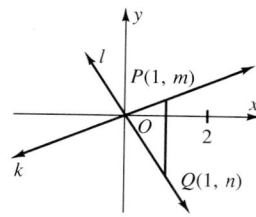

40. Prove that if the equations of two perpendicular lines are $ax + by = c$ and $dx + ey = f$, where neither one is vertical, then $ad + be = 0$. Since the 2 lines are $\perp$, $-\frac{a}{b} \cdot -\frac{d}{e} = -1$. $\frac{ad}{be} = -1$; $ad = -be$; $ad + be = 0$.

Applications

41. Crafts The pattern for a needlepointed pillow cover is shown. If this pattern appeared on a grid, what would be the slopes of the lines? 1 and -1

42. Technology Use Logo to generate the needlepoint pillow cover in Exercise 41. See Solutions Manual.

Algebra Review

Solve and check.

43. $\sqrt{a} = 7$ 49

44. $\sqrt{2x} = 12$ 72

45. $3\sqrt{5m} = 30$ 20

46. $\sqrt{y} = \frac{1}{2}$ $\frac{1}{4}$

47. $\sqrt{\frac{n}{2}} = 3$ 18

48. $2\sqrt{\frac{c}{3}} = 16$ 192

49. $\sqrt{b + 3} = 5$ 22

50. $\sqrt{3z} - 5 = 7$ 48

51. $12 - 2\sqrt{p} = 0$ 36

13.6 Slopes of Parallel and Perpendicular Lines **569**

Teacher's Resource Book

Follow-Up Investigation, *Chapter 13*, p. 16.

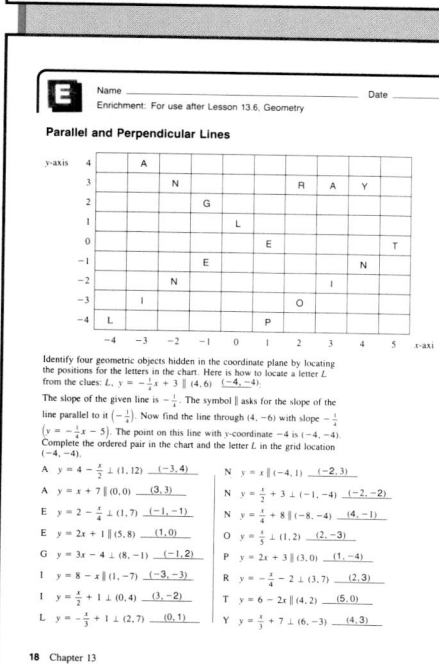

13.7

Strategy: Use Coordinate Geometry in Proofs

Coordinate geometry makes it possible to use algebra in geometric proofs by
placing figures on the coordinate plane.

Locate the figures so that the algebra will be as simple as possible. The
problem solving steps can be used to develop coordinate geometry proofs.

EXAMPLE 1 **Prove by coordinate geometry: If a segment joins the midpoints of two**
sides of a triangle, then it is parallel to the third side.

Understand
The Problem
Draw and label a figure. State the *Given* and *Prove*.

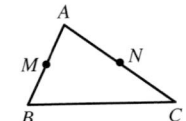

Given: $\triangle ABC$; M and N are midpoints
 of $\overline{AB}$ and $\overline{AC}$, respectively.

Prove: $\overline{MN} \parallel \overline{BC}$

Plan Your
Approach
Place the figure on the coordinate plane so that the algebraic
computations will be as simple as possible.

Look Ahead from the *Given*.
The coordinates of A, B, and C must be used to compute the
coordinates of M and N by the Midpoint Formula; if the coordinates
chosen are even, then fractions can be avoided.

Look Back from the *Prove*.
The slopes of $\overline{MN}$ and $\overline{BC}$ must be computed and compared.

Here are three possibilities for locating $\triangle ABC$ on the coordinate plane.

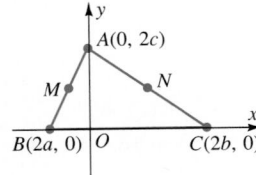
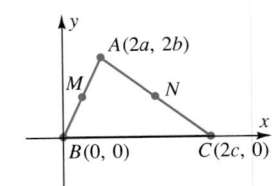
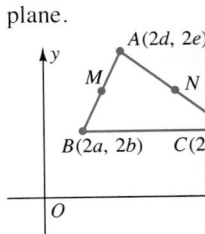

Developing Mathematical Power
Cooperative Learning The Practice Exercises 10–32 and the Project can be
done by students working in groups. Encourage students to discuss their choices of
placement of the figure for the coordinate proof before they begin the proof. Have
each group challenge the other groups with their problem for the Project.

It is usually helpful to have one of the sides of a polygon coincide with one of the axes. Thus the first two figures provide better choices. Locating a vertex at the origin can facilitate computations. However, for demonstration purposes the first figure will be used.

Implement The Plan

Proof, using Figure 1:

Statements	Reasons
1. $M(a, c)$ and $N(b, c)$	1. Midpoint Formula
2. Slope of $\overline{MN} = 0$ Slope of $\overline{BC} = 0$	2. Def. of slope
3. Slope of $\overline{MN} =$ slope of $\overline{BC}$	3. Trans. prop.
4. $\overline{MN} \parallel \overline{BC}$	4. If 2 lines have $=$ slopes, they are $\parallel$.

Interpret The Results

Using the Midpoint Formula and the definition of slope, it can be shown that the segment connecting the midpoints of two sides of a triangle has the same slope as the third side. Thus, that segment is parallel to the third side.

Problem Solving Reminders

- Some geometric proofs can be done by placing figures on the coordinate plane and applying algebraic properties.
- Placing a polygon so that one of its sides coincides with an axis can make the proof easier.
- Choosing even coordinates such as $2a$, $2b$, and so on, may make the computations simpler.

EXAMPLE 2   **Prove: If the diagonals of a parallelogram are perpendicular, then the parallelogram is a rhombus.**

Understand The Problem

Draw and label a figure. State the *Given* and *Prove*.

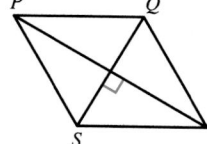

Given: $\square PQRS;\ \overline{PR} \perp \overline{QS}$

Prove: $PQRS$ is a rhombus.

TEACHING SUGGESTION

Make sure that students get ample practice assigning general coordinates to figures before they attempt coordinate proofs, which most students find very difficult.

CHALKBOARD EXAMPLES

- **For Example 1**
  Use the center figure on p. 570 to prove: If a segment joins the midpoints of two sides of a triangle, it is parallel to the third side.
  See the student text for the figure and the Given and the Prove.
  Proof:

Statements	Reasons
1. M and N have coordinates (a,b) and $(a + c,b)$, respectively	1. Midpt. formula
2. Slope of $\overline{MN} = 0$; slope of $\overline{BC} = 0$	2. Def. of slope
3. Slope of $\overline{MN} =$ slope of $\overline{BC}$	3. Trans. prop.
4. $\overline{MN} \parallel \overline{BC}$	4. Lines with $=$ slopes are $\parallel$

- **For Example 2**

  Use the figure on p. 571 to prove: If a parallelogram is a rhombus, the diagonals are perpendicular.

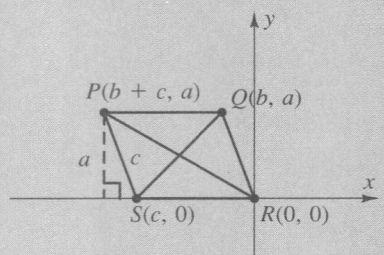

Given: Rhombus $PQRS$

Prove: $\overline{PR} \perp \overline{QS}$

Proof:

Statements	Reasons
1. Rhombus $PQRS$	1. Given
2. $PQ = QR = RS = SP = c$	2. Def. of rhombus
3. Slope of $\overline{QS} = \dfrac{a}{b-c}$ Slope of $\overline{PR} = \dfrac{a}{b+c}$	3. Def. of slope
4. $a^2 + b^2 = c^2$	4. Pyth. Th.
5. $a = \sqrt{c^2 - b^2}$	5. Algebraic prop.
6. $\dfrac{a}{b-c} \cdot \dfrac{a}{b+c} = -1$	6. Algebraic prop.
7. $\overline{PR} \perp \overline{QS}$	7. Slopes of $\perp$ lines have prod. -1

Common Error

- Some students will have difficulty assigning letter coordinates to figures and working them into proofs. Have students label coordinates to understand their relationships before assigning formal proofs.
- See *Teacher's Resource Book*, for additional remediation.

▢ **Plan Your Approach**

Place one vertex at the origin and make one side coincide with the x-axis.

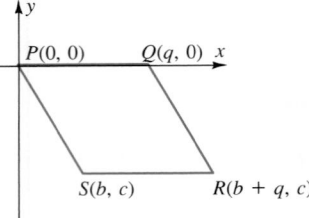

Look ahead from *Given*:
P is $(0, 0)$; Q is $(q, 0)$. Assign (b, c) to S. Thus, R has coordinates $(b + q, c)$.

Look back from *Prove*:
It is necessary to show that all sides of $PQRS$ are of length q.

▢ **Implement The Plan**

Proof:

Statements	Reasons
1. $\square PQRS$; $\overline{PR} \perp \overline{QS}$	1. Given
2. $PQ = RS = q$	2. Opp. sides of a $\square$ are $=$ in leng
3. $PS = QR = \sqrt{c^2 + b^2}$	3. Distance Formula
4. Slope of $\overline{PR} = \dfrac{c}{b+q}$ Slope of $\overline{QS} = \dfrac{c}{b-q}$	4. Def. of slope
5. $\dfrac{c}{b+q} \cdot \dfrac{c}{b-q} = -1$	5. Slopes of $\perp$ lines have a produc of -1.
6. $c^2 = q^2 - b^2$ $c^2 + b^2 = q^2$ $\sqrt{c^2 + b^2} = q$	6. Algebraic prop. from Step 5.
7. $PQ = RS = PS = QR$	7. Trans. prop.
8. $PQRS$ is a rhombus.	8. Def. of rhombus.

Conclusion:
If, in $\square PQRS$, $\overline{PR} \perp \overline{QS}$, then $PQRS$ is a rhombus.

▢ **Interpret The Results**

Placing one vertex of $\square PQRS$ at the origin and one side along the x-axis resulted in

1. the use of $(q, 0)$ for Q, where q is the length of $\overline{PQ}$;

2. the assigning of $(b + q, c)$ to R after S was assigned to (b, c).

Then appropriate equations could be written that led to the conclusion.

Thinking Critically

Suppose this theorem were proven by using coordinate geometry: **If a triangle is isosceles, then the perpendicular to the base from the vertex angle bisects the base.**

1. Here are three ways to place the axes. Which seems to be best? Explain.
Answers may vary. Fig. 2, since the ⊥ lies along an axis.

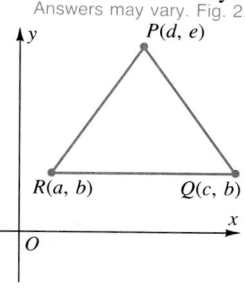

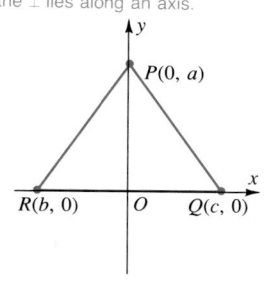

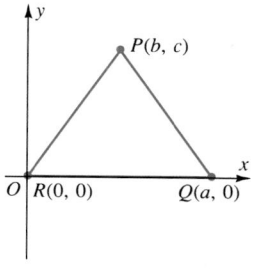

1   2   3

2. If Figure 2 were chosen, then it must be proven that $c = -b$. Discuss why. Then do so. If $c = -b$, then $|c| = |-b|$, which means that the base has been bisected. See side column.

3. If Figure 3 were chosen, then it must be proven that $2b = a$. Discuss why. Then do so. The ⊥ from P to $\overline{RQ}$ must bisect it at $(b, 0)$. See side column.

Suppose this theorem were proven by using coordinate geometry: **If the diagonals of a parallelogram are equal in length, then the parallelogram is a rectangle.** See side column, pp. 573–574.

4. Draw a parallelogram $ABCD$. State the *Given* and the *Prove*.

5. Using the third figure above as a model, let the origin be A. Discuss where to place the *x*-axis and how to assign coordinates to B, C, and D.

Suppose you were to prove this theorem by using coordinate geometry: **The opposite sides of a parallelogram are equal in length.**

6. Using this figure, you can first prove that $d - b = a$. Why? Do so by using the fact that the slopes of $\overline{AD}$ and $\overline{BC}$ are equal.

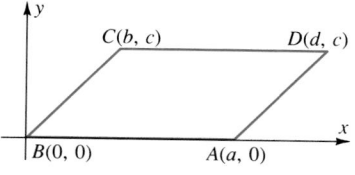

7. Knowing that $d - b = a$, the *x*-coordinate of D becomes $a + b$. Discuss why. Replace d with $a + b$, then prove that $BC = DA$.

4. Given: $\square ABCD$; $AC = BD$
Prove: $\square ABCD$ is a rect.

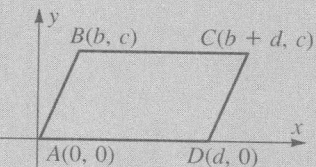

---

2. Given: $\triangle PQR$ is isos.;
$\overline{PR} \cong \overline{PQ}$; $\overline{PO} \perp \overline{RQ}$
Prove: $\overline{RO} \cong \overline{OQ}$ or $b = -c$
Plan: Use the given coords. and the Pyth. Th. to arrive at concl.
Proof:

Statements	Reasons
1. $\overline{PR} \cong \overline{PQ}$; $\overline{PO} \perp \overline{RQ}$	1. Given
2. $PR = PQ$	2. Def. of ≅ segs.
3. $PR = \sqrt{a^2 + b^2}$ $PQ = \sqrt{a^2 + c^2}$	3. Pyth. Th.
4. $\sqrt{a^2 + b^2} = \sqrt{a^2 + c^2}$	4. Subst. prop.
5. $a^2 + b^2 = a^2 + c^2$	5. Alg. prop.
6. $b^2 = c^2$	6. Subtr. prop.
7. $b = \pm c$; but $b \neq c$ from the figure; hence $b = -c$ and $RO = OQ$.	7. Alg. prop.
8. $\overline{RO} \cong \overline{OQ}$	8. Def. of ≅ segs.

Concl.: In an isos. △, the ⊥ from the vertex ∠ to the base bisects the base.

3. Given: $\triangle PQR$ is isos.; $\overline{PR} \cong \overline{PQ}$; $\overline{PM} \perp \overline{RQ}$
Prove: $\overline{RM} \cong \overline{MQ}$ or $a = 2b$

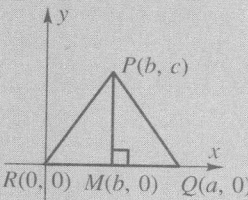

Plan: Use the given coords. and the Pyth. Th. to arrive at concl.
Proof:

Statements	Reasons
1. $\overline{PR} \cong \overline{PQ}$; $\overline{PM} \perp \overline{RQ}$	1. Given
2. $PR = PQ$	2. Def. of ≅ seg.
3. $PR = \sqrt{b^2 + c^2}$ $PQ = \sqrt{c^2 + (a-b)^2}$	3. Pyth. Th.
4. $\sqrt{b^2 + c^2} = \sqrt{c^2 + (a-b)^2}$	4. Trans. prop.
5. $2b = a$; hence the midpt. of $\overline{RQ}$ is $(\frac{2b}{2}, 0)$ or $(b, 0)$.	5. Alg. prop.

Concl.: See Ex. 2.

573

Lesson Quiz

Given: □*ERIC* ≅ □*ACEL*

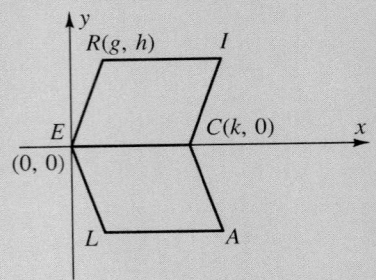

1. Label *I*; *L*; *A*.
2. Find the slope of diagonal $\overline{RC}$.
3. Find the slope of diagonal $\overline{CL}$.
4. Write a plan to prove diagonal *IE* = *EA*.

1. *I*(*g* + *k*, *h*); *L*(*g*, −*h*); *A*(*g* + *k*, −*h*)

2. $\frac{h}{g-k}$ 3. $\frac{h}{k-g}$

4. Use the Distance Formula to find the length of each diagonal. Make sure coordinates relate to each other.

Additional Answers for p. 573

5. Answers may vary. Place *A* at the origin, $\overline{AD}$ on the x-axis. Assign *B*(*b*, *c*) and *D*(*d*, 0). Then, the coords. of *C* are (*b* + *d*, *c*).

6. slope of $\overline{BC} = \frac{c}{b}$ and slope of $\overline{AD} = \frac{c}{d-a}$; since $\overline{BC} \parallel \overline{AD}$, $\frac{c}{b} = \frac{c}{d-a}$. Then *b* = *d* − *a*, *a* + *b* = *d*, and *a* = *d* − *b*.

7. If *d* − *b* = *a*, *d* = *a* + *b*. *BC* = $\sqrt{b^2 + c^2}$ and *AD* = $\sqrt{(a + b - a)^2 + c^2}$ = $\sqrt{b^2 + c^2}$. Thus *BC* = *AD*.

8. If lines *r* and *s* are coplanar and *r* ⊥ *l* and *s* ⊥ *l*, then (slope of *r*)(slope of *l*) = −1 and (slope of *s*)(slope of *l*) = −1. Therefore (slope of *r*)(slope of *l*) = (slope of *s*)(slope of *l*) and slope of *r* = slope of *s*. Thus *r* ∥ *s*.

---

8. Prove this theorem by using coordinate geometry: If two coplanar lines are perpendicular to the same line, then the two lines are parallel.
In doing so, it makes little difference where you put the axes, as there are no points to which you must assign coordinates. However, no line must be vertical. Why? The slope of a vert. line is undefined.
See side column.

PRACTICE EXERCISES

A   **In Exercises 1–6, supply the missing coordinates.**

1. *ABCD* is a rectangle where *AB* = *a* and *BC* = *b*.
B(*a*, 0), *C*(*a*, *b*), *D*(0, *b*)

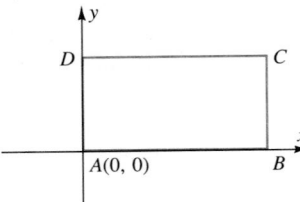

2. *EFGH* is a square where *EF* = 2*a*. The axes bisect the sides.
E(−*a*, −*a*), *F*(*a*, −*a*), *G*(*a*, *a*), *H*(−*a*, *a*)

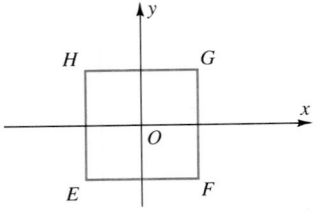

3. Each leg of isosceles right △*IJK* has length *a*.
J(*a*, 0), *K*(0, *a*)

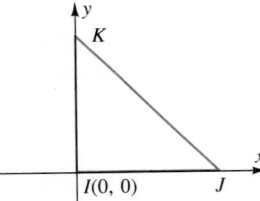

4. Each leg of isosceles △*LMN* has length $\sqrt{a^2 + b^2}$.
M(*b*, 0), *N*(−*b*, 0)

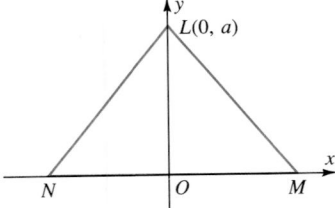

5. △*PQR* is equilateral. Each side has length 2*a*.
P(0, *a*$\sqrt{3}$), *Q*(*a*, 0), *R*(−*a*, 0)

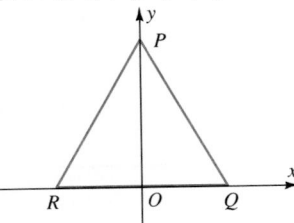

6. Each side of rhombus *STUV* has length *a*.
S(0, 0), *T*(*a*, 0), *U*(*b* + *a*, *c*)

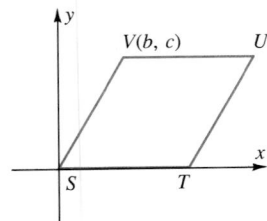

In Exercises 7–9, use coordinate geometry.

7. Given: right $\triangle ABC$

Show that the coordinates of midpoint M are (a, b). Use that fact to show that $MA = MB$.

$\left(\dfrac{2a + 0}{2}, \dfrac{2b + 0}{2}\right) = (a, b)$

$MA = \sqrt{(0 - a)^2 + (2b - b)^2} = \sqrt{a^2 + b^2}$

$MB = \sqrt{(a - 2a)^2 + (b - 0)^2} = \sqrt{a^2 + b^2}$

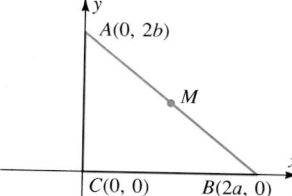

8. Given: isosceles $\triangle DEF$

Show that the coordinates of midpoint M are $(-a, b)$ and of midpoint N are (a, b). Use those facts to show that the medians to the legs of $\triangle DEF$ are equal in length.

For Exercises 8–32, see Additional Answers, p. 702, for answers that do not appear in side column.

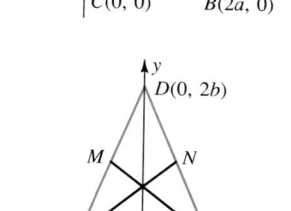

9. Given: any $\triangle GHI$; See Solutions Manual.
line k bisects side $\overline{GH}$
and is parallel to $\overline{GI}$.

a. Show that the coordinates of midpoint M are (a, b).

b. Show that, since slope of k = slope of $\overline{GI}$, the y-coordinate of W is b.

c. Also show that, since
slope of $\overline{HW}$ = slope of $\overline{WI}$, $\dfrac{b}{-x} = \dfrac{b}{x - 2c}$.

d. Show that $x = c$ by solving for x in $\dfrac{b}{-x} = \dfrac{b}{x - 2c}$.

e. Since the coordinates of W are (c, b), show that W is the midpoint of $\overline{HI}$.

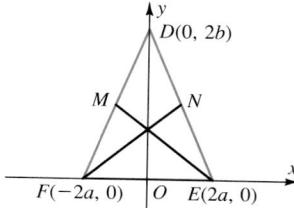

Use coordinate geometry to prove each theorem.

10. If a triangle is isosceles, then the perpendicular to the base from the vertex angle bisects the base. See side column.

11. The opposite sides of a parallelogram are equal in length.

12. If a line is perpendicular to one of two parallel lines, it is also perpendicular to the other.

13. The midpoint of the hypotenuse of any right triangle is equidistant from the triangle's vertices.

13.7 Strategy: Use Coordinate Geometry in Proofs **575**

---

10. Given: Isos. $\triangle ABC$; $BC = AC$;
$\overline{CP} \perp \overline{BA}$

Prove: $\overline{CP}$ bisects $\overline{BA}$.

Plan: Use the coords. and the Pyth. Th. to show $BP = AP$. the concl. follows.

Proof:

Statements	Reasons
1. Isos. $\triangle ABC$; $BC = AC$; $CP \perp BA$	1. Given
2. $BC = \sqrt{(0 - b)^2 + y^2} = \sqrt{b^2 + y^2}$ $AC = \sqrt{(0 - a)^2 + y^2} = \sqrt{a^2 + y^2}$	2. Pyth. Th.
3. $\sqrt{b^2 + y^2} = \sqrt{a^2 + y^2}$ $b^2 = a^2$ $b = \pm a$	3. Alg. props.
4. $BP = b$; $AP = a$	4. Distance Form.
5. $BP = AP$	5. Subst. prop
6. $\overline{BP} \cong \overline{AP}$	6. Def. $\cong$ seg.
7. $\overline{CP}$ bisects $\overline{BA}$.	7. Def. of bis.

Concl.: If a $\triangle$ is isos., then the $\perp$ to the base from the vertex $\angle$ bisects the base.

11. Use the figure for Class Ex. 6–7. D has coords. $(a + b, c)$.

$CD = \sqrt{(a + b - b)^2 + (c - c)^2} = \sqrt{a^2} = a$

$BA = \sqrt{(a - 0)^2 + (0 - 0)^2} = \sqrt{a^2} = a$

$BC = \sqrt{(b - 0)^2 + (c - 0)^2} = \sqrt{b^2 + c^2}$

$DA = \sqrt{(a + b - a)^2 + (c - 0)^2} = \sqrt{b^2 + c^2}$

Connections

Coordinate approach ⟷ Synthetic approach

Ex. 10 p. 575	Ex. 15 p. 178
Ex. 11 p. 575	Ex. 28 p. 222
Ex. 12 p. 575	Ex. 18 p. 89
Ex. 13 p. 575	Ex. 22 p. 237

Use coordinate geometry to prove each theorem.

14. The medians from the base angles to the legs of any isosceles triangle are equal in length.

15. If two medians of a triangle are congruent, then it is isosceles.

16. The diagonals of a square are perpendicular.

B 17. The diagonals of a rectangle are equal in length.

18. The diagonals of a rhombus are perpendicular.

19. If a line segment joins the midpoints of two sides of a triangle, then its length is equal to one-half the length of the third side.

20. If a line from the vertex angle of an isosceles triangle bisects the base, then it is perpendicular to the base.

21. If a line from any angle of a scalene triangle is perpendicular to the opposite side, then it does *not* bisect the base.

22. If a line bisects one side of a triangle and its parallel to a second side, then it bisects the third side.

23. If the diagonals of a parallelogram are equal in length, then the parallelogram is a rectangle.

24. If two sides of a quadrilateral are parallel and equal in length, then the quadrilateral is a parallelogram.

25. The diagonals of a parallelogram bisect each other.

26. If the diagonals of a quadrilateral bisect each other, the quadrilateral is a parallelogram.

C 27. The line segment joining the midpoints of the diagonals of any trapezoid is equal in length to one-half of the difference of the bases and is parallel to the bases.

28. If a line bisects one of the nonparallel sides of a trapezoid and is parallel to the base, it bisects the other nonparallel side.

29. The altitudes of any triangle are concurrent.

30. The medians of any triangle are concurrent, and this point of concurrency is located two-thirds of the distance from each vertex to the midpoint of the opposite side.

31. The locus of all points equidistant from two given points is the perpendicular bisector of the line segment joining the two points.

32. The perpendicular bisectors of the sides of any triangle are concurrent.

576 Chapter 13 Coordinate Geometry

Project

This Project integrates the material covered in this lesson. Students who have mastered the concepts could apply this to more complex theorems, while others might benefit from applying more basic ones.

Test Yourself

See *Teacher's Resource Book, Tests*, pp. 139–140.

Connections

Coordinate approach	Synthetic approach
Ex. 16 p. 576	Ex. 24 p. 237
Ex. 17 p. 576	Ex. 17 p. 236
Ex. 18 p. 576	Ex. 16 p. 237
Ex. 19 p. 576	Ex. 19 p. 243
Ex. 20 p. 576	Ex. 15 p. 178
Ex. 22 p. 576	Ex. 21 p. 231
Ex. 23 p. 576	Ex. 27 p. 237
Ex. 24 p. 576	Ex. 17 p. 226
Ex. 25 p. 576	Ex. 27 p. 222
Ex. 26 p. 576	Ex. 25 p. 227
Ex. 32 p. 576	Ex. 21 p. 410
Ex. 16 p. 577	Ex. 24 p. 243

Use this figure to show that the diagonals of a parallelogram bisect each other by first correctly labeling point P. Then choose one of the theorems from this lesson and formulate a problem such as this one, in which a vertex must first be located.

See Solutions Manual.

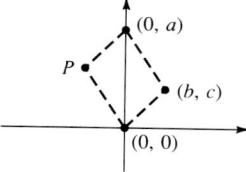

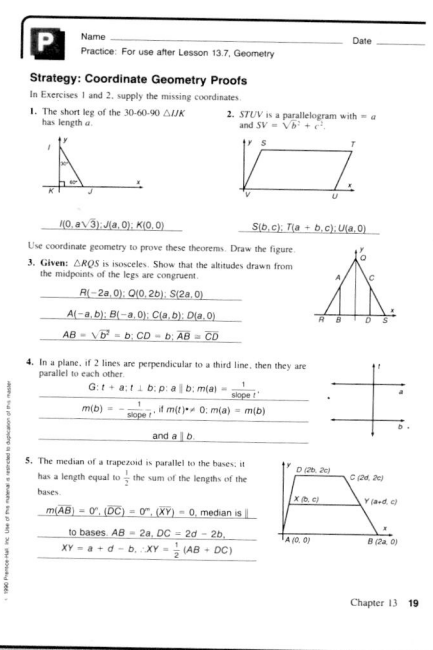

TEST YOURSELF

Find the slope of each line determined by the given points.

1. $(4, 0)$, $(0, 4)$ -1 2. $(-4, 3)$, $(4, 2)$ $-\frac{1}{8}$ 3. $(5, -6)$, $(-3, -4)$ $-\frac{1}{4}$ **13.4**

4. Compute the slope of each side of $\triangle ABC$, with $A(-8, 1)$, $B(0, 3)$, and $C(4, -5)$. $\overline{AB}: m = \frac{1}{4}$; $\overline{BC}: m = -2$; $\overline{AC}: m = -\frac{1}{2}$

5. A line intersecting the y-axis at $(0, 6)$ has slope $-\frac{2}{3}$. Find the coordinates of its x-intercept. $(9, 0)$

Find the slope and y-intercept of the line with the given equation.

6. $y = 2x - 6$ $2; -6$ 7. $2x - 5y = -10$ $\frac{2}{5}; 2$ 8. $(y - 3) = -3(x + 5)$ $-3; -12$ **13.5**

Write the equation in standard form for each line defined.

9. y-intercept $= -8$, slope $= \frac{1}{2}$ $x - 2y = 16$

10. Containing $(3, -4)$ and with slope of -2 $2x + y = 2$

11. Containing $(-4, -5)$ and $(7, -3)$ $2x - 11y = 47$

Tell whether the two lines are parallel, perpendicular, or neither.

12. $y = -5x + 7$ and $y = -5x - 7$ ∥ **13.6**

13. $(y - 3) = 4(x + 5)$ and $(y - 4) = -4(x + 6)$ neither

14. $2x + 7y = 5$ and $7x - 2y = 4$ ⊥

15. Write the equation in point-slope form for the line containing $(-2, 3)$ that is parallel to the line whose equation is $(y - 1) = -6(x + 4)$. $(y - 3) = -6(x + 2)$

16. Use coordinate geometry to prove that the diagonals of an isosceles trapezoid are equal in length. **13.7**

13.7 Strategy: Use Coordinate Geometry in Proofs **577**

Test Yourself
16. **Given:** Isos. trap. $ABCD$, $AD = BC$
    Prove: $AC = BD$
    Plan: Use the Distance Formula for AD and BC. Then use the variable coords. to compare AC and BD.

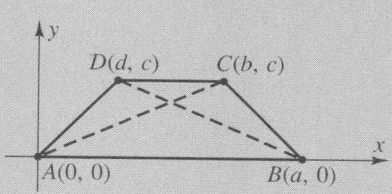

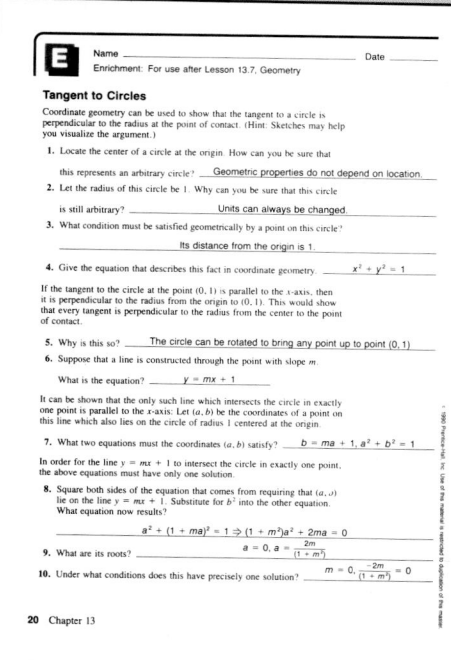

See *Teacher's Resource Book*, Follow-up *Technology*, pp. 17–18.

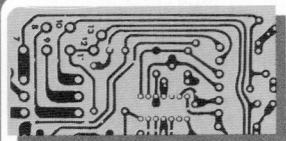

TECHNOLOGY:
Embedded Recursion and Dragon Curves

Embedded recursion takes place when the recursive call is within a procedure as opposed to **tail-end recursion,** when the recursive call is at the end of a procedure. With embedded recursion, commands within a procedure are stacked and then executed when the recursion is stopped. Wonderful graphics are created with embedded recursion: fractals, trees, dragon curves, and space-filling curves.

A tree is built from branches; the following procedure draws two branches:

```
to branch :length
lt 45 fd :length bk :length
rt 90 fd :length bk :length
lt 45
end
```

branch 30

Embedded recursion means that the procedure *branch* is called within itself after each drawing of a branch. But another variable is needed to tell the procedure how small the branches are to be. In the procedure, this variable is called :small, and the procedure stops drawing on that branch and goes to another when the :length of the branch is less than :small.

```
to branch :length :small
if :length < :small [stop]
lt 45 fd :length
branch :length / 2 :small
bk :length rt 90 fd :length
branch :length / 2 :small
bk :length lt 45
end
```

branch 30 1

The procedure for dragon curves uses embedded recursion differently. For dragon curves, the recursive calls alternate between left and right so that the figure does not come back to connect with itself.

EXAMPLE Run the following procedures, which demonstrate the famous dragon curves. Notice the alternation between the *ldragon* and the *rdragon*. The :length is the length of each "arm" of the dragon, and the :small in these procedures is slowly decreased by subtraction.

```
to begin.dragon
pu setpos [−50 −50] rt 180
ht
pd ldragon 3 11
end
```

```
to ldragon :length :small
if :small = 0 [fd :length stop]
ldragon :length :small − 1
lt 90
rdragon :length :small − 1
end
```

```
to rdragon :length :small
if :small = 0 [fd :length stop]
ldragon :length :small − 1
rt 90
rdragon :length :small − 1
end
```

EXERCISES

See Solutions Manual.

1. Try the second branch procedure shown above with the same number for :length, but different numbers for :small.

2. Try Exercise 1 again, but change both variables.

3. Rewrite the branch procedure used in Exercises 1 and 2 so that the quantity that divides :length can also change.

4. In the dragon curve procedures in the example above, change the :length and :small to obtain different shapes and sizes.

5. Rewrite the dragon curve procedures in the example above so that :small decreases by division. What kind of picture is drawn?

Technology: Embedded Recursions and Dragon Curves **579**

- See *Teacher's Resource Book, Spanish Chapter Summary and Review*, pp. 25–26.
- See Extra Practice, p. 655.

Vocabulary

coordinate plane (536)	quadrants (537)	slope of a vertical line (553)
Distance Formula (537)	slope (552)	x-axis (536)
equation of a circle (542)	slope-intercept form of a linear equation (559)	x-coordinate (536)
linear equation (558)		x-intercept (559)
Midpoint Formula (547)	slope of a horizontal line (553)	y-axis (536)
ordered pair (536)		y-coordinate (536)
origin (536)	standard form of a linear equation (558)	y-intercept (559)
point-slope form of a linear equation (559)		

The Distance Formula   The distance d between any two points (x_1, y_1) and (x_2, y_2) is given by $d = \sqrt{(x_2 - x_1)^2 + (y_2 - y_1)^2}$.   **13.1**

Find the distance between the points.

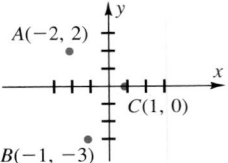

A(−2, 2)

C(1, 0)

B(−1, −3)

1. A and B $\sqrt{26}$

2. B and C $\sqrt{13}$

3. C and A $\sqrt{13}$

4. Find the distance between $E(4, 5)$ and $F(0, -3)$. $4\sqrt{5}$

The Equation of a Circle   An equation of the circle with center *(h, k)* and radius length r is $(x - h)^2 + (y - k)^2 = r^2$.   **13.2**

5. What are the coordinates of the center and the radius length of the circle whose equation is given by $(x + 3)^2 + (y + 4)^2 = 8$? (−3,−4); 2√2

6. What are the coordinates of the center and the radius length of the circle whose equation is given by $x^2 + (y - 5)^2 = 4$? (0,5); 2

7. Give the equation of the circle with $(6, -2)$ as center and radius length 5.
$(x − 6)^2 + (y + 2)^2 = 25$

The Midpoint Formula   If the coordinates of any two points P and R are (x_1, y_1) and (x_2, y_2), respectively, then the coordinates of the midpoint of $\overline{PR}$ are $\left(\dfrac{x_1 + x_2}{2}, \dfrac{y_1 + y_2}{2}\right)$.   **13.3**

8. Find the coordinates of the midpoint of $\overline{AB}$: $A(7, -6)$ and $B(-3, -4)$. (2,−5)

9. What are the coordinates of D of $\overline{DE}$, with $E(7, -1)$ and midpoint $M(0, -4)$? (−7, −7)

Slope of a Line   Given any two points on a line with coordinates (x_1, y_1) and (x_2, y_2), the slope m of the line is given by: 13.4

$$m = \frac{y_2 - y_1}{x_2 - x_1} \qquad \text{provided that } x_2 \neq x_1$$

Find the slopes of lines determined by the given points.

10. $(-5, 0), (0, -10)$ -2

11. $(-3, -6), (2, -2)$ $\frac{4}{5}$

Equations of a Line   The graph of an equation is a line if and only if the equation is of the form $ax + by = c$, where a and b are not both 0.   13.5

The point-slope form of an equation of a line containing the point (x_1, y_1) and having slope m is $(y - y_1) = m(x - x_1)$.

The slope-intercept form of an equation of a line with y-intercept b and slope m is $y = mx + b$.

Give the slope and y-intercept of each line with the given equation.

12. $y = \left(\frac{3}{2}\right)x + 5$ $\frac{3}{2}$; 5

13. $4x - 2y = 1$ $2; \frac{-1}{2}$

14. $(y - 2) = 3(x + 4)$ $3; 14$

15. Write the equation in point-slope form for the line with slope -5 and y-intercept -4. $(y + 4) = -5(x - 0)$, or $y + 4 = -5x$

Slopes of Parallel and Perpendicular Lines   Two nonvertical lines are parallel if and only if their slopes are equal. Two nonvertical lines are perpendicular if and only if the product of their slopes is -1.   13.6

16. Write the equation in point-slope form for the line containing $(-2, -4)$ that is parallel to the line with equation $y = 4x - 3$. $(y + 4) = 4(x + 2)$

17. Write the equation in point-slope form for the line containing $(-2, -4)$ that is perpendicular to the line with the equation $y = -3x + 3$. $(y + 4) = \frac{1}{3}(x + 2)$

Solve each problem.   13.7

18. Find the coordinates of vertex D of $\square ABCD$ with $A(0, 0)$, $B(a, 0)$, and $C(a + b, c)$. $D(b, c)$

19. Use coordinate geometry to prove that the diagonals of a square are equal in length.   See Solutions Manual.

Chapter 13 Summary and Review   **581**

Connections
Coordinate approach ⟷ Synthetic approach
Ex. 19 p. 581   Ex. 26 p. 237

See *Teacher's Resource Book, Tests,* pp. 141–144.

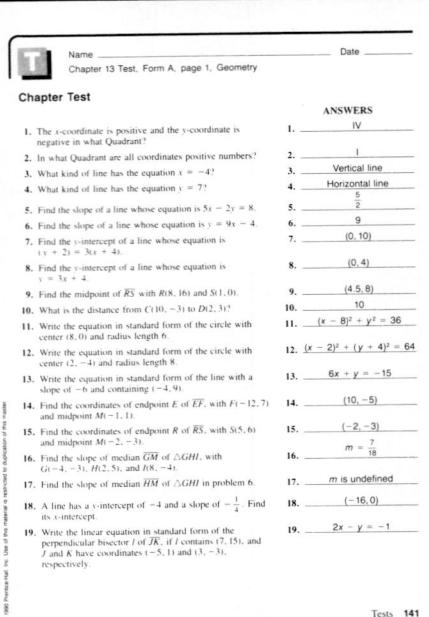

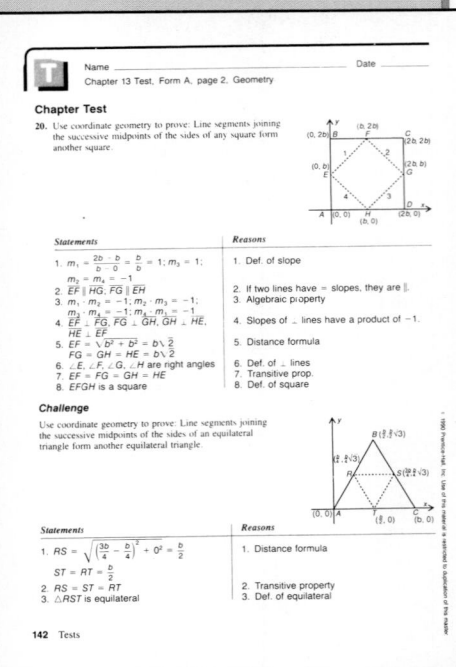

Complete.

1. All coordinates in Quadrant ___ are negative numbers. III

2. All *x*-coordinates are positive in Quadrants ___ and ___. I; IV

3. $y = -5$ is the equation of a ___ line. horizontal

4. $3x - 4y = -8$ is the equation of a line with slope ___. $\frac{3}{4}$

5. $(y - 3) = -4(x - 5)$ is the equation of a line with *y*-intercept ___. 23

6. Find the midpoint of $\overline{AB}$, with $A(-3, -8)$ and $B(5, -12)$. (1, −10)

7. What is the distance from $C(7, -6)$ to $D(-1, 0)$? 10

8. Write the equation in standard form of the circle with center $(0, -5)$ and radius length 4. $x^2 + (y + 5)^2 = 16$

9. Write the equation in standard form of the line with slope $-\frac{3}{5}$ and containing $(5, -6)$. $3x + 5y = -15$

10. Find the coordinates of endpoint E of $\overline{EF}$, with $F(-7, 3)$ and midpoint $M(-2, -1)$. (3, −5)

11. Find the slope of the median $\overline{GM}$ of $\triangle GHI$, with $G(-5, -3)$, $H(3, 7)$, and $I(9, 5)$. $\frac{-4}{11}$

12. A line has *y*-intercept 12 and slope $-\frac{3}{4}$. Find its *x*-intercept. 16

13. Write the equation in standard form of the perpendicular bisector k of $\overline{JK}$, if J and K have coordinates $(-8, -2)$ and $(6, 4)$, respectively. 7x + 3y = −4

14. Use coordinate geometry to prove: Line segments joining the successive midpoints of the sides of any quadrilateral form a parallelogram. See page 780.

15. Which subset of the coordinate plane is given by $y < 3$? half-plane below y = 3

16. Which subset of the coordinate plane is given by $x \geq -2$? x = −2 and the half-plane to the right

17. Give the center and radius length of the circle with equation $x^2 - 4x + y^2 + 6y = 23$. (2, −3); 6

18. Write the equation in standard form of the line that contains the point $(5, -2)$ and is parallel to the line whose equation is $4x - 12y = 9$. x − 3y = 11

19. Find the coordinates of the intersection of the lines with equations $3x - 2y = -6$ and $2x + 3y = 9$. (0, 3)

Challenge

Use coordinate geometry to prove that the opposite sides of a regular hexagon are parallel. See Solutions Manual.

582   Chapter 13 Coordinate Geometry

Alternative Assessment   Have students complete the Critical Thinking activity, p. 13, in the *Teacher's Resource Book.* For each exercise, the students should support their explanations with numerical examples and a graph where appropriate.

Select the best choice for each question.

1. If the following numbers are arranged in numerical order, which would be in the middle?

   A

   A. $\dfrac{3}{2\sqrt{2}}$ **B.** $\dfrac{2}{3\sqrt{2}}$ **C.** $\sqrt{2}$

   D. $\dfrac{3}{\sqrt{2}}$ **E.** $\dfrac{1}{\sqrt{2}}$

2. $k = \dfrac{3x^2}{y}$, for x, y, and k nonzero real numbers. Doubling x and tripling y would multiply k by:

   C

   A. $\dfrac{2}{3}$ **B.** $\dfrac{3}{4}$ **C.** $\dfrac{4}{3}$

   D. $\dfrac{3}{2}$ **E.** 4

3. Find the area of $\triangle PQR$ for points $P(0, 0)$, $Q(8, 0)$, and $R(6, 10)$.

   E

   A. 80   **B.** 64   **C.** 60
   D. 48   **E.** 40

4. When $x = -5$, what is the value of $x^4 + 5x^3 + x^2 + 5x + 15$?

   E

   A. -10 **B.** -5 **C.** 5
   D. 10   **E.** 15

5. What are the coordinates of vertex D of rectangle $ABCD$ for $A(1, 7)$, $B(3, 2)$, and $C(8, 4)$?

   C

   A. $(-4, 5)$ **B.** $(5, 7)$ **C.** $(6, 9)$
   D. $(3, 12)$ **E.** $(10, 9)$

6. Jo takes 3 h 20 min to mow a lawn. When Tim helps, they finish in 2 h. How long would it take Tim to do it alone?

   A

   A. 5 h   **B.** 4 h 40 min
   C. 4 h 24 min   **D.** 4 h
   E. 3 h 54 min

7. This summer the price of gas will vary from \$0.81 to \$1.10 per gal. Mr. Ford plans an 800-mile trip and expects to average 25–32 mi per gal. What is the least amount he must include in his trip budget to be sure to cover the cost of gas?

   D

   A. \$25.92   **B.** \$27.50   **C.** \$31.52
   D. \$35.20   **E.** \$37.50

8. The vertices of $\triangle ABC$ are $A(2, 7)$, $B(4, -3)$, and $C(0, -1)$. What is the equation of the line containing the altitude through C?

   B

   A. $5x - y = 1$ **B.** $x - 5y = 5$
   C. $x - y = 1$ **D.** $x - 5y = 19$
   E. $x - 4y = 4$

Use this definition for 9–11.

The operation # is defined as:

$$x \# y = \frac{x^2 - y^2}{x + y}$$

9. Find the value of $(5 \# 3) \# 4$.

   B

   A. -6 **B.** -2 **C.** 1
   D. 2   **E.** 6

10. Which is undefined?

   D

   A. $1 \# 1$ **B.** $1 \# 0$
   C. $(-1) \# (-1)$ **D.** $1 \# (-1)$
   E. none of these

11. If $x \# 7 = 3$, then $x =$

   E

   A. -10 or 7   **B.** -7 or 10
   C. -4 or 7   **D.** 4 or -10
   E. 10

The individual comments provided for certain problems may help the students in solving them.

1. An alternate method of solution could be to use 1.4 as the value of $\sqrt{2}$ and give approximate values for each choice. Then, choice A becomes 1.06, B is .46, C is 1.4, D is 2.1, and E is .7, and they can then be arranged in order.

4. Other methods of solution would include direct calculation, or writing the expression as $(-5)^4 + 5(-5)^3 + (-5)^2 + 5(-5) + 15 = 5^4 - 5^4 + 5^2 - 5^2 + 15 = 15$.

5. Another algebraic method of solution would be to write the equations of $\overleftrightarrow{CD}$ and $\overleftrightarrow{AD}$, and then solve the two simultaneously.

8. An observant student might note that only the equations in B and D have slopes of $\dfrac{1}{5}$, and point C satisfies only equations in A, B, C, and E. Then B is the one having both properties.

9–10. If this problem were to be worked using $\dfrac{x^2 - y^2}{x + y} = x - y$, care must be taken to be sure $x + y \neq 0$ in the denominator.

See *Teacher's Resource Book* for *Preparing for College Entrance Exams*.

ALGEBRA REVIEW

State the range of each function.

Example $f(x) = 3x + 1$; the domain $D = \{-3, 0, 1, 4\}$

$$f(-3) = 3(-3) + 1 = -8$$
$$f(0) = 3(0) + 1 = 1$$
$$f(1) = 3(1) + 1 = 4$$
$$f(4) = 3(4) + 1 = 13$$

The range $R = \{-8, 1, 4, 13\}$.

1. $g(x) = 4 - x$, $D = \{-4, 1, 6\}$ {−2, 3, 8}   **2.** $h(x) = x^3$, $D = \{-3, -1, 4\}$
                                                                                 {−27, −1, 64}

3. $k(p) = p^2 - p$, $D = \{-5, -2, 3\}$ {6, 30}   **4.** $f(r) = 3r^2$, $D = \{-2, 1, 5\}$ {3, 12, 75}

5. $j(k) = \dfrac{2}{k + 2}$, $D = \{-7, -4, 6\}$ **6.** $p(k) = \dfrac{k^2 + 1}{k - 1}$, $D = \{-3, 0, 5\}$
{−1, −$\frac{2}{5}$, $\frac{1}{4}$}   {−$\frac{5}{2}$, −1, $\frac{13}{2}$}

Find x if $f(x) = 0$.

Example   **a.** $f(x) = 2x - 12$ **b.** $f(x) = x^2 - 3x - 4$
                       $0 = 2x - 12$ $0 = x^2 - 3x - 4$
                       $12 = 2x$ $0 = (x - 4)(x + 1)$
                       $6 = x$ $x - 4 = 0$ or $x + 1 = 0$
                                                                     $x = 4$ $x = -1$

7. $f(x) = -\dfrac{1}{2}x + 5$ 10   **8.** $f(x) = 2x^2 + x - 3$ $-\frac{3}{2}$, 1   **9.** $f(x) = x - x^3$ −1, 0, 1

Find x if $f(x) = -2$.

10. $f(x) = x^2 - 7x + 8$ 2, 5   **11.** $f(x) = \dfrac{x + 1}{x - 2}$ 1

Given $f(x) = x^2 + 2$, $g(x) = 2x - 1$, and $h(x) = \dfrac{1}{2}x$, find the following.

Example $f(g(3)) = f(2(3) - 1)$
                         $= f(5)$
                         $= 5^2 + 2 = 27$

12. $f(h(0))$ 2   **13.** $f(g(0))$ 3   **14.** $h(g(3))$ $\frac{5}{2}$

15. $g(f(0))$ 3   **16.** $g(h(3))$ 2   **17.** $f(h(-6))$ 11

18. $h(f(-6))$ 19   **19.** $g(g(-5))$ −23   **20.** $g(h(f(-10)))$ 101

OVERVIEW • Chapter 14

SUMMARY

In Chapter 14, students are introduced to the concept of mappings. They study reflections, translations, rotations, and dilations in a plane. Students then learn to combine these mappings through composition of mappings. Relationships of identity and inverse transformations are discussed. Finally, students concentrate on identifying different symmetries in plane figures.

CHAPTER OBJECTIVES

- To recognize and use the terms and properties of basic mappings

- To locate images of figures by reflections, translations, glide reflections, rotations, and dilations

- To use vectors to represent translations

- To locate images of figures by composition of mappings

- To recognize and use the terms identity and inverse in relation to mappings

- To describe the symmetry of figures

- To identify types of symmetry in a plane geometric figure

- To *use transformations* in developing alternative methods of proof and construction

CHAPTER HIGHLIGHTS

DEVELOPING MATHEMATICAL POWER

Problem Solving

Lesson 14.8 incorporates the four problem solving steps and uses transformations to prove such things as the Isosceles Triangle Theorem.

Communication

The side column suggests reading topics such as topology. Paper-folding is an alternative learning style. Students are asked to write in their journals, comparing and contrasting dilations and other isometries, and point, line, and rotational symmetries. There is a Chapter Summary and Review in Spanish in the *Teacher's Resource Book*.

Reasoning

A thinking critically exercise asks students to analyze a triangle's orientation, given the different isometries.

Connections

Real-world applications include such topics as sports, optics, and linguistics. The historical reference to Isaac Newton's reflecting telescope provides an example of the variety of cultural influences on mathematics.

Technology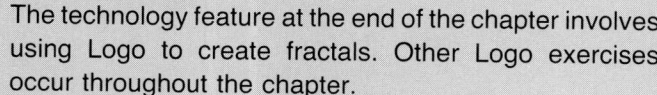

The technology feature at the end of the chapter involves using Logo to create fractals. Other Logo exercises occur throughout the chapter.

STUDENT TEXT

Chapter Content	Basic		Average		Enriched		NCTM STANDARDS*
14.1 Mappings	D:	589/3-8, 16, MR	D:	589/1-10, 16, MR	D:	589/1-10, 13-16, MR	2, 6, 8, 12, 14
14.2 Reflections	D:	594/1-9, 28, 30	D:	594/1-19, 28-31	D:	594/1-19, 25-31	3, 4, 8, 14
	R:	589/9, 10	R:	589/11, 12	R:	589/11, 12	
14.3 Translations	D:	598/1, 3-10, 24	D:	598/1-17, 24, 25	D:	598/1-17, 20-25	3, 6, 8, 14
	R:	594/10-13	R:	594/20-24	R:	594/20-24	
14.4 Rotations	D:	603/3-15, 40, 41	D:	603/1-27, 40, 41	D:	603/1-27, 33-41	4, 6, 8, 14
	R:	598/2, 11, 12	R:	598/18, 19	R:	598/18, 19	
14.5 Dilations	D:	609/1-14, 31, 42-44, AR	D:	609/1-22, 32, 42-44, AR	D:	609/1-22, 29-32, 42-46, AR	1, 3, 6, 8, 14
	R:	603/16-18	R:	603/28-32	R:	603/28-32	
14.6 Composition of Mappings			D:	615/1-16, 26, 27	D:	615/1-16, 22-27	1, 3, 6, 8, 14
			R:	609/23-28	R:	609/23-28	
14.7 Identity and Inverse Transformations	D:	619/1-16, 44, 46	D:	619/1-30, 44-46	D:	619/1-30, 39-46	3, 6, 8
	R:	609/15-18	R:	615/17-21	R:	615/17-21	
14.8 Strategy: Use Transformations			D:	624/1-6	D:	624/3-8	1, 3, 7, 8, 13
			R:	619/31-38	R:	619/31-38	
14.9 Symmetry	D:	628/1-16, 31	D:	628/1-26, 31, 32	D:	628/6-32	4, 6, 8
	R:	619/17-23	R:	624/7	R:	624/9-11	

D = Daily   R = Review   MR = Mixed Review   AR = Algebra Review

*For a complete list of NCTM Standards, see p. T7.

STUDENT TEXT

Review/Assessment

Mixed Review 590

Algebra Review 611

Summary and Review 634

College Ent. Exam Rev. 637

Cumulative Review 638

Extra Practice 656

Test Yourself 606, 631

Chapter Test 636

Chapter Project 585

Special Features

Historical Note 616

Technology 590, 595, 600, 611, 616, 631, 632–633

Devel. Math. Power 595, 600, 611, 616, 621

Applications 590, 595, 600, 606, 611, 616, 621, 630-631

Project 625

RESOURCES

Teacher's Resource Book

Ch. 14: Investigation/Practice/ Enrichment 1-26

Spanish Sum. and Rev. 27-28

Quizzes 145-148

Chapter Tests 149-152

Semester and Final Tests 153-168

Perf. Assessment Proj. Ch. 14

Critical Thinking 14

Reading and Writing in Geom. 14

Technology 19-20

Teaching Aid 14

Transparencies 26-28

Teaching Transparencies 92-100

Computer Test Bank 865-910

Connections 27-36

PH Graph. Utility

Overhead Manip. Kit

14 Transformational Geometry

Coming or going?

Developing Mathematical Power

C. Escher (1898–1972) is a Dutch graphic artist whose art reflects his interest science and mathematics.

Many of his works have been used to illustrate mathematics and science textbooks.

Transformations of triangles, squares, rectangles, and other parallelograms are the basis of many Escher tessellations. A tessellation is an arrangement of figures that completely cover a plane with no overlapping.

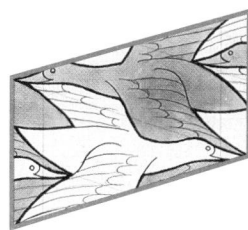

The tessellation used in the art below is based on a parallelogram.

Project

Use transformational procedures to create an Escher-type tessellation. Start with a polygon that will tessellate. Use translations, rotations, reflections, and/or dilations to form a new shape (or shapes) that will tessellate. Explain the transformations that you use.

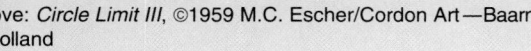

MODELING

This project involves creating a graphic design. The model is developed by using transformational geometry skills.

Cooperative Learning

This project is accomplished through a succession of tasks, each of which is well-suited to a cooperative learning situation. These tasks include:

1. Applying concepts of transformational geometry, including mapping, reflections, translations, and rotations.
2. Choosing a polygon that will tessellate.
3. Performing reflections, translations, and rotations.
4. Analyzing tessellations.

Students should be encouraged to use a computer drawing program.

Alternative Assessment

See the *Teacher's Resource Book*, Assessment, Chapter 14. This project and the TRB page may be used as an alternative form of assessment for selected topics in Chapter 14.

585

Vocabulary

Image
Isometry
Mapping
One-to-one
Preimage
Projection onto the *x*-axis
Transformation

Materials/Manipulatives

Graph paper
Protractors
*Teacher's Resource Book,
Transparency 26*
Teaching Transparency 92

Technology

*Computer Test Bank, pp.
865–869*

LESSON FOCUS

Review
• Review nongeometric and geometric examples of mappings. Pairing a student with his or her locker number, a segment with its length, and an angle with its measure all illustrate a mapping from one set to another.
• The Mixed Review, Exercises 17–19, involves area and volume.

Alternative Learning Styles
• The Investigation provides an opportunity to introduce students to a transformation using congruent triangles. Show students how $\triangle A'B'C'$ could be obtained from $\triangle ABC$ by folding along the *y*-axis and tracing.
• The musical learner may benefit from the mapping between the notes on a sheet of music and the notes played on an instrument.

14.1

Mappings

Objective: To recognize and use the terms and properties of basic mappings

You have studied one-to-one correspondences between geometric figures. You have also studied the properties of both congruent and similar figures. In this chapter, you will identify features of figures that are changed or unchanged by moving them in a plane. These motions are described mathematically as correspondences between sets of points.

Investigation—*Thinking Critically*

Congruence of triangles was defined as a correspondence between triangles so that corresponding sides and corresponding angles are congruent. Consider $\triangle ABC$ and $\triangle A'B'C'$ shown on the grid.

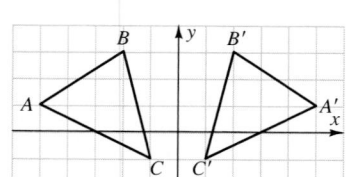

1. Measure the angles of each triangle and compare the measures. $m\angle A = 60 = m\angle A'$; $m\angle B = 70 = m\angle B'$; $m\angle C = 50 = m\angle C'$
2. Use the distance formula to find *AB, BC, AC, A'B', B'C'*, and *A'C'*. How do these measures compare? $AB = \sqrt{13} = A'B'$; $BC = \sqrt{17} = B'C'$; $AC = \sqrt{20} = A'C'$
3. Is $\triangle ABC \cong \triangle A'B'C'$? yes; corr. $\angle$s $\cong$, corr. sides $\cong$
4. If (*x, y*) is a point of $\triangle ABC$, what is the corresponding point of $\triangle A'B'C'$? $(-x, y)$
5. If $P = (x, y)$ is a point of $\triangle ABC$, let $P' = (x + 1, y - 1)$. Plot points *D, E*, and *F* that correspond to *A, B*, and *C* using this rule. Is $\triangle DEF \cong \triangle ABC$? Justify your answer. $D = (-4, 0), E = (-1, 2), F = (0, -2)$ yes; corr. sides $\cong$, corr. $\angle$s $\cong$

The idea of correspondence between two sets (same set or different sets) is used to describe the effects of motion on a figure. Examples of correspondences previously introduced include the Protractor Postulate, which establishes a correspondence between the numbers 0 to 180 and certain rays, and congruence of geometric figures, which represents a correspondence between their sides and angles.

The word *mapping* is often used in mathematics to describe certain types of correspondences between sets.

Definition   A correspondence between sets *A* and *B* is a **mapping** of *A* to *B* if and only if each member of *A* corresponds to one and only one member of *B*.

586   Chapter 14 Transformational Geometry

Developing Mathematical Power

Keeping a Portfolio   Have students describe how they would explain the concepts in this lesson to a classmate who was absent. They should cover all the vocabulary introduced and provide illustrations of concepts wherever possible.

Mappings are usually represented by capital letters. The notation $M: A \rightarrow B$ represents a mapping from set A to set B. If P is a member of set A and P' is the corresponding member of set B, write $M(P) = P'$. P' is called the **image** of P under mapping M and P is called the **preimage** of P'.

EXAMPLE 1 For which of the following is M a mapping from A to B? For the correspondences that are mappings, what is the image of c? What is the preimage of e?

a. 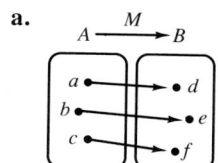 **b.** 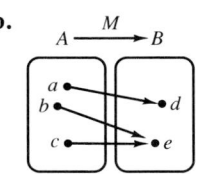 **c.** 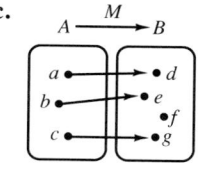 **d.**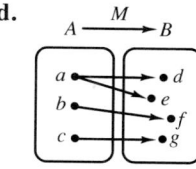

a. This is a mapping. The image of c is f, or $M(c) = f$, and the preimage of e is b, or $M(b) = e$.

b. This is a mapping. The image of c is e, or $M(c) = e$; e has two preimages, b and c, or $M(b) = e$ and $M(c) = e$.

c. This is a mapping. The image of c is g, or $M(c) = g$ and the preimage of e is b, or $M(b) = e$.

d. This is not a mapping because a member of A (a) is associated with two different members of B (d and e).

In Example 1, parts (a) and (c) show a type of mapping, called **one-to-one,** in which every image in B has exactly one preimage. Thus the mapping in part (b) is not one-to-one. Note in part **c** that although f is not the image of any element of A under the mapping M, the necessary conditions for a one-to-one mapping still exist.

Special mappings called *transformations* describe motions in geometry.

Definition A mapping is a **transformation** if and only if it is a one-to-one mapping of the plane onto itself.

A transformation is a correspondence between points of the plane such that every point in the plane is the image of a point of the plane and no two points have the same image. Although transformations are defined as mappings of the entire plane to itself, mappings of geometric figures such as lines, triangles, or other figures are usually of more interest.

Ordered pairs can represent points of a plane. If T is a transformation, then $T(x, y) = (x', y')$ indicates that point (x', y') is the image of point (x, y) under the transformation T.

14.1 Mappings **587**

TEACHING SUGGESTIONS

- Stress the concepts of *mapping, transformation, image, preimage, one-to-one, onto,* and *isometry.*
- Students should understand that the sentence after the definition of *transformation* restates the definition by paraphrasing "one-to-one" and "onto." The condition that *every point in the plane is the image of another point of the plane* is a description of "onto," and *no two points have the same image* describes "one-to-one."
- Point out to students that most of the mappings that will be studied in this chapter are isometries, or congruence mappings, although dilations are similarity mappings.

CHALKBOARD EXAMPLES

- **For Example 1**
  For which of the following is M a mapping from C to D? For those that are mappings, is the mapping one-to-one? What is the image of k? What is the preimage of o?

a. $C \xrightarrow{M} D$ 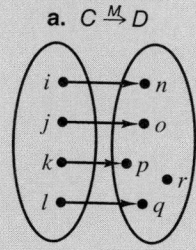 **b.** $C \xrightarrow{M} D$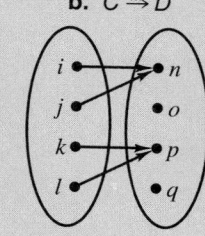

c. $C \xrightarrow{M} D$ **d.** $C \xrightarrow{M} D$

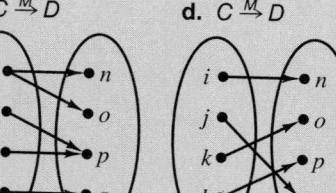

a. yes; yes; p; j
b. yes; no; p; no preimage
c. no
d. yes; yes; o; k

• For Example 2

$T(x, y) = (2x, y + 4)$ is a transformation. Find the following:

a. $T(0, 0)$ **b.** $T(3, -4)$
c. $T(-2, 1)$ **d.** Preimage of $(8, -5)$

a. $T(0, 0) = (2 \cdot 0, 0 + 4)$
    $= (0, 4)$
b. $T(3, -4) = (2 \cdot 3, -4 + 4)$
    $= (6, 0)$
c. $T(-2, 1) = (2 \cdot -2, 1 + 4)$
    $= (-4, 5)$
d. $(8, -5) = (2x, y + 4)$, so $x = 4$, $y = -9$. Thus, $T(4, -9) = (8, -5)$.

• For Example 3

Plot points $P(3, -1)$ and $Q(-2, 4)$ and the P' and Q' where $T(P) = P'$ and $T(Q) = Q'$. Draw $\overline{PQ}$ and $\overline{P'Q'}$. Find PQ and $P'Q'$ using the distance formula. Compare PQ to $P'Q'$.

a. $T(x, y) = (2x, -y)$
b. $T(x, y) = (-y, x - 1)$

a.

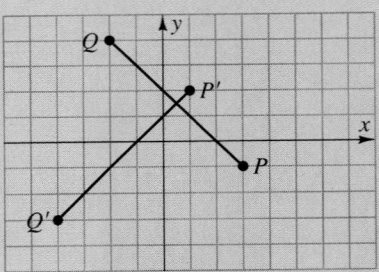

$P' = (6, 1)$; $Q' = (-4, -4)$; $PQ = 5\sqrt{2}$;
$P'Q' = 5\sqrt{5}$; $PQ \neq P'Q'$

b.

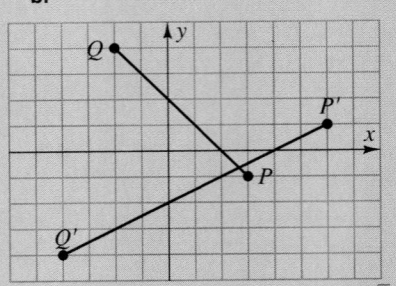

$P' = (1, 2)$, $Q' = (-4, -3)$; $PQ = 5\sqrt{2}$;
$P'Q' = 5\sqrt{2}$; $P'Q' = PQ$

EXAMPLE 2   Suppose $T(x, y) = (x + 1, 3y)$ is a transformation. Find the following.

a. The image of $(2, 5)$ under T **b.** $T(0, 3)$
c. $T(3, -2)$ **d.** The preimage of $(4, 9)$

a. $T(2, 5) = (2 + 1, 3 \cdot 5) = (3, 15)$
b. $T(0, 3) = (0 + 1, 3 \cdot 3) = (1, 9)$
c. $T(3, -2) = (3 + 1, 3 \cdot -2) = (4, -6)$
d. $(4, 9) = (x + 1, 3y)$, so $4 = x + 1$ and $9 = 3y$. Thus, $x = 3$ and $y = 3$. The preimage of $(4, 9)$ is $(3, 3)$, or $T(3, 3) = (4, 9)$.

EXAMPLE 3   Plot points $A(1, 4)$ and $B(-2, -1)$ and then A' and B' where $T(A) = A'$ and $T(B) = B'$. Draw $\overline{AB}$ and $\overline{A'B'}$. Find AB and $A'B'$ by using the distance formula. How do AB and $A'B'$ compare?

a. $T(x, y) = (-x, y)$ **b.** $T(x, y) = (2x, y - 1)$

a. $A' = T(1, 4) = (-1, 4)$; $B' = T(-2, -1) = (2, -1)$;
$AB = \sqrt{9 + 25} = \sqrt{34}$; $A'B' = \sqrt{9 + 25} = \sqrt{34}$; so $AB = A'B'$

b. $A' = T(1, 4) = (2, 3)$; $B' = T(-2, -1) = (-4, -2)$; $A'B' = \sqrt{36 + 25} = \sqrt{61}$; $AB = \sqrt{34}$; so $A'B' > AB$.

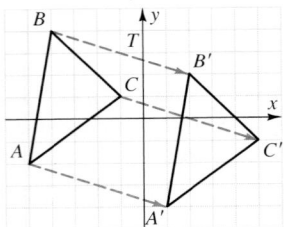

T maps $\triangle ABC \rightarrow \triangle A'B'C'$
Since $\triangle ABC \cong \triangle A'B'C'$,
T is an *isometry*.

Observe that the transformation in Example 3a preserves the distance between points, whereas the one in Example 3b does not. A mapping M preserves the distance between A and B if $AB = A'B'$, where $M(A) = A'$ and $M(B) = B'$. A transformation that preserves the distance between points is called an **isometry,** or a **congruence** mapping. If a figure is mapped by an isometry, the image of the figure is congruent to the original figure. Transformations can describe movements and the effects of those movements upon the figures. Some transformations preserve distance and produce images congruent to the original figure.

CLASS EXERCISES

$A = \{\ldots, -2, -1, 0, 1, 2, \ldots\}$, all the integers, and $B = \{0, 1, 4, 9, \ldots\}$, all the perfect squares. Let C be a correspondence between each integer and its square.

1. Find $C(-5)$, $C(3)$, $C(0)$, and $C(5)$.
25; 9; 0; 25
2. Is C a mapping? Explain. Yes; each member of A is associated with one member of B.
3. Find the preimage(s) of 0; of 16.
0; ± 4
4. Is C one-to-one? Explain. No; each member of B, except 0, has two preimages in A.

588   Chapter 14 Transformational Geometry

Suppose $T(x, y) = (x, y - 2)$ is a transformation.

$T(A) = (-4, 0); T(B) = (-2, 2); T(C) = (2, -1)$
5. Find the images of A, B, C, D, and E.
$T(D) = (-3, -4); T(E) = (4, -6)$
6. Find the preimage of the points $(3, 6)$,
$(-2, -6), (0, 0), (4, -1)$, and $(-3, 5)$.
$(3, 8); (-2, -4); (0, 2); (4, 1); (-3, 7)$
7. Is T an isometry? Justify your answer. Yes; the
transformation preserves distances between points.
8. Repeat Exercises 5–7, using the transformation

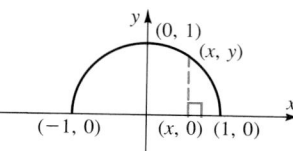

$T(x, y) = (2x, 2y)$. 5. $(-8, 4), (-4, 8), (4, 2), (-6, -4), (8, -8)$ 6. $(\frac{3}{2}, 3), (-1, -3),$
$(0, 0), (2, -\frac{1}{2}), (-\frac{3}{2}, \frac{5}{2})$ 7. No; the transformation doesn't preserve distance between points.
9. Repeat Exercises 5–7, using the transformation
$T(x, y) = (x - 2, -2y)$. See below.

Each point (x, y) of this semicircle can be associated
with a point of the x-axis between -1 and 1 by
drawing a line from (x, y) perpendicular to the x-axis
so that (x, y) is associated with $(x, 0)$. This is called
the **projection** onto the x-axis of the semicircle.

10. Does this correspondence map the semicircle to the x-axis? Explain. Yes;
each point on the semicircle corr. to one pt. on the axis.
11. If this is a mapping, is it one-to-one? Explain. Yes; each image has one
preimage.
12. What is the image of $(0, 1)$? $(-1, 0)$? Any (x, y) on the semicircle?
$(0, 0); (-1, 0); (x, 0)$
13. What is the preimage of $(\frac{1}{2}, 0)$? $(-\frac{1}{4}, 0)$? $(x, 0)$ between -1 and 1?
$(\frac{1}{2}, \frac{\sqrt{3}}{2}); (-\frac{1}{4}, \frac{\sqrt{15}}{4}); (x, +\sqrt{1 - x^2})$

PRACTICE EXERCISES   Use technology where appropriate.

There are six $\triangle$ congruences between an equilateral triangle and itself.

A **1.** Write these possible congruences using $\triangle ABC$. $\triangle ABC \cong \triangle ABC \cong \triangle ACB$
$\cong \triangle BAC \cong \triangle BCA \cong \triangle CAB \cong \triangle CBA$
2. Suppose $\triangle ABC$ is mapped onto itself by the isometry $\triangle ABC \rightarrow \triangle BCA$.
Find the images of A, B, C, $\overline{AB}$, $\overline{AC}$, and $\overline{BC}$. $B, C, A, \overline{BC}, \overline{BA}, \overline{CA}$

**Does the correspondence represent
a mapping of set C to set D? If L
is a mapping, is it one-to-one?
Explain.**

3.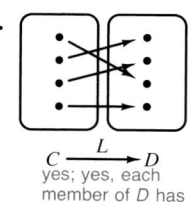

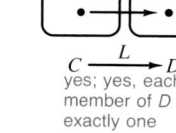
yes; yes, each
member of D has
exactly one
preimage

4.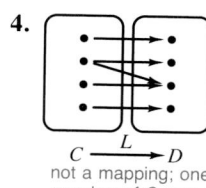

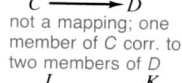
not a mapping; one
member of C corr. to
two members of D

Suppose sets J and K are as shown.

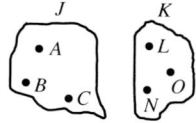

5. Define a one-to-one mapping from J to K by giving the
image of each member of J. $M(A) = L; M(B) = O; M(C) = N$
Answers may vary.
6. Define a mapping from J to K that is not one-to-one.
Answers may vary. $M(A) = L; M(B) = O; M(C) = O$

14.1 Mappings   **589**

Common Errors

- Some students will confuse the
definition of a mapping with the
concepts of *one-to-one* and *onto*.
Use many examples to alleviate
this.

- Some students may assume that if
a transformation preserves distances for two particular points,
then it is an isometry. Ask them if
$T(x, y) = (-2x, \frac{y}{2})$ is an isometry.

First have them find AB and A'B'
for $A(-1, 2)$ and $B(1, -2)$, then
have them find AC and A'C' for
$C(1, -4)$.

- See *Teacher's Resource Book* for
additional remediation.

LESSON FOLLOW-UP

Assignment Guide
See p. 584B for assignments.

Lesson Quiz
Suppose $T(x, y) = (-y, -x + 2)$ is a
transformation. Find the following:

1. $T(3, 4)$ **2.** $T(0, 0)$
3. The preimage of $(6, -1)$
4. The preimage of $(2, 0)$
5. Is T an isometry? Justify.
1. $(-4, -1)$ 2. $(0, 2)$
3. $(3, -6)$ 4. $(2, -2)$
5. For $P_1(x_1, y_1)$ and $P_2(x_2, y_2)$,
$P_1' = T(P_1) = (-y_1, -x_1 + 2),$
$P_2' = T(P_2) = (-y_2, -x_2 + 2).$
$P_1P_2 = \sqrt{(x_2 - x_1)^2 + (y_2 - y_1)^2},$
$P_1'P_2' =$
$\sqrt{(-y_2 - (-y_1))^2 + ((-x_2 + 2) - (-x_1 + 2))^2}$
$= \sqrt{(y_1 - y_2)^2 + (x_1 - x_2)^2}$
$= P_1P_2$. T is an isometry.

Additional Answer

9. 5. $(-6, -4), (-4, -8), (0, -2), (-5, 4), (2, 8)$ **6.** $(5, -3), (0, 3), (2, 0), (6, \frac{1}{2}), (-1, -\frac{5}{2})$
7. No; the transformation does not preserve distance between points.

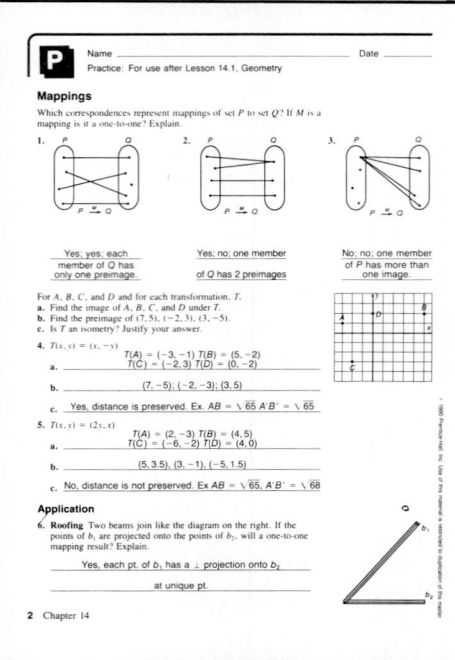

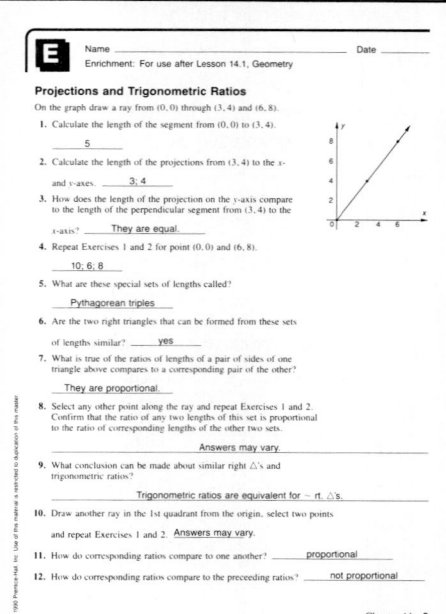

For *A, B, C,* and *D* and for each transformation *T*

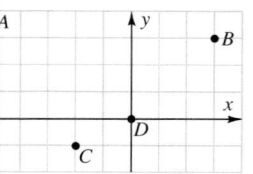

a. Find the image of *A, B, C,* and *D* under *T*.

b. Find the preimage of (4, 2), (−3, 4), and (2, −3).

c. Is *T* an isometry? Justify your answer.
See Additional Answers, p. 702.

7. $T(x, y) = (x, -y)$ 8. $T(x, y) = (y, x)$

9. $T(x, y) = (-3x, 3y)$ 10. $T(x, y) = (-x, -y)$

Define a mapping *M*

a. if *P* is on *l*, then $M(P) = P = P'$.

b. if *P* is not on *l*, then $M(P) = P'$, where *P'* is the point at
which $\overline{PP'}$ intersects *l* and $\overline{PP'} \perp l$.

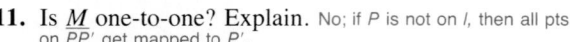

11. Is *M* one-to-one? Explain. No; if *P* is not on *l*, then all pts.
on $\overline{PP'}$ get mapped to *P'*.

12. Does *M* preserve the distance between points? Justify your answer.
See Additional Answers, p. 702.

13. If *l* is a line and *T* is an isometry, show that *T(l)* is also a line. (Let *A, B,* and
C be points of *l* with *B* between *A* and *C* and consider $A' = T(A)$, $B' = T(B)$, and
$C' = T(C)$. Show that *A', B',* and *C'* must be collinear.)

14. *T* is an isometry and $k \parallel l$. Use an indirect argument to show that $T(k) \parallel T(l)$.

Applications

15. **Cartography**   In creating polar maps of the earth, points on the surface of
the globe are projected to a plane that is perpendicular to a pole. Does this
suggest a one-to-one mapping? Explain. Yes; every pt. on the globe maps to a
unique point on the plane.

16. **Technology**   Use Logo to generate a pentomino (a design made of five
congruent squares) and show its image under the transformation:
$T(x, y) = (-x, -y)$. See Solutions Manual.

Mixed Review

Find the lateral area, total area, and volume of each solid.

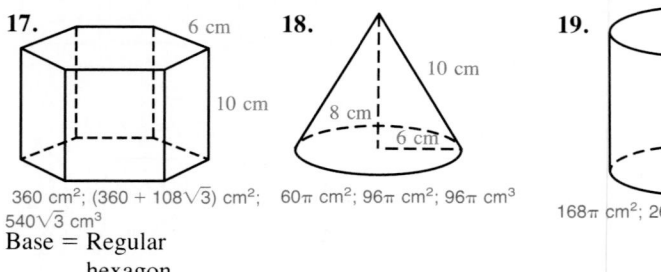

17. 6 cm, 10 cm
360 cm²; (360 + 108√3) cm²;
540√3 cm³
Base = Regular
   hexagon

18. 10 cm, 8 cm, 6 cm
60π cm²; 96π cm²; 96π cm³

19. 7 cm, 12 cm
168π cm²; 266π cm²; 588π cm³

14.2

Reflections

Objective: To locate images of figures by reflections

Reflections of objects in mirrors, pools of water, or in almost any shiny surface are common everyday occurrences. An object and its reflected image can be described mathematically using a geometric transformation called a *reflection*.

Investigation—*Visualizing the Concept*

A computer program draws a figure, "flips" the figure over the y-axis in a coordinate plane, and then draws the flip image. Draw △ABC and the computer will produce the output shown. Notice the correspondence: $A \leftrightarrow A'$, $B \leftrightarrow B'$, and $C \leftrightarrow C'$.

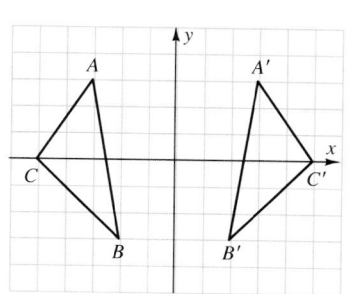

1. Is $\triangle ABC \cong \triangle A'B'C'$? Justify your answer. Yes; <u>distance is preserved.</u>
2. Draw $\overline{AA'}$, $\overline{BB'}$, and $\overline{CC'}$. Construct the perpendicular bisector of each segment. What do you observe? The y-axis is the ⊥ bisector of the segments.

Your reflection in a mirror appears to be as far in "back" of the mirror as you are in "front." If you reflect an object in it, you can think of the mirror as the perpendicular bisector of the segments connecting corresponding points of the object and its image.

Definition A transformation is a **reflection** in line *l* if and only if the following conditions are satisfied:
   a. if *A* is a point of *l*, then the image of *A* is *A*;
   b. if *A* is not on *l*, then the image of *A* is *A'*, such that *l* is the perpendicular bisector of $\overline{AA'}$.

Write R_l to show that *R* is a reflection in line *l*, the **line of reflection.** The notation $R_l(A) = A'$ is used to show that *A'* is the image of *A* under reflection in line *l*.

Given a point *A* and a line of reflection *l*, the image of *A* can be found by paper folding, by drawing with a ruler, by construction, or by locating the point and line on a grid. If *A* and *A'* are given and *l* is to be found, construction is usually used.

14.2 Reflections **591**

Developing Mathematical Power

Keeping a Portfolio Have students use their own words to describe the reflection of a figure over the y-axis and a reflection of a figure over the x-axis. They should provide examples to illustrate their descriptions. Then have them experiment with and describe the reflection of a figure over a diagonal line in a coordinate plane.

LESSON PLAN

Vocabulary
Line of reflection
Orientation
Reflection in a line
Reflection through a point

Materials/Manipulatives
Graph paper
Compasses and straightedges
Teaching Transparencies 93–93B

Technology
Computer
Computer Test Bank, pp. 869–874
The Geometric Supposer: Triangles
Geometry Problems and Projects: Triangles, Worksheets T50, T51

LESSON FOCUS

Review
If $T(x, y) = (x - 2, 5y)$ is a transformation, find the following:

1. The image of $(2, -1)$ under *T*
2. $T(-3, 2)$
3. The preimage of $(-2, -5)$
   1. $(0, -5)$ **2.** $(-5, 10)$ **3.** $(0, -1)$

Alternative Learning Styles
- The Investigation provides an opportunity to visualize the reflection of a figure over the y-axis.
- The kinesthetic learner may benefit from folding the coordinate plane (with a figure drawn on it) along the y-axis and then putting a pencil point through the vertices of the figure (preimage). When the plane is unfolded, students will see the vertices of the image, and they can connect them to create the image.

591

- Tell students that since any point on a line of reflection is mapped onto itself under the reflection, each such point is called a *fixed point*.
- Be sure to cover Class Exercises 14–16. You may also wish to ask students to find the coordinates of the image of (x, y) under reflection in the line $y = -x$. $(-y, -x)$ These four reflections are particularly important in later lessons such as Lesson 14.6.
- If you don't assign Practice Exercises 25–27, you may wish to discuss reflection through a point in class. Note that the Class Exercises in Lesson 14.4 refer to Exercise 27.

CHALKBOARD EXAMPLES

- **For Example 1**
  Use this figure to find each image.

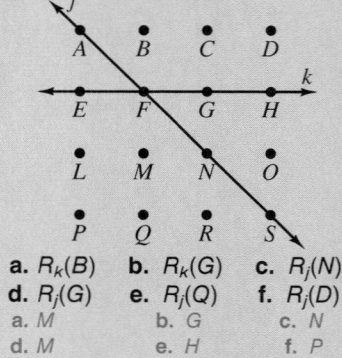

a. $R_k(B)$ b. $R_k(G)$ c. $R_j(N)$
d. $R_j(G)$ e. $R_j(Q)$ f. $R_j(D)$
a. M b. G c. N
d. M e. H f. P

EXAMPLE 1 **Use this figure to answer each question.**

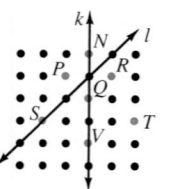

a. $R_k(P) = \underline{\ ?\ }$ b. $R_l(S) = \underline{\ ?\ }$
c. $R_l(P) = \underline{\ ?\ }$ d. $R_l(Q) = \underline{\ ?\ }$
e. $R_k(S) = \underline{\ ?\ }$ f. $R_k(N) = \underline{\ ?\ }$
a. R b. S c. Q d. P e. T f. N

Geometric figures can be reflected in a line by reflecting each point or enough points to determine the figure. The reflection images are in blue.

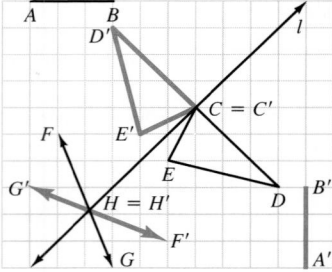

$$R_l(\overline{AB}) = \overline{A'B'} \qquad R_l(\triangle CDE) = \triangle C'D'E'$$
$$R_l(\overleftrightarrow{FG}) = \overleftrightarrow{F'G'}$$

Observe that reflection in a line preserves betweenness of points, collinearity, angles, angle measure, and segment length. Theorem 14.1 verifies that reflection preserves distance between points.

> **Theorem 14.1** A reflection in a line is an isometry.

One proof of this theorem uses coordinate geometry. Another type of justification follows.

Suppose $R_l(\overline{AB}) = \overline{A'B'}$ as shown. If $\overline{AA'}$ and $\overline{BB'}$ are drawn, then quad.$(ACDB) \cong$ quad.$(A'CDB')$ by SASAS. Thus $\overline{AB} \cong \overline{A'B'}$ because these are corresponding parts.

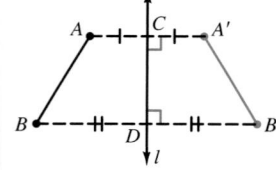

Since a reflection is an isometry, the reflected image of any figure is congruent to the original figure.

EXAMPLE 2 **Consider points A, B, and C as shown.**

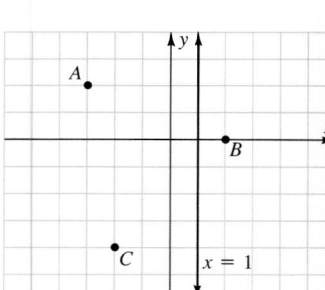

a. Give the coordinates of the image of each point by reflecting in the y-axis.

b. Repeat, reflecting in the x-axis.

c. Repeat, reflecting in the line $x = 1$.

d. Verify that a reflection in the line $x = 1$ is an isometry by finding AB and $A'B'$.

e. Draw $\triangle ABC$ and reflect it in the x-axis, forming $\triangle A'B'C'$. Is $\triangle ABC \cong \triangle A'B'C'$? Explain.

592   Chapter 14 Transformational Geometry

a. $A'(3, 2)$; $B'(-2, 0)$; $C'(2, -4)$

b. $A'(-3, -2)$; $B'(2, 0)$; $C'(-2, 4)$

c. $A'(5, 2)$; $B'(0, 0)$; $C'(4, -4)$

d. $AB = \sqrt{(-3-2)^2 + (2-0)^2} = \sqrt{29}$
   $A'B' = \sqrt{(5-0)^2 + (2-0)^2} = \sqrt{29}$

e. $\triangle ABC \cong \triangle A'B'C'$ because reflection in a line is an isometry.

CLASS EXERCISES

True or false? Justify your answers.

1. If k is the perpendicular bisector of $\overline{MN}$, then $R_k(M) = N$. True; the def. of reflection

2. If l is the bisector of $\angle CDE$, then $R_l(\overrightarrow{DC}) = \overrightarrow{DE}$. True; see Additional Answers, p. 702.

3. Given points P and P', it is possible to find two distinct lines j and k such that $R_j(P) = P'$ and $R_k(P) = P'$. False; there is only one ⊥ bisector of $\overline{PP'}$ (k coincides with j)

4. The set of points equidistant from the endpoints of $\overline{CD}$ is a line l with $R_l(D) = C$. True; l is the ⊥ bisector of $\overline{CD}$. Therefore, it is the line of reflection.

5. If $R_j(C) = C'$ and $R_j(D) = D'$, then $\overline{CD} \cong \overline{C'D'}$. True; reflection in a line is an isometry.

6. Given line l and point A, construct A', the image of A under reflection in l. See Additional Answers, p. 702.

7. Given two points A and A', construct line l such that $R_l(A) = A'$.

Complete the following.

8. $R_k(D) = \underline{?}$ J

9. $R_l(H) = \underline{?}$ H

10. $R_k(G) = \underline{?}$ E

11. $R_j(K) = \underline{?}$ M

12. $R_l(I) = \underline{?}$ D

13. $R_j(B) = \underline{?}$ B

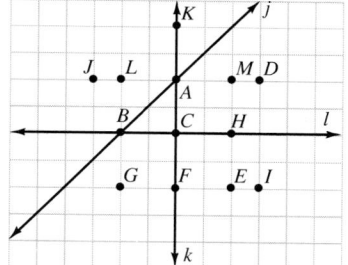

Sketch the image of each figure and give the coordinates of the vertices of the image if the figure is reflected in

14. x-axis See Additional Answers, p. 702.

15. y-axis

16. line z

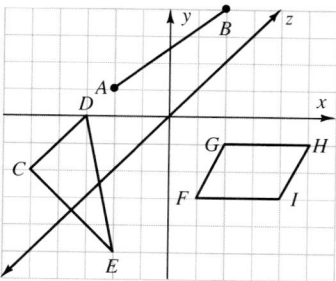

14.2 Reflections **593**

• **For Example 2**
   Give the coordinates of the image of each point under each reflection.

   a. R_y **b.** R_x **c.** R_k **d.** R_j

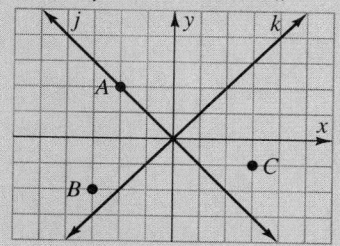

   a. $A'(2, 2)$; $B'(3, -2)$; $C'(-3, -1)$
   b. $A'(-2, -2)$; $B'(-3, 2)$; $C'(3, 1)$
   c. $A'(2, -2)$; $B'(-2, -3)$; $C'(-1, 3)$
   d. $A'(-2, 2)$; $B'(2, 3)$; $C'(1, -3)$

Common Error

• Some students may incorrectly apply the definition of reflection in a line. Paper folding and/or the use of transparencies will be helpful here.

• See *Teacher's Resource Book* for additional remediation.

LESSON FOLLOW-UP

Assignment Guide
See p. 584B for assignments.

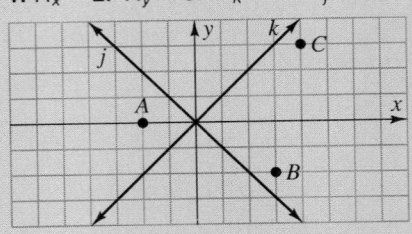
PRACTICE EXERCISES   〜 Use technology where appropriate.

Trace each figure and find the image by reflecting in line *l*.

A   **1.** 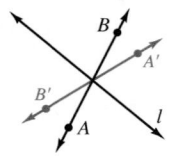   **2.** 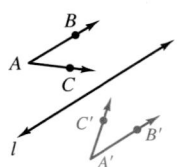   **3.** 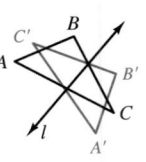   **4.**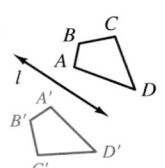

Copy onto graph paper and find the image of each figure under R_l.

5. 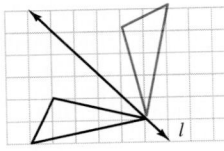   **6.** 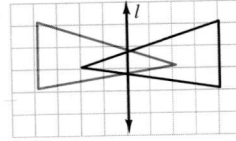   **7.**

Each dashed figure is the image of the solid figure under relection in a line *l*. Copy each figure onto graph paper and find *l*.

8. 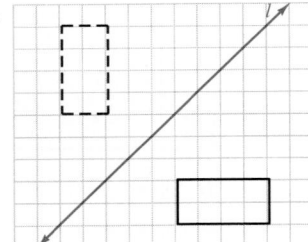   **9.**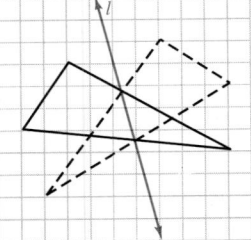

If (x, y) is any point in the plane, give the coordinates of the image of (x, y) under each of the following.

10. R_x $(x, -y)$ **11.** R_y $(-x, y)$ **12.** Reflection in the line $y = x$ (y, x)

13. Draw square *ABCD* and locate the line of reflection *l* such that $R_l(A) = A$, $R_l(B) = D$, $R_l(C) = C$, and $R_l(D) = B$. $l = \overleftrightarrow{AC}$

The justification of Theorem 14.1 was outlined for *A* and *B* on the same side of *l*.

Draw a figure, state the *Given* and *Prove*, and write a complete proof for

B   **14.** *A* or *B* (not both) on *l*.   **15.** *A* and *B* on opposite sides of *l*.
See Solutions Manual.

594   Chapter 14 Transformational Geometry

Find the equation of line j. Then find the equation of the image of j under the following. $y = \frac{4}{3}x + 4$
See below.

16. R_x **17.** R_y **18.** $R_{y=x}$ **19.** $R_{y=-x}$

20. Repeat Exercises 16–19 using line k.

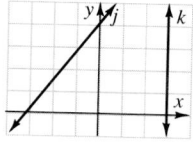

Consider point A and its image A' under reflection in a line l.
a. Find the equation of line l.   **b.** If (x, y) is any point, find $R_l(x, y)$.

21. $A = (3, 4)$; $A' = (-3, 4)$
     a. $x = 0$; **b.** $(-x, y)$
22. $A = (-1, 5)$; $A' = (5, -1)$
     a. $y = x$; **b.** (y, x)
23. $A = (2, 8)$; $A' = (-6, 8)$
     a. $x = -2$; **b.** $(x - 8, y)$
24. $A = (-4, -1)$; $A' = (3, 7)$
     a. $y = -\frac{7}{8}x + \frac{41}{16}$; **b.** $(x + 7, y + 8)$

Suppose P is a given point, with each point Q of the plane mapping to Q' such that Q, P, and Q' are collinear and $PQ = P'Q'$. This mapping is a *reflection through point P*.

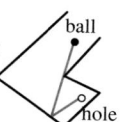

Trace this figure. Draw the image of $\triangle ABC$
See Solutions Manual.

C   **25.** reflected through C **26.** reflected through P

27. If P is the origin, give the coordinates of the image of any point (x, y) reflected through the origin.
$(-x, -y)$

Applications

28. Sports In miniature golf, if a ball has no spin on it, it will rebound off a wall at the same angle it strikes the wall. Explain how the ball can be put into the hole in one shot by striking appropriate wall(s). See Solutions Manual.

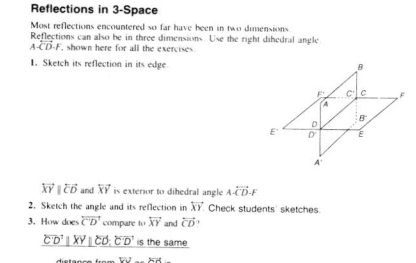

29. Technology Use Logo to simulate a ball moving around a pool table.

Developing Mathematical Power

30. Thinking Critically Naming the triangle vertices in clockwise or counterclockwise order gives the *orientation* of the triangle. Would any line *reflection* of $\triangle ABC$ preserve orientation? Why?
No; line reflection changes the order.

31. Thinking Critically Suppose your entire image in a wall mirror is exactly the height of the mirror. Recall that the angle at which light strikes the mirror *(the angle of incidence)* is congruent to the angle at which it is reflected from the mirror *(angle of reflection)*. Using this fact, what is the minimum length mirror needed to allow you to see your entire image? Justify your answer. See Additional Answers, p. 702.

16. $y' = -\frac{4}{3}x - 4$

17. $y' = -\frac{4}{3}x + 4$

18. $y' = \frac{3}{4}x - 3$

19. $y' = \frac{3}{4}x + 3$

20. for $k = 3$:
   16) $x = 3$
   17) $x = -3$
   18) $y = 3$
   19) $y = -3$

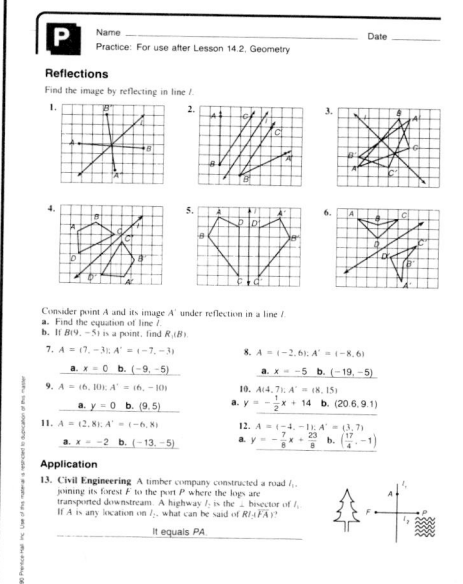
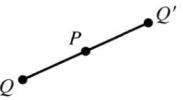
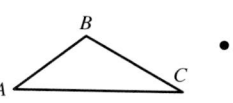

Vocabulary

Glide   Translation
 reflection   Vector
Tessellation

Materials/Manipulatives

Graph paper and colored pencils
Compasses and straightedges
*Teaching Transparancies 94 and
94A*

Technology

*Computer Test Bank, pp.
875–878*

LESSON FOCUS

Review

Review graphing figures on a coordinate plane.

Alternative Learning Styles

- The Investigation provides an opportunity to visualize translations in a plane.
- The visual learner will benefit from seeing how the translation of a figure glides over the plane.

Show a transparency with △*ABC* on a grid. Superimpose △*A'B'C'* on △*ABC* and glide it to a new position, describing the motion as a translation. Show students how the translation can be represented by a *vector* such as $\overrightarrow{DD'}$.

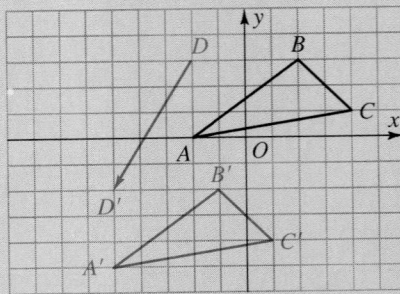

14.3

Translations

Objectives: To use vectors to represent translations
To locate images of figures by translations and glide
reflections

Sliding down a sliding board or gliding on ice illustrates a class of motions that play an important part in real life.

Investigation—*Visualizing the Concept*

In this diagram, tiles are being arranged to completely cover a surface. This illustrates one of the *semiregular tessellations* of the plane. Assuming that the pattern extends beyond what is shown, describe at least six different ways it could glide (with no twisting or turning) and be made to coincide with itself. Answers may vary.

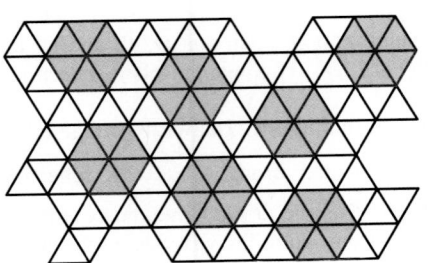

If △*XYZ* glides along the path indicated by the arrow, △*XYZ* will coincide with △*X'Y'Z'*. This motion describes a transformation of the plane called a *translation*. A translation glides all points of a plane the same *distance* and in the same *direction*. Arrows called **vectors** indicate the distance and direction of the glide. Vector $\overrightarrow{AA'}$ is shown in this figure.

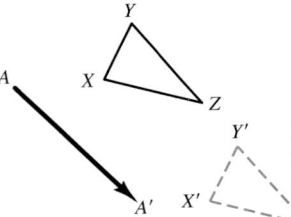

Definition If *A* and *B* are points, and *A'* and *B'* are their images under a transformation *T*, then *T* is a **translation** if and only if:

a. $AA' = BB'$ **b.** $\overline{AA'} \parallel \overline{BB'}$ **c.** $\overline{AB} \parallel \overline{A'B'}$

Condition (a) verifies that all points of the plane are glided the *same distance* under a translation. Conditions (b) and (c) guarantee that points are glided in the *same direction*.
Under these conditions, *AA'B'B* is a parallelogram.
Hence $AB = A'B'$. Thus a *translation is an isometry*.
Translations are easily represented using the coordinate plane.

596   Chapter 14 Transformational Geometry

Developing Mathematical Power

Cooperative Learning Working in groups, students can create translations and glide reflections. Have groups challenge each other to identify the vector that describes the translations and glide reflections that they have created. Points can be given for speed and accuracy.

EXAMPLE 1 **a.** Describe the transformation represented by $\overrightarrow{AA'}$.

b. Sketch the image of $\triangle MNQ$ under the same translation.

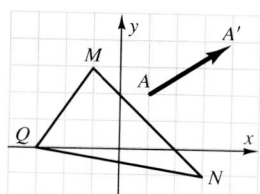

a. The vector $\overrightarrow{AA'}$ moves each point 3 units right and 2 units up.

b.

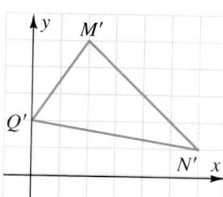

EXAMPLE 2 Give the coordinates of the vertices of the image of $\triangle ABC$ under the translation represented by:

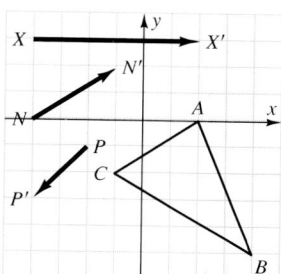

a. $\overrightarrow{PP'}$ **b.** $\overrightarrow{XX'}$ **c.** $\overrightarrow{NN'}$

a. $A' = (0, -2)$, $B' = (2, -7)$, $C' = (-3, -4)$

b. $A' = (8, 0)$, $B' = (10, -5)$, $C' = (5, -2)$

c. $A' = (5, 2)$, $B' = (7, -3)$, $C' = (2, 0)$

> **Theorem 14.2** If a transformation T maps any point (x, y) to $(x + a, y + b)$, then T is a translation.
> Proved in Practice Exercise 20

EXAMPLE 3 Is the given transformation a translation? Justify your answer.

a. $T(x, y) = (x + 1, y - 2)$ **b.** $T(x, y) = (2x, y)$ **c.** $T(x, y) = (x - 3, y)$

a. Yes; $T(x, y) = (x + 1, y - 2) = (x + a, y + b)$ where $a = 1$ and $b = -2$.

b. No; $T(x, y) = (2x, y) \neq (x + a, y + b)$.

c. Yes; $T(x, y) = (x - 3, y) = (x + a, y + b)$ where $a = -3$ and $b = 0$.

The motion here is a combination of two transformations: a glide and a reflection, and so is called a **glide reflection.**
$\triangle A'B'C'$ is the glide image of $\triangle ABC$.
$\triangle A''B''C''$ is the reflection image of $\triangle A'B'C'$.
$\triangle A''B''C''$ is the glide reflection image of $\triangle ABC$.

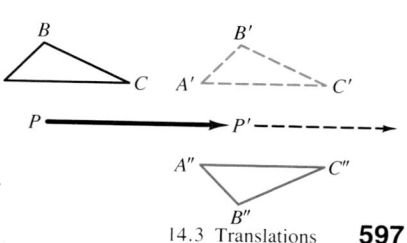

14.3 Translations   **597**

TEACHING SUGGESTIONS

- The concept of *vector* will likely be new to students. Here vectors are being used to represent motions in the plane. Point out to students that later mathematics courses will deal extensively with vectors.
- Point out that condition *c* prevents the situations shown below.

- Tell students that $T(x, y) = (x, y)$ is considered a translation with *zero vector*.
- The glide reflection is the students' first example of a composite motion. (They will see more examples in Lesson 14.6.) Make certain students understand the basis for this idea—that one motion (a glide, or translation in this case) is followed by another (a reflection).

CHALKBOARD EXAMPLES

- **For Example 1**
  a. Describe the transformation represented by $\overrightarrow{PP'}$.
  b. Sketch the image of $\triangle ABC$ under the translation of $\overrightarrow{PP'}$.

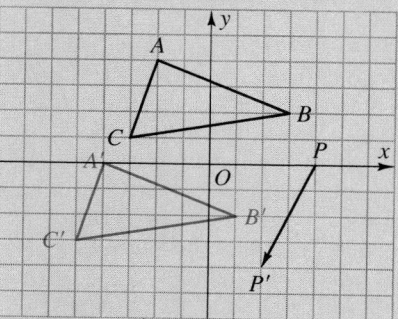

  a. The translation represented by $\overrightarrow{PP'}$ is 2 units left, 4 units down.
  b. See diagram.

598

• **For Example 2**

Give the coordinates of the vertices of the image of △JKL under the translation represented by:

a. $\vec{AA'}$ **b.** $\vec{BB'}$ **c.** $\vec{CC'}$

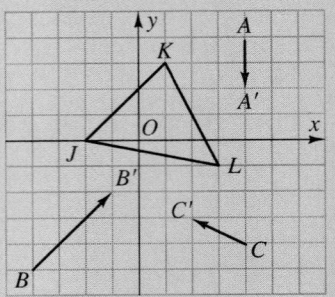

	J'	K'	L'
a.	(−2, −2)	(1, 1)	(3, −3)
b.	(1, 3)	(4, 6)	(6, 2)
c.	(−4, 1)	(−1, 4)	(1, 0)

• **For Example 3**

Is the given transformation a translation? Justify your answer.

a. $T(x, y) = (x, y − 2)$
b. $T(x, y) = (−x, y + 1)$
c. $T(x, y) = (x, 4y)$

a. Yes; $T(x, y) = (x, y − 2) = (x + a, y + b)$ where $a = 0$ and $b = −2$.
b. No; $−x$ is not of the form $x + a$.
c. No; $4y$ is not of the form $y + b$.

Common Error

• Some students may have difficulty interpreting the motion represented by a vector. Have them check vertical and horizontal measures to be repeated for each vertex of a figure.
• See *Teacher's Resource Book* for additional remediation.

LESSON FOLLOW-UPS

Assignment Guide
See p. 584B for assignments.

598

CLASS EXERCISES

True or false? Justify your answers.

1. If $\vec{AA'}$ is a vector and if line l is parallel to $\vec{AA'}$, then $T_{AA'}(l) = l$. True; a line is an infinite set of points in both directions.
2. The translation image of a triangle can have at most one fixed point. False; has no fixed points unless all are fixed.
3. Translations preserve figure orientation. True; a figure stays in the same orientation as it slides or glides.
4. It is possible to find two vectors $\vec{AA'}$ and $\vec{BB'}$ such that $T_{AA'}(P) = P'$ and $T_{BB'}(P) = P'$. True; vectors having the same direction and length produce equivalent translations.
5. If $l \nparallel \vec{AA'}$, describe the image of l when mapped by $\vec{AA'}$. $l' \parallel l$

6. Would a reflection followed by a glide produce the same result as a glide reflection? Explain. Yes; the points of the original figure are moved the same distance and direction and are reflected regardless of which is applied first.
7. There is only one line of reflection that maps point P to point P', but there are many vectors $\vec{AA'}$ that translate P to P'. Explain. Any vector having the same length and direction as the original one will work.

Suppose T is a translation and $T(7, 2) = (3, 7)$.

8. $T(−3, −2) = \underline{?}$ (−7, 3)   9. $T(4, 1) = \underline{?}$ (0, 6)   10. $T(0, 0) = \underline{?}$ (−4, 5)

11. $T(x, y) = \underline{?}$ (x − 4, y + 5)   12. Find the preimage of (x, y). (x + 4; y − 5)

Suppose T is a translation and $T(5, 2) = (0, −5)$.

13. $T(4, 9) = \underline{?}$ (−1, 2)   14. $T(−1, 3) = \underline{?}$ (−6, −4)   15. $T(0, 0) = \underline{?}$ (−5, −7)

16. $T(x, y) = \underline{?}$ (x − 5, y − 7)   17. Find the preimage of (x, y). (x + 5, y + 7)

PRACTICE EXERCISES ⌇ Use technology where appropriate.

A **Thinking Critically** Which of the possible images represent reflections, translations, or glide reflections of the original figure?

Figure   Possible Images

| | (a) | (b) | (c) | (d) | (e) |

1.

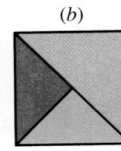 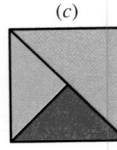 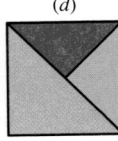 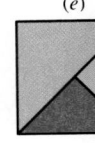

a, b, and e; d; a and e could be glide reflections.

2.

(a)   (b)   (c)   (d)   (e)

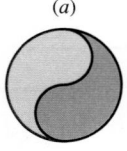 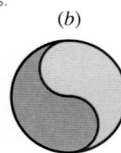 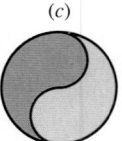 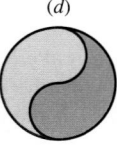 

a, c, and d; b; a, c, and d could be glide reflections.

598 Chapter 14 Transformational Geometry

A

Copy each specified figure onto graph paper. Use a different color to represent the image under the translation.

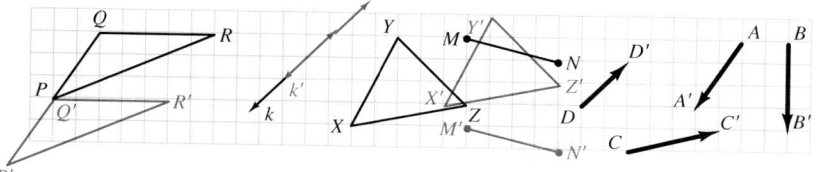

3. $T_{AA'}(\triangle PQR)$ **4.** $T_{BB'}(\overline{MN})$ **5.** $T_{DD'}(k)$ **6.** $T_{CC'}(\triangle XYZ)$

$\overline{M'N'}$: ∥ and ≅ to $\overline{MN}$, 4 units above

Copy each specified figure onto graph paper and draw two vectors that will map it onto its image.

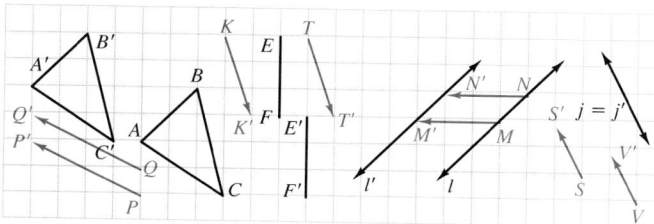

7. $T(\triangle ABC) = \triangle A'B'C'$ $\overrightarrow{PP'}, \overrightarrow{QQ'}$

8. $T(\overline{EF}) = \overline{E'F'}$ $\overrightarrow{KK'}, \overrightarrow{TT'}$

9. $T(l) = l'$ $\overrightarrow{MM'}, \overrightarrow{NN'}$

10. $T(j) = j'$ $\overrightarrow{SS'}, \overrightarrow{VV'}$ (can also go in opp. direction)

For vectors $\overrightarrow{PP'}$ and $\overrightarrow{XX'}$:

11. Describe in words the motion represented by the vector. $\overrightarrow{PP'}$ 2 units left and 4 units down; $\overrightarrow{XX'}$ 6 units right and 1 unit up

12. Give the coordinates of the vertices of the image of $\triangle ABC$ under the translation. $\overrightarrow{PP'}$: $A' = (-4, -2)$, $B' = (2, 0)$, $C' = (1, -8)$; $\overrightarrow{XX'}$: $A' = (4, 3)$, $B' = (10, 5)$, $C' = (9, -3)$

B

13. If (x, y) is any point, find $T(x, y)$ under this translation. $\overrightarrow{PP'}$ $(x - 2, y - 4)$; $\overrightarrow{XX'}$ $(x + 6, y + 1)$

14. Find the preimage of $(1, 3)$; $(-2, 0)$; and (x, y).
$\overrightarrow{PP'}$ $(3, 7)$, $(0, 4)$, $(x + 2, y + 4)$; $\overrightarrow{XX'}$ $(-5, 2)$, $(-8, -1)$, $(x - 6, y - 1)$

Consider the translation $T(x, y) = (x + 3, y - 1)$.

15. On graph paper, sketch a vector that corresponds to this translation. From a given point on the vector, a second point is 3 units right and 1 unit down.

16. If $\square ABCD$ has vertices $A = (2, -1)$, $B = (1, 1)$, and $C = (4, 4)$, find the coordinates of vertex D and the coordinates of the vertices of $T(\square ABCD)$.
$D = (5, 2)$; $A' = (5, -2)$, $B' = (4, 0)$, $C' = (7, 3)$, $D' = (8, 1)$

17. Rectangle $MNPQ$ has coordinates $M = (a, b)$, $N = (a, -b)$, $P = (-a, -b)$, and $Q = (-a, b)$. Find the coordinates of the vertices of $T(MNPQ)$. $M' = (a + 3, b - 1)$, $N' = (a + 3, -b - 1)$, $P' = (-a + 3, -b - 1)$, $Q' = (-a + 3, b - 1)$

14.3 Translations   **599**

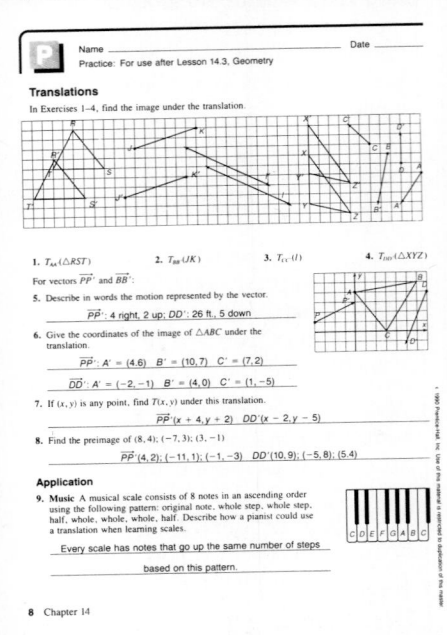

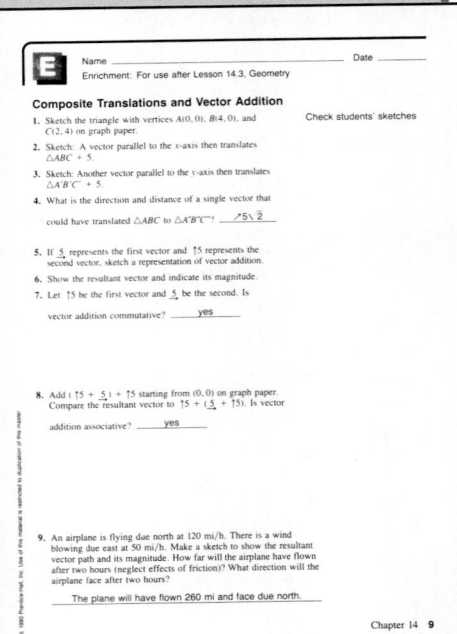

See side column.

18. Repeat Exercises 15–17 using the translation $T(x,y) = (x - 2, y)$.

19. P' is the image of P under a glide reflection. Describe a way to construct $\overrightarrow{AA'}$, the translation vector, and $\overleftrightarrow{AA'}$, the line of reflection.

C **20.** Prove Theorem 14.2. See Additional Answers, p. 702.

21. Is a glide reflection an isometry? Justify your answer.

Copy onto graph paper and observe that $T_{PP'}(\triangle ABC) = \triangle A'B'C'$.

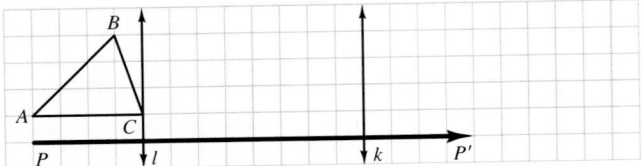

22. Draw $\triangle A''B''C'' = R_l(\triangle ABC)$. Then draw $\triangle A'B'C' = R_k(\triangle A''B''C'')$.

23. What observation can be made? Describe the location of l and k and the distance between l and k in relationship to $\overrightarrow{PP'}$. The double reflection of $\triangle ABC$ through l and k results in the translation $\overrightarrow{PP'}$. The distance between l and k is half the length of vector $\overrightarrow{PP'}$ and $l \parallel k$.

Applications See Solutions Manual.

24. Technology   Using Logo, design a simple pattern and then create a border of your pattern around the edges of the computer screen.

25. Art   Describe the translations and glide reflections in this border.

Developing Mathematical Power

26. Reading in Geometry   Transformations are the basis of innumerable devices that serve us in the twentieth century. In a generator, motion is transformed to electrical energy; in a motor, electrical energy is transformed to motion. Photocells transform light to electrical signals; radio receivers transform electrical signals to sound; and television receivers transform electrical signals to pictures, as well as to sound. Research one of these transformations.

600   Chapter 14 Transformational Geometry

18. a. ←———• $T(x, y) = (x - 2, y)$
b. $D(5,2);\ A'(0,-1),\ B'(-1,1),$ $C'(2,4),\ D'(3,2)$
c. $M'(a - 2,b),\ N'(a - 2, -b),$ $P'(-a - 2, -b),\ Q'(-a - 2,b)$

19. a. Draw $\overline{PP'}$ and find its midpoint M. **b.** Construct rt. $\triangle PQP'$ having $\overline{PP'}$ as a hypo. **c.** Draw $\overleftrightarrow{MN} \parallel \overline{PQ}$. **d.** Locate A and A' on $\overleftrightarrow{MN}$ such that $\overline{AA'}$ has the same length as $\overline{PQ}$. $\overline{AA'}$ is the translation vector and line $\overleftrightarrow{MN}$ is the line of reflection.

<table>
<tr><td>

14.4

</td><td colspan="2">

Rotations

Objective: To locate images of figures by rotations

</td></tr>
</table>

Turning a doorknob, winding a tape measure on a reel, and rolling down a car window all involve turning motions called *rotations*.

Investigation—*Visualizing the Concept*

Christy drew *ABCD* on a transparent sheet for use on the overhead projector. Suzanne traced the figure on a sheet of colored acetate. Then the girls pushed a pin through point P and turned the acetate.

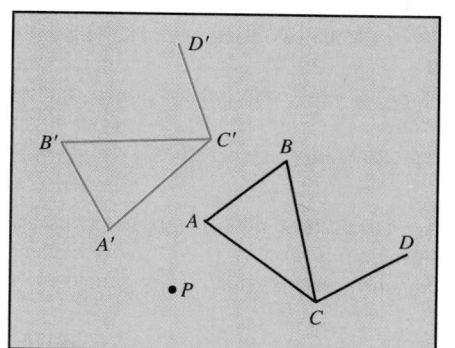

1. Find *PA, PB, PC,* and *PD,* and compare them to *PA', PB', PC',* and *PD'.* PA = PA'   PC = PC'
   PB = PB'   PD = PD'
2. Compare $m\angle DPD'$ to $m\angle APA'$. =

3. Compare $m\angle BPB'$ to $m\angle APA'$. =

4. Generalize for any point Q and its image Q' under this motion. PQ = P'Q
   and $m\angle QPQ' = m\angle APA'$

A record on a turntable revolving around the center spindle describes a transformation of the plane called a *rotation*.

Definition   A transformation is a **rotation** having center O and angle measure α if and only if each point P in the plane is associated with point P' such that:

a. If P is different from O, then OP = OP' and $m\angle POP' = \alpha$. (angle of rotation)
b. O is a fixed point.

In circle O with point P, move counterclockwise along the circle from P to P' until $m\angle POP' = \alpha$. Since OP = OP', P' is the image of point P under the rotation with center O and measure α. Write $\mathcal{R}_{O,\alpha}$ to represent the rotation with center O and measure α.

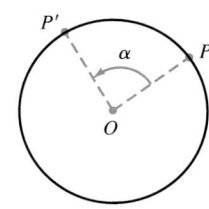

If α is a positive angle measure, the rotation is counterclockwise; if α is negative, the rotation is clockwise.

14.4 Rotations   **601**

Developing Mathematical Power

Keeping a Portfolio   Have students write a paragraph that describes how to find the center of rotation and the angle of rotation when the preimage and image of a figure on a coordinate plane are given. They should illustrate their descriptions with a specific figure, preimage, and image.

- Emphasize that many different rotations can produce the same result. Make certain that students know how to represent a given rotation as an equivalent one having a measure α such that $-180 \leq \alpha \leq 180$.
- Remind students that representing "counterclockwise" motions with positive numbers and "clockwise" motions with negative numbers is an agreed-upon convention.
- Review the use of the term *fixed point*, and point out to students that the center is the only point fixed by a rotation (unless the rotation has measure 0).
- Stress that *any* point of the plane can be the center of a rotation.
- Make certain that students can do both of the following:

  1. Given a figure and its rotation image, locate the center and determine the measure of the rotation.
  2. Given a figure and the center and measure of a rotation, draw or construct the image under that rotation.

CHALKBOARD EXAMPLES

- **For Example 1**

  Name a rotation that maps the first point onto the second point.

  a. $A \rightarrow B$ **b.** $C \rightarrow B$

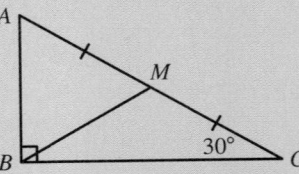

  a. $BM = AM = MC$; since $m\angle A = 60$, $\triangle AMB$ is equil., and $m\angle AMB = 60$. $\mathscr{R}_{M, 60}$ maps A onto B.
  b. $m\angle BMC = 120$. $\mathscr{R}_{M, -120}$ maps C onto B.

EXAMPLE 1 $\triangle A'B'C'$ is the image of $\triangle ABC$ under a rotation. Represent each rotation using the appropriate notation.

a.
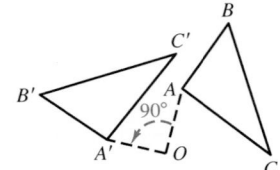

b.
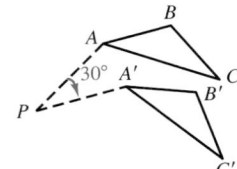

c.
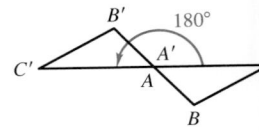

a. $\mathscr{R}_{O,90}$ **b.** $\mathscr{R}_{P,-30}$ **c.** $\mathscr{R}_{A,180}$

Compare the two rotations. The left figure maps P to P' by $\mathscr{R}_{O,45}$ and the right figure maps P to P' by $\mathscr{R}_{O,-315}$. Note that the two rotations produce the same result. Any rotation can be represented by $\mathscr{R}_{O,\alpha}$, where $-180 \leq \alpha \leq 180$.

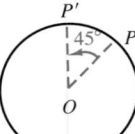 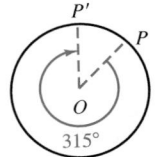

A rotation through $360°$ maps P to its original location. Such a rotation is called a *full turn*. A rotation with center O through $180°$ or $-180°$ is called a *half-turn*, and is usually represented as H_O.

EXAMPLE 2   Find an equivalent rotation $\mathscr{R}_{O,\alpha}$, where $-180 \leq \alpha \leq 180$.

a. $\mathscr{R}_{O,270}$ **b.** $\mathscr{R}_{O,-400}$ **c.** $\mathscr{R}_{O,720}$ **d.** $\mathscr{R}_{O,-210}$

a. $\mathscr{R}_{O,-90}$ **b.** $\mathscr{R}_{O,-40}$ **c.** $\mathscr{R}_{O,0}$ **d.** $\mathscr{R}_{O,150}$

Consider $\overline{AB}$ and $\mathscr{R}_{O,\alpha}(\overline{AB}) = \overline{A'B'}$. By the definition of rotation, $OA = OA'$, $OB = OB'$ and $m\angle BOB' = \alpha = m\angle AOA'$. Since it can be shown that $\angle BOA \cong \angle B'OA'$, it follows that $\triangle AOB \cong \triangle A'OB'$ and so $AB = A'B'$. Theorem 14.3 verifies this.

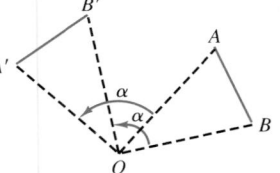

> **Theorem 14.3**   A rotation is an isometry.
> Proved in Practice Exercise 26

Besides distance between points, rotations also preserve betweenness, collinearity, angles and their measures, segments, rays, and lines. Since rotations are isometries, the image of a figure under a rotation is congruent to the original figure. Rotations are distance-preserving transformations about one fixed point.

CLASS EXERCISES

Thinking Critically

1. Given a point P, a center O, and an angle of measure α, explain how to construct the image P' of P under $\mathcal{R}_{O,\alpha}$.

> 1. Draw $\overrightarrow{OP}$; using O as a vertex and $\overrightarrow{OP}$ as initial side, copy the angle of measure α; using OP as radius, P' is located on the line that is $\alpha°$ from $\overrightarrow{OP}$ at the same distance.

2. If (x, y) is rotated 180° in a counterclockwise direction about the origin, what are the coordinates of the image of (x, y)? (Observe that this rotation corresponds to a reflection of (x, y) through the origin. See Exercise 27, Lesson 14.2.) $(-x, -y)$

Each blue figure is the image of the black figure under a rotation. Copy onto graph paper and find the center and measure of each rotation.

3.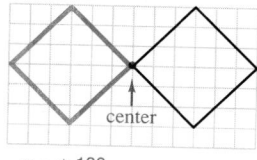
α = ± 180

4.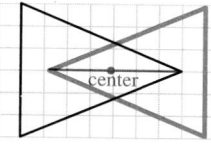
α = ± 180

5.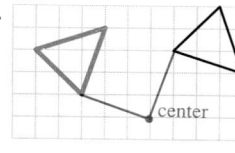
α = 90

Find an equivalent rotation $\mathcal{R}_{O,\alpha}$, where $-180 \leq \alpha \leq 180$.

6. $\mathcal{R}_{O,230}$ $\mathcal{R}_{O,-130}$

7. $\mathcal{R}_{O,-190}$ $\mathcal{R}_{O,170}$

8. $\mathcal{R}_{O,415}$ $\mathcal{R}_{O,55}$

Consider square $ABCD$ with center O. Find the image of each point or segment under the given rotation.

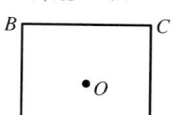

9. $\mathcal{R}_{O,90}(A) = \underline{}$ D

10. $H_O(\overline{BC}) = \underline{}$ $\overline{DA}$

11. $\mathcal{R}_{O,-270}(C) = \underline{}$ B

12. $\mathcal{R}_{O,450}(\overline{DC})\underline{}$ $\overline{CB}$

Find the image under a 90° counterclockwise rotation about the origin.

13. $A(4, -1)$
$A'(1, 4)$

14. $B(3, -2)$
$B'(2, 3)$

15. $C(3, 1)$
$C'(-1, 3)$

PRACTICE EXERCISES

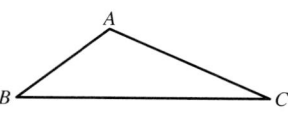

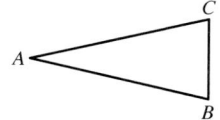

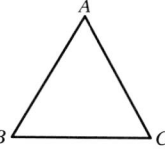

Trace these figures and for each triangle,

1. Determine if the triangle can be rotated through a center within the figure and made to coincide with itself. yes; yes; yes

2. If so, give the center and measure of all rotations that map $\triangle ABC$ to itself.
Each ctr. is the intersection of the ⊥ bis. of the sides; scal. and isos. can be rotated only through integral multiples of 360; equil. can be rotated through integral multiples of 120.

14.4 Rotations **603**

Draw points O and P on your paper and use your protractor and compass to draw the image of P under the rotation.

3. $\mathcal{R}_{O,45}$

4. $\mathcal{R}_{O,-90}$

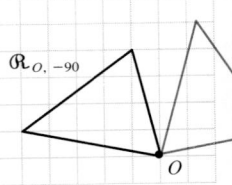

Draw the image of the figure under the given rotation.

5. $\mathcal{R}_{O,90}$

6. H_O
See Additional Answers, p. 702.

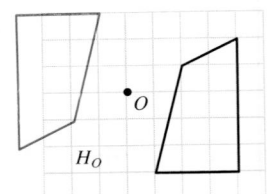

Find an equivalent rotation $\mathcal{R}_{O,\alpha}$, where $-180 \leq \alpha \leq 180$.

7. $\mathcal{R}_{O,1460}$ $\mathcal{R}_{O,20}$ 8. $\mathcal{R}_{O,-600}$ $\mathcal{R}_{O,120}$ 9. $\mathcal{R}_{O,-290}$ $\mathcal{R}_{O,70}$ 10. $\mathcal{R}_{O,315}$ $\mathcal{R}_{O,45}$

Copy onto graph paper and draw the image of each figure under the given rotation.

11.
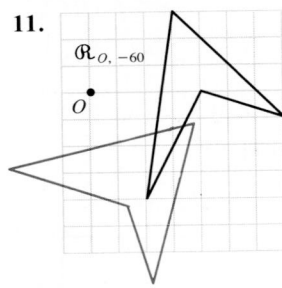
$\mathcal{R}_{O,-60}$
O

12.

13.
$\mathcal{R}_{O,-90}$

The blue figure is the image of the black figure under a rotation $\mathcal{R}_{O,\alpha}$. Copy onto graph paper and find O and α.

14.
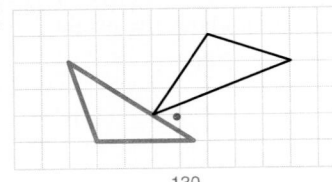
130

15.
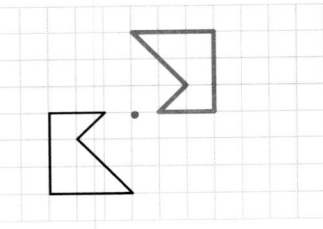
H_O

If rectangle $MNPQ$ has vertices $M = (-2, 1)$, $N = (2, 1)$, $P = (2, -1)$, and $Q = (-2, -1)$, find the coordinates of the vertices of $MNPQ$ under each.

16. $\mathcal{R}_{O,90}$
See side column page 605.

17. H_O

18. $\mathcal{R}_{O,-90}$

If rectangle $CDEF$ has vertices $C = (x, y)$, $D = (-x, y)$, $E = (-x, -y)$, and $F = (x, -y)$, find the coordinates of the vertices under each.

19. $\mathcal{R}_{O,90}$

20. H_O

21. $\mathcal{R}_{O,-90}$

Assignment Guide
See p. 584B for assignments.

$\mathcal{R}_{O,\alpha}$ is a rotation and $\mathcal{R}_{O,\beta}$ is a rotation.

B **22.** Are there any points P such that $\mathcal{R}_{O,\alpha}(P) = P$? Yes; if $P = O$

23. Are there any lines l such that $\mathcal{R}_{O,\alpha}(l) = l$? Yes, if the line is through the center and α is an integral mult. of 180.

24. If $\beta > 360$, what α, where $-180 \le \alpha \le 180$, produces the same result? Subtract the largest integral multiple of 360 from β that leaves a positive difference α. If $0 \le \alpha \le 180$,

25. If $180 < \beta < 360$, how can α be determined? use α; if $180 < \alpha < 360$, use $\alpha - 360$.
$\beta - 360$

26. Write a complete proof of Theorem 14.3.
See Additional Answers, p. 702.

27. This regular hexagon has center O.
For what α is $\mathcal{R}_{O,\alpha}(V_1) = V_3$? 120

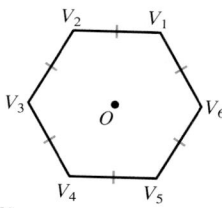

28. If a regular octagon has center O and vertices labeled $V_1, V_2, \ldots, V_8$ in a counterclockwise direction, for what α is $\mathcal{R}_{O,\alpha}(V_1) = V_3$? 90

29. Repeat Exercise 28, using any regular n-gon. $2 \cdot \frac{360}{n}$

30. **Given:** $\mathcal{R}_{O,\alpha}(l) = l'$; $\mathcal{R}_{O,\alpha}(A) = A'$, where
$\overline{OA} \perp l$ and $\overline{OA'} \perp l'$
Prove: $m\angle ABC' = \alpha$

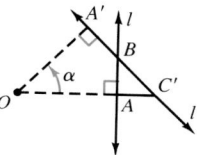

Write a statement that describes the result given in this theorem.
See Additional Answers, p. 702.

31. **Given:** $H_O(l) = l'$
Prove: $l \parallel l'$

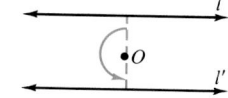

32. Construct a parallelogram with a pair of consecutive vertices on circles I and II. (*Hint:* Use H_O.) Verify that the figure is a parallelogram.
Construct $H_O(M) = M'$ and $H_O(N) = N'$. Draw $MNM'N'$.
$\overline{MN} \parallel M'N'$ by Ex. 31; $\overline{MN} \cong \overline{M'N'}$ by CPCTC. Thus, $MNM'N'$ is a $\square$.

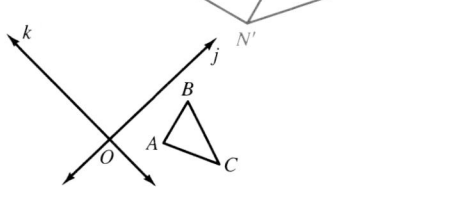

C **33.** Construct $\triangle A''B''C'' = R_j(\triangle ABC)$.

34. Construct $\triangle A'B'C' = R_k(\triangle A''B''C'')$.

35. Compare $\triangle A'B'C'$ to the image of $\triangle ABC$ if $\triangle ABC$ is rotated about O through some angle α. What do you observe? As α approaches 180, $\triangle ABC$ approaches $\triangle A'B'C'$.

36. Use a protractor to measure the acute angle between lines j and k. How does this measure compare to α? 90; $\alpha = 2$ times meas. of $\angle$ between j and k

14.4 Rotations **605**

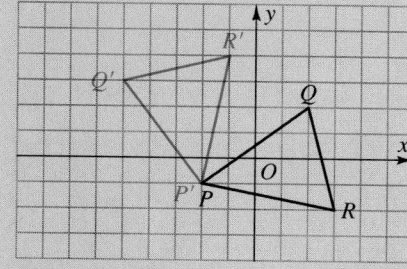
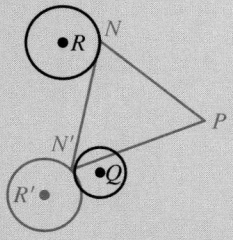
	M'	N'	P'	Q'			C'	D'	E'	F'
16.	$(-1,-2)$	$(-1,2)$	$(1,2)$	$(1,-2)$		19.	$(-y,x)$	$(-y,-x)$	$(y,-x)$	(y,x)
17.	$(2,-1)$	$(-2,-1)$	$(-2,1)$	$(2,1)$		20.	$(-x,-y)$	$(x,-y)$	(x,y)	$(-x,y)$
18.	$(1,2)$	$(1,-2)$	$(-1,-2)$	$(-1,2)$		21.	$(y,-x)$	(y,x)	$(-y,x)$	$(-y,-x)$

Teacher's Resource Book

Follow-Up Investigation, *Chapter 14*, p. 10

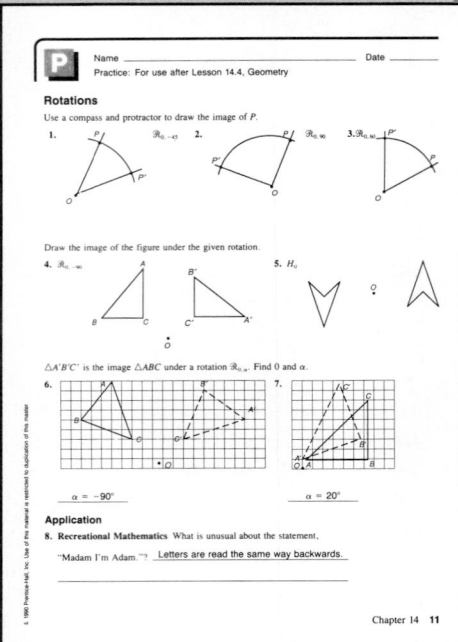

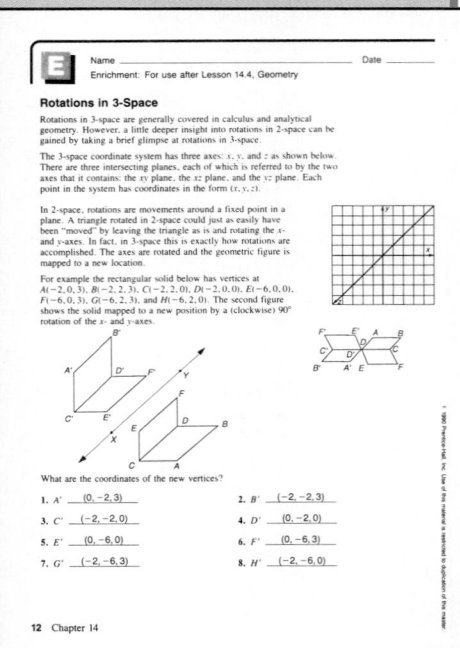

$\triangle A'B'C'$ is the image of $\triangle ABC$ under a half-turn.

37. Find the center of the half-turn.

38. Find lines j and k such that $R_j(\triangle ABC) = \triangle A''B''C''$ and $R_k(\triangle(A''B''C'')) = \triangle A'B'C'$.

39. What is the measure of the angle between lines j and k? How do you know? 90; they are ⊥.

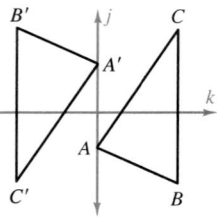

Applications

40. Astronomy What appears to be the center of rotation? North Star

41. Recreational Mathematics Why is this an unusual sign? Rotating through 180° produces the same sign (a palindrome).

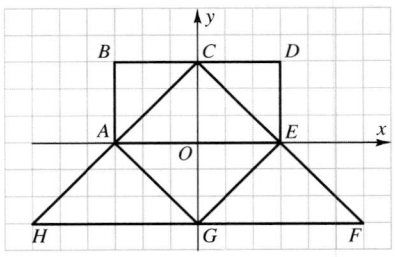

TEST YOURSELF

Consider the mapping $T(x, y) = (x - 2, y + 3)$.

1. Find the image of $(3, -1)$ under this mapping. (1, 2)   14.1

2. Find $T(0, 0)$. (-2, 3)

3. Find the preimage of $(8, -2)$. (10, -5)

4. Is T an isometry? Justify your answer. Yes; T is a translation and translations are isometries.

5. If $T(\triangle ABC) = \triangle A'B'C'$, $T(\overline{AC}) = \underline{\ ?\ }$. $\overline{A'C'}$

Complete the following.

6. $H_O(\overline{CE}) = \underline{\ ?\ }$ $\overline{GA}$ 14.2–14.4

7. $T_{HG}(A) = \underline{\ ?\ }$ E

8. $R_x(\triangle AGE) = \underline{\ ?\ }$ $\triangle ACE$

9. $\mathcal{R}_{O,90}(E) = \underline{\ ?\ }$ C

10. $R_y(\triangle HCF) = \underline{\ ?\ }$ $\triangle FCH$

$\triangle XYZ$ has vertices $X(3, 1)$, $Y(-4, 2)$, and $Z(0, -2)$. Find the coordinates of the vertices of the image of $\triangle XYZ$ under the given transformation.

11. R_y **12.** H_O **13.** $T(x, y) = (x + 1, y)$ See side column.

14. $\mathcal{R}_{O,-90}$ **15.** R_l where l is the line $y = x$

606   Chapter 14 Transformational Geometry

	X'	Y'	Z'
11.	$(-3,1)$	$(4,2)$	$(0,-2)$
12.	$(-3,-1)$	$(4,-2)$	$(0,2)$
13.	$(4,1)$	$(-3,2)$	$(1,-2)$
14.	$(1,-3)$	$(2,4)$	$(-2,0)$
15.	$(1,3)$	$(2,-4)$	$(-2,0)$

Dilations

Objective: To locate images of figures by dilations

Some transformations produce images that are similar to the original figure, but not necessarily congruent to it.

Investigation—*Coordinate Geometry*

A scale drawing of one of the designs submitted in a competition for a company logo appeared as shown.

1. Give the coordinates of points *A–I*. To find the logo's actual size, multiply each of the coordinates by 3 $3(x, y) = (3x, 3y)$. Plot the new points.
   See Additional Answers, p. 702.
2. Is the new figure similar to the scale drawing? yes

3. How do the perimeters compare? the areas? 1 to 3; 1 to 9

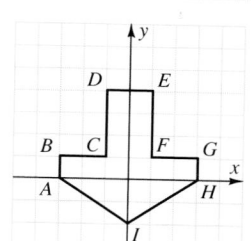

Transformations that result in size changes are called *dilations*. A dilation has a *center* and a nonzero *scale factor*, or *magnitude*, *k*. The dilation with center *O* and magnitude *k* is represented $D_{O,k}$. The dilation $D_{O,k}$ maps each point *P* as defined below.

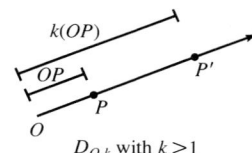

$D_{O,k}$ with $k > 1$

Definition A transformation is a **dilation with center *O* and magnitude *k*** ($D_{O,k}$) if and only if each point *P* maps to a point *P'* such that

a. If $k > 0$, *P'* is on $\overrightarrow{OP}$ and $OP' = k \cdot OP$.
b. If $k < 0$, *P'* is on the ray opposite $\overrightarrow{OP}$ and $OP' = |k| \cdot OP$.
c. *O* is a fixed point; that is, $D_{O,k}(O) = O$.

If $|k| > 1$, the dilation is an **expansion** of the original figure. If $|k| < 1$, the dilation is a **contraction.**

EXAMPLE 1 For each, $D_{O,k}(P) = P'$. Find *k*.

a. 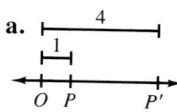 **b.** 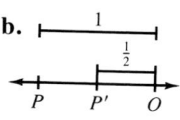 **c.** 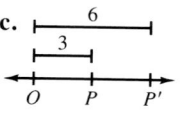 **d.**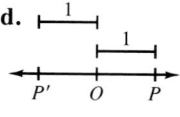

a. $k = 4$ **b.** $k = \dfrac{1}{2}$ **c.** $k = 2$ **d.** $k = -1$

14.5 Dilations **607**

Developing Mathematical Power

Keeping a Portfolio Have students compare and contrast dilations with the isometries studied thus far. They should make a chart showing which properties of the original figure are preserved under each. Have them include an explanation of how to determine whether a dilation is an expansion or a contraction.

LESSON PLAN

Vocabulary
Center of a dilation
Contraction
Dilation
Expansion
Magnitude
Scale factor

Materials/Manipulatives
Graph paper
Rulers .nd protractors
Teaching Transparencies 96 and 96A

Technology
Computer Test Bank, pp. 884–890

LESSON FOCUS

Review
- Ask students to graph $\triangle ABC$ with vertices $A(4, 6)$, $B(-2, 0)$, and $C(2, -4)$, and then graph its images $\triangle A'B'C'$ and $\triangle A''B''C''$ under $T_1(x, y) = \left(\dfrac{3x}{2}, \dfrac{3y}{2}\right)$ and $T_2(x, y) = \left(-\dfrac{x}{2}, -\dfrac{y}{2}\right)$, respectively. $A'(6, 9)$, $B'(-3, 0)$, $C'(3, -6)$; $A''(-2, -3)$, $B''(1, 0)$; $C''(-1, 2)$
- The Algebra Review, Exercises 33–41, involves the quadratic formula.

Alternative Learning Styles
- The Investigation uses the coordinate plane to illustrate a dilation. Distribute graph paper and have students complete the Investigation. They should recognize that multiplying coordinates by a constant produces an image similar to the original.
- The visual learner will benefit from seeing examples of dilations. Teaching Transparencies 96 and 96A provide an opportunity for this.

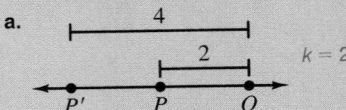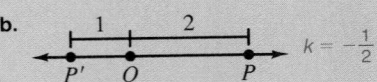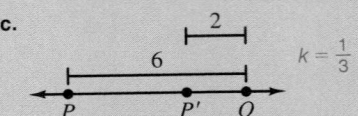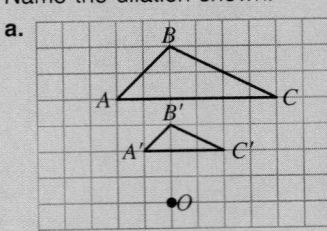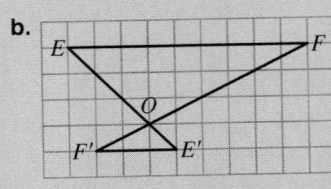
EXAMPLE 2   Find the dilation of the image of each figure.

a.
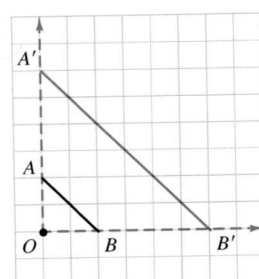

b.
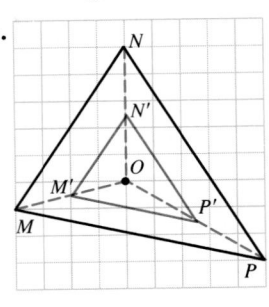

c.
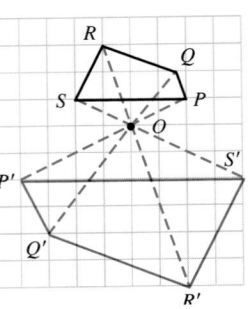

a. $D_{O,3}$ b. $D_{O,\frac{1}{2}}$ c. $D_{O,-2}$

> **Theorem 14.4**   The dilation $D_{O,k}$ maps every line segment to a parallel line segment that is $|k|$ times as long.

Given: $D_{O,k}(\overline{PQ}) = \overline{P'Q'}$

Prove: $\overline{P'Q'} \parallel \overline{PQ}$; $P'Q' = |k| \cdot PQ$

Plan: Consider two cases: $|k| > 1$ and $|k| < 1$. In both cases, $\triangle POQ \sim \triangle P'OQ'$ by the SAS similarity theorem. Since $\angle OPQ \cong \angle OP'Q'$, $\overline{P'Q'} \parallel \overline{PQ}$. Also, $P'Q'$ and PQ are proportional.

Proved in Practice Exercises 27 and 28

Case 1: $|k| > 1$

Case 2: $|k| < 1$

If $D_{O,k}$ is *any* dilation whose center is the origin, $D_{O,k}(x, y) = k(x, y) = (kx, ky)$.

EXAMPLE 3   Copy this figure onto graph paper.

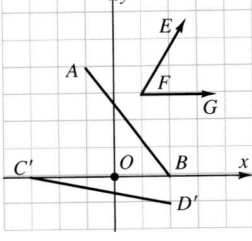

a. $AB = \underline{\ ?\ }$

b. Draw $D_{O,2}(\overline{AB}) = \overline{A'B'}$. Compare $A'B'$ to AB.

c. Suppose $\overline{C'D'} = D_{O,-1}(\overline{CD})$. Draw $\overline{CD}$, and give the coordinates of its endpoints. Compare $C'D'$ and CD.

d. $D_{O,2}(\angle EFG) = \angle E'F'G'$. Compare their measures.

a. $AB = \sqrt{3^2 + 4^2} = \sqrt{25} = 5$

b. $A' = (-2, 8)$ and $B' = (4, 0)$. $A'B' = \sqrt{6^2 + 8^2} = 10 = 2 \cdot AB$

c. $C = (3, 0)$ and $D = (-2, 1)$. $CD = \sqrt{5^2 + 1^2} = \sqrt{26} = C'D'$

d. $m\angle EFG = 60 = m\angle E'F'G'$

608   Chapter 14 Transformational Geometry

Dilations not only preserve angle measure, but they also preserve the ratio of distances between points. Thus they produce similar images.

CLASS EXERCISES

These points are equally spaced. Find the image of the given point under the given dilation and identify each as an *expansion* or a *contraction*.

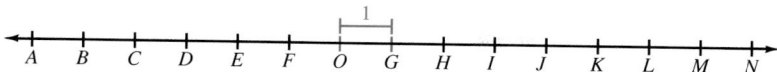

1. $D_{O,3}(G)$
I, expansion

2. $D_{O,-2}(I)$
A, expansion

3. $D_{O,4}(F)$
C, expansion

4. $D_{O,\frac{1}{2}}(A)$
D, contraction

Find the images of *A*, *B*, and *C* under the dilation and identify each as an *expansion* or a *contraction*.

5. $D_{O,3}$ expansion

6. $D_{O,2}$ expansion

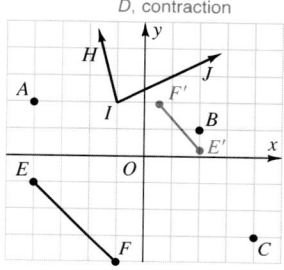

	A′	B′	C′
5.	(−12, 6)	(6, 3)	(12, −9)
6.	(−8, 4)	(4, 2)	(8, −6)

Complete.

7. Draw $D_{O,-\frac{1}{2}}(\overline{EF}) = \overline{E'F'}$

8. $E'\ (\underline{\ ?\ },\ \underline{\ ?\ })$,
$F'\ (\underline{\ ?\ },\ \underline{\ ?\ })$

9. What is EF? $E'F'$? $3\sqrt{2}; \frac{3}{2}\sqrt{2}$ $(2, \frac{1}{2}); (\frac{1}{2}, 2)$

10. Suppose $D_{O,k}(\frac{1}{2}, 3) = (2, 12)$. Find k. 4

PRACTICE EXERCISES   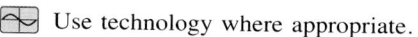 Use technology where appropriate.

Copy this figure onto graph paper and use your ruler to draw the image of points *A* to *E* under the given dilation.

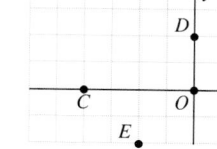

A

1. $D_{O,3}$ **2.** $D_{O,\frac{1}{2}}$

	A′	B′	C′	D′	E′
1.	(6, 0)	(12, 12)	(−12, 0)	(0, 6)	(−6, −6)
2.	(1, 0)	(2, 2)	(−2, 0)	(0, 2)	(−1, −1)

Find *k* such that $D_{O,k}(P) = P'$.

3. $k = -1$
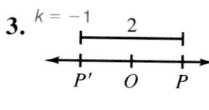

4. $k = \frac{1}{2}$
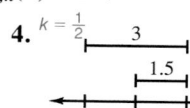

5. $k = 2$

6. $k = \frac{7}{3}$

Copy onto graph paper and draw the image under the given dilation.
See Additional Answers, p. 702.

7. $D_{O,2}$
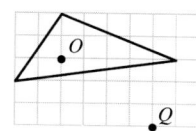

8. $D_{Q,\frac{1}{2}}$

9. $D_{O,3}$
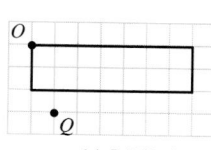

10. $D_{Q,-2}$

14.5 Dilations   **609**

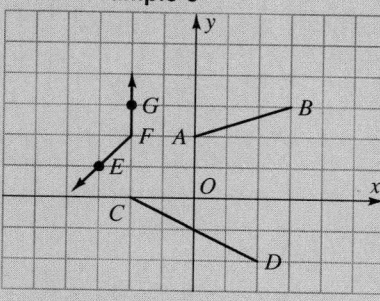

For Example 3

a. Suppose $D_{O,-2}(\overline{AB}) = \overline{A'B'}$. Give the coordinates of A' and B' and compare $A'B'$ to AB.

b. Suppose $D_{A,\frac{1}{2}}(\overline{CD}) = \overline{C'D'}$. Give the coordinates of C' and D' and compare $C'D'$ to CD.

c. $D_{O,\ 3}(\angle EFG) = \angle E'F'G'$. Compare their measures.

a. $A'(0, -4)$, $B'(-6, -6)$; $AB = \sqrt{3^2 + 1^2} = \sqrt{10}$; $A'B' = \sqrt{6^2 + 2^2} = \sqrt{40} = 2\sqrt{10}$; $A'B' = 2AB$

b. $C'(-1, 1)$, $D'(1, 0)$; $CD = \sqrt{4^2 + 2^2} = \sqrt{20} = 2\sqrt{5}$; $C'D' = \sqrt{2^2 + 1^2} = \sqrt{5}$; $C'D' = \frac{1}{2} \cdot CD$

c. $m\angle EFG = m\angle E'F'G'$

Common Error

- Some students will have trouble working with negative magnitudes. Give them ample practice.
- See *Teacher's Resource Book* for additional remediation.

LESSON FOLLOW-UP

Discussion
Ask for a summary of properties that are preserved under dilations, and properties that are not preserved. Ask whether a dilation ever produces an image congruent to the original. Yes, if $k = \pm 1$.

Assignment Guide
See p. 584B for assignments.

Suppose $\triangle A'B'C' = D_{O,3}(\triangle ABC)$.

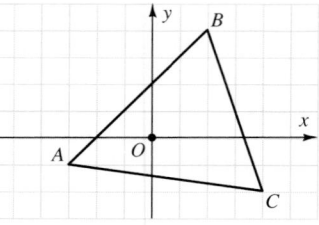

11. Find A', B', and C'.
   $A'(-9, -3)$, $B'(6, 12)$, $C'(12, -6)$
12. If $m\angle BCA = 50$, $m\angle B'C'A' = \underline{?}$. 50

13. Find AB and $A'B'$. $AB = 5\sqrt{2}$; $A'B' = 15\sqrt{2}$

14. $\dfrac{AC}{A'C'} = \underline{?}$ $\frac{1}{3}$

Suppose $\triangle X'Y'Z' = D_{O,-\frac{2}{3}}(\triangle XYZ)$.
   $X'(2, \frac{2}{3})$, $Y'(0, -2)$, $Z'(-2, \frac{2}{3})$
15. Find X', Y', and Z', and draw $\triangle X'Y'Z'$.

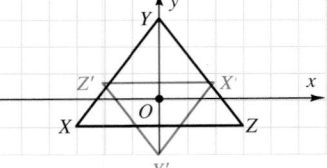

16. $\overline{YZ} \underline{?} \overline{Y'Z'}$ ∥   **17.** $X'Y' = \underline{?} \cdot XY$ $\frac{2}{3}$

18. If $m\angle XYZ = 70$, $m\angle X'Y'Z' = \underline{?}$. 70

$D_{O,k}(\triangle MNP) = \triangle JKL$ **is an expansion.**

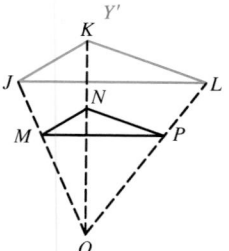

B **19.** If $MN = 3$, $NP = 8$, $JK = 9$, and $JL = 30$, find k, MP, and KL. 3, 10, 24

20. If $JL = 50$, $KL = 35$, $MP = 20$, and $MN = 8$, find k, JK, and NP. $\frac{5}{2}$, 20, 14

21. If $KL = 24$, $NP = 18$, and $PL = 9$, find OP. 27

22. If $JK = 25$, $MN = 5$, and $OJ = 30$, find MJ. 24

$D_{O,k}(\triangle ABC) = \triangle A'B'C'$ **is a contraction.**

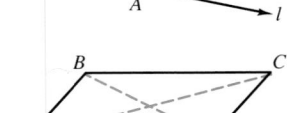

23. The perimeter of $\triangle ABC$ is 18 cm and of $\triangle A'B'C'$ is 12 cm. If $A'B' = 3$ cm and $B'C' = 4$ cm, find the side lengths of $\triangle ABC$.

24. If $OA = 8$ in. and $OA' = 2$ in., then $\dfrac{BC}{B'C'} = \underline{?}$. 4
   23. $k = \frac{2}{3}$; $AB = \frac{9}{2}$ cm, $BC = 6$ cm, $AC = \frac{15}{2}$ cm

25. If O is a point of l and if $D_{O,k}(B) = B'$, explain how to construct A' such that $D_{O,k}(A) = A'$.
   See Additional Answers, p. 702.

26. Consider $\square ABCD$. Is there a dilation $D_{O,k}$ such that $D_{O,k}(\overline{AD}) = \overline{CB}$? If so, find O and k; if not, explain why not. Yes; $D_{O,-1}(\overline{AD}) = \overline{CB}$; O is the point where diagonals intersect.

27. Prove Case 1 of Theorem 14.4.   **28.** Prove Case 2 of Theorem 14.4.
   See Additional Answers, p. 702.

C **29.** Consider a dilation $D_{Q,k}$ having center Q (r, s). If $D_{Q,k}(0, 2) = (-3, 6)$ and $D_{Q,k}(4, 2) = (5, 6)$, find (r, s) and the magnitude k. $(r, s) = (3, -2)$; $k = 2$

610   Chapter 14 Transformational Geometry

30. Generalize the method of Exercise 29: If $D_{Q,k}$ is a dilation having center Q (r, s) and magnitude k and if $D_{Q,k}(A) = A'$ and $D_{Q,k}(B) = B'$, describe a method for finding the center Q and magnitude k of the dilation. To find the center, find the equation of the lines through $\overleftrightarrow{AA'}$ and $\overleftrightarrow{BB'}$. The center is their point of intersection. To find the magnitude, find $\frac{A'B'}{AB}$.

Applications

31. Technology Using Logo, dilate any given polygon and print out the magnitude of the dilation. See Solutions Manual.

32. Optics A flashlight projects an image of square $ABCD$ on a wall 4 ft away. If $ABCD$ measures 4 in. on a side, how far from the light should $ABCD$ be held so that the area of $A'B'C'D'$ is 1 ft²? 16 in.

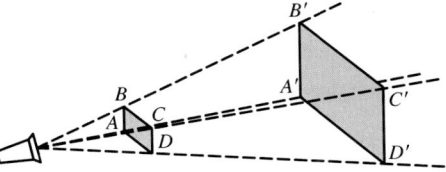

Algebra Review

Quadratic formula: If $ax^2 + bx + c = 0$, where a, b, and c are real numbers and $a \neq 0$, then $x = \frac{-b \pm \sqrt{b^2 - 4ac}}{2a}$.

Solve by using the quadratic formula.

33. $x^2 - 5x + 6 = 0$ 3, 2   **34.** $x^2 + 2x - 8 = 0$ 2, −4   **35.** $x^2 + 4x + 2 = 0$ $-2 \pm \sqrt{2}$

36. $2x^2 - 3x + 1 = 0$ 1, $\frac{1}{2}$ **37.** $2x^2 - 5x + 3 = 0$ 1, $\frac{3}{2}$ **38.** $3x^2 - 2x - 1 = 0$ 1, $-\frac{1}{3}$

39. $3x + 2x^2 = 2$ 1, −2   **40.** $-2x - 1 = x^2$ −1, −1   **41.** $2x^2 = 6x - 3$ $\frac{3 \pm \sqrt{3}}{2}$

Developing Mathematical Power

Extension Copy this figure onto graph paper.

42. Plot the following points.
A $(-4, 2)$, B $(0, 6)$, C $(4, 2)$, D $(2, 2)$,
E $(2, -3)$, F $(-2, -3)$, and G $(-2, 2)$.
Join them in alphabetical order. Join G to A.

43. What is the area of this figure? 36 square units

44. Give the coordinates A' to G' of the image of the figure under a dilation $D_{O,k}$ if the area of the resulting figure is to be 4 times the area of the original. A' $(-8, 4)$, B' $(0, 12)$, C' $(8, 4)$, D' $(4, 4)$, E' $(4, -6)$, F' $(-4, -6)$, G' $(-4, 4)$

45. What is the perimeter of the new figure? Justify your answer. $P_{OLD} = 18 + 8\sqrt{2}$, $k = 2$; so, $P_{NEW} = 36 + 16\sqrt{2}$

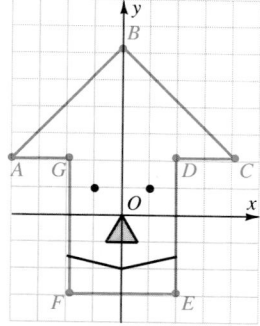

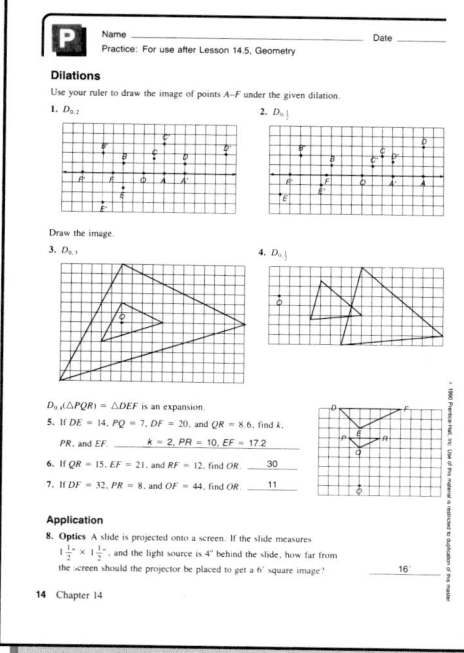
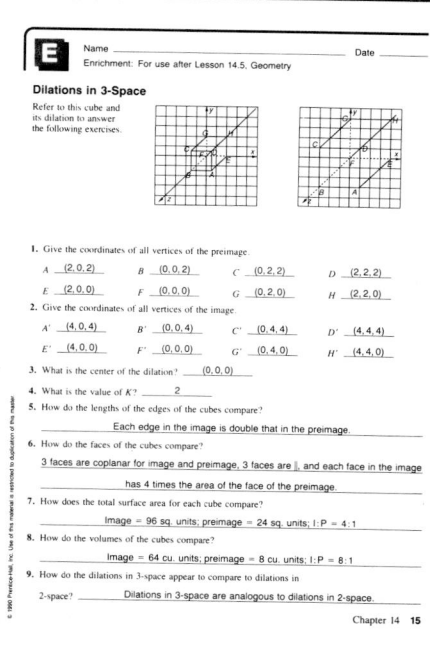

14.6 Composition of Mappings

Objective: To locate the images of figures by composition of mappings

Most motions consist of more than one of the simple transformations carried out in succession.

Investigation—*Visualizing the Concept*

Copy figure F and points A and B onto graph paper.

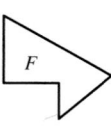

1. Draw the image of figure F under H_A. Label it F'.
   See Solutions Manual.
2. Find the image of F' under H_B. Label it F''.

3. How does F'' seem to compare with F? $F'' \cong F$

4. How does the distance between F and F'' compare to AB?
   Dist. bet. corr. parts of F and $F'' = 2(AB)$
5. What single transformation produces the same result as H_A followed by H_B? Translation $T_{2(AB)}$

Combinations of mappings carried out in succession are **compositions,** or **products, of mappings.** If a transformation F maps P to P' and another transformation G then maps P' to P'', a mapping that takes P directly to P'' is the *composition of F and G.* This mapping, $G \circ F$, is accomplished by first finding $F(P) = P'$, then $G(P') = P''$. So, $G \circ F(P) = G(F(P)) = G(P') = P''$. $G \circ F$ is read ''G composed with F,'' or ''G of F.''

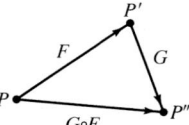

If $F(P) = P'$ and
$G(P') = P''$, then
$G \circ F(P) = P''$.

EXAMPLE 1   Describe each composite mapping.

   a. $R_y \circ R_x(P)$ **b.** $R_{AB} \circ T_{AB}(\triangle XYZ)$

   a. Reflect point P about the x-axis and the image P' about the y-axis.
   b. Translate $\triangle XYZ$ in the direction and distance of $\overleftrightarrow{AB}$; reflect the image over $\overleftrightarrow{AB}$.

EXAMPLE 2   Find the image under the composite mapping.

   a. $R_x \circ R_y(A) = \underline{\ ?\ }$ **b.** $R_y \circ R_x(B) = \underline{\ ?\ }$
   c. $R_z \circ R_x(D) = \underline{\ ?\ }$ **d.** $H_o \circ R_x(F) = \underline{\ ?\ }$

   a. E **b.** F **c.** G **d.** H

612   Chapter 14 Transformational Geometry

Developing Mathematical Power

Cooperative Learning   Working in small groups, students should complete the Enrichment activity, p. 18, in the *Teacher's Resource Book* (see side column, p. 616). Challenge them to create their own "Tic-Tac Transformation." Will their choice of the figure change the answer to Exercise 3?

EXAMPLE 3   **Draw the image of each figure under the composite mapping.**

a.

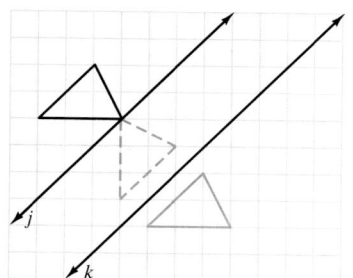

b.

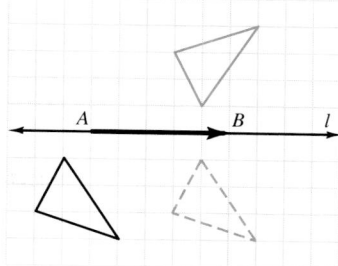

a. $R_k \circ R_j$

b. $R_l \circ T_{AB}$

Observe in Example 3 that both mappings are the product of isometries, and the images appear to be congruent to the original figure. Theorem 14.5 verifies this.

> **Theorem 14.5**   The composition of two isometries is an isometry.

Given: Isometries F and G **Prove:** $G \circ F$ is an isometry.

Plan: To show that $G \circ F$ is an isometry, show that it preserves the distance between points; that is, if X and Y are any points with $G \circ F(\overline{XY}) = \overline{X''Y''}$, show that $XY = X''Y''$. Use the definition of composition, the fact that F and G are isometries, and the transitive property.
Proved in Practice Exercise 20

Reflections are the most ''basic'' of the isometries because translations are the composition of two reflections in parallel lines and rotations are the result of two reflections in intersecting lines.

> **Theorem 14.6**   A composition of reflections in two parallel lines is a translation. The translation glides all points through twice the distance between the lines.

Given: Parallel lines l and m with a distance of d between l and m

Prove: $R_m \circ R_l$ is a translation; the distance between a point and its image under $R_m \circ R_l$ is $2d$.
(plan on next page)

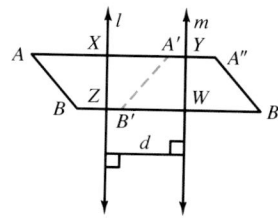

14.6 Composition of Mappings   **613**

613

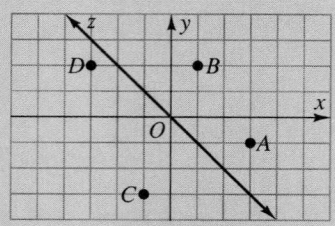
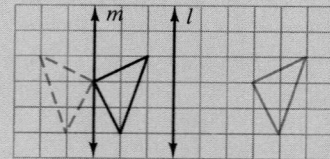
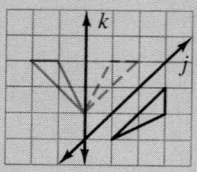
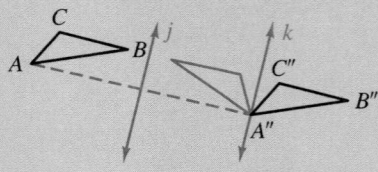
Plan: Given A and B and their images, A'' and B'' under $R_m \circ R_l$. $R_m \circ R_l$ is an isometry (why?); thus it suffices to show $AA'' = BB''$ to verify that it is a translation. If $R_l(A) = A'$ and $R_m(A') = A''$, then, since A, A', and A'' are collinear, $AA'' = AX + XA' + A'Y + YA''$. Use the fact that l and m are the respective perpendicular bisectors of $\overline{AA'}$ and $\overline{A'A''}$ to get:
$$AA'' = 2XA' + 2A'Y = 2(XA' + A'Y) = 2d.$$
Similarly, $BB'' = BZ + ZB' + B'W + WB'' = 2(ZB' + B'W) = 2d.$
Thus $AA'' = BB''$ and the distance between a point and its image is twice the distance between the parallel lines of reflection.
Proved in Practice Exercise 21

EXAMPLE 4 $\triangle A''B''C''$ **is the translation image of** $\triangle ABC$.

a. If $(0,0)$ is the endpoint of a translation vector $\overrightarrow{OP}$, what are the coordinates of P?

b. If $y \parallel k$, and if $R_k \circ R_y(\triangle ABC) = \triangle A''B''C''$, what is the distance between y and k?

c. Explain how to locate k.

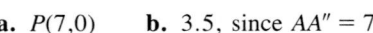

a. $P(7,0)$ **b.** 3.5, since $AA'' = 7$ **c.** Locate k so that $k \parallel y$ and 3.5 from y.

Theorem 14.7 A composition of reflections in two intersecting lines is a rotation about the point of intersection of the two lines. The measure of the angle of rotation is twice the measure of the angle from the first line of reflection to the second.

Given: Lines l and m intersecting in O; $m\angle SOR = \alpha$

Prove: $R_m \circ R_l = \mathcal{R}_{O, 2\alpha}$

Plan: Suppose $R_l(A) = A'$ and $R_m(A') = A''$. To show that $R_m \circ R_l$ is a rotation with center O and measure 2α, show that $OA = OA''$ and $m\angle AOA'' = 2\alpha$. Since Theorem 14.5 showed that the composition of two isometries is an isometry and since reflections are isometries, then $OA = OA''$. Further, since reflections preserve angle measure, $\angle AOS \cong \angle SOA'$ and $\angle A'OR \cong \angle ROA''$. So $m\angle AOA'' = 2m\angle SOA' + 2m\angle A'OR = 2m\angle SOR = 2\alpha$.
Proved in Practice Exercise 22

Corollary A composition of reflections in perpendicular lines is a half-turn about the point where the lines intersect. Proved in Practice Exercise 23

CLASS EXERCISES

Describe a transformation or composition of transformations that maps this figure to each of the following.

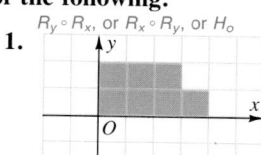

1. $R_y \circ R_x$, or $R_x \circ R_y$, or H_O

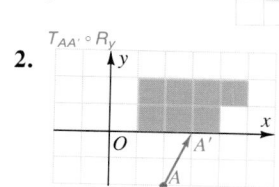

2. $T_{AA'} \circ R_y$

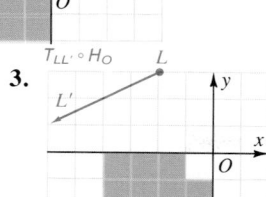

3. $T_{LL'} \circ H_O$

Find the coordinates of the image of each point.

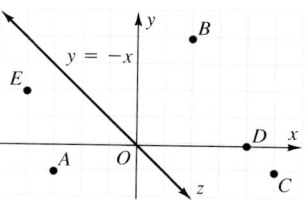

4. $R_y \circ R_x(A) = \underline{?}$. (3, 1)

5. $R_z \circ R_x(B) = \underline{?}$
(4, −2)

6. $R_y \circ H_O(C) = \underline{?}$ (5, 1)

7. $R_x \circ R_y(D) = \underline{?}$
(−4, 0)

8. $R_y \circ R_x \circ R_z(E) = \underline{?}$
(2, −4)

9. $R_x \circ R_y \circ R_z(E) = \underline{?}$
(2, −4)

PRACTICE EXERCISES

〰️ Use technology where appropriate.

Trace each figure. Find the image under the given mapping.

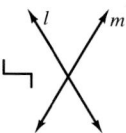
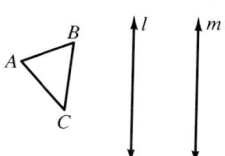
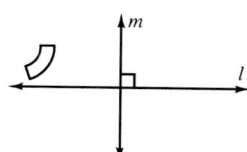

A **1.** $R_m \circ R_l$; $R_l \circ R_m$
See Additional Answers, p. 702.

2. $R_m \circ R_l$; $R_l \circ R_m$

3. $R_m \circ R_l$; $R_l \circ R_m$

Consider the rotations $\mathcal{R}_1 = \mathcal{R}_{O,45}$, $\mathcal{R}_2 = \mathcal{R}_{O,60}$, and $\mathcal{R}_3 = \mathcal{R}_{O,-90}$. Find a single rotation that produces the same result.

4. $\mathcal{R}_2 \circ \mathcal{R}_1(P)$ $\mathcal{R}_{O,105}$

5. $\mathcal{R}_3 \circ \mathcal{R}_2(P)$ $\mathcal{R}_{O,-30}$

6. $\mathcal{R}_3 \circ \mathcal{R}_1(P)$ $\mathcal{R}_{O,-45}$

7. $\mathcal{R}_3 \circ \mathcal{R}_3(P)$ $\mathcal{R}_{O,180}$ or $\mathcal{R}_{O,-180}$

8. Generalize the results of Exercises 4–7: If $\mathcal{R}_1$ and $\mathcal{R}_2$ are rotations having the same center O and measures α_1 and α_2, respectively, then $\mathcal{R}_2 \circ \mathcal{R}_1$ is $\underline{?}$.
rotation having center O and measure $\alpha_1 + \alpha_2$

G_{AB} is a glide reflection. Copy onto graph paper.
See Additional Answers, p. 702.

9. Draw the image of $\triangle CDE$ under $G_{AB} \circ G_{AB}$.

10. Describe a single transformation that would produce the same result as $G_{AB} \circ G_{AB}$. $T_{2(AB)}(\triangle CDE)$

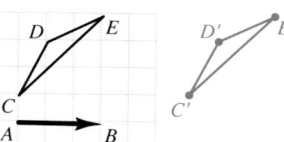

14.6 Composition of Mappings **615**

LESSON FOLLOW-UP

Discussion
Ask students why reflections are considered the most basic isometry. Rotations and translations (and hence glide reflections) can be expressed as compositions of reflections.

Assignment Guide
See p. 584B for assignments.

Historical Note
Some students might know how Newton was able to "bend" a ray of light. Others might want to research it and create a simple model.

Lesson Quiz
Give the coordinates of the image under the composite mapping.

1. $R_w \circ R_y$ (A) (1, 2)

2. $R_y \circ R_w$ (B) (−1, −2)

3. $R_w \circ R_z$ (C) (3, 3)

4. $H_0 \circ R_x$ (D) (2, −1)

5. $R_x \circ R_z$ (E) (1, 2)

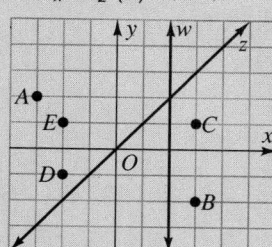

Describe a single mapping that would produce the same result as:

6. $R_y \circ R_w$ $T(x, y) = (x − 4, y)$

7. $R_x \circ R_z$ $\mathcal{R}_{O, −90}$

Developing Mathematical Power

Keeping a Portfolio Have students use Exercises 17 and 18 to show that the composition of mappings need not be commutative (Exercise 19). Ask students to test the associative and distributive properties for the composition of mappings. They should also experiment to see if there is an identity mapping.

615

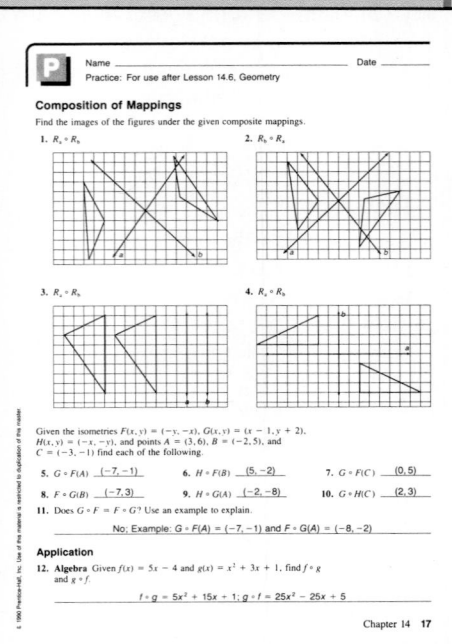

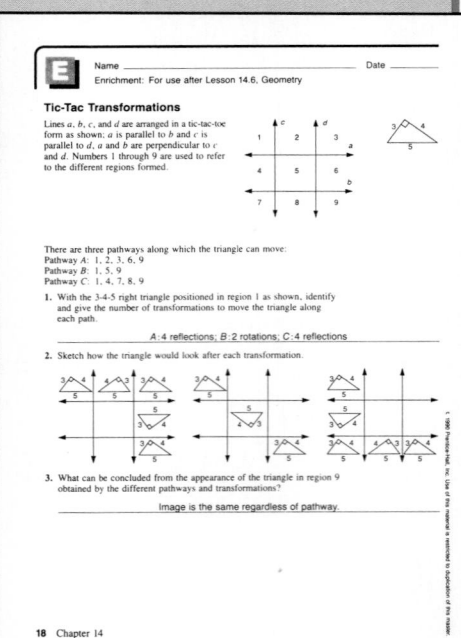

Given the isometries $F(x, y) = (y, x)$, $G(x, y) = (x + 1, y - 2)$, and $H(x, y) = (-x, -y)$, and the points $A(3, 2)$, $B(-1, 4)$, and $C(-2, -4)$, find each of the following:

B

11. $G \circ F(A)$ (3, 1)   **12.** $H \circ F(B)$ (−4, 1)   **13.** $F \circ G(B)$ (2, 0)

14. $G \circ H(C)$ (3, 2)   **15.** $H \circ G \circ F(B)$ (−5, 3)   **16.** $G \circ F \circ H(A)$ (−1, −5)

17. $G \circ F(x, y)$ (y + 1, x − 2)   **18.** $F \circ G(x, y)$ (y − 2, x + 1)   **19.** Is $G \circ F = F \circ G$? Explain.
no; compare 17 to 18.

Prove. See Additional Answers, p. 702.

20. Theorem 14.5   **21.** Theorem 14.6

22. Theorem 14.7   **23.** Corollary of Theorem 14.7

C
24. When is the composition of two reflections commutative? $R_1 \circ R_2 = R_2 \circ R_1$
when lines 1 and 2 are ⊥

25. Verify that $F \circ (G \circ H) = (F \circ G) \circ H$ if F is the mapping R_x, G is R_y, and $H(x, y) = (x + 1, y + 1)$. $F \circ (G \circ H) = F \circ (G(H(x, y))) = F \circ (G(x + 1, y + 1)) = F(-(x + 1), (y + 1)) = (-(x + 1), -(y + 1))$; $(F \circ G) \circ H(x, y) = (F \circ G)(H(x, y)) = (F \circ G)(x + 1, y + 1) = F(G(x + 1, y + 1)) = F(-(x + 1), y + 1) = (-(x + 1), -(y + 1))$

Applications

26. Design Describe all isometries that will map the design in this picture onto itself.

27. Technology Using Logo, draw your initials and use the glide reflection transformation to generate a computer graphic.
See Solutions Manual.

Developing Mathematical Power

28. Extension Copy these congruent triangles. Find an isometry that maps $\triangle ABC \rightarrow \triangle A'B'C'$. $R_m \circ R_l$

(*Hint:* Try an isometry of two reflections.)

Draw $\overline{AA'}$; construct its ⊥ bis., *l*, and reflect $\triangle ABC$ in *l*, getting $\triangle A''B''C''$. Draw $\overline{B''B'}$; construct its ⊥ bis., *m*, and reflect $A''B''C''$ in *m*.

HISTORICAL NOTE

By building the first working model of a reflecting telescope, Sir Isaac Newton, the famous scientist and mathematician, solved the problem "How can a ray of light be sent on a path that changes direction by 90°?"

The same principle is used in the periscope, through which submarine crews look along the surface of the water. The light rays have to be bent twice in this instrument. Represent their path by a composition mapping.

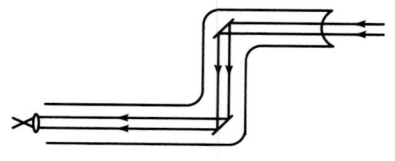

14.7 Identity and Inverse Transformations

Objective: To recognize and use the terms identity and inverse in relation to mappings

The mappings previously studied usually have described motions of geometric figures. Mappings and compositions of mappings that leave all points of a figure in their original positions are the focus of this lesson.

Investigation—*Visualizing the Concept*

This caution sign is attached to the back of a wagon by a fastener through its center. The sign is loose and turns freely about the center.

1. Through what angle has the equilateral triangle rotated if it is in position *A*? 120° or −240°

2. If the sign is in its original position, but then it slips to position *B*, what is the angle of this rotation? 240° or −120°

3. Suppose the sign makes one complete revolution about its center. Through what angle has it been rotated? 360°

4. If the sign were in position *A*, through what angle would it have to be rotated in order to be returned to its original position? Is more than one answer possible? yes; −120° or 240°

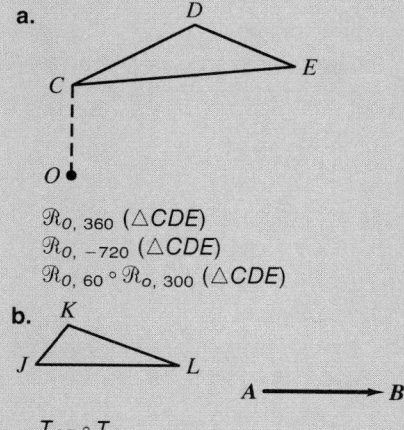

Transformations such as reflections, translations, rotations, and compositions of these mappings usually result in the movement of a figure in the plane. Mappings that leave all points of the plane in their original positions are called *identity mappings* or *identity transformations*.

Definition   A transformation *I* is an **identity transformation** if and only if $I(P) = P$ for every point *P* in the plane.

This may be compared to the identity property in algebra in which the number 0 is added to any real number: if *a* is a real number, $a + 0 = 0 + a = a$. Adding 0 to any number does not change the number; 0 is called the *identity* for addition.

If an identity mapping *I* is composed with any other transformation *T*, the result is $T \circ I(P) = I \circ T(P) = T(P)$.

Developing Mathematical Power

Keeping a Portfolio   Have students complete the Investigation activity, p. 19, in the *Teacher's Resource Book.* They should show the transformations that they listed to verify their answers. Have them alternate colors on the triangles and determine that answer.

LESSON PLAN

Vocabulary
Identity transformation
Inverse transformation
Similarity mapping

Materials/Manipulatives
A model of the sign in the Investigation
Teaching Transparency 98

Technology
Computer Test Bank, pp. 896–899

LESSON FOCUS

Review
Draw each of these diagrams on the chalkboard and ask students to describe the result when each transformation is applied.

a.

$\mathcal{R}_{O,\,360}\ (\triangle CDE)$
$\mathcal{R}_{O,\,-720}\ (\triangle CDE)$
$\mathcal{R}_{O,\,60°} \circ \mathcal{R}_{O,\,300}\ (\triangle CDE)$

b.

$T_{AB} \circ T_{BA}$

Students should observe that these transformations return the figure to its original location. Introduce the term *identity mapping* to describe such situations.

Alternative Learning Styles
In the Investigation, using a model of the caution sign as a manipulative would help students visualize an identity transformation.

617

- Draw analogies between identity mappings and algebraic counterparts. For example, under addition, zero is the identity; under multiplication, one is the identity.
- Show the relationship between mappings that are inverses of each other and algebraic counterparts. Under the operation of addition, the opposite of a number is its inverse; under multiplication, the reciprocal of any nonzero number is its inverse. Point out that the result of combining an element and its inverse is the identity.
- Emphasize how to find the inverse of any of the basic transformations studied so far: the inverse of a reflection is the same reflection; the inverse of T_{AB} is T_{BA}; the inverse of $\mathcal{R}_{o,\alpha}$ is $\mathcal{R}_{o,-\alpha}$ (or equivalent); and the inverse of $D_{o,k}$ is $D_{o,\frac{1}{k}}$.

CHALKBOARD EXAMPLES

- **For Example 1**

  Which of the following represent identity mappings?

  a. $\mathcal{R}_{o,360}$
  b. $T(x, y) = (x + 0, y + 0)$
  c. $R_x \circ R_y$
  d. $\mathcal{R}_{o,-1080}$

  a, b, and d are identity mappings.

- **For Example 2**

  Find the inverse of each transformation described.

  a. translation 5 units right and 3 units down
  b. H_o **c.** $D_{o,-3}$ $(\overline{AB})$ **d.** $\mathcal{R}_{o,170}$

  a. translation 5 units left and 3 units up
  b. H_o c. $D_{o,-\frac{1}{3}}$
  d. $\mathcal{R}_{o,-170}$ (or $\mathcal{R}_{o,190}$)

EXAMPLE 1   **Which of the following represent identity mappings?**

  a. $\mathcal{R}_{O,0}$ **b.** $R_l \circ R_l$ **c.** T_{AB}, where $AB = 0$ **d.** $\mathcal{R}_{O,240}$

  a. Identity mapping; **b.** Identity mapping; $R_l(P) = P'$ and $R_l(P') = P$;
  c. Identity mapping (the translation vector has zero distance)
  d. No (240° rotation)

  Example 1b shows that the composition of a reflection about a line l with itself results in point P being mapped to itself. Therefore $R_l \circ R_l = I$, an identity mapping. When the composition of two mappings is an identity mapping, these two mappings are called *inverses* of each other.

  Definition   If T is a transformation that maps set A to set B, the transformation S is the **inverse** of T if and only if S maps each image in set B back to its preimage in set A.

  A transformation T always has an inverse transformation, denoted T^{-1}. The inverse mapping "undoes" the effect of the original mapping. For example, if P is any point and $T(P) = P'$, then $T^{-1}(P') = P$. Thus $T^{-1} \circ T(P) = I(P) = P$.

  You saw earlier that 0 is the identity for addition in algebra. If a is any real number, $-a$ is the additive inverse of a because $a + (-a) = (-a) + a = 0$; therefore a number and its inverse add up to the identity.

EXAMPLE 2   **Find the inverse of each transformation described.**

  a. Reflection of $\overline{AB}$ about line k

  b. Rotation of point P about center O through a measure of 90

  c. Translation of $\triangle ABC$ 5 units to the right

  d. Dilation of $\overline{CD}$ with center O and magnitude 2

  a. Reflection of the image of $\overline{AB}$ about line k **b.** $\mathcal{R}_{O,-90}$; $\mathcal{R}_{O,270}$
  c. Translation of the image of $\triangle ABC$ 5 units to the left
  d. Dilation of the image of $\overline{CD}$ using center O and magnitude $\frac{1}{2}$

EXAMPLE 3   **Each of the following describes a transformation T. Describe T and find $T^{-1}(x, y)$.**

  a. $T(x, y) = (x + 1, y - 2)$ **b.** $T(x, y) = (-3x, -3y)$ **c.** $T(x, y) = (-x, y)$

  a. T is a translation that moves point P 1 unit to the right and 2 units down.
  $T^{-1}(x, y) = (x - 1, y + 2)$
  b. T is a dilation having center O and magnitude $|-3| = 3$.
  $T^{-1}(x, y) = (-\frac{1}{3}x, -\frac{1}{3}y)$
  c. T is a reflection about the y-axis. $T^{-1}(x, y) = (-x, y)$.

618   Chapter 14 Transformational Geometry

CLASS EXERCISES

True or false? Justify your answers.

1. A reflection is its own inverse. <small>true; reflect the image to obtain original figure</small>

2. If I is an identity transformation and T is any transformation, then $T \circ I = I \circ T = I$. <small>false; equals T</small>

3. The inverse of any dilation $D_{O,k}$ is $D_{O,-k}$. <small>false; inverse is $D_{O,\frac{1}{k}}$</small>

4. Under an identity mapping, all points are fixed. <small>true; def. of identity mapping</small>

5. The inverse of a contraction is an expansion. <small>true; inverse magnitude</small>

Suppose $\mathcal{R}_1 = \mathcal{R}_{O,90}$, $\mathcal{R}_2 = H_O$, $\mathcal{R}_3 = \mathcal{R}_{O,270}$, **and** $\mathcal{R}_4 = \mathcal{R}_{O,360}$. **Identify the equivalent mapping.**

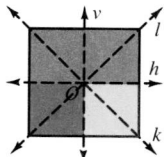

6. $\mathcal{R}_1{}^{-1} = \underline{\ ?\ }$ $\mathcal{R}_3$

7. $\mathcal{R}_2{}^{-1} = \underline{\ ?\ }$ $\mathcal{R}_2$

8. $\mathcal{R}_3 \circ \mathcal{R}_1 = \underline{\ ?\ }$ $\mathcal{R}_4$

9. $\mathcal{R}_4{}^{-1} = \underline{\ ?\ }$ $\mathcal{R}_4$

10. $\mathcal{R}_3{}^{-1} = \underline{\ ?\ }$ $\mathcal{R}_1$

11. $\mathcal{R}_2{}^{-1} \circ \mathcal{R}_1 = \underline{\ ?\ }$ $\mathcal{R}_3$

12. $\mathcal{R}_2 \circ \mathcal{R}_2 = \underline{\ ?\ }$ $\mathcal{R}_4$

13. $\mathcal{R}_4{}^{-1} \circ \mathcal{R}_1{}^{-1} \circ \mathcal{R}_2{}^{-1} = \underline{\ ?\ }$ $\mathcal{R}_1$

Give the inverse of each of the following transformations.

14. R_l R_l

15. $\mathcal{R}_{O,\alpha}$ $\mathcal{R}_{O,-\alpha}$

16. T_{AB} T_{BA}

17. $D_{O,k}$ $D_{O,\frac{1}{k}}$

18. G_{AB} (glide reflection) G_{BA}

19. H_O H_O

PRACTICE EXERCISES

This square of plastic is colored on both sides as shown. The following transformations of this figure are possible:
R_l, R_k, R_h, R_v, $\mathcal{R}_{O,90}$, H_O, $\mathcal{R}_{O,270}$, and I

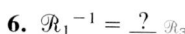

If the square is in the position shown, give the transformation that will take it back to its original position.

A

1.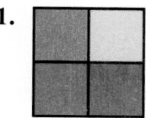
$\mathcal{R}_{O,270}$

2.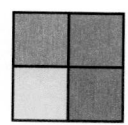
R_v

3.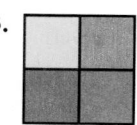
R_l

4.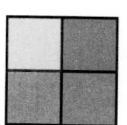
H_O

5.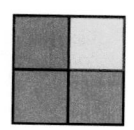
R_h

Give the inverse of each transformation.

6. $\mathcal{R}_{O,40}$ $\mathcal{R}_{O,-40}$ or $\mathcal{R}_{O,320}$

7. R_k R_k

8. $\mathcal{R}_{O,-150}$ $\mathcal{R}_{O,150}$ or $\mathcal{R}_{O,-210}$

9. $D_{O,4}$ $D_{O,\frac{1}{4}}$

10. $D_{O,-\frac{1}{2}}$ $D_{O,-2}$

14.7 Identity and Inverse Transformations **619**

• **For Example 3**

Each of the following describes a transformation T. Describe T and find $T^{-1}(x, y)$.

a. $T(x, y) = (y, x)$

b. $T(x, y) = (x - 3, y + 4)$

c. $T(x, y) = (\dfrac{x}{2}, \dfrac{y}{2})$

a. T is a reflection about the line $y = x$; $T^{-1}(x, y) = (y, x)$.

b. T is a translation that moves a point 3 units left and 4 units up; $T^{-1}(x, y) = (x + 3, y - 4)$.

c. T is a dilation having center O and magnitude $\frac{1}{2}$; $T^{-1}(x, y) = (2x, 2y)$.

Common Errors

• Some students will have difficulty understanding the concepts of identity and inverse mappings. Emphasizing the analogies between mappings and the algebraic examples they are familiar with should help.

• Some students may make mistakes when writing the inverse of a dilation with center O and magnitude k, thinking it is one with center O and magnitude $-k$. Remind students of additive and multiplicative inverses and the uses of each.

• See *Teacher's Resource Book* for additional remediation.

LESSON FOLLOW-UP

Discussion

If you do not assign Practice Exercises 42 and 43, you may wish to cover them in class, or have students do them in small groups.

Assignment Guide

See p. 584B for assignments.

Developing Mathematical Power

Reading in Geometry Students are given a brief description of topology. Encourage them to do additional reading and to write a report to display on the bulletin board.

Lesson Quiz

Which of the following represent identity transformations? If a transformation is not an identity, give its inverse.

1. $R_y \circ R_x$ **2.** $\mathscr{R}_{O,-50}$
3. $R_y \circ R_y$ **4.** $T_{BA} \circ T_{AB}$
5. $(\mathscr{R}_{O,120})^{-1} \circ \mathscr{R}_{O,120}$
Suppose $F(x, y) = (x, y + 2)$ and $G(x, y) = (x - 1, y - 3)$. Find:
6. $F^{-1}(x, y)$ **7.** $G^{-1}(x, y)$
8. $F \circ G(x, y)$ **9.** $G \circ F(x, y)$
10. $G^{-1} \circ F^{-1}(x, y)$

1. Not an identity; this is equivalent to H_O; hence the inverse is H_O.
2. Not an identity; inverse is $\mathscr{R}_{O,50}$
3. identity
4. identity
5. identity
6. $F^{-1}(x, y) = (x, y - 2)$
7. $G^{-1}(x, y) = (x + 1, y + 3)$
8. $F \circ G(x, y) = F(x - 1, y - 3)$
   $= (x - 1, y - 1)$
9. $G \circ F(x, y) = G(x, y + 2)$
   $= (x - 1, y - 1)$
10. $G^{-1} \circ F^{-1}(x, y) = G^{-1}(x, y - 2)$
    $= (x + 1, y + 1)$

Draw the image of each figure under the transformation T_{BA}.

11.

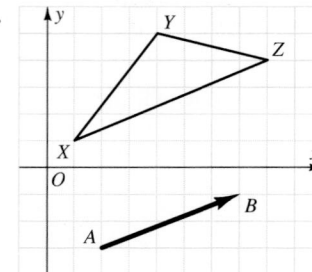

12.

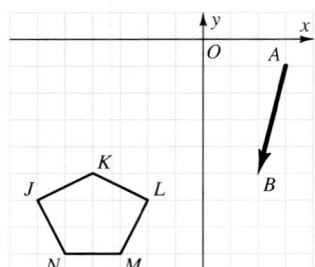

Suppose $T(x, y) = (x - 3, y + 2)$ and $S(x, y) = (x + 1, y + 1)$.

13. $T^{-1}(x, y) = \underline{?}$ $(x + 3, y - 2)$ **14.** $S^{-1}(x, y) = \underline{?}$ $(x - 1, y - 1)$

15. $S \circ T(x, y) = \underline{?}$ $(x - 2, y + 3)$ **16.** $T \circ S(x, y) = \underline{?}$ $(x - 2, y + 3)$

17. $T^{-1} \circ T(x, y) = \underline{?}$ (x, y) **18.** $T \circ T^{-1}(x, y) = \underline{?}$ (x, y)

19. $S^{-1} \circ T^{-1}(x, y) = \underline{?}$ $(x + 2, y - 3)$ **20.** $T^{-1} \circ S^{-1}(x, y) = \underline{?}$ $(x + 2, y - 3)$

$\triangle ABC$ **is equilateral with center O. Consider the rotations $\mathscr{R}_{O,0}$, $\mathscr{R}_{O,120}$, and $\mathscr{R}_{O,240}$ of $\triangle ABC$.**

21. $\mathscr{R}_{O,120}(\triangle ABC) = \triangle \underline{?}$ BCA   **22.** $\mathscr{R}_{O,240}(\triangle ABC) = \triangle \underline{?}$ CAB

23. What is the identity mapping? $\mathscr{R}_{O,0}$

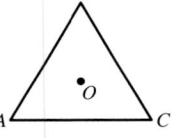

Find the inverse of each.

B **24.** $\mathscr{R}_{O,0}$ $\mathscr{R}_{O,360}$ **25.** $\mathscr{R}_{O,120}$ $\mathscr{R}_{O,240}$ or $\mathscr{R}_{O,-120}$ **26.** $\mathscr{R}_{O,240}$ $\mathscr{R}_{O,120}$ or $\mathscr{R}_{O,-240}$

27. $\mathscr{R}_{O,120} \circ \mathscr{R}_{O,580} = \underline{?}$ $\mathscr{R}_{O,-340}$ **28.** $\mathscr{R}_{O,600} \circ \mathscr{R}_{O,240} = \underline{?}$ $\mathscr{R}_{O,-120}$

29. $\mathscr{R}_{O,120} \circ \mathscr{R}_{O,240}$ $\mathscr{R}_{O,0}$ **30.** $\mathscr{R}_{O,360} \circ \mathscr{R}_{O,-150} = \underline{?}$ $\mathscr{R}_{O,150}$

Consider the *similarity mapping* $T(x, y) = (2x - 2, 2y + 6)$.

31. Find $Q = (kx, ky)$ and $S = (x + a, y + b)$ such that $T(x, y) = Q \circ S(x, y)$.
   $Q = (2x, 2y); k = 2; S = (x - 1, y + 3)$
32. Is $Q \circ S = S \circ Q$? Justify your answer. no; $Q \circ S = (2x - 2, 2y + 6)$; $S \circ Q = (2x - 1, 2y + 3)$; hence, not equal
33. $Q^{-1}(x, y) = \underline{?}$ $\left(\frac{x}{2}, \frac{y}{2}\right)$ **34.** $S^{-1}(x, y) = \underline{?}$ $(x + 1, y - 3)$

35. $Q^{-1} \circ S^{-1}(x,y) = \underline{?}$ $\left(\frac{x+1}{2}, \frac{y-3}{2}\right)$ **36.** $S^{-1} \circ Q^{-1}(x, y) = \underline{?}$ $\left(\frac{x}{2}+1, \frac{y}{2}-3\right)$

37. Either $T^{-1} = Q^{-1} \circ S^{-1}$ or $T^{-1} = S^{-1} \circ Q^{-1}$. Which is correct?
   Explain. $S^{-1} \circ Q^{-1}$; $T \circ (S^{-1} \circ Q^{-1})(x, y) = T \circ (S^{-1}(\frac{x}{2}, \frac{y}{2})) = T(\frac{x}{2} + 1, \frac{y}{2} - 3) = [2(\frac{x}{2} + 1) - 2, 2(\frac{y}{2} - 3) + 6] = (x, y)$
38. If $T = (kx + ka, ky + kb)$ is a similarity transformation, what is T^{-1}?
   $T^{-1}(x, y) = \frac{1}{k}(x - ka, y - kb)$

See Additional Answers, p. 702.

C **39.** If S and T are transformations with inverses S^{-1} and T^{-1}, respectively, and if $T \circ S(M) = N$, show that $S^{-1} \circ T^{-1}(N) = M$. (*Hint:* Recall that composition of mappings is an associative operation; that is, if A, B, and C are mappings, then $(A \circ B) \circ C = A \circ (B \circ C)$.)

40. Generalize the result of Exercise 39: If S and T are transformations having inverses S^{-1} and T^{-1}, respectively, then $(T \circ S)^{-1} = \underline{\ ?\ }$. $S^{-1} \circ T^{-1}$

41. Given H_A a half-turn about a point A, prove that $H_A \circ H_A = I$.

In a coordinate plane, consider the mappings R_x, R_y, H_o and I. All possible compositions of these mappings can be summarized in a table. The entries in the table represent the product of the mappings in the first row and column of the table. For example, $R_y \circ R_x(x,y) = R_y(x,-y) = (-x,-y) = H_o$.

42. Complete the table.

43. Give the inverse of:
R_x, R_y, H_o, I.
$R_x;\ R_y;\ H_o;\ I$

	I	R_x	R_y	H_o
I	I	R_x	R_y	H_o
R_x	R_x	I	H_o	R_y
R_y	R_y	H_o	I	R_x
H_o	H_o	R_y	R_x	I

Applications

44. Numerical Analysis Does every real number have an inverse under multiplication? If so, what is it? If not, tell why not. Is there any real number other than 1 that is its own inverse? All real numbers except 0 have a mult. inv. (the reciprocal of the number); -1 is its own inv.

45. Linguistics The word *inverse* has been used in two different ways in this book. Compare its meanings in *Logic* and in *Mappings*. In Logic: Statement—If p, then q. Inverse—If not p, then not q. In Mappings: Inverse represents a mapping that "undoes" the effect of the original mapping

Developing Mathematical Power

46. Reading in Geometry In Euclidean geometry, figures are compared on the basis of size and shape. In *topology*, two figures are equivalent if one can be obtained from the other by distortions such as stretching, shrinking, bending, and twisting. These figures can be obtained from one another without cutting the figure or puncturing a hole.

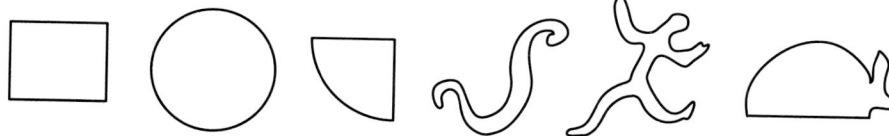

14.7 Identity and Inverse Transformations **621**

Teacher's Resource Book
Follow-Up Investigation, *Chapter 14*, p. 19

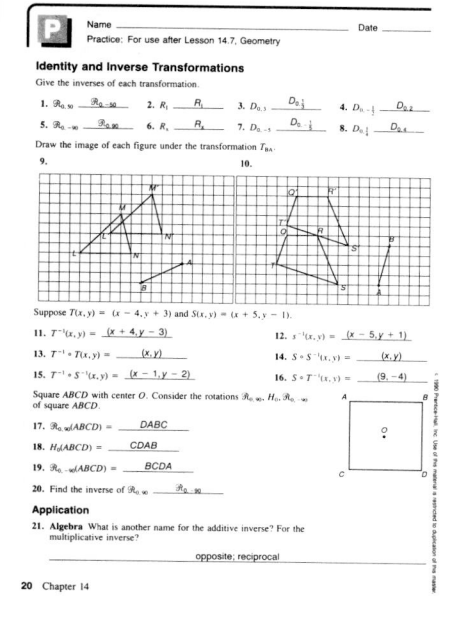

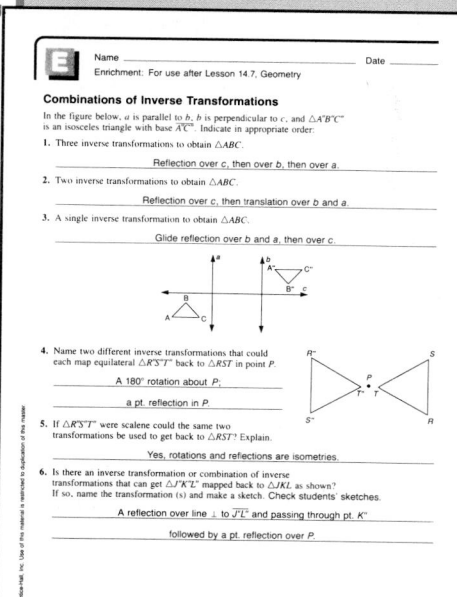

Materials/Manipulatives

Compasses and straightedges
Overhead transparency
Teaching Transparencies
99–99B

Technology

Computer Test Bank, pp.
900–904

LESSON FOCUS

Review

- Review the Isosceles Triangle Theorem.
- Review constructing a square.

Alternative Learning Styles

- Teaching Transparencies 99–99B provide a means to motivate the lesson and illustrate how transformations can be used to solve many types of problems. The use of the overlays allows for a step-by-step development of the proof and should appeal to visual learners.
- The logical learner may benefit from looking at the conclusion or the diagram in earlier proofs to determine the mapping that is needed to produce the desired result.

Connections

Transformational ↔ Synthetic
approach   approach
EXAM. 1 p. 622   Th. 5.1 p. 175

14.8	# Strategy: Use Transformations

Transformations can be applied to a variety of problems. The problem solving steps can aid in using this strategy.

EXAMPLE 1   Use transformations to prove the Isosceles Triangle Theorem.

▪ **Understand the Problem**

Draw a figure. What is given?

$\triangle ABC$ with $\overline{AB} \cong \overline{AC}$

What is to be proven?

$\angle B \cong \angle C$

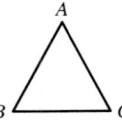

▪ **Plan Your Approach**

Plan:

Draw l, the bisector of $\angle A$, and label point D on $\overline{BC}$.
$R_l(A) = A$, $R_l(D) = D$, and $R_l(\overrightarrow{AB}) = \overrightarrow{AC}$.
Since $R_l(B) = B'$ is on $\overrightarrow{AC}$, it can be deduced that B' is C. So,
$R_l(\triangle ABD) = \triangle ACD$, and $\triangle ABD \cong \triangle ACD$.
The conclusion follows by CPCTC.

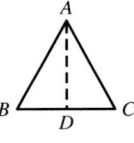

▪ **Implement the Plan**

Proof:

Statements	*Reasons*
1. Isosceles $\triangle ABC$; $\overline{AB} \cong \overline{AC}$	1. Given
2. Draw the bisector of $\angle A$; label D.	2. Every $\angle$ has a bis.
3. $R_l(A) = A$; $R_l(D) = D$	3. Def. of reflection
4. $R_l(\overrightarrow{AB}) = \overrightarrow{AC}$; hence, $R_l(B) = B'$ is on $\overrightarrow{AC}$.	4. The bis. of an $\angle$ is a line of reflection for the sides of the $\angle$.
5. $AB = AB'$	5. A reflection is an isometry.
6. $AB = AC$	6. Def. of $\cong$ segs.
7. $AB' = AC$	7. Subst. prop.
8. B' is C	8. On a ray, there is exactly 1 pt. that is at a given distance from the endpoint of the ray.

Developing Mathematical Power

Cooperative Learning   Working in groups, students can complete the Enrichment activity, p. 23, in the *Teacher's Resource Book* (see side column, p. 625). It provides a method for establishing different transformations of an equilateral triangle that will bring it into congruence with itself.

Statements	Reasons
9. $R_l(B) = C$	9. Subst. prop.
10. $R_l(\triangle ADB) = \triangle ADC$	10. Steps 3 and 9
11. $\triangle ADB \cong \triangle ADC$	11. Def. of isometry
12. $\angle B \cong \angle C$	12. CPCTC

Interpret the Results   Transformations can be used to prove the Isosceles Triangle Theorem.

EXAMPLE 2   Given $\odot O$ with sector AOB, construct a square having two of its vertices on the arc of the sector and one vertex on each of the two radii.

Understand the Problem

What is given?

$\odot O$ with sector AOB.

What is to be found?

A square having two of its vertices on arc $\overarc{AB}$ and the other vertices on $\overline{OA}$ and $\overline{OB}$, respectively.

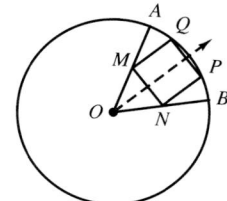

Make a sketch.

Plan Your Approach

Look ahead.

In the sketch, the square appears to be placed so that the bisector of $\angle AOB$ is a line of reflection of the desired square. If one vertex could be located on $\overline{OA}$ or $\overline{OB}$, a reflection could be used to find its image and hence a side of the square.

Look for a pattern.

Suppose a series of squares approaching the solution is constructed. $\overline{M_{i+1}N_{i+1}}$ is a dilation of $\overline{M_iN_i}$ with center O and $\overline{P_{i+1}Q_{i+1}}$ is a dilation of $\overline{P_iQ_i}$ with center O.

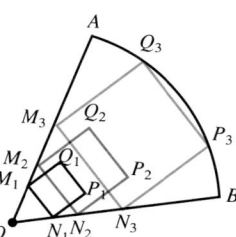

Plan:

Construct the bisector l of $\angle AOB$ and choose a point M' on $\overline{OA}$. Reflect M' in l to find N'. Using $M'N'$ as the length of a side, construct square $M'N'P'Q'$. Since the desired square is similar to $M'N'P'Q'$, use O as the center of a dilation and find $D_{o,k}(P') = P$ such that P is on $\overarc{AB}$. Since the dilation maps $M'N'P'Q'$ onto $MNPQ$, locating point P and $R_l(P) = Q$ will determine the solution square.

14.8 Strategy: Use Transformations   **623**

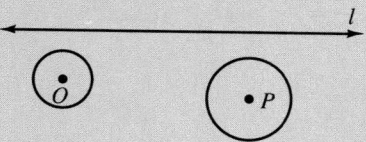

Imagine that the problem has been solved.

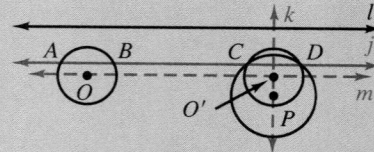

Translate ⊙O along j a distance of AC; call its image ⊙O'. Since AB = CD, AB coincides with CD; hence P and O' both lie on the ⊥ bis. of CD. To const. j, do the following: Through P, const. k ⊥ l. Then const. m through O ∥ to l. Let O' be the intersection of k and m. Translate ⊙O along m a distance of OO'. The line j through the pts. of intersections of ⊙O' and ⊙P is the solution.

LESSON FOLLOW-UP

Assignment Guide

See p. 584B for assignments.

Project

This project provides an opportunity to synthesize knowledge acquired in this course.

Lesson Quiz

Construct an equilateral △ with vertices at A, on ⊙B, and on ⊙C.

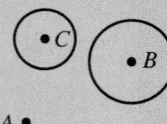

Let ⊙C' = $\mathcal{R}_{A, -60}$ (⊙C). Let D' be one of the pts. of intersection of ⊙C' and ⊙B; let D be the preimage of D'. △ADD' is the required equil. △.

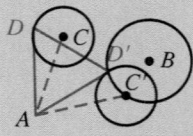

| **Implement the Plan** | Construct l and choose any point M' on $\overrightarrow{OA}$. Find $R_l(M') = N'$. Use M'N' as the length of a side and construct square M'N'P'Q'. Construct $D_{o,k}(P') = P$ such that P is on $\overset{\frown}{AB}$. Find $R_l(P) = Q$. PQ is the length of the side of the desired square, so square MNPQ can be constructed. |

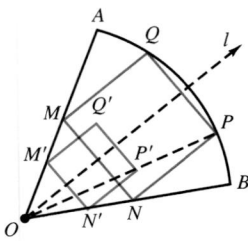

| **Interpret the Results** | **Conclusion:** A dilation of a square having two of its vertices on the sides of ∠AO* produces the solution square. |

> ### Problem Solving Reminders
> - Transformations can provide a means for proving theorems.
> - Some construction problems can be solved using a transformational approach.

CLASS EXERCISES For Class and Practice Exercises, see Additional Answers, p. 702.

Given a line l, construct each figure.

1. Rectangle ABCD such that R_l(rectangle ABCD) = rectangle BADC

2. Pentagon EFGHI such that R_l(pentagon EFGHI) = pentagon IHGFE

3. Triangle ABC such that $R_l(\triangle ABC) = \triangle ACB$

4. Nonrectangular parallelogram JKLM such that $R_l(\square JKLM) = \square LKJM$

PRACTICE EXERCISES

A 1. Explain how to construct rectangle EFGH in scalene △ABC so that the vertices are placed as shown.

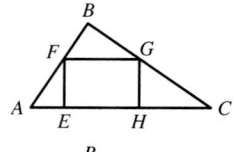

2. Explain how to construct square EFGH in scalene △ABC so that the vertices are placed as shown.

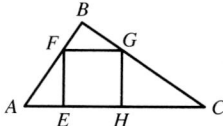

Use transformations to prove Exercises 3 and 4.

3. The diagonals of a parallelogram bisect each other. (*Hint:* Use half-turns.)

4. The diagonals of a rhombus are perpendicular. (*Hint:* Use reflections.)

5. Suppose *P* and *Q* are on ⊙*O* and line *k* is tangent to ⊙*O*. Use transformations to construct ⊙*O*.

6. Given lines *j*, *k*, and *l* as shown, construct △*ABC* such that *j*, *k*, and *l* are the bisectors of the angles of △*ABC*.

B   7. Given lines *m*, *n*, and *p*, as shown, construct △*ABC* such that *M* is the midpoint of $\overline{BC}$ and *m*, *n*, and *p* are the perpendicular bisectors of the sides of △*ABC*.

Use this figure for Exercises 8 and 9.

8. Construct an equilateral triangle with one vertex on line *l* and the other vertices on each of the circles.

9. Construct a square with two vertices on line *l* and the other vertices on each of the circles.

C   10. If *j* ∥ *k* ∥ *l*, construct equilateral △*ABC* having vertex *A* on *j*, *B* on *k*, and *C* on *l*.

11. The SAS postulate was accepted as true previously in this book. Use transformations to prove SAS.
   Given: <u>s</u>△*ABC* and *DEF*; $\overline{AB} \cong \overline{DE}$; $\overline{BC} \cong \overline{EF}$; ∠*B* ≅ ∠*E*
   Prove: △*ABC* ≅ △*DEF*
   (*Hint:* Translate △*ABC* so that *B* maps onto *E* and then use a reflection.)

PROJECT

Choose a postulate or theorem about triangle congruence and write a plan for proving the postulate or theorem with transformations.

Connections

Transformational → approach	Coordinate → approach	Synthetic approach
Ex. 3 p. 625	Ex. 25 p. 576	Ex. 32 p. 222
Ex. 4 p. 625	Ex. 18 p. 576	Ex. 19 p. 237
Ex. 11 p. 625		Post. 15 p. 134

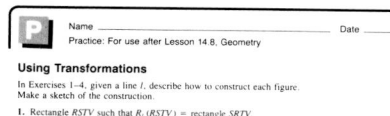

Teacher's Resource Book

Name _____ Date ____
Practice: For use after Lesson 14.8, Geometry

Using Transformations

In Exercises 1–4, given a line *l*, describe how to construct each figure. Make a sketch of the construction.

1. Rectangle *RSTV* such that R_l(*RSTV*) = rectangle *SRTV*. Let *l* be the ⊥ bisector of $\overline{RS}$ and $\overline{VT}$. Then R_l(*RSTV*) = *SRVT*.

2. Regular pentagon *ABCDE* such that R_l(*ABCDE*) = regular pentagon *EDCBA*. Let *l* bisect ∠*C* and extend through $\overline{AE}$; *l* is the ⊥ bisector of $\overline{AE}$. Then R_l(*ABCDE*) = *EDCBA*.

3. Isosceles △*JKL* with vertex ∠*J* such that R_l(△*JKL*) = isosceles △*JLK*. Let *l* be the bisector of ∠*J*. Then *l* is the ⊥ bisector of $\overline{KL}$, so R_l(*JKL*) = △*JLK*.

4. Nonrectangular □*PQRS* such that R_l(□*PQRS*) = □*RQPS*. Let *l* contain the diagonal $\overline{QS}$. Then R_l(□*PQRS*) = □*RQPS*.

5. Explain how to construct rectangle *ABCD* in scalene △*XYZ* such that *A* and *D* lie on $\overline{XZ}$, *C* lies on $\overline{YZ}$, and *B* lies on $\overline{XY}$. Choose any point *B* between *X* and *Y*. Construct a ⊥ to $\overline{XY}$ from *B*; call the point where this ⊥ intersects $\overline{XZ}$ point *A*. Then construct through *B* a line ∥ $\overline{XZ}$; locate *C* where this line intersects $\overline{YZ}$. Drop a ⊥ to $\overline{XZ}$ from *C*. *ABCD* is a rectangle since it is a ▱ with a right ∠.

6. Explain how to construct square *ABCD* in scalene △*XYZ* such that *A* and *D* lie on $\overline{XZ}$, *C* lies on $\overline{YZ}$, and *B* lies on $\overline{XY}$. A square having a side on $\overline{XZ}$ and a vertex on $\overline{XY}$ may not have its fourth vertex on $\overline{YZ}$. A dilation of this square, using *X* as the center will meet all conditions. Choose point *J* on $\overline{XY}$ and construct $\overline{JK}$ ⊥ $\overline{XZ}$. Construct square *JKLM* having sides of length *JK*. Draw $\overline{XM}$ to intersect $\overline{YZ}$ at *C*. Construct *CD* ⊥ $\overline{XZ}$. Using *CD* as a side length, construct square *ABCD*.

22   Chapter 14

Name _____ Date ____
Enrichment: For use after Lesson 14.8, Geometry

Transformational Congruences of an Equilateral Triangle

There are a number of transformations of an equilateral triangle that will bring it into congruence with itself. These can be brought together in a systematic way.

Draw an equilateral triangle *ABC* with *O* the point of concurrency of the medians. Now consider the following transformations.

$R_{0,120}$ and $R_{0,240}$ are rotations around point *O*. $R_{\overline{AD}}$, $R_{\overline{BE}}$ and $R_{\overline{CF}}$ are reflections about the given axis. *I* leaves the triangle in the same position.

Let • represent the operation "is followed by." For example, $R_{0,120} • R_{0,240}$ first rotates the triangle about *O* through 120° and then rotates the triangle about *O* 240°. The result of this combined operation is to put the triangle back into the original position. This is equivalent to applying *I*. Hence, $R_{0,120} • R_{0,240} = I$.

Fill in the empty spaces of the table with the result of • operation.

•	*I*	$R_{0,120}$	$R_{0,240}$	$R_{\overline{AD}}$	$R_{\overline{BE}}$	$R_{\overline{CF}}$
I	*I*	$R_{0,120}$	$R_{0,240}$	$R_{\overline{AD}}$	$R_{\overline{BE}}$	$R_{\overline{CF}}$
$R_{0,120}$	$R_{0,120}$	$R_{0,240}$	*I*	$R_{\overline{BE}}$	$R_{\overline{CF}}$	$R_{\overline{AD}}$
$R_{0,240}$	$R_{0,240}$	*I*	$R_{0,120}$	$R_{\overline{CF}}$	$R_{\overline{AD}}$	$R_{\overline{BE}}$
$R_{\overline{AD}}$	$R_{\overline{AD}}$	$R_{\overline{CF}}$	$R_{\overline{BE}}$	*I*	$R_{0,240}$	$R_{0,120}$
$R_{\overline{BE}}$	$R_{\overline{BE}}$	$R_{\overline{AD}}$	$R_{\overline{CF}}$	$R_{0,120}$	*I*	$R_{0,240}$
$R_{\overline{CF}}$	$R_{\overline{CF}}$	$R_{\overline{BE}}$	$R_{\overline{AD}}$	$R_{0,240}$	$R_{0,120}$	*I*

Chapter 14   **23**

LESSON FOCUS

Review
- Review transformations made by reflections and rotations.
- The Chapter Summary and Review, pp. 634–635, gives vocabulary and concepts and review exercises by lesson.
- The end of the chapter features a Cumulative Review on pp. 638–642.

Alternative Learning Styles
- The Investigation provides real-life examples to help students visualize line and point symmetry.
- Kinesthetic learners may benefit from making a tracing of the figure to be investigated. They can then cut and fold the tracing to determine line symmetry and rotate the tracing about a point to determine point symmetry.

14.9

Symmetry

Objectives: To describe the symmetry of figures
To identify types of symmetry in a plane geometric figure

Most living things have a certain regularity or balance of form. These regularities often can be described in terms of the symmetry of the figure.

Investigation—*Visualizing the Concept*

Here are the flags of four different countries.

Canada

Switzerland

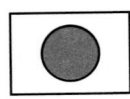
Japan

Israel

1. Which could be folded about some line so that the halves would coincide? all

2. Which could be hung upside down and still appear the same? all except Canada

A figure is said to possess *symmetry* or to be *symmetric* if there is an isometry other than the identity that maps the figure onto itself.

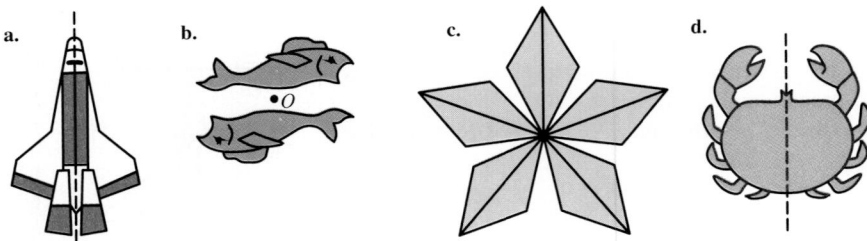

a. b. c. d.

Figures (a), (c), and (d) have *line symmetry*. Each of them could be folded about some line and the two halves of the figure would coincide. Figure (b) has *point symmetry;* a half-turn about point *O* would cause the figure to coincide with itself. Figure (c) also has *rotational symmetry*. It can be rotated through 72° and mapped onto itself. What other angles of rotation would map it onto itself?
144°, 216°, 288°

626   Chapter 14 Transformational Geometry

Developing Mathematical Power

Keeping a Portfolio   Have students compare and contrast line, point, and rotational symmetry. They should illustrate each type with sketches or pictures of both natural and artificial examples. Have them design a logo that includes more than one type of symmetry.

Any figure has **line symmetry,** or **reflectional symmetry,** if there is a line l such that the reflection image of any point P of the figure about line l is also a point of the figure. Line l is called the **line of symmetry.** Objects in nature that have a line of symmetry are said to have *bilateral symmetry.*

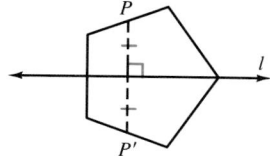

Point symmetry is a special case of rotational symmetry. A figure has **rotational symmetry** if there is some point O about which the figure can be rotated and made to coincide with itself. If an angle of rotation of 180° maps the figure onto itself, the figure has **point symmetry.**

Rotational symmetries are identified by the measure of the angle of rotation required to have the figure coincide with itself. The figure at the right has 90° rotational symmetry as well as 180° (point symmetry), 270°, and 360° rotational symmetry. If a figure has *only* 360° rotational symmetry (the identity mapping), it is not considered to be symmetric.

EXAMPLE   Identify the type of symmetry, if any, each figure possesses.

a. 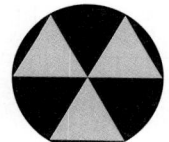   b.    c.    d.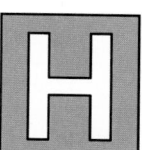

a. 120° and 240° rotational and line symmetry
c. none
b. bilateral (line) symmetry
d. point and line symmetry

CLASS EXERCISES

True or false? If false, give a counterexample.

1. If a figure has line symmetry, it also has point symmetry. false; isos. △

2. If a figure has point symmetry, it also has line symmetry. false; ▱

3. If a figure has point symmetry, it also has rotational symmetry. true

4. If a figure has rotational symmetry, it also has point symmetry. false; equilateral △

5. If a figure has point and line symmetry, it also has rotational symmetry. true

6. In a figure, the intersection of two lines of symmetry is a point of symmetry. false; only true if lines are ⊥

 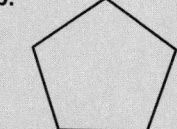

Common Error

• Some students may have difficulty understanding the relationship between point and rotational symmetry. Although a figure having point symmetry has rotational symmetry, the converse is not necessarily true. Use the example of an equilateral triangle.

• See *Teacher's Resource Book* for additional remediation.

LESSON FOLLOW-UP

Discussion

Distribute paper and scissors to students. Have them experiment with various ways of folding and cutting the paper to produce designs that illustrate various symmetries, or else have no symmetry. Challenge them to produce figures that have line symmetry, but no rotational symmetry, and so on.

Critical Thinking

Application Ask students to create examples of figures that have various types of symmetries.

Assignment Guide

See p. 584B for assignments.

Find all lines of symmetry. Identify any rotational symmetries.

7. nonsquare rectangle ⊥ bis. of sides; 180° rotational

8. rhombus diagonals; 180° rotational

9. nonrectangular ▱ none; 180° rotational

10. square ⊥ bis., diagonals; rotation 90°, 180°, and 270°

11. isosceles trapezoid ⊥ bis. of bases; no rotational

12. kite (quad. with 2 pairs of ≅ adjacent sides) one diag.; no rotational

Equilateral triangle *ABC* has center *O*.

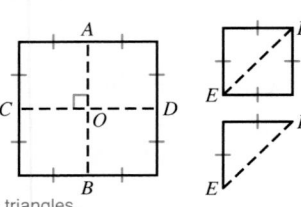

13. Identify all rotational symmetries of △*ABC*. $\mathcal{R}_{o,120}$, $\mathcal{R}_{o,240}$

14. Does △*ABC* have point symmetry? no

15. Identify all lines of symmetry. $\overline{AO}$, $\overline{BO}$, $\overline{CO}$

16. How many lines of symmetry does a regular pentagon have? a regular hexagon? 5 lines; 6 lines

PRACTICE EXERCISES   ⟳ Use technology where appropriate.

Fold a square sheet of paper as shown. Fold along diagonal *EF* and then unfold the paper.

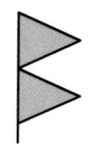

A   1. What lines of symmetry does this figure have? What rotational symmetry? the fold lines; $\mathcal{R}_{o,90}$, H_o, $\mathcal{R}_{o,270}$

2. Can you find a way to cut the triangle so that the figure is not symmetric? yes; cut through one layer of the paper when folded into triangles.

Find all lines of symmetry. Then identify any rotational symmetries and figures with point symmetry.

3.

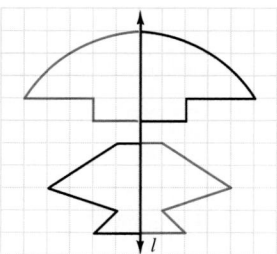

a. 1 vert., 2 diag., 1 horiz. line
b. 60°, 120°, 180°, 240°, 300°   c. yes

4.

a. 1 vert. line
b. no rotational
c. no point

5.

a. none
b. none
c. none

Complete each figure so that it has the given symmetry.

6.

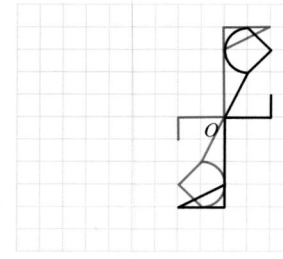

about line *l*

7.

about point *O*

Complete each figure so that it has the indicated rotational symmetry.

8.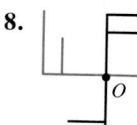

$\mathcal{R}_{O,90}$; $\mathcal{R}_{O,270}$ and point symmetry about O

9.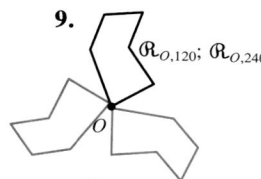

$\mathcal{R}_{O,120}$; $\mathcal{R}_{O,240}$

Consider the letters of the alphabet in block form:

A   B   C   D   E   F   G   H   I
J   K   L   M   N   O   P   Q   R
S   T   U   V   W   X   Y   Z

10. Which letters have line symmetry in a vertical line? A, H, I, M, O, T, U, V, W, X, Y

11. Which letters have line symmetry in a horizontal line? B, C, D, E, H, I, O, X

12. Which letters have line symmetry in both a vertical and a horizontal line? H, I, O, X

13. Which letters have point symmetry? H, I, N, O, X, Z, S

14. Which letters have both point and line symmetry? H, I, O, X

Create a tessellation of the plane using the given figure. Answers may vary.

15.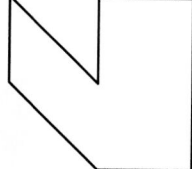

16.

Draw a figure meeting the specified conditions. If no such figure is possible, explain why.

B

17. Quadrilateral having point symmetry but no line symmetry
any nonrectangular □ except a rhombus

18. Triangle having exactly one line of symmetry isos. △

19. Figure having 120° rotational symmetry, but no line of symmetry
equilateral △ with irregular design at each vertex

20. Pentagon with exactly four lines of symmetry not possible; only rotational symmetry

14.9 Symmetry   **629**

Lesson Quiz

a. Describe all lines of symmetry.
b. Describe all rotational symmetries.
c. Does the figure have point symmetry?

1.

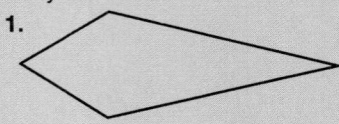

2.

3. A regular octagon.

1. a. the horizontal diagonal
   b. none
   c. no
2. a. none
   b. 180° rotational symmetry
   c. yes
3. a. 8 lines of symmetry: 4 that join pairs
      of opposite vertices and 4 that join
      midpoints of opposite sides
   b. 45°, 90°, 135°, 180°, 225°, 270°, 315°
      rotational symmetry
   c. yes

Connections

Transformational ⟷ Synthetic
approach   approach
Cl. Ex. 2 p. 593   Ex. 29 p. 630

Suppose a figure *F* is symmetric and *P* = (*x*, *y*) is any point of *F*. Identify
the isometry that maps *P* to its image *P′* and give the coordinates of *P′*, if
F is symmetric with respect to the following.

21. *x*-axis
$R_x(x, y) = (x, -y)$

22. *y*-axis
$R_y(x, y) = (-x, y)$

23. origin
$H_O(x, y) = (-x, -y)$

24. line $y = x$
$R_{y=x}(x, y) = (y, x)$

Pentominoes are figures composed of five squares joined so that they touch
only along a complete side. Some examples are:

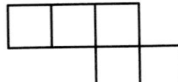   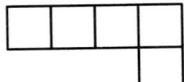

25. Use graph paper to draw the twelve distinct pentominoes. (Do not include
figures that are reflections or rotations of each other.)
See side column page 629.
26. Classify your pentominoes for line symmetry, point symmetry, and 90°
rotational symmetry.

Consider any regular *n*-gon with center *O*.

27. How many lines of symmetry does the figure have? Describe them. *n* lines; if *n* is
even, from vertices through center and through midpts. of opposite sides; if *n* is odd, from vertex to midpt. of opp. side
28. How many rotational symmetries does the figure have? Describe them.
$(n-1)$ rotations of vertices

Write paragraph proofs in Exercises 29 and 30.

29. Prove that the angles formed by an angle bisector are symmetric to each
other with respect to the bisector. See side column.

30. Prove that the point of intersection of two perpendicular lines of symmetry
of a figure is a point of symmetry for the figure.
See side column page 631.

Applications

31. Design   Recall that a tessellation of the
plane is an arrangement of figures that
completely covers the plane with no
overlapping. In addition to the types of
symmetries described above,
tessellations also may have *translational
symmetry*. A figure has translational
symmetry if there is a translation that
maps the figure onto itself. How many
different types of symmetries can you
find in the tessellation shown? If color
is ignored, what additional symmetries
may be found? line and point symmetry;
rotational symmetry

29. Given: ∠*EBF*, bis. *l*
Prove: ∠*ABD* is sym-
metric to ∠*CBD* with
respect to *l*.

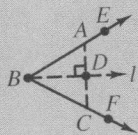

Proof: Draw $\overline{AC} \perp l$ at *D*. Then △*ABD* ≅
△*CBD* by LA. $\overline{AB} \cong \overline{CB}$ and $\overline{AD} \cong \overline{CD}$ by
CPCTC. Thus, line *l* is the line of refl.
of ∠*ABC*, where *A* is the reflection of *C*
through *l*. Therefore, ∠*ABD* is symmetric
to ∠*CBD* with respect to *l*.

32. Computer Using Logo, take your school logo, or any other logo, and generate a computer graphic around a line of symmetry.
See Solutions Manual.

TEST YOURSELF

Find the coordinates of the image of the given point under the given mapping.

1. $D_{0,3}(A)$ $(-9, -6)$

2. $R_x \circ R_y(B)$ $(-4, 1)$

3. $T_{AB} \circ R_y(C)$ $(9, 1)$

4. $D_{0,-2}(D)$ $(-2, -6)$

5. $\mathcal{R}_{0,90} \circ H_A(E)$ $(-3, 5)$

14.5, 14.6

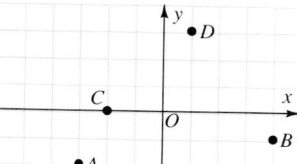

Copy this figure and draw the image of $\triangle ABC$ under the given mapping.

6. $R_l \circ R_k$. What single mapping will produce the same result? $\mathcal{R}_{P,220}$

7. $R_l \circ H_P$
See Solutions Manual.

8. $D_{P,2}$

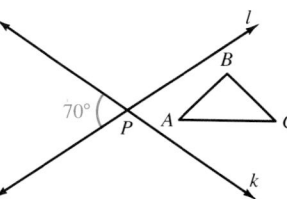

Suppose $F(x, y) = (3x, 3y)$ and $G(x, y) = (x - 2, y + 4)$.

9. $F \circ G(x, y) = \underline{\ ?\ }$ $(3x - 6, 3y + 12)$

10. $G \circ F(x, y) = \underline{\ ?\ }$ $(3x - 2, 3y + 4)$

14.7, 14.8

11. $F^{-1}(x, y) = \underline{\ ?\ }$ $\left(\frac{x}{3}, \frac{y}{3}\right)$

12. $G^{-1}(x, y) = \underline{\ ?\ }$ $(x + 2, y - 4)$

13. If $F(\triangle ABC) = \triangle A'B'C'$ and if $AB = 10$ cm, then $A'B' = \underline{\ ?\ }$. Why? 30 cm;
F is a dilation of magnitude 3.

14. If $G(\triangle XYZ) = \triangle X'Y'Z'$ and if $m\angle Y = 50$, then $m\angle Y' = \underline{\ ?\ }$. Why? 50;
Translations preserve ∠ meas.

Describe all symmetries of each figure.

15.

3 lines of symmetry; 120° and 240° rotational symmetry

16.

14.9

2 diag. lines of symmetry; point symmetry

14.9 Symmetry **631**

30. Given: $l \perp k$ at O
Prove: O is a point of symmetry.

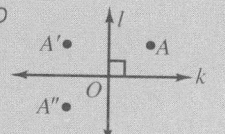

Proof:
The corollary of Th. 14.7 showed that a composition of reflections in ⊥ lines is a half-turn about the point where the lines intersect. Since $R_l \circ R_k = \mathcal{R}_{0,180} = H_0$, then O is a point of symmetry by definition.

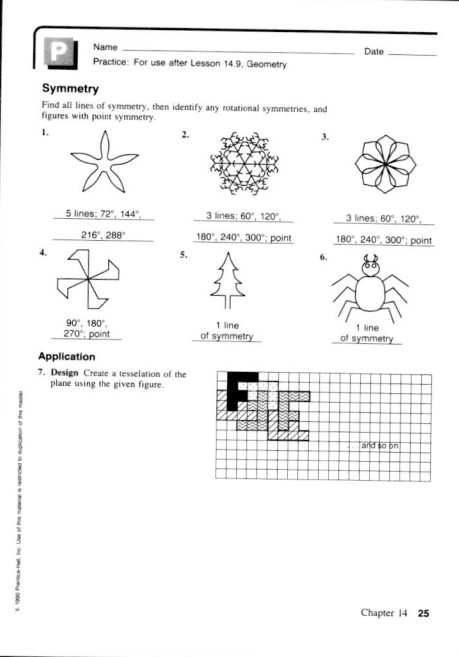
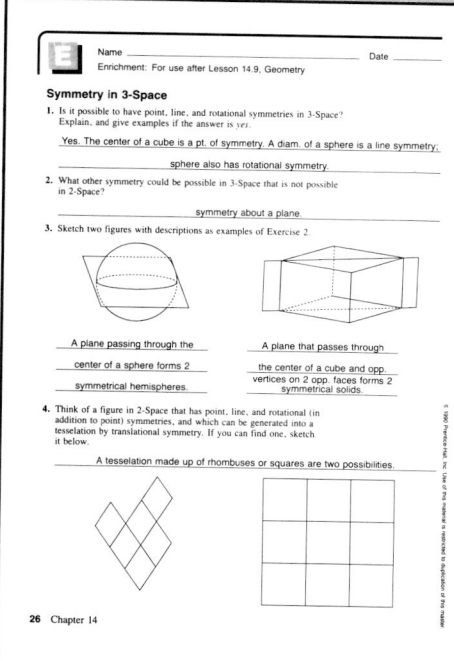

See *Teacher's Resource Book*, Follow-up *Technology*, pp. 19–20.

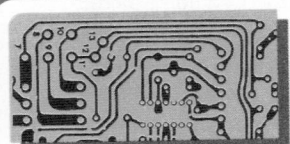

TECHNOLOGY:
Fractals

Computers have paved the way for mathematical and scientific discoveries in many fields. The field of fractal geometry—the geometry of self-similar forms—is one of them. The word *fractal* was first used in the 1960s by the mathematician Benoit Mandelbrot. The ideas he discovered are being applied in many scientific, mathematical, and artistic disciplines: studying the circulatory systems in plants and animals; tracking and predicting earthquakes, weather patterns, and the flow of turbulent liquids; understanding the biological forms of trees and leaves, the formation of soap bubbles, and price fluctuations on the stock market; and drawing realistic computer graphic simulations of ocean waves and mountain ranges.

The **fractal,** or self-similar curve, shown in the figure is the Logo approximation of an infinite curve called a *Koch snowflake*. Koch snowflakes are named after Helge Von Koch, the Swedish mathematician who first described the curve in 1904. The Koch snowflake demonstrates the idea of self-similar forms. The section of the curve from A to C is exactly similar to the section from A to B. The section from A to C can be enlarged to be identical to the section from A to B. Both sections are also similar to the section from A to D, and so on. No matter how small a section you examine, it can be enlarged to look exactly like the section from A to B.

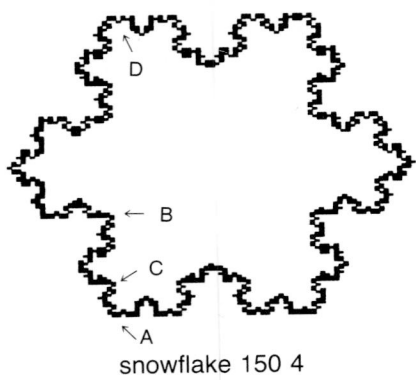

snowflake 150 4

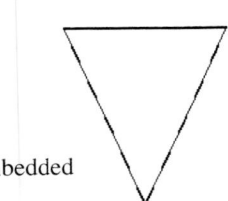

The construction of a Koch snowflake uses the idea of embedded recursion based on an equilateral triangle.

632   Chapter 14 Transformational Geometry

The first step is to divide each side into thirds and replace the middle third by two sides of equal length. The procedure is:

```
to side :length :order
if :order = 0 [forward :length stop]
side :length/3 :order-1
left 60 side :length/3 :order-1
right 120 side :length/3 :order-1
left 60 side :length/3 :order-1
end
```

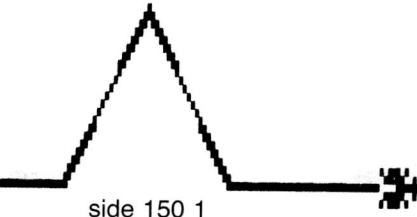

side 150 1

Then the snowflake is the simple procedure:

```
to snowflake :length :order
repeat 3 [side :length :order right 120]
end
```

The result is a 12-sided star with a perimeter that is $\frac{4}{3}$ as long as the perimeter of the first triangle. If you divided each of the unbroken sides into thirds and replaced the middle third by two more sides of equal length (order 2), the snowflake procedure would result in a 48-sided snowflake with a perimeter that is $\frac{4}{3} \cdot \frac{4}{3}$, or $\frac{16}{9}$ as long as the perimeter of the first triangle. A third time (order-3) would result in a 192-sided snowflake with a perimeter $\frac{4}{3} \cdot \frac{4}{3} \cdot \frac{4}{3}$, or $\frac{64}{27}$ as long as the original perimeter; and so on. snowflake 150 4 on page 632 has 762 sides. If you could continue the process an infinite number of times, you would have something rather strange—a curve of infinite length enclosing a finite area!

EXERCISES

See Solutions Manual.

1. The fractal described above is based on a triangle. Write a procedure to generate a fractal based on a square, pentagon, or hexagon. Can you write a procedure which would generate a fractal based on any regular polygon?

2. Generate a quadric Koch island which is a Koch snowflake based on a square. Reflect the sides of the square to obtain a Koch cross.

3. Calculate the perimeters of a series of snowflakes with length 150 and orders 1–6. Calculate the areas of the same snowflakes. Can you predict a value for the area of an infinite-order snowflake? What about the length of an infinite-order snowflake? Will its length really be infinite, or will it reach some finite limit?

4. Design your own fractal monster using more than one type of fractal side.

5. Fractals are used extensively to generate computer landscapes by filmmakers. Generate a fractal landscape.

Technology: Fractals   **633**

633

- See *Teacher's Resource Book*
  Spanish Chapter Summary and
  Review, pp. 27–28.
- See Extra Practice, p. 656.

CHAPTER 14   SUMMARY AND REVIEW

Vocabulary

composition of
   mappings (612)
contraction (607)
dilation (607)
expansion (607)
glide reflection (597)
identity
   transformation (617)
image (587)

inverse
   transformation (618)
isometry (588)
line symmetry (627)
mapping (586)
one-to-one mapping (587)
point symmetry (627)
preimage (587)
projection (589)

reflection (591)
rotation (601)
rotational symmetry (627)
similarity mapping (620)
symmetry (626)
tesselation (596, 630)
transformation (587)
translation (596)
vector (596)

Mappings   A **mapping** is a correspondence between sets that associates each   **14.1**
member of the first set with one and only one member of the second set. If
$M: A \rightarrow B$ with $M(P) = P'$, then P' is the image of P under M. Transformations
that preserve distances are isometries, or congruence mappings.

Given the transformation $T(x, y) = (x - 2, 3y)$:

1. Find the image of $(-2, 4)$, $(5, 0)$, and $(6, -2)$ under T. (−4, 12); (3, 0); (4, −6)
2. Find the preimage of $(10, 9)$, $(-3, -6)$, and (a, b). (12, 3); (−1, −2); $(a + 2, \frac{b}{3})$
3. Use $A = (3, 1)$ and $B = (-4, -2)$ to decide whether or not T is an isometry.
   $A'(1, 3)$; $B'(-6, -6)$; $AB = \sqrt{58}$; $A'B' = \sqrt{130}$; $AB \neq A'B'$, so T is not an isometry

Reflections   A reflection is a transformation that produces a mirror image of   **14.2**
a figure. If l is a line, R_l associates each point P not on l with point P' such
that l is the perpendicular bisector of $\overline{PP'}$. Reflections are isometries.

Give the coordinates of the image of each
point under the given reflection.

4. $R_x(A) = \underline{\ ?\ }$ (−3, 1)   5. $R_y(B) = \underline{\ ?\ }$ (−2, 2)
6. $R_x(C) = \underline{\ ?\ }$ (−5, 0)   7. $R_z(D) = \underline{\ ?\ }$ (1, 3)
8. If $\overline{M'N'}$ is the image of $\overline{MN}$ under R_z,
   find the coordinates of M and N.
   $M = (-1, 4)$; $N = (-3, 4)$

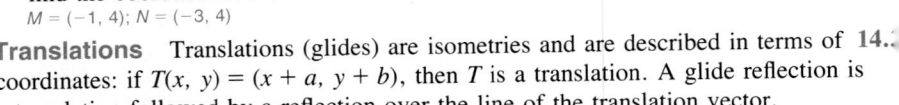

Translations   Translations (glides) are isometries and are described in terms of   **14.3**
coordinates: if $T(x, y) = (x + a, y + b)$, then T is a translation. A glide reflection is
a translation followed by a reflection over the line of the translation vector.

9. Copy onto graph paper
   and draw the image of
   each figure under $\overrightarrow{QQ'}$.

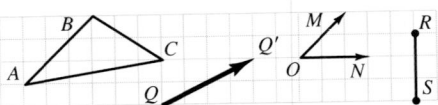

9.

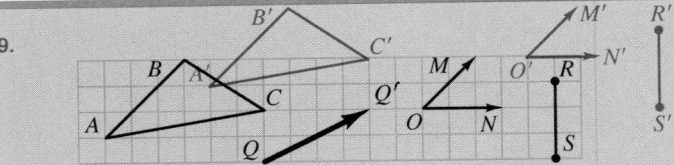

Rotations   A rotation of a figure in the plane involves turning the figure   **14.4**
about a fixed point, the center of the rotation. $\mathcal{R}_{o,\alpha}$ leaves point O fixed, but
maps all other points P to P' such that $m\angle POP' = \alpha$.

Give an equivalent name for $\mathcal{R}_{0,\alpha}$, where $-180 \le \alpha \le 180$.

10. $\mathcal{R}_{o,580}$ $\mathcal{R}_{o,-140}$ **11.** $\mathcal{R}_{o,-200}$ $\mathcal{R}_{o,160}$

Dilations   A dilation produces an enlargement or a contraction. A dilation   **14.5**
$D_{o,k}$ maps a segment to a parallel segment $|k|$ times as long: $D_{o,k}(x, y) = (kx, ky)$.

If $D_{o,k}(P) = P'$, find k.

12.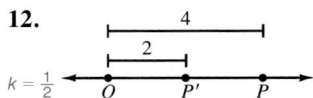

13.

Composition of Mappings   The composition of mappings F and G, $F \circ G$,   **14.6**
takes point P to P'' by applying G to P, producing P', then applying F to P'.

Suppose $\triangle A'B'C'$ is the image of $\triangle ABC$. Give
the coordinates of $A'B'C'$ and, where
appropriate, describe a single transformation that
produces the same result.

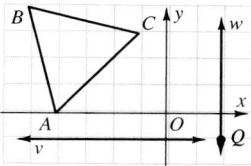

                 $A'(0, 0)$, $B'(-1, 4)$, $C'(3, 3)$;
14. $R_w \circ R_y$ **15.** $R_y \circ R_w$ $A'(8, -2)$,
   translating 4 units to rt. $B'(9, -6)$, $C'(5, -5)$; H_O

Identity and Inverse Transformations   An identity transformation   **14.7, 14.8**
leaves all points of the plane fixed; $R_l \circ R_l$ and $\mathcal{R}_{O,360}$ are examples. If the
product of two mappings A and B is the identity mapping, A and B are inverses.

$\triangle PQR$ is equilateral with center O. For $\triangle PQR$,
define R_j, R_k, R_l, $\mathcal{R}_{o,120}$, $\mathcal{R}_{o,240}$, and I. Find the
following.

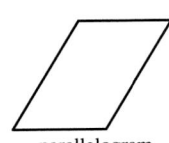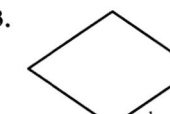

16. $\mathcal{R}_{o,120}{}^{-1}$ $\mathcal{R}_{O,-120}$ or   **17.** $R_j(\triangle PQR)$ $\triangle PRQ$
18. $\mathcal{R}_{o,240} \circ R_l$ R_j $\mathcal{R}_{O,240}$ **19.** $(\mathcal{R}_{o,120} \circ \mathcal{R}_{o,120})^{-1}$ $\mathcal{R}_{O,120}$ or $\mathcal{R}_{O,-240}$
20. $(R_k)^{-1} \circ \mathcal{R}_{o,240}$ R_j **21.** $I \circ R_l(\triangle PQR)$ $\triangle RQP$

Symmetry   A figure is symmetric if there is an isometry other than the   **14.9**
identity that maps the figure onto itself. Figures may have line symmetry,
point symmetry, rotational symmetry, or translational symmetry.

a. Draw all lines of symmetry.   **22.**   **23.**
b. Describe any rotational
   symmetries.
c. Does it have point
   symmetry?   parallelogram   rhombus

  22. a. no lines, b. rotational 180°,
  c. yes   **23.** a. diagonals, b.
  rotational 180°, c. yes

See *Teacher's Resource Book, Tests,* pp. 149–152.

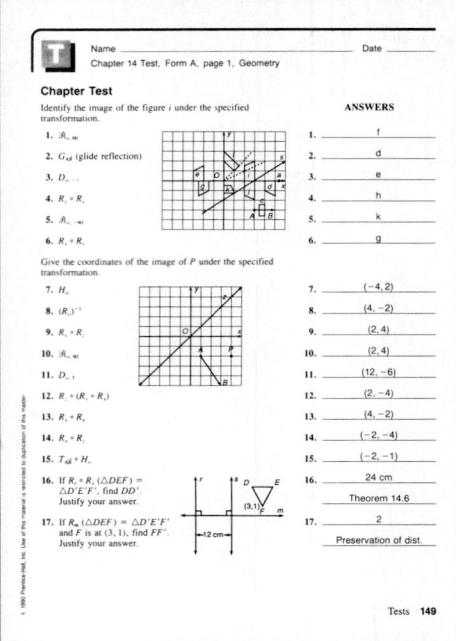

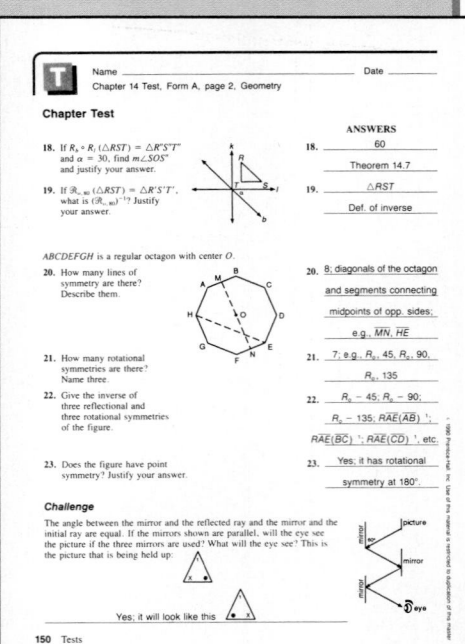

Draw the image of the figure under the specified transformation.
See Solutions Manual.

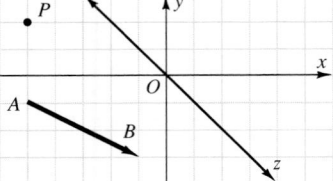

1. $R_{P,60}$ **2.** G_{AB} (glide reflection)

3. $D_{P,-1}$ **4.** $R_l \circ R_j$

Give the coordinates of the image of P under the specified transformation.

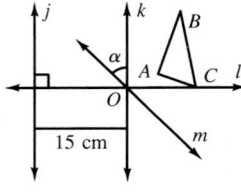

5. H_O (5, −2) **6.** $(R_z)^{-1}$ **7.** $R_{y,} \circ R_z$
  (−2, 5) (2, 5)

8. $\mathscr{R}_{O,90}$ **9.** $D_{O,3}$ **10.** $R_x \circ R_x$
  (−2, −5) (−15, 6) (−5, 2)

11. $R_z \circ (R_y \circ R_x)$ (2, −5) **12.** $T_{AB} \circ H_O$ (9, −4)

Justify each answer.

13. If $R_j \circ R_k(\triangle ABC) = \triangle A'B'C'$, then $BB' = \underline{\;?\;}$
  30 cm; Theorem 14.6
14. If $R_l(\triangle ABC) = \triangle A''B''C''$, then $CC' = \underline{\;?\;}$. 0, since $j \| k$
  Cel; preservation of distance
15. **a.** If $R_m \circ R_l(\triangle ABC) = \triangle A''B''C''$ and $\alpha = 40°$,
  then $m\angle AOA'' = \underline{\;?\;}$. 100, Th. 14.7
  b. If $\mathscr{R}_{O,70}(\triangle ABC) = \triangle A'B'C'$, what is $(\mathscr{R}_{O,70})^{-1}$?
  $\mathscr{R}_{O,-70}$ or $\mathscr{R}_{O,290}$, because their composition is I

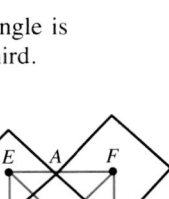

15 cm

***ABCDEF* is a regular hexagon with center O.**

16. How many lines of symmetry are there? Describe them.
  6; lines through O to each vertex and through midpts. of opp. sides
17. How many rotational symmetries? Name them.
  5; $\mathscr{R}_{O,60}$; $\mathscr{R}_{O,120}$; $\mathscr{R}_{O,180}$; $\mathscr{R}_{O,240}$; $\mathscr{R}_{O,300}$
18. Give the inverse of R_{CF}; $\mathscr{R}_{O,300}$. R_{CF}; $\mathscr{R}_{O,60}$

19. Does the figure have point symmetry? Justify your answer. yes; 180° rotational
20. Use transformations to verify the following theorem:
  The line segment joining the midpoints of two sides of a triangle is parallel to the third side and has one-half the length of the third.
  See page 787.

Challenge

$\triangle ABC$ has squares on sides $\overline{AC}$ and $\overline{AB}$. E and F are the centers of those squares and M is a midpoint. $H_M(E) = E'$ and $H_M(F) = F'$. Prove that $EFE'F'$ is a rhombus.

Chapter 14 Transformational Geometry

Alternative Assessment Have students complete the Critical Thinking activity, p. 14, in the *Teacher's Resource Book*. For Exercise 1, they should define the three transformations in their explanation. For Exercise 3, they should locate $\triangle ABC$ on a coordinate grid and then illustrate each of the transformations studied to show which ones preserve orientation. Have them draw a regular triangle and identify all types of symmetry in it.

Directions: In each item, compare a quantity in Column 1 with a quantity in Column 2. Write the letter of the correct answer from these choices:

A. The quantity in Column 1 is greater than the quantity in Column 2.
B. The quantity in Column 2 is greater than the quantity in Column 1.
C. The quantity in Column 1 is equal to the quantity in Column 2.
D. The relationship cannot be determined from the given information.

Notes: A symbol that appears in both columns has the same meaning in each column. All variables represent real numbers. Most figures are not drawn to scale.

Column 1	Column 2
1. Sum of prime factors of 32	Sum of prime factors of 15
2. $2\frac{2}{3} + 3\frac{1}{4}$	$6\frac{2}{3} - 1\frac{1}{8}$

$$\frac{x}{3} = \frac{5}{6}$$

Column 1	Column 2
3. $4x$	$\dfrac{25}{x}$
4. Slant height of a right circular cone with height 15 cm and base diameter 16 cm	Slant height of regular square pyramid with height 12 cm and base edge 18 cm

$$s > 0,\ t < 0$$

Column 1	Column 2
5. $\sqrt{\dfrac{s^2}{t^2}}$	$\dfrac{s}{t}$

$$A(-2,\ 1)$$
$$B(0,\ 4)$$
$$C(4,\ 9)$$

Column 1	Column 2
6. AC	$AB + BC$
7. $\sqrt{5^3 + 4^2}$	$(2\sqrt{3})^2$

Column 1   **Column 2**

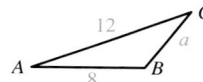

	Column 1	Column 2
8.	a	20
9.	a	10
10.	$m\angle B$	$m\angle C$

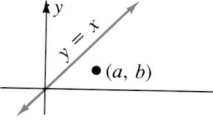

	Column 1	Column 2
11.	a	b

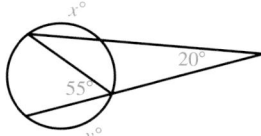

	Column 1	Column 2
12.	x	y
13.	$x + y$	180

The individual comments provided for certain problems may help students in solving them.

1. Some students may need to be reminded that 1 is not considered a prime number.
2. Improper fractions could also be used to answer this question.

Then, $\dfrac{8}{3} + \dfrac{13}{4} = \dfrac{32 + 39}{12} = \dfrac{71}{12} = \dfrac{142}{24}$

$\dfrac{20}{3} - \dfrac{9}{8} = \dfrac{160 - 27}{24} = \dfrac{133}{24}$

6. Any student trying to use direct calculation of the distances for this problem could find it difficult to answer the question since the values to be compared are $\sqrt{13} + \sqrt{41}$ and 10, and it is not readily apparent that $\sqrt{13} + \sqrt{41} > 10$.

See *Teacher's Resource Book* for *Preparing for College Entrance Exams.*

637

True or false? Justify each answer.

1. If $\angle RST$ and $\angle RSM$ are congruent adjacent angles, then $\overline{RS} \perp \overline{TM}$.   1.6
   false; ∠s must be rt. ∠s

2. "It is wet." is the negation of "It is dry." false; "It is not wet."   2.1

3. The formula to find the sum of the measures of the interior angles of a convex polygon with n sides is $(n - 2)180$. true; Th. 3.13   3.7

4. In $\triangle RAS$, if $\angle A \cong \angle S$, then $\overline{RA} \cong \overline{RS}$. true; conv. of isos. △ th.   5.1

5. If a base angle of an isosceles triangle has measure d, then the vertex angle has measure $180 - d$. false; 180 − 2d   3.4

6. If the numbers m and n are given, then $m > n$, $m = n$, or $m < n$.   5.2
   true; trichotomy

7. All plane angles of the same dihedral angle are congruent. true; Th. 5.11   5.7

8. An equiangular rectangle is a square. false; an equilateral rect. is a square   6.4

9. The geometric mean between 6 and 16 is 11. false; $\sqrt{96} = 4\sqrt{6}$ 7.2

10. If two triangles are similar, then they are also congruent.   7.4
    false; true only if corr. sides are ≅

11. A triangle with side lengths 2, 3, and $\sqrt{5}$ is a right triangle.   8.2
    true; $2^2 + (\sqrt{5})^2 = 3^2$

12. If an angle inscribed in a circle intercepts a major arc, then the measure of the angle is greater than 180. false; ∠ meas. is between 90 and 180   9.4

13. The lines that contain the altitudes of a triangle intersect at the orthocenter. true; def.   10.5

14. The area of a parallelogram with side lengths 8 and 10 is 80 square units.   11.2
    false; true only if ▱ is a rect.

15. If a trapezoid has a median of 9 units and a height of 10 units, then the area is 90 square units. true; median $= \frac{b_1 + b_2}{2}$ 11.3

16. If two similar cones have heights of 9 and 15, then the ratio of their volumes is $18:30$. false; $3^3:5^3$ 12.7

17. The midpoint between $(-2, -4)$ and $(4, 8)$ is $(2, 4)$. false; $(\frac{-2+4}{2}, \frac{-4+8}{2}) = (1,2)$ 13.3

18. A transformation is a one-to-one mapping from the whole plane to the whole plane. true; def. of transformation   14.1

Is each statement true *sometimes*, *always*, or *never*? Justify each answer.

19. If two lines are parallel to the third line, then they are __?__ parallel to each other. always; Th. 3.10   3.3

20. Supplementary angles are __?__ adjacent. sometimes; when ∠s form a linear pair   1.5

638   Chapter 14 Transformational Geometry

Connections for p. 636

Transformational approach	$\longleftrightarrow$	Coordinate approach	$\longleftrightarrow$	Synthetic approach

Ex. 20 p. 636   EXAM. 1 p. 570   Ex. 19 p. 243
                Ex. 19, p. 576

21. If $\angle ABC \cong \angle ABD$, then $\overrightarrow{AB}$ is $\underline{\ ?\ }$ the angle bisector. always; def. ∠ bis.   1.4

22. If $\triangle YMA \cong \triangle NOD$, then $\angle A$ is $\underline{\ ?\ }$ congruent to $\angle D$. always; CPCTC   4.1

23. If plane P is perpendicular to plane Q, and plane Q is parallel to plane R, then plane P is $\underline{\ ?\ }$ perpendicular to plane R. always; Th. 3.1 and 3.5   3.1

24. If two lines have a transversal, and a pair of alternate interior angles are congruent, then the lines are $\underline{\ ?\ }$ parallel. always; Th. 3.6   3.3

Given $\triangle ABC$ with $\overrightarrow{AC}$ extended to D.

25. $m\angle 3$ is $\underline{\ ?\ }$ less than $m\angle 4$. sometimes; if ∠3 is acute   3.4

26. $m\angle 1 + m\angle 2$ is $\underline{\ ?\ }$ equal to $m\angle 4$. always; Th. 3.12   5.2

27. $m\angle 1$ is $\underline{\ ?\ }$ equal to $m\angle 4$. never; Th. 5.5   3.4

28. $m\angle 1 + m\angle 2$ is $\underline{\ ?\ }$ greater than $m\angle 3$. sometimes; when $m\angle 3 < 90$ 5.2

29. In $\triangle BUD$, if $m\angle B < m\angle D$, then $BD \underline{\ ?\ } < BU$. sometimes; when $m\angle D > m\angle U$ 5.5

30. An equiangular triangle is $\underline{\ ?\ }$ equilateral. always; cor. to Th. 5.2   3.4

31. The measures of the sides of a triangle can $\underline{\ ?\ }$ be 1, 2, and 3. never; △inequality Th.   5.6

32. An equiangular parallelogram is $\underline{\ ?\ }$ a rectangle. always; def. of rect.   6.4

33. If $2:3$ as $11:x$, then $x \underline{\ ?\ } = 33$. never; $x = \frac{33}{2}$ 7.1

34. If $\triangle RIT \sim \triangle USC$, then $\angle T \cong \angle S$. sometimes; when $\angle S \cong \angle C$ 7.3

35. Two circles are $\underline{\ ?\ }$ similar. always   7.3

36. In a 30°-60°-90° triangle, the ratio of the legs is $\underline{\ ?\ }$ $1:2$. never; $1:\sqrt{3}$ 8.4

37. The tangent of an acute angle of a right triangle is $\underline{\ ?\ }$ less than 1. sometimes; when the adj. leg is longer than the opp. leg   8.6

38. If a line is drawn tangent to a circle, then it will $\underline{\ ?\ }$ be perpendicular to the radius drawn to the point of tangency. always; Th. 9.1   9.2

39. If an angle is inscribed in a semicircle, then it is $\underline{\ ?\ }$ a right angle. always; Th. 9.9   9.4

40. If an angle inscribed in a circle measures 40°, then its intercepted arc $\underline{\ ?\ }$ measures 40°. never; ∠ meas. 80°   9.4

41. The centroid of a triangle can $\underline{\ ?\ }$ be found by constructing the angle bisectors. sometimes; when the triangle is equilateral   10.5

Is each statement true *sometimes*, *always*, or *never*? Justify each answer.

42. The locus of points equidistant from two points is $\underline{\ ?\ }$ two intersecting circles. never; locus is the ⊥ bis. of the seg. joining the pts.   10.6

43. If a radius is perpendicular to a chord, then it $\underline{\ ?\ }$ bisects the chord. always; Th. 9.5   9.3

93. Plan: Show △AEL ≅ ∠RLE by SAS.

Then $\overline{AL} \cong \overline{RE}$ by CPCTC.

Proof:

Statements	Reasons
1. ∠OEL ≅ ∠OLE; A midpt. of $\overline{OE}$; R midpt. of $\overline{OL}$	1. Given
2. $\overline{OE} \cong \overline{OL}$	2. Conv. of Isos. △ Th.
3. $OE = OL$	3. Def. ≅ seg.
4. $\frac{1}{2}OE = \frac{1}{2}OL$	4. Mult. prop.
5. $AE = \frac{1}{2}OE$; $RL = \frac{1}{2}OL$	5. Midpt. Th.
6. $AE = RL$	6. Subst. prop.
7. $\overline{AE} \cong \overline{RL}$	7. Def. ≅ seg.
8. $\overline{EL} \cong \overline{LE}$	8. Refl. prop.
9. △AEL ≅ △RLE	9. SAS
10. $\overline{AL} \cong \overline{RE}$	10. CPCTC

Concl.: In the given figure, if ∠OEL ≅ ∠OLE and A and R are midpts., then $\overline{AL} \cong \overline{ER}$.

94. Plan: Show △AEP ≅ △RLP by SAS. Then use ≅ corr. parts $\overline{AE}$ and $\overline{RL}$ to show △AEL ≅ △RLE by SSS. Then ∠AEL ≅ ∠RLE by CPCTC.

Proof:

Statements	Reasons
1. $\overline{AP} \cong \overline{PR}$; $\overline{EP} \cong \overline{PL}$	1. Given
2. ∠APE ≅ ∠RPL	2. Vert. ∠s are ≅.
3. △AEP ≅ △RLP	3. SAS
4. $\overline{AE} \cong \overline{RL}$	4. CPCTC
5. $AP = PR$; $EP = PL$	5. Def. ≅ seg.
6. $AP + PL = PR + EP$	6. Add. prop.
7. $AP + PL = AL$; $PR + EP = RE$	7. Def. of betw.
8. $AL = RE$	8. Subst. prop.
9. $\overline{AL} \cong \overline{RE}$	9. Def. of ≅ seg.
10. $\overline{EL} \cong \overline{EL}$	10. Refl. prop.
11. △AEL ≅ △RLE	11. SSS
12. ∠AEL ≅ ∠RLE	12. CPCTC

Concl.: In the given figure, if $\overline{AP} \cong \overline{PR}$ and $\overline{EP} \cong \overline{PL}$, then ∠AEL ≅ ∠RLE.

640

---

44. The area of a regular polygon is ___?___ equal to one-half the product of the apothem and the perimeter. always; Th. 11.5 — 11.1

45. In a right pyramid, the height is ___?___ equal in length to a slant height. — 12.2
never; slant height is the hyp. of a rt. △.

46. The base of a prism is ___?___ a regular polygon. — 12.1
sometimes; when the prism is regular

47. If the slopes of two lines are $\frac{2}{3}$ and $-\frac{3}{2}$, then the lines are ___?___ parallel. — 13.6
never; lines are ⊥

48. A glide followed by a reflection in a line parallel to the glide ___?___ yields a glide reflection. always; def. of glide reflection — 14.2

Complete.

49. If two parallel lines have a transversal, then the interior angles on the same side of the transversal are ___?___. supp. — 3.2

Given △ABC and △XYZ.

50. If ∠A ≅ ∠Z, ∠B ≅ ∠Y, and $\overline{AB} \cong \overline{YZ}$, then ___?___ ≅ ___?___ because ___?___. — 4.2
△ABC ≅ △ZYX; ASA

51. If ∠B ≅ ∠Z, $\overline{BC} \cong \overline{ZY}$, and $\overline{AB} \cong \overline{XZ}$, then ___?___ because ___?___.
△ABC ≅ △XZY; SAS

52. If ∠A ≅ ∠Z, $\overline{AB} \cong \overline{XZ}$, and $\overline{BC} \cong \overline{XY}$, then ___?___ because ___?___.
no concl.; no SSA Post. or Th.

53. If $\overline{AC} \cong \overline{ZX}$, $\overline{BC} \cong \overline{YZ}$, and ∠B ≅ ∠Z, then ___?___ because ___?___.
no concl.; need another pair of corr. parts ≅.

Given △STE and △MUR. — 5.6

54. If $\overline{SE} \cong \overline{RM}$, $\overline{ST} \cong \overline{MU}$, and $m\angle S > m\angle M$, then ET ___?___ RU. >

55. If $ET < RU$, $\overline{TS} \cong \overline{MU}$, and $\overline{ES} \cong \overline{RM}$, then $m\angle S$ ___?___ $m\angle M$. <

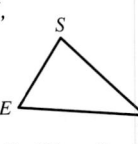

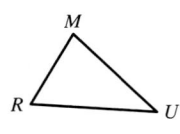

Polygon ABCD has diagonals intersecting at E. Give the best name for each. — 6.1, 6.4

56. If $\overline{AB} \cong \overline{DC}$ and $\overline{AB} \parallel \overline{DC}$, then it is a ___?___. ▱

57. If $\overline{AC}$ and $\overline{BD}$ bisect each other, then it is a ___?___. ▱

58. If $\overline{AD} \cong \overline{BC}$ and $\overline{AB} \parallel \overline{DC}$, then it is a ___?___. isos. trap.

59. If $\overline{AB} \cong \overline{DC} \cong \overline{BC} \cong \overline{AD}$, then it is a ___?___. rhombus

60. If $\overline{AC} \cong \overline{BD}$ and $\overline{AC} \perp \overline{BD}$, then it is a ___?___. quad.

61. If $\overline{AD} \cong \overline{BC}$ and $\overline{AE} \cong \overline{BE}$, then it is a ___?___. quad.

CD and UE intersect at N. Complete.

62. If $\dfrac{UN}{NE} = \dfrac{DN}{NC}$, then △ ___?___ ~ △ ___?___ because ___?___. — 7.5
UND   ENS   SAS Th.

63. △ ___?___ ~ △ ___?___ if $\dfrac{DU}{EC} = \dfrac{UN}{NC} = $ ___?___ because ___?___.
DUN   ECN $\frac{DN}{NE}$ SSS Th.

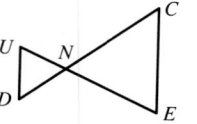

△ABC has side lengths _a_, _b_, and _c_. 8.3

64. If $a^2 + c^2 = b^2$, then △ABC is __?__. a rt. △

65. If $a^2 + c^2 < b^2$, then △ABC is __?__. obtuse

66. An equilateral triangle with a height of $10\sqrt{3}$ has a perimeter = __?__ 60

△RGT has a right ∠G. 8.6

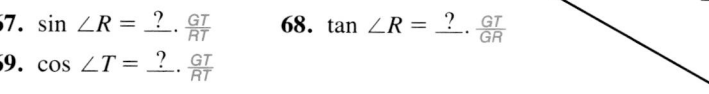

67. sin ∠R = __?__. $\frac{GT}{RT}$ **68.** tan ∠R = __?__. $\frac{GT}{GR}$

69. cos ∠T = __?__. $\frac{GT}{RT}$

70. The angle down from the line of sight of the horizon is called the angle of __?__. depression 8.7

71. If two chords of a circle are unequal in length, then the __?__ chord is nearer to the center of the circle. longer 9.3

72. If two arcs of a circle are included between parallel secants, then the arcs are __?__. ≅ 9.4

73. The circumcenter of a triangle is the intersection of the __?__. 10.3
⊥ bisectors of the sides

74. The locus of points equidistant from the sides of an angle is __?__. ∠bis. 10.6

75. If the diagonals of a rhombus have lengths 6 and 8, then the area is __?__ and the perimeter is __?__. 24; 20 11.2

76. If a square has a radius of 5, then its area is __?__. 50 11.4

77. If the radii of two circles have the ratio 3 : 7, then the ratio of circumferences is __?__ and the ratio of areas is __?__. 3 : 7; 9 : 49 11.6

78. The volume of a sphere with radius 6 in. is __?__. 288 π in.³ 12.6

79. The distance between the points (1, −5) and (−4, −2) is __?__. $\sqrt{34}$ 13.1

80. The slope of the line through (1, −5) and (−4, −2) is __?__. $-\frac{3}{5}$ 13.4

81. If isometry _S_ maps _A_ to _A′_ and _B_ to _B′_, then $\overline{AB}$ __?__ $\overline{A′B′}$. ≅ 14.1

82. If a transformation $S:(x, y) \rightarrow (2x, y - 2)$, then the image of (3, 3) is __?__, and the preimage of (3, 3) is __?__. (6, 1); ($\frac{3}{2}$, 5) 14.1

Complete.

83. Similar pentagons 7.2

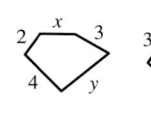 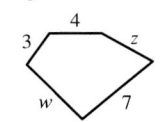

$w =$ __?__ 6
$x =$ __?__ $\frac{8}{3}$
$y =$ __?__ $\frac{14}{3}$
$z =$ __?__ $\frac{9}{2}$

84. 7.7

$x =$ __?__ $\frac{27}{7}$
$y =$ __?__ $\frac{100}{7}$

Additional Answers for p. 642

95. Plan: Concl. follows immediately from the Conv. of the Hinge Th.
Proof:

Statements	Reasons
1. $\overline{RV} \cong \overline{VS} \cong \overline{ST}$; $RS > VT$	1. Given
2. $m\angle 1 > m\angle 2$	2. Conv. of the Hinge Th.

Concl.: In the given figure, if $RV \cong VS \cong ST$ and $RS > VT$, then $m\angle 1 > m\angle 2$.

96. Plan: Concl. follows from the △ ∠-bis. Th. and prop. properties.
Proof:

Statements	Reasons
1. ∠S is a rt. ∠.	1. Given
2. △RST is a rt △ with hyp. $\overline{RT}$.	2. Defs. of rt △ and hyp.
3. $\overline{SV} \perp \overline{RT}$	3. Given
4. $\overline{SV}$ is an alt.	4. Def. of alt.
5. $\frac{RV}{RS} = \frac{RS}{RT}$	5. The alt. to the hyp. of a rt. △ intersects it so that the length of each leg is the geometric mean between the length of its adj. segment and the length of the entire hyp.
6. $RS^2 = RV \cdot RT$	6. Means-extremes prop. of a prop.

Concl.: In the given △, if ∠S is a rt. ∠ and $\overline{SV} \perp \overline{RT}$, then $RS^2 = RV \cdot RT$.

641

642

97. Plan: Assume the negation of the concl. and show that it leads to a contradiction.

Proof:

Assume $k \parallel l$ Negation of the concl.

$\angle 1 \cong \angle 2$ If lines are $\parallel$, alt. ext. $\angle$s are $\cong$.

$m\angle 1 = m\angle 2$ Def. of $\cong \angle$s

Contradiction: $m\angle 1 \neq m\angle 2$

Conclusion: Since the assumption $k \parallel l$ leads to a contradiction of the given information, the assumption is false. Hence, $k \nparallel l$.

98. Given: $\square ABCD$

Prove: $\overline{AC}$ and $\overline{BD}$ bisect each other.

Plan: Use the coords. and the Midpt. formula to show that $\overline{AC}$ and $\overline{BD}$ have the same midpts.

Proof:

Statements	Reasons
1. $\square ABCD$	1. Given
2. Midpt. of $\overline{AC}$ has coords. $(\frac{a+b}{2}, \frac{c}{2})$, and the midpt. of $\overline{BD}$ has coords. $(\frac{b+a}{2}, \frac{c}{2})$	2. Midpt. formula
3. $\overline{AC}$ and $\overline{BD}$ have the same midpt.	3. Subst. prop.
4. $\overline{AC}$ and $\overline{BD}$ bisect each other.	4. Def. of bis.

Concl.: If $ABCD$ is a $\square$, then $\overline{AC}$ and $\overline{BD}$ bisect each other.

---

85.   8.1

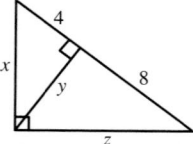

$x = \underline{\ ?\ }$ $y = \underline{\ ?\ }$ $z = \underline{\ ?\ }$

   $4\sqrt{3}$ $4\sqrt{2}$ $4\sqrt{6}$

86.   8.4, 11.2

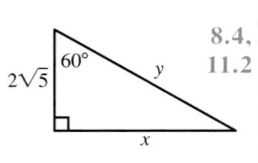

$x = \underline{\ ?\ }$ $y = \underline{\ ?\ }$

  $2\sqrt{15}$ $4\sqrt{5}$

87.   9.2

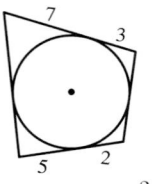

Perimeter $= \underline{\ ?\ }$

            34

88.   9.7

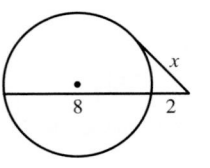

$x = \underline{\ ?\ }$

  $2\sqrt{5}$

89.   8.4, 11.3

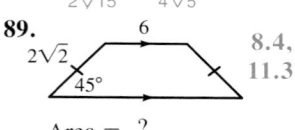

Area $= \underline{\ ?\ }$

       16

Perimeter $= \underline{\ ?\ }$

           $16 + 4\sqrt{2}$

90. Regular hexagon   11.4

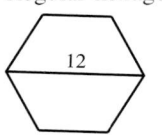

Apothem $= \underline{\ ?\ }$

          $3\sqrt{3}$

Perimeter $= \underline{\ ?\ }$

          36

Area $= \underline{\ ?\ }$

        $54\sqrt{3}$

91.   11.6, 11.7

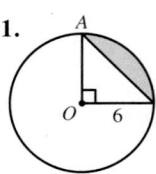

Length of $\overparen{AB} = \underline{\ ?\ }$

              3π

Area of sector $AOB = \underline{\ ?\ }$

                 9π

Area of shaded segment $= \underline{\ ?\ }$

             $9\pi - 18$

See side column pages 640–642.

92.   12.5

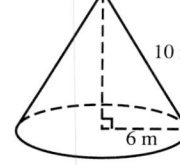

$L = \underline{\ ?\ }$

      60π

$T = \underline{\ ?\ }$

      96π

$V = \underline{\ ?\ }$

      96π

93. Given: $\angle OEL \cong \angle OLE$;
       A midpoint of $\overline{OE}$;
       R midpoint of $\overline{OL}$

Prove: $\overline{AL} \cong \overline{RE}$

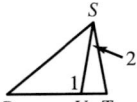

94. Given: $\overline{AP} \cong \overline{PR}$;
       $\overline{EP} \cong \overline{PL}$

Prove: $\angle AEL \cong \angle RLE$

95. Given: $\overline{RV} \cong \overline{VS} \cong \overline{ST}$;
       $RS > VT$

Prove: $m\angle 1 > m\angle 2$

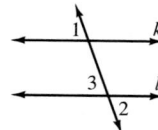

96. Given: S is a rt. $\angle$;
       $\overline{SV} \perp \overline{RT}$.

Prove: $RS^2 = RV \cdot RT$

97. Write an indirect proof.

Given: $m\angle 1 \neq m\angle 2$

Prove: $k \nparallel l$

98. Write a coordinate proof for this theorem: The diagonals of a parallelogram bisect each other.

Chapter 1   The Language of Geometry

Use the figure to name the following.

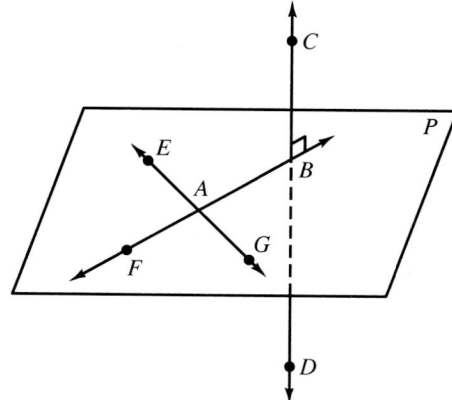

1. Three lines Answers may vary. $\overleftrightarrow{EG}$, $\overleftrightarrow{FB}$, $\overleftrightarrow{CD}$

2. Two right angles ∠CBA, ∠ABD

3. Two angles adjacent to ∠EAF
   ∠EAB, ∠GAF

4. Three collinear points
   Answers may vary. E, A, G; B, A, F

5. Three noncollinear points
   Answers may vary. E, A, D; C, A, F

6. Two skew lines $\overleftrightarrow{EG}$, $\overleftrightarrow{CD}$

7. Two supplementary angles Answers
   may vary. ∠EAF and ∠GAF, ∠EAB and ∠BAG

8. Two pairs of vertical angles
   ∠EAB and ∠GAF, ∠EAF and ∠BAG

9. Two perpendicular lines $\overleftrightarrow{FB}$ and $\overleftrightarrow{CD}$

10. The intersection of plane P and $\overleftrightarrow{CD}$ B

11. The ray opposite $\overrightarrow{AB}$ $\overrightarrow{AF}$

For Exercises 12–14, use $\overleftrightarrow{ED}$.

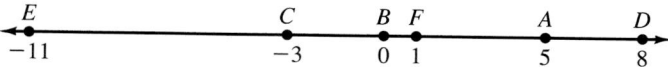

12. What is the distance from D to C? 11

13. What is the midpoint of $\overline{AC}$? F

14. Which two points are equidistant from C? E, A

For Exercises 15–20, use the figure at the right.

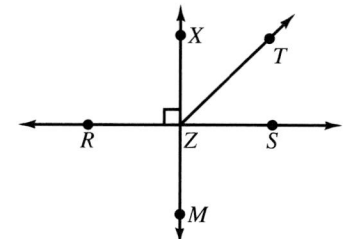

15. Name two complementary angles. ∠XZT and ∠TZS

16. What angle is supplementary to ∠TZS? ∠TZR

17. If $\overline{RZ} \cong \overline{ZS}$, then $\overleftrightarrow{XM}$ is called the ? . ⊥ bis.

18. If ∠XZT ≅ ∠TZS, then $\overrightarrow{ZT}$ is called the ? . ∠ bis.

19. Name two obtuse angles. ∠TZR, ∠TZM

20. If $m∠XZT = 42$, then $m∠TZS = $? , $m∠TZM = $? ,
    and $m∠TZR = $? . 48 138 132

21. If an angle exceeds its supplement by 42, find the measure of each angle.
    69, 111

Chapter 2   The Logic of Geometry

Give the postulate, property, definition, or theorem that justifies each statement.

1. If $\angle A \cong \angle B$ and $\angle B \cong \angle C$, then $\angle A \cong \angle C$. Trans. prop.

2. If $2AM = AB$, then $AM = \frac{1}{2}AB$. Division

3. If $\angle A \cong \angle B$ and $m\angle A + m\angle M = 180$, then $m\angle B + m\angle M = 180$.
   Subst. prop.

4. If $\overline{RS} \cong \overline{MT}$, then $\overline{RT} \cong \overline{SM}$. Add. prop.   R━━━━S━T━━━M

5. $\overline{PX} \cong \overline{PX}$. Refl. prop.

6. If $\angle 1$ is a supplement of $\angle 2$ and $\angle 2$ is a supplement of $\angle 3$, then $\angle 1 \cong \angle 3$. Th. 2.3: ∠s that are supp. of the same ∠ are ≅.

7. If $\frac{2}{3}x = 12$, then $x = 18$. Mult. prop.

8. Write the conditional, converse, inverse, and contrapositive of *Vertical angles are congruent*. State the truth value of each. See Solutions Manual.

9. Write the biconditional of the statement in Exercise 8.

10. If vertical angles are complementary, find the measure of each angle. 45

11. If $\angle 1$ and $\angle 2$ are complementary, $\angle 2$ and $\angle 3$ are complementary, and $\angle 3$ and $\angle 4$ are supplementary, then $\angle 1$ and $\angle 4$ are ___?___. supp.

12. **Given:** $\angle 1 \cong \angle 3$
    Prove: $\angle 2 \cong \angle 4$ See Solutions Manual.

13. **Given:** $\angle 1 \cong \angle 2$
    Prove: $\angle 3 \cong \angle 4$

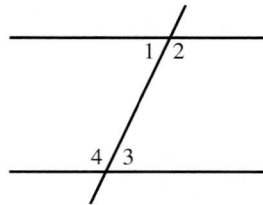

14. **Given:** $\angle ABC \cong \angle ACB$,
    $\overline{BE}$ bisects $\angle ABC$,
    $\overline{EC}$ bisects $\angle ACB$.
    Prove: $\angle 1 \cong \angle 2$

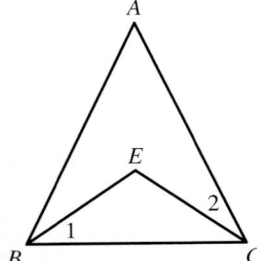

Chapter 3   Parallelism

If $l \parallel m$, give the name for each angle pair and the relationship that exists.

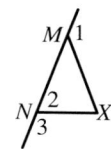

1. $\angle 6$ and $\angle 1$. same-side int., supp.

2. $\angle 4$ and $\angle 2$. alt. ext., $\cong$

3. $\angle 7$ and $\angle 5$. corr., $\cong$

4. $\angle 3$ and $\angle 1$. alt. int., $\cong$

5. $\angle 5$ and $\angle 8$. vert., $\cong$

6. If $a \parallel b$, $b \parallel c$, and $a \perp d$, then c _?_ d. $\perp$

7. If $r \perp m$ and $m \perp n$, then r _?_ n. $\parallel$

8. In a right triangle, one acute angle measures twice the other. Find the measures of the three angles. 30, 60, 90

9. If $a \parallel b$ and $m\angle 1 = 70$, find the measures of all the other angles.
$m\angle 3 = m\angle 5 = m\angle 7 = 70$;
$m\angle 2 = m\angle 4 = m\angle 6 = m\angle 8 = 110$

10. In $\triangle MNX$, if $\angle 2 \cong \angle X$ and $m\angle 1 = 110$, find the measure of $\angle 3$. 125

11. If one side of a regular heptagon measures 10.2 m, what is the length of the perimeter of the heptagon? 71.4 m

12. The sum of the measures of the exterior angles of a polygon with 20 sides is _?_. 360

13. Each interior angle of a regular quadrilateral measures _?_. 90°

14. Find the sum of the measures of the interior angles of a decagon. 1440

15. Find the number of sides of a regular polygon if each interior angle has a measure of 150. 12

16. Given: $\overline{AB} \parallel \overline{CD}$, $\overline{AD} \parallel \overline{BC}$
Prove: $\angle A \cong \angle C$
See Solutions Manual.

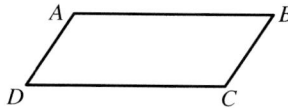

17. Given: $\angle 1$ and $\angle 4$ are supp.
Prove: $n \parallel p$

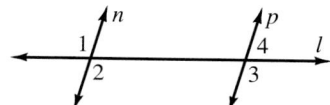

Chapter 4   Congruent Triangles

1. Name eight ways of proving triangles congruent.
   SSS, SAS, ASA, AAS, HL, HA, LA, LL
2. If $\triangle MAP \cong \triangle CAR$, then $\triangle ARC$ is congruent to what triangle? $\triangle APM$

State and verify each triangle congruence.

3.

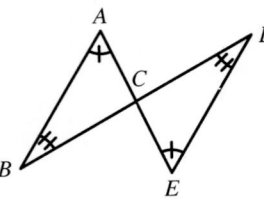

not enough information

4.

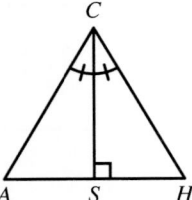

$\triangle CAS \cong \triangle CHS$, LA

5.

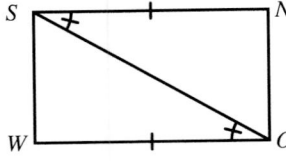

$\triangle SNO \cong \triangle OWS$, SAS

6.

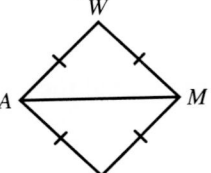

$\triangle AWM \cong \triangle ARM$, SSS

7.

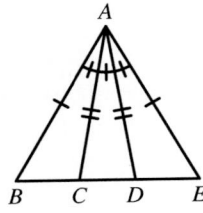

$\triangle ABC \cong \triangle AED$, SAS;
$\triangle BAD \cong \triangle EAC$, SAS

8.

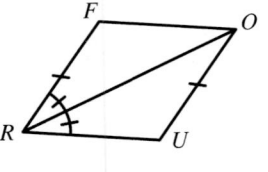

not enough information

Write *altitude, angle bisector,* or *median* to name each segment in $\triangle ABC$.

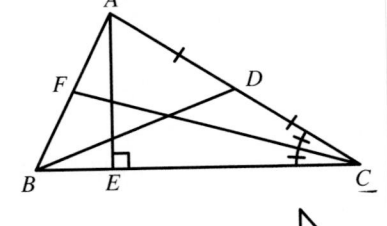

9. $\overline{AE}$
   altitude

10. $\overline{BD}$
   median

11. $\overline{FC}$
   $\angle$bis.

12. The triangles are congruent.
   Find each indicated measure.
   w = 9, x = 50, y = 15, z = 40

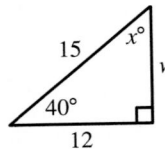

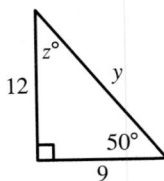

13. **Given:** $\overline{AC} \parallel \overline{BD}$, $\overline{AC} \cong \overline{BD}$,
   D is the midpoint of $\overline{CE}$.
   Prove: $\angle A \cong \angle B$ See Solutions Manual.

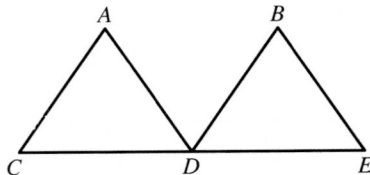

14. **Given:** $\overline{PB}$ is the $\perp$ bisector of $\overline{AC}$.
   Prove: $\angle A \cong \angle C$

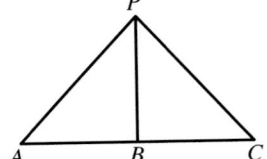

Chapter 5 Inequalities in Triangles

Find each indicated measure.

1.
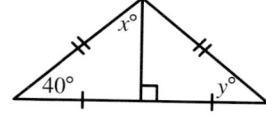
$x = 50$
$y = 40$

2.
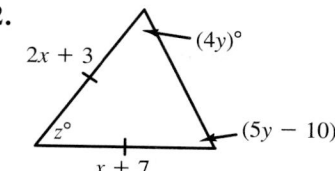
$x = 4$
$y = 10$
$z = 100$

3. Given isosceles $\triangle ABC$ with base $\overline{BC}$, isosceles $\triangle BCD$ with base $\overline{BD}$, and $m\angle D = 25$, find $m\angle A$. 80

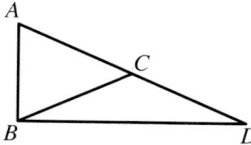

Draw $\triangle ABC$ and $\triangle XYZ$. Write <, >, or =.

4. If $AB > BC$, then $m\angle C$ _?_ $m\angle A$. >

5. If $\overline{AC} \cong \overline{XY}$, $\overline{AB} \cong \overline{YZ}$, and $m\angle A > m\angle Y$, then XZ _?_ BC. <

6. If $\overline{XY} \cong \overline{YZ}$, then $\angle X$ _?_ $\angle Z$. ≅

7. If $\overline{AB} \cong \overline{XY}$, $\overline{AC} \cong \overline{XZ}$, and $\angle A \cong \angle X$, then $\angle B$ _?_ $\angle Y$. ≅

8. If $\overline{XZ} \cong \overline{AB}$, $AC > XY$, and $\overline{BC} \cong \overline{YZ}$, then $m\angle B$ _?_ $m\angle Z$. >

Draw $\triangle ANG$ where $\angle N$ is 90° and G is between N and L on $\overrightarrow{NG}$.

9. AN _?_ AG <

10. $m\angle A$ _?_ $m\angle AGL$ <

11. If $m\angle A > m\angle AGN$, then NG _?_ AN. >

Can the three lengths be sides of a triangle?

12. 7, 8, 10 yes

13. 2.1, 2.1, 4 yes

14. 3, 4, 10 no

15. Name the dihedral angle with edge $\overline{NC}$. Answers may vary. R-NC-A

16. Name the dihedral angle with edge $\overline{RN}$. Answers may vary. G-RN-E

17. What is the intersection of the two dihedral angles named in Exercises 15 and 16? face RNCE

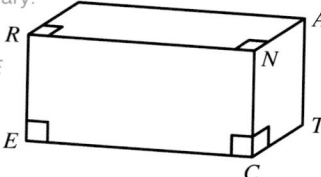

Write an indirect proof. See Solutions Manual.

18. Given: $AB \neq BC$
Prove: $m\angle C \neq m\angle A$

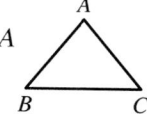

19. Given: $PR = PT$, $RS \neq ST$
Prove: $\triangle PRS \not\cong \triangle PTS$

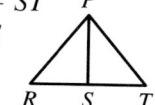

Extra Practice **647**

Chapter 6   Quadrilaterals

Complete each statement for a parallelogram.

1. Opposite sides are _?_ and _?_. ≅;∥

2. Opposite angles are _?_. ≅

3. Diagonals _?_ each other. bisect

4. Consecutive angles are _?_. supp.

Complete each statement.

5. An equilateral parallelogram is a _?_. rhombus

6. An equiangular parallelogram is a _?_. rectangle

7. An equiangular rhombus is a _?_. square

8. An equilateral rectangle is a _?_. square

9. A regular quadrilateral is a _?_. square

10. If the diagonals of a quadrilateral are perpendicular bisectors of each other, then the quadrilateral is a _?_. rhombus

11. Name the two ways of proving quadrilaterals congruent. ASASA, SASAS

Find the value of each variable.

12.
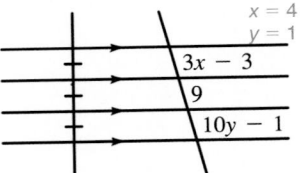
$x = 4$
$y = 1$
$3x - 3$
9
$10y - 1$

13.
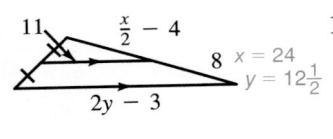
11
$\frac{x}{2} - 4$
8
$2y - 3$
$x = 24$
$y = 12\frac{1}{2}$

14.
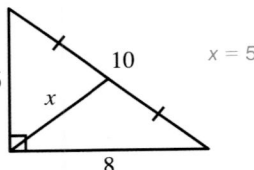
10
6
x
8
$x = 5$

15.
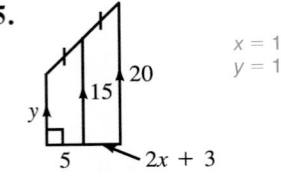
20
15
y
5
$2x + 3$
$x = 1$
$y = 10$

16.
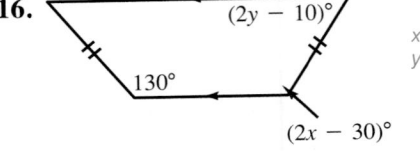
$(2y - 10)°$
$130°$
$(2x - 30)°$
$x = 80$
$y = 30$

17. Given: Quad. *QTAU* and quad. *LRDA* are rectangles, $TA = \frac{1}{2}LA$, $AD = \frac{1}{2}UA$, $\overline{RD} \cong \overline{QT}$.
Prove: Quad. $QTAU \cong$ quad. $LRDA$
See Solutions Manual

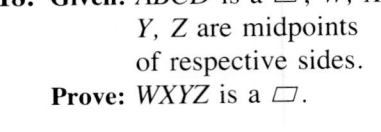

18. Given: *ABCD* is a ▱, *W*, *X*, *Y*, *Z* are midpoints of respective sides.
Prove: *WXYZ* is a ▱.

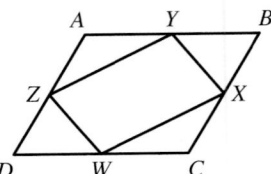

Chapter 7 Similarity

Given $4p = 5m$, complete each proportion.

1. $\dfrac{4}{m} = \dfrac{?}{?} \;\; {}^{5}_{p}$

2. $\dfrac{9}{?} = \dfrac{m+p}{?} \;\; {}_{5;\,p}$

3. $p = \dfrac{?}{?} \;\; {}^{5m}_{4}$

4. Find the measures of the angles of a triangle with sides in the ratio $1:6:11$. 10, 60, 110

Solve each proportion for x.

5. $\dfrac{6}{x} = \dfrac{x}{9}$ $3\sqrt{6}$

6. $\dfrac{x}{2} = \dfrac{9}{3x}$ $\sqrt{6}$

7. $\dfrac{a}{3b} = \dfrac{x}{12}$ $\frac{4a}{b}$

8. The two polygons are similar. Find each indicated measure.
$a = 130,\; b = 110,\; w = \frac{55}{4},\; x = \frac{48}{11},$
$y = \frac{24}{11},\; z = \frac{33}{4}$

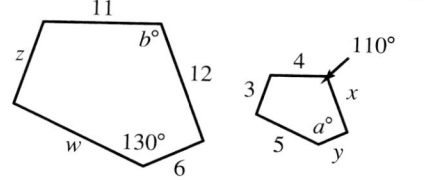

If two triangles are similar, write a similarity statement. Justify.

9.

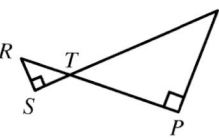

$\triangle RTS \sim \triangle MTP$, AA

10.

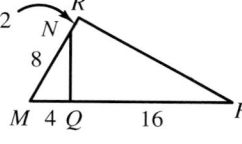

$\triangle NMQ \sim \triangle PMR$ SAS

11.

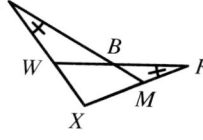

$\triangle WAB \sim \triangle MRB$, AA,
$\triangle AXM \sim \triangle RXW$, AA

Find the value of each variable.

12.

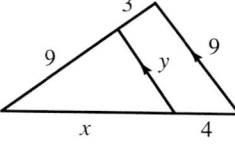

$x = 12,\; y = \frac{27}{4}$

13.

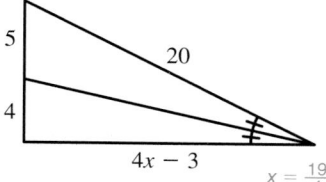

$x = \frac{19}{4}$

14. If the corresponding sides of two similar polygons are 4 and 9, respectively, and the perimeter of the smaller polygon is 20, what is the perimeter of the larger? 45

15. Given: $\overline{AB} \parallel \overline{DE}$
Prove: $\dfrac{CA}{BC} = \dfrac{CE}{CD}$ See Solutions Manual.

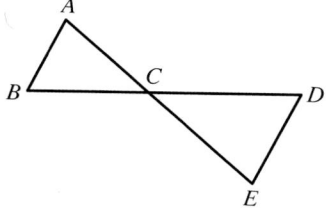

16. Given: $\angle 1 \cong \angle R$
Prove: $RS \cdot XZ = XT \cdot ZS$

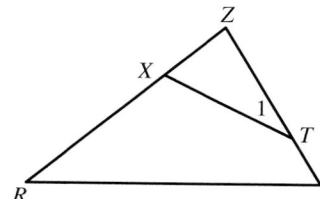

Chapter 8   Right Triangles

Find the value of each variable.

1.

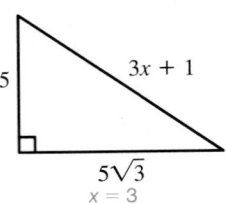

5, $3x + 1$, $5\sqrt{3}$
$x = 3$

2.

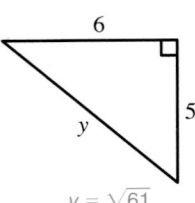

6, 5, y
$y = \sqrt{61}$

3.

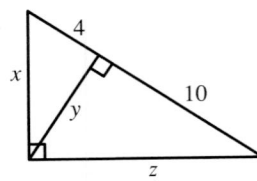

4, x, 10, y, z
$x = 2\sqrt{14}$, $y = 2\sqrt{10}$, $z = 2\sqrt{35}$

4.

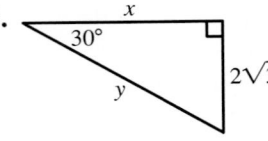

x, $30°$, y, $2\sqrt{3}$
$x = 6$, $y = 4\sqrt{3}$

5.

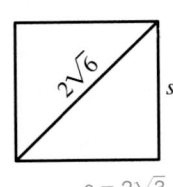

$2\sqrt{6}$, s
$s = 2\sqrt{3}$

6.

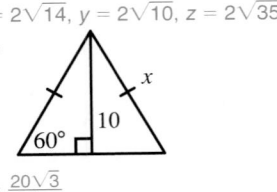

x, 10, $60°$
$x = \dfrac{20\sqrt{3}}{3}$

7.

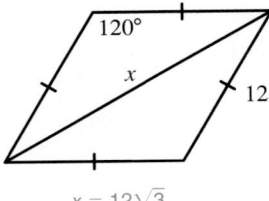

$120°$, x, 12
$x = 12\sqrt{3}$

8.

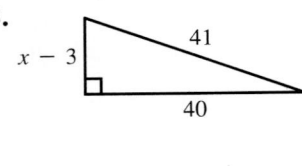

41, $x - 3$, 40
$x = 12$

9.

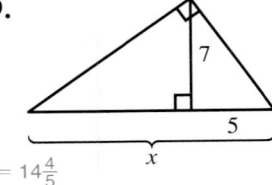

7, 5, x
$x = 14\frac{4}{5}$

10. Given right triangle ABC, complete the following.

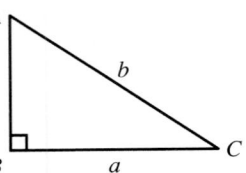

$\sin A = \underline{\ ?\ }\ \frac{a}{b}$ $\tan A = \underline{\ ?\ }\ \frac{a}{c}$ $\cos C = \underline{\ ?\ }\ \frac{a}{b}$

$\sin C = \underline{\ ?\ }\ \frac{c}{b}$ $\cos A = \underline{\ ?\ }\ \frac{c}{b}$ $\tan C = \underline{\ ?\ }\ \frac{c}{a}$

What kind of triangle, if any, has the given side measures?

11. 5, 7, 12 _{not a triangle}   **12.** 3, 3, 5 _{obt. isos.}   **13.** $\sqrt{5}$, $\sqrt{13}$, $2\sqrt{2}$
rt. scalene

Use a calculator or the table of trigonometric ratios on page 658 to find each indicated measure to the nearest tenth.

14. $x \approx 48.4$

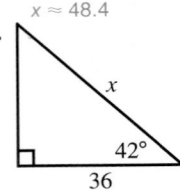

x, $42°$, 36

15. $x \approx 53.1$ $y \approx 36.9$

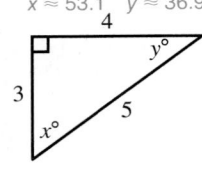

4, $y°$, 3, 5, $x°$

16. $x \approx 1.1$

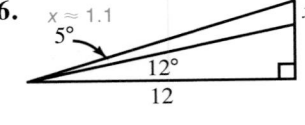

x, $5°$, $12°$, 12

17. A radio tower casts a shadow of 62 ft when the angle of elevation to the sun is 62°. How high is the tower to the nearest tenth of a foot? 116.6 ft

18. If the diagonals of a rhombus measure 15 and 18, what are the angle measures of the rhombus to the nearest tenth? 79.6, 100.4

650   Extra Practice

Chapter 9   Circles

Find the indicated measures.

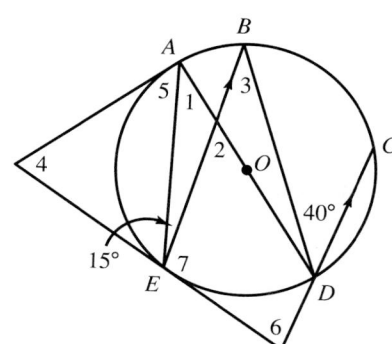

1. $m\widehat{BC}$ 80

$m\angle2$ 55

$m\widehat{CD}$ 70

$m\widehat{AB}$ 30

$m\widehat{AE}$ 100

$m\widehat{ED}$ 80

2. $m\angle1$ 40

$m\angle3$ 40

$m\angle4$ 80

$m\angle5$ 50

$m\angle6$ 65

$m\angle7$ 115

Find the value of x.

3.

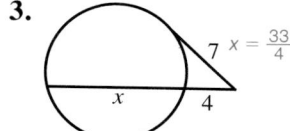

$x = \dfrac{33}{4}$

4.

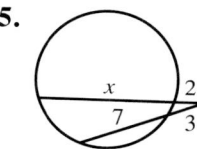

$x = 2\sqrt{6}$

5.

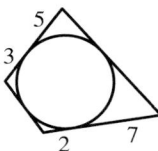

$x = 13$

6. In the figure at the right, what is the perimeter of the circumscribed quadrilateral? 34

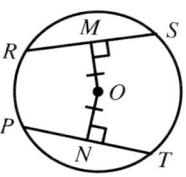

Complete each statement.

7. If $RM = 9$, then $PT = \underline{\ ?\ }$. 18

8. If $PT = 24$ and $MO = 5$, then the measure of the radius is $\underline{\ ?\ }$. 13

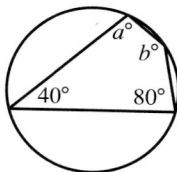

9. Find each indicated measure.

$a = 100,\ b = 140$

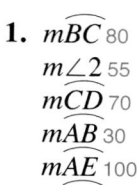

See Solutions Manual.

10. **Given:** Inscribed trapezoid. TRAP

Prove: *TRAP* is isosceles

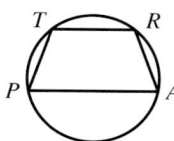

Chapter 10 Constructions and Loci

Construct the following. See Solutions Manual.

1. An equilateral triangle with a given side length

2. A parallelogram with a 30° angle, in which the length of one side is twice the length of the other

3. A square with a given side length

4. A rhombus with a 120° angle

5. The incenter of a given obtuse triangle

6. The circumcenter of a given obtuse triangle

7. The orthocenter of a given obtuse triangle

8. The centroid of a given obtuse triangle

9. Two segments tangent to a given circle from a given exterior point

Do the following constructions.

10. Inscribe a circle in a given acute triangle.

11. Circumscribe a circle around a given obtuse triangle.

12. Divide a given segment into three equal lengths.

13. A segment whose length is the geometric mean between the lengths of two given segments.

Describe each locus in a plane.

14. Points 6 m from a given point *R* Circle, r = 6 m, center *R*

15. Points equidistant from two given points ⊥ bis. of seg. betw. 2 pts.

16. Points equidistant from the sides of a given angle ∠ bis.

17. All points that are centers of circles tangent to a given line at a given point on the line line ⊥ to given line at given point excluding the given point

Describe each locus in space.

18. Point 6 m from given point *M* sphere, r = 6 m, center *M*

19. All points equidistant from the endpoints of a given segment
plane, ⊥ bis. of seg.

20. Points equidistant from two given parallel planes plane, ∥ to and equidistant from 2 given planes

Chapter 11   Area

Find the perimeter (circumference) and area of each polygon (circle).

1.

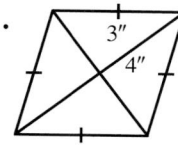

$P = 20$ in., $A = 24$ in.^{2}

2.

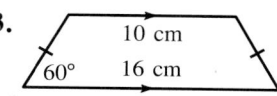

$P = 34$ ft, $A = 60$ ft^2

3.

10 cm
60°   16 cm

$P = 38$ cm, $A = 39\sqrt{3}$ cm^2

4.

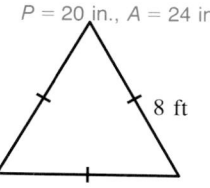

8 ft

$P = 24$ ft, $A = 16\sqrt{3}$ ft^2

5.

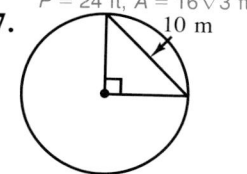

12 m
45°
13 m

$P = 50$ m, $A = 78\sqrt{2}$ m^2

6.

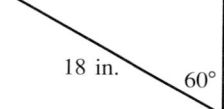

10 in.   10 in.
12 in.

$P = 32$ in., $A = 48$ in.^{2}

7.

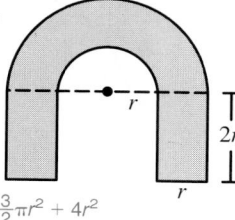

10 m

$C = 10\sqrt{2}\,\pi$m, $A = 50\pi$m^2

8.

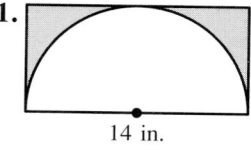

45°
10
6

$P = 20 + 4\sqrt{2}$ cm, $A = 32$ cm^2

9.

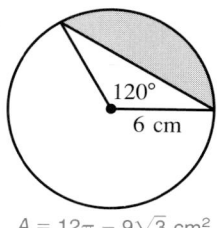

18 in.   60°

$P = 27 + 9\sqrt{3}$ in., $A = \frac{81}{2}\sqrt{3}$ in.^{2}

Find the area of each shaded region.

10.

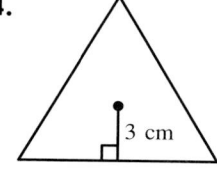

r
$2r$
r

$A = \frac{3}{2}\pi r^2 + 4r^2$

11.

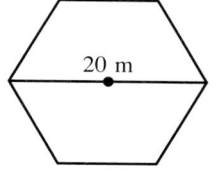

14 in.

$A = 98 - \frac{49}{2}\pi$ in.^{2}

12.

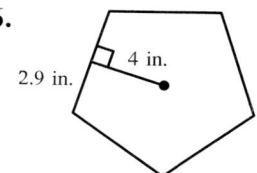

120°
6 cm

$A = 12\pi - 9\sqrt{3}$ cm^2

13. If two similar polygons have areas of 147 m^2 and 48 m^2, respectively, and the larger perimeter is 35 m, find the smaller perimeter. 20 m

Find the perimeter and area of each regular polygon.

14.

3 cm

$P = 18\sqrt{3}$ cm, $A = 27\sqrt{3}$ cm^2

15.

20 m

$P = 60$ m, $A = 150\sqrt{3}$ m^2

16.

4 in.
2.9 in.

$P = 29$ in., $A = 58$ in.^{2}

Chapter 12 Area and Volume of Solids

Find the lateral area, total area, and volume of each right polyhedron or sphere.

1.
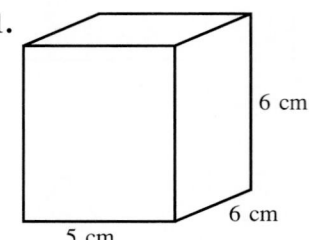

$L = 132$ cm^2
$T = 192$ cm^2
$V = 180$ cm^3

6 cm

6 cm

5 cm

2.
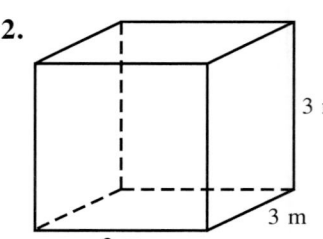

$L = 36$ m^2
$T = 54$ m^2
$V = 27$ m^3

3 m

3 m

3 m

3.
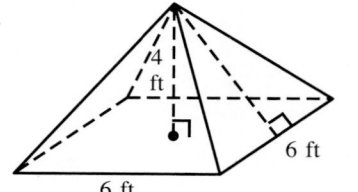

4 ft

6 ft

6 ft

$L = 60$ ft^2
$T = 96$ ft^2
$V = 48$ ft^3

4.
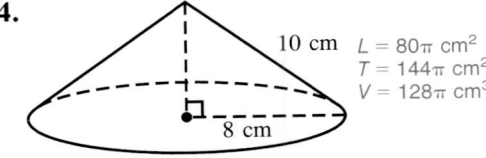

10 cm

8 cm

$L = 80\pi$ cm^2
$T = 144\pi$ cm^2
$V = 128\pi$ cm^3

5.
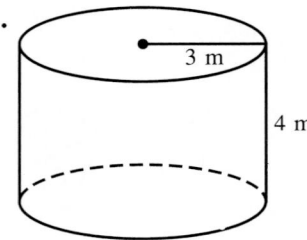

3 m

4 m

$L = 24\pi$ m^2
$T = 42\pi$ m^2
$V = 36\pi$ m^3

6.
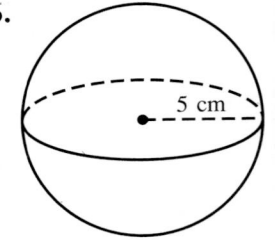

5 cm

$A = 100\pi$ cm^2
$V = \dfrac{500}{3}\pi$ cm^3

True or false? Justify your answer.

7. All cones are similar. false

8. All cubes are similar. true

9. All spheres are similar. true

10. All prisms are similar. false

11. If two similar cylinders have lateral areas of 81π ft^2 and 144π ft^2, respectively, find the ratios of their heights, total areas, and volume.
    3:4; 9:16; 27:64

12. Two similar pyramids have volumes of 3 m^3 and 375 m^3, respectively. What are the ratios of their slant heights, base areas, and total areas?
    1:5; 1:25; 1:25

Chapter 13   Coordinate Geometry

Give the coordinates of these points.

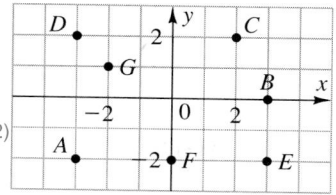

1. C (2, 2)   2. A (−3, −2)   3. E

(3, −2)

Name the points having these coordinates.

4. (−3, 2) D 5. (0, −2) F 6. (−2, 1) G

7. What is the distance between (−3, −8) and (2, 4)? 13

8. What kind of triangle has vertices (3, −1), (5, 1), and (−1, 1)?
   Obtuse scalene

9. What is the area of the rectangle that has consecutive vertices (8, 0), (2, −9), (−1, −7), and (5, 2)? 39

10. What is the equation of the circle with center (2, 5) and radius length 3? $(x - 2)^2 + (y - 5)^2 = 9$

11. What is the midpoint between (5, −1) and (2, 2)? (3.5, .5)

12. The point (−6, 8) is the midpoint between (−1, 2) and what point?
    (−11, 14)

13. Find the length of the median of the trapezoid with vertices (−4, −3), (−1, 4), (4, 4), and (7, −3). 8

14. What is the slope of the line containing points (8, −1) and (2, −9)? $\frac{4}{3}$

15. If the slopes of two lines are 4 and $-\frac{1}{4}$, respectively, what is the relationship between the lines? ⊥

16. Are points (1, −3), (−3, 1), and (−9, 6) collinear? no

17. Find the point of intersection of the lines $7x + 2y = -4$ and $2x + y = 1$. (−2, 5)

18. Given $A(-3, 5)$ and $B(-1, -4)$, find the slope of $\overleftrightarrow{AB}$, the slope of any line parallel to $\overleftrightarrow{AB}$, and the slope of any line perpendicular to $\overleftrightarrow{AB}$. $-\frac{9}{2}, -\frac{9}{2}, \frac{2}{9}$

19. Determine what kind of quadrilateral has consecutive vertices (−1, −6), (1, −3), (11, 1), and (9, −2). ▱

See Solutions Manual.

Use coordinate geometry to prove the following theorems.

20. The altitude to the base of an isosceles triangle bisects the base.

21. The midpoint of the hypotenuse of a right triangle is equidistant from the three vertices.

22. The diagonals of a rhombus are perpendicular.

Chapter 14   Transformational Geometry

1. An isometry is a transformation that preserves ?. <small>distance between points</small>

2. If $T(x, y) \rightarrow (x + 2, y - 5)$, what is the image of $(-2, -6)$? What is the preimage of $(-2, -6)$? <small>$(0, -11)$; $(-4, -1)$</small>

Find the following.

3. $R_x(2, -5)$ <small>$(2, 5)$</small>

4. $R_y(-5, 2)$ <small>$(5, 2)$</small>

5. $H_o(-6, 3)$ <small>$(6, -3)$</small>

6. $\mathcal{R}_{o, 90}(0, 7)$ <small>$(-7, 0)$</small>

Square $ABCD$ has center O. Find the following.

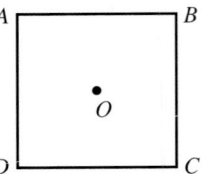

7. $\mathcal{R}_{o, -90}(A)$ <small>B</small>

8. $R_{AC}(B)$ <small>D</small>

9. $H_o(C)$ <small>A</small>

10. $\mathcal{R}_{B, 90}(A)$ <small>C</small>

11. $R_{BD}(\overline{AB})$ <small>$\overline{BC}$</small>

12. $D_{o, -1}(D)$ <small>B</small>

Write *translation, reflection, rotation,* or *half-turn* to complete each statement.

13. A ? maps △1 to △4. <small>translation</small>

14. A ? maps △3 to △7. <small>half-turn</small>

15. A ? maps △5 to △7. <small>reflection</small>

16. A ? maps △1 to △5. <small>rotation</small>

17. A glide ? maps △8 to △1. <small>reflection</small>

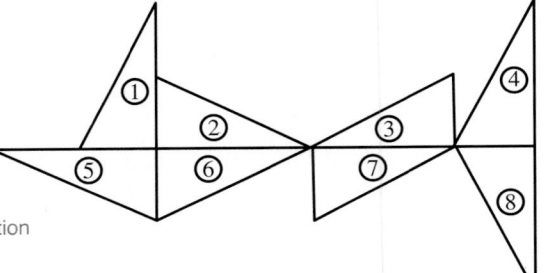

$\triangle ABC$ is equilateral, points X, Y, and Z are midpoints, and O is the center of the triangle. Find the following.

18. $T_{BZ}(Y)$ <small>X</small>

19. $D_{o, -2}(Z)$ <small>A</small>

20. $\mathcal{R}_{C, 60}(A)$ <small>B</small>

21. $D_{A, 2}(X)$ <small>C</small>

22. $\mathcal{R}_{o, 480}(Z)$ <small>X</small>

23. $H_x \circ H_y(B)$ <small>C</small>

24. $D_{B, \frac{1}{2}} \circ H_x(A)$ <small>Z</small>

25. $\mathcal{R}_{o, 120} \circ R_z(C)$ <small>C</small>

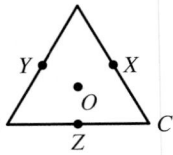

26. If $T(x, y) \rightarrow (x - 3, y + 2)$, find T^{-1}. <small>$(x + 3, y - 2)$</small>

Each letter has how many lines of symmetry?

27. A <small>1</small>

28. O <small>2</small>

29. R <small>0</small>

30. X <small>2</small>

Squares and Approximate Square Roots

Number n	Square n^2	Positive Square Root $\sqrt{n}$	Number n	Square n^2	Positive Square Root $\sqrt{n}$	Number n	Square n^2	Positive Square Root $\sqrt{n}$
1	1	1.000	51	2,601	7.141	101	10,201	10.050
2	4	1.414	52	2,704	7.211	102	10,404	10.100
3	9	1.732	53	2,809	7.280	103	10,609	10.149
4	16	2.000	54	2,916	7.348	104	10,816	10.198
5	25	2.236	55	3,025	7.416	105	11,025	10.247
6	36	2.449	56	3,136	7.483	106	11,236	10.296
7	49	2.646	57	3,249	7.550	107	11,449	10.344
8	64	2.828	58	3,364	7.616	108	11,664	10.392
9	81	3.000	59	3,481	7.681	109	11,881	10.440
10	100	3.162	60	3,600	7.746	110	12,100	10.488
11	121	3.317	61	3,721	7.810	111	12,321	10.536
12	144	3.464	62	3,844	7.874	112	12,544	10.583
13	169	3.606	63	3,969	7.937	113	12,769	10.630
14	196	3.742	64	4,096	8.000	114	12,996	10.677
15	225	3.873	65	4,225	8.062	115	13,225	10.724
16	256	4.000	66	4,356	8.124	116	13,456	10.770
17	289	4.123	67	4,489	8.185	117	13,689	10.817
18	324	4.243	68	4,624	8.246	118	13,924	10.863
19	361	4.359	69	4,761	8.307	119	14,161	10.909
20	400	4.472	70	4,900	8.367	120	14,400	10.954
21	441	4.583	71	5,041	8.426	121	14,641	11.000
22	484	4.690	72	5,184	8.485	122	14,884	11.045
23	529	4.796	73	5,329	8.544	123	15,129	11.091
24	576	4.899	74	5,476	8.602	124	15,376	11.136
25	625	5.000	75	5,625	8.660	125	15,625	11.180
26	676	5.099	76	5,776	8.718	126	15,876	11.225
27	729	5.196	77	5,929	8.775	127	16,129	11.269
28	784	5.292	78	6,084	8.832	128	16,384	11.314
29	841	5.385	79	6,241	8.888	129	16,641	11.358
30	900	5.477	80	6,400	8.944	130	16,900	11.402
31	961	5.568	81	6,561	9.000	131	17,161	11.446
32	1,024	5.657	82	6,724	9.055	132	17,424	11.489
33	1,089	5.745	83	6,889	9.110	133	17,689	11.533
34	1,156	5.831	84	7,056	9.165	134	17,956	11.576
35	1,225	5.916	85	7,225	9.220	135	18,225	11.619
36	1,296	6.000	86	7,396	9.274	136	18,496	11.662
37	1,369	6.083	87	7,569	9.327	137	18,769	11.705
38	1,444	6.164	88	7,744	9.381	138	19,044	11.747
39	1,521	6.245	89	7,921	9.434	139	19,321	11.790
40	1,600	6.325	90	8,100	9.487	140	19,600	11.832
41	1,681	6.403	91	8,281	9.539	141	19,881	11.874
42	1,764	6.481	92	8,464	9.592	142	20,164	11.916
43	1,849	6.557	93	8,649	9.644	143	20,449	11.958
44	1,936	6.633	94	8,836	9.695	144	20,736	12.000
45	2,025	6.708	95	9,025	9.747	145	21,025	12.042
46	2,116	6.782	96	9,216	9.798	146	21,316	12.083
47	2,209	6.856	97	9,409	9.849	147	21,609	12.124
48	2,304	6.928	98	9,604	9.899	148	21,904	12.166
49	2,401	7.000	99	9,801	9.950	149	22,201	12.207
50	2,500	7.071	100	10,000	10.000	150	22,500	12.247

Tables

Trigonometric Ratios

Angle	Sin	Cos	Tan	Angle	Sin	Cos	Tan
0°	0.0000	1.0000	0.0000	45°	0.7071	0.7071	1.0000
1	0.0175	0.9998	0.0175	46	0.7193	0.6947	1.0355
2	0.0349	0.9994	0.0349	47	0.7314	0.6820	1.0724
3	0.0523	0.9986	0.0524	48	0.7431	0.6691	1.1106
4	0.0698	0.9976	0.0699	49	0.7547	0.6561	1.1504
5	0.0872	0.9962	0.0875	50	0.7660	0.6428	1.1918
6	0.1045	0.9945	0.1051	51	0.7771	0.6293	1.2349
7	0.1219	0.9925	0.1228	52	0.7880	0.6157	1.2799
8	0.1392	0.9903	0.1405	53	0.7986	0.6018	1.3270
9	0.1564	0.9877	0.1584	54	0.8090	0.5878	1.3764
10	0.1736	0.9848	0.1763	55	0.8192	0.5736	1.4281
11	0.1908	0.9816	0.1944	56	0.8290	0.5592	1.4826
12	0.2079	0.9781	0.2126	57	0.8387	0.5446	1.5399
13	0.2250	0.9744	0.2309	58	0.8480	0.5299	1.6003
14	0.2419	0.9703	0.2493	59	0.8572	0.5150	1.6643
15	0.2588	0.9659	0.2679	60	0.8660	0.5000	1.7321
16	0.2756	0.9613	0.2867	61	0.8746	0.4848	1.8040
17	0.2924	0.9563	0.3057	62	0.8829	0.4695	1.8807
18	0.3090	0.9511	0.3249	63	0.8910	0.4540	1.9626
19	0.3256	0.9455	0.3443	64	0.8988	0.4384	2.0503
20	0.3420	0.9397	0.3640	65	0.9063	0.4226	2.1445
21	0.3584	0.9336	0.3839	66	0.9135	0.4067	2.2460
22	0.3746	0.9272	0.4040	67	0.9205	0.3907	2.3559
23	0.3907	0.9205	0.4245	68	0.9272	0.3746	2.4751
24	0.4067	0.9135	0.4452	69	0.9336	0.3584	2.6051
25	0.4226	0.9063	0.4663	70	0.9397	0.3420	2.7475
26	0.4384	0.8988	0.4877	71	0.9455	0.3256	2.9042
27	0.4540	0.8910	0.5095	72	0.9511	0.3090	3.0777
28	0.4695	0.8829	0.5317	73	0.9563	0.2924	3.2709
29	0.4848	0.8746	0.5543	74	0.9613	0.2756	3.4874
30	0.5000	0.8660	0.5774	75	0.9659	0.2588	3.7321
31	0.5150	0.8572	0.6009	76	0.9703	0.2419	4.0108
32	0.5299	0.8480	0.6249	77	0.9744	0.2250	4.3315
33	0.5446	0.8387	0.6494	78	0.9781	0.2079	4.7046
34	0.5592	0.8290	0.6745	79	0.9816	0.1908	5.1446
35	0.5736	0.8192	0.7002	80	0.9848	0.1736	5.6713
36	0.5878	0.8090	0.7265	81	0.9877	0.1564	6.3138
37	0.6018	0.7986	0.7536	82	0.9903	0.1392	7.1154
38	0.6157	0.7880	0.7813	83	0.9925	0.1219	8.1443
39	0.6293	0.7771	0.8098	84	0.9945	0.1045	9.5144
40	0.6428	0.7660	0.8391	85	0.9962	0.0872	11.4301
41	0.6561	0.7547	0.8693	86	0.9976	0.0698	14.3007
42	0.6691	0.7431	0.9004	87	0.9986	0.0523	19.0811
43	0.6820	0.7314	0.9325	88	0.9994	0.0349	28.6363
44	0.6947	0.7193	0.9657	89	0.9998	0.0175	57.2900
45	0.7071	0.7071	1.0000	90	1.0000	0.0000	

Tables

		Page
$\lvert x \rvert$	absolute value of x	13
adj. $\angle$s	adjacent angles	18
alt. ext. $\angle$s	alternate exterior angles	81
alt. int. $\angle$s	alternate interior angles	81
alt.	altitude	150
$\angle$, $\angle$s	angle(s)	18
AA Post.	angle-angle postulate of similarity	277
AAS	angle-angle-side congruence of triangles	134
ASA	angle-side-angle congruence of triangles	134
ASASA	angle-side-angle-side-angle congruence of quadrilaterals	249
a	apothem	455
$\overarc{AB}$	arc with endpoints A and B	362
A	area of a polygon	440
b	length of base	441
b	y-intercept	559
B	area of base	491
$p \leftrightarrow q$	biconditional statement, p iff q	53
bis.	bisector (angle)	20
	(segment)	14
	(triangle)	149
$\odot O$	circle with center O	352
C	circumference	466
coll.	collinear	3
comp. $\angle$s	complementary angles	23
$S \circ T$	composition of S and T	612
concl.	conclusion	47
$p \rightarrow q$	conditional statement, if p then q	47
$\cong$	congruent, is congruent to (segments)	13
	(angles)	20
	(quadrilaterals)	248
const.	construct, construction	17
ctpos.	contrapositive	51
$\sim q \rightarrow \sim p$	contrapositive of $p \rightarrow q$	51
conv.	converse	51
$q \rightarrow p$	converse of $p \rightarrow q$	51

		Page
cor.	corollary	14
$\leftrightarrow$	corresponds to	128
corr. $\angle$s	corresponding angles	81
CPCTC	corresponding parts of congruent triangles are congruent	139
cos	cosine	333
def.	definition	3
diag.	diagonal	106
d	diameter, length of diameter	352
d	distance	13, 151, 537
$D_{o,k}$	dilation with center O and magnitude k	607
dist.	distributive property	56
div.	division property	56
e	edge length	491
endpt.	endpoint	13
$=$	equal(s), equality, is equal to	13
ext. $\angle$	exterior angle (triangle)	97
	(parallel lines)	81
fig.	figure	67
geom.	geometric	268
$>$	greater than	179
$\geq$	greater than or equal to	179
HA	hypotenuse-angle congruence of right triangles	159
HL	hypotenuse-leg congruence of right triangles	159
H_O	half-turn about point O	602
h	height, length of altitude	441
hyp.	hypotenuse	159
I	identity tranformation	617
iff	if and only if	3
ineq.	inequality	179
int.	interior	81
inv.	inverse	51
$\sim p \rightarrow \sim q$	inverse of $p \rightarrow q$	51
T^{-1}	inverse of transformation T	618
isos.	isosceles (triangle)	96
	(trapezoid)	239
L	lateral area	491

LA	leg-angle congruence of right triangles	159
LL	leg-leg congruence of right triangles	159
AB	length of $\overline{AB}$, distance between points A and B	13
$<$	less than	179
$\leq$	less than or equal to	179
$a_n \rightarrow L$	limit of a sequence is L	461
$\overleftrightarrow{AB}$	line containing points A and B	2
$\overset{\frown}{ABC}$	major arc with endpoints A and C	362
$M:$ $A \rightarrow A'$	M maps point A to point A'	587
meas.	measure	13
$m\angle A$	measure of angle A	19
$m\overset{\frown}{AB}$	measure of arc AB	362
midpt.	midpoint	14
mult.	multiplication property	56
$\sim p$	negation of p, not p	46
$\neq$	not equal	179
$\not>$	not greater than	179
$\not<$	not less than	179
obt.	obtuse (angle)	19
	(triangle)	96
opp. $\angle$s	opposite angles	24
(x, y)	ordered pair	536
$\parallel$	parallel, is parallel to	80
$\square$	parallelogram	218
P	perimeter	106
$\perp$	perpendicular, is perpendicular to	28
π	pi	467
pt.	point	2
$P(x, y)$	point P with coordinates x and y	536
n-gon	polygon with n sides	106
Post.	Postulate	7
prop.	property	56
quad.	quadrilateral	106
r	radius	352
a/b, $a:b$	ratio of a to b	262
$\overrightarrow{AB}$	ray with endpoint A, passing through point B	13
rect.	rectangle	233

R_j	reflection in line j	591
refl.	reflexive property	56
rt. $\angle$	right angle	19
rt. $\triangle$	right triangle	96
$\mathcal{R}_{O,\ 90}$	rotation about point O through 90 degrees	601
s.-s. int. $\angle$s	same-side interior angles	86
seg.	segment	13
$\overline{AB}$	segment with endpoints A and B	13
SAS	side-angle-side congruence of triangles	134
SAS Th.	side-angle-side theorem of similarity	282
SASAS	side-angle-side-angle-side congruence of quadrilaterals	249
SSS	side-side-side congruence of triangles	133
SSS Th.	side-side-side theorem of similarity	283
$\sim$	similar, is similar to	271
sin	sine	332
l	slant height	496
m	slope	552
subst.	substitution property	56
subtr.	subtraction property	56
supp. $\angle$s	supplementary angles	23
sym.	symmetric property	56
tan	tangent (trigonometry)	333
T	total area	491
Th.	theorem	8
$T(x, y) = (x', y')$	transformation	587
trans.	transitive property	56
$T(x, y) = (x + a, y + b)$	translation	597
transv.	transversal	81
$\triangle$ $\triangle$	triangle(s)	95
$\rightarrow$	vector	254
vert. $\angle$s	vertical angles	24
V	volume	491

Chapter 1

Practice Exercises, pages 5–6   1. intersection
2. intersection   **4.** noncollinear; also coplanar
6. coll., coplanar   **16.** false; H is not in R.
18. true   **20.** false; B is in y.   **22.** true   **24.** false;
P and R are not opposite half-planes.   **27.** 4: $\overleftrightarrow{AE}$,
$\overleftrightarrow{BE}$, $\overleftrightarrow{CE}$, $\overleftrightarrow{DE}$ **29.** ABD, ABE, ADE   **31.** ADE,
ABD   **32.** They do not intersect.   **36.** A line that
contains an edge of the base.

Practice Exercises, pages 10–11   1. Post. 4
3. no; noncollinear.   **5.** Two   **7.** noncoll.
9. noncoplanar   **17.** Th. 1.1   **19.** Post. 3
21. Post. 4   **23.** Th. 1.1   **25.** 3   **27.** 4   **29.** Two
distinct lines int. in at least one pt. Two distinct
lines int. in only one pt.   **31.** 10   **33.** 3   **35.** 4
37. Four noncoll. pts. may be noncoplanar.   **39.** 5
40. 3   **41.** 9   **42.** 1

Practice Exercises, pages 15–17   2. 2   **4.** 5.5
6. π **8.** FH or 1.5   **12.** 8; 6; 4   **14.** none
17. 16   **19.** 28   **23.** $\overrightarrow{FD}$ or $\overrightarrow{FE}$ **25.** no
27. 0.25; 0.50; 1.75   **29.** none   **31.** 36   **33.** RS;
ST **35.** B; $AB + BX = AX$ **37.** X; $AX + XB = AB$
38. (1) def. of midpt.; (2) def. of $\cong$ segments; (3)
def. of betweenness; (4) subst.; (5) distrib. prop.
41. 10; 10   **43.** C **45.** $4x - 5 = 19$ **46.** $2(x +
3) = 20$ **47.** $x = 90 - x$ **48.** 12   **49.** 9   **50.** -1

Practice Exercises, pages 21–22   3. obtuse
5. obtuse   **7.** acute   **10.** $m\angle AOX + m\angle XOB =
m\angle AOB$ **12.** distributive   **14.** $m\angle AOB$; $\frac{1}{2}$
16. $\angle C$, $\angle 4$, $\angle ACG$ **18.** ABD
20. 45   **22.** All rt. $\angle$s are $\cong$.   **24.** $m\angle 1 = 54$;
$m\angle 2 = 18$ **26.** $m\angle 1 = 5.5$; $m\angle 2 = 66.5$

Test Yourself, page 22   1. A, B, C **2.** D, E, F
3. G, B, C **4.** line; postulate   **5.** one plane;
theorem   **6.** $XY + YZ = XZ$; definition   **7.** 9; 1.5
8. W; $\overrightarrow{WA}$ and $\overrightarrow{WB}$ **9.** I; E **10.** $\angle AWE \cong \angle BWE$

Practice Exercises, pages 26–27   3. comp.: 52
supp.: 142   **5.** comp.: $(90 - x)$ supp.: $(180 - x)$
8. $\angle RVU$ and $\angle UVT$ or $\angle RUV$ and $\angle VUS$; $\angle UVT$
and $\angle T$ or $\angle VUS$ and $\angle S$ **10.** $\angle UVT$ **12.** $\angle 3$;
$\angle 4$; $\angle 1$; $\angle 2$ **14.** 75, 75, 105   **16.** $\angle EOF$ or
$\angle IOH$ **18.** They are not adj.   **20.** $5x =
(180 - x) + 48$; $x = 38$; $180 - x = 142$
23. $m\angle 4 + m\angle 3 = 180$, Linear Pair Post.

25. Trans. prop.   **27.** 22.5, 67.5, 157.5   **29.** $\angle 1$
and $\angle 3$ and $\angle 2$ and $\angle 4$ are supp.; $m\angle 1 + m\angle 3 =
180$ and $m\angle 2 + m\angle 4 = 180$, $m\angle 3 = 180 - m\angle 1$;
$m\angle 4 = 180 - m\angle 2$ or $m\angle 4 = 180 - m\angle 1$; Thus,
$\angle 3 \cong \angle 4$ **31.** $\angle 1$ and $\angle 2$ must be comp.

Practice Exercises, pages 31–32   1. 45°N of E
3. 67.5°W of N   **5** cor. of Th. 1.12   **7.** def. of $\perp$
9. Th. 1.13   **11.** impossible   **13.** Th. 1.11
15. def of $\perp$ **17.** $90 - x$ **19.** $180 - x - y$
21. no   **23.** no   **25.** yes; same as Ex. 20 plus def.
of between ray   **27.** yes; def. of between ray, def.
of $\cong \angle$s, and Th. 1.11   **29.** $m\angle 1 = 81$, $m\angle 2 = 9$;
$m\angle 3 = 81$, $m\angle 4 = 18$, $m\angle 5 = 162$, $m\angle 6 = 9$
31. Protractor Post.: In a half-plane with edge $\overrightarrow{AB}$
and P between A and B, there exists a one-to-one
correspondence between the rays that originate at P
in that half-plane and the real numbers between 0
and 180.   **33.** 35°S of E; 55°W of N

Test Yourself, page 37   1. $\angle 3$ **2.** $\angle 1$ and $\angle 2$,
$\angle 2$ and $\angle 3$, $\angle 3$ and $\angle 4$, $\angle 1$ and $\angle 4$ **3.** $\angle 2$, $\angle 4$
4. 55, 55, 125   **5.** yes; Th. 1.11   **6.** no   **7.** no
8. yes, defs. of rt. $\angle$ and $\perp$ **10.** $\angle ROT$ and
$\angle TOM$ are adj. $\angle$s. T is an interior pt. of $\angle ROM$;
$m\angle ROT + m\angle TOM = m\angle ROM$.

Summary and Review, pages 40–41   1. $\overleftrightarrow{DE}$; Post.
2   **3.** Q; Post. 3   **5.** Q; Th. 1.2   **7.** 4, Y **9.** $\overline{XZ}$,
$\overline{XB}$ **11.** $\overrightarrow{OX}$, $\overrightarrow{OY}$, O **13.** $\angle POW \cong \angle XOP$
15. PQV and TQR; supp. $\angle$s   **17.** def. of $\perp$
19. Th. 1.13   **21.** 58   **23.** 90   **25.** 29

Chapter 2

Practice Exercises, pages 49–50   1. true;
$m\angle BAC \neq 90$; false   **3.** true; $\angle 1$ is not a comp. of
$\angle 2$; false   **5.** false; $m\angle 1 + m\angle 2 \neq 180$; true
7. If 2 lines are $\perp$, then the lines form 4 rt. $\angle$s.
9. If 2 numbers are even, then their sum is even.
11. false; vert. $\angle$s are $\cong$ but need not be rt. $\angle$s.
17. false; they lie in the intersection of many planes
19. true   **21.** false; let $a = -3$ and $b = 3$ **23.** If
two $\angle$s are supp. and not $\cong$, ...   **26.** If the track
team finishes third, then it will win a bronze medal.
28. 11   **29.** 4   **30.** 7   **31.** Acute angles measure
less than 90°. Possible explanation: "less than" can
be thought of as the negation of "equal to or more
than."

Answers (side text, rotated)

Practice Exercises, pages 54–55 **1.** False; If 2 $\angle$s are comp., then the 2 $\angle$s are adj. False; If 2 $\angle$s are not adj., then the 2 $\angle$s are not comp. False; If 2 $\angle$s are not comp., then they are not adj. False **8.** Two $\angle$s are adj. iff the 2 $\angle$s are comp. False **11.** If the meas. of an $\angle$ is > 90 and < 180, then the $\angle$ is obt. If an $\angle$ is obt., then its meas. is > 90 and < 180. **13.** If a youngster's allowance is not stopped, then the youngster has not misbehaved. **15.** If 2 int. are neg., then their sum is neg.; and if the sum of 2 int. is not neg, then the 2 int. are not both neg. If the sum of 2 int. is neg., then the 2 int. are neg.; and if 2 int. are not both neg., then their sum is not neg. **17.** true; two lines lie in one plane iff they are intersecting; false **19.** If $x = 6$, then $3x - 7 = 11$: True; If $3x - 7 \neq 11$, then $x \neq 6$: True; If $x \neq 6$, then $3x - 7 \neq 11$: True **21.** If M is between X and Y and the midpt. of $\overline{XY}$, then $XM = MY$. If $XM = MY$, then M is between X and Y and the midpt. of $\overline{XY}$. If $XM \neq MY$, then M is between X and Y but not the midpt. of $\overline{XY}$. **23.** If 2 $\angle$s are $\cong$, then the 2 $\angle$s are vert. If 2 $\angle$s are vert., then they are $\cong$. If 2 $\angle$s are not vert., then the 2 $\angle$s are not $\cong$. **25.** The baseball game was not rained out. **26.** 3 **27.** 11 **28.** 14 **29.** 24, 24 **30.** 38, 19 **31.** 67.5, 22.5 **32.** 30, 60 **33.** contrapositive **35.** inverse **37.** contrapositive **39.** conditional

Practice Exercises, pages 58–60 **1.** sym. prop. of congruence **3.** subtr. prop. **5.** Distrib. prop. **7.** Subst. prop. **9.** $m\angle A + m\angle B$ **11.** $\overline{CZ}$ **13.** Add. prop., distrib. prop., subtr. prop., div. prop., sym. prop. **20.** Given, def. of $\cong$ seg., sym. prop., def. of $\cong$ seg. **22.** Given; def. of $\cong$ $\angle$s; sym. prop; def. of $\cong$ $\angle$s. **24.** Given; distrib. prop.; subtr. prop.; div. prop.; sym. prop. **26.** Given; Given; $m\angle A + m\angle B = 180$; subst. prop. $6m\angle B = 180$; distrib. prop.; 30, div. prop.; 150, subst. prop. **27.** $\frac{2(x - 6)}{5} = 4$, given; $2(x - 6) = 20$, mult. prop.; $2x - 12 = 20$, distrib. prop.; $2x = 32$, add. prop.; $x = 16$, div. prop. **31.** If $50X = 30B$ and $30B = 20Y$, then $50X = 20Y$ by the Trans. prop. **32.** One 5-g, one 3-g, one 2-g or two 3-g, two 2-g; subst. prop.

Test Yourself, page 61 **1.** true; -4 is not the solution of $-3x = 12$; false **3.** false; an odd integer is not divisible by 2; true **4.** false: the sum of the measures of two supp. $\angle$s is not 90; true **7.** If a number is even, then it has an even ones digit. **8.** If an angle is a right angle, then its measure is less than 180. **9.** false; an $\angle$ measuring between

90 and 100 is also ob. **10.** false; the measures of any pair of noncongruent adj. $\angle$s whose sum is 180 could be used as a counterexample **11.** true **12.** cond. and contr.; conv. and inv.

Practice Exercises, pages 70–71 **1.** comp.; $\angle 1$; 3; 2; Given; comp.; def. of comp. $\angle$s; $\angle 3$ and $\angle 1$ are comp.; 3; 2; comp. **7.** 37 **8.** $m\angle 7 = 80$, $m\angle 8 = 80$

Test Yourself, page 72 **1.** If the exterior sides of 2 adj. acute $\angle$s are $\perp$, then the $\angle$s are comp. **2.** def of $\angle$ bisector **3.** $\angle$ Bisector Th.; $\angle$ Bisector Th.; def of $\cong$ $\angle$s; mult. prop.; subst. prop.; def of $\cong$ $\angle$s

Summary and Review, pages 74–75 **1.** true; $\angle 2$ is not a comp. of $\angle 1$; false **3.** true; $m\angle 1 + m\angle 2 \neq 90$; false **5.** If 3 pts. are noncoll., then they determine a unique plane. **7.** It cannot, because the conv. is false. Both the cond. and the conv. must be true in order for the bicond. to be true. **9.** Given; def. of $\cong$ $\angle$s; refl. prop.; def. of betweenness of rays; subst. prop.; subtr. prop.; def. of $\cong$ $\angle$s.

Chapter 3

Practice Exercises, pages 83–84 **1.** $\parallel$ segments **3.** intersecting rays **5.** skew lines **7.** skew segments **19.** corr. $\angle$s **21.** alt. ext$\angle$s **23.** alt. int.$\angle$s **25.** $\angle 2$, $\angle 3$, $\angle 7$, $\angle 8$ **27.** $\angle 1$ and $\angle 6$; $\angle 4$ and $\angle 5$. **29.** yes; by using the Vert. $\angle$Th. and Linear Pair Post. **31.** $\overleftrightarrow{DF}$ **33.** $\overleftrightarrow{DF}$, $\overleftrightarrow{EF}$, $\overleftrightarrow{AC}$ **35.** false; there are also infinitely many $\parallel$ lines such as those determined by selected edges.

Practice Exercises, pages 89–91 **2.** $m\angle 1 = m\angle 3 = m\angle 5 = m\angle 7 = 75$, $m\angle 2 = m\angle 4 = m\angle 6 = m\angle 8 = 105$ **4.** $x = 36$; $m\angle 1 = m\angle 3 = m\angle 5 = m = 7 = 72$; $m\angle 2 = m\angle 4 = m\angle 6 = m\angle 8 = 108$ **6.** $m\angle B = m\angle D = 128$; $m\angle C = 52$ **11.** 100: vert $\angle$s are $\cong$. **14.** 100; if lines are $\parallel$, alt. ext. $\angle$s are $\cong$. **22.** $\angle 5$; $\angle 14$ **24.** $\angle 5$; $\angle 7$; $\angle 14$ **26.** 90; Th. 3.5 means $\overline{DE} \perp \overline{BC}$ **28.** 45; alt. int $\angle$s $\cong$ **33.** $\angle 1 \cong \angle 2$; if $6L \parallel 6R$, $\angle$s 1 and 2 are $\cong$ because they are corr. $\angle$s **36.** contrapositive **38.** $DF = KL$ **40.** 0.5 **42.** 1 **44.** -0.5 **46.** 165

Practice Exercises, pages 95–96 **2.** If 2 coplanar lines are $\perp$ to the same line, the lines are $\parallel$. **6.** $x \parallel y$; Th. 3.8; If 2 lines have a transv. and the int. $\angle$s on the same side of the transv. are supp., $m = 7 = 72$; $m\angle 2 = m4 = m\angle 6 = m\angle 8 = 108$ then the lines are $\parallel$. **13.** $m\angle 1 = 72$ **17.** Th. 3.9

662 Answers to Selected Exercises

Practice Exercises, pages 100–102 1. yes; 3 more. They are formed by extending $\overrightarrow{AB}$, $\overrightarrow{CA}$, and $\overrightarrow{BC}$. **3.** $m\angle B = 65$ **5.** $m\angle B = 30$; $m\angle C = 120$ **7.** $m\angle 4 = 70$; $m\angle 5 = 110$; acute isos. **9.** true; def. of isos. $\triangle$ **11.** true; sides of a rt. $\triangle$ may or may not be $\cong$. **15.** $m\angle 1 = 35$, $m\angle 2 = 105$, $m\angle 3 = 75$ **18.** $m\angle A = 20$; $m\angle B = 60$; $m\angle C = 100$ **22.** $m\angle A = 96$; $m\angle B = 32$; $m\angle C = 52$ **24.** $m\angle J = 40$; $m\angle K = 110$; $m\angle JLM = 150$ **26.** 19, 71

Test Yourself, page 102 1. ABC, GDE **5.** $\overrightarrow{HC}$ **6.** $\overleftrightarrow{HC}$ or $\overrightarrow{GD}$ **7.** $\angle 3$ and $\angle 16$, $\angle 4$ and $\angle 15$, $\angle 1$ and $\angle 14$, $\angle 2$ and $\angle 13$ **8.** $\angle 6 \cong \angle 9$ (alt. int. $\angle$s); $\angle 1 \cong \angle 9$ (corr. $\angle$s) **9.** 60, 120, 120, 60, 60, 120, 120, 60 **11.** $m\angle B = m\angle C = 42$ **12.** $m\angle A = 60$: $m\angle B = 90$; $m\angle C = 30$ **15.** not possible by def. of isos.

Practice Exercises, pages 107–109 1. concave; some lines that contain sides also contain interior points. **3.** convex; it satisfies the def. **5.** not a polygon; one vertex is the endpt. of 4 segs. **16.** false **18.** true; a regular nonagon has $9 \cong$ side lengths **20.** true; multiply a side length by the no. of sides in the reg. polygon **22.** 72 cm **24.** $t = 3$; 21, 9, 13, 11, 6 **26.** 2, 3; 3, 4; 4, 5; 5, 6, 7; 7, 8 **28.** $n - 3$; $n - 2$ **34.** $\frac{3}{2}$ **35.** 3 **36.** 5 **37.** 4 **38.** 2 **39.** 2 **40.** 3 **41.** -6 **42.** 84.5 **43.** 15% **44.** 2% **45.** 150% **46.** $t < 7$ **47.** $x \geq 13$ **48.** $x \leq -4$ **49.** $y < 4$ **50.** $p \leq 3$ **51.** $k < -6$ **52.** $x = y - 10$ **53.** $l = \dfrac{P - 2w}{2}$ **54.** $P = \dfrac{A}{1 + rt}$

Practice Exercises, pages 117–119 1. $\triangle$s **3.** $n - 2$ **5.** 900, 360 **7.** 3240, 360 **9.** $128\frac{4}{7}$, $51\frac{3}{7}$ **11.** 162, 18 **13.** 3 **15.** 12 **17.** 175 **19.** 30 **21.** 6 **23.** 16 **25.** 18 **27.** 5 **29.** 14 or 15 **31.** 8 **33.** 72 **35.** $\dfrac{360}{n}$ **37.** 90°, 90°, 90°, 90°, 135°, 45°, 90°, 90°, 135°, 45°

Test Yourself, page 119 1. 33, 33, 165, 129 **2.** 27 cm **3.** 65536, 4294967296 **4.** 10, 0 **5.** 1440, 360 **6.** $128\frac{4}{7}$ **7.** 18 **8.** yes

Summary and Review, pages 122–123 1. $\angle 1$, $\angle 7$; $\angle 2$, $\angle 8$ **3.** $\angle 1$, $\angle 5$; $\angle 2$, $\angle 6$; $\angle 3$, $\angle 7$; $\angle 4$, $\angle 8$ **5.** $\cong$; alt. ext. $\angle$s **7.** Supp.; Same side int. $\angle$s **9.** Supp.; $\angle 2$ is supp. to $\angle 3$, $\angle 3 \cong \angle 8$ **11.** $\cong$; if alt. int. $\angle$s are $\cong$, lines are $\parallel$ **13.** $\cong$; if alt. ext. $\angle$s $\cong$, lines are $\parallel$. **15.** $\cong$; if alt. ext.

$\angle$s $\cong$, lines are $\parallel$. **17.** $m\angle 4 = 101$; $m\angle 5 = 79$ **19.** $m\angle A = 90$; $m\angle ABC = 36$; $m\angle C = 54$, $m\angle ABX = 144$ **21.** Through B, draw a line $\parallel \overleftrightarrow{AC}$. Then use the corr. $\angle$s formed and the alt. int. $\angle$s formed to relate $m\angle C$ and $m\angle A$ to $m\angle ABX$ **23.** 1440, 144 **25.** Octagon; 18.4 cm

Chapter 4

Practice Exercises, pages 131–132 1. I and IV **3.** yes **5.** no; $YZX \leftrightarrow NQM$ **7.** $\overline{AM}$ **9.** $\overline{IN}$ **11.** 8 **13.** 24 **15.** 24 **17.** $\triangle ABG \cong \triangle YBO$ (or equiv.) **19.** a. $\overline{PQ}$ b. $\overline{PR}$ c. $\overline{QR}$ d. $\angle N$ e. $\angle R$ f. $\angle P$ g. $\triangle MON \cong \triangle PRQ$ (or equiv). **21.** $\angle X \cong \angle R$, $\angle Y \cong \angle S$, $\angle Z \cong \angle T$, $\overline{XY} \cong \overline{RS}$, $\overline{XZ} \cong \overline{RT}$, $\overline{YZ} \cong \overline{ST}$ **23.** 55 **25.** 8 **27.** 9 **29.** 7 **31.** $\triangle ABC \cong \triangle ABC$, $\triangle ABC \cong \triangle BAC$, $\triangle ABC \cong \triangle ACB$, $\triangle ABC \cong \triangle BCA$, $\triangle ABC \cong \triangle CAB$, $\triangle ABC \cong \triangle CBA$ **33.** No; need corr sides. **35.** Yes; all corr sides are $\cong$. **37.** $\triangle RST \cong \triangle RSW \cong \triangle RVW \cong \triangle RVT$

Practice Exercises, pages 136–138 2. $\angle O$ **4.** $\overline{YT}$ and $\overline{TO}$ or o and y **6.** $\angle C$ **8.** $\overline{AC}$ or b **10.** not enough information **12.** AAS **14.** AAS **16.** $\overline{XY} \cong \overline{MN}$, $\overline{YZ} \cong \overline{NQ}$, $\overline{ZX} \cong \overline{QM}$; $\triangle XYZ \cong \triangle MNQ$; SSS **18.** $\angle M \cong \angle S$; $\angle MAN \cong \angle SAW$; $\overline{MN} \cong \overline{SW}$, $\triangle MNA \cong \triangle SWA$; AAS **20.** $\angle TRS \cong \angle VRS$, $\overline{RS} \cong \overline{RS}$, $\angle RST \cong \angle RSV$, $\triangle TRS \cong \triangle VRS$; ASA; **23.** $\angle A \cong \angle D$ or $\angle B \cong \angle E$ **25.** $\overline{AC} \cong \overline{DF}$ **27.** $\overline{QK} \cong \overline{QA}$, $\overline{QB}$ bisects $\angle KQA$; KQB, AQB, def. of $\angle$ bis.; refl. prop.; $\triangle BQK$, $\triangle BQA$, SAS **31.** If $\angle BET \cong \angle RTE$ and $\angle BTE \cong \angle RET$, then $\triangle BET \cong \triangle RTE$. **33.** If $\overline{YG} \cong \overline{AR}$ and $\overline{GA} \cong \overline{RY}$, then $\triangle YGA \cong \triangle ARY$ **35.** not necessarily—the second peak could have sides: 5 ft, 6 ft, 7 ft **37.** $m\angle A = m\angle C = 30$ **38.** $m\angle B = 100$; $m\angle C = 30$ **39.** $m\angle B = 70$ **40.** 135° **41.** 60° **43.** No; one $\triangle$ cannot be superimposed exactly over the other. **45.** Having 2 sides and a nonincluded $\angle$ of one $\triangle$ $\cong$ to corr. parts of another $\triangle$ is insufficient to guarantee $\cong$ $\triangle$s.

Practice Exercises, pages 141–144 2. $\triangle JAS \cong \triangle KCS$; AAS; $\overline{AS}$ **4.** $\triangle ASC \cong \triangle KSC$; SAS; $\angle 4$ **6.** $\angle ITG$, $\angle TGN$; ITN, GTN, def. of $\angle$ bis.; $\overline{TN}$, $\overline{TN}$, refl. prop.; AAS; CPCTC **11.** $\angle 1 \cong \angle 2$; $\overline{LP}$ bis. $\overline{MR}$ at N.; Linear Pair Post.; Supp. of $\cong$ $\angle$s are $\cong$; def. of bis.; LNM, PNR, vert. $\angle$s are $\cong$; $\triangle MLN \cong \triangle RPN$; $\overline{LN} \cong \overline{PN}$, CPCTC **28.** Since the $\triangle$ are $\cong$; the corr. sides have = meas. By add. prop., the sums are =.

Test Yourself, page 144 **1.** a, b, c **2.** $\angle M$ **3.** $\overline{MA}$ **4.** $\angle A$ **5.** $\overline{EO}$ **6.** not enough information **7.** $\triangle OCW \cong \triangle GPI$ by SAS **8.** $\triangle NOM \cong \triangle LKM$ by AAS; $\triangle JNK \cong \triangle JLO$ by SAS or ASA

Practice Exercises, pages 152–154 **1.** $\overline{OR} \cong \overline{OS}$; $\overline{PR} \cong \overline{PS}$; $\overline{QR} \cong \overline{QS}$; $\angle$s *ROQ*, *SOP*, *QOS* and *ROP* are rt. $\angle$s **3.** median **5.** altitude **7.** *AQS*, *BQS*, ASA; CPCTC **9.** $\overline{SP} \perp \overline{RT}$ **11.** $\overline{SP} \cong \overline{PQ}$ **13.** $\overline{TP} \perp \overline{SQ}$ **17.** $\overleftrightarrow{PQ}$ is $\perp$ bis. of $\overline{MN}$; def. of $\perp$ lines; $\angle ROM \cong \angle RON$; $\overline{OM} \cong \overline{ON}$; $\overline{OR}$, Refl. prop.; $\triangle ORM \cong \triangle ORN$; $\overline{RM} \cong \overline{RN}$, CPCTC

Practice Exercises, pages 161–163 **2.** not enough information **5.** $\triangle RGH \cong \triangle HTR$ by AAS or HA **7.** 9 **11.** $m\angle T = 60$, $m\angle G = 30$ **13.** 19 **15.** 4 **28.** isos.; LL or HL **29.** $<$ **30.** $=$ **31.** $>$ **32.** $>$ **33.** $=$ **34.** $>$ **35.** $x < 22$ **36.** $x \le 24$ **37.** $x > 9$ **38.** {all real nos. less than 1) **39.** (all real nos. greater than 1) **40.** 1

Test Yourself, page 163 **1.** *C* is midpt. of $\overline{KA}$ **2.** *R* lies on $\perp$ bis. of $\overline{PQ}$ **3.** $\overline{IJ} \perp \overline{JM}$; $\triangle JIM$ is a rt. $\triangle$. **4.** $\overrightarrow{OC}$ bis. $\angle AOB$ **6.** not enough information **7.** LA or ASA **8.** LL or SAS **9.** HL

Summary and Review, pages 166–167
1. $\overline{EF} \leftrightarrow \overline{HI}$, $\overline{EG} \leftrightarrow \overline{HJ}$, $\overline{FG} \leftrightarrow \overline{IJ}$, $\angle E \leftrightarrow \angle H$, $\angle F \leftrightarrow \angle I$, $\angle G \leftrightarrow \angle J$ **3.** SAS **5.** not enough information **7.** *BCD* and *FED* **9.** *DGE* and *DAC* or *DFG* and *DBA* **13.** $\angle ABE \cong \angle CBE$ **15.** $\overline{CG}$ is a median, and $\overline{AG} \cong \overline{BG}$. **19.** LA or AAS **21.** HL

Chapter 5

Practice Exercises, pages 177–178 **2.** 30 **4.** 15 **6.** 105 **8.** equilateral, equilangular **10.** $\angle MRN$ **13.** $\overline{MN}$ **15.** $\overline{MR}$, $\overline{NR}$ **17.** 65 **19.** 5 **30.** 6 **31.** 35 **32.** 55 **33.** 10 **34.** 12 **35.** 70

Practice Exercises, pages 182–183 **2.** mult. **4.** trans. **6.** (a) cannot determine, (b) true, Th. 5.4; (c) true, Th. 5.4; (d) cannot determine **8.** $\angle GBC$, $\angle GCB$ **10.** $\angle EFG$ **12.** $EH > AF$ **14.** *BED: BDE* **15.** Th. 5.4 **17.** Add prop. of ineq.

Practice Exercises, pages 192–193 **1.** $AB \ne GH$ **3.** $\angle 1 \cong \angle 2$ **5.** $m\angle LPM \le m\angle YOP$ **7.** It is not Saturday. **9.** $\triangle TRP$ is not isosceles. **11.** $m\angle CVF \ge 90$ **14.** false; $\angle B$ is acute or a rt. $\angle$ **16.** true **18.** acute; a rt. $\angle$ **20.** $\ne$ **28.** Assume the planes are on intersecting courses or skew courses. Then reason to contradictions of meanings of E and W.

Test Yourself, page 193 **1.** $\angle I \cong \angle PAI$ **2.** $\overline{AP} \cong \overline{AN}$ **3.** 20 **4.** $\cong$ **5.** $\angle NAP$ or $\angle NPI$ **6.** $\angle PAN$, $\angle NPA$ **7.** subtraction **8.** tricotomy

Practice Exercises, pages 197–198 **1.** $=$ **3.** cannot be determined **5.** $<$ **7.** $m\angle S < m\angle R < m\angle T$ **9.** longest: $\overline{BC}$; shortest: $\overline{AB}$ **11.** longest: $\overline{AC}$; shortest: $\overline{AB}$ **13.** $m\angle G$, $m\angle H$ **17.** $JC < JR$, Th. 5.7 **19.** Given: Equilateral $\triangle ABC$ with alt. $\overline{BD}$; Prove: $BD < AC$ (or $BD < AB$ or $BD < BC$) **21.** Given: Square *WXYZ* with diag. $\overline{XZ}$, Prove: $XZ > XY$ (or any other side) **27.** In the fig., the greater the distance between *R* and other pts. of $\overline{MQ}$, the longer the seg. joining *P* to that pt. **29.** subtr. **30.** div. **31.** add.

Practice Exercises, pages 202–203 **2.** yes **4.** no **6.** *LR;* $\triangle$ Ineq. Th. **8.** $>$; Th. 5.6 **10.** *RI*, $\overrightarrow{IF}$; $\triangle$ Ineq. Th. **12.** $<$; Hinge Th. **16.** Extend $\overline{BC}$ through *C* to pt. *E* such that $CE = AC$. Draw $\overline{EA}$. Then, $\angle CAE \cong \angle CEA$. Since *C* is between *B* and *E*, $BC + EC = BE$. $AC = EC$, so $AC + BC = BE$. Also, $m\angle EAB > m\angle EAC$ and $m\angle EAB > m\angle AEC$, so $BE > AB$ and $AC + BC > AB$.

Practice Exercises, pages 207–209 **2.** *P*-$\overleftrightarrow{JA}$-*M*; *P*-$\overleftrightarrow{AC}$-*E*; *P*-$\overleftrightarrow{JK}$-*R*; *P*-$\overleftrightarrow{KC}$-*R* **4.** $\angle AMH$; $\angle CER$ **6.** *P*-$\overleftrightarrow{KC}$-*R* **8.** face *KCER* **10.** 90 **12.** 90 **14.** $=$ **16.** false; true if plane intersects the edge and is $\perp$ to the edge. **18.** no; not unless $m\angle XAC = 90$ **20.** no; must know $\overleftrightarrow{AB} \perp \overleftrightarrow{XY}$ also. **22.** $180 - 2x$ **26.** The one through $\overline{PD}$; $\overline{PD}$ is $\perp$ to the edge. **28.** Answers may vary depending on how $\overline{NO}$ is cut; the $\angle$s are $\ne$ in meas.

Test Yourself, page 209 **1.** $\angle AFR$; largest $\angle$ is opp. longest side **2.** $\overline{FA}$; hypotenuse is longest side **3.** $\overline{AE}$: longest side is opp. largest $\angle$ **4.** $\angle EFR$; $\angle FRE$; larger $\angle$ opp. longer side **5.** $>$; $\triangle$Inequality Th. **6.** 9 cm; $\triangle$ Inequality Th. **8.** $=$; SAS; CPCTC; $\cong$ seg. **9.** $<$; Hinge Th. **10.** $\angle ECD$; $\angle BCA$; conv. of Hinge Th. **11.** *M*-$\overleftrightarrow{PA}$-*Y*

Summary and Review, pages 212–213 **1.** 60 **3.** 120 **5.** 30 **7.** Th. 5.4 **9.** subtr. prop of $\ne$ **11.** add. prop. of $\ne$ **13.** Assume $\triangle ABC$ is isos.; then (1) $\overline{AB} \cong \overline{AC}$ (2) $\overline{AB} \cong \overline{BC}$ or (3) $\overline{AC} \cong \overline{BC}$ **17.** *SKC; C* **19.** no **21.** no **23.** *YR*, *YT*; *AT*, $\overline{AR}$; $\triangle$ Ineq. Th. **25.** *I*-$\overleftrightarrow{AN}$-*D* **27.** face *PIRE* and $\overleftrightarrow{AI}$

Chapter 6

Practice Exercises, pages 221–222 1. 16 **3.** 7.5
5. 7.5 **7.** $\overline{OR}$ **9.** $\angle K$ or $\angle O$ **11.** $\triangle KMO \cong$
$\triangle ORK$ **13.** $\angle M \cong \angle R$; $\angle K \cong \angle O$ **15.** 60
17. $\angle NWS$ **19.** 120 **21.** SO **23.** 20
25. $m\angle E = 75$, $m\angle D = 105$, $m\angle Q = 75$, $m\angle U =$
105 **39.** =; Th. 3.2 **40.** >; Th. 5.5 **41.** <; Th.
5.6 **42.** =; Th. 5.3 **43.** <; Th. 5.3 **44.** <;
trans. prop. and subst. **45.** =; Linear Pair Post.,
Th. 32.2, and subst. **46.** $m\angle$ABC; Th. 3.12

Practice Exercises, pages 225–226 1. $PC = d +$
DC, $MA = d + AB$, and $DC = AB$ so $\overline{PC} \cong \overline{MA}$;
$\angle NAM$ and $\angle QCP$ are supp. respectively of $\cong \angle$s
DAB and DCB, so $\angle NAM \cong \angle QCP$; $\overline{NA} \cong \overline{QC}$, so
$\triangle NAM \cong \triangle QCP$ and $\overline{NM} \cong \overline{PQ}$ (CPCTC).
Similarly, $\overline{PN} \cong \overline{MQ}$, so $MNPQ$ is a $\square$. **3.** yes;
both pairs of opp. sides are $\cong$ **5.** no; no 2 sides
are ∥ **7.** yes; by CPCTC, a pair of opp sides
both $\cong$ and ∥ **9.** no; this is true for any quad
11. $\cong$; both are $\cong$ to $\overline{EF}$ since $HJ + JG = JG + GI$.
13. $\cong$; SSS **15.** Supp.; $\angle D \cong \angle B$, $\angle B$ is supp.
to $\angle BEG$ **29.** Reposition $\overline{CD}$ so that $\overline{AB}$ and $\overline{CD}$
bis. each other.

Practice Exercises, pages 230–232 1. 18; Th. 6.9
or its cor. **3.** 17; Th. 6.9 or its cor. **5.** 10; Th.
6.9 or its cor. **7.** 27; Th. 6.9 or its cor.
9. $LA = 16.5$ cm; Th. 6.9 **11.** $OR = 16$ cm; Th.
6.9 or its cor. **13.** $RE = 15$ cm; Th. 6.9 or its cor.
15. The conv. of Th. 6.9 is not true. **17.** 40
19. When $t_1 \parallel t_2$ or $LO = PS$ **33.** $\overline{DE} \cong \overline{EF}$, Th.
5.2 **34.** $m\angle C > m\angle B$, Th. 5.6 **35.** $\cong$, CPCTC
36. 180, Th. 6.3 **37.** yes **38.** no **39.** yes
40. yes

Practice Exercises, pages 236–238
3. rect. **5.** rhombus **7.** rhombus **9.** none
10. rhombus **12.** midpt.; def. of median
14. $6y + 4 = 5y + 8$; $y = 4$; $AC = CK = KJ = 28$
16. $PR = 28$ cm **18.** $OT = 13$ cm

Test Yourself, page 238 1. 115; 65; 115; 65
2. 10; 7; 7 **3.** yes; def. of $\square$ **4.** yes; $TY \parallel OR$,
$TO \parallel YR$ **5.** no, could be a trapezoid **6.** yes;
opp. sides are $\cong$ **10.** $\square$, rhombus **11.** $\square$,
rhombus, rect., square **12.** $\square$, rect. **13.** none

Practice Exercises, pages 242–243 1. $m\angle W =$
70; $m\angle R = 110$; $m\angle E = 70$ **3.** $x = 14$;
$m\angle W = m\angle E = 83$ **5.** $WI = ER = 9$ cm
7. 12 cm **9.** 12 cm **11.** $x = 3$, $ZD = 13$ cm,
$OI = 13$ cm **13.** 24.5 **15.** 19 **17.** $2y$ **20.** $x =$

2, $KR = 11$ cm, $PA = 21$ cm **22.** $PA = 31$ cm,
$KR = 25$ cm, $ED = 28$ cm **32.** 2 rects.; top and
bottom; 2 rects. on the left and right; 2 isos. trap. on
front and back **34.** $\frac{1}{2}y$ **35.** $\frac{a}{b}$ **36.** $\frac{1}{x} + 2$
37. $\frac{3}{x} + 3$ **38.** 9 **39.** $5\sqrt{2}$
40. $3x$ **41.** $3y\sqrt{5y}$ **42.** 6 **43.** 32 **44.** 10
45. 7

Practice Exercises, pages 250–253 1. Methods
may vary. Start with a line and a pt. to represent C'.
Const. an $\angle \cong$ to $\angle OCB$. ($\angle C'$) Const. a seg. $\cong$
$\overline{CB}$. ($\overline{C'B'} \cong \overline{CB}$). Const. an $\angle \cong$ to $\angle RBC$ with
vertex B'. Const. a seg. $\cong \overline{BR}$ ($\overline{B'R'} \cong \overline{BR}$). Const.
an $\angle \cong \angle R$ at R'. Extend a side of $\angle R'$ to intersect
the sides of $\angle C'$ (ASASA). **3.** 60 **5.** 105 **7.** 7
9. Not enough information **11.** ASASA
13. SASAS **15.** not enough information
17. $\overline{JA} \cong \overline{JO}$ **19.** $\angle A \cong \angle O$ **21.** 60; 60; 60; 120
23. 6.5, 12.5 cm, 12.5 cm **25.** 12 cm **27.** 12
cm, 15 cm, 12 cm

Test Yourself, page 253 1. 20 cm; 10 cm **2.** 3
5. The statement underdetermines a trap., which has
only one pair of ∥ sides.

Summary and Review, pages 256–257 1. $\overline{NG}$
3. supp. **5.** yes; has a pair of $\cong$ ∥ sides: **7.** not a
$\square$; opp. sides are $\neq$ **9.** 16 **11.** rect.
13. rhombus **15.** $q = 2.5$; $TY = 1.5$ cm
17. $x = 6$, $TU = 31$ cm, $PQ = 51$ cm **21.** not
enough information **23.** Quad. $EFGH \cong$ quad.
$EDIH$ by SASAS.

Chapter 7

Practice Exercises, pages 265–266 2. $5x:1$
4. 4:3 **6.** 4:3 **8.** 4:3 **10.** $AB:BC$, $BC:BE$,
$DB:BE$ **12.** 12, 7 means; x, 18 extremes;
$x = 4\frac{2}{3}$ **14.** x, x means; 4, 9 extremes; $x = 6$
16. 15, 75 **18.** 13.74 **20.** $m\angle 1 = m\angle 5 =$
$m\angle 8 = m\angle 4 = 132$; $m\angle 3 = m\angle 7 = m\angle 2 = m\angle 6 =$
48 **23.** $x = 1$ **25.** $x = 15$; $y = 28$ **27.** $x = \sqrt{3}$
29. hexagon **31.** length, 15 mm; width, 10 mm
33. 8 counselors **36.** false: unless they are right
angles **37.** true **38.** false: conditional and its
converse **39.** true **40.** $\overline{BC}$ or $\overline{AD}$ **41.** $\overline{AC}$
42. $\overline{EC}$ **43.** $\overline{AD}$ **44.** $\angle BCD$, $\angle CDA$, or $\angle DAB$
45. $\angle ADB$, $\angle BCA$, or $\angle DAC$

Practice Exercises, pages 269–270 1. $BC \cdot DE$
4. $AB + DE$ **6.** 8 **9.** $2\sqrt{95}$ **12.** $8\sqrt{2}$ **14.** 3;
9; 8 **16.** 9; 5; 10; 2.5 **18.** 12 **20.** $2\sqrt{6}$ **22.** 9
24. 1, 18; 2, 9; 3, 6 **30.** 3 **32.** 270 **34.** $6\sqrt[3]{7}$

Practice Exercises, pages 273–276 1. 1 in. = 3 ft is best, since 45 and 48 are both multiples of 3.
3. Yes; $\triangle GHI \sim \triangle KJL$; Scale factor $\frac{2}{3}$
5. $c = 115$; $d = 65$; $e = 115$; $a = 4$; $b = 2$; $j = 6$; $k = l = 3$; $f = h = 115$; $g = 65$ **7.** $g = 12$; $i = 20$; $h = 25$; measures of $\angle$s cannot be determined.
9. 45 **11.** true **13.** true **15.** false **17.** false; corr. sides may not be proportion **19.** $\overline{BC} \| \overline{DE}$; corr. $\angle$s are $\cong$. **21.** 2; 6; 4.5 **23.** Yes; corr. $\angle$s $\cong$, corr. sides are proportional.
25. $\triangle ABD \sim \triangle CBA$; scale factor $1:\sqrt{3}$ **27.** 5:3
29. $x = 3$, $HI = 5$, $IE = 6$, $HE = 7$, $OW = 20$, $WL = 24$ **31.** $11\frac{3}{7}$ in.

Test Yourself, page 276 1. 15:17 **2.** $\frac{(x + 5)}{6}$
3. extremes 4 and 9; means x, x; $x = 6$
4. extremes 9, $(x - 5)$; means 4, x; $x = 9$ **5.** 40, 60, 80 **6.** 36, 54, 144 **7.** $5\sqrt{15}$ **8.** $\frac{BX}{CY}$; means may be interchanged. **9.** $\frac{CY}{AY}$; if $\frac{a}{b} = \frac{c}{d}$, then $\frac{b}{a} = \frac{d}{c}$. **10.** $\frac{AC}{AY}$; if $\frac{a}{b} = \frac{c}{d}$, then $\frac{a+b}{b} = \frac{c+d}{d}$.
11. false **12.** true **13.** false **14.** true
15. $BC = 6$, $CD = 8$, $FG = 12$, $GH = EF = 16$, $m\angle A = m\angle C = m\angle G = m\angle E = 130$, $m\angle B = m\angle D = m\angle F = m\angle H = 50$

**Practice Exercises, pages 279–281
2.** $\triangle ABX \sim \triangle CDX$ **4.** Alt int. $\angle$s are $\cong$ and $\triangle$ are $\sim$ by AA Post.; $x = 9$, $z = 2$ **6.** ML; MN; LN **8.** $3\frac{1}{5}$; $7\frac{1}{2}$ **11.** 10 m **19.** $x = 12$; $y = 12$ **23.** $33\frac{1}{3}$ yd; 25 yd **26.** 21 **27.** 3
28. 15 **29.** 30 **30.** $\frac{5}{6}$ **31.** 27 **32.** 21 **33.** 40

Practice Exercises, pages 284–286 1. $x = 7\frac{1}{2}$; $y = 9\frac{1}{3}$ **3.** $x = 7\frac{1}{2}$; $y = 12\frac{1}{2}$ **5.** $\triangle ABD \sim \triangle DBC$; SAS Th. **7.** $\triangle ACL \sim \triangle ECI$; SAS Th.; $AL = 48$
9. $\triangle APR \sim \triangle YDI$; SAS Th.; $YI = 22$ **13.** 20
15. $9\sqrt{2}$ **17.** 20 **23.** If 2 $\triangle$ are $\sim$ and have medians drawn to corr. sides, then the $\triangle$ formed in one $\triangle$ are $\sim$ to the corr. $\triangle$ formed in the other.
31. No; the side lengths are not proportional.

Practice Exercises, pages 295–297 2. 20; 7; 21
4. 6 cm; 4 cm **6.** $17\frac{1}{2}$; 22 **8.** 6; $5 + 2\sqrt{5}$
11. 15 m **13.** $\frac{45}{2}$ mm **15.** $MH = 21$ m; $KP = 15$ m **19.** $BC = 12$; $FH = 9$ **21.** $RX = 8$; $RA = 18$ **23.** $\frac{3}{5} = \frac{4.5}{7.5}$ is a true proportion. **27.** $2\frac{2}{5}$ in., $2\frac{3}{5}$ in. **29.** 80 ft, 100 ft **31.** 65°; 115° **32.** 38

Test Yourself, page 297 1. If 2 sides of one $\triangle$ are respectively proportional to 2 corr. sides of a 2nd

$\triangle$, and the included $\angle$s are $\cong$, then the $\triangle$ are $\sim$.
2. If a ray bisects an $\angle$ of a $\triangle$, then it separates the opp. side into segments proportional to the other 2 sides of the $\triangle$. **3.** $\overline{DY} \| \overline{CB}$ (2 lines $\perp$ to the same line are $\|$); $\angle C \cong \angle DYX$ (alt. int. $\angle$s of $\|$ lines are $\cong$); $\angle D \cong \angle B$ (all rt. $\angle$s are $\cong$); $\triangle CBA \sim \triangle YDX$; (AA Post). $\frac{CB}{YD} = \frac{BA}{DX} = \frac{AC}{XY}$
4. no **5.** $\triangle MON \sim \triangle TRB$; SAS Th. or AA Post.
6. $\triangle GRE \sim \triangle DTF$; SSS Th. **7.** Make a scale drawing and let 1 yd = 1 in.; distance = 32.5 yd.
8. $CP = 6$, $BP = 10$ **9.** $\frac{40}{3}$

Summary and Review, page 300 1. $\frac{2}{3}$
3. $\frac{2(x - 4)}{}$ **5.** means x, 12; extremes 8, 20; $x = \frac{40}{3}$ **7.** $\frac{RY}{UR}$ **9.** $AM + RY$ **11.** 18
13. $RSVP \sim ADHO$; 3:2 **15.** $\triangle QER \sim \triangle DCR$; AA Post. **17.** $\triangle ABC \sim \triangle EFD$; SSS Th. **19.** 15
21. 4

Chapter 8

Practice Exercises, pages 308–310 1. $2\sqrt{3}$; 4; $4\sqrt{3}$ **3.** $\angle TAR$, $\angle B$ **5.** $\angle R$ **7.** $\angle RTA$, $\angle RAB$
9. $\frac{BT}{AT} = \frac{BA}{AR} = \frac{TA}{TR}$ **11.** $\overline{BT}$ **13.** $\frac{RT}{AR} = \frac{AR}{RB}$
15. $c = 29$; $h = 10$; $a = 2\sqrt{29}$; $b = 5\sqrt{29}$
17. $x = 9$; $c = 12$; $a = 6\sqrt{3}$; $b = 6$ **19.** $x = 4$; $h = 4\sqrt{3}$; $a = 8$; $b = 8\sqrt{3}$ **21.** $a = 5\sqrt{5}$; $b = 10\sqrt{5}$; $c = 25$; $y = 20$ **23.** $b = 6\sqrt{3}$; $x = 3$; $y = 9$; $h = 3\sqrt{3}$ **25.** Rt. $\triangle ABC$; rt $\angle BCA$; $\overline{CP}$ is an altitude to $\overline{AB}$; $\overline{CP} \perp \overline{AB}$; def. of $\perp$ lines; All rt. $\angle$s are $\cong$; Refl. prop.; ACP; CPB; AA Post.; Acute $\angle$s of a rt. $\triangle$ are comp.; B; PCA; $\angle$s comp. to the same $\angle$ are $\cong$; $\triangle PBC \sim \triangle PCA$; AA Post. **27.** $BC = 16.5$
29. $PC = 2$ **31.** $AC = 6$; $AB = 3\sqrt{5}$ **33.** $\sqrt{5}$ cm, $2\sqrt{5}$ cm **35.** alt. = 3 ft, each leg = $3\sqrt{2}$ ft
39. $h = \frac{12}{5}$, or 2.4 **41.** $\frac{12}{35}$ ft **43.** 20 ft

Practice Exercises, pages 314–315 3. 61 **5.** 40
7. $\sqrt{2}$ **9.** 6 **11.** $5\sqrt{3}$ **13.** $h = 24$ **15.** $s = 3\sqrt{29}$ **18.** $h = 12$ **21.** $AG = 15\sqrt{5}$ **23.** $AP = 4\sqrt{3}$ **25.** $4\sqrt{17}$ cm **27.** Four rt. $\triangle$s are formed with hyp. s and legs $\frac{p}{2}$ and $\frac{q}{2}$. Thus, by the Pyth. Th.; $4[(\frac{p}{2})^2 + (\frac{q}{2})^2 = s^2]$, or $p^2 + q^2 = 4s^2$.
29. $PT \approx 64.944$ ft **30.** $\angle ABD$; alt. int. $\angle$s are $\cong$. **31.** $\overline{AC}$; def. of altitude **32.** 180; $\angle EBA$ and $\angle FBA$ are linear pairs; use alt. int. $\angle$s are $\cong$, and subst. **33.** $m\angle DBC$; remote int. $\angle$s **34.** $\triangle ADB$; $\triangle BDC$; Th. 8.1 **35.** $\angle SBD$; corr. $\angle$s of $\sim \triangle$s
36. DC; $\triangle$ Inequality Th.

Practice Exercises, pages 318–320   **2.** yes; acute
4. yes; rt.   **6.** no   **8.** yes; acute   **10.** yes; rt.
12. yes; acute   **14.** yes; acute   **16.** no   **19.** $AC =$
$\sqrt{128} = 8\sqrt{2}$ **20.** $RT = 14$ **22.** $MP = 17$
24. 10 cm, 24 cm   **26.** $RS = 9$ cm; $SQ = 5$ cm
32. 28 cm, 96 cm

Test Yourself, page 320   **1.** $x = 20$ **2.** $h = 6$
3. $y = 16$; $c = 25$ **4.** $a = 4\sqrt{7}$ **5.** 10   **6.** 12
7. $10\sqrt{3}$ **8.** each side = 5   **9.** perimeter = 28
10. yes; yes   **11.** yes; no   **12.** no   **13.** Ex. 11

Practice Exercises, pages 324–325   **1.** $a = 3$;
$b = 3$; $c = 3\sqrt{2}$ **3.** $x = 5\sqrt{3}$; $y = 5$; $z = 10$
5. $\frac{3}{4}$; $\frac{3\sqrt{2}}{4}$ **7.** 9; 9   **9.** $2\sqrt{30}$; $2\sqrt{30}$ **11.** 36;
$24\sqrt{3}$ **13.** 6; 12   **15.** $\frac{3\sqrt{3}}{4}$; $\frac{3}{2}$ **17.** $3\sqrt{2}$ m $\approx$
4.24 m   **19.** 36 in.   **22.** $c = 20$, $d = 10\sqrt{3}$, $e =$
10, $f = 20$, $g = 10\sqrt{2}$ **26.** $d = s\sqrt{3}$ **28.** $(-5,$
$3\sqrt{3})$ **31.** 13   **32.** 22   **33.** 35   **34.** 25   **35.** 31
36. $\frac{8\sqrt{3}}{3}$ **37.** $\frac{3\sqrt{5}}{5}$ **38.** $6\sqrt{2}$ **39.** $7\sqrt{3}$
40. $5\sqrt{7}$ **41.** 15   **42.** 5   **43.** 2   **44.** 7

Practice Exercises, pages 335–336   **1.** $\sin 13 =$
$\frac{y}{12}$; $y \approx 2.70$ **3.** $\tan x = \frac{50}{30}$; $x \approx 59°$ **5.** $\sin x =$
$\frac{13}{18}$; $x \approx 46°$ **8.** $x = 9.04$; The answers are different
by one hundredth   **10.** $5^2 + (EF)^2 = 13^2$; $25 +$
$(EF)^2 = 169$; $(EF)^2 = 144$; $EF = 12$; $\tan x = \frac{5}{12}$;
$\tan x \approx 0.4167$; $x \approx 23°$; Using the sine ratio
takes fewer steps.   **12.** $x \approx 53°$ **14.** each side is
73.10 mm   **16.** 10.46 cm   **18.** $\frac{b}{c}$
20. $\sqrt{3} \approx 1.7321$; trig table: 1.7321   **22.** $\frac{1}{2} =$
0.5000; trig table: 0.5000   **24.** $\sin 45° \approx 0.7071$;
$\cos 45° \approx 0.7071$ **26.** They are =.   **28.** 28 ft
31. 250.43 ft

Practice Exercises, pages 339–341   **1.** 78 ft
3. 2864 m   **5.** 3817 ft   **7.** line of sight = 4000 ft;
horizontal distance = 3500 ft   **9.** 769 ft; 46,140 ft/h
11. 45° and 135°   **13.** 34 m

Test Yourself, page 341   **1.** $\sqrt{2}$ **2.** $\sqrt{3}$; 1
3. leg = 10 cm; hyp. = $10\sqrt{2}$ cm   **4.** 15 mm;
$15\sqrt{3}$ mm   **5.** $\sin x = \frac{\text{leg opp. } \angle x}{\text{hyp.}}$ **6.** 0.5736
7. 0.6157   **8.** 6.3138   **9.** 25   **10.** 0.5   **11.** $\frac{\sqrt{3}}{2} =$
0.8660254; table: 0.8660   **12.** $\tan 43° = \frac{BC}{40}$; $BC =$
37 ft   **13.** 34

Summary and Review, pages 344–345   **1.** $3\sqrt{5}$
cm   **3.** $2\sqrt{14}$ **5.** yes; $8^2 = 4^2 + (4\sqrt{3})^2$

7. 12 cm, $12\sqrt{3}$ cm, 24 cm   **9.** 37   **11.** $\frac{\sqrt{3}}{2}$
13. $\frac{\sqrt{3}}{2}$

Chapter 9

Practice Exercises, pages 355–356   **1.** Isos.; the
radii (sides of the $\triangle$) are $\cong$.
3. A $\triangle$ with 1 vertex at the center of a $\odot$ and the
other 2 vertices located on the $\odot$ is an isos. $\triangle$.
5. $\overline{QW}$; $\overline{QS}$; $\overline{QU}$ **7.** $\overline{XY}$; $\overline{SY}$ **9.** $\overrightarrow{SY}$ **11.** rt.
13. true   **15.** false   **17.** false   **20.** False
22. $x = 5\sqrt{2}$ **24.** 4 mm   **26.** $QC = 8\sqrt{3}$
30. infinitely many

Practice Exercises, pages 360–361   **1.** 4   **3.** 2
5. 2   **8.** 8   **10.** $\sqrt{21}$ **12.** 5   **14.** 62   **16.** Rt.
$\triangle$; $BC^2 + CA^2 = AB^2$ **18.** 2 pts.   **20.** 0, 1, or 2
pts.   **26.** 26, 20, 23

Practice Exercises, pages 365–367   **1.** Answers
may vary; $\overset{\frown}{AB}$, $\overset{\frown}{BC}$, $\overset{\frown}{CD}$, $\overset{\frown}{DE}$, $\overset{\frown}{EF}$ **3.** $\angle FQC \cong$
$\angle FQE$, $\angle AQC \cong \angle GQE$, $\angle CQD \cong \angle DQE$,
$\angle AQD \cong \angle GQD$, $\angle AQE \cong \angle CQG$ **5.** $m\overset{\frown}{AB} = 50$,
$m\overset{\frown}{AC} = 85$, $m\overset{\frown}{AD} = 130$, $m\overset{\frown}{AE} = 160$, $m\overset{\frown}{BC} = 35$,
$m\overset{\frown}{BD} = 80$, $m\overset{\frown}{BE} = 110$, $m\overset{\frown}{CD} = 45$, $m\overset{\frown}{CE} = 75$,
$m\overset{\frown}{DE} = 30$ **7.** $\overset{\frown}{AE}$, $\overset{\frown}{AD}$, $\overset{\frown}{BE}$, $\overset{\frown}{AC}$, $\overset{\frown}{BD}$, $\overset{\frown}{CE}$, $\overset{\frown}{AB}$, $\overset{\frown}{CD}$,
$\overset{\frown}{BC}$, $\overset{\frown}{DE}$ **9.** $\cong$, $\cong$ **11.** $<$ **13.** $>$ **15.** 8;
16   **17.** 7   **21.** Isos. $\triangle$ **23.** $m\angle OAB =$
$m\angle OBA = 65$, $m\angle AOB = 50$ **25.** $m\overset{\frown}{AB} = 70$,
$m\angle A = m\angle B = 55$ **37.** right   **38.** $\triangle ACD$; $\triangle CBD$
39. $2.5\sqrt{3}$ **40.** 30   **41.** 10   **42.** $5\sqrt{3}$ **43.** 2.5

Test Yourself, page 367   **1.** A $\odot$ is the set of pts.
in a plane, every one of which is at a given distance
from a given pt.   **2.** $\overline{OA}$, $\overline{OB}$, $\overline{OC}$ **3.** $\overline{BC}$ **4.** $\overline{AC}$,
$\overline{AB}$, $\overline{CB}$ **5.** $\triangle ABC$ **6.** The line is tan. to the
circle at that pt.   **8.** 12   **9.** 90   **10.** 1   **11.** an $\angle$
that has its vertex at the center of the circle   **12.** a
diameter is $\perp$ to a chord   **13.** $\overset{\frown}{BC} \cong \overset{\frown}{AD}$; $\overset{\frown}{ABC} \cong$
$\overset{\frown}{DAB}$; $\overset{\frown}{BCD} \cong \overset{\frown}{ADC}$, $\overset{\frown}{ACD} \cong \overset{\frown}{BDC}$ **14.** BC, DC, AB
15. 8

Practice Exercises, pages 371–372   **2.** $m\angle A = 50$;
$m\angle B = 45$; $m\angle C = 85$; $m\overset{\frown}{AB} = 170$ **4.** $m\angle A = 25$;
$m\angle B = m\angle C = 77.5$; $m\overset{\frown}{AC} = m\overset{\frown}{AB} = 155$
6. $m\angle A = 30$; $m\angle B = 90$; $m\angle C = 60$; $m\overset{\frown}{AB} = 120$;
$m\overset{\frown}{AC} = 180$; $m\overset{\frown}{BC} = 60$ **8.** $m\angle A = 60$; $m\angle B = 80$;
$m\angle C = 40$; $m\overset{\frown}{AB} = 80$; $m\overset{\frown}{BC} = 120$; $m\overset{\frown}{CA} = 160$
10. $m\angle A = 85$; $m\angle C = 5$; $m\overset{\frown}{AC} = 180$; $m\overset{\frown}{BC} = 170$
12. They intercept the same arc.   **14.** $\triangle ADE \sim$
$\triangle CBE$; corresponding sides $\cong$ **16.** $m\angle P = 116$;
$m\overset{\frown}{PS} = 90$; $m\overset{\frown}{PQ} = 38$; $m\overset{\frown}{QR} = 122$ **18.** $m\angle P =$
120; $m\angle Q = 110$; $m\overset{\frown}{PS} = m\overset{\frown}{PQ} = 60$; $m\overset{\frown}{QR} = 80$;
$m\overset{\frown}{SR} = 160$ **20.** $m\angle P = m\angle R = 90$; $m\angle Q = 110$;

$m\angle S = 70$; $m\overarc{PS} = 110$; $m\overarc{QR} = 70$; $m\overarc{RS} = 110$;
22. $m\angle P = m\angle R = 90$; $m\angle Q = 110$; $m\angle S = 70$;
$m\overarc{PQ} = 80$; $m\overarc{PS} = 100$; $m\overarc{QR} = 60$; $m\overarc{RS} = 120$
24. 45

Practice Exercises, pages 375–377 **1.** $x = 65$
3. $x = 50$, $y = 230$ **5.** $m\angle 1 = 30$; $m\angle 2 = 30$;
$m\angle 3 = 90$; $m\angle 4 = 30$; $m\overarc{AB} = 10$; $m\overarc{CD} = 140$;
$m\overarc{DE} = 20$ **9.** 40 **11.** 240, 120 **24.** $(x + 9)$
$(x + 1)$ **25.** $(x + 4)(x + 2)$ **26.** $(x - 3)(x - 7)$
27. $(x - 3)(x - 8)$ **28.** $(x - 6)(x + 6)$
29. $(x + 4)^2$ **30.** $(x + 5)(x - 3)$
31. $(x - 6)(x + 3)$ **32.** $(x + 3)(x - 2)$ **33.** $x = 9$,
$x = -9$ **34.** $x = -1$, $x = 12$ **35.** $x = 4$, $x = 1$
36. $x = 5$, $x = -4$ **37.** $x = -6$, $x = 5$ **38.** $x = -4$, $x = 8$

Practice Exercises, pages 385–387 **1.** $x = 14$
3. $x = 6$ **5.** $x = 2$ **7.** $x = 6$ **9.** $x = 5$; $y = 3$
11. $y = 6$; $x = 4\sqrt{10}$ **13.** $8\sqrt{3}$ **19.** 24 cm
21. If $5x = 8(x + 6)$, then $x = -16$, which cannot
be the length of a seg.; change $x + 6$ to $x - 6$; then
$x = 16$. **25.** 24.6 mi

Test Yourself, page 387 **1.** 60 **2.** 30 **3.** 80
4. 40 **5.** 100 **6.** 110 **7.** 30, 60, 90; 60, 120,
180 **8.** False; they are supplementary. **9.** False; it
is the sum. not the difference of the meas. **10.** 5;
95; 90; 50 **11.** the product of the lengths of 1
secant seg. and its external seg. = prod. of the
lengths of the other secant seg. and its external seg.
12. the prod. of the lengths of the seg. of 1 chord =
prod. of the lengths of the seg. of the other chord.
14. $x = 1$ **15.** $x = 6$ **16.** $x = 8$

Summary and Review, pages 390–391 **1.** $\odot C$
with pt. B, $\odot C$ with pt. O **3.** $\overline{AB}$, $\overline{AD}$, $\overline{XY}$ **5.** 18
9. 80 **11.** 110 **13.** $x = 50$; $y = 130$ **17.** $x = 12$

Chapter 10

Practice Exercises, pages 400–402 **13.** Const. the
bis. of any $\angle$ of $\triangle MNO$. $(30 = \frac{1}{2}60)$ **15.** Answers
may vary. Const. an $\angle$ whose meas. = the sum of
the meas. of the $\angle$s constructed in Ex. 15 and 16.
$(45 = 30 + 15)$ **17.** Answers may vary. Const. on
$\angle$ whose meas. = the sum of the meas. of the $\angle$s
constructed in Ex. 15. $(90 = 60 + 30)$ **19.** Answers
may vary. Const. an $\angle$ whose meas. = sum of the
meas of the $\angle$ constructed in Ex. 19, and $\angle$ of
$\triangle MNO$. $(150 = 90 + 60)$ **21.** Since the sum of the
meas. of the $\angle$s of a $\triangle = 180$, if 2 $\angle$s are known,
the third is determined. No, since $\overline{PQ}$ can be any

length, the $\triangle$s will be $\sim$ but not nec. $\cong$. **31.** no;
$WX + XY \not> YW$ **33.** at the midpoint **40.** 2
41. -1 **42.** -7 **43.** 2 **44.** 1; 20 **45.** -5; 6
46. Given $\angle AVC$, fold so that $\overrightarrow{VA}$ coincides with
$\overrightarrow{VC}$. Unfold and label the crease $\overrightarrow{VX}$.

Practice Exercises, pages 405–406 **1.** Construct
$\perp$ lines, then bisect one $\angle$. **11.** a $\square$; both pairs of
opp. sides are $\parallel$ **13.** Make $\angle AVB$ a rt. $\angle$.
15. $\overline{XP} \cong \overline{YP}$ and $\overline{XZ} \cong \overline{YZ}$. Since Z is equidistant
from the endpts. of a seg., it lies on the $\perp$ bis. of
the seg. **17.** $\angle 1 \cong \angle 2$ by construction. If 2 lines
have a transv. and $\cong$ corr. $\angle$s, then the lines are $\parallel$.
19. Const. $\overline{XY} \cong \overline{CD}$; at X, const. the $\perp$; with center
Y and radius AB draw an arc intersecting the $\perp$; label
the intersection Z; draw $\overline{YZ}$. **21.** Const $\angle X \cong \angle E$;
then const. remaining sides. **24.** The intersection is
in the ext. of the $\triangle$. **26.** The $\triangle$s are $\sim$. SSS Th.
28. Const. the $\perp$ bis. of the base; the peak should be
a pt. on it. **30.** By the Pyth. Th., $(2x)^2 + (x)^2 =$
h^2; $h = x\sqrt{5}$; $\dfrac{x\sqrt{5}}{x} = \sqrt{5}$

Practice Exercises 410–411 **1.** All 4 are the same
pt. **5.** 16; 8 **7.** 3; 9 **9.** 24; 36; 9; 18; 27
11. equilateral **13.** rt. $\triangle$ **15.** obtuse $\triangle$ **17.** 3
19. 8; -2; 12 or 72 **21.** In $\triangle PQR$, $\overline{ST} \parallel \overline{RQ}$, and
in $\triangle ROQ$, $\overline{XY} \parallel \overline{RQ}$ because a line that intersects the
midpts. of 2 sides of a $\triangle$ is $\parallel$ to the third side.
Hence, $\overline{ST} \parallel \overline{XY}$. Also, $\overline{ST} = \frac{1}{2}\overline{RQ}$ and $\overline{XY} = \frac{1}{2}\overline{RQ}$.
Hence, $\overline{ST} \cong \overline{XY}$. Since a pair of sides of $STYX$ are
both $\parallel$ and $\cong$, $STYX$ is a $\square$. **27.** By the def. of
median, X has been constructed to be the common
pt. of medians $\overline{CM}$ and $\overline{AN}$. Since, by Th. 10.4, all
3 medians will intersect at X, X is the centroid.
29. $4\sqrt{3}$ **31.** Draw an isos. $\triangle$. Use Const. 4 to
find the incenter. Using the dist. from the incenter to
one side as a radius, draw the $\odot$ with center at the
incenter.

Practice Exercises, pages 415–416 **1.** Fold non-$\parallel$
chords $\overline{AB}$ and $\overline{CD}$. Then fold along the $\perp$ bis. of
each chord. The intersection of the $\perp$ bisectors is the
center. **3.** Tangents are $\parallel$. **14.** $\angle CPD$ is an inscr.
$\angle$ that intercepts a semi-$\odot$; hence $m\angle CPD = 90$,
and $\overleftrightarrow{CP} \perp \overleftrightarrow{AB}$ at P.

Practice Exercises, pages 419–421 **12.** $\overline{AY}$ in Ex.
11 is a seg. such that $AY:AB = 3:5$. **14.** isos.
24. Use the lengths from Ex. 18 to copy the given
const. Then const. a $\odot$ with radius length 1 cm.
Choose a pt. of the $\odot$ and use X to mark off ten $=$
arcs. Connect the pts. to form a decagon.
31. 12 **32.** $5\sqrt{3}$ **33.** $4\sqrt{2}$ **34.** 13 **35.** 5

Practice Exercises, pages 424–426 2. the diag. of the square excluding the endpts. which passes through the intersection of the given sides. **4.** all interior pts. of the cube that are also on the plane that bisects the dihedral $\angle$ formed by the 2 given faces **6.** a $\odot$ with the same center and radius length 15 cm **8.** the intersection of the 2 lines that join the midpts. of the opp. sides of a rect. **10.** the circumcenter; the intersection of the $\perp$ bis. of each side of the $\triangle$ **12.** all pts. on $\odot$ whose center is the midpt. of the hyp. except those on hyp. **14.** the intersection of a line $\parallel$ to each of the given lines and midway between them; and the $\odot$ with center P and radius of 4 cm **16.** 4 pts. that are the intersection of the bis. of the $\angle$s formed by the given lines and the $\odot$ with center at the intersection of the given lines and a radius length of the given distance **18.** the pt. of intersection of the line $\parallel$ to and halfway between k and l and the $\perp$ bis. of $\overline{AB}$ **20.** a curve consisting of pts. equidistant from the given line and the given pt. **22.** 2 planes $\perp$ to each other and bis. the dihedral $\angle$s formed by the given planes. **24.** Answers may vary; the intersection of the $\odot$ with center P at a given dist. d and the $\angle$ bis. **26.** the diam. of $\odot O$ that is $\perp$ to the given diam., excluding pt. O. **28.** m is the line $\parallel$ to and midway between k and l; if m is the $\perp$ bis. of $\overline{AB}$, then the locus is m; if m is $\perp$ to $\overline{AB}$ but not the bis., the locus is $\varnothing$; if $\overline{AB}$ is not $\perp$ to m, the locus is the intersection of the $\perp$ bis. of $\overline{AB}$ and line m. **30.** Answers may vary. There are 10 possible intersections for 2 $\parallel$ planes and 2 concentric spheres: 4 $\odot$s, 3 $\odot$s, 2 $\odot$s, 1 $\odot$, 3$\odot$s and 1 pt., 2 $\odot$s and 1 pt., 1 $\odot$ and 1 pt., 2 pts., 1 pt., and no pts. **34.** at the intersection of the $\perp$ bis. of $\overline{SF}$ and the line $\parallel$ to the school at 9 ft E of the school

Test Yourself page 431 5. 2 planes $\parallel$ to the given plane, 10 cm above and below the given plane. **6.** the intersection of the two $\angle$bis. of the two intersecting lines and the circle centered at the intersection of the two lines with radius length 5 cm **7.** the 2 $\angle$ bis. of the 4 $\angle$s created by the 2 intersecting lines, excluding the intersection of the given lines

Summary and Review, pages 434–435 13. Draw any 2 non-$\parallel$ chords and construct the $\perp$ bis. of each. The pt. of intersection is the center of the disk. **19.** a $\odot$ with radius length = to the given dist. and centered at the given pt. **21.** All the locus of pts. equidistant from k and l; line m; If the $\perp$ bis. of $\overline{AB}$

is m, then m is the locus; if the $\perp$ bis. of $\overline{AB}$ is not m, there are no pts. in the locus. **23.** Answers may vary. Post. 19

Chapter 11

Practice Exercises, pages 442–444 1. Add the areas: $5 \cdot 35$, $5 \cdot 20$, $5 \cdot 40$, $20 \cdot 20$, and $10 \cdot 35$ **3.** 5 cm; 16 cm **5.** 4 in.; 20 in.^{2} **7.** rect.; 84 in.^{2} **9.** both; 25 in.^{2} **11.** $n = 4$; $AL = 5$ cm **13.** $x = 9$; $b = 12$ cm, $h = 6$ cm **15.** $A = (4a^2 + 12a + 9)$ dm^2 **17.** $s = y - 3$, $A = (y - 3)^2 = (y^2 - 6y + 9)$ cm^2 **19.** 25 in.^{2} **21.** 24 cm **23.** $A = 2r^2$ **25.** new area $= 4A$ **27.** $\frac{2}{3}h^2$; $\frac{3}{2}b^2$

Practice Exercises, pages 447–449 1. new area $= 2A$ **3.** 55 cm^2 **5.** 40 cm^2 **7.** 21 in.; 14 in. **9.** 21 cm^2 **11.** 40 cm **13.** 150 in.^{2} **15.** $16\sqrt{3} = \frac{s^2\sqrt{3}}{4}$; $s = 8$ cm, $h = 4\sqrt{3}$ cm **17.** $9\sqrt{3}$ and $18\sqrt{3}$ **19.** $75\sqrt{2}$ cm^2 **21.** $128\sqrt{3}$ ft^2 **23.** $A = \frac{1}{2} \cdot 45 \cdot 28 = 630$ cm^2 **27.** A of $\square = 2$ times A of $\triangle$ **35.** 12 in.^{2}

Practice Exercises, pages 452–454 1. $A = hm$; $h = \frac{A}{m}$; $h = 16.76$ ft **3.** 47.5 cm^2 **5.** 38 cm^2 **7.** 324 cm^2 **9.** 4 ft; 12 ft **11.** 5 ft; 10 ft; 16 ft **13.** $A = 60$ in.^{2} **15.** $P = (32 + 16\sqrt{2})$ in.; $A = 128$ in.^{2} **17.** 24 cm^2 **19.** $A = 7921$ mm^2 **21.** $A = 144$ **23.** (a) It is $=$ to A. (b) new $A = \frac{1}{2}(h + 1)(c + d) = A + \frac{1}{2}(c + d)$ **25.** 315 in.^{2} **27.** No; $A(BCDE) = \frac{h(b_2 + m)}{4}$, $A(ABEF) = \frac{h(b_1 + m)}{4}$ and $b_1 \neq b_2$. **29.** $A = 2[\frac{1}{2}(4.29)$ $(10.4 + 12.48) + \frac{1}{2}(4.29)(8.32 + 6.24)] +$ $(10.4)(6.24) = 160.6176 + 64.896 = 225.5136 \approx$ 226 in.^{2} **30.** $4\sqrt{3}$ **31.** $8\sqrt{3}$ **32.** 12 **33.** 60 **34.** $\frac{\sqrt{3}}{2}$ **35.** $\sqrt{3}$ **37.** 120 **38.** 180 **39.** the $\perp$ bis. of $\overline{MN}$ **40.** obtuse **41.** right **42.** acute **43.** right

Practice Exercises, pages 457–460 1. $m\angle 1 = 54$, $m\angle 2 = 36$, $m\angle 3 = 72$, $m\angle 4 = 54$, $m\angle 5 = 54$, $m\angle 6 = 108$ **3.** $A \approx 247.5$ in.^{2} **5.** 12 cm **7.** $6\sqrt{3}$ cm **9.** 72 cm **11.** $a = \sqrt{3}$ cm, $s = 2\sqrt{3}$ cm, $P = 8\sqrt{3}$ cm, $A = 12$ cm^2 **13.** $a = 2\sqrt{3}$ cm, $r = 4$ cm, $A = 24\sqrt{3}$ cm^2 **15.** $864\sqrt{3}$ in.^{2} **17.** $150\sqrt{3}$ in.^{2} **19.** $\frac{360}{10 \text{ sides}} = 36$ **21.** 6.2 **23.** $a = 3\sqrt{3}$ cm;

$P = 36$ cm   **25.** $A_\triangle = 9\sqrt{3}$ cm²; $A_{hex} = 24\sqrt{3}$ cm²; $24\sqrt{3} - 9\sqrt{3} = 15\sqrt{3}$ cm²
27. $m\angle 1 = 45$, $m\angle 2 = 135$, $m\angle 3 = 45$, $m\angle 4 = 45$; $a = \frac{s}{2}(1 + \sqrt{2})$ **31.** $h = 3a$, $h = \frac{s}{2}\sqrt{3}$, $3a = \frac{s}{2}\sqrt{3}$; $s = 2a\sqrt{3}$ **33.** $A_{hex} = 6a^2\sqrt{3}$, $A_\triangle = 3a^2\sqrt{3}$ $A_{hex} = 2A_\triangle$ **35.** approx. 135,100 m^2

Test Yourself, page 460   1. 32 cm²   **2.** 12 cm²
3. 84 cm²   **4.** $9\sqrt{3}$ cm²   **5.** 35 cm²   **6.** 60 cm²
7. 172.5 cm²   **8.** 20 cm²   **9.** 13.5 cm²
10. $96\sqrt{3}$ cm²   **11.** 60 cm²   **12.** $50\sqrt{3}$ cm²

Practice Exercises, pages 468–470   1. 24,492 in.;
14,695.2 in.; 7041.45 in.   **3.** 3; 6π **5.** $\frac{5}{\pi}$; $\frac{10}{\pi}$
7. 70; 220   **9.** $\frac{49}{11}$; $\frac{98}{11}$ **11.** 9π cm   **13.** 36π cm
15. 6π cm; $\frac{6\pi}{5}$ cm   **17.** 72 cm; 144π cm
19. 96π cm; 72π cm   **21.** $\sqrt{2}$:1   **25.** 3.14 ft
27. $8\pi\sqrt{3}$ cm   **31.** $3\sqrt{3}$ cm   **33.** $6\pi + 6\sqrt{3}$ cm

Practice Exercises, pages 474–475   1. the 14 in.
pizza; $\frac{49\pi}{6} > \frac{64\pi}{8}$ **3.** 2; 45; 2π; $\frac{\pi}{8}$ **5.** 12; $\frac{6\pi}{5}$;
12π; 3.6π **7.** $\frac{\pi}{4}$ **9.** 32π **11.** $\frac{\pi r^2}{2}$; this is the
limit of a segment whose chord approaches a
diameter and whose central angle approaches 180°.
13. 72π **15.** $64\sqrt{3} - 32\pi$ **17.** A of sector, $A_s = \frac{m}{360}\pi r^2$; area of $\odot$, $A_\odot = \pi r^2$. Thus, $\frac{A_s}{A_\odot} = \frac{A_s}{\pi r^2} = \frac{\frac{m}{360}\pi r^2}{\pi r^2} = \frac{m}{360}$ **19.** $A_{(shaded\ region)}$ + sector ROP =
$2 \cdot \frac{\pi r^2}{6} - \frac{r^2}{4}\sqrt{3} = r^2(\frac{\pi}{3} - \frac{\sqrt{3}}{4})$.
21. $9(\sqrt{3} - \frac{1}{2}\pi)$ in.²   **23.** $6(15) - 10(\frac{3}{2})^2\pi = (90 - 22.5\pi)$ in.²   **24.** $2\sqrt{6}$ **25.** $-12\sqrt{10}$
26. $6\sqrt{3} - 30$

Practice Exercises, pages 478–481   1. No; they
should mult. the dimensions by $\sqrt{2}$.   **3.** 2:3, 2:3,
4:9   **5.** 5; 1; 25; 1   **7.** 1; 2; 1; 4   **9.** 4; 3; 4; 3
11. 1:4   **13.** $\frac{3}{2}$ **15.** 15 in.   **17.** $P(\triangle CED) = 66$
in.; $P(\triangle BEA) = 44$ in.   **19.** 200 in.²   **21.** $\sqrt{2}$:1
23. $\frac{\sqrt{2}}{1}$ **25.** $\frac{2}{1}$ **27.** $PR = 6$; $PQ = 12$
31. $\frac{P(H_1)}{P(H_2)} = \frac{a_1}{a_2} = \frac{r_1}{r_2}$ **33.** The perimeters of
2 regular polygons having the same number of sides
have the same ratio as the corr. linear parts.
35. 1225 ft²

Test Yourself, page 481   1. 8π cm   **2.** 16π cm²
3. 2π cm   **4.** 4π cm²   **5.** $(4\pi - 8)$ cm²   **6.** $C_A =$

$\frac{1}{2}C_B$ **7.** $\frac{5}{4}$ **8.** $\frac{P_1}{P_2} = \frac{2}{3}, \frac{A_1}{A_2} = \frac{4}{9}$ **9.** $(100 - 25\pi)$
cm²

Summary and Review, pages 484–485   1. 40 cm²
3. 24 cm²   **5.** 18 cm²   **7.** $\frac{75\sqrt{3}}{2}$ in.²   **9.** 2
11. $a_n = \frac{10}{10^n}$; limit = 0   **13.** 10π in.   **15.** $\frac{12\pi}{5}$
in.   **17.** 36π cm²   **19.** 12π cm²   **21.** 3:2; 3:2;
9:4

Chapter 12

Practice Exercises, pages 493–494   2. 7 in.
4. 12 in.   **6.** $L = 14$ in.²; $T = 38$ in.²; $V = 12$ in.³
8. $L = 80$ m^2; $T = 125$ m²; $V = 90$ m³   **10.** $L = 450$ cm²; $T = 510$ cm²; $V = 450$ cm³   **12.** $L = 144$
cm²; $T = 144 + 48\sqrt{3}$ cm²; $V = 144\sqrt{3}$ cm³
14. $T \approx 4,896$ ft²; $V = 19,500$ ft³   **16.** $e = \sqrt{38} \approx 6.2$ ft   **18.** yes; if an edge is 6 in. long   **24.** $d = \sqrt{w^2 + l^2 + h^2}$ **26.** 448 in.²   **28.** no; 4 trips; 117
ft³ ≈ 875.16 gal.; $\frac{875.16}{250} \approx 3.5 \to 4$ trips

Practice Exercises, pages 498–501   2. $L = 260$
cm²; $T = 360$ cm²; $V = 400$ cm³   **4.** 4, $2\sqrt{3}$;
$30\sqrt{3}$, $48\sqrt{3}$ **6.** $\sqrt{3}$, 2; $6\sqrt{3}$, $6(\sqrt{3} + \sqrt{6})$; 6
8. $14\sqrt{3}$; $882\sqrt{3}$; $1218\sqrt{3}$, $2100\sqrt{3}$; $5880\sqrt{3}$
10. 400   **12.** 72   **14.** $s = 6$ in.; $l = 12$ in.; $T = 180$ in.²   **16.** 192   **18.** $L = 108\sqrt{3}$ cm²; $T = 144\sqrt{3}$ cm²   **20.** \$0.25 since $V_p = \frac{1}{3}V_b$ **22.** $T = 8,400 + 400\sqrt{10}$; $V = 44,000$ **24.** $144(1 + \sqrt{10})$
cm²; 864 cm³   **26.** The base edges of the bottom
base are ∥ to the base edges of the top base. If a
pyramid is regular, the lateral edges are ≅.
Therefore, the lateral edges all have the same length.
28. $W = 1,404,928,400$ lb

Practice Exercises, pages 504–506   1. the height
and base of the rect.   **3.** 40π, 72π; 80π **5.** 3.5;
9π; $\frac{7}{2}\pi$ **7.** 14, 10; 480π **9.** 5; 125.6, 282.6
11. $64\pi\sqrt{3}$ **13.** =; $T_A = 2T_B$ **15.** $T = 210\pi$
in.²; $V = 400\pi$ in.³   **17.** $T = 144 + 288\sqrt{2}$ cm²;
$V = 864$ cm³   **19.** $r = \frac{4h}{h - 4}$; $h > 4$
21. $T + 10\% \approx 4663$ in.²   **23.** $96.5 = \pi r^2(2r)$;
$\pi r^3 = 48.25$, $r = \sqrt[3]{15.366} \approx 2.5$ in., $h \approx 5$ in.
25. Half is filled.

Test Yourself, page 506   1. $L = 156 + 12\sqrt{41}$;
$T = 188 + 12\sqrt{41}$; $V = 192$ **2.** $L = 75\pi$; $T = 87.5\pi$; $V = 93.75\pi$ **3.** $L = 28\sqrt{305}$; $T = 196 + 28\sqrt{305}$; $V = 1045\frac{1}{3}$ **4.** $L = 676$; $T = 756$; $V = 1040$ **5.** $L = 9\sqrt{259}$; $T = 9\sqrt{259} + 3\sqrt{3}$; $V = 48\sqrt{3}$ **6.** $L = 96\pi$; $T = 128\pi$; $V = 192\pi$

670   Answers to Selected Exercises

Practice Exercises, pages 513–515 **1.** $\dfrac{r_1}{r_2} = \dfrac{h_1}{h_2}$; lengths of corr. sides of similar $\triangle$s are proportional **3.** 24; 175π, 224π; 392π **6.** 8, 15, 17; 600π **7.** $h = r = 5\sqrt{2}$; $L = 50\pi\sqrt{2}$; $T = 50\pi(\sqrt{2}+1)$; $V = \dfrac{250\pi\sqrt{2}}{3}$ **9.** $h = 5\sqrt{3}$; $r = 5$; $L = 50\pi$; $T = 75\pi$; $V = \dfrac{125\pi\sqrt{3}}{3}$ **11.** $\dfrac{1024\pi}{3}$ **13.** $\dfrac{a^3\pi}{9}$ **15.** $\dfrac{s^3\pi\sqrt{3}}{24}$ **17.** $\dfrac{250\pi}{3}$ cm^3 **19.** $\sqrt{2}$ **27.** $V = \pi r^2 h_1 + \dfrac{1}{3}\pi r^2 h_2 = 147\pi$ ft^3 **29.** $A = \pi r l + 20$, $l \approx 15.4$; $A = 189.246$ in.^{2} **30.** 8 **31.** 180° **32.** 80° **33.** 20° **34.** 100° **35.** 13 **36.** 80° **37.** $\sqrt{39}$ **38.** $\dfrac{13\sqrt{39}}{2}$ **39.** 50 **40.** The $\perp$ bis. of the seg. joining the two pts.

Practice Exercises, pages 518–520 **1.** 288π m^3 **3.** π, 4π; $\dfrac{4}{3}\pi$ **5.** 7; 196π; $\dfrac{1372\pi}{3}$ **7.** 4; 16π, 64π **9.** $2\sqrt{6}$; 96π; $64\pi\sqrt{6}$ **12.** 256π in.^{2} **14.** 36π in.^{3} **16.** $\dfrac{\pi}{6}$ **18.** $A = 160\pi$ in.^{2}; $V = \dfrac{832\pi}{3}$ in.^{3} **20.** $4\sqrt{15}$ in. **23.** $\dfrac{4}{3}\pi r^3 = 4 \cdot 6 \cdot 2$, $r^3 = \dfrac{36}{\pi}$; $r \approx 2.25$ **24.** (6, 5) **25.** (−2, 6) **26.** (−9, 20)

Practice Exercises, pages 523–525 **1.** $\dfrac{1}{2}e$; $\dfrac{1}{2}e\sqrt{3}$ **3.** $\sqrt{3}$:9 **5.** 5:6; 25:36; 25:36; 25:36; 125:216 **7.** 3:4; 3:4; 9:16; 9:16; 27:64 **9.** 3:7; 3:7; 9:49; 9:49; 27:343 **11.** 3:4; 3:4; 9:16; 9:16; 9:16 **13.** 27:64 **15.** 7:11 **17.** 2:5 **19.** 4:25 **21.** 16 cm; 24 cm **23.** 512 cm^3; 1728 cm^3 **25.** mult. by $\dfrac{1}{4}$ **27.** doubled **29.** $\sqrt[3]{2}$

Test Yourself, page 525 **1.** $L = 65\pi$ cm^2; $T = 90\pi$ cm^2; $V = 100\pi$ cm^3 **2.** 5π cm^2 **3.** 36π cm^3 **4.** $5\sqrt{2}$ in. **5.** 972π in.^{3} **6.** $8\pi r + 4\pi$ cm^2 **7.** $\dfrac{(e+2)^3}{e^3}$ **8.** 27:64

Summary and Review, page 528 **1.** *CDEFGH*; *JKLMNO* **3.** 768; 768 + 192$\sqrt{3}$; 1536$\sqrt{3}$ **5.** 64 in.^{3} **7.** $V = 540\pi$ in.^{3} **9.** $L = 8\pi\sqrt{29}$ in.^{2}; $T = 16\pi + 8\pi\sqrt{29}$ in.^{2}; $V = \dfrac{160\pi}{3}$ in.^{3} **11.** 196π in.^{2}; $\dfrac{1372\pi}{3}$ in.^{3} **13.** scale factor = 3:1; $P_1:P_2 = 3:1$; $T_1:T_2 = 9:1$; $V_1:V_2 = 27:1$

Chapter 13

Practice Exercises, pages 538–540 **2.** (−6, −4) **4.** (6, −8) **6.** *C* **8.** *H* **10.** 12 **12.** $4\sqrt{10}$ **14.** $y = 8$ **16.** $x = 6$ **18.** $\overleftrightarrow{AF}$ **20.** y-axis

23. $x = -6$ and the half-plane to the left **25.** $y = -5$ and the half-plane below **26–29.**

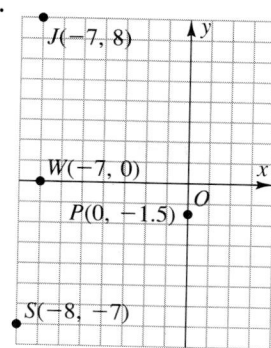

31. $x > -6$ **33.** $x \le 2$ **35.** IV **37.** I **39.** $DF = EF$; isos $\triangle$.

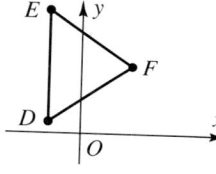

41. $JK = KL$ and $m\angle K = 90$; rt. isos. $\triangle$

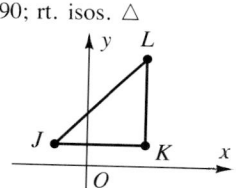

43. $\square$; $EF = HG$ and $EH = FG$

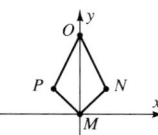

45. kite; $OP = ON$ and $MP = MN$

47. 2:1 **49.** yes; −3 **51.** $18 + 9\sqrt{2}$; 30.7 **53.** yes; 6; (1, 5), (1, −7), (−5, 5), (−5, −7), (−2, 2), or (−2, −4) **55.** yes; 2: (−2, 3) and (−2, −5) **56.** $4\sqrt{2}$ ft by $2\sqrt{2}$ ft, or approx. 5.6 ft by 2.8 ft

Practice Exercises, pages 544–545 **2.** (−1, 2); 6

4. (0, 0); 7

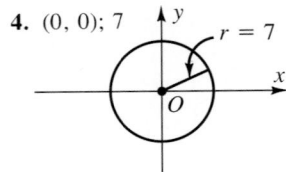

6. (4, 0); $\sqrt{2}$ **8.** (0, 0); 2.5 **10.** $(-a, -b)$; $2\sqrt{3}$
12. $(x + 2)^2 + (y - 4)^2 = 16$ **14.** $x^2 + y^2 = 2.25$
16. $(x - 4)^2 + y^2 = 3$ **18.** $(x - d)^2 + (y + 4)^2 = $
4.5

20.

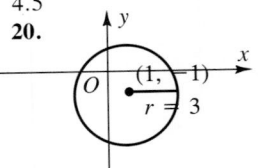

22.

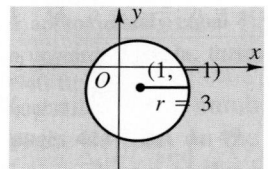

24.

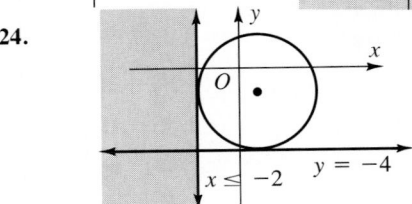

26. $(x + 3)^2 + y^2 \geq 25$ **28.** $x = 2$; $x = -8$
30. $(x + 3)^2 + (y + 2)^2 = 4$; yes **32.** $(x + 5)^2 + $
$(y + 2)^2 = 25$; yes **34.** $x^2 + y^2 = 16$ and $x^2 + y^2 = $
36 **36.** $(x + 2)^2 + (y - 8)^2 = 9$ **38.** $(x - 2)^2 + $
$(y + 3)^2 = 16$ **40.** $x^2 + y^2 = 4$, $x^2 + y^2 = 16$, $x^2 + $
$y^2 = 36$, $x^2 + y^2 = 64$, $x^2 + y^2 = 100$, $x^2 + y^2 = $
144, $x^2 + y^2 = 196$

Practice Exercises, pages 548–550

2. (3, −4) **4.** (−7, −4) **6.** (5.5, −1) **8.** (0, 0)
10. (3.5, $c + 1$) **12.** A(10, −1) **14.** B(−7, −5)
16. A(5, 2c −4) **18.** M_{DE} (0, 0); M_{EF} (2, −3);
M_{DF} (5, 1) **20.** M_{KL} (4, 5); M_{LM} (5, −2);
M_{MN} (−2, −3); M_{NK} (−3, 4) **22.** M_{SU} (2, 0);
M_{TV} (2, 0) **24.** $4\sqrt{2}$ **26.** M_{EH} (−3, 3);
M_{GF} ($\frac{3}{2}$, −3) **28.** no; midpts. of diag. do not
coincide; M_{BD} ($\frac{11}{2}$, $\frac{10}{2}$); M_{AC} ($\frac{11}{2}$, $\frac{11}{2}$) **30.** length
of median = $\frac{1}{2}$ length of hyp.; $PR = 10$, $QM = 5$
32. P(−11, −2) **34.** (3, 2) **37.** 31.4 or 10π
38. 20 **39.** 58 **40.** 78.5 or 25π **41.** 30
42. 10 **43.** 119 **44.** 238

Test Yourself, page 551 **1.** (−4, 3) **2.** (1, −3)
3. (−2, −2) **4.** (0, 3) **5.** B **6.** J **7.** E **8.** C
9. I: B, J; II: A, C; III: H, D; IV: G **10.** True; x-
and y-coordinates must be pos. to be in Quad. I
11. False; x-coordinates are pos. **12.** False;

x-coordinates are neg., y-coordinates are pos.
13. false; horizontal **14.** true; vertical line with all
values of $x = 7.5$ **15.** 13 **16.** $6\sqrt{5}$ **17.** (2,
−5); 2 **18.** (0, 0); 4 **19.** $(x - 5)^2 + y^2 = 9$
20. $(x + 4)^2 + (y - 3)^2 = 5$ **21.** (5, −8) **22.** (3,
0) **23.** A(3, 4) **24.** 5

Practice Exercises, pages 555–557 **1.** Slope
increases in abs. val.; slope decreases in abs. val.
3. a, b, c, d; f, g, h, i; answers may vary.
5. $\overleftrightarrow{AB}$, $\overleftrightarrow{EF}$ **7.** $\overrightarrow{IJ}$ **9.** $\frac{2}{3}$ **11.** 0 **13.** 2 **15.** −1
17. $\frac{1}{2}$ **19.** undefined **21.** $\overline{DE}$:$m = -\frac{1}{5}$; $\overline{EF}$:m is
undefined; $\overline{FG}$:$m = 0$; $\overline{DG}$:$m = -\frac{9}{2}$

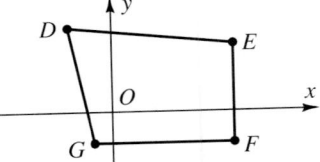

23. $\overline{LM}$:$m = 1$; $\overline{MN}$:$m = -1$; $\overline{NO}$:$m = 1$;
$\overline{LO}$:$m = -1$

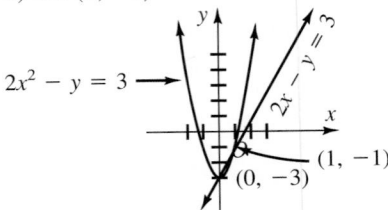

25. midpt. of $\overline{SU}$:M_1 (0, 10); midpt. of
$\overline{TU}$:M_2 (−2, 4); $\overline{ST}$:$m = 3$; M_1M_2:$m = 3$
29. Yes; slope of $\overline{GH}$ = slope of $\overline{HI}$ = $-\frac{4}{3}$

33. (0, 6) **35.** −1 **37.** $-\frac{b}{a}$ **39.** $ED = 5$,
$EF = 10$, $DF = \sqrt{125}$; by Pyth Th., slope of
$\overline{ED} = \frac{3}{4}$, slope of $\overline{EF} = -\frac{4}{3}$ **41.** Answers may
vary; $(-2\frac{1}{2}, 4)$, $(-4\frac{1}{2}, 0)$ **43.** $\tan A = \frac{4}{3}$,
$\angle A = 53°$ **47.** The rise is 0, or the roof is flat.
49. 48 ft **50.** 5.9 ft **51.** 27 cm **52.** 48 cm

Practice Exercises, pages 561–564 **1.** The graph
of $2x^2 - y = 3$ is a curve. The graphs intersect at
(0, −3) and (1, −1).

3. $y = 2x - \dfrac{9}{4}$ **5.** $y = 2x - 5$ **7.** $(-3, 4)$;

$m = -\dfrac{2}{3}$ **9.** $m = 0.5$; -3 **11.** $y = -8x + \dfrac{1}{2}$

13. $y = x\sqrt{3} + 0.5$ **15.** $y + 6 = \dfrac{2}{5}(x + 5)$

17. Answers may vary; $(y + 1) = 1(x - 1)$;
$x - y = 2$ **19.** Answers may vary; $(y - 2) = 3(x + 3)$; $3x - y = -11$ **21.**

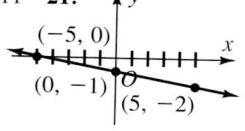

(−5, 0)
(0, −1)
(5, −2)

23.

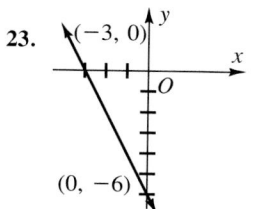

(−3, 0)
(0, −6)

25. $(4, -5)$ **27.**

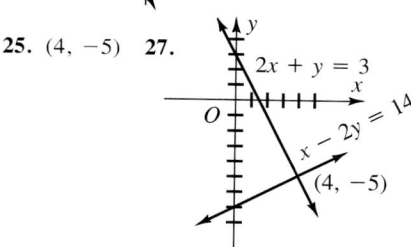

$2x + y = 3$
$x - 2y = 14$
$(4, -5)$

29. $(\dfrac{5}{4}, \dfrac{105}{8})$ **31.** Solving algebraically gives precise answers. With fractional coords. it can be hard to determine the coords. of intersect. pt.
33. $5x - 2y = -10$ **35.** $2x + y = 0$ **37.** $(2, -1)$
39. $3x + 2y = 1$ **41.** $\overleftrightarrow{AB}: x + y = 1$; $\overleftrightarrow{BC}: x + 4y = -2$; $\overleftrightarrow{CA}: x - 2y = -2$ **43.** $\overleftrightarrow{BD}: 4x + 7y = 40$; $\overleftrightarrow{AC}: 4x - 13y = 0$ **45.** $m = -\dfrac{4}{3}$, $b = 4$
47. $m = \dfrac{3}{4}$, $b = -3$ **51.** $y = b$ or $y = \dfrac{c}{b}$
57. $y = 2x - 5$; The graph is a line that crosses the y-axis at -5 and has a slope of 2.

Practice Exercises, pages 567–569
1. (a) $ax + by = 0$ (b) $bx - ay = 0$ **3.** $b \parallel c$; $b \perp d$, $c \perp d$ **5.** $b \parallel d$ **7.** $\dfrac{3}{7}$; $\dfrac{3}{7}$; $-\dfrac{7}{3}$ **9.** $-\dfrac{1}{4}$; $-\dfrac{1}{4}$; 4
11. $-\dfrac{1}{5}$ **13.** $-\dfrac{1}{3}$ **15.** $\parallel$ **17.** $\perp$ **19.** neither
21. $\parallel$; $(y - 2) = -5(x + 4)$; $\perp$; $(y - 2) = \dfrac{1}{5}(x + 4)$
23. $\parallel$; $(y + 2) = -\dfrac{1}{2}(x + 3)$; $\perp$; $(y + 2) = 2(x + 3)$

25. $3x - y = 11$ **27.** $x + 3y = -3$; since
$4 + 3 \cdot 1 \neq -3$, it does not contain A. **29.** trap.;
$\overline{BC} \parallel \overline{AD}$, $\overline{AB} \nparallel \overline{CD}$ **31.** rect.; $\overline{BC} \parallel \overline{AD}$, $\overline{AB} \parallel \overline{CD}$,
$\overline{AB} \perp \overline{BC}$ **33.** If 2 nonvert. lines are $\parallel$, then their slopes are $=$. If 2 nonvert. lines have $=$ slopes, then

they are $\parallel$. **35.** $L(2, 4)$; length of consecutive sides is 5 **37.** $3x + 2y = 11$ **43.** 49 **44.** 72 **45.** 20
46. $\dfrac{1}{4}$ **47.** 18 **48.** 192 **49.** 22 **50.** 48
51. 36

Practice Exercises, pages 574–576 **1.** $B(a, 0)$,
$C(a, b)$, $D(0, b)$ **3.** $J(a, 0)$, $K(0, a)$
5. $P(0, a\sqrt{3})$, $Q(a, 0)$, $R(-a, 0)$ **7.** $(\dfrac{2a + 0}{2}$,
$\dfrac{2b + 0}{2}) = (a, b)$; $MA = \sqrt{(0 - a)^2 + (2b - b)^2} = \sqrt{a^2 + b^2}$; $MB = \sqrt{(a - 2a)^2 - (b - 0)^2} = \sqrt{a^2 + b^2}$

Test Yourself, page 577 **1.** -1 **2.** $-\dfrac{1}{8}$ **3.** $-\dfrac{1}{4}$
4. $\overline{AB}$: $m = \dfrac{1}{4}$; $\overline{BC}$; $m = -2$; $\overline{AC}$; $m = -\dfrac{1}{2}$ **5.** $(9, 0)$
6. 2; -6 **7.** $\dfrac{2}{5}$; 2 **8.** -3; -12 **9.** $x - 2y = 16$ **10.** $2x + y = 2$ **11.** $2x - 11y = 47$ **12.** $\parallel$
13. neither **14.** $\perp$ **15.** $(y - 3) = -6(x + 2)$

Summary and Review, page 580 **1.** $\sqrt{26}$
3. $\sqrt{13}$ **5.** $(-3, -4)$; $2\sqrt{2}$ **7.** $(x - 6)^2 + (y + 2)^2 = 25$ **9.** $(-7, -7)$ **11.** $\dfrac{4}{5}$ **13.** 2;
$-\dfrac{1}{2}$ **15.** $(y + 4) = -5(x - 0)$ or $y + 4 = -5x$
17. $(y + 4) = \dfrac{1}{3}(x + 2)$

Chapter 14

Practice Exercises, pages 589–590 **1.** $\triangle ABC \cong \triangle ABC \cong \triangle ACB \cong \triangle BAC \cong \triangle BCA \cong \triangle CAB \cong \triangle CBA$ **3.** yes; yes, each member of D has exactly 1 preimage **5.** Answers may vary; $M(A) = L$; $M(B) = 0$; $M(C) = N$ **7.** (a) $(-5, -4)$, $(3, -3)$, $(-2, 1)$, $(0, 0)$; (b) $(4, -2)$, $(-3, -4)$, $(2, 3)$; (c) Yes; T preserves distance between pts. **9.** (a) $(15, 12)$, $(-9, 9)$, $(6, -3)$, $(0, 0)$; (b) $(-\dfrac{4}{3}, \dfrac{2}{3})$, $(1, \dfrac{4}{3})$, $(-\dfrac{2}{3}, -1)$; (c) No; distances are not preserved. **11.** No; if P is not on l, then all pts. on $\overline{PP'}$ get mapped to P'. **15.** yes; every pt. on the globe maps to a unique pt. on the plane **17.** 360 cm^2; $(360 + 108\sqrt{3})$ cm^2; $540\sqrt{3}$ cm^3 **18.** 60π cm^2; 96π cm^2; 96π cm^3 **19.** 168π cm^2; 266π cm^2; 588π cm^3

Practice Exercises pages 594–595 **10.** $(x, -y)$
12. (y, x) For Ex. 17, 19 line j: $y = \dfrac{4}{3}x + 4$
17. $y' = -\dfrac{4}{3}x + 4$ **19.** $y' = \dfrac{3}{4}x + 3$ **21.** (a)
$x = 0$; (b) $(-x, y)$ **23.** (a) $x = -2$; (b) $(x - 8, y)$
27. $(-x, -y)$

Practice Exercises, pages 598–600   1. a, b, and e; d; a and e could be glide reflections   **7.** $\overrightarrow{PP'}$, $\overrightarrow{QQ'}$ **9.** $\overrightarrow{MM'}$, $\overrightarrow{NN'}$ **11.** $\overrightarrow{PP'}$ 2 units left and 4 units down; $\overrightarrow{XX'}$ 6 units right and 1 unit up   **13.** $\overrightarrow{PP'}(x - 2, y - 4)$; $\overrightarrow{XX'}(x + 6, y + 1)$ **17.** $M' = (a + 3, b - 1)$, $N' = (a + 3, -b - 1)$, $P' = (-a + 3, -b - 1)$, $Q' = (-a + 3, b - 1)$ **19.** (a) Draw $\overrightarrow{PP'}$ and find its midpt. M. (b) Const. rt. $\triangle PQP'$ having $\overrightarrow{PP'}$ as a hyp. (c) Draw $\overleftrightarrow{MN} \parallel \overrightarrow{PQ}$. (d) Locate A and A' on $\overleftrightarrow{MN}$ such that $\overrightarrow{AA'}$ has the same length as $\overrightarrow{PQ}$. $\overrightarrow{AA'}$ is the translation vector and line $\overleftrightarrow{MN}$ is the line of reflection.   **23.** The double reflection of $\triangle ABC$ through l and k results in the translation $\overrightarrow{PP'}$. The distance between l and k is half the length of vector $\overrightarrow{PP'}$ and $l \parallel k$.   **25.** Answers may vary.

Practice Exercises, pages 603–606   1. yes; yes; yes   **7.** $\mathcal{R}_{o,20}$ **9.** $\mathcal{R}_{o,70}$ **17.** $M' = (2, -1)$; $N' = (-2, -1)$; $P' = (-2, 1)$; $Q' = (2, 1)$ **19.** $C' = (-y, x)$; $D' = (-y, -x)$; $E' = (y, -x)$; $F' = (y, x)$ **21.** $C' = (y, -x)$; $D' = (y, x)$; $E' = (-y, x)$; $F' = (-y, -x)$ **23.** Yes, if the line is through the center and α is an integral mult. of 180.   **25.** $\beta - 360$ **27.** 120   **29.** $2 \cdot \dfrac{360}{n}$ **35.** As α approaches 180, $\triangle ABC$ approaches $\triangle A'B'C'$ **39.** 90; they are $\perp$ **41.** Rotating through 180° produces the same sign.

Test Yourself, page 606   1. $(1, 2)$ **2.** $(-2, 3)$ **3.** $(10, -5)$ **4.** Yes; T is a translation and translations are isometries.   **5.** $\overline{A'C'}$ **6.** $\overline{GA}$ **7.** E **8.** $\triangle ACE$ **9.** C **10.** $\triangle FCH$ **11.** $(-3, 1)$; $(4, 2)$; $(0, -2)$ **12.** $(-3, -1)$; $(4, -2)$; $(0, 2)$ **13.** $(4, 1)$; $(-3, 2)$; $(1, -2)$ **14.** $(1, -3)$; $(2, 4)$; $(-2, 0)$ **15.** $(1, 3)$; $(2, -4)$; $(-2, 0)$

Practice Exercises, pages 609–611   3. $k = -1$ **5.** $k = 2$ **11.** $A' = (-9, -3)$, $B' = (6, 12)$, $C' = (12, -6)$ **13.** $AB = 5\sqrt{2}$; $A'B' = 15\sqrt{2}$ **15.** $X' = (2, \frac{2}{3})$, $Y' = (0, -2)$, $Z' = (-2, \frac{2}{3})$ **17.** $\frac{2}{3}$ **19.** 3, 10, 24   **21.** 27   **23.** $k = \frac{2}{3}$; $AB = \frac{9}{2}$ cm, $BC = 6$ cm, $AC = \frac{15}{2}$ cm   **25.** Know Q is on l and $D_{o,k}(B) = B'$. (1) Draw $\overleftrightarrow{AB}$. Know that $\overline{AB}$ gets mapped onto $\overline{A'B'}$ where $\overline{A'B'} \parallel \overline{AB}$ and $A'B' = |k| \cdot AB$. (2) Through B', const. $\overleftrightarrow{A'B'}$ such that $\overline{A'B'} \parallel \overline{AB}$. A' is the pt. at which the line intersects l.   **30.** $(r, s) = (3, -2)$; $k = 2$ **33.** $3, \frac{3}{2}$ **34.** $2, \frac{-4}{3}$ **35.** $-2 \pm \sqrt{5}$ **36.** $1, \frac{1}{2}$ **37.** $1, \frac{3}{2}$ **38.** $1, -\frac{1}{3}$ **39.** $\frac{1}{2}, -2$ **40.** $-1, -1$ **41.** $\dfrac{3 \pm \sqrt{3}}{2}$

Practice Exercises, pages 615–616   4. $\mathcal{R}_{o,105}$ **8.** rotation having center O and measure $\alpha_1 + \alpha_2$ **10.** $T_{2(AB)}(\triangle CDE)$ **12.** $(-4, 1)$ **14.** $(3, 2)$ **16.** $(-1, -5)$ **18.** $(y - 2, x + 1)$ **25.** $F \circ (G \circ H) = F \circ (G(H(x, y))) = F \circ (G(-x + 1, y + 1)) = F(-(x + 1), (y + 1)) = (-(x + 1), -(y + 1))$; $(F \circ G) \circ H(x, y) = (F \circ G)(H(x, y)) = (F \circ G)(x + 1, y + 1) = F(G(x + 1, y + 1)) = F(-(x + 1), (y + 1)) = (-(x + 1)), -(y + 1))$

Practice Exercises, pages 619–621   1. $\mathcal{R}_{o,270}$ **3.** R_l **5.** R_h **7.** R_k **9.** $D_{o,\frac{1}{4}}$ **13.** $(x + 3, y - 2)$ **15.** $(x - 2, y + 3)$ **17.** (x, y) **19.** $(x + 2, y - 3)$ **21.** BCA **23.** $\mathcal{R}_{o,0}$ **25.** $\mathcal{R}_{o,240}$ or $\mathcal{R}_{o,-120}$ **27.** $\mathcal{R}_{o,-340}$ **29.** $\mathcal{R}_{o,0}$ **31.** $Q = (2x, 2y)$; $k = 2$; $S = (x - 1, y + 3)$ **33.** $(\frac{x}{2}, \frac{y}{2})$ **35.** $(\frac{x + 1}{2}, \frac{y - 3}{2})$ **37.** $S^{-1} \circ Q^{-1}$ **43.** R_y; R_y; H_o; I **45.** In Logic: Statement: If p, then q. Inv.: If not p, then not q. In mappings: Inv. represents a mapping that "undoes" the effect of the original mapping.

Practice Exercises, pages 628–631   1. The fold lines; $\mathcal{R}_{o,90}$, H_o, $\mathcal{R}_{o,270}$ **3.** (a) 1 vert., 2 diag., 1 horiz. line (b) 60°, 120°, 180°, 240°, 300°; (c) yes   **5.** (a) none (b) none (c) none   **11.** B, C, D, E, H, I, O, X   **13.** H, I, N, O, S, X, Z   **15.** Answers may vary.   **17.** any nonrectangular $\square$ except a rhombus   **19.** Equilateral $\triangle$ with irregular design at each vertex.   **21.** $R_y(x, y) = (x, -y)$ **23.** $H_o(x, y) = (-x, -y)$ **27.** n lines; if n is even, from vertices through center and through midpts. of opp. sides; if n is odd, from vertex to midpt. of opp. side   **31.** line and pt. sym.; rotational sym.

Test Yourself, page 631   1. $(-9, -6)$ **2.** $(-4, 1)$ **3.** $(9, 1)$ **4.** $(-2, -6)$ **5.** $(-3, 5)$ **9.** $(3x - 6, 3y + 12)$ **10.** $(3x - 2, 3y + 4)$ **11.** $(\frac{x}{3}, \frac{y}{3})$ **12.** $(x + 2, y - 4)$ **13.** 30 cm: F is a dilation of magnitude 3.   **14.** 50: translations preserve $\angle$ meas.   **15.** 3 lines of symmetry; 120° and 240° rotational symmetry   **16.** 2 diag. lines of symmetry; point symmetry

Summary and Review, pages 634–635   1. $(-4, 12)$; $(3, 0)$; $(4, -6)$ **3.** $A' = (1, 3)$; $B' = (-6, -6)$; $AB = \sqrt{58}$; $A'B' = \sqrt{130}$; $AB \neq A'B'$, so T is not on isometry.   **5.** $(-2, 2)$ **7.** $(1, 3)$ **11.** $\mathcal{R}_{o,160}$ **13.** $k = 3$ **15.** $A'(8, -2)$, $B'(9, -6)$, $C'(5, -5)$; H_Q **17.** $\triangle PRQ$ **19.** $\mathcal{R}_{o,120}$ or $\mathcal{R}_{o,-240}$ **21.** $\triangle RQP$ **23.** a. diagonals; b. rotational 180°; c. yes

674   Answers to Selected Exercises

Postulate 1   A line contains at least two distinct points. A plane contains at least three noncollinear points. Space contains at least four noncoplanar points. **(1.2)**

Postulate 2   If two distinct points are given, then a unique line contains them. **(1.2)**

Postulate 3   Through any two points there are infinitely many planes. Through any three points there is at least one plane. Through any three noncollinear points there is exactly one plane. **(1.2)**

Postulate 4   If two points are in a plane, then the line that contains those points lies entirely in the plane. **(1.2)**

Postulate 5   If two distinct planes intersect, then their intersection is a line. **(1.2)**

Theorem 1.1   If two distinct lines intersect, then they intersect in exactly one point. **(1.2)**

Theorem 1.2   If there is a line and a point not in the line, then there is exactly one plane that contains them. **(1.2)**

Theorem 1.3   If two distinct lines intersect, then they lie in exactly one plane. **(1.2)**

Postulate 6   Given any two points there is a unique distance between them. **(1.3)**

Postulate 7   **The Ruler Postulate**   There is a one-to-one correspondence between the points of a line and the set of real numbers such that the distance between two distinct points of the line is the absolute value of the difference of their coordinates. **(1.3)**

Theorem 1.4   On a ray there is exactly one point that is at a given distance from the endpoint of the ray. **(1.3)**

Corollary   Each segment has exactly one midpoint. **(1.3)**

Theorem 1.5   **Midpoint Theorem** If M is the midpoint of a segment $\overline{AB}$, then:

$$\text{and } \begin{array}{l} 2AM = AB \\ AM = \frac{1}{2}AB \end{array} \qquad \text{and } \begin{array}{l} 2MB = AB \\ MB = \frac{1}{2}AB. \end{array} \quad \textbf{(1.3)}$$

Postulate 8   Given any angle, there is a unique real number between 0 and 180 known as its degree measure. **(1.4)**

Postulate 9   **The Protractor Postulate**   In a half-plane with edge $\overleftrightarrow{AB}$ and any point S between A and B, there exists a one-to-one correspondence between the rays that originate at S in that half-plane and the real numbers between 0 and 180. **(1.4)**

Theorem 1.6   In a half-plane, through the endpoint of a ray lying in the edge of the half-plane, there is exactly one other ray such that the angle formed by the two rays has a given measure between 0 and 180. **(1.4)**

Theorem 1.7   All right angles are congruent. **(1.4)**

Postulates
Theorems

Theorem 1.8	**Angle Bisector Theorem** If $\overrightarrow{OX}$ is the bisector of $\angle AOB$, then:

$$\text{and } \begin{array}{l} 2m\angle AOX = m\angle AOB \\ m\angle AOX = \frac{1}{2}m\angle AOB \end{array} \quad \text{and } \begin{array}{l} 2m\angle XOB = m\angle AOB \\ m\angle XOB = \frac{1}{2}m\angle AOB. \end{array} \quad \textbf{(1.4)}$$

Postulate 10	**Linear Pair Postulate** If two angles form a linear pair, then they are supplementary angles. **(1.5)**
Theorem 1.9	If two angles are vertical, then they are congruent. **(1.5)**
Theorem 1.10	If two lines are perpendicular, then the pairs of adjacent angles they form are congruent. **(1.6)**
Corollary 1	If two lines are perpendicular, then all four angles they form are congruent. **(1.6)**
Corollary 2	If two lines are perpendicular, then all four angles they form are right angles. **(1.6)**
Theorem 1.11	If two lines intersect to form a pair of congruent adjacent angles, then the lines are perpendicular. **(1.6)**
Theorem 1.12	If there is given any point on a line in a plane, then there is exactly one line in that plane perpendicular to the given line at the given point. **(1.6)**
Corollary	If there is given any segment in a plane, then in that plane there is exactly one line that is a perpendicular bisector of the segment. **(1.6)**
Theorem 1.13	If the exterior sides of two adjacent acute angles are perpendicular, then the angles are complementary. **(1.6)**
Theorem 1.14	If there is a point not on a line, then there is exactly one line perpendicular to the given line through the given point. **(1.6)**
Theorem 2.1	Congruence of segments is reflexive, symmetric, and transitive. **(2.3)**
Theorem 2.2	Congruence of angles is reflexive, symmetric, and transitive. **(2.3)**
Theorem 2.3	If two angles are supplements of congruent angles or of the same angles, then the two angles are congruent. **(2.5)**
Theorem 2.4	If two angles are complements of congruent angles or of the same angle, then the two angles are congruent. **(2.5)**
Theorem 3.1	If two parallel planes are intersected by a third plane, then the lines of intersection are parallel. **(3.1)**
Postulate 11	If parallel lines have a transversal, then corresponding angles are congruent. **(3.2)**
Theorem 3.2	If parallel lines have a transversal, then alternate interior angles are congruent. **(3.2)**
Theorem 3.3	If parallel lines have a transversal, then alternate exterior angles are congruent. **(3.2)**
Theorem 3.4	If parallel lines have a transversal, then interior angles on the same side of the transversal are supplementary. **(3.2)**

Postulates
Theorems

Theorem 3.5	If a transversal intersecting two parallel lines is perpendicular to one of the lines, it is also perpendicular to the other line. (**3.2**)
Postulate 12	Through a point not on a line, there is exactly one line parallel to the given line. (**3.3**)
Postulate 13	If two lines have a transversal and a pair of congruent corresponding angles, then the lines are parallel. (**3.3**)
Theorem 3.6	If two lines have a transversal and a pair of congruent alternate interior angles, then the lines are parallel. (**3.3**)
Theorem 3.7	If two lines have a transversal and a pair of congruent alternate exterior angles, then the lines are parallel. (**3.3**)
Theorem 3.8	If two lines have interior angles on the same side of the transversal that are supplementary, then the lines are parallel. (**3.3**)
Theorem 3.9	If two coplanar lines are perpendicular to the same line, then they are parallel. (**3.3**)
Theorem 3.10	If two lines are parallel to a third line, then they are parallel to each other. (**3.3**)
Theorem 3.11	The sum of the measures of the angles of a triangle is 180. (**3.4**)
Corollary 1	If two angles of one triangle are congruent respectively to two angles of a second triangle, then the third angles are congruent. (**3.4**)
Corollary 2	Each angle of an equiangular triangle measures 60°. (**3.4**)
Corollary 3	In a triangle, there can be at most one right angle, or at most one obtuse angle. (**3.4**)
Corollary 4	The acute angles of a right triangle are complementary. (**3.4**)
Theorem 3.12	The measure of an exterior angle of a triangle is equal to the sum of the measures of the two remote interior angles. (**3.4**)
Theorem 3.13	The sum of the measures of the interior angles of a convex polygon with n sides is $(n - 2)180$. (**3.7**)
Theorem 3.14	The sum of the measures of the exterior angles of any convex polygon, one angle at each vertex, is 360. (**3.7**)
Postulate 14	**SSS Postulate** If three sides of one triangle are congruent to three sides of another triangle, then the two triangles are congruent. (**4.2**)
Postulate 15	**SAS Postulate** If two sides and the included angle of one triangle are congruent to two sides and the included angle of another triangle, then the two triangles are congruent. (**4.2**)
Postulate 16	**ASA Postulate** If two angles and the included side of one triangle are congruent to two angles and the included side of another triangle, then the two triangles are congruent. (**4.2**)
Theorem 4.1	**AAS Theorem** If two angles and the nonincluded side of one triangle are congruent, respectively, to the corresponding angles and nonincluded side of another triangle, then the two triangles are congruent. (**4.2**)

Theorem 4.2	If a point lies on the perpendicular bisector of a segment, then the point is equidistant from the endpoints of the segment. **(4.5)**
Theorem 4.3	If a point is equidistant from the endpoints of a segment, then it lies on the perpendicular bisector of the segment. **(4.5)**
Corollary	If two points are each equidistant from the endpoints of a segment, then the line joining the points is the perpendicular bisector of the segment. **(4.5)**
Theorem 4.4	If a point lies on the bisector of an angle, then the point is equidistant from the sides of the angle. **(4.5)**
Theorem 4.5	If a point is equidistant from the sides of an angle, then the point lies on the bisector of the angle. **(4.5)**
Theorem 4.6	**LA Theorem** If a leg and an acute angle of one right triangle are congruent to the corresponding parts of another right triangle, then the triangles are congruent. **(4.7)**
Theorem 4.7	**HA Theorem** If the hypotenuse and an acute angle of one right triangle are congruent to the corresponding parts of another right triangle, then the triangles are congruent. **(4.7)**
Theorem 4.8	**LL Theorem** If the two legs of one right triangle are congruent to the two legs of another right triangle, then the triangles are congruent. **(4.7)**
Theorem 4.9	**HL Theorem** If the hypotenuse and a leg of one right triangle are congruent to the corresponding parts of another right triangle, then the triangles are congruent. **(4.7)**
Theorem 5.1	**Isosceles Triangle Theorem** If two sides of a triangle are congruent, then the angles opposite those sides are congruent. **(5.1)**
Corollary 1	An equilateral triangle is also equiangular. **(5.1)**
Corollary 2	Each angle of an equilateral triangle has a measure of 60. **(5.1)**
Corollary 3	The bisector of the vertex angle of an isosceles triangle is perpendicular to the base at its midpoint. **(5.1)**
Theorem 5.2	If two angles of a triangle are congruent, then the sides opposite those angles are congruent. **(5.1)**
Corollary	An equiangular triangle is also equilateral. **(5.1)**
Theorem 5.3	If B is between A and C, then $AC > AB$ and $AC > BC$. **(5.2)**
Theorem 5.4	If $\overrightarrow{OB}$ is between $\overrightarrow{OA}$ and $\overrightarrow{OC}$, then $m\angle AOC > m\angle AOB$ and $m\angle AOC > m\angle BOC$. **(5.2)**
Theorem 5.5	**The Exterior Angle Theorem** The measure of an exterior angle of a triangle is greater than the measure of either remote interior angle. **(5.2)**
Theorem 5.6	If two sides of a triangle are unequal, then the angles opposite them are unequal and the larger angle is opposite the longer side. **(5.5)**
Theorem 5.7	If two angles of a triangle are unequal, then the sides opposite them are unequal and the longer side is opposite the larger angle. **(5.5)**

Postulates
Theorems

Corollary 1	The perpendicular segment from a point to a line is the shortest segment from the point to the line. **(5.5)**
Corollary 2	The perpendicular segment from a point to a plane is the shortest segment from the point to the plane. **(5.5)**
Theorem 5.8	**The Triangle Inequality** The sum of the lengths of any two sides of a triangle is greater than the length of the third side. **(5.6)**
Theorem 5.9	**Hinge Theorem** If two sides of one triangle are congruent to two sides of a second triangle, and the included angle of the first is larger than the included angle of the second, then the third side of the first triangle is longer than the third side of the second triangle. **(5.6)**
Theorem 5.10	**Converse of the Hinge Theorem** If two sides of one triangle are congruent to two sides of a second triangle, and the third side of the first is longer than the third side of the second, then the included angle of the first triangle is larger than the included angle of the second triangle. **(5.6)**
Theorem 5.11	All plane angles of dihedral angles are congruent. **(5.7)**
Theorem 6.1	Opposite sides of a parallelogram are congruent. **(6.1)**
Corollary 1	A diagonal of a parallelogram forms two congruent triangles. **(6.1)**
Corollary 2	If two lines are parallel, then all points on one line are equidistant from the other line. **(6.1)**
Theorem 6.2	Opposite angles of a parallelogram are congruent. **(6.1)**
Theorem 6.3	Consecutive angles of a parallelogram are supplementary. **(6.1)**
Theorem 6.4	The diagonals of a parallelogram bisect each other. **(6.1)**
Theorem 6.5	If both pairs of opposite sides of a quadrilateral are congruent, then the quadrilateral is a parallelogram. **(6.2)**
Theorem 6.6	If one pair of opposite sides of a quadrilateral is both congruent and parallel, then the quadrilateral is a parallelogram. **(6.2)**
Theorem 6.7	If both pairs of opposite angles of a quadrilateral are congruent, then the quadrilateral is a parallelogram. **(6.2)**
Theorem 6.8	If the diagonals of a quadrilateral bisect each other, then the quadrilateral is a parallelogram. **(6.2)**
Theorem 6.9	If three or more parallel lines cut off congruent segments on one transversal, then they cut off congruent segments on every transversal. **(6.3)**
Corollary	A line that contains the midpoint of one side of a triangle and is parallel to another side bisects the third side. **(6.3)**
Theorem 6.10	The diagonals of a rectangle are congruent. **(6.4)**
Theorem 6.11	The diagonals of a rhombus are perpendicular. **(6.4)**
Theorem 6.12	Each diagonal of a rhombus bisects two angles of the rhombus. **(6.4)**
Theorem 6.13	The midpoint of the hypotenuse of a right triangle is equidistant from the three vertices. **(6.4)**

Theorem 6.14	Base angles of an isosceles trapezoid are congruent. **(6.5)**
Theorem 6.15	If the base angles of a trapezoid are congruent, then the trapezoid is isosceles. **(6.5)**
Theorem 6.16	The diagonals of an isosceles trapezoid are congruent. **(6.5)**
Theorem 6.17	If the diagonals of a trapezoid are congruent, then the trapezoid is isosceles. **(6.5)**
Theorem 6.18	**The Midsegment Theorem** The segment that joins the midpoints of two sides of a triangle is parallel to the third side, and its length is half the length of the third side. **(6.5)**
Theorem 6.19	The median of a trapezoid is parallel to the bases, and has a length equal to one-half the sum of the lengths of the bases. **(6.5)**
Theorem 6.20	**SASAS Theorem** Two quadrilaterals are congruent if any three sides and the included angles of one are congruent, respectively, to the corresponding three sides and the included angles of the other. **(6.7)**
Theorem 6.21	**ASASA Theorem** Two quadrilaterals are congruent if any three angles and the included sides of one are congruent, respectively, to the three corresponding angles and the included sides of the other. **(6.7)**
Postulate 17	**AA Postulate** If two angles of one triangle are congruent to two angles of a second triangle, then the triangles are similar. **(7.4)**
Theorem 7.1	**SAS Theorem** If an angle of one triangle is congruent to an angle of another triangle, and the lengths of the sides including those angles are in proportion, then the triangles are similar. **(7.5)**
Theorem 7.2	**SSS Theorem** If the corresponding sides of two triangles are in proportion, then the triangles are similar. **(7.5)**
Theorem 7.3	**Triangle Proportionality Theorem** If a line parallel to one side of a triangle intersects the other two sides, then it divides those sides proportionally. **(7.7)**
Corollary	If three parallel lines have two transversals, then they divide the transversals proportionally. **(7.7)**
Theorem 7.4	If a line divides two sides of a triangle proportionally, then it is parallel to the third side of the triangle. **(7.7)**
Theorem 7.5	Corresponding medians of similar triangles are proportional to the corresponding sides. **(7.7)**
Theorem 7.6	Corresponding altitudes of similar triangles are proportional to the corresponding sides. **(7.7)**
Theorem 7.7	**Triangle Angle-Bisector Theorem** If a ray bisects an angle of a triangle, then it divides the opposite side into segments proportional to the other two sides of the triangle. **(7.7)**
Theorem 8.1	The altitude to the hypotenuse of a right triangle forms two triangles that are similar to the original triangle and to each other. **(8.1)**

Corollary 1	The length of the altitude drawn to the hypotenuse of a right triangle is the geometric mean between the lengths of the segments of the hypotenuse. **(8.1)**
Corollary 2	The altitude to the hypotenuse of a right triangle intersects it so that the length of each leg is the geometric mean between the length of its adjacent segment of the hypotenuse and the length of the entire hypotenuse. **(8.1)**
Theorem 8.2	**Pythagorean Theorem** In a right triangle, the square of the length of the hypotenuse is equal to the sum of the squares of the lengths of the legs. **(8.2)**
Theorem 8.3	**Converse of Pythagorean Theorem** If the sum of the squares of the lengths of two sides of a triangle is equal to the square of the length of the third side, then the triangle is a right triangle. **(8.3)**
Theorem 8.4	If the square of the length of the longest side of a triangle is greater than the sum of the squares of the lengths of the other two sides, then the triangle is an obtuse triangle. **(8.3)**
Theorem 8.5	If the square of the length of the longest side of a triangle is less than the sum of the squares of the lengths of the other two sides, then the triangle is an acute triangle. **(8.3)**
Theorem 8.6	**45°-45°-90° Theorem** In a 45°-45°-90° triangle, the length of the hypotenuse is $\sqrt{2}$ times the length of a leg. **(8.4)**
Theorem 8.7	**30°-60°-90° Theorem** In a 30°-60°-90° triangle, the length of the hypotenuse is twice the length of the shorter leg, and the length of the longer leg is $\sqrt{3}$ times the length of the shorter leg. **(8.4)**
Theorem 9.1	If a line is tangent to a circle, then the line is perpendicular to the radius at the point of tangency. **(9.2)**
Corollary 1	Two tangent segments from a common external point are congruent. **(9.2)**
Corollary 2	The two tangent rays from a common external point determine an angle that is bisected by the ray from the external point to the center of the circle. **(9.2)**
Theorem 9.2	If a line in the plane of a circle is perpendicular to a radius at its endpoint on the circle, then the line is tangent to the circle. **(9.2)**
Postulate 18	The measure of an arc formed by two adjacent nonoverlapping arcs is the sum of the measures of those two arcs. **(9.3)**
Theorem 9.3	In the same circle, or in congruent circles, two minor arcs are congruent if and only if their central angles are congruent. **(9.3)**
Theorem 9.4	In the same circle, or in congruent circles, two minor arcs are congruent if and only if their chords are congruent. **(9.3)**
Theorem 9.5	If a diameter is perpendicular to a chord, then it bisects the chord and its arcs. **(9.3)**
Theorem 9.6	In the same circle, or in congruent circles, two chords are equidistant from the center(s) if and only if they are congruent. **(9.3)**
Theorem 9.7	If two chords of a circle are unequal in length, then the longer chord is nearer to the center of the circle. **(9.3)**

Theorem 9.8	If two chords of a circle are not equidistant from the center, then the longer chord is nearer to the center of the circle. **(9.3)**
Theorem 9.9	The measure of an inscribed angle is equal to one-half of the measure of its intercepted arc. **(9.4)**
Corollary 1	If two inscribed angles of a circle intercept the same arc or congruent arcs, then the angles are congruent. **(9.4)**
Corollary 2	If a quadrilateral is inscribed in a circle, then its opposite angles are supplementary. **(9.4)**
Corollary 3	If an inscribed angle intercepts a semicircle, the angle is a right angle. **(9.4)**
Corollary 4	If two arcs of a circle are included between parallel segments, then the arcs are congruent. **(9.4)**
Theorem 9.10	If two chords intersect within a circle, then the measure of the angle formed is equal to one-half the sum of the measures of the intercepted arcs. **(9.5)**
Theorem 9.11	If a tangent and a chord intersect in a point on the circle, then the measure of the angle they form is one-half the measure of the intercepted arc. **(9.5)**
Theorem 9.12	If a tangent and a secant, two secants, or two tangents intersect in a point in the exterior of a circle, then the measure of the angle is equal to one-half the difference of the measures of the intercepted arcs. **(9.5)**
Theorem 9.13	If two chords intersect inside a circle, then the product of the lengths of the segments of one chord is equal to the product of the lengths of the segments of the other chord. **(9.7)**
Theorem 9.14	If two secants intersect in the exterior of a circle, then the product of the lengths of one secant segment and its external segment is equal to the product of the lengths of the other secant segment and its external segment. **(9.7)**
Theorem 9.15	If a secant and a tangent intersect in the exterior of a circle, then the product of the lengths of the secant segment and its external segment is equal to the square of the length of the tangent segment. **(9.7)**
Theorem 10.1	The bisectors of the angles of a triangle intersect in a point that is equidistant from the three sides of the triangle. **(10.3)**
Theorem 10.2	The perpendicular bisectors of the sides of a triangle intersect in a point that is equidistant from the vertices of the triangle. **(10.3)**
Theorem 10.3	The lines that contain the altitudes of a triangle intersect in one point. **(10.3)**
Theorem 10.4	The medians of any triangle are concurrent, intersecting in a point that is $\frac{2}{3}$ of the distance from each vertex to the midpoint of the opposite side. **(10.3)**
Postulate 19	In a plane, the locus of points at a given distance d from a given point P is a circle with center P and with d the length of a radius. **(10.6)**
Postulate 20	In a plane, the locus of points a given distance d from a given line l is a pair of lines each parallel to l and at the distance d from l. **(10.6)**
Postulate 21	In a plane, the locus of points equidistant from two given parallel lines is a line midway between and parallel to each of the given lines. **(10.6)**

Theorem 10.5	In a plane, the locus of points equidistant from two given points is the perpendicular bisector of the segment joining the points. **(10.6)**
Theorem 10.6	In a plane, the locus of points equidistant from the sides of an angle is the angle bisector. **(10.6)**
Postulate 22	**Area Postulate** Every polygonal region corresponds to a unique positive number, called the *area* of the region. **(11.1)**
Postulate 23	**Area Congruence Postulate** If two polygons are congruent, then the polygonal regions determined by them have the same area. **(11.1)**
Postulate 24	**Area Addition Postulate** If a region can be subdivided into nonoverlapping parts, the area of the region is the sum of the areas of those nonoverlapping parts. **(11.1)**
Postulate 25	The area of a square is the square of the length of its side. $(A = s^2)$ **(11.1)**
Theorem 11.1	The area of a rectangle equals the product of its base and height. $(A = bh)$ **(11.1)**
Theorem 11.2	The area of a parallelogram equals the product of the length of a base and its corresponding height. $(A = bh)$ **(11.2)**
Theorem 11.3	The area of a triangle is equal to one-half the product of the length of a base and its corresponding height. $(A = \frac{1}{2}bh)$ **(11.2)**
Corollary 1	The area of a rhombus equals one-half the product of the lengths of its diagonals. $(A = \frac{1}{2}d_1 \cdot d_2)$ **(11.2)**
Corollary 2	The area of an equilateral triangle equals one-fourth the product of $\sqrt{3}$ and the length of the side squared. $(A = \frac{s^2\sqrt{3}}{4})$ **(11.2)**
Theorem 11.4	The area of a trapezoid equals one-half the product of the height and the sum of the lengths of the bases. $[A = \frac{h}{2}(b_1 + b_2)]$ **(11.3)**
Theorem 11.5	The area of a regular polygon is equal to one-half the product of the apothem and the perimeter. $[A = \frac{1}{2}aP]$ **(11.4)**
Theorem 11.6	For all circles, the ratio of the circumference to the length of the diameter is the same. **(11.6)**
Corollary 1	The circumferences of any two circles have the same ratio as their radii. **(11.6)**
Corollary 2	If C is the circumference of a circle with a diameter of length d and a radius of length r, then $C = \pi d$, or $C = 2\pi r$. **(11.6)**
Corollary 3	In a circle, the ratio of the length l of an arc to the circumference C equals the ratio of the degree measure m of the arc to 360. $[\frac{l}{C} = \frac{m}{360}$, or $l = \frac{m}{360}(2\pi r)]$ **(11.6)**
Theorem 11.7	The area A of a circle with radius of length r is given by the formula $A = \pi r^2$. **(11.7)**
Corollary 1	The areas of two circles have the same ratio as the squares of their radii. **(11.7)**

Corollary 2	In a circle with radius r, the ratio of the area A of a sector to the area of the circle (πr^2) equals the ratio of the degree measure m of the arc of the sector to 360. $[\frac{A}{\pi r^2} = \frac{m}{360}$, or $A = \frac{m}{360}(\pi r^2)]$ **(11.7)**
Theorem 11.8	If the scale factor of two similar figures is $a:b$, then the ratio of corresponding perimeters is $a:b$, and the ratio of corresponding areas is $a^2:b^2$. **(11.8)**
Theorem 12.1	The lateral area L of a right prism equals the perimeter of a base P times the height h of the prism. ($L = Ph$) **(12.1)**
Theorem 12.2	The total area T of a right prism is the sum of the lateral area L and the area of the two bases, $2B$. ($T = L + 2B$) **(12.1)**
Theorem 12.3	The volume V of a right prism equals the area of a base B times the height h of the prism. ($V = Bh$) **(12.1)**
Corollary	The volume of a cube with edge e is the cube of e. ($V = e^3$) **(12.1)**
Theorem 12.4	The lateral area L of a regular pyramid equals one-half the product of the slant height l and the perimeter P of the base. ($L = \frac{1}{2}lP$) **(12.2)**
Theorem 12.5	The total area T of a regular pyramid equals the lateral area L plus the area of the base B. ($T = L + B$) **(12.2)**
Theorem 12.6	The volume V of a pyramid is one-third the product of its height h and the area B of its base. ($V = \frac{1}{3}Bh$) **(12.2)**
Theorem 12.7	The lateral area L of a right circular cylinder equals the product of the circumference C of the base and the height h of the cylinder. ($L = C \cdot h = 2\pi rh$) **(12.3)**
Theorem 12.8	The total area T of a right circular cylinder equals the sum of the lateral area L and the area of the two bases $2B$. ($T = L + 2B = 2\pi rh + 2\pi r^2 = 2\pi r(h + r)$) **(12.3)**
Theorem 12.9	The volume V of a cylinder equals the product of the area of the base B and the height of the cylinder. ($V = B \cdot h = \pi r^2 h$) **(12.3)**
Theorem 12.10	The lateral area L of a right circular cone having slant height l and circumference $C = 2\pi r$, where r is the radius of the base, is one-half the product of the circumference and the slant height. ($L = \frac{1}{2}(2\pi r)l = \pi rl$) **(12.5)**
Theorem 12.11	The total area T of a right circular cone is the sum of the lateral area L and the area of the base B. ($T = L + B = \pi rl + \pi r^2 = \pi r(l + r)$) **(12.5)**
Theorem 12.12	The volume V of a cone is one-third the product of the area of the base B and the height h. ($V = \frac{1}{3}Bh = \frac{1}{3}\pi r^2 h$) **(12.5)**
Theorem 12.13	The area A of a sphere of radius r is four times the area of a great circle. ($A = 4\pi r^2$) **(12.6)**
Theorem 12.14	The volume V of a sphere of radius r is $\frac{4}{3}\pi r^3$. ($V = \frac{4}{3}\pi r^3$) **(12.6)**

Theorem 12.15	If the scale factor of two similar solids is $a:b$, then
	i. the ratio of corresponding perimeters or circumferences is $a:b$
	ii. the ratios of base areas, lateral areas, and total areas are $a^2:b^2$
	iii. the ratio of volumes is $a^3:b^3$. **(12.7)**
Theorem 13.1	The distance d between any two points (x_1, y_1) and (x_2, y_2) is $d = \sqrt{|x_2 - x_1|^2 + |y_2 - y_1|^2}$. **(13.1)**
Theorem 13.2	An equation of the circle with center (h, k) and radius length r is $(x - h)^2 + (y - k)^2 = r^2$. **(13.2)**
Theorem 13.3	The midpoint of the segment with endpoint coordinates (x_1, y_1) and (x_2, y_2) is the point with coordinates $(\frac{x_1 + x_2}{2}, \frac{y_1 + y_2}{2})$. **(13.3)**
Theorem 13.4	The graph of an equation that can be written in the form $ax + by = c$, with a and b not both zero, is a line. **(13.5)**
Theorem 13.5	An equation of a line containing point (x_1, y_1) and having slope m is $(y - y_1) = m(x - x_1)$. **(13.5)**
Theorem 13.6	An equation of a line that has y-intercept b and slope m is $y = mx + b$. **(13.5)**
Theorem 13.7	Two nonvertical lines are parallel if and only if their slopes are equal. **(13.6)**
Theorem 13.8	Two nonvertical lines are perpendicular if and only if the product of their slopes is -1. **(13.6)**
Theorem 14.1	A reflection in a line is an isometry. **(14.2)**
Theorem 14.2	If a transformation T maps any point (x, y) to $(x + a, y + b)$, then T is a translation. **(14.3)**
Theorem 14.3	A rotation is an isometry. **(14.4)**
Theorem 14.4	The dilation $D_{o, k}$ maps every line segment to a parallel line segment that is $|k|$ times as long. **(14.5)**
Theorem 14.5	The composition of two isometries is an isometry. **(14.6)**
Theorem 14.6	A composition of reflections in two parallel lines is a translation. The translation glides all points through twice the distance between the lines. **(14.6)**
Theorem 14.7	A composition of reflections in two intersecting lines is a rotation about the point of intersection of the two lines. The measure of the angle of rotation is twice the measure of the angle from the first line of reflection to the second. **(14.6)**
Corollary	A composition of reflections in perpendicular lines is a half-turn about the point where the lines intersect. **(14.6)**

Construction 1 To construct a segment congruent to a given segment **(397)**

Construction 2 To construct the midpoint of a given segment **(397)**

Construction 3 To construct an angle congruent to a given angle **(398)**

Construction 4 To construct the bisector of a given angle **(398)**

Construction 5 To construct the perpendicular bisector of a given segment **(403)**

Construction 6 To construct the perpendicular to a given line at a given point on the line **(404)**

Construction 7 To construct the perpendicular to a given line from a given point not on the line **(404)**

Construction 8 To construct a line parallel to a given line and through a point not on the given line **(404)**

Construction 9 To construct the orthocenter of a given triangle **(408)**

Construction 10 To construct the centroid of a given triangle **(409)**

Construction 11 To construct a tangent to a circle at a point on the circle **(412)**

Construction 12 To construct a tangent to a circle through a point in the circle's exterior **(413)**

Construction 13 To locate the center of a given circle **(413)**

Construction 14 To circumscribe a circle about a given triangle **(414)**

Construction 15 To inscribe a circle in a given triangle **(414)**

Construction 16 To divide a given segment into a specified number of congruent segment **(417)**

Construction 17 To construct a fourth segment in proportion with three given segments **(418)**

Construction 18 To construct a segment whose length is the geometric mean between the lengths of two given segments **(418)**

Constructions

acute angle (p. 19)   Angle whose measure is between 0 and 90.

acute triangle (p. 98)   Triangle with three acute angles.

adjacent angles (p. 18)   Two coplanar angles that have a common vertex, a common side, and have no common interior points.

adjacent dihedral angles (p. 205)   Dihedral angles that share a common edge and a common face.

adjacent nonoverlapping arcs (p. 363)   Arcs with exactly one point in common.

alternate exterior angles (p. 81)   Pair of nonadjacent angles, both exterior, on opposite sides of the transversal.

alternate interior angles (p. 81)   Pair of nonadjacent angles, both interior, on opposite sides of the transversal.

altitude (cone) (p. 511)   Perpendicular segment joining the vertex to the plane of the base.

altitude (cylinder) (p. 503)   Perpendicular segment joining the bases.

altitude (parallelogram) (p. 441)   Segment perpendicular to the base and joining the base to the opposite side.

altitude (prism) (p. 491)   Segment perpendicular to the planes of both bases.

altitude (trapezoid) (p. 450)   Segment that is perpendicular to, and has its endpoints on, the bases of the trapezoid.

altitude (triangle) (p. 150)   Segment that is perpendicular from a vertex to the line containing the opposite side.

angle (triangle) (p. 18)   Union of two noncollinear rays with a common endpoint.

angle bisector (of a triangle) (p. 149)   Segment that bisects an angle of a triangle and has one endpoint on the opposite side.

angle of depression (p. 337)   Angle drawn down from the horizontal.

angle of elevation (p. 337)   Angle drawn up from the horizontal.

apothem (regular polygon) (p. 455)   Distance from the center to a side.

arc length (p. 468)   Portion of the circumference of a circle.

area (p. 440)   Size of the region enclosed by the figure.

auxiliary line (p. 98)   Lines, segments, rays, or points added to a figure in order to facilitate a proof or an understanding of a problem.

axis (cone) (p. 511)   Perpendicular segment joining the vertex to the base.

axis (cylinder) (p. 502)   Segment joining the centers of the bases.

base (isosceles triangle) (p. 174)   The side opposite the vertex angle.

base angles (isosceles triangle) (p. 174)   Angles that include the base.

base angles (trapezoid) (p. 239)   Angles that include each base.

base edges (pyramid) (p. 495)   Edges of the base.

base (parallelogram) (p. 441)   One side of the parallelogram.

base (pyramid) (p. 495)   Face that does not contain the vertex.

bases (prism) (p. 490)   Two congruent, parallel faces.

bases (trapezoid) (p. 239)   The parallel sides.

between (points) (p. 13)   Given three collinear points X, Y, and Z, Y is between X and Z if and only if $XY + YZ = XZ$.

between (rays) (p. 20)   Given three coplanar rays $\overrightarrow{OA}$, $\overrightarrow{OT}$, and $\overrightarrow{OB}$, $\overrightarrow{OT}$ is between $\overrightarrow{OA}$ and $\overrightarrow{OB}$ if and only if $m\angle AOT + m\angle TOB = m\angle AOB$.

biconditional (p. 53)   "If and only if" statement formed by combining a conditional and its converse into one statement.

bisector (angle) (p. 20)   Ray that separates an angle into two angles of equal measures.

bisector (segment) (p. 14)   Any line, segment, ray, or plane that intersects a segment at its midpoint.

center (circle) (p. 352)   The given point from which every point is equidistant.

center (regular polygon) (p. 455)   Center of the circumscribed circle.

central angle (circle) (p. 362)   Angle whose vertex is the center of the circle and whose sides are radii.

central angle (regular polygon) (p. 455)   Angle with its vertex at the center and its sides two consecutive radii.

centroid (p. 409)   Point of concurrency of the medians of a triangle.

chord (p. 353)   Segment joining two points on a circle.

circle (p. 352)   Set of all points in a plane that are a given distance from a given point called the center.

circumcenter (p. 408)   Point of concurrency of the perpendicular bisectors of the sides of a triangle.

circumscribed around the polygon (p. 353)   Each vertex of the polygon is a point on the circle.

circumference (p. 466)   Distance around a circle.

collinear (p. 3)   Points that lie on the same line.

common external tangent (p. 359)   Line tangent to two coplanar circles that does not intersect the segment joining the centers of the two circles.

common internal tangent (p. 359)   Line tangent to two coplanar circles that intersects the segment joining the centers of the two circles.

complementary angles (p. 23)   Two angles whose measures sum to 90.

composition of mappings (p. 612)   Combinations of mappings carried out in succession.

concave polygon (p. 105)   Polygon in which any of the lines containing the sides also contain points in the polygon's interior.

conclusion (p. 47)   "Then" part of a conditional statement.

conditional (p. 47)   Statement formed by joining two statements, p and q, with the words *if* and *then*.

cone (p. 511)   Pyramid-like solid with a circular base.

congruent angles (p. 20)   Angles that have equal measures.

congruent arcs (p. 363)   Arcs in the same or congruent circles with equal measures.

congruent circles (p. 353)   Circles having congruent radii.

congruent quadrilaterals (p. 248)   Quadrilaterals with corresponding angles and corresponding sides congruent.

congruent segments (p. 13)   Segments having equal measures.

congruent triangles (p. 129)   Triangles whose corresponding angles and corresponding sides are congruent.

concentric circles (p. 353)   Coplanar circles having the same center.

concurrent (p. 407)   Three or more lines that intersect in the same point.

construction (p. 396)   Creating a figure using only a straightedge and a compass.

contraction (p. 607)   Dilation that reduces the size of a figure.

contrapositive (p. 51)   Statement related to a conditional statement in the form: If $\sim q$, then $\sim p$.

converse (p. 51)   Statement related to a conditional statement in the form: If q, then p.

convex polygon (p. 105)   Polygon in which the lines containing the sides do not contain points in the polygon's interior.

coordinate (p. 12)   Number paired with each point on a number line.

coordinate plane (p. 536)   Plane of the x-axis and the y-axis.

coplanar (p. 3)   Points that lie on the same plane.

corollary (p. 14)   Theorem whose justification follows from another theorem.

corresponding angles (p. 81)   Pair of nonadjacent angles—one interior, one exterior—both on the same side of the transversal.

cos x (p. 333)   In a right triangle, the length of the side adjacent to an acute angle divided by the length of the hypotenuse.

cylinder (p. 502)   Prism-like solid with circular bases.

decagon (p. 105)   A 10-sided polygon.

deductive reasoning (p. 62)   Reasoning logically from given statements to a desired conclusion.

diagonal (polygon) (p. 105)   Segment that joins two nonconsecutive vertices.

diameter (p. 353)   Chord containing the center of a circle.

dihedral angle (p. 204)   Union of two noncoplanar half-planes that have the same edge.

dilation (p. 607)   Transformation that produces an enlargement or a contraction.

distance (p. 12)   Absolute value of the difference of the coordinates of two distinct points on a line.

distance (from point to line) (p. 151)   Length of the perpendicular from the point to the line.

edge (dihedral angle) (p. 204)   Intersection of the two noncoplanar half-planes.

edge (plane) (p. 4)   Line that separates a plane into two half-planes.

edges (polyhedron) (p. 490)   Intersections of the sides.

equation (circle) (p. 542)   Equation with center (h, k) and radius r, is in the form $(x - h)^2 + (y - k)^2 = r^2$.

equiangular triangle (p. 98)   Triangle in which all angles are congruent.

equilateral triangle (p. 98)   Triangle in which all sides are congruent.

expansion (p. 607)   Dilation that enlarges a figure.

exterior (circle) (p. 352)   Set of all points E in the plane of $\odot O$ such that $OE > r$.

externally tangent circles (p. 359)   All points of one circle are exterior to those of the other, except the point where the circles are tangent to the same line.

extremes (p. 263)   First and fourth terms of a proportion.

faces (dihedral angle) (p. 204)   The non-coplanar half-planes forming the angle.

formal proof (p. 67)   A logical argument in which each statement requires justification.

geometric mean (p. 268) x is the geometric mean between positive numbers p and q if and only if $p/x = x/q$, where $x > 0$.

Given (p. 62)   Hypothesis of a proof.

glide reflection (p. 597)   Transformation composed of a glide followed by a reflection.

great circle (p. 353)   Intersection of a sphere and a plane that contains the center of the sphere.

greater than (p. 179)   For real numbers a and b, a is *greater than* b, written $a > b$, if and only if there is a positive real number c such that $a = b + c$.

half-planes (p. 4)   Two halves of a plane that are separated by a line.

height (cylinder) (p. 503)   Length of the altitude.

height (cone) (p. 511)   Length of the altitude.

height (prism) (p. 491)   Length of the altitude.

height (pyramid) (p. 495)   Distance from the vertex to the base.

hexagon (p. 105)   A 6-sided polygon.

hypothesis (p. 47)   "If" part of a conditional statement.

hypotenuse (p. 159)   Side of a right triangle that is opposite the right angle.

identity transformation (p. 617)   Mapping that leaves each point fixed.

image (p. 587)   Point mapped from a pre-image.

incenter (p. 407)   Point of concurrency of the angle bisectors of a triangle.

inscribed angle (p. 368)   Angle with its vertex on the circle and its sides containing chords of the circle.

inscribed in a circle (p. 353)   Polygon with each vertex being a point on the circle.

interior (circle) (p. 352)   Set of all points I in the plane of $\odot O$ such that $OI < r$.

internally tangent circles (p. 359)   One circle in the interior of the other, except for the point where the circles are tangent to the same line.

intersection (two figures) (p. 3)   The set of points that lie in both figures.

inverse (p. 51)   Statement related to a conditional statement in the form: If $\sim p$, then $\sim q$.

inverse transformation (p. 618)   Mapping that "undoes" the effect of the original mapping.

isometry (p. 588)   Transformation that preserves distance between points.

isosceles trapezoid (p. 239)   Trapezoid with congruent legs.

isosceles triangle (p. 98)   Triangle in which at least two sides are congruent.

lateral area (p. 491)   Sum of the areas of the lateral faces.

lateral edges (prism) (p. 490)   Intersections of the lateral faces.

lateral edges (pyramid) (p. 495)   Intersections of the lateral faces.

lateral faces (prism) (p. 490)   Parallelogram faces.

lateral faces (pyramid) (p. 495)   Faces that contain the vertex.

lateral surface (cone) (p. 511)   Set of all points not in the base.

legs (isosceles triangle) (p. 174)   Two congruent sides.

legs (right triangle) (p. 159)   Sides opposite the acute angles.

legs (trapezoid) (p. 239)   Nonparallel sides.

line (p. 2)   Infinitely many points extending in both directions.

linear equation (p. 558)   Equation in the form $ax + by = c$, with a and b not both zero.

linear pair (p. 23)   Two angles that are adjacent and whose noncommon sides are opposite rays.

line of reflection (p. 591)   Perpendicular bisector of the segment between a preimage and its reflected image.

line symmetry (p. 627)   Isometry other than the identity that reflects the figure onto itself.

locus (p. 422)   Set of points satisfying one or more given conditions.

logically equivalent (p. 52)   Statements that have the same truth value.

major arc (p. 362)   Arc with measure > 180.

mapping (p. 586)   Correspondence that associates each member of a set with a unique member of another set.

means (p. 263)   Second and third terms of a proportion.

measure (dihedral angle) (p. 205)   Measure of a plane angle of the dihedral angle.

measure (major arc) (p. 362)   Difference between the measure of its related minor arc and 360.

measure (minor arc) (p. 362)   Measure of its central angle.

measure (length) (segment) (p. 13)   Distance between the endpoints of the segment.

measure (semicircle) (p. 362)   180.

median (trapezoid) (p. 241)   Segment that joins the midpoints of the legs.

median (triangle) (p. 149)   Segment that extends from a vertex to the midpoint of the opposite side.

midpoint (segment) (p. 14)   Point that divides a segment into two congruent segments.

minor arc (p. 362)   Less than a semicircle.

negation (statement) (p. 46)   Formed by using the word *not*.

noncollinear (p. 3)   Points that are not collinear.

noncoplanar (p. 3)   Points that are not coplanar.

oblique cone (p. 511)   Axis is not perpendicular to the base.

oblique cylinder (p. 502)   Axis not perpendicular to the bases.

oblique prism (p. 491)   Lateral edges not perpendicular to the planes of the bases.

obtuse angle (p. 19)   Angle whose measure is between 90 and 180.

obtuse triangle (p. 98)   Triangle with one obtuse angle.

octagon (p. 105)   An 8-sided polygon.

opposite rays (p. 13) $\overrightarrow{TS}$ and $\overrightarrow{TX}$ are called opposite rays if T is between S and X.

ordered pair (p. 536)   Unique point on the coordinate plane.

origin (p. 536)   Point of intersection of the axes on the coordinate plane.

orthocenter (p. 408)   Point of concurrency of the altitudes of a triangle.

parallel lines (p. 80)   Two lines that lie in the same plane and do not intersect.

parallel planes (p. 80)   Two planes that do not intersect.

parallel rays or segments (p. 80)   Two segments or rays, or the lines that contain them, that do not intersect.

parallelogram (p. 218)   Quadrilateral with both pairs of opposite sides parallel.

pentagon (p. 105)   A 5-sided polygon.

perimeter (of a polygon) (p. 106)   Sum of the lengths of the sides.

perpendicular (lines) (p. 28)   Two lines that intersect to form right angles.

perpendicular bisector of a segment (p. 29)   Line, ray, segment, or plane that is perpendicular to a segment at its midpoint.

pi (π) (p. 467)   Ratio of circumference to the diameter of a circle.

plane (p. 2)   A flat surface with no thickness that extends without end in all directions.

plane angle (dihedral angle) (p. 205)   Angle formed by a plane that is perpendicular to its edge.

point (p. 2)   Has no size and no dimension, merely position.

point-slope form (linear equation) (p. 559)   Equation of a line containing point (x_1, y_1) and having slope m, in the form $(y - y_1) = m(x - x_1)$.

point symmetry (p. 627)   Special case of rotational symmetry.

polygon (p. 104)   Figure consisting of three or more coplanar segments intersecting only at endpoints with no two segments collinear.

polyhedron (p. 490)   Geometric figure made up of a finite number of polygons that are joined by pairs along their sides and that enclose a finite portion of space.

postulate (axiom) (p. 7)   Statement accepted as true.

preimage (p. 587)   Point mapped to an image.

prism (p. 490)   Polyhedron with two congruent faces contained in parallel planes, and its other faces parallelograms.

projection onto the *x*-axis (p. 589)   Line drawn from (x, y) perpendicular to the *x*-axis.

proof (p. 57) Logical sequence of statements with their supporting reasons.

proportion (p. 263) Equality of two ratios.

protractor (p. 19) Instrument used to determine the measure of an angle in degrees.

Prove (p. 62) Conclusion to be reached in a proof.

pyramid (p. 495) Polyhedron with all faces except one having a common vertex.

quadrant (p. 537) One of four regions of the coordinate plane.

quadrilateral (p. 105) A 4-sided polygon.

radius (circle) (p. 352) Segment extending from the center to any point on the circle.

radius (regular polygon) (p. 455) Segment that joins the center to a vertex.

ratio (p. 262) Given two numbers x and y, $y \neq 0$, a ratio is the quotient x divided by y.

ray (p. 13) Set of points on a line that consists of a segment, $\overline{ST}$, and all points X such that T is between X and S.

rectangle (p. 233) Parallelogram that has a right angle.

reflection (p. 591) Transformation that produces a mirror image of a figure.

regular polygon (p. 106) Polygon that is both equilateral and equiangular.

regular prism (p. 491) Prism with regular polygons as bases.

regular pyramid (p. 495) Pyramid with a regular polygonal base and congruent lateral edges.

rhombus (p. 233) Parallelogram with consecutive sides congruent.

right angle (p. 19) Angle whose measure is 90.

right circular cone (p. 511) Axis is perpendicular to the base.

right cylinder (p. 502) Axis perpendicular to the bases.

right prism (p. 491) Prism with lateral edges perpendicular to the planes of the bases.

right triangle (p. 98) Triangle with one right angle.

rotation (p. 601) Transformation that turns a figure about a fixed point through a given number of degrees.

rotational symmetry (p. 627) Isometry other than the identity that rotates a figure onto itself.

scale factor (p. 271) Ratio between the corresponding sides of similar polygons.

scale factor (similar solids) (p. 521) Ratio of corresponding lengths.

scalene triangle (p. 98) Triangle in which no sides are congruent.

secant (p. 353) Line, ray, or segment that contains a chord of a circle.

sector (circle) (p. 472) Region bounded by two radii and their intercepted arc.

segment (p. 13) Set of points on a line that consist of two points called the endpoints, and all points between them.

segment (circle) (p. 473) Region bounded by an arc and the chord of the arc.

semicircle (p. 362) Arc whose endpoints are the endpoints of a diameter.

sides (polygon) (p. 105) Segments that determine a polygon.

sides (angle) (p. 18) Rays that form an angle.

similar (p. 271) Polygons with corresponding angles congruent and lengths of corresponding sides in proportion.

similar solids (p. 521) Solids having similar bases and corresponding lengths proportional.

sin x (p. 332) In a right triangle, the length of the side opposite an acute angle divided by the length of the hypotenuse.

skew lines (p. 80) Two lines that do not lie in the same plane and do not intersect.

slant height (regular pyramid) (p. 495) Distance from the vertex to the base edge.

slant height (right circular cone) (p. 511)   Distance from the vertex to any point of the circle that forms the base.

slope (line) (p. 552)   Steepness of the line.

slope-intercept form (linear equation) (p. 559)   Equation of a line that has y-intercept b and slope m, in the form $y = mx + b$.

space (p. 3)   The set of all points.

sphere (p. 353)   Set of all points in space that are a given distance from a given point called the center.

square (p. 233)   Equilateral, equiangular parallelogram.

square unit (p. 441)   Square region having sides that measure one unit in length.

standard form (linear equation) (p. 558) $ax + by = c$, with a and b not both zero.

supplementary angles (p. 23)   Two angles whose measures sum to 180.

tangent to a circle (p. 357)   Line in the plane of the circle that intersects the circle in exactly one point.

tan x (p. 333)   In a right triangle, the length of the side opposite an acute angle divided by the length of the side adjacent to the angle.

theorem (p. 8)   Statement that must be proven true.

total area (p. 491)   Sum of the lateral area and the area of the base(s).

transformation (p. 587)   One-to-one mapping of the plane onto itself.

translation (p. 596)   Transformation in one direction, indicated by a vector.

transversal (p. 81)   Line that intersects two or more coplanar lines at different points.

trapezoid (p. 239)   Quadrilateral with exactly one pair of parallel sides.

triangle (p. 95)   Set of points that consists of the figure formed by three segments connecting three noncollinear points.

vertex (angle) (p. 18)   Common endpoint of the rays that form an angle.

vertex angle (p. 174)   Angle opposite the base of an isosceles triangle.

vertex (polygon) (p. 105)   Intersection point of two consecutive sides of a polygon.

vertex (pyramid) (p. 495)   The common vertex.

vertical angles (p. 24)   Two nonadjacent angles formed by two intersecting lines.

vertices (polyhedron) (p. 490)   Points where the edges intersect.

vector (p. 596)   Arrow used to indicate distance and direction of a glide.

volume (p. 491)   Amount of space occupied by a figure.

x-axis (p. 536)   Horizontal number line on the coordinate plane.

x-coordinate (p. 536)   First component of an ordered pair.

x-intercept (p. 559)   x-coordinate of the point where a linear equation intersects the x-axis.

y-axis (p. 536)   Vertical number line on the coordinate plane.

y-coordinate (p. 536)   Second component of an ordered pair.

y-intercept (p. 559)   y-coordinate of the point where a linear equation intersects the y-axis.

AA postulate, 277
AAS theorem, 134
Acute angle, 19
Acute triangle, 98–99, 317
Algebra
    absolute value, 13
    additive inverse, 618
    Boolean, 66
    cross products, 267
    decimal approximation for radical expressions, 323
    estimating square roots, 327
    geometric mean, 268, 418–419
    greater than, 179
    identity for addition, 617
    less than, 179
    means-extremes property, 267
    operations with radicals, 268, 322
    product property of square roots, 268
    properties of equality, 56
    properties of inequality, 179–181
    properties of a proportion, 267
    real numbers, 56, 180
    reciprocals, 267
    simplifying radicals, 268
    triangular numbers, 109
Algebra Review (*see* Table of Contents, iii–x)
Algorithm, 545
Alternate Assessment (*see* Chapter Projects), 1, 45, 79, 127, 173, 217, 261, 305, 351, 395, 439, 489, 535, 585
Altitude(s)
    concurrent, 408
    of cones, 511
    corresponding, of similar triangles, 294
    of cylinders, 503
    of parallelograms, 441
    of prisms, 491
    of pyramids, 495
    of right triangles, 306–307
    of trapezoids, 450
    of triangles, 150, 407–408
Angle(s) 18–20
    acute, 19

adjacent, 18
alternate exterior, 81, 86
alternate interior, 81, 86
base, 174, 239
bisector, 20, 398
central, 362, 368, 455
classifying, 19
complementary, 23, 69
congruent, 20, 27, 57, 68–69, 85–86, 398
consecutive, 104
constructing, 27, 398–399
corresponding, 81, 85, 129
of depression, 337
dihedral, 204–206
of elevation, 337
exterior, 81, 86
exterior points of, 18
formed by secant and tangent, 374
formed by tangent and chord, 374
formed by a transversal, 81, 85–87
formed by two chords, 373
formed by two secants, 374
formed by two tangents, 374
of incidence, 594
included, 134
inscribed, 368–369
interior, 81, 86
interior points of, 18
linear pair, 23
measure of, 19
obtuse, 19
opposite, 218–219
of parallax, 342
of parallelograms, 218–220
plane, 205–206
of polygons, 114–116
of reflection, 594
remote interior, of triangles, 180
right, 19
sides of, 18
solving problems involving, 34–35
supplementary, 23, 68, 86
theorems about, 19–20, 25, 57, 68–69
of triangles, 97–100
vertex, 174–175
vertex of, 18
vertical, 24–25

Angle bisector(s), 20, 398
    locus as, 422–423
    in triangles, 149, 151, 294, 407
Angle bisector theorem, 20
Angle pairs, 23–25, 81
Apothem, 455
Applications (*see also* Developing Mathematical Power, x)
    Approximations of Area, 482–483
    Astronomy, 342–343
    Longitude and Latitude, 120–121
    Precision and Accuracy, 164–165
    Vectors and Scalars, 254–255
Arc(s), 362–363
    adjacent nonoverlapping, 363
    congruent, 363, 369
    intercepted, 368–369, 373–375
    length, 468
    major, 362
    measures of, 362–363
    minor, 362
    semicircle, 362
Archimedes, 475, 482–483
Archimedian solids, 501
Area, 440
    approximation of, 482–483
    of circles, 471–472
    computer applications, 444, 449, 460, 470, 481, 506, 525
    of congruent polygons, 440
    of equilateral triangles, 446
    of parallelograms, 445
    of polygons, 440–441
    of rectangles, 441
    of regular polygons, 455–457
    of rhombuses, 446
    of sectors of circle, 472
    of segments of circle, 473
    of similar polygons, 476–477
    of similar solids, 521–522
    of spheres, 516
    of squares, 440
    of trapezoids, 450–451
    of triangles, 446, 449
Area addition postulate, 440
Area congruence postulate, 440
Area postulate, 440
ASA postulate, 134
ASASA theorem, 249
Assessment
    alternative (*see* Chapter Projects), 1, 45, 79, 127, 173, 217, 261, 305, 351, 395, 439, 489, 535, 585

tests (*see* Table of Contents, iii–x)
Astronomy, 2, 342–343, 356, 606
Auxiliary
  figures, 378–380
  lines, 99
  segments, 155–156
Axiom, 7, 84
Axis
  of cones, 511
  of cylinders, 502

Base(s)
  of cones, 511
  of cylinders, 502
  of isosceles triangles, 174
  of prisms, 490
  of pyramids, 495
  of trapezoids, 239
Base angles
  of isosceles triangles, 174
  of trapezoids, 239
Base edges, 495
Betweenness, 13, 20
Biconditional(s), 53, 151, 244
Biographical Note, 426, 540, 545, 564
Bisector(s)
  angle, 20, 398
  concurrent, 407–408
  locus as, 423
  perpendicular, 29, 150–151, 154, 403
  segment, 14
  in triangles, 149, 151, 294, 407–408
Boolean Algebra, 66

Calculator, 17
  scientific, 264, 323, 327, 332, 337–338, 343, 383–384, 449
Career
  applied mathematician, 426
  archaeologist, 12
  computer programmer, 46
  construction worker, 28, 204
  designer, 6
  draftsperson, 6
  engineer, 6, 426
  lawyer, 50
  layout artist, 262
  metallurgist, 506
  navigator, 378
  packager, 500
  pilot, 23, 340, 422
  ranger, 340
  surveyor, 7, 18, 228, 316, 329
Cavalieri's Principle, 520
Center
  of a circle, 352, 413
  of a dilation, 607
  of regular polygons, 455

of a rotation, 601
Central angle
  of circles, 362
  of regular polygons, 455
Centroid, 409
Chapter Project (*see* Table of Contents, iii–x)
Chapter Summary and Review (*see* Table of Contents, iii–x)
Chapter Test (*see* Table of Contents, iii–x)
Chord, 353, 363–364, 373–374, 382
Circle(s), 352–384
  arc of, 362–363 (*see also* Arc)
  area of, 471–472
  center of, 352, 413
  central angle, 362
  chord of, 353, 363–364, 373–374, 382
  circumference of, 466–467
  circumscribed, 353, 356, 395, 414, 455
  computer applications, 356, 361, 367, 372, 377, 388–389, 416, 470, 545
  concentric, 353
  congruent, 353
  constructions involving, 356, 377, 412–414
  diameter of, 353
  equation of, 541–543
  exterior of, 352
  great, 353
  inequalities in, 364
  inscribed, 359, 414
  interior of, 352
  locus as, 423
  measure of, 362
  products of segment lengths of, 382–383
  radius of, 352
  secant of, 353, 374, 382–383
  sector of, 472
  tangent, 359
  tangent to, 357–359 (*see also* Tangent)
Circumcenter, 408
Circumference
  of circles, 466–467
  of cylinders, 502
Circumscribed
  circles, 353, 356, 395, 414, 455
  polygons, 359
College Entrance Exam Review (*see* Table of Contents, iii–x)
Collinear points, 3
Communication (*see* Developing Mathematical Power, x)
Compass, 396
Coplanar points, 3
Complementary angles, 23, 69
  sine and cosine of, 331–333

Computer
  applications, 38–39, 73, 84, 96, 108, 109, 119, 132, 138, 154, 162, 178, 183, 198, 203, 210–211, 222, 227, 238, 243, 253, 266, 276, 281, 286, 297, 298–299, 308, 310, 315, 320, 325, 335, 336, 341, 356, 361, 367, 372, 377, 388–389, 402, 406, 411, 416, 421, 426, 432, 444, 449, 460, 470, 481, 494, 506, 515, 520, 525–527, 540, 545, 550, 557, 564, 569, 578–579, 590, 600, 611, 616, 631, 632–633
  and Boolean Algebra, 66
  graphics, 210–211, 298–299, 388–389, 432–433, 470, 481, 578–579, 631, 632–633
  graphs, 545
  Logo commands, 38–39, 108–109, 138, 210–211, 298–299, 310, 320, 336, 341, 388–389, 432–433, 494, 526–527, 540, 550, 557, 578–579, 632–633
  using Logo, 38–39, 73, 84, 96, 108, 109, 119, 132, 138, 154,162, 178, 183, 198, 203, 210–211, 222, 227, 238, 243, 253, 266, 276, 281, 286, 297, 298–299, 310, 315, 320, 325, 336, 341, 356, 361, 367, 372, 377, 388–389, 402, 406, 411, 416, 421, 426, 432–433, 444, 449, 460, 470, 481, 494, 506, 515, 520, 525, 526–527, 540, 545, 550, 557, 564, 569, 578–579, 590, 600, 611, 616, 631, 632–633
Conclusion, 47
Concurrent lines, 407
  constructions involving, 407–409
Conditional(s), 46–53
  proving, 62–63
Cone(s), 511–512
  lateral area of, 512
  lateral surface of, 511
  oblique, 511
  right circular, 511
  total area of, 512
  volume of, 512
Congruence, 128–130
  AAS theorem, 134
  and area, 440
  ASASA theorem, 249
  identity, 174
  in an isosceles triangle, 174–176
  of quadrilaterals, 248–249
  and reflections, 592
  of right triangles, 159–160
  and rotations, 602
  SAS theorem, 282

SASAS theorem, 249
in space, 204–206
SSS theorem, 283
of triangles, 129–130 (see also
Congruent triangles)
Congruent angles, 20, 27, 57, 68–
69, 85–86, 398
Congruent arcs, 363, 369
Congruent chords, 363–364
Congruent circles, 353
Congruent segments, 13, 17, 57,
228–229, 397, 417
Congruent triangles, 129–130
AAS theorem, 134
application of, 164–165
computer applications, 132, 138
congruent sides of, 133–134
corresponding angles of, 129–
130
corresponding sides of, 129–130
CPCTC, 139
included angle, 134
included side, 134
postulates about, 133–134
proving, 133–135, 139–140
right, 159–160
Conjunction, 66
Connections (see Developing
Mathematical Power, x)
Consecutive
angles, 104
sides, 104
vertices, 104
Construction(s), 396–419
of angle bisector, 398
of centroid of triangle, 409
of circle circumscribed about triangle, 356, 414
of circle inscribed in triangle, 414
computer applications, 402, 406,
411, 416, 421
of congruent angles, 27, 398
of congruent segments, 17, 397,
417
of geometric shapes, 38–39
of Golden Rectangle, 444
list of, 686
location of center of circle, 413
location of point dividing segment according to Golden
Mean, 310
of midpoint of segment, 397,
403
of orthocenter of triangle, 408
of parallel lines, 404
of perpendicular bisector of segment, 154, 403
of perpendicular line, 32, 404
of segment as geometric mean of
two segments, 418–419
of segment in proportion with
three segments, 418

of segment into congruent segments, 417
of tangents to circle, 377, 412–413
of triangles, 203, 395, 399
using locus in, 427–430
using Logo in, 38–39, 432–433
Contrapositive, 51–52
Converse, 51–53
of Hinge theorem, 200–201
of Pythagorean theorem, 316
Coordinate(s), 536
of midpoint of segment, 546–
547
of point on number line, 12
in space, 540, 550
Coordinate geometry, 536–573
coordinate plane, 536–537
distance formula, 536–537
equation of a circle, 541–543
equations of a line, 558–561
midpoint formula, 546–547
proofs, 570–572
slope of a line, 552–554, 565–
566
Coordinate plane, 536–537
in Logo, 526–527
Coplanar points, 3
Corollary, 14
Correspondence, 128–130, 586–
587, 591–592
Corresponding angles formed by a
transversal, 81
Corresponding parts
of congruent quadrilaterals, 248–
249
of congruent triangles, 129–130,
139–140
of similar polygons, 271–272
of similar triangles, 293–294
Cosecant ratio, 336
Cosine ratio, 333
Cotangent ratio, 336
Counterexample, 47
CPCTC, 139
Critical Thinking (see Developing
Mathematical Power, Thinking
Critically, x)
Cube, 490
volume of, 491
Cumulative Review (see Table of
Contents, iii–x)
Cylinder(s), 502–503
circumference of, 502
lateral area of, 503
lateral surface of, 502
oblique circular, 502
right circular, 502
total area of, 503
volume of, 503

Decagon, 105
Deductive reasoning, 62–63
Definition, 3, 9, 244–246
Degree measure, 19
Descartes, René, 540
Developing Mathematical Power
(see x)
Diagonal(s)
of parallelograms, 219–220
of polygons, 105
of quadrilaterals, 225
of rectangles, 234
of rhombuses, 234
of squares, 234
of trapezoids, 240
Diameter, 353
Dihedral angle(s), 204–206
adjacent, 205
measure of, 205
plane angle of, 205–206
Dilation(s), 607–608
Discrete mathematics (see Algorithm; Boolean Algebra; Computer; Fractals; Graph; Inductive
reasoning; Linear equa-
tion; Logic; Proof; Recursion;
Sequences; Triangular numbers;
Truth table)
Disjunction, 66
Distance(s)
between two points, 12–13, 199
between two points in coordinate plane, 536–538
between two points in space, 540
estimating, 291
finding inaccessible, 287–288,
326–328, 337–338
from a point to a line, 151
Distance Formula, 536–537
Drawing in Geometry (see Developing Mathematical Power, x)
Dudeney, Henry, 439

Edge(s)
of dihedral angles, 204
of half-planes, 4
of polyhedra, 490
Equation(s)
linear, 558
of a circle, 541–543
of a line, 558–561
standard form, 558
Equiangular
polygons, 106

triangles, 98–99, 175–176
Equidistant, 150–151
Equilateral
  polygons, 106
  triangles, 98–99, 175–176, 395, 439, 446
Escher, Maurits Cornelis, 238, 585
Euclidean geometry, 84, 92, 132, 621
Euler, Leonhard, 545
Exterior angle theorem, 180
Extra Practice (*see* Table of Contents, iii–x)
Extension (*see* Developing Mathematical Power, x)
Extremes of a proportion, 263

Face(s)
  of dihedral angles, 204
  of polyhedra, 490
  of prisms, 490
  of pyramids, 495
Fibonacci sequence, 465
Formal proof(s)
  steps of, 67
  of theorems, 67–69, 145–147
  two-column format, 68
  writing, 67–69
Formula(s)
  area (*see* Area; Lateral area; Total area)
  distance, 537
  Heron's, 449
  measure of an interior angle of a regular polygon, 115
  midpoint, 547
  volume (*see* Volume)
45° - 45° - 90° theorem, 321
Fractals, 632–633

Geometric mean, 268, 418–419
Given, 62
Glide reflection(s), 597
Golden Mean, 310
Golden Ratio, 270, 421, 444, 465
Golden Rectangle, 217, 444
Gomez, Selma Maria, 426
Graph(s)
  computer applications, 545
  in coordinate geometry proofs, 570–572
  of equation of a circle, 542–543
  of intersection of two linear equations, 561
  of a linear equation, 559–561
  on a number line, 13–14
  of polygons, 554, 572–573
Graphing calculator (*see* Calculator)
Great circle(s), 353
  application of, 120–121

HA theorem, 159
Half-plane, 4, 204

Height
  of cones, 511
  of cylinders, 503
  of parallelograms, 441
  of prisms, 491
  of pyramids, 495
  of trapezoids, 450
Heptagon, 105
Heron's formula, 449
Hexagon, 105
Hinge theorem, 200
  converse of, 200–201
Historical Note (*see* Developing Mathematical Power, x)
HL theorem, 160
Hypotenuse, 159
Hypothesis, 47

Identity congruence, 174
Identity transformation, 617
If-and-only-if statement(s), 3, 53
If-then form, 47, 51–53
Image, 587
Incenter, 407
Indirect proof(s), 184–191
Indirect reasoning, 184, 190
Inductive reasoning, 110–112
Inequality(ies)
  in circles, 364
  indirect proof and, 189–191
  properties of, 179–181
  in scalene triangles, 190
  transitive property of, 180
  in one triangle, 194–196, 199
  in two triangles, 200–201
Inscribed
  angles, 368–369
  circles, 359, 414
  polygons, 353, 455–456
Integrating Geometry (*see* Developing Mathematical Power, x)
Intersection, 3
  of lines, 8–9, 81
  of loci, 423
  of a plane and a solid, 353, 507–509
  of planes, 8, 81, 205
  point of, 8–9, 561
Inverse, 51–52
Inverse transformation, 618
Investigations (*see* Developing Mathematical Power, x)
Isometry, 588
Isosceles trapezoid, 239–240
Isosceles triangle(s), 98–99
  base angles of, 174
  computer applications, 178, 198, 432
  congruence in an, 174–176

legs of, 174
  right, 321–322
  vertex angle of, 174–175
Isosceles triangle theorem, 175, 622

LA theorem, 159
Lateral area
  of cones, 512
  of cylinders, 503
  of prisms, 491
  of pyramids, 496
Lateral edge(s), 490, 495
Lateral face(s), 490, 495
Lateral surface, 502, 511
Leg(s)
  of isosceles triangles, 174
  of right triangles, 159
  of trapezoids, 239
Length(s)
  arc, 468
  products of segment, 382–383
  of a segment, 13
  sum of segments, 62–63
Limit of a sequence, 461–464
Line(s), 2, 7–9
  auxiliary, 99, 155–156
  concurrent, 407–409
  equations of, 558–561
  horizontal, 537
  intersection of, 8–9, 81
  parallel, 80–97 (*see also* Parallel lines)
  perpendicular, 28–30
  of reflection, 591
  skew, 80
  slope of, 552–554, 565–566
  of symmetry, 627
  transversal, 81
  vertical, 536
Line symmetry, 626–627
Linear equation(s), 558–561
  point of intersection of two, 561
  point-slope form of, 559
  slope-intercept form of, 559
  standard form of, 558
Linear pair postulate, 23
LL theorem, 159
Loci, 422–430
  computer applications, 426, 432–433
  conditions for, 422
  and constructions, 427–430
  intersection of, 423
  in space, 424
  theorems about, 423
Logic, 46–63
Logical Reasoning (*see* Developing Mathematical Power, x)
Logo (*see* Computer)
Longitude, 120–121

Magnitude, 607
Manipulatives (*see* Developing

Mathematical Power, x)
Mapping(s), 586–588
    composition of, 612–614
    identity, 617–618
    inverse, 618
    similarity, 620
Mathematical induction, 115
Mathematical Power (*see* Developing Mathematical Power, x)
Mean(s)
    geometric, 268, 418–419
    Golden, 310
    of a proportion, 263
Measure(s)
    of angles, 19
    of arcs, 362–363
    of circles, 362
    of dihedral angles, 205
    of latitudes, 120, 351
    of longitudes, 120
    of segments, 13
    of semicircles, 362
Measurement, precision and accuracy of, 164–165
Median(s)
    concurrent, 409
    corresponding, of similar triangles, 293
    of trapezoids, 241
    of triangles, 149, 409
Midpoint, 14
    computer application, 550
    coordinates of, 546–547
    coordinates of, in space, 550
    of a segment, 14, 397
Midpoint formula, 546–547
Midpoint theorem, 14
Midsegment theorem, 240
Minimal condition, 244–245
Mixed Review, (*see* Table of Contents, iii–x)
Modeling (*see* Visualizing the Concept *and* Using Manipulatives, Developing Mathematical Power, x)
Moebius strip, 372
Multicultural contributions, 6, 7, 12, 23, 45, 50. 84, 204, 217, 238, 261, 262, 305, 351, 395, 426, 439, 449, 475, 482, 520, 540, 545, 564, 585, 616

Negation, 46, 189
Newton, Isaac, 616
Nonagon, 105
Noncoplanar points, 3
Number line, 12–14
    coordinate of point on, 12

Oblique
    circular cylinder, 502
    cone, 511
    prism, 491

Obtuse angle, 19
Obtuse triangle, 98–99, 317
Octagon, 105
One-to-one correspondence, 128
One-to-one mapping, 587
Ordered pair, 536
Origin, 536
Orthocenter, 408
Overdetermined figure, 155–157

Pantograph, 79
Parallel line(s), 80–100
    computer applications, 84, 96, 406
    constructing, 404
    locus as, 423
    properties of, 85–87
    proving, 92–94
    slope of, 565
    theorems about, 86–87, 93–94
    and triangles, 97–100
Parallel planes, 80–81
    application of, 120–121
Parallel postulate, 92
Parallelogram(s), 218–220
    altitude of, 441
    area of, 445
    base of, 441
    computer applications, 222, 227, 238
    congruent, 249
    consecutive angles in, 220
    diagonals of, 219–220
    height of, 441
    opposite angles of, 218–219
    opposite sides of, 218–219
    properties of, 218–220
    proving quadrilateral as, 223–225
    proving rhombus as, 571–572
    special, 233–235
Patterns
    and polygons, 114–115
    and squares of numbers, 327
    and triangular numbers, 109
Pentagon, 105
Pentominoes, 590, 630
Perimeter
    computer applications, 470, 525
    of polygons, 106
    of similar polygons, 476–477
Perpendicular bisector(s), 29, 150–151, 154, 403
    locus as, 423
    in triangles, 408
Perpendicular line(s), 28–30
    constructing, 32, 404
    slope of, 566

Perpendicular planes, 28
    application of, 120–121
Perpendicular rays, 28
Perpendicular segments, 28
Pi(π), 467, 475
Plane(s), 2, 7–9
    half-planes, 4, 204
    intersection of, 8, 81, 205
    intersection of a solid and, 353, 507–509
    parallel, 80–81
    perpendicular, 28, 120–121
Plane angle, 205–206
Platonic solids, 494, 510
Point(s), 2, 7–9
    collinear, 3
    of concurrency, 407–409
    coordinates of, 536, 540
    coplanar, 3
    distance between, 12–13, 199
    exterior, 18
    interior, 18
    of intersection, 8–9, 561
    locus of, 422–423
    sets of, 3
    symmetry, 626–627
    of tangency, 357
Point-slope form, 559
Pólya, George, 564
Polygon(s), 104–106
    angles of, 114–116
    area of, 440–441, 445–446, 455–457, 476–477
    classifying, 105–106
    circumscribed, 359
    computer applications, 38–39, 108, 109, 119, 210–211, 298–299, 460, 470, 481, 526–527
    concave, 105
    convex, 105
    on coordinate plane, 570–572
    diagonals of, 105
    equiangular, 106
    equilateral, 106
    exterior angles of convex, 115–116
    inscribed, 353, 455–456
    interior angles of convex, 114–115
    perimeter of, 106, 476–477
    regular, 106 (*see also* Regular polygon)
    sides of, 104–105
    similar, 271–272, 476–477
    sum of angle measures of, 114–116
    vertices of, 104
Polyhedron, 490, 494

Postulate(s), 7–9, 84
  list of, 675–685
Preimage, 587
Prism(s), 490–492
  cross section of, 507–508
  lateral area of, 491–492
  oblique, 491
  regular, 491
  right, 491
  total area of, 491
  volume of, 491–492
Problem solving
  steps, 33
  strategies (see Table of Contents, iii–x)
Project (see Developing Mathematical Power, x)
Proof(s), 57
  coordinate geometry, 570–572
  formal, 67–69, 145–147
  indirect, 184–191
  by mathematical induction, 115
Property(ies)
  of congruence, 57
  of equality, 56
  of inequality, 179–181
  means-extremes, 267
  product, of square roots, 268
  of a proportion, 267
  reflexive, 56–57
  symmetric, 56–57
  transitive, 56–57, 180
Proportion(s), 262–264
  cross products of, 267
  extended, 264
  properties of, 267
Proportional segments, 292–294, 417–418
Proportionality in triangles, 292–294
Protractor, 19
Protractor postulate, 19
Prove, 62
Pyramid(s), 495–497
  cross section of, 509
  lateral area of, 496–497
  regular, 495
  total area of, 496–497
  vertex of, 495
  volume of, 497
Pythagorean Theorem, 311–313, 326–328
  converse of, 316–317
Pythagorean triples, 320

Quadrants, 537
Quadrilateral(s), 105, 218–249
  ASASA theorem, 249
  computer applications, 222, 227, 238, 243, 253
  congruent, 248–249
  diagonals of, 225

  opposite angles of, 218, 224
  opposite sides of, 218, 223–224
  parallelogram as, 218–225
  quadriplex as, 245
  SASAS theorem, 249
  trapezoid as, 239–241

Radius (radii)
  of circles, 352
  of regular polygons, 455
Ratio, 262–264
  Golden, 270, 421, 444, 465
Ray(s), 13
  opposite, 13
  parallel, 80
  perpendicular, 28
Reading in Geometry (see Developing Mathematical Power, x)
Reasoning
  deductive, 62–63
  indirect, 184, 190
  inductive, 110–112
  logical, 62–63
  Thinking Critically (see Developing Mathematical Power, x)
Rectangle(s), 233–235
  area of, 441
  Golden, 217, 444
Recursion, 210, 578–579
Reflection(s), 591–593
Reflexive property of congruence, 57
Regular polygon(s), 106
  apothem of, 455
  area of, 456–457
  center of, 455
  central angle of, 455
  inscribed, 455
  measures of angles of, 114–116
  radius of, 455
Reviews
  Algebra, 11, 17, 44, 50, 109, 126, 163, 198, 216, 243, 281, 304, 325, 377, 394, 402, 475, 488, 520, 569, 584, 611
  Chapter Summary and, 40–41, 74–75, 122–123, 166–167, 212–213, 256–257, 300–301, 344–345, 390–391, 434–435, 484–485, 528–529, 580–581, 634–635
  College Entrance Exam, 43, 77, 125, 169, 215, 259, 303, 347, 393, 437, 487, 531, 583, 637
  Cumulative, 78, 170–172, 260, 348–350, 438, 532–534, 638–642
  Extra Practice, 643–656
  Mixed, 55, 91, 138, 178, 222, 232, 266, 297, 315, 367, 421, 454, 515, 550, 557, 590
Rhombus(es), 233–235, 572–573
  area of, 446
Right angle, 19–20

Right circular cone, 511
Right circular cylinder, 502
Right prism, 491
Right triangle(s), 98–99
  altitude of, 306–307
  computer applications, 162, 310, 315, 320, 325, 336, 341
  congruent, 159–160
  hypotenuse of, 159
  isosceles, 321–322
  legs of, 159
  opposite angle, 159
  opposite side, 159
  similarity, 306–307
  special, 321–323
  theorems about, 159–160, 235, 306, 312, 316–317, 321–322
  trigonometric ratios in, 331–338
Rotation(s), 601–602
Rotational symmetry, 626–627
Ruler postulate, 12

SAS postulate, 134
SAS theorem, 282
SASAS theorem, 249
Scale factor
  of dilations, 607
  of similar polygons, 271
  of similar solids, 521
Scalene triangle, 98–99, 190
Scientific calculator (see Calculator)
Secant, 353, 374, 382–383
Secant ratio, 336
Sector, 472
Segment(s), 13
  addition of, 62–63
  auxiliary, 155–156
  bisector, 14
  of a circle, 473
  congruent, 13, 17, 57, 228–229, 397, 417
  constructions involving, 17, 154, 310, 397, 403–404, 417–419
  lengths, related to circles, 382–384
  measure of, 13
  midpoint of, 14, 397, 403
  parallel, 80
  perpendicular, 28
  perpendicular bisector of, 29, 150–151, 154, 403
  proportional, 292–294, 417–418
  secant, 382
  in space, 550
  tangent, 357–358
Semicircle, 362
Semiperimeter, 449

Sequence(s), 113
  Fibonacci, 465
  limit of, 461–464
Side(s)
  of angles, 18
  of congruent triangles, 133–134
  consecutive, 104
  corresponding, 129
  included, 134
  nonincluded, 134
  opposite, 218–219
  of parallelograms, 218–219
  of polygons, 104–105
  of triangles, 97–98
Similar
  polygons, 271–272, 476–477
  right triangles, 306–307
  solids, 521–522
  triangles, 261, 277–288, 293–294
Similarity
  AA postulate, 277
  computer applications, 266, 276, 281, 286, 297, 298–299, 525
  and dilations, 608
  mapping, 620
  properties of, 271–272, 521–522
  proportional segments, 292–294
  ratio and proportion, 262–264
  SAS theorem, 282
  scale factor of, 271, 521
  SSS theorem, 283
Sine ratio, 332
Skew lines, 80
Slant height
  of regular pyramids, 495
  of right circular cones, 511
Slope, 552
  computer applications, 557, 564
  of horizontal lines, 553
  negative, 553
  of parallel lines, 565
  of perpendicular lines, 566
  positive, 553
  undefined, 553
  of vertical lines, 553
  of zero, 553
Slope-intercept form, 559
Solid(s), 490–522
  Archimedian, 501
  computer applications, 494, 506, 515, 520, 525
  cross sections of, 507–509
  intersection of a plane and, 353, 507–509
  Platonic, 494, 510
  regular, 491, 494, 495, 501
  similar, 521–522

Space, 3
  congruence in, 206
  coordinates in, 540, 550
  loci in, 423–424
Sphere(s), 353
  area of, 516
  great circle of, 353
  intersection of a plane and, 353
  volume of, 517
Spiral, 535
Square(s), 233–234
  area of, 440
  table of, 657
  unit, 441
Square root(s), 268
  computer applications, 310, 540
  estimating, 326–328
  table of approximate, 657
SSS postulate, 133
SSS theorem, 283
Statement(s)
  biconditional, 53, 151, 244
  conditional, 46–53
  existence, 9
  if-and-only-if, 3, 53
  if-then, 47, 51–53
  logically equivalent, 52–53
  negation, 46
  uniqueness, 9
Supplementary angles, 23, 68, 86
Symbols (*see* Symbols and Abbreviations, 659–660)
Symmetric property of congruence, 57
Symmetry, 626–627, 630

Tangent(s), 357–359
  circles, 359
  common, 359
  computer applications, 361, 416
  constructing, 412–413
  intersection of, 374
  intersection of a chord and, 374
  intersection of a secant and, 374, 383
  segment, 357–358
Tangent ratio, 333
Technology
  Constructing Geometric Shapes Using Logo, 38–39
  Embedded Recursion and Dragon Curves, 578–579
  Fractals, 632–633
  Recursions and Tessellations, 210–211
  Similarity in Computer Graphics, 298–299
  Solving Problems Using Logo, 73

  The Coordinate System in Logo, 526–527
  Using Logo in Constructions, 432–433
  (*see also* Calculator, Computer)
Tessellations, 211, 596, 630
  computer applications, 210–211, 222, 227, 238, 243, 253, 325
  Penrose, 243
Tests
  Chapter, 42, 76, 124, 168, 214, 258, 302, 346, 392, 436, 486, 530, 582, 636
  Test Yourself, 22, 37, 61, 72, 102, 119, 144, 163, 193, 209, 238, 253, 276, 297, 320, 341, 367, 387, 411, 431, 460, 481, 506, 525, 551, 577, 606, 631
Thales, 261
Theorem(s), 8–9, 675–685
  formal proof of, 67–69, 145–147
30°–60°–90° theorem, 322
Thinking Critically (*see* Developing Mathematical Power, x)
Topology, 621
Total area
  of cones, 512
  of cylinders, 503
  of prisms, 491
  of pyramids, 496
Transformation(s), 587–588
  identity, 617
  inverse, 618
Transformational geometry, 586–627
  composite mappings, 612–614
  computer applications, 590, 600, 611, 616, 631
  dilations, 607–608
  glide reflections, 597
  isometries, 588, 592, 602, 613
  mappings, 586–588
  reflections, 591–593
  rotations, 601–602
  symmetry, 626–627, 630
  transformations, 587–588, 617–624
  translations, 596–597
Transitive property
  of congruence, 57
  of inequality, 180
Translation(s), 596–597
Translational symmetry, 630
Transversals, 81–94
Trapezoid(s), 239–241
  area of, 450–451
  base angles of, 239
  isosceles, 239–240
  legs of, 239
  median of, 241

Triangle(s), 97–100, 105
  acute, 98–99, 317
  adjacent interior angles of, 99
  altitudes of, 150, 407–408
  angle bisectors of, 149, 151, 294, 407
  angle relationships in, 99
  area of, 446, 449
  centroid of, 409
  circumcenter of, 408
  classifying by angles, 98
  classifying by sides, 98, 316–317
  computer applications, 132, 138, 154, 162, 178, 183, 198, 203, 281, 286, 297, 298, 432, 632–633
  concurrent lines in, 407–409
  congruent, 129–130 (see also Congruent Triangles)
  congruent angles in, 98–99
  congruent sides in, 98–99
  constructions involving, 203, 356, 395, 399, 407–409, 414, 418
  corresponding parts of congruent, 129–130, 139–140
  equiangular, 98–99, 175–176
  equilateral, 98–99, 175–176, 395, 439, 446
  exterior angles of, 99, 180, 191
  incenter of, 407
  inequalities in, 179–201
  interior angles of, 99
  isosceles, 98–99

  medians of, 149, 409
  obtuse, 98–99, 317
  orthocenter of, 408
  overlapping, 140
  parallax, 342–343
  perpendicular bisectors in, 408
  proportional segments in, 292–294, 418
  proportionality in, 292–294
  reflected image of, 591–592
  remote interior angles of, 99
  right, 98–99 (see also Right Triangle)
  rigidity of, 138
  scalene, 98–99, 190
  semiperimeter of, 449
  sides of, 97–98
  similar, 261, 277–288, 293–294
  sum of angle measures of, 98
  vertices of, 97
Triangle angle–bisector theorem, 294
Triangle inequality theorem, 199
Triangle proportionality theorem, 292
Triangular numbers, 109
Triangular prism, 490
Trichotomy property, 181
Trigonometric ratios, 331–338
  application of, 342–343
  computer applications, 336, 432
  reciprocals of, 336
  table of, 658
Truth table, 66
Truth value, 52–53

Undefined terms, 2–3
Underdetermined figure, 155–157

Vectors, 254–255, 596
Venn diagram, 236
vertex, 18, 104, 174, 495
Vertical angles, 24–25
Vocabulary, 40, 74, 122, 166, 212, 256, 300, 344, 390, 434, 484, 528, 580, 634
Volume
  and Cavalieri's principle, 520
  computer applications, 494, 506, 515, 520, 525
  of cones, 512
  of cubes, 491
  of cylinders, 503
  of prisms, 491
  of pyramids, 497
  of similar solids, 521–522
  of spheres, 517

Writing in Mathematics (see Developing Mathematical Power, x)

x-axis, 536
x-coordinate, 526–527, 536
x-intercept, 559

y-axis, 536
y-coordinate, 526–527, 536
y-intercept, 559

z-axis, 540
Zeno's Paradox, 45

Additional Answers

PAGE 51 INVESTIGATION

1. If Candidate Lee wins in California

2. She will win her party's presidential nomination.

3. a. If Candidate Lee wins her party's presidential nomination, then she won in California.
  b. If Candidate Lee does not win in California, then she will not win her party's presidential nomination.
  c. If Candidate Lee does not win her party's presidential nomination, then she did not win in California.

4. The headline implies that b is true.

5. If the headline is true, it is possible that each statement could be true.

PAGE 53

Exercise	Truth Value	Converse	Inverse	Contrapositive
3	False	If 2 ∠s are complementary, then the 2 ∠s are acute. True	If 2 ∠s are not both acute, then they are NOT complementary. True	If 2 ∠s are NOT complementary, then they are NOT both acute. False
4	True	If one ∠ is obtuse and the other is acute, then the 2 ∠s are supplementary. False	If 2 non-rt ∠s are NOT supplementary, then it is not the case that one must be obtuse and the other is acute. False	If one angle is NOT obtuse or the second ∠ is NOT acute, then the two non-rt ∠s are not supplementary. True OR If two non-rt ∠s are such that it is not the case that one is obtuse and the other is acute, then the ∠s are NOT supplementary. True
5	True	If the sum of the measures of 2 ∠s is 180, then the ∠s are supplementary. True	If 2 ∠s are NOT supplementary, then the sum of their measures is NOT 180. True	If the sum of the measures of 2 ∠s is not 180, then the ∠s are not supplementary. True
6	False	If 2 ∠s form a linear pair, then they are supplementary. True	If 2 ∠s are NOT supplementary, then they are NOT a linear pair. True	If 2 ∠s do NOT form a linear pair, then they are NOT supplementary. False

7. Ex 3: Two ∠s are acute iff they are complementary. False
8. Ex 4: Two non-rt ∠s are supplementary iff one is obtuse and the other is acute. False
9. Ex 5: Two ∠s are supplementary iff the sum of their measures is 180. True
10. Ex 6: Two ∠s are supplementary iff they are a linear pair. False

PAGE 54

Problem	Truth Value	Converse	Inverse	Contrapositive
1.	False	If 2 ∠s are complementary then the 2 ∠s are adjacent. False	If 2 ∠s are NOT adjacent, then the 2 ∠s are NOT complementary. False	If 2 ∠s are NOT complementary, then they are NOT adjacent. False
2.	False	If 2 ∠s are rt ∠s, then the 2 ∠s are ≅. True	If 2 ∠s are NOT ≅, then the 2 ∠s are NOT rt ∠s. True	If 2 ∠s are not rt ∠s, then the 2 ∠s are NOT ≅. False
3.	True	If 2 lines intersect to form a rt ∠, then the 2 lines are ⊥. True	If 2 lines are NOT ⊥, then the 2 lines do NOT form a rt ∠. True	If 2 lines do NOT intersect to form a rt ∠, then the 2 lines are Not ⊥. True
4.	True	If 2 segments have = measures, then the 2 segments are ≅. True	If 2 segments are NOT congruent, then the 2 segments do NOT have = measures. True	If 2 segments do NOT have = measures, then the 2 segments are NOT congruent. True
5.	True	If $m\angle 2 = m\angle 1$, then $m\angle 1 = m\angle 2$. True	If $m\angle 1 \neq m\angle 2$, then $m\angle 2 \neq m\angle 1$. True	If $m\angle 2 \neq m\angle 1$, then $m\angle 1 \neq m\angle 2$. True
6.	False	If $m\angle 4 < m\angle 3$, then $m\angle 3 < m\angle 4$. False	If $m\angle 3 \nless m\angle 4$, then $m\angle 4 \nless m\angle 3$. False	If $m\angle 4 \nless m\angle 3$, then $m\angle 3 \nless m\angle 4$. False
7.	True	If Sam bought flowers, then Sam went to the prom. False	If Sam did NOT go to the prom, then Sam did NOT buy flowers. False	If Sam did NOT buy flowers, then Sam did NOT go to the prom. True

8. Ex 1: Two ∠s are adjacent iff the 2 ∠s are complementary. False
9. Ex 2: Two ∠s are ≅ iff they are rt. ∠s. False
10. Ex 7: Sam will go to the prom iff he buys flowers.

15. If 2 integers are negative, then their sum is negative; and if the sum of 2 integers is not negative, then the 2 integers are not both negative. If the sum of 2 integers is negative, then the 2 integers are negative; and if 2 integers are not both negative, then their sum is not negative.

16. If points are coplanar, then they lie in the same plane; and if points do not lie in the same plane, then they are not coplanar; If points lie in the same plane, the points are coplanar; and if points are not coplanar, then they do not lie in the same plane.

Problem	Converse	Inverse	Contrapositive
19.	If $x = 6$, then $3x - 7 = 11$. True	If $3x - 7 \neq 11$, then $x \neq 6$. True	If $x \neq 6$, then $3x - 7 \neq 11$. True
20.	If $y^2 - 1 = 80$, then $y = 9$. False	If $y \neq 9$, then $y^2 - 1 \neq 80$. False	If $y^2 - 1 \neq 80$, then $y \neq 9$. True

PAGE 55

Problem	Conditional	Converse	Contrapositive
21.	If M is between X and Y and the midpoint of $\overline{XY}$, then $XM = MY$.	If $XM = MY$, then M is between X and Y and is midpoint of $\overline{XY}$.	If $XM \neq MY$, then M is between X and Y but not the midpoint of $\overline{XY}$.
22.	If $\overrightarrow{OX}$ is not the bisector of $\angle AOB$, then $2m\angle AOX \neq m\angle AOB$.	If $2m\angle AOX \neq m\angle AOB$, then $\overrightarrow{OX}$ is not the bisector of $\angle AOB$.	If $2m\angle AOX = m\angle AOB$, then $\overrightarrow{OX}$ is the bisector of $\angle AOB$.
23.	If 2 $\angle$s are $\cong$, then the 2 $\angle$s are vertical.	If 2 $\angle$s are vertical, then they are $\cong$.	If 2 $\angle$s are not vertical, then the 2 $\angle$s are not $\cong$.

PAGE 60

28.
$$\begin{cases} 3x + 6y = 9 \\ 6x - 5y = -33 \end{cases} \quad \text{Given}$$

Change $3x + 6y = 9$ Division
to $x + 2y = 3$

$x = 3 - 2y$ Subtraction

$6(3 - 2y) - 5y = -33$	Substitution
$18 - 12y - 5y = -33$	Distributive prop.
$18 - 17y = -33$	Distributive prop.
$-17y = -51$	Subtraction
$y = 3$	Division

29. Let $180 - m\angle R =$ Supp. of $\angle R$
$90 - m\angle R =$ Comp. of $\angle R$

$180 - m\angle R = 7(90 - m\angle R)$	Given
$180 - m\angle R = 630 - 7m\angle R$	Distributive prop.
$180 + 6m\angle R = 630$	Add. prop.
$6m\angle R = 450$	Subtraction prop.
$m\angle R = 75$	Div. prop.

30. Let $180 - m\angle D =$ Supp. of $\angle D$
$90 - m\angle D =$ Comp. of $\angle D$

$180 - m\angle D = 4(90 - m\angle D) + 15$	Given
$180 - m\angle D = 360 - 4m\angle D + 15$	Dist. prop.
$3m\angle D = 195$	Add. and Subt. props.
$m\angle D = 65$	Div. prop.

PAGE 61

11. Converse: If 2 $\angle$s are comp., then their measures are 35 and 55; false
Inverse: If the measures of two $\angle$s are not 35 and 55, then the $\angle$s are not comp. false
Contrapositive: If 2 $\angle$s are not comp., then their measures are not 35 and 55; true

13. A biconditional is formed by combining a conditional and its converse into one statement, connecting the hypothesis and conclusion with "if and only if." A biconditional is true whenever both the conditional and its converse are true.

PAGE 65

13. M and X are midpoints of $\overline{AB}$ and $\overline{CD}$, respectively; $\overline{AM} \cong \overline{CX}$ } Given

$\overline{AM} \cong \overline{MB}$; $\overline{CX} \cong \overline{XD}$	Def. of midpt.
$\overline{MB} \cong \overline{CX}$	Trans. prop.
$\overline{MB} \cong \overline{XD}$	Trans. prop.

PAGE 66

14. $\overrightarrow{XS}$ and $\overrightarrow{XW}$ are bisectors of $\angle RXT$ and $\angle YXV$ respectively; $\angle 2 \cong \angle 3$ } Given

$\angle 1 \cong \angle 2$; $\angle 3 \cong \angle 4$	Def. of $\angle$ bis.
$\angle 1 \cong \angle 3$	Trans. prop.
$\angle 1 \cong \angle 4$	Trans. prop.

PAGE 66

15. $\angle 4 \cong \angle 1, \angle 2 \cong \angle 3$
$\angle 1 \cong \angle 4$
$m\angle 1 + m\angle 2 = m\angle 4 + m\angle 2$
$m\angle 1 + m\angle 2 = m\angle 4 + m\angle 3$
$m\angle RXT = m\angle YXV$
$\angle RXT \cong \angle YXV$

Given
Sym. prop.
Add. prop.
Subst. prop.
Def. of betw. of rays
Def. of $\cong \angle$s

16. $\angle YXS \cong \angle RXW$
$\angle SXW \cong \angle SXW$
$m\angle YXS - m\angle SXW = m\angle RXW - m\angle SXW$
$m\angle 1 = m\angle 2$
$\angle 1 \cong \angle 2$

Given
Refl. prop.
Subtr. prop.
Def. of betw. of rays
Def. of $\cong \angle$s

17. $\angle 1 \cong \angle 4, \angle 2 \cong \angle 3$
$m\angle 1 + m\angle 2 = m\angle 4 + m\angle 2$
$m\angle 1 + m\angle 2 = m\angle 4 + m\angle 3$
$\angle RXT \cong \angle YXV$

$\angle TXV \cong \angle TXV$
$m\angle RXT + m\angle TXV = m\angle YXV + m\angle TXV$
$\angle RXV \cong \angle TXY$

Given
Add. prop.
Subst. prop.
Def. of betw. of rays;
def. of $\cong \angle$s
Refl. prop.
Add. prop.
Def. of betw. of rays;
def. of $\cong \angle$s

18. $\angle 1 \cong \angle 2, \angle 3 \cong \angle 4$
$\angle RXW \cong \angle YXS$
$\angle SXW \cong \angle SXW$
$m\angle RXW - m\angle SXW = m\angle YXS - m\angle SXW$
$m\angle 1 = m\angle 4$
$\angle 1 \cong \angle 4$

Given
Refl. prop.
Subtr. prop.
Def. of betw. of rays
Def. of $\cong \angle$s

PAGE 71

12. Plan: Use the given, the def. of complementary, and the Transitive prop. to show $m\angle 1 + m\angle 3 = m\angle 2 + m\angle 4$. Use algebraic properties and def. of $\cong \angle$s to reach the conclusion.

Proof:

Statements	Reasons
1. $\angle 1$ and $\angle 3$ are complementary. $\angle 2$ and $\angle 4$ are complementary.	1. Given
2. $m\angle 1 + m\angle 3 = 90$ $m\angle 2 + m\angle 4 = 90$	2. Def. of comp. $\angle$s
3. $\angle 3 \cong \angle 4$	3. Given
4. $m\angle 3 = m\angle 4$	4. Def. of $\cong \angle$s
5. $m\angle 1 + m\angle 3 = m\angle 2 + m\angle 4$	5. Trans. prop.
6. $m\angle 1 + m\angle 3 = m\angle 2 + m\angle 3$	6. Subst.
7. $m\angle 1 = m\angle 2$	7. Subtr.
8. $\angle 1 \cong \angle 2$	8. Def. of $\cong \angle$s

Conclusion: In the given figure, if $\angle 1$ is compl. to $\angle 3$ and $\angle 2$ is compl. to $\angle 4$ and $\angle 3 \cong \angle 4$, then $\angle 1 \cong \angle 2$.

13. Plan: Use the Given and the def. of $\angle$ bisector to get $m\angle 1 = m\angle 2$ and $m\angle 3 = m\angle 4$. Then use add. prop. and betweenness to show $\angle DBP \cong \angle EBP$. The conclusion follows by the theorem that says if

intersecting lines form $\cong$ adj. $\angle$s, then the lines are $\perp$.

Proof:

Statements	Reasons
1. $\angle 1 \cong \angle 2$; $\overrightarrow{BP}$ is $\angle$ bisector of $\angle ABC$.	1. Given
2. $\angle 3 \cong \angle 4$	2. Def. of $\angle$ Bisector
3. $m\angle 1 = m\angle 2$ $m\angle 3 = m\angle 4$	3. Def. of $\cong \angle$s
4. $\overrightarrow{BA}$ is between the sides of $\angle DBP$. $\overrightarrow{CB}$ is between sides of $\angle EBP$.	4. Given
5. $m\angle 1 + m\angle 3 = m\angle DBP$ $m\angle 2 + m\angle 4 = m\angle EBP$	5. Def. of betweenness of rays
6. $m\angle 1 + m\angle 3 = m\angle 2 + m\angle 3$	6. Addition prop.
7. $m\angle 1 + m\angle 3 = m\angle 2 + m\angle 4$	7. Substitution
8. $m\angle DBP = m\angle EBP$	8. Substitution
9. $\angle DBP \cong \angle EBP$	9. Def. of $\cong \angle$s
10. $\overrightarrow{BP} \perp \overleftrightarrow{DE}$	10. If two lines intersect so that the pair of adj. $\angle$s formed are $\cong$, then the lines are $\perp$.

Conclusion: In the given figure, if $\overrightarrow{BP}$ is the $\angle$ bisector of $\angle ABC$ and $\angle 1 \cong \angle 2$, then $\angle 3 \cong \angle 4$.

14. Plan: Use the def. of comp $\angle$s and algebraic properties to show $m\angle 4 + m\angle 2 = 90$. Concl. follows by def. of comp. $\angle$s.

Proof:

Statements	Reasons
1. $\angle 3$ and $\angle 1$ are complementary $\angle$s.	1. Given
2. $m\angle 3 + m\angle 1 = 90$	2. Def. of comp. $\angle$s
3. $m\angle 4 + m\angle 2 + m\angle 3 + m\angle 1 = 180$	3. Sum of measures of $\angle$s on same side of line and with common vertex is 180°.
4. $90 + m\angle 4 + m\angle 2 = 180$	4. Substitution
5. $m\angle 4 + m\angle 2 = 90$	5. Subtraction
6. $\angle 4$ and $\angle 2$ are complementary	6. Def. of comp. $\angle$s

Conclusion: In the given figure, if $\angle 3$ and $\angle 1$ are complementary $\angle$s, then so are $\angle 4$ and $\angle 2$.

PAGE 76

14. Plan: Use the $\cong \angle$s and the def. of $\angle$ bisector to show $\angle AOB \cong \angle DOE$.

Proof:

Statements	Reasons
1. $\angle AOC \cong \angle COE$	1. Given
2. $m\angle AOC = m\angle COE$	2. Def. of $\cong$ $\angle$s
3. $\frac{1}{2}m\angle AOC = \frac{1}{2}m\angle COE$	3. Multiplication prop.
4. $\overrightarrow{OB}$ bisects $\angle AOC$; $\overrightarrow{OD}$ bisects $\angle COE$.	4. Given
5. $m\angle AOB = \frac{1}{2}m\angle AOC$ $m\angle DOE = \frac{1}{2}m\angle COE$	5. $\angle$ Bis. Th.
6. $m\angle AOB = m\angle DOB$	6. Substitution
7. $\angle AOB \cong \angle DOB$	7. Def. of $\cong$ $\angle$s

Conclusion: In the given figure, if $\overrightarrow{OB}$ bisects $\angle AOC$ and $\overrightarrow{OD}$ bisects $\angle COE$ and $\angle AOC \cong \angle COE$, then $\angle AOB \cong \angle DOB$.

PAGE 78

12. Cond.: If 2 $\angle$s are vert. then they are $\cong$. (true) **Conv.:** If 2 $\angle$s are $\cong$, then they are vert. (false) **Inv.:** If 2 $\angle$s are not vert., then they are not $\cong$. (false) **C pos.:** If 2 $\angle$s are not $\cong$, then they are not vert. (true)

PAGE 89

9. Plan: Since $k \parallel l$, $\angle 2$ and $\angle 1$ are suppl. $\angle 1 \cong \angle 3$ and $\angle 2 \cong \angle 4$ because they are corr. $\angle$s. Conclusion follows by substitution.

Proof:

Statements	Reasons
1. $k \parallel l$	1. Given
2. $\angle 2$ and $\angle 1$ are suppl.	2. If 2 $\parallel$ lines have a transv., then the int. $\angle$s on the same side of the transv. are suppl.
3. $m\angle 2 + m\angle 1 = 180$	3. Def. of suppl.
4. $\angle 3 \cong \angle 1$, $\angle 2 \cong \angle 4$	4. If 2 $\parallel$ lines have a transv., the corr. $\angle$s are $\cong$.
5. $m\angle 3 = m\angle 1$; $m\angle 2 = m\angle 4$	5. Def. of $\cong$

| 6. $m\angle 4 + m\angle 3 = 180$ | 6. Substitution |
| 7. $\angle 4$ and $\angle 3$ are suppl. | 7. Def. of suppl. |

Conclusion: If 2 $\parallel$ lines have a transv., then ext. $\angle$s on the same side of the transv. are suppl.

17. Use the figure and given for Theorem 3.2 on p. 86
Plan: Since $\angle 2$ is $\cong$ to both $\angle 1$ and $\angle 4$, you can use the tran. prop. of $\cong$ to show that $\angle 1 \cong \angle 4$.

Proof:

Statements	Reasons
1. $h \parallel k$ with transv. t	1. Given
2. $\angle 4 \cong \angle 2$	2. If $\parallel$ lines have a transv., then corr. $\angle$s are $\cong$.
3. $\angle 2 \cong \angle 1$	3. Vert. $\angle$s are $\cong$.
4. $\angle 1 \cong \angle 4$	4. Trans. prop. of $\cong$

Conclusion: Whenever h is parallel to k, then the alt. ext. $\angle$s, $\angle 1$ and $\angle 4$, are $\cong$.

18. Given: $l \parallel m$; $l \perp t$
Prove: $m \perp t$

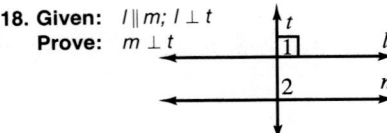

Plan: Since $l \parallel m$, $\angle 1 \cong \angle 2$. By the def. of $\perp$, $\angle 1$ is a rt. $\angle$. It follows that $\angle 2$ is also a rt. $\angle$ and so $m \perp t$.

Proof:

Statements	Reasons
1. $l \parallel m$, and $l \perp t$	1. Given
2. $\angle 1 \cong \angle 2$	2. Post. 10 (If 2 $\parallel$ lines have a transv., corr. $\angle$s are $\cong$.)
3. $\angle 1$ is a right angle.	3. Def. of $\perp$
4. $m\angle 1 = m\angle 2$	4. Def. of $\cong$ $\angle$s
5. $m\angle 1 = 90$	5. Def. of rt. $\angle$
6. $m\angle 2 = 90$	6. Trans. prop.
7. $\angle 2$ is a rt. $\angle$.	7. Def. of rt. $\angle$
8. $m \perp t$	8. Def. of $\perp$

Conclusion: If $t \perp l$ and $l \parallel m$, then t is also $\perp m$.

19. Plan: Since $\overleftrightarrow{AO} \parallel \overleftrightarrow{BQ}$, alt. int. $\angle$s AOQ and OQB are $\cong$. Then use the $\angle$ Bis. Th. to show that halves of measures of $\cong$ $\angle$s have the same measure. The conclusion follows by def. of $\cong$ $\angle$s.

Proof:

Statements	Reasons
1. $\overleftrightarrow{AO} \parallel \overleftrightarrow{BQ}$; $\overrightarrow{OP}$ bisects $\angle AOQ$, and QR bisects $\angle OQB$.	1. Given
2. $\angle AOQ \cong \angle OQB$	2. Th. 3.2 (If 2 $\parallel$ lines have a transv., the alt. int. $\angle$s are $\cong$.)
3. $m\angle AOQ = m\angle OQB$	3. Def. of $\cong$ $\angle$s
4. $m\angle 2 = \frac{1}{2}m\angle AOQ$, $m\angle 4 = \frac{1}{2}m\angle OQB$	4. $\angle$ Bis. Th. (Th. 1.8)
5. $\frac{1}{2}m\angle AOQ = \frac{1}{2}m\angle OQB$	5. Mult. prop.
6. $m\angle 2 = m\angle 4$	6. Substitution
7. $\angle 2 \cong \angle 4$	7. Def. of $\cong$ $\angle$s

Conclusion: In the given figure, if $\overleftrightarrow{AO} \parallel \overleftrightarrow{BQ}$ and $\angle AOQ$ and $\angle OQB$ are bisected, then $\angle 2 \cong \angle 4$

20. Plan: Since lines are $\parallel$, the pairs of alt. int $\angle$s, $\angle AOQ$ and $\angle OQB$ and $\angle 2$ and $\angle 3$ are $\cong$. Use betw. of rays and subst. to relate these $\angle$s to $\angle 1$ and $\angle 4$.

Proof:

Statements	Reasons
1. $\overleftrightarrow{AO} \parallel \overleftrightarrow{BQ}$, $\overrightarrow{OP} \parallel QR$	1. Given
2. $\angle AOQ \cong \angle OQB$, $\angle 2 \cong \angle 3$	2. Th. 3.2 (alt. int. $\angle$s of $\parallel$ lines are $\cong$).
3. $m\angle AOQ = m\angle OQB$ $m\angle 2 = m\angle 3$	3. Def. of $\cong$ $\angle$s
4. $m\angle AOQ = m\angle 1 + m\angle 2$ $m\angle OQB = m\angle 3 + m\angle 4$	4. Def. of betweenness of rays
5. $m\angle 1 + m\angle 2 = m\angle 3 + m\angle 4$	5. Substitution

6. $m\angle 1 + m\angle 2 =$ 6. Substitution
    $m\angle 2 + m\angle 4$

7. $m\angle 1 = m\angle 4$ 7. Subtraction

8. $\angle 1 \cong \angle 4$ 8. Def. of $\cong \angle$s

Conclusion: In the given figure, if $\overrightarrow{AO} \parallel$ $\overrightarrow{BQ}$ and $\overrightarrow{OP} \parallel \overrightarrow{QR}$, then $\angle 1 \cong \angle 4$.

PAGE 90

31. Given: $\overleftrightarrow{BA} \parallel \overleftrightarrow{ED}$; $\overleftrightarrow{BC} \parallel \overleftrightarrow{EF}$
    Prove: $\angle B \cong \angle DEF$

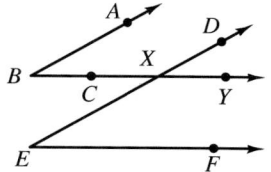

Plan: Since $\overleftrightarrow{BA} \parallel \overleftrightarrow{ED}$, corr. $\angle$s B and DXY are $\cong$.
Since $\overleftrightarrow{BC} \parallel \overleftrightarrow{EF}$, corr. $\angle$s DXY and E are $\cong$.
Conclusion follows by trans. prop.

Proof:

Statements	Reasons
1. $\overleftrightarrow{BA} \parallel \overleftrightarrow{ED}$; $\overleftrightarrow{BC} \parallel$ $\overleftrightarrow{EF}$	1. Given
2. Extend $\overrightarrow{BC}$ to intersect $\overleftrightarrow{ED}$ in point X.	2. 2 lines intersect in exactly 1 point.
3. $\angle B \cong \angle DXY$ $\angle DXY \cong \angle E$	3. Post. 10 (If 2 $\parallel$ lines have a transv., corr. $\angle$s are $\cong$.)
4. $\angle B \cong \angle DEF$	4. Trans. prop.

Conclusion: In the given figure, when $\overleftrightarrow{BA} \parallel \overleftrightarrow{ED}$ and $\overleftrightarrow{BC} \parallel \overleftrightarrow{EF}$, then $\angle B \cong \angle E$.

PAGE 95

5. $v \parallel y$; Thm 3.9: If 2 coplanar lines are $\perp$ to same line, then they are $\parallel$.
$x \parallel z$; Thm 3.9: same as above
Thm 3.6 could also be used: If 2 lines have a transv. and a pair of alt. int. $\angle$s are $\cong$, then the lines are $\parallel$.

6. $x \parallel y$; Thm 3.8: If 2 lines have a transv. and the int. $\angle$s on the same side of the transv. are supp., then the lines are $\parallel$.

7. $\overleftrightarrow{BE} \parallel \overleftrightarrow{CD}$ by Post. 13, since $m\angle CDE = 40$ by Linear Pair Post.

$\overleftrightarrow{BE} \parallel \overleftrightarrow{GH}$ by Th. 3.9 or Post. 13, since $\overleftrightarrow{BE} \perp \overleftrightarrow{AC}$ by def. of rt. $\angle$ and $\perp$ lines.
$\overleftrightarrow{CD} \parallel \overleftrightarrow{GH}$ by Th. 3.10

11. Given: $\overleftrightarrow{AB}$, $\overleftrightarrow{EF}$; transv. $\overleftrightarrow{CD}$;
    $\angle 1$ supp. to $\angle 2$

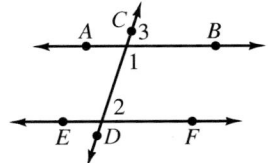

Prove: $\overleftrightarrow{AB} \parallel \overleftrightarrow{EF}$
Plan: Since $\angle 1$ is supp. to $\angle 2$ and $\angle 1$ is supp. to $\angle 3$, $\angle 2 \cong \angle 3$. Since $\angle 2$ and $\angle 3$ are $\cong$ corr. $\angle$s, $\overleftrightarrow{AB} \parallel \overleftrightarrow{EF}$.

Proof:

Statements	Reasons
1. $\angle 1$ is supp. to $\angle 2$	1. Given
2. $m\angle 1 + m\angle 2 = 180$	2. Def. of supp.
3. $\angle 1$ and $\angle 3$ are a linear pair.	3. Def. of linear pair
4. $m\angle 1 + m\angle 3 = 180$	4. Linear Pair Post.: def. supp.
5. $m\angle 1 + m\angle 2 = m\angle 1 + m\angle 3$	5. Substitution
6. $m\angle 2 = m\angle 3$	6. Subt. prop.
7. $\angle 2 \cong \angle 3$	7. Def. of $\cong \angle$s
8. $\overleftrightarrow{AB} \parallel \overleftrightarrow{EF}$	8. If corr $\angle$s are $\cong$, the lines are $\parallel$.

Conclusion: In the given figure, if $\angle 1$ is supp. to $\angle 2$, then $\overleftrightarrow{AB} \parallel \overleftrightarrow{EF}$.

12. Given: $l \parallel m$; $l \parallel n$;
    Prove: $m \parallel n$

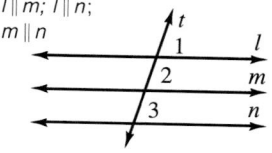

Plan: Since $l \parallel m$ and $l \parallel n$, corr. $\angle$s 1 and 2 are $\cong$ and corr. $\angle$s 1 and 3 are $\cong$. By the trans. prop. $\angle 2 \cong \angle 3$. Concl. follows by Post. 13.

Proof:

Statements	Reasons
1. $l \parallel m$; $l \parallel n$	1. Given
2. $\angle 1 \cong \angle 3$; $\angle 1 \cong$ $\angle 2$	2. If lines are $\parallel$, corr. $\angle$s are $\cong$.

3. $\angle 3 \cong \angle 2$ 3. Trans. prop.

4. $m \parallel n$ 4. If corr. $\angle$s are $\cong$, lines are $\parallel$.

Conclusion: If lines m and n are each $\parallel$ to line l, then $m \parallel n$.

PAGE 96

21. Given: $m\angle BAD = 110$; $m\angle ABC = 100$; $m\angle BCE = 30$
    Prove: $k \parallel l$

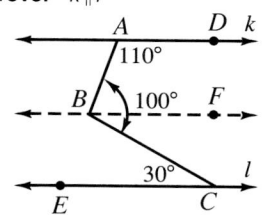

Plan: Construct $\overleftrightarrow{BF} \parallel \overleftrightarrow{AD}$; then $m\angle ABF = 70$ and $m\angle FBC = 30$. $\angle FBC$ and $\angle BCE$ are $\cong$ alt. int. $\angle$s of $\overleftrightarrow{BF}$ and l. Since $\overleftrightarrow{BF} \parallel l$ and $\overleftrightarrow{BF} \parallel k$, $k \parallel l$.

Proof:

Statements	Reasons
1. Through B, construct $\overleftrightarrow{BF} \parallel \overleftrightarrow{AD}$.	1. Post. 12
2. $m\angle DAB +$ $m\angle ABF = 180$	2. If 2 $\parallel$ lines have a transv., the int. $\angle$s on the same side of the transv. are supp.
3. $m\angle BAD =$ 110, $m\angle ABC =$ 100, $m\angle BCE = 30$	3. Given
4. $110 +$ $m\angle ABF = 180$	4. Substitution
5. $m\angle ABF = 70$	5. Subtraction
6. $m\angle ABC =$ $m\angle ABF +$ $m\angle FBC$	6. Def. of betw.
7. $100 = 70 +$ $m\angle FBC$	7. Substitution
8. $m\angle FBC = 30$	8. Subtraction
9. $m\angle FBC =$ $m\angle BCE$	9. Transitive prop.
10. $\angle FBC \cong$ $\angle BCE$	10. Def. of $\cong$

11. $\overleftrightarrow{BF} \parallel l$ | **11.** If 2 lines have a transv. and alt. int. $\angle$s are $\cong$, the lines are $\parallel$

12. $k \parallel l$ | **12.** 2 lines $\parallel$ to the same line are $\parallel$.

Conclusion: In the given figure, if $m\angle BAD = 110$, $m\angle ABC = 100$ and $m\angle BCE = 30$, then $k \parallel l$.

22. Given: $\overleftrightarrow{AD} \parallel \overleftrightarrow{BC}$, transv. $\overleftrightarrow{BE}$; $\overrightarrow{AM}$ bisects $\angle EAD$; $\overrightarrow{BN}$ bisects $\angle ABC$.
Prove: $\overleftrightarrow{AM} \parallel \overleftrightarrow{BN}$

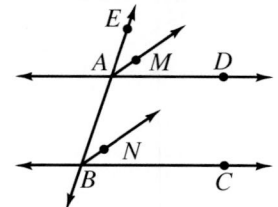

Plan: Since $\overleftrightarrow{AD} \parallel \overleftrightarrow{BC}$, corr. $\angle$s EAD and ABC are $\cong$. Use $\angle$ Bis. Th. and algebraic properties to show $m\angle EAM = m\angle ABN$. Concl. follows by def. of $\cong \angle$s and Post. 13.

Proof:

Statements	Reasons
1. $\overleftrightarrow{AD} \parallel \overleftrightarrow{BC}$, $\overrightarrow{AM}$ bisects $\angle EAD$, $\overrightarrow{BN}$ bisects $\angle ABC$.	1. Given
2. $\angle EAD \cong \angle ABC$	2. Post. 10; corr. $\angle$s of $\parallel$ lines are $\cong$.
3. $m\angle EAD = m\angle ABC$	3. Def. of $\cong \angle$s
4. $m\angle EAM = \frac{1}{2}m\angle EAD$, $m\angle ABN = \frac{1}{2}m\angle ABC$	4. $\angle$Bis. Th.
5. $\frac{1}{2}m\angle EAD = \frac{1}{2}m\angle ABC$	5. Mult. prop.
6. $m\angle EAM = m\angle ABN$	6. Substitution
7. $\angle EAM \cong \angle ABN$	7. Def. of $\cong$
8. $\overleftrightarrow{AM} \parallel \overleftrightarrow{BN}$	8. Post. 13

Conclusion: In the given figure, if $\overleftrightarrow{AD} \parallel \overleftrightarrow{BC}$, $\overrightarrow{AM}$ bisects $\angle EAD$, and $\overrightarrow{BN}$ bisects

$\angle ABC$, then $\overrightarrow{AM} \parallel \overrightarrow{BN}$.

Construction

PAGE 100

2.

4.

5.

6.

PAGE 101

13. Proof:

Statements	Reasons
1. $m\angle A + m\angle B + m\angle C = 180$, $m\angle X + m\angle Y + m\angle Z = 180$	1. The sum of the measures of the $\angle$s of a $\triangle$ is 180
2. $m\angle A + m\angle B + m\angle C = m\angle X + m\angle Y + m\angle Z$	2. Trans. prop.
3. $\angle A \cong \angle X$; $\angle B \cong \angle Y$	3. Given
4. $m\angle A = m\angle X$; $m\angle B = m\angle Y$	4. Def. of $\cong \angle$s
5. $m\angle A + m\angle B + m\angle C = m\angle A + m\angle B + m\angle Z$	5. Subst. prop.
6. $m\angle C = m\angle Z$	6. Subtr. prop.
7. $\angle C \cong \angle Z$	7. Def. of $\cong \angle$s

Conclusion: If you are given $\triangle ABC$ and $\triangle XYZ$ with $\angle A \cong \angle X$ and $\angle B \cong \angle Y$, then $\angle C \cong \angle Z$.

PAGE 102

27. Proof:

Statements	Reasons
1. $\angle 1$ is ext $\angle$ of $\triangle ABC$	1. Given

2. $\angle 1$ and $\angle CAB$ are a linear pair.	2. Def. of linear pair
3. $\angle 1$ and $\angle CAB$ are suppl.	3. Linear Pair Post.
4. $m\angle 1 + m\angle CAB = 180$	4. Def. of supp. $\angle$s
5. $m\angle B + m\angle C + m\angle CAB = 180$	5. Sum of measures of $\angle$s of $\triangle$ is 180.
6. $m\angle B + m\angle C + m\angle CAB = m\angle 1 + m\angle CAB$	6. Trans. prop.
7. $m\angle B + m\angle C = m\angle 1$	7. Subtr. prop.

Conclusion: In the given triangle, the measure of exterior $\angle 1$ is equal to the sum of the measures of the remote interior $\angle$s, $\angle B$ and $\angle C$.

28. Given: equiangular $\triangle ABC$
Prove: $m\angle A = m\angle B = m\angle C = 60$
Plan: Since $\triangle ABC$ is equiangular, $m\angle A$, $m\angle B$ and $m\angle C$ are equal. Using the substitution and division properties results in the conclusion.

Proof:

Statements	Reasons
1. $\triangle ABC$ is equiangular.	1. Given
2. $m\angle A = m\angle B = m\angle C$	2. Def. of equiangular
3. $m\angle A + m\angle B + m\angle C = 180$	3. Sum of measures of $\angle$s of a $\triangle$ is 180.
4. $m\angle A + m\angle A + m\angle A = 180$	4. Substitution
5. $3m\angle A = 180$	5. Distrib. prop.
6. $m\angle A = 60$	6. Division prop.
7. $m\angle B = 60$, $m\angle C = 60$	7. Substitution

Conclusion: In equiangular $\triangle ABC$, the measure of each $\angle = 60$.

30. Plan: By Th. 3.12 $m\angle 1 = m\angle B + m\angle C$. Likewise for $m\angle 2$ and $m\angle 3$, the other ext. $\angle$s. Using $m\angle A + m\angle B + m\angle C = 180$ and the addition of $m\angle 1 + m\angle 2 + m\angle 3$ results in the conclusion.

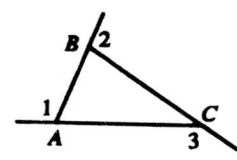

Proof:

Statements	Reasons
1. ∠1, ∠2, ∠3 are the ext. ∠s of △ABC.	1. Given
2. m∠1 = m∠B + m∠C m∠2 = m∠C + m∠A m∠3 = m∠A + m∠B	2. measure of ext. ∠s of a △ = sum of measures of remote int. ∠s.
3. m∠1 + m∠2 + m∠3 = (m∠B + m∠C) + (m∠C + m∠A) + (m∠A + m∠B) = (m∠A + m∠B + m∠C) + (m∠A + m∠B + m∠C)	3. addition prop. + other alg. properties
4. m∠A + m∠B + m∠C = 180	4. Sum of the measures of the ∠s of △ is 180.
5. m∠1 + m∠2 + m∠3 = 180 + 180 = 360	5. Substitution

Conclusion: The sum of the exterior ∠s, ∠1, ∠2, and ∠3 is 360.

PAGE 108

30. Plan: $\overline{RT}$ partitions RSTV into two △. The sum of the measures of the ∠s of each △ is 180. The conclusion follows.

Proof:

Statements	Reasons
1. Quad. RSTV; diag. $\overline{RT}$	1. Given
2. In △RTV: m∠1 + m∠2 + m∠v = 180 In △RST: m∠4 + m∠5 + m∠S = 180	2. Sum of measures of the ∠s of a △ is 180.
3. (m∠1 + m∠2 + m∠V) + (m∠4 + m∠5 + m∠s) = 360	3. Add. prop.

4. (m∠2 + m∠4) + (m∠1 + m∠5) + m∠v + m∠S = 360	4. Comm. and assoc. props.
5. m∠2 + m∠4 = m∠STV m∠1 + m∠5 = m∠SRV	5. Def. of betw. of rays
6. m∠STV + m∠SRV + m∠S + m∠v = 360	6. Substitution

Conclusion: Given quad. RSTV, the sum of its ∠ measures is 360.

PAGE 109

57.

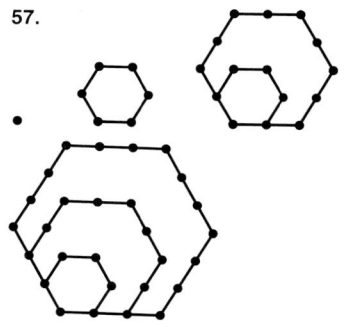

PAGE 137

29. Plan: Use the def. of ⊥ bisector to show △JON ≅ △HON.

Proof:

Statements	Reasons
1. $\overrightarrow{ON}$ is the ⊥ bisector of $\overline{JH}$.	1. Given
2. ∠JNO and ∠HNO are rt. ∠s.	2. Def. of ⊥
3. ∠JNO ≅ ∠HNO	3. All rt. ∠s are ≅.
4. $\overline{JN} \cong \overline{HN}$	4. Def. of bisector
5. $\overline{ON} \cong \overline{ON}$	5. Refl. prop. of ≅
6. △JON ≅ △HON	6. SAS

Conclusion: When a segment drawn from a vertex of a △ to the opposite side is the ⊥ bisector of that side, then 2 ≅ △ are formed.

30. Plan: Use the def. of ∠ bisector and the trans. prop. to show △NOJ ≅ △NOH.

Proof:

Statements	Reasons
1. $\overrightarrow{ON}$ bisects ∠JOH.	1. Given

2. ∠JON ≅ ∠HON	2. Def. ∠ bis.
3. m∠J = x; m∠H = x	3. Given
4. m∠J = m∠H	4. Trans. prop.
5. ∠J ≅ ∠H	5. Def. of ≅ ∠s.
6. $\overline{ON} \cong \overline{ON}$	6. Refl. prop. of ≅
7. △NOJ ≅ △NOH	7. AAS

Conclusion: In the given figure, if $\overrightarrow{ON}$ bisects ∠JOH and ∠J and ∠H have the same measure, then △NOJ ≅ △NOH.

PAGE 142

14. Use the given and the refl. prop. to show that △ACD ≅ △ABE. Concl. follows by CPCTC.

15. Use the given and the refl. prop. to show △BDC ≅ △CEB by SSS. Concl. follows by CPCTC.

PAGE 143

22. Plan: First prove △HIJ ≅ △HOP. Then ∠IHJ ≅ ∠OHP by CPCTC, and m∠IHJ = m∠OHP. Use add prop. and betweenness to reach concl.

Proof:

Statements	Reasons
1. $\overline{HI} \cong \overline{HO}$; $\overline{IJ} \cong \overline{PO}$; ∠I ≅ ∠O	1. Given
2. △HIJ ≅ △HOP	2. SAS
3. ∠IHJ ≅ ∠OHP	3. CPCTC
4. m∠IHJ = m∠OHP	4. Def. of ≅ ∠s
5. m∠IHJ + m∠JHP = m∠OHP + m∠JHP	5. Add. prop.
6. m∠IHJ + m∠JHP = m∠IHP; m∠OHP + m∠JHP = m∠OHJ	6. Def. of betweenness
7. m∠IHP = m∠OHJ	7. Subst. prop.
8. ∠IHP ≅ ∠OHJ	8. Def. of ≅ ∠s

Conclusion: In the figure, if $\overline{HI} \cong \overline{HO}$, $\overline{IJ} \cong \overline{PO}$ and ∠I ≅ ∠O, then ∠IHP ≅ ∠OHJ.

23. Plan: Use the defs. of reg. hex. and bis. to prove △KLP ≅ △NOP. Then ∠KLP ≅ ∠NOP by CPCTC and the concl. follows, since they are alt. int. ∠s.

Proof:

Statements	Reasons
1. *JKLMNO* is a reg. hexagon.	1. Given
2. $\overline{KL} \cong \overline{NO}$	2. Def. of reg. polygon
3. $\overline{KN}$ and $\overline{OL}$ bisect each other.	3. Given
4. $\overline{LP} \cong \overline{OP}$; $\overline{KP} \cong \overline{NP}$	4. Def. of bisector
5. $\triangle KLP \cong \triangle NOP$	5. SSS
6. $\angle KLP \cong \angle NOP$	6. CPCTC
7. $\overline{KL} \parallel \overline{NO}$	7. If alt. int. $\angle$s are $\cong$, then lines are $\parallel$.

Conclusion: The opposite sides of a regular hexagon are parallel.

24. Given: Points *M* and *N* on opposite sides of $\overleftrightarrow{PQ}$; $\overline{MP} \cong \overline{NP}$ and $\overline{MQ} \cong \overline{NQ}$
Prove: $\angle M \cong \angle N$

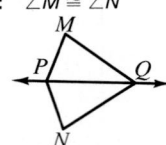

Plan: Draw a figure from the Given. Show $\triangle MPQ \cong \triangle NPQ$. Concl. follows by CPCTC.
Proof:

Statements	Reasons
1. Points *M* and *N* on opposite sides of $\overleftrightarrow{PQ}$	1. Given
2. $\overline{MP} \cong \overline{NP}$; $\overline{MQ} \cong \overline{NQ}$	2. Given
3. $\overline{PQ} \cong \overline{PQ}$	3. Refl. prop. of $\cong$
4. $\triangle MPQ \cong \triangle NPQ$	4. SSS
5. $\angle M \cong \angle N$	5. CPCTC

Conclusion: If points *M* and *N* are on opposite sides of $\overleftrightarrow{PQ}$ with $\overline{MP} \cong \overline{NP}$ and $\overline{MQ} \cong \overline{NQ}$, then $\angle M \cong \angle N$.

25. Given: Points *M* and *N* on opposite sides of $\overleftrightarrow{PQ}$; $\overline{MP} \cong \overline{NQ}$; $\overline{MP} \parallel \overline{NQ}$.
Prove: $\overline{MQ} \cong \overline{NP}$

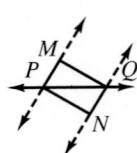

Plan: Draw a figure from the Given. Show $\triangle MPQ \cong \triangle NQP$. Concl. follows by CPCTC.
Proof:

Statements	Reasons
1. Points *M* and *N* on opposite sides of $\overleftrightarrow{PQ}$	1. Given
2. $\overline{MP} \cong \overline{NQ}$; $\overline{MP} \parallel \overline{NQ}$	2. Given
3. $\angle MPQ \cong \angle NQP$	3. Th. 3.2
4. $\overline{PQ} \cong \overline{QP}$	4. Refl. prop. of $\cong$
5. $\triangle MPQ \cong \triangle NQP$	5. SAS
6. $\overline{MQ} \cong \overline{NP}$	6. CPCTC

Conclusion: If *M* and *N* are on opposite sides of $\overleftrightarrow{PQ}$ with $\overline{MP} \cong \overline{NQ}$ and $\overline{MP} \parallel \overline{NQ}$, then $\overline{MQ} \cong \overline{NP}$.

26. Plan: Show $\triangle \cong$ by showing pairs of alt. int. $\angle$s $\cong$ and using the refl. prop. of $\cong$. Concl. follows by CPCTC.
Proof:

Statements	Reasons
1. $\overleftrightarrow{KL} \parallel \overleftrightarrow{NO}$	1. Given
2. $\angle 3 \cong \angle 5$	2. Th. 3.2
3. $\overleftrightarrow{OK} \parallel \overleftrightarrow{LN}$	3. Given
4. $\angle 2 \cong \angle 4$	4. Th. 3.2
5. $\overline{KN} \cong \overline{NK}$	5. Refl. prop. of $\cong$
6. $\triangle OKN \cong \triangle LNK$	6. ASA
7. $\overline{OK} \cong \overline{LN}$	7. CPCTC

Conclusion: If $\triangle OKN$ and LNK have $\parallel$ sides $\overline{KL}$ and $\overline{NO}$ and $\overline{OK}$ and $\overline{LN}$, then $\overline{OK} \cong \overline{LN}$.

27. Plan: Show $\triangle FAM \cong \triangle GBM$ by ASA. Then $\overline{FM} \cong \overline{GM}$ and it can be shown that $\triangle FMC \cong \triangle GMC$ by SAS. Concl. follows.
Proof:

Statements	Reasons
1. $\overline{AM} \cong \overline{BM}$; $\angle A \cong \angle B$; $\angle 1 \cong \angle 4$	1. Given
2. $\triangle FAM \cong \triangle GBM$	2. ASA
3. $\overline{FM} \cong \overline{GM}$	3. CPCTC
4. $\angle 2 \cong \angle 3$	4. Given
5. $\overline{MC} \cong \overline{MC}$	5. Refl. prop. $\cong$
6. $\triangle FMC \cong \triangle GMC$	6. SAS
7. $\overline{FC} \cong \overline{GC}$	7. CPCTC

Conclusion: If $\overline{AM} \cong \overline{BM}$, $\angle A \cong \angle B$, $\angle 1 \cong \angle 4$, and $\angle 2 \cong \angle 3$, then $\overline{FC} \cong \overline{GC}$.

28. Plan: First show $\angle KBT \cong \triangle KBU$ by SAS. Then use corr. parts $\overline{KT}$ and $\overline{KU}$ to show $\triangle KCU \cong \triangle KET$. Concl. follows.
Proof:

Statements	Reasons
1. $\angle 1 \cong \angle 2$; $\overline{BT} \cong \overline{BU}$	1. Given
2. $\overline{KB} \cong \overline{KB}$	2. Refl. prop. $\cong$
3. $\triangle KBT \cong \triangle KBU$	3. SAS
4. $\overline{KT} \cong \overline{KU}$	4. CPCTC
5. $\angle 3 \cong \angle 4$	5. Given
6. $\angle CKU \cong \angle EKT$	6. Vert. $\angle$s are $\cong$.
7. $\triangle KCU \cong \triangle KET$	7. ASA
8. $\overline{KC} \cong \overline{KE}$	8. CPCTC

Conclusion: If $\angle 1 \cong \angle 2$, $\overline{BT} \cong \overline{BU}$ and $\angle 3 \cong \angle 4$, then $\overline{KC} \cong \overline{KE}$.

PAGE 148

3. Plan: Use the Given, the def. of betweenness, and the refl. prop. ($\angle C \cong \angle C$) to prove $\triangle ACF \cong \triangle BCD$ by SAS. Then $\angle A \cong \angle B$ by CPCTC.
Intermediate goals: Show: $\overline{AC} \cong \overline{BC}$; $\triangle ACF \cong \triangle BCD$

4. Plan: Use the Given, the def. of betweenness, and vert. $\angle$s to prove $\triangle AED \cong \triangle BEF$. Then $\angle ADE \cong \angle BFE$ by CPCTC. Thus, $\angle EDC \cong \angle EFC$ because they are supplements of $\cong$ $\angle$s.
Intermediate goals: Show: $\overline{AE} \cong \overline{BE}$; $\triangle AED \cong \triangle BEF$; $\angle ADE \cong \angle BFE$

5. Plan: Use the Given and the Trans. prop. to get $\overline{ML} \cong \overline{ON}$. Then prove $\triangle ONJ \cong \triangle MLN$ by SAS. $\angle 3$ and $\angle 4$ are $\cong$ by CPCTC.
Proof:

Statements	Reasons
1. $\angle 1 \cong \angle 2$; *M* and *N* are midpts.	1. Given
2. $\overline{JN} \cong \overline{NL}$; $\overline{ML} \cong \overline{KM}$	2. Def. of midpt.
3. $\overline{KM} \cong \overline{ON}$	3. Given
4. $\overline{ML} \cong \overline{ON}$	4. Trans. prop.

5. △MLN ≅ △ONJ | 5. SAS
6. ∠3 ≅ ∠4 | 6. CPCTC

Concl.: In the given fig., if M and N are midpts., ∠1 ≅ ∠2, and ON ≅ KM, then ∠3 ≅ ∠4.

Intermediate goals: ML ≅ ON; △ONJ ≅ △MLN

6. Plan: Use the Given to get ∠3 ≅ ∠4; then prove △EDC ≅ △FDC by SAS. EC ≅ FC by CPCTC.

Proof:

Statements	Reasons
1. CD ⊥ AB; ∠1 ≅ ∠2; DE ≅ DF	1. Given
2. ∠3 is the comp. of ∠1; ∠4 is the comp. of ∠2.	2. If 2 adj. ∠s have their ext. sides in ⊥ lines, the ∠s are comp.
3. ∠3 ≅ ∠4	3. Complements of ≅ ∠s are ≅.
4. DC ≅ DC	4. Refl. prop.
5. △EDC ≅ △FDC	5. SAS
6. EC ≅ FC	6. CPCTC

Concl.: In the given fig., if CD ⊥ AB, ∠1 ≅ ∠2, and DE ≅ DF, then EC ≅ FC.

Intermediate goals: ∠3 ≅ ∠4; △EDC ≅ △FDC

7. Plan: Show △JKM ≅ △LKM by SAS to get JK ≅ LK by CPCTC. The concl. follows by def. of isosc. △.

Proof:

Statements	Reasons
1. KM is the ⊥ bisector of JL.	1. Given
2. JM ≅ ML	2. Def. of bisector
3. ∠JMK and ∠LMK are rt. ∠s.	3. Def. of ⊥
4. ∠JMK ≅ ∠LMK	4. All right ∠s are ≅.
5. KM ≅ KM	5. Refl. prop.
6. △JKM ≅ △LKM	6. SAS
7. JK ≅ LK	7. CPCTC
8. △JKL is isosc.	8. Def. of isosc. △

Conclusion: In △JKL, if KM is the ⊥ bisector of JL, then △JKL is isosc.

Intermediate goals: △JKM ≅ △LKM

8. Plan: Show △JKM ≅ △LKM by SSS to get ∠JMK ≅ ∠LMK. The concl. follows by Th. 1.11.

Proof:

Statements	Reasons
1. △JKL is isos.	1. Given
2. JK ≅ LK	2. Def. of isosc. △
3. KM ≅ KM	3. Refl. prop.
4. KM bisects JL.	4. Given
5. JM ≅ LM	5. Def. of bisector
6. △JKM ≅ △LKM	6. SSS
7. △JMK ≅ △LMK	7. CPCTC
8. KM ⊥ JL	8. Th. 1.11

Conclusion: In △JKL, if KM is the ⊥ bisector of JL, △JKL is isosc.

Intermediate goal: △JKM ≅ △LKM

PAGE 153

15. Given: △RST with median TM; TS ≅ TR

Prove: ∠S ≅ ∠R

Plan: Prove △MST ≅ △MRT by SSS, then ∠S ≅ ∠R by CPCTC.

Statements	Reasons
1. TS ≅ TR	1. Given
2. TM ≅ TM	2. Refl. prop.
3. TM is median.	3. Given
4. MS ≅ MR	4. Def. of median
5. △MST ≅ MRT	5. SSS
6. ∠S ≅ ∠R	6. CPCTC

Conclusion: In △RST, if TM is a median and TS ≅ TR, then ∠S ≅ ∠R.

16. Given: TM bisects ∠RTS; ∠R ≅ ∠S

Prove: TM is an altitude of △RTS

Plan: Prove △MST ≅ △MRT by AAS, then ∠SMT ≅ ∠RMT. Use Th. 1.11 to show TM ⊥ RS.

Proof:

Statements	Reasons
1. ∠R ≅ ∠S	1. Given
2. TM bisects ∠RTS.	2. Given
3. ∠RTM ≅ ∠STM	3. Def. of bisector
4. TM ≅ TM	4. Refl. prop.
5. △MST ≅ △MRT	5. AAS
6. ∠SMT ≅ ∠RMT	6. CPCTC
7. TM ⊥ RS	7. Th. 1.11
8. TM is an altitude of △RTS.	8. Def. of altitude

Conclusion: If TM bisects ∠RTS in △RTS and ∠R ≅ ∠S, then TM is an altitude of △RTS.

17. Proof:

Statements	Reasons
1. PQ is ⊥ bisector of MN.	1. Given
2. ∠ROM and ∠RON are rt. ∠s.	2. Def. of ⊥ lines
3. ∠ROM ≅ ∠RON	3. all rt. ∠s are ≅
4. OM ≅ ON	4. Def. of ⊥ bisector
5. OR ≅ OR	5. Refl. prop.
6. △ORM ≅ △ORN	6. SAS
7. RM ≅ RN	7. CPCTC

Conclusion: If R is on the ⊥ bisector of MN, then RM ≅ RN.

18. Given: △ABC with AD bisecting ∠A; AD ⊥ BC

Prove: △ABC is isosceles.

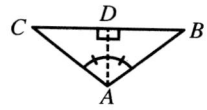

Plan: In order to show △ABC isosceles, show AB ≅ AC. Show that AB and AC are corr. parts of △ ADB and ADC. Use the ASA theorem to prove △ADB ≅ △ADC.

19. Given: Isosceles △ABC with AB ≅ AC; CD and BE are altitudes

Prove: CD ≅ BE

Plan: Show that CD and BE are corr. parts of ≅ △ ACD and ABE. These △ are ≅ by AAS (sides AB and AC, rt. ∠s ADC and AEB, and ∠A).

21. Given: P and Q are each equi-distant from A and B; i.e., PA ≅ PB and QA ≅ QB

Prove: PQ is the ⊥ bisector of AB.

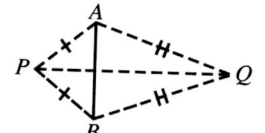

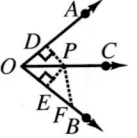

Plan: Use Theorem 4.3 to show that P and Q are on the ⊥ bisector of $\overline{AB}$. Then use the postulate that states that two points determine a unique line.

Statements	Reasons
1. P and Q are each equidistant from points A and B; i.e., $\overline{PA} \cong \overline{PB}$ and $\overline{QA} \cong \overline{QB}$.	1. Given
2. P lies on the ⊥ bisector of $\overline{AB}$.	2. Th 4.3
3. Q lies on the perpendicular bisector of $\overline{AB}$	3. Th 4.3
4. Consider $\overrightarrow{PQ}$.	4. Two points determine a line.
5. $\overrightarrow{PQ}$ is the ⊥ bisector of $\overline{AB}$.	5. In a plane, a segment has exactly one ⊥ bisector.

Conclusion: If two points are each equidistant from the endpoints of a segment, then the line joining the points is the perpendicular bisector of the segment.

22. Proof:

Statements	Reasons
1. $\overrightarrow{AR}$ bisects $\angle CAT$; P on $\overrightarrow{AR}$	1. Given
2. $\angle QAP \cong \angle SAP$	2. Def. of ∠ bis.
3. $\overrightarrow{PQ} \perp \overrightarrow{AC}$; $\overrightarrow{PS} \perp \overrightarrow{AT}$	3. Def. of dist. from pt. to line
4. $\angle PQA$ and $\angle PSA$ are rt. ∠s	4. Def. of ⊥ lines
5. $\angle PQA \cong \angle PSA$	5. All rt. ∠s ≅
6. $\overline{PA} \cong \overline{PA}$	6. Refl. prop.
7. $\triangle PQA \cong \triangle PSA$	7. AAS
8. $\overline{PQ} \cong \overline{PS}$	8. CPCTC

Conclusion: In the given figure if $\overrightarrow{AR}$ bis. $\angle CAT$, then $\overline{PQ} \cong \overline{PS}$.

23. Given: $\angle AOB$ with interior $\overrightarrow{OC}$; P is on $\overrightarrow{OC}$ and equidistant from $\overrightarrow{OA}$ and $\overrightarrow{OB}$; i.e., $\overline{PD} \cong \overline{PE}$.

Prove: $\overrightarrow{OC}$ bisects $\angle AOB$.

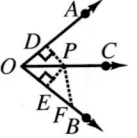

Plan: Use auxiliary figures to form △PFE and show △POD ≅ △PFE. Then show △PFE ≅ △POE. The conclusion follows by the transitive prop.

Statements	Reasons
1. Locate F on $\overrightarrow{OB}$ such that $\overline{EF} \cong \overline{OD}$.	1. On a ray there is exactly one pt. at a given dis. from the ray's endpt.
2. Draw $\overline{PF}$.	2. Two points determine a line.
3. P is equidistant from $\overrightarrow{OA}$ and $\overrightarrow{OB}$; $\overline{PD} \cong \overline{PE}$.	3. Given
4. $\overline{PD} \perp \overrightarrow{OA}$; $\overline{PE} \perp \overrightarrow{OB}$	4. Def. of dist. from a pt. to a line
5. $\angle PDO$ and $\angle PEF$ are rt. ∠s.	5. Def. of ⊥ lines
6. $\angle PDO \cong \angle PEF$	6. All rt ∠s ≅
7. $\triangle POD \cong \triangle PFE$	7. SAS
8. $\overline{PO} \cong \overline{PF}$	8. CPCTC
9. $\overline{PE}$ is the ⊥ bisector of $\overline{OF}$.	9. Th. 4.3
10. E is the midpt. of $\overline{OF}$.	10. Def. of ⊥ bisector
11. $\overline{OE} \cong \overline{FE}$	11. Def. of midpt.
12. $\triangle PFE \cong \triangle POE$	12. SSS
13. $\triangle POD \cong \triangle POE$	13. Trans. prop.
14. $\angle POD \cong \angle POE$	14. CPCTC
15. $\overrightarrow{OC}$ bisects $\angle AOB$.	15. Def. of bisector

Conclusion: If a point is equidistant from the sides of an ∠, then the point lies on the bisector of the ∠.

PAGE 154

24. Plan: Use the given information to prove △JOM ≅ △HNP. Then $\overline{OM}$ and $\overline{NP}$ are ≅ corr. parts.

Statements	Reasons
1. $\overline{OM}$ is an alt. of △JOH; $\overline{NP}$ is an alt. of △HNJ.	1. Given
2. $\overline{OM} \perp \overline{JH}$; $\overline{NP} \perp \overline{JH}$	2. Def. of altitude
3. $\angle JMO$ and $\angle HPN$ are rt. ∠s.	3. Def. of ⊥ lines
4. $\angle JMO \cong \angle HPN$	4. All rt. ∠s are ≅.
5. $\angle 1 \cong \angle 2$; $\overline{JM} \cong \overline{HP}$	5. Given
6. $\triangle JOM \cong \triangle HNP$	6. ASA
7. $\overline{OM} \cong \overline{NP}$	7. CPCTC

Conclusion: In the given figure, if $\angle 1 \cong \angle 2$, $\overline{JM} \cong \overline{HP}$, and $\overline{OM}$ and $\overline{NP}$ are altitudes of △ JOH and HNJ, respectively, then $\overline{OM} \cong \overline{NP}$.

25. Plan: First show △OMH ≅ △NPJ by AAS. Then use corr. ≅ parts $\overline{OH}$ and $\overline{NJ}$ to prove △OHJ ≅ △NJH by SAS. Then $\overline{OJ}$ and $\overline{NH}$ are ≅ corr. parts.

Statements	Reasons
1. $\overline{OH} \parallel \overline{JN}$	1. Given
2. $\angle OHM \cong \angle NJP$	2. If lines are ∥, alt. int. ∠s are ≅.
3. $\overline{OM}$ is an alt. of △JOH; $\overline{NP}$ is an alt. of △HNJ.	3. Given
4. $\overline{OM} \perp \overline{JH}$; $\overline{NP} \perp \overline{JH}$	4. Def. of altitude
5. $\angle OMH$ and $\angle NPJ$ are rt. ∠s	5. Def. of ⊥ lines
6. $\angle OMH \cong \angle NPJ$	6. All rt. ∠s are ≅
7. $\overline{OM} \cong \overline{NP}$	7. Given
8. $\triangle OMH \cong \triangle NPJ$	8. AAS
9. $\overline{OH} \cong \overline{NJ}$	9. CPCTC
10. $\overline{HJ} \cong \overline{JH}$	10. Refl. prop.
11. $\triangle OHJ \cong \triangle NJH$	11. SAS
12. $\overline{OJ} \cong \overline{NH}$	12. CPCTC

Conclusion: In the given figure, if $\overline{OH} \parallel \overline{JN}$, $\overline{OM} \cong \overline{NP}$, and $\overline{OM}$ and $\overline{NP}$ are altitudes of △ JOH and HNJ, respectively, then $\overline{OJ} \cong \overline{NH}$.

PAGE 160

5. Plan: Use the given and the th. about vert. ∠s to prove the △ ≅ by HA.

Proof:

Statements	Reasons
1. $\overline{YA} \perp \overline{MR}$; $\overline{MT} \perp \overline{YR}$	1. Given
2. $\angle SAM$ and $\angle STY$ are right angles.	2. Def. of $\perp$ lines
3. $\triangle SAM$ and $\triangle STY$ are right triangles.	3. Def. of rt. $\triangle$
4. $\overline{SM} \cong \overline{SY}$	4. Given
5. $\angle ASM \cong \angle TSY$	5. Vert. $\angle$s are $\cong$.
6. $\triangle SAM \cong \triangle STY$	6. HA

Conclusion: In the given figure, if $\overline{YA} \perp \overline{MR}$, $\overline{MT} \perp \overline{YR}$ and $\overline{SM} \cong \overline{SY}$, then $\triangle SAM \cong \triangle STY$

6. Given: $\triangle YAM$ and $\triangle MTY$ are rt. $\triangle$s; $\overline{AM} \cong \overline{TY}$; $\angle AYM \cong \angle TMY$
Prove: $\triangle YAM \cong \triangle MTY$
Plan: Since $\angle A$ and $\angle T$ are rt. $\angle$s, they are $\cong$. Thus, $\triangle YAM \cong \triangle MTY$ by AAS.

Proof:

Statements	Reasons
1. $\triangle YAM$, $\triangle MTY$ rt. $\triangle$s; $\overline{AM} \cong \overline{TY}$; $\angle AYM \cong \angle TMY$	1. Given
2. $\angle A$, $\angle T$ rt. $\angle$s	2. Def. rt. $\triangle$
3. $\angle A \cong \angle T$	3. All rt. $\angle$s $\cong$
4. $\triangle YAM \cong \triangle MTY$	4. AAS

Conclusion: If a leg and an acute angle of a rt. $\triangle$ are $\cong$ to the corr. parts of another rt. $\triangle$, then the triangles are $\cong$.

PAGE 161

9. Plan: Since rt. $\angle$s A and O are $\cong$, the $\triangle$s are $\cong$ by SAS.

Proof:

Statements	Reasons
1. $\triangle TAG$ and HOP are rt. $\triangle$s; $\overline{AG} \cong \overline{OP}$; $\overline{TA} \cong \overline{HO}$	1. Given
2. $\angle A$ and $\angle O$ are rt. $\angle$s	2. Def. of rt. $\triangle$
3. $\angle A \cong \angle O$	3. All rt. $\angle$s are $\cong$.
4. $\triangle TAG \cong \triangle HOP$	4. SAS

Conclusion If the legs of one rt. $\triangle$ are $\cong$ to the legs of another rt. $\triangle$, then the $\triangle$s are $\cong$.

16. Proof:

Statements	Reasons
1. Right $\triangle$s ABC and DEF; $\overline{AC} \cong \overline{DF}$; $\overline{AB} \cong \overline{DE}$	1. Given
2. $\angle ABC$ and $\angle DEF$ are right angles.	2. Def. of rt. $\triangle$
3. $\angle ABC \cong \angle DEF$	3. All rt. $\angle$s are $\cong$.
4. Extend $\overrightarrow{FE}$ so that $\overline{EG} \cong \overline{BC}$.	4. On a ray there is exactly 1 pt that is at a given distance from the endpoint of a ray.
5. Draw $\overline{DG}$.	5. 2 pts. determine a line.
6. $\overline{DE} \perp \overline{FG}$	6. Def. of $\perp$
7. $\angle DEG$ is a right angle.	7. If 2 lines are $\perp$, then all 4 $\angle$s they form are rt. $\angle$s.
8. $\angle ABC \cong \angle DEG$	8. All rt. $\angle$s are $\cong$.
9. $\triangle ABC \cong \triangle DEG$	9. SAS
10. $\overline{AC} \cong \overline{DG}$	10. CPCTC
11. $\overline{DG} \cong \overline{DF}$	11. Subst. prop.
12. $\overline{DE}$ is the perpendicular bisector of $\overline{EG}$.	12. If a pt. is equidistant from the endpoints of a segment, then it lies on the $\perp$ bisector of the segment.
13. E is the midpoint of $\overline{FG}$.	13. Def. of $\perp$ bisector
14. $\overline{EG} \cong \overline{EF}$	14. Def. of midpt.
15. $\overline{BC} \cong \overline{EF}$	15. Subst. prop.
16. $\triangle ABC \cong \triangle DEF$	16. SSS (or SAS)

Conclusion If the hypotenuse and a leg of right triangle ABC are congruent to the corresponding parts of right triangle DEF, then $\triangle ABC \cong \triangle DEF$.

PAGE 162

17. Plan: Show $\triangle AEB \cong \triangle CEB$ by LA. Concl. follows by CPCTC.

Proof:

Statements	Reasons
1. $\overline{BE} \perp \overline{AC}$	1. Given
2. $\angle AEB$ and $\angle CEB$ are rt. $\angle$s	2. Def. of $\perp$ lines
3. $\triangle AEB$ and $\triangle CEB$ are rt. $\triangle$.	3. Def. of rt. $\triangle$.
4. $\angle A \cong \angle C$	4. Given
5. $\overline{EB} \cong \overline{EB}$	5. Refl. prop.
6. $\triangle AEB \cong \triangle CEB$	6. LA
7. $\angle ABE \cong \angle CBE$	7. CPCTC

Conclusion: If $\overline{BE} \perp \overline{AC}$ in $\triangle ABC$ and if $\angle A \cong \angle C$, then $\angle ABE \cong \angle CBE$.

18. Plan: Show rt. $\triangle$s AEB and $CEB \cong$ Then corr. sides $\overline{AB}$ and $\overline{CB}$ are congruent.

Proof:

Statements	Reasons
1. $\overline{BE} \perp \overline{AC}$	1. Given
2. $\angle AEB$ and $\angle CEB$ are rt. $\angle$s.	2. Def. of $\perp$ lines
3. $\triangle AEB$ and $\triangle CEB$ are rt. $\triangle$.	3. Def. of rt. $\triangle$
4. $\overline{AE} \cong \overline{CE}$	4. Given
5. $\overline{BE} \cong \overline{BE}$	5. Refl. prop.
6. $\triangle AEB \cong \triangle CEB$	6. LL
7. $\overline{AB} \cong \overline{CB}$	7. CPCTC
8. $\triangle ABC$ is isos.	8. Def. of isos. $\triangle$

Conclusion: If $\overline{BE} \perp \overline{AC}$ in $\triangle ABC$ and $\overline{AE} \cong \overline{CE}$, then $\triangle ABC$ is isosceles.

19. Plan: Show $\triangle XYT \cong \triangle ZYW$. Then $\angle X$ and $\angle Z$ are $\cong$ corr. parts.

Proof:

Statements	Reasons
1. $\overline{YX} \cong \overline{YZ}$; $\overline{TY} \perp \overline{YX}$; $\overline{WY} \perp \overline{YZ}$	1. Given
2. $\angle XYT$ and $\angle ZYW$ are rt. $\angle$s.	2. Def. of $\perp$ lines
3. $\triangle XYT$ and $\triangle ZYW$ are rt. $\triangle$.	3. Def. of rt. $\triangle$
4. Y is on $\perp$ bisector of $\overline{TW}$.	4. Given

5. *Y* is equidistant from *T* and *W*, or *YT* = *YW*.

5. Th. 4.2

6. $\overline{YT} \cong \overline{YW}$

6. Def. of ≅ segments

7. △*XYT* ≅ △*ZYW*

7. LL

8. ∠*X* ≅ ∠*Z*

8. CPCTC

Conclusion: In the given figure, if $\overline{YX} \cong \overline{YZ}$, $\overline{TY} \perp \overline{YX}$, $\overline{WY} \perp \overline{YZ}$, and *Y* is on the ⊥ bisector of $\overline{TW}$, then ∠*X* ≅ ∠*Z*.

20. Plan: Show △*XYT* ≅ △*ZYW*. Thus, *YT* = *YW* and *Y* is on the ⊥ bisector of $\overline{TW}$. Draw ⊥ bisector $\overline{YS}$ and show △*YTS* ≅ △*YWS*. Conclusion follows by CPCTC.

Proof:

Statements	Reasons
1. △*XYT* and △*ZYW* are rt. ⓢ; ∠*X* ≅ ∠*Z* and $\overline{XY} \cong \overline{ZY}$.	1. Given
2. △*XYT* ≅ △*ZYW*	2. LA
3. $\overline{YT} \cong \overline{YW}$	3. CPCTC
4. *YT* = *YW*	4. Def. of ≅ segments
5. *Y* is on the ⊥ bisector of $\overline{TW}$.	5. Th. 4.3
6. Draw $\overline{YS}$, the ⊥ bisector of $\overline{TW}$.	6. Through a point not on a line exactly one perpendicular can be drawn to the line.
7. ∠*YST* and ∠*YSW* are rt. ∠s.	7. Def. of ⊥ lines
8. △*YST* and △*YSW* are rt. ⓢ.	8. Def. of rt. ⓢ
9. $\overline{YS} \cong \overline{YS}$	9. Refl. Prop.
10. △*YST* ≅ △*YSW*	10. HL
11. ∠*YTW* ≅ ∠*YWT*	11. CPCTC

Conclusion: In the given figure, if ∠*X* ≅ ∠*Z*, $\overline{XY} \cong \overline{ZY}$, and △*XYT* and △*ZYW* are rt. ⓢ, then ∠*YTW* ≅ ∠*YWT*.

21. Plan: Show △*TOD* ≅ △*ADO*. Use corr. ≅ ∠s to show rt. ⓢ *DFT* and *OEA* ≅ . Then $\overline{OE} \cong \overline{DF}$ by CPCTC.

Proof:

Statements	Reasons
1. $\overline{DT} \cong \overline{OA}$; $\overline{TO} \cong \overline{AD}$	1. Given
2. $\overline{OD} \cong \overline{DO}$	2. Refl. prop.
3. △*TOD* ≅ △*ADO*	3. SSS
4. ∠*T* ≅ ∠*A*	4. CPCTC
5. $\overline{OE}$ is an altitude of △*ODA*; $\overline{DF}$ is an altitude of △*DTO*.	5. Given
6. $\overline{OE} \perp \overline{DA}$; $\overline{DF} \perp \overline{TO}$	6. Def. of altitude
7. ∠*OEA* and ∠*DFT* are rt. ∠s.	7. Def. of ⊥ lines
8. △*OEA* and △*DFT* are rt. ⓢ.	8. Def. of a rt. △
9. △*OEA* ≅ △*DFT*	9. HA
10. $\overline{OE} \cong \overline{DF}$	10. CPCTC

Conclusion: In the given figure, if $\overline{DT} \cong \overline{OA}$, $\overline{TO} \cong \overline{AD}$, and $\overline{DF}$ and $\overline{OE}$ are altitudes of ⓢ *DTO* and *ODA*, respectively, then $\overline{OE} \cong \overline{DF}$.

22. Plan: Show △*NRH* ≅ △*HON*. Then use ≅ corr. parts to show rt. ⓢ *RND* and *OHA* congruent. Conclusion follows by CPCTC.

Proof:

Statements	Reasons
1. $\overline{RH} \cong \overline{ON}$; $\overline{RH} \parallel \overline{NO}$	1. Given
2. ∠*RHN* ≅ ∠*ONH*	2. If lines are ∥, alt. int. ∠s are ≅.
3. $\overline{NH} \cong \overline{HN}$	3. Refl. prop.
4. △*NRH* ≅ △*HON*	4. SAS
5. $\overline{RN} \cong \overline{OH}$; ∠*RND* ≅ ∠*OHA*	5. CPCTC
6. $\overline{RD} \perp \overline{NH}$; $\overline{OA} \perp \overline{NH}$	6. Given
7. ∠*RDN* and ∠*OAH* are rt. ∠s.	7. Def. of ⊥ lines

8. △*RND* and △*OHA* are rt. ⓢ.

8. Def. of rt. △

9. △*RND* ≅ △*OHA*

9. HA

10. $\overline{ND} \cong \overline{HA}$

10. CPCTC

Conclusion: In the given figure, if $\overline{RH} \parallel \overline{NO}$, $\overline{RH} \cong \overline{ON}$, $\overline{RD} \perp \overline{NH}$, and $\overline{OA} \perp \overline{NH}$, then $\overline{ND} \cong \overline{HA}$.

23. Given: △*MBS* and △*RCN* are rt. ⓢ; $\overline{SM} \cong \overline{NR}$; ∠*S* ≅ ∠*N*.

Prove: △*MBS* ≅ △*RCN*

Plan: Use the given information and the AAS Theorem.

Statements	Reasons
1. △*MBS* and △*RCN* are rt. ⓢ; $\overline{SM} \cong \overline{NR}$; ∠*S* ≅ ∠*N*.	1. Given
2. ∠*B* and ∠*C* are rt. ∠s.	2. Def. of rt. △
3. ∠*B* ≅ ∠*C*	3. All right ∠s are ≅.
4. △*MBS* ≅ △*RCN*	4. AAS or HA

Conclusion: If the hypotenuse and an acute ∠ of one rt. △ are ≅ to the corr. parts of another rt. △, then the ⓢ are ≅.

24. Given: Isosceles rt. △*END*

Prove: ∠*E* ≅ ∠*D*

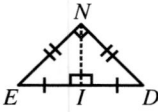

Plan: Use the fact that *N* is equidistant from the endpoints of $\overline{ED}$ to draw ⊥ bisector $\overline{NI}$. Thus, the two ⓢ formed can be proven ≅, and ∠*E* and ∠*D* are ≅ corr. parts.

Statements	Reasons
1. △*END* is an isosceles rt. △.	1. Given
2. $\overline{NE} \cong \overline{ND}$	2. Def. of isosceles △
3. *NE* = *ND*	3. Def. of ≅ segments
4. *N* is on the ⊥ bisector of $\overline{ED}$.	4. Th. 4.3

714

5. Draw $\overline{NI}$, the ⊥ bisector of $\overline{ED}$.

6. ∠EIN and ∠DIN are rt. ∠s.

7. △EIN and △DIN are rt. △.

8. $\overline{IE} \cong \overline{ID}$

9. △NIE ≅ △NID

10. ∠E ≅ ∠D

5. Through a point not on a line, exactly one ⊥ line can be drawn.

6. Def. of ⊥ lines

7. Def. of rt. △

8. Def. of bisector

9. HL

10. CPCTC

Conclusion: If a rt. △ is isosceles, then its acute ∠s are ≅.

25. Given: Rt. △ MAR and SOL are ≅ ; $\overline{RC}$ is an altitude of △MAR; $\overline{LB}$ is an altitude of △SOL.

Prove: $\overline{RC} \cong \overline{LB}$

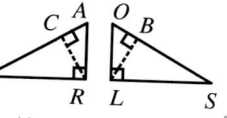

Plan: Use corr. parts of ≅ △ to show △RCA ≅ △LBO by HA. Then $\overline{RC} \cong \overline{LB}$ by CPCTC.

Statements	Reasons
1. Rt. △ MAR and SOL are ≅.	1. Given
2. $\overline{RA} \cong \overline{LO}$; ∠A ≅ ∠O	2. CPCTC
3. $\overline{RC}$ is an altitude of △MAR; $\overline{LB}$ is an altitude of △SOL.	3. Given
4. $\overline{RC} \perp \overline{MA}$; $\overline{LB} \perp \overline{SO}$	4. Def. of altitude
5. ∠RCA and ∠LBO are rt. ∠s.	5. Def. of ⊥ lines
6. △RCA and △LBO are rt. △.	6. Def. of rt. △
7. △RCA ≅ △LBO	7. HA
8. $\overline{RC} \cong \overline{LB}$	8. CPCTC

Conclusion: If two rt. △ are ≅ , then the altitudes from their right ∠s are ≅ .

PAGE 163

5. Plan: Show △ABE ≅ △DBC. Then ∠A and ∠D are ≅ corr. parts.

Statements	Reasons
1. $\overline{EC} \perp \overline{CD}$; $\overline{CE} \perp \overline{EA}$	1. Given
2. ∠C and ∠E are rt. ∠s.	2. Def. of ⊥
3. △ABE and △DBC are rt. △.	3. Def. of rt. △
4. ∠EBA ≅ ∠CBD	4. Vertical ∠s are ≅.
5. $\overline{AE} \cong \overline{DC}$	5. Given
6. △ABE ≅ △DBC	6. LA (or AAS)
7. ∠A ≅ ∠D	7. CPCTC

Conclusion: In the given figure, if $\overline{AE} \cong \overline{DC}$, $\overline{EC} \perp \overline{CD}$ and $\overline{CE} \perp \overline{EA}$, then ∠A ≅ ∠D.

PAGE 167

17. Given: $\overleftrightarrow{RS}$ is ⊥ bisector of $\overline{AB}$; P is a point on $\overline{RS}$ not on $\overline{AB}$.

Prove: △PAB is isosceles.

Plan: Since P is on the ⊥ bisector of $\overline{AB}$, P is equidistant from A and B. It follows that $\overline{PA} \cong \overline{PB}$ and △PAB is isosceles.

Statements	Reasons
1. $\overleftrightarrow{RS}$ is the ⊥ bisector of $\overline{AB}$; P is any point on $\overline{RS}$ not on $\overline{AB}$.	1. Given
2. P is equidistant from A and B.	2. Th. 4.2
3. PA = PB	3. Def. equidist.
4. $\overline{PA} \cong \overline{PB}$	4. Def. of ≅ seg.
5. △PAB is isosceles.	5. Def. of isos. △

Conclusion: If P is a point on the ⊥ bisector of $\overline{AB}$ such that P is not on $\overline{AB}$, then △PAB is isosceles.

22. Plan: Prove rt. △ AKP and OKM ≅. Then $\overline{AP}$ and $\overline{OM}$ are ≅ corr. parts.

Statements	Reasons
1. $\overline{AO} \perp$ bis. $\overline{PM}$. $\overline{PM} \perp$ bis. $\overline{AO}$.	1. Given
2. $\overline{AK} \cong \overline{OK}$; $\overline{PK} \cong \overline{MK}$	2. Def. of bisector
3. ∠AKP is a rt. ∠. ∠OKM is a rt. ∠.	3. Def. of ⊥
4. △AKP is a rt. △; △OKM is a rt. △.	4. Def. of rt. △.

| 5. △AKP ≅ △OKM | 5. LL |
| 6. $\overline{AP} \cong \overline{MO}$ | 6. CPCTC |

Conclusion: In the given figure, if $\overline{AO}$ is the ⊥ bisector of $\overline{PM}$ and $\overline{PM}$ is the ⊥ bisector of $\overline{AO}$, then $\overline{AP} \cong \overline{MO}$.

PAGE 168

10. Plan: Use the def. of median and vertical ∠s to show △ESP ≅ △RSA. Then $\overline{EP} \cong \overline{RA}$ by CPCTC.

Proof:

Statements	Reasons
1. $\overline{ES}$ is a median of △EPA; $\overline{AS}$ is a median of △AER.	1. Given
2. S is the midpoint of $\overline{PA}$; S is the midpoint of $\overline{ER}$.	2. Def. of median
3. $\overline{SP} \cong \overline{SA}$; $\overline{SE} \cong \overline{SR}$	3. Def. of midpt.
4. ∠ESP ≅ ∠RSA	4. Vert. ∠s are ≅.
5. △ESP ≅ △RSA	5. SAS
6. $\overline{EP} \cong \overline{RA}$	6. CPCTC

Conclusion: If $\overline{ES}$ is a median of △EPA and $\overline{AS}$ is a median of △AER, then $\overline{EP} \cong \overline{RA}$.

11. Plan: Use the given to prove △AED ≅ △BFD. Then use corr. ≅ parts to prove △CED ≅ △CFD. Use corresp. ≅ parts again to prove △ACD ≅ △BCD. The conclusion follows by CPCTC.

Proof:

Statements	Reasons
1. $\overline{DE} \perp \overline{AC}$; $\overline{DF} \perp \overline{BC}$	1. Given
2. ∠AED and ∠BFD are rt. ∠s; ∠CED and ∠CFD are rt. ∠s.	2. Def. of ⊥
3. △AED and △BFD are rt. △. △CED and △CFD are rt. △.	3. Def. of rt. △
4. $\overline{DE} \cong \overline{DF}$	4. Given
5. $\overline{AD} \cong \overline{BD}$	5. Given
6. △AED ≅ △BFD	6. HL

7. ∠A ≅ ∠B
8. $\overline{CD} \cong \overline{CD}$
9. △CED ≅ △CFD
10. ∠ACD ≅ ∠BCD
11. △ACD ≅ △BCD
12. $\overline{AC} \cong \overline{BC}$

7. CPCTC
8. Refl. prop. of ≅
9. HL
10. CPCTC
11. AAS
12. CPCTC

Conclusion: In the given figure if $\overline{DE} \perp \overline{AC}$, $\overline{DF} \perp \overline{BC}$, $\overline{DE} \cong \overline{DF}$, and $\overline{AD} \cong \overline{BD}$, then $\overline{AC} \cong \overline{BC}$.

12. Given: △ABC ≅ △DEF; $\overline{BX}$ is an altitude of △ABC; $\overline{EY}$ is an altitude of △DEF.
Prove: $\overline{BX} \cong \overline{EY}$

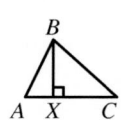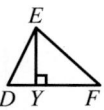

Plan: Use the corr. parts of ≅ △s ABC and DEF and the def. of altitude to prove rt. △s BXC and EYF ≅. Then $\overline{BX} \cong \overline{EY}$ by CPCTC.

Proof:

Statements	Reasons
1. $\overline{BX}$ is an alt. of △ABC; $\overline{EY}$ is an alt. of △DEF.	1. Given
2. $\overline{BX} \perp \overline{AC}$; $\overline{EY} \perp \overline{DF}$	2. Def. of altitude
3. ∠BXC is a rt. ∠. ∠EYF is a rt. ∠.	3. Def. of ⊥
4. △BXC is a rt. △. △EYF is a rt. △.	4. Def. of rt. △
5. △ABC ≅ △DEF	5. Given
6. $\overline{BC} \cong \overline{EF}$; ∠C ≅ ∠F	6. CPCTC
7. △BXC ≅ △EYF	7. HA
8. $\overline{BX} \cong \overline{EY}$	8. CPCTC

Conclusion: If 2 △s are ≅, then the corr. altitudes are ≅.

PAGE 172

54. Plan: Use the Given to prove △UYV ≅ △XVY by SSS. Then corr. ≅ parts, ∠UYV and ∠XVY, are alt. int. ∠s for $\overline{UY}$ and $\overline{VX}$.

Proof:

Statements	Reasons
1. △UYV ≅ △VXW	1. Given
2. $\overline{UY} \cong \overline{VX}$; $\overline{UV} \cong \overline{VW}$	2. CPCTC
3. UV = VW	3. Def. of ≅ seg.
4. UV + VW = UW	4. Def. of betw.
5. UV + UV = UW	5. Subst. prop.
6. 2UV = UW	6. Distrib. prop.
7. $UV = \frac{1}{2}UW$	7. Mult. prop.
8. $XY = \frac{1}{2}UW$	8. Given
9. XY = UV	9. Subst. prop.
10. $\overline{XY} \cong \overline{UV}$	10. Def. of ≅ seg.
11. $\overline{YV} \cong \overline{VY}$	11. Refl. prop.
12. △UYV ≅ △XVY	12. SSS
13. ∠UYV ≅ ∠XVY	13. CPCTC
14. $\overline{UY} \parallel \overline{VX}$	14. If 2 lines have a transv. and ≅ alt. int. ∠s, then the lines are ∥.

Concl.: In the given figure, if △UYV ≅ △VXW and $XY = \frac{1}{2}UW$, then $\overline{UY} \parallel \overline{VX}$.

55. Plan: Use corr. parts of the Given ≅ △s to show △AEB ≅ △DEC by SAS.

Proof:

Statements	Reasons
1. △AEC ≅ △DEB	1. Given
2. $\overline{AE} \cong \overline{DE}$; ∠A ≅ ∠D; $\overline{AC} \cong \overline{DB}$	2. CPCTC
3. $\overline{BC} \cong \overline{BC}$	3. Refl. prop.
4. AC = DB; BC = BC	4. Def. of ≅ seg.
5. AC − BC = DB − BC	5. Subtr. prop.
6. AC − BC = AB; DB − BC = DC	6. Def. betw.
7. AB = DC	7. Subst.
8. $\overline{AB} \cong \overline{DC}$	8. Def. of ≅ seg.
9. △AEB ≅ △DEC	9. SAS

Concl.: In the given figure, if △AEC ≅ △DEB, then △AEB ≅ △DEC.

56. Plan: Use the Given, betw. of rays, and the Th. about supplements of ≅ ∠s to show △AEB ≅ △DEC by AAS.

Proof:

Statements	Reasons
1. $\overline{AB} \cong \overline{CD}$; ∠EBC ≅ ∠ECB	1. Given
2. ∠ABE ≅ ∠DCE	2. Supplements of ≅ ∠s are ≅.
3. ∠AEC ≅ ∠DEB	3. Given
4. ∠BEC ≅ ∠BEC	4. Refl. prop.
5. m∠AEC = m∠DEB; m∠BEC = m∠BEC	5. Def. of ≅ ∠s
6. m∠AEC − m∠BEC = m∠DEB − m∠BEC	6. Subtr. prop.
7. m∠AEC − m∠BEC = m∠AEB; m∠BED − m∠BEC = m∠DEC	7. Def. betw.
8. m∠AEB = m∠DEC	8. Subst.
9. ∠AEB ≅ ∠DEC	9. Def. of ≅ ∠s
10. △AEB ≅ △DEC	10. AAS

Concl.: In the given figure, if ∠EBC ≅ ∠ECB, ∠AEC ≅ ∠DEB, and $\overline{AB} \cong \overline{CD}$, then △AEB ≅ △DEC.

PAGE 178

20. Plan: Use the Isos. △ Th. to show ∠AYT ≅ ∠ATY. Since ∠AYM and ∠AYT are a linear pair, as are ∠ATY and ∠ATR, they are supp. The conclusion follows because supp. of ≅ ∠s are ≅.

Proof:

Statements	Reasons
1. $\overline{YA} \cong \overline{TA}$	1. Given
2. ∠AYT ≅ ∠ATY	2. Isos. △ Th.
3. ∠AYM and ∠AYT are a linear pair; ∠ATR and ∠ATY are a linear pair.	3. Def. of linear pair
4. ∠AYM and ∠AYT are supp. ∠ATR and ∠ATY are supp.	4. Linear Pair Postulate
5. ∠AYM ≅ ∠ATR	5. Supp. of ≅ ∠s are ≅.

Conclusion: In the figure, if $\overline{YA} \cong \overline{TA}$, then $\angle AYM \cong \angle ATR$.

21. Plan: Since $\angle AYM$ and $\angle AYT$ are a linear pair and therefore supp., and since the same is true for $\angle ATR$ and $\angle ATY$, it follows that $\angle AYT \cong \angle ATY$. Hence, $\overline{AY} \cong \overline{AT}$, and the conclusion follows.

Proof:

Statements	Reasons
1. $\angle AYM$ and $\angle AYT$ are a linear pair; $\angle ATR$ and $\angle ATY$ are a linear pair.	1. Def. of linear pair
2. $\angle AYM$ and $\angle AYT$ are supp. $\angle ATR$ and $\angle ATY$ are supp.	2. Linear Pair Postulate
3. $\angle AYM \cong \angle ATR$	3. Given
4. $\angle AYT \cong \angle ATY$	4. Supp. of $\cong \angle$s are $\cong$.
5. $\overline{AY} \cong \overline{AT}$	5. If two $\angle$s of a $\triangle$ are $\cong$, the sides opposite them are $\cong$.
6. $\triangle AYT$ is isos.	6. Def. of isos. $\triangle$

Conclusion: In the figure, if $\angle AYM \cong \angle ATR$, $\triangle AYT$ is isos.

22. Given: Equilateral $\triangle MNP$
Prove: $\angle M \cong \angle N \cong \angle P$

Plan: Use the Isos. $\triangle$ Th. twice to get $\angle M \cong \angle P$ and $\angle P \cong \angle N$ (or equivalent choices). Then $\angle M \cong \angle N \cong \angle P$

Proof:

Statements	Reasons
1. Consider equilateral $\triangle MNP$.	1. Given
2. $\overline{MN} \cong \overline{PN} \cong \overline{MP}$	2. Def. of equilateral $\triangle$
3. $\angle P \cong \angle M \cong \angle N$	3. Isos. $\triangle$ Th.

Conclusion: An equilateral $\triangle$ is also equiangular.

23. Given: Equilateral $\triangle MNP$
Prove: $m\angle M = m\angle N = m\angle P = 60$

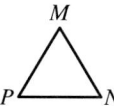

Plan: Since an equilateral $\triangle$ is also equiangular by Cor. 1, and since the sum of the measures of the $\angle$s of a $\triangle$ is 180, the conclusion follows.

Proof:

Statements	Reasons
1. Equilateral $\triangle MNP$.	1. Given
2. $\angle M \cong \angle N \cong \angle P$	2. An equilateral $\triangle$ is also equiangular.
3. $m\angle M = m\angle N = m\angle P$	3. Def. of $\cong \angle$s
4. $m\angle M + m\angle N + m\angle P = 180$	4. The sum of the measures of the $\angle$s of a $\triangle$ is 180.
5. $3 \cdot m\angle M = 180$	5. Subst. prop.
6. $m\angle M = 60$	6. Div. prop. of $=$
7. $m\angle M = m\angle N = m\angle P = 60$	7. Subst. prop.

Conclusion: Each angle of an equilateral triangle measures 60°.

24. Given: $\triangle CAT$ with $\angle C \cong \angle T$
Prove: $\overline{AT} \cong \overline{AC}$

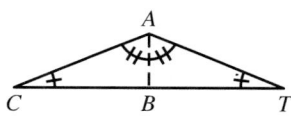

Plan: Draw $\overline{AB}$, the segment that bis. $\angle A$ and intersects $\overline{CT}$ in point B. Show that $\triangle ABC \cong \triangle ABT$, and then the sides will be $\cong$ corr. parts.

Proof:

Statements	Reasons
1. In $\triangle CAT$, draw the bis. of $\angle A$. Label it $\overline{AB}$.	1. Every $\angle$ has a bis.
2. $\angle CAB \cong \angle TAB$	2. Def. of $\angle$ bis.
3. $\angle C \cong \angle T$	3. Given
4. $\overline{AB} \cong \overline{AB}$	4. Refl. prop.
5. $\triangle ABC \cong \triangle ABT$	5. AAS Th.
6. $\overline{AC} \cong \overline{AT}$	6. CPCTC

Conclusion: In $\triangle CAT$, whenever $\angle C \cong \angle T$, then $\overline{AT} \cong \overline{AC}$.

25. Given: $\triangle ABC$ with $\angle A \cong \angle B \cong \angle C$
Prove: $\overline{AB} \cong \overline{BC} \cong \overline{CA}$

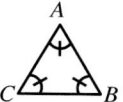

Plan: Use the converse to the Isos. $\triangle$ Th. twice to get a congruence statement that involves all three sides of $\triangle ABC$.

Proof:

Statements	Reasons
1. Consider $\triangle ABC$ having $\angle A \cong \angle B \cong \angle C$.	1. Given
2. $\overline{AB} \cong \overline{BC}$ and $\overline{BC} \cong \overline{CA}$	2. If two $\angle$s of a $\triangle$ are $\cong$, the sides opp. them are $\cong$.
3. $\overline{AB} \cong \overline{CA}$	3. Trans. prop. of $\cong$

Conclusion: An equiangular triangle is also equilateral.

26. Given: $\triangle DEF$ with alt. and median $\overline{EA}$
Prove: $\triangle DEF$ is isos.

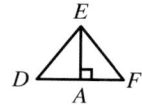

Plan: Show $\triangle EAD \cong \triangle EAF$ by the LL Theorem. Then $\overline{ED} \cong \overline{EF}$ by corr. parts; hence, $\triangle DEF$ is isos.

Proof:

Statements	Reasons
1. Consider $\triangle DEF$ with altitude and median $\overline{EA}$.	1. Given
2. $\overline{EA} \perp \overline{DF}$	2. Def. of alt.
3. $\angle EAD$ and $\angle EAF$ are rt. $\angle$s.	3. Def. of $\perp$ lines
4. $\triangle EAD$ and $\triangle EAF$ are rt. $\triangle$.	4. Def. of rt. $\triangle$
5. A is the midpt. of $\overline{DF}$.	5. Def. of median
6. $\overline{AD} \cong \overline{AF}$	6. Def. of midpt.
7. $\overline{EA} \cong \overline{EA}$	7. Refl. prop. of $\cong$
8. $\triangle EAD \cong \triangle EAF$	8. LL Theorem
9. $\overline{ED} \cong \overline{EF}$	9. CPCTC
10. $\triangle DEF$ is isos.	10. Def. of isos. $\triangle$

Conclusion: If a segment is both an alt. and a median of a $\triangle$, the $\triangle$ is isos.

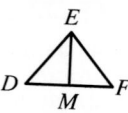

27. Given: Isos. △DEF with base $\overline{DF}$ and median $\overline{EM}$

Prove: $\overline{EM}$ bisects ∠E.

Plan: Show △EDM ≅ △EFM by the SAS Postulate. Then ∠DEM ≅ ∠FEM by corr. parts; hence, $\overline{EM}$ bisects ∠E.

Proof:

Statements	Reasons
1. Consider isos. △DEF with base $\overline{DF}$ and median $\overline{EM}$	1. Given
2. $\overline{ED} \cong \overline{EF}$	2. Def. of isos. △
3. ∠D ≅ ∠F	3. Isos. △ Th.
4. M is the midpt. of $\overline{EM}$.	4. Def. of median
5. $\overline{DM} \cong \overline{FM}$	5. Def. of midpt.
6. △EDM ≅ △EFM	6. SAS postulate
7. ∠DEM ≅ ∠FEM	7. CPCTC
8. $\overline{EM}$ bisects ∠E	8. Def. of ∠ bis.

Conclusion: The median from the vertex angle to the base of an isosceles △ bisects the vertex angle.

PAGE 183

19. Proof:

Statements	Reasons
1. B is between A and C.	1. Given
2. AB + BC = AC, where AB, BC, and AC are positive	2. Def. of betweenness
3. AC > AB; AC > BC	3. Def. of greater than

Conclusion: If B is between A and C, then AC > AB and AC > BC.

20. Proof:

Statements	Reasons
1. Consider △XYZ with $\overline{XZ}$.	1. Given
2. m∠4 = m∠1 + m∠2	2. The measure of any ext. ∠ of a △ is equal to the sum of the measures of the two remote int. ∠s.

| 3. m∠4 > m∠2; m∠4 > m∠1 | 3. Def. of greater than |

Conclusion: The measure of an ext. ∠ of a △ is greater than the measure of either remote int. ∠.

21. Plan: Show △MIS ≅ △EIX by SAS. Then ∠SMI ≅ ∠XEI by corr. parts. Since m∠MSR > m∠SMI, subst. leads to the conclusion.

Proof:

Statements	Reasons
1. I is the midpt. of $\overline{ME}$ and $\overline{XS}$.	1. Given
2. $\overline{MI} \cong \overline{EI}$; $\overline{IS} \cong \overline{IX}$	2. Def. of midpt.
3. ∠MIS ≅ ∠EIX	3. Vert. ∠s are ≅.
4. △MIS ≅ △EIX	4. SAS
5. ∠SMI ≅ ∠XEI	5. CPCTC
6. m∠SMI = m∠XEI	6. Def. of ≅ ∠s
7. m∠MSR > m∠SMI	7. Ext. ∠ Th.
8. m∠MSR > m∠XEI	8. Subst. prop.

Conclusion: In the given figure, if I is the midpt. of $\overline{ME}$ and $\overline{XS}$, then m∠MSR > m∠XEI.

22. Plan: Since ∠DCA and ∠ACB are supp., and since m∠DCA > m∠A, properties of inequality and equality verify the conclusion.

Proof:

Statements	Reasons
1. △ABC with $\overrightarrow{BC}$ extended through D	1. Given
2. m∠DCA > m∠A	2. Ext. ∠ Th.
3. ∠DCA and ∠ACB are a linear pair.	3. Def. of linear pair
4. ∠DCA and ∠ACB are supp.	4. Linear pair post.
5. m∠DCA + m∠ACB = 180	5. Def. of supp. ∠s
6. m∠DCA = 180 − m∠ACB	6. Subtraction prop.
7. 180 − m∠ACB > m∠A	7. Subst. prop.
8. 180 > m∠A + m∠ACB	8. Addition prop. of inequality

Generalization: The sum of the measures of two angles of a triangle is less than 180.

23. Given: $\overrightarrow{OB}$ is between $\overrightarrow{OA}$ and $\overrightarrow{OC}$.

Prove: m∠AOC > m∠AOB; m∠AOC > m∠BOC

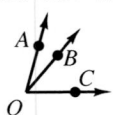

Plan: Since $\overrightarrow{OB}$ is between $\overrightarrow{OA}$ and $\overrightarrow{OC}$, m∠AOB + m∠BOC = m∠AOC. The conclusion follows by the definition of greater than for angles.

Proof:

Statements	Reasons
1. $\overrightarrow{OB}$ is between $\overrightarrow{OA}$ and $\overrightarrow{OC}$	1. Given
2. m∠AOB + m∠BOC = m∠AOC	2. Def. of betweenness
3. m∠AOC > m∠AOB; m∠AOC > m∠BOC	3. Def. of greater than

Conclusion: If $\overrightarrow{OB}$ is between $\overrightarrow{OA}$ and $\overrightarrow{OC}$, then m∠AOC is greater than the measure of either ∠AOB or ∠BOC.

24. Prove the addition property of inequalty by proving the two cases: (a) If a > b and c = d, then a + c > b + d, and (b) If a > b and c > d, then a + c > b + d

Case (a):

Plan: Use the def. of greater than and the add. prop. of equality to write an expression involving the quantities (a + c) and (b + d).

Proof:

Statements	Reasons
1. a > b	1. Given
2. There is a pos. number k with a = b + k.	2. Def. of greater than
3. c = d	3. Given
4. a + c = b + k + d	4. Add. prop. of equality
5. a + c = b + d + k	5. Commutative prop. of addition
6. a + c > b + d	6. Def. of >

Conclusion: If equal quantities are added to both sides of an inequality, the resulting sums are unequal in the same direction as the original inequality.

Case (b)

Plan: Use the def. of greater than on the two inequality statements given. Application of addition properties verifies the conclusion.

Proof:

Statements	Reasons
1. $a > b$; $c > d$	1. Given
2. There exist pos. numbers k_1 and k_2 with $a = b + k_1$ and $c = d + k_2$.	2. Def. of greater than
3. $a + c = b + k_1 + d + k_2$	3. Add. prop. of equality
4. $a + c = b + d + k_1 + k_2$	4. Commutative prop. of addition
5. $k_1 + k_2$ is a pos. number.	5. Closure prop. of addition
6. $a + c > b + d$	6. Def. of $>$

Conclusion: If $a > b$ and $c > d$, then $a + c > b + d$.

25. Given: real numbers a, b, and c; $a > b$ and $b > c$

Prove: $a > c$

Proof:

Statements	Reasons
1. real numbers a, b, and c; $a > b$ and $b > c$	1. Given
2. $a = b + d$, $d > 0$; $b = c + e$, $e > 0$	2. Def. of greater than
3. $a = (c + e) + d$	3. Subst. prop.
4. $a = c + (e + d)$	4. Assoc. prop.
5. $e + d > 0$	5. Closure
6. $a > c$	6. Def. of $>$

Conclusion: If a, b, and c are real numbers and $a > b$ and $b > c$, then $a > c$.

26. Plan: Use the def. of greater than and the mult. prop. of equality to verify the conclusion.

Proof:

Statements	Reasons
1. $a > b$	1. Given
2. There is a positive number k with $a = b + k$.	2. Def. of greater than
3. $c > 0$	3. Given

4. $a \cdot c = (b + k) \cdot c$	4. Mult. prop.
5. $a \cdot c = b \cdot c + k \cdot c$	5. Distrib. prop.
6. $k \cdot c > 0$	6. The product of two pos. numbers is pos.
7. $a \cdot c > b \cdot c$	7. Def. of $>$

Conclusion: If both sides of an inequality are multiplied by a positive number, the resulting products are unequal in the same direction as the original inequality.

PAGE 187

1. Plan: Assume that $\overline{OM}$ does bisect $\angle PMN$ and show that it leads to a contradiction.

Proof:

Assume:	
$\overline{OM}$ bisects $\angle PMN$.	Negation of concl.
$\angle NMO \cong \angle PMO$	Def. of bis.
$\overline{MO} \cong \overline{MO}$	Refl. prop.
$\overline{MN} \cong \overline{MP}$	Given
$\triangle MNO \cong \triangle MPO$	SAS
$\overline{NO} \cong \overline{PO}$	CPCTC

Contradiction: $\overline{ON} \not\equiv \overline{OP}$

Concl.: Since the assumption $\overline{OM}$ bisects $\angle PMN$ leads to a contradiction of the given, then the assumption is false. Therefore, $\overline{OM}$ does not bisect $\angle PMN$.

2. Plan: Assume that $\overline{OM} \perp \overline{NP}$ and show that it leads to a contradiction.

Proof:

Assume:	
$\overline{OM} \perp \overline{NP}$	Negation of concl.
$\angle NRM$ and $\angle PRM$ are rt. $\angle$s.	Def. of $\perp$
$\triangle NRM$ and $\triangle PRM$ are rt. $\triangle$s.	Def. of rt. $\triangle$
$\overline{MN} \cong \overline{MP}$	Given
$\overline{MR} \cong \overline{MR}$	Refl. prop.
$\triangle MNR \cong \triangle MPR$	HL
$\angle NMO \cong \angle PMO$	CPCTC
$\overline{MO} \cong \overline{MO}$	Refl. prop.
$\triangle MNO \cong \triangle MPO$	SAS
$\overline{NO} \cong \overline{PO}$	CPCTC

Contradiction: $\overline{NO} \not\equiv \overline{PO}$

Concl.: Since the assumption $\overline{OM} \perp \overline{NP}$ leads to a contradiction of the given, the assumption is false. Therefore, $\overline{OM} \not\perp \overline{NP}$.

PAGE 188

3. Plan: Assume the negation of the concl. and show that it leads to a contradiction.

Proof:

Assume:

$\angle 3$ and $\angle 4$ are supp.	Negation of concl.
$k \parallel l$	If int. $\angle$s on same side of transv. are supp., lines are $\parallel$.
$\angle 1 \cong \angle 3$	If lines are $\parallel$, corr. $\angle$s are $\cong$.

Contradiction: $\angle 1 \not\equiv \angle 3$

Conclusion: Since the assumption that $\angle 3$ and $\angle 4$ are supp. leads to a contradiction of the given, the assumption is false. Therefore, $\angle 3$ and $\angle 4$ are not supp.

4. Plan: same as above

Proof:

Assume:

$\angle 3$ and $\angle 4$ are supp.	Negation of concl.
$k \parallel l$	If int. $\angle$s on same side of transv. are supp., lines are $\parallel$.
$\angle 1 \cong \angle 3$; $\angle 4 \cong \angle 5$	If lines are $\parallel$, corr. $\angle$s are $\cong$.
$\angle 1$ and $\angle 5$ are supp.	Subst.

Contradiction: $\angle 1$ and $\angle 5$ are not supp.

Conclusion: Since the assumption that $\angle 3$ and $\angle 4$ are supp. leads to a contradiction of the given, the assumption is false. Therefore, $\angle 3$ and $\angle 4$ are not supp.

5. Plan: Assume the negation of the concl. and show that it leads to a contradiction.

Proof:

Assume:

$k \parallel l$	Negation of conclusion
$\angle 2 \cong \angle 3$	If lines are $\parallel$, alt. int. $\angle$s are $\cong$

Contradiction: $\angle 2 \not\equiv \angle 3$

Conclusion: Since the assumption $k \parallel l$ leads to a contradiction of the given, the assumption is false. Therefore, $k \not\parallel l$.

6. Plan: Same as above
Proof:
Assume:

∠1 ≅ ∠3   Negation of concl.
k ∥ l   If corr. ∠s are ≅,
                  lines are ∥.
Contradiction: k ∦ l
Conclusion: Since the assumption
∠1 ≅ ∠3 leads to a contradiction,
∠1 ≅ ∠3 is false. Therefore,
∠1 ≇ ∠3.

7. Plan: Same as above
Proof:
Assume:

∠S is a rt. ∠.   Negation of concl.
△RST is a rt. △.   Def. of rt. △
∠R and ∠T   The acute ∠s of a
are comp.   rt. △ are comp.
Contradiction: ∠R and ∠T are not
                            comp.
Conclusion: Since the assumption
that ∠S is a rt. ∠ leads to a
contradiction, the assumption is false.
Therefore, ∠S is not a rt. ∠.

8. Plan: Assume the negation of the
concl. and show that this leads
to a contradiction.
Proof:
Assume:

△RSU ≅ △VST   Negation of concl.
∠R ≅ ∠V   CPCTC
RU ∥ TV   If alt. int. ∠s are ≅,
                          lines are ∥.
Contradiction: RU ∦ TV
Conclusion: Since the assumption
△RSU ≅ △VST leads to a
contradiction of the given, the
assumption is false. Therefore,
△RSU ≇ △VST.

9. Plan: Same as above
Proof:
Assume:

RU ∥ TV   Negation of concl.
∠R ≅ ∠V;   If lines are ∥, alt.
∠U ≅ ∠T   int. ∠s are ≅.
RU ≅ VT   Given
△RSU ≅ △VST   ASA
Contradiction: △RSU ≇ △VST
Conclusion: Since the assumption
RU ∥ TV leads to a contradiction, the
assumption is false. Therefore,
RU ∦ TV.

10. Given: Obt. △ABC with obt. ∠A
Prove: △ABC does not contain a rt.
∠.

Plan: Assume the negation of the
concl. and show that this leads
to a contradiction.

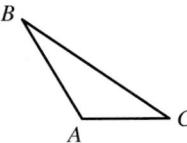

Proof: Assume that △ABC does
contain a rt. ∠. Since there can be at
most one rt. ∠ this contradicts the
given fact that ∠A is obt. Therefore,
the assumption is false. Hence,
△ABC does not contain a rt. ∠.

11.

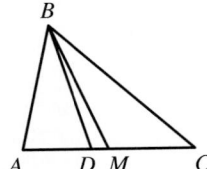

Given: scalene △ABC with alt. BD
and median BM.
Prove: (BD and BM are
not the same seg.)
Plan: Show that the negation of the
concl. leads to a contradiction.
Proof: Assume BD and BM are the
same. Then BD is both the alt. and
median from B to AC (or BM is both
the median and alt. from B to AC)
(Given) Thus BD (or BM) is the ⊥ bis.
of AC (Def. of ⊥ bis.) Then ∠BDA
and ∠BDC (or ∠BMA and ∠BMC)
are rt. ∠s and are ≅. (Def. ⊥ lines)
also, AD ≅ DC (or AM ≅ MC) (Def. of
bis. or median) and BD ≅ BD (or
BM ≅ BM). (Refl. prop.) It follows that
△ABD ≅ △CBD (or △ABM ≅ △CBM)
(SAS Post.) and AB ≅ BC (CPCTC).
But this contradicts the given fact that
△ABC is scalene. Therefore, the
assumption that BD and BM are the
same must be false; hence the alt. to
a side of a scalene △ cannot also be
a median of the △.

12.

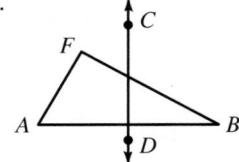

Given: AB with ⊥ bis. CD;
AF ≠ FB

Prove: F does not lie on the
⊥ bisector of AB.
Plan: Show that the negation of the
concl. leads to a contradiction.
Proof: Assume F lies on the ⊥ bis. of
AB. Then by Th. 4.6 AF = FB (If a pt.
lies on the ⊥ bis. of a seg., then the
pt. is equidistant from the endpt. of
the seg.) But this contradicts the
given fact that AF ≠ FB. Therefore,
the assumption that F lies on the ⊥
bis. of AB must be false; hence, F
does not lie on the ⊥ bis. of AB.

13.

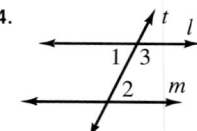

Given: ∠ABC with ∠bis. BD;
EG ≠ FG
Prove: G does not lie on the
∠bis. of ∠ABC.
Plan: Show that the negation of the
concl. leads to a contradiction.
Proof: Assume G does lie on the ∠
bis. of ∠ABC. Then by Th. 4.8 EG =
FG (If a pt. lies on the bis. of an ∠,
then the pt. is equidistant from the
sides of the ∠.) But this contradicts
the given fact that EG ≠ FG.
Therefore, the assumption that G lies
on the ∠ bis. of ∠ABC must be false;
hence, G does not lie on the ∠ bis.
of ∠ABC.

14.

Given: l ∥ m; transversal t
Prove: ∠1 ≅ ∠2
Plan: Show that the negation of the
concl. leads to a contradiction.
Proof: Assume ∠1 ≇ ∠2. ∠1 and ∠3
are supp. by the Linear Pair Post.
However, by subst. (since ∠1 ≇ ∠2),
∠2 and ∠3 are not supp. If ∠2 and
∠3 are not supp., then l ∦ m since, if
they were supp., the lines would be ∥.
But this contradicts the given fact that
l ∥ m. Therefore, the assumption that
∠1 ≇ ∠2 must be false; hence ∠1 ≅
∠2.

15.

$\xleftrightarrow{\hspace{2cm}}$ *l*

$\xleftrightarrow{\hspace{2cm}}$ *m*

$\xleftrightarrow{\hspace{2cm}}$ *n*

Given: *l* ∥ *m*; *n* ∥ *m*
Prove: *l* ∥ *n*
Plan: Show that the negation of the concl. leads to a contradiction.
Proof: Assume *l* ∦ *n*. Then *l* and *n* intersect. Since *l* ∥ *m*, then *n* also intersects *m* and is the transversal of *l* and *m*. If *n* intersects *m*, then *n* ∦ *m*. But this contradicts the given fact that *n* ∥ *m*. Therefore, the assumption that *l* ∦ *n* must be false; hence *l* ∥ *m*.

PAGE 192

21. Plan: Assume the negation of $\overline{CW} \not\cong \overline{PG}$. Show that this leads to a contradiction.
Proof:
Assume:

$\overline{CW} \cong \overline{PG}$	Negation of the conclusion
$\overline{CO} \cong \overline{PI}$; $\overline{OW} \cong \overline{IG}$	Given
$\triangle COW \cong \triangle PIG$	SSS
$\angle O \cong \angle I$	CPCTC

Contradiction: $\angle O \not\cong \angle I$
Conclusion: The assumption leads to a contradiction of the given information that $\angle O \not\cong \angle I$. Therefore, the assumption that $\overline{CW} \cong \overline{PG}$ is false, and so $\overline{CW} \not\cong \overline{PG}$.

22. Plan: Assume the negation of $\angle O \not\cong \angle I$ and show that this leads to a contradiction.
Proof:
Assume:

$\angle O \cong \angle I$	Negation of the conclusion
$\overline{CO} \cong \overline{PI}$; $\overline{OW} \cong \overline{IG}$	Given
$\triangle COW \cong \triangle PIG$	SAS
$\overline{CW} \cong \overline{PG}$	CPCTC

Contradiction: $\overline{CW} \not\cong \overline{PG}$
Conclusion: Since the assumption leads to a contradiction of given information, the assumption $\angle O \cong \angle I$ is false, and so $\angle O \not\cong \angle I$.

PAGE 193

23. Plan: Assume the negation of the conclusion and show that this leads to a contradiction.

Proof:
Assume:

$\overline{AD}$ bisects ∠A.	Negation of the conclusion
$\angle BAD \cong \angle CAD$	Def. of ∠ bis.
$\overline{BA} \cong \overline{CA}$	Given
$\overline{AD} \cong \overline{AD}$	Refl. prop.
$\triangle BAD \cong \triangle CAD$	SAS
$\overline{BD} \cong \overline{CD}$	CPCTC
D is midpt. of $\overline{BC}$	Def. of midpt.
$\overline{AD}$ is a median of $\triangle ABC$.	Def. of △ median

Contradiction: $\overline{AD}$ is *not* a median of $\triangle ABC$.
Conclusion: Since the assumption leads to a contradiction, the assumption is false, and so $\overline{AD}$ does not bisect ∠A.

24. Plan: Assume the negation of the conclusion and show that this leads to a contradiction.
Proof:
Assume:

D is the midpt. of $\overline{BC}$.	Negation of conclusion
$\overline{BD} \cong \overline{CD}$	Def. of midpt.
$\overline{AD} \cong \overline{AD}$	Reflexive prop.
$\overline{BA} \cong \overline{CA}$	Given
$\triangle BAD \cong \triangle CAD$	SSS
$\angle BDA \cong \angle CDA$	CPCTC
$\overline{AD} \perp \overline{BC}$	If lines intersect to form ≅ adj. ∠s, then they are ⊥.
$\overline{AD}$ is an altitude of $\triangle ABC$.	Def. of △ altitude

Contradiction: $\overline{AD}$ is not an altitude of $\triangle ABC$.
Conclusion: Since the assumption leads to a contradiction of given information, it follows that the assumption is false, and so, D is not the midpt. of $\overline{BC}$.

25. Plan: Assume the negation of the conclusion and show that this leads to a contradiction.
Proof:
Assume:

$\overline{BA} \cong \overline{CA}$	Negation of conclusion
$\angle B \cong \angle C$	Isos. △ Th.
$\overline{AD}$ is a median.	Given
$\overline{BD} \cong \overline{CD}$	Def. of median and midpt.

$\triangle BAD \cong \triangle CAD$	SAS
$\angle BAD \cong \angle CAD$	CPCTC

Contradiction: $\angle BAD \not\cong \angle CAD$
Conclusion: Since the assumption leads to a contradiction of given information, the assumption is false. Thus, $\overline{BA} \not\cong \overline{CA}$.

26. Given: $\triangle ABC$ with $\angle B \not\cong \angle C$
Prove: $\overline{AB} \not\cong \overline{AC}$

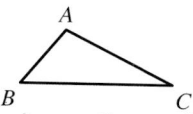

Plan: Assume the negation of the conclusion: $\overline{AB} \cong \overline{AC}$. Show that this leads to a contradiction.
Proof:
Assume:

$\overline{AB} \cong \overline{AC}$	Negation of conclusion
$\angle B \cong \angle C$	Isosceles △ Th.

Contradiction: $\angle B \not\cong \angle C$
Conclusion: Since the assumption $\overline{AB} \cong \overline{AC}$ leads to a contradiction, then $\overline{AB} \cong \overline{AC}$ must be false. Therefore $\overline{AB} \not\cong \overline{AC}$ is true.

27. Given: $a > b$ and $c = d$
Prove: $a - c > b - d$
Plan: Assume the negation of the conclusion: $a - c \not> b - d$. This leads to two alternatives: (1) $a - c < b - d$ and (2) $a - c = b - d$.
Proof:
(1) Assume:

$a - c < b - d$	Negation of conclusion
$a - c + k = b - d\ (k > 0)$	Def. of greater than
$c = d$	Given
$a + k = b$	Add prop
$a < b$	Def. of greater than

Contradiction: $a > b$
(2) Assume:

$a - c = b - d$	Negation of conclusion
$c = d$	Given
$a = b$	Add. prop.

Contradiction: $a > b$
Conclusion: Since both alternative assumptions produce contradictions, the negation of the conclusion is false, and so $a - c > b - d$.

TEST YOURSELF

9. Plan: Since $\angle LFU \cong \angle LUF$ and since $\angle LFT \cong \angle LUT$, it can be shown that $\angle UFT \cong \angle FUT$. Then, by the converse to the isos. $\triangle$ th., $\overline{FT} \cong \overline{UT}$; hence, $\triangle FUT$ is isos.

Proof:

Statements	Reasons
1. Isos. $\triangle LUF$ with base $\overline{UF}$	1. Given
2. $\overline{FL} \cong \overline{UL}$	2. Def. of isos. $\triangle$
3. $\angle LFU \cong \angle LUF$	3. Isos. $\triangle$ Th.
4. $m\angle LFU = m\angle LUF$	4. Def. of $\cong \angle$s
5. $\angle LFT \cong \angle LUT$	5. Given
6. $m\angle LFT = m\angle LUT$	6. Def. of $\cong \angle$s
7. $m\angle LFT = m\angle LFU + m\angle UFT$; $m\angle LUT = m\angle LUF + m\angle FUT$	7. Def. of betweenness
8. $m\angle LFU + m\angle UFT = m\angle LUF + m\angle FUT$	8. Subst. prop.
9. $m\angle UFT = m\angle FUT$	9. Subt. prop.
10. $\angle UFT \cong \angle FUT$	10. Def. of $\cong \angle$s
11. $\overline{FT} \cong \overline{UT}$	11. Converse of isos. $\triangle$ th.
12. $\triangle FUT$ is isos.	12. Def. of isos. $\triangle$

Conclusion: In the given figure, if $\triangle LUF$ is isos. with base $\overline{UF}$ and $\angle LFT \cong \angle LUT$, then $\triangle FUT$ is isos.

10. Given: $\triangle ABC$ with $\overline{AB} \not\cong \overline{BC}$
Prove: $\angle A \not\cong \angle C$

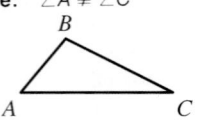

Plan: Assume the negation of the conclusion, $\angle A \cong \angle C$, and show that this leads to a contradiction.

Proof:
Assume:

$\angle A \cong \angle C$	
$\overline{AB} \cong \overline{BC}$	Negation of conclusion If 2 $\angle$s of a $\triangle$ are $\cong$, then the sides opp. those $\angle$s are $\cong$.

Contradiction: $\overline{AB} \not\cong \overline{BC}$
Conclusion: The assumption leads to a contradiction of the given. Therefore, the assumption is false, and so the conclusion $\angle A \not\cong \angle C$ is true.

PAGE 197

15. Proof:

Statements	Reasons
1. $m\angle FEG > m\angle GED$	1. Given
2. $m\angle GED > m\angle EGF$	2. Ext. $\angle$ Th.
3. $m\angle FEG > m\angle EGF$	3. Tran. prop.
4. $FG > EF$	4. If the measures of two $\angle$s of a $\triangle$ are unequal the longer side is opp. the larger $\angle$.

Conclusion: In the given figure, if $m\angle FEG > m\angle GED$, then $FG > EF$.

Page 198

18.

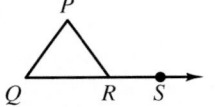

Given: Isos. $\triangle PQR$ with base $\overline{QR}$; QR extended through point S
Prove: $\angle PRS$ is obtuse.

19.

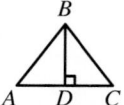

Given: Equilateral $\triangle ABC$ with alt. $\overline{BD}$
Prove: $BD < AC$ (or $BD < AB$ or $BD < BC$)

20.

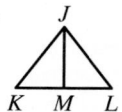

Given: Isos. $\triangle JKL$ with base $\overline{KL}$ and median $\overline{JM}$
Prove: $JK > JM$ (or $JL > JM$)

21. W X Z Y

Given: Square $WXYZ$ with diagonal $\overline{XZ}$
Prove: $XZ > XY$ (or any other side)

22. Plan: Use Theorem 5.6 with the def. of betw. to verify the conclusion.

Proof:

Statements	Reasons
1. $DF > DG$; $FE > EG$	1. Given
2. In $\triangle DGF$, $m\angle DGF > m\angle DFG$; in $\triangle GEF$, $m\angle FGE > m\angle GFE$	2. If the lengths of two sides of a $\triangle$ are unequal, the larger $\angle$ is opp. the longer side.
3. $m\angle DGF + m\angle FGE > m\angle DFG + m\angle GFE$	3. Add. prop. of inequality
4. $m\angle DGF + m\angle FGE = m\angle DGE$; $m\angle DFG + m\angle GFE = m\angle DFE$	4. Def. of betw.
5. $m\angle DGE > m\angle DFE$	5. Subst. prop.

Conclusion: In the given figure, if $DF > DG$ and $FE > EG$, then $m\angle DGE > m\angle DFE$.

23. Plan: Since $\triangle DGF \cong \triangle EGF$, $\angle 4 \cong \angle 1$ and $\angle 3 \cong \angle 2$. Use the given and subst. to verify the conclusion.

Proof:

Statements	Reasons
1. $\triangle DGF \cong \triangle EGF$	1. Given
2. $\angle 4 \cong \angle 1$; $\angle 3 \cong \angle 2$	2. CPCTC
3. $m\angle 4 = m\angle 1$; $m\angle 3 = m\angle 2$	3. Def. $\cong \angle$s
4. $m\angle 4 > m\angle 3$	4. Given
5. $m\angle 1 > m\angle 2$	5. Subst. prop.
6. $DF > DG$	6. If the measures of 2 $\angle$s of a $\triangle$ are unequal, the longer side is opposite the larger $\angle$.

Conclusion: If $\triangle DGF \cong \triangle EGF$ and $m\angle 4 > m\angle 3$, then $DF > DG$.

24. Given: $\triangle ABC$ with a rt. $\angle$ at B
Prove: $AC > AB$; $AC > BC$

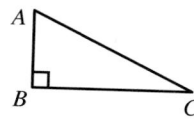

Plan: Use the def. of rt. ∠, and the fact that the ⊥ segment from a point is the shortest distance to a line.

Proof:

Statements	Reasons
1. △ABC with a rt. ∠ at B	1. Given
2. $\overline{AB} \perp \overline{BC}$	2. Def. of rt. ∠
3. $AB < AC$; $BC < AC$	3. The ⊥ segment from a point to a line is the shortest distance from the point to the line.

Conclusion: The hypo. of a rt. △ is the longest side of the △.

25. Plan: To show $XW > XZ$, try to show that $m\angle WZX > m\angle XWY$. Since $m\angle WZX > m\angle Y$ and since $m\angle Y > m\angle XWY$ in rt. △XYW, the tran. prop. verifies the conclusion.

Proof:

Statements	Reasons
1. Rt. △XYZ with $\overline{YZ}$ extended to W	1. Given
2. $m\angle WZX > m\angle Y$	2. Ext. ∠ The.
3. In right △XYZ, $m\angle Y > m\angle XWY$	3. A △ has at most one rt. ∠ (the other ∠s are acute).
4. $m\angle WZX > m\angle XWY$	4. Trans. prop. of inequality
5. $XW > XZ$	5. If the measures of 2 angles of a △ are unequal, the longer side is opp. the larger ∠.

Conclusion: In rt. △XYZ having $\overrightarrow{YZ}$ extended to W, $XW > XZ$.

26. Plan: Use auxiliary segment $\overline{KJ_1}$ to form rt. △s KPJ and KPJ₁. These △s are ≅ by LL. Since $m\angle J = m\angle KJ_1J$ and $m\angle KJ_1J > m\angle L$, subst. verifies the conclusion.

Proof:

Statements	Reasons
1. △JKL with alt. $\overline{KP}$; $LP > PJ$	1. Given
2. On $\overline{PL}$, locate J_1 such that $\overline{PJ} \cong \overline{PJ_1}$	2. On a ray there is exactly 1 pt. a given dist. from the endpt.
3. $\overline{KP} \perp \overline{JL}$	3. Def. of alt.
4. ∠KPJ and ∠KPJ₁ are rt. ∠s.	4. Def. of ⊥ lines
5. △KPJ and △KPJ₁ are rt ∠s.	5. Def. of rt. ∠s.
6. $\overline{KP} \cong \overline{KP}$	6. Refl. prop.
7. △KPJ ≅ △KPJ₁	7. LL
8. $\angle J \cong \angle KJ_1J$	8. CPCTC
9. $m\angle J = m\angle KJ_1J$	9. Def. of ≅ ∠s.
10. $m\angle KJ_1J > m\angle L$	10. Ext. ∠ Th.
11. $m\angle J > m\angle L$	11. Subst. prop.
12. $KL > KJ$	12. Th. 5.7

Conclusion: If an altitude divides a side of a △ into 2 segments of unequal length, then the longer of the two remaining sides is the greater distance from the foot of the altitude.

PAGE 202

14. Plan: Use the △ inequality on △s PQR, RST, and TUP to verify the conclusion.

Proof:

Statements	Reasons
1. Hexagon PQRSTU with vertices P, R, T joined to form △PRT.	1. Given
2. $PR < PQ + QR$; $RT < RS + ST$; $TP < TU + UP$	2. Triangle Inequality
3. $PR + RT + TP < PQ + QR + RS + ST + TU + UP$	3. Add. prop. of inequality
4. Perimeter (△PRT) < Perimeter (PQRSTU)	4. Def. of perimeter

Conclusion: If the vertices P, R, T of hexagon PQRSTU are joined to form △PRT, the perimeter of △PRT is less than the perimeter of the hexagon.

15. Proof:

Statements	Reasons
1. Extend $\overrightarrow{CB}$ through D such that $DB = AB$.	1. On a ray there is exactly one point that is a given distance from the endpoint of the ray.
2. $\overline{DB} \cong \overline{AB}$	2. Def. of ≅ segments
3. Draw $\overline{DA}$	3. Two points determine a line.
4. $\angle 1 \cong \angle 2$	4. Isos. △ Th.
5. $m\angle 1 = m\angle 2$	5. Def. of ≅ ∠s.
6. $DB + BC = DC$	6. Def. of betw.
7. $AB + BC = DC$	7. Subst. prop.
8. $m\angle DAC > m\angle 2$	8. Whole is > any of parts.
9. $m\angle DAC > m\angle 1$	9. Subst. prop.
10. $DC > AC$	10. If the measures of two ∠s of a △ are unequal, the longer side is opp. the larger ∠.
11. $AB + BC > AC$	11. Subst. prop.

Conclusion: In △ABC, $AB + BC > AC$

16. Extend $\overrightarrow{BC}$ through C to point E such that $CE = AC$. Draw $\overline{EA}$. Then $\angle CAE \cong \angle CEA$. Since C is between B and E, $BC + EC = BE$. $AC = EC$, so $AC + BC = BE$. Also, $m\angle EAB > m\angle EAC$ and $m\angle EAB > m\angle AEC$, so $BE > AB$ and $AC + BC > AB$.

17. Given: △ABC
Prove: $AB + AC > BC$

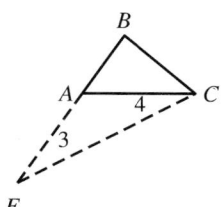

Plan: Extend $\overrightarrow{BA}$ through A to F, such that $\overline{AF} \cong \overline{AC}$. Draw $\overline{FC}$. Then $\angle 3 \cong \angle 4$. Since A is between B and F, $BA + AF = BF$. Since $AF = AC$, it follows that $AB + AC = BF$. Since it can be shown that $m\angle BCF > m\angle 4$, $m\angle BCF > m\angle 3$. Thus $BF > BC$, and it follows that $AB + AC > BC$.

Proof:

Statements	Reasons
1. $\triangle ABC$.	1. Given
2. Extend $\overrightarrow{BA}$ through A to F, such that $\overline{AF} \cong \overline{AC}$.	2. There is exactly 1 point on a ray at a given distance from the endpoint.
3. $AF = AC$	3. Def. $\cong$ seg.
4. Draw $\overline{FC}$.	4. Two pts. determine a unique segment.
5. $\angle 3 \cong \angle 4$	5. Isos. $\triangle$ Th.
6. $m\angle 3 = m\angle 4$	6. Def. $\cong \angle s$
7. $AB + AF = BF$	7. Def. of betw.
8. $AB + AC = BF$	8. Subst. prop.
9. $m\angle BCF > m\angle 4$	9. Whole > any of its parts
10. $m\angle BCF > m\angle 3$	10. Subst. prop.
11. $BF > BC$	11. If the measures of two $\angle s$ of a $\triangle$ are unequal, the longer side is opp. the larger $\angle$.
12. $AB + AC > BC$	12. Subst. prop.

Conclusion: In $\triangle ABC$, $AB + AC > BC$.

18. Given: $\triangle ABC$
Prove: $AB - BC < AC$

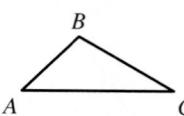

Plan: Since $AC + BC > AB$, or $AB < AC + BC$, the subt. prop. verifies the conclusion.

Proof:

Statements	Reasons
1. $\triangle ABC$	1. Given
2. $AC + BC > AB$ or $AB < AC + BC$	2. $\triangle$ Inequality Th.
3. $AB - BC < AC$	3. Subtr. prop. of inequality

Conclusion: The difference between the lengths of any two sides of a $\triangle$ is less than the length of the third side.

19. Plan: Use the converse of the Hinge Theorem.

Proof:

Statements	Reasons
1. $\triangle QRT$; median $\overline{QS}$.	1. Given
2. S is the midpt. of $\overline{RT}$.	2. Def. of median
3. $\overline{RS} \cong \overline{ST}$	3. Def. of midpt.
4. $\overline{SQ} \cong \overline{SQ}$	4. Refl. prop. of $\cong$
5. $TQ > RQ$	5. Given
6. $m\angle TSQ > m\angle RSQ$	6. Converse of Hinge Theorem

Conclusion: In the figure, if $\overline{QS}$ is a median of $\triangle QRT$ and $TQ > RQ$, then $m\angle TSQ > m\angle RSQ$.

PAGE 203

20. Proof:

Statements	Reasons
1. In $\triangle ABC$, $\triangle DEF$, $\overline{AB} \cong \overline{DE}$, $\overline{BC} \cong \overline{EF}$, $m\angle ABC > m\angle DEF$	1. Given
2. Draw $\overrightarrow{BR}$ such that $\angle ABR \cong \angle DEF$.	2. Through endpt. of ray there is exactly 1 ray such that the $\angle$ formed by the 2 rays has a given meas.
3. Select pt R on $\overrightarrow{BR}$ such that $\overline{BR} \cong \overline{EF}$	3. On a ray there is exactly 1 pt. at a given dist. from endpt.
4. Draw $\overline{AR}$.	4. Two points determine exactly 1 line segment.
5. $\triangle ABR \cong \triangle DEF$	5. SAS
6. $\overline{AR} \cong \overline{DF}$	6. CPCTC
7. $\overline{BC} \cong \overline{BR}$	7. Subst. prop.
8. Draw $\overrightarrow{BQ}$ bisecting $\angle RBC$.	8. An $\angle$ has a unique bisector.
9. $\angle RBQ \cong \angle CBQ$	9. Def. of bis.
10. $\overline{BQ} \cong \overline{BQ}$	10. Refl. prop.
11. $\triangle BQR \cong \triangle BQC$	11. SAS
12. $\overline{QR} \cong \overline{QC}$	12. CPCTC
13. $QR = QC$	13. Def. of $\cong$ seg.
14. In $\triangle AQR$, $AQ + QR > AR$	14. $\triangle$ inequality
15. $AQ + QC > AR$	15. Subst. prop.
16. $AQ + QC = AC$	16. Def. of betw.
17. $AC > AR$	17. Subst. prop.

Conclusion: If $\triangle ABC$ and DEF have $\overline{AB} \cong \overline{DE}$, $\overline{BC} \cong \overline{EF}$, and $m\angle ABC > m\angle DEF$, then $AC > DF$.

21. Given: Scalene $\triangle JKL$ with $\overline{KM}$ bisecting $\angle K$ and altitude $\overline{KA}$
Prove: $KM > KA$

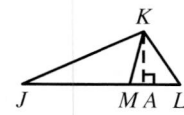

Plan: Since $\overline{KM}$ and $\overline{KA}$ are distinct, consider right $\triangle KAM$. $KM > KA$ since the hyp. is the longest side.

Proof:

Statements	Reasons
1. Scalene $\triangle JKL$ with $\angle$ bis. $\overline{KM}$ and alt. $\overline{KA}$	1. Given
2. $\overline{KA} \perp \overline{JL}$	2. Def. of altitude
3. $\angle KAM$ is a rt. $\angle$.	3. Def. of $\perp$ lines
4. $\triangle KAM$ is a rt. $\triangle$.	4. Def. of rt. $\triangle$.
5. $KM > KA$	5. The hyp. of a rt. $\triangle$ is the longest side.

Conclusion: In a scalene $\triangle$, the lengths of the angle bisector of any angle of the $\triangle$ is greater than the length of the altitude from that vertex.

PAGE 209

7. Plan: Since $AC > AB$, $m\angle ABC > m\angle ACB$. Since $\angle DCA$ is ext. to the $\triangle$, $m\angle DCA > m\angle ABC$. The trans. prop. verifies the conclusion.

Proof:

Statements	Reasons
1. △ABC with $\overrightarrow{BC}$ extended through D	1. Given
2. AC > AB	2. Given
3. m∠ABC > m∠ACB	3. If the lengths of two sides of a △ are unequal, the larger ∠ is opposite the longer side.
4. m∠DCA > m∠ABC	4. Ext. ∠ The.
5. m∠DCA > m∠ACB	5. Trans. prop. of inequality

Conclusion: In the given figure, if AC > AB, then m∠DCA > m∠ACB.

PAGE 213

15. Plan: Assume the negation of the conclusion; i.e. $\overline{DG} \perp \overline{EF}$. Then reason to a contradiction.

Proof:
Assume:

$\overline{DG} \perp \overline{EF}$	Negation of conclusion
∠DGE and ∠DGF are rt ∠s.	Def. of ⊥ lines
△DGE and △DGF are rt △.	Def. of rt △
△DEF is isos.	Given
$\overline{DE} \cong \overline{DF}$	Def. of isos. △
∠E ≅ ∠F	Isos. △ Th.
△DGE ≅ △DGF	HA
∠EDG ≅ ∠FDG	CPCTC
$\overline{DG}$ bisects ∠EDF.	Def. of ∠ bis.

Contradiction: $\overline{DG}$ does not bisect ∠EDF.

Conclusion: Since the assumption leads to a contradiction, $\overline{DG}$ must not be ⊥ to $\overline{EF}$.

PAGE 214

8. Plan: In right △QAB, QA < QB. Show QB < QM. This would be true if m∠MBQ > m∠QMB. Since m∠MBQ > m∠QAM and since, in △QAM, m∠QAM > m∠QMB, the trans. prop. verifies the conclusion.

Proof:

Statements	Reasons
1. △PQR with alt. $\overline{QA}$, angle bis. $\overline{QB}$, and median $\overline{QM}$, with B betw. A and M	1. Given
2. $\overline{QA} \perp \overline{PR}$	2. Def. of alt.
3. ∠QAB is a right ∠.	3. Def. of ⊥ lines
4. △QAB is a right △.	4. Def. of rt. △
5. QA < QB	5. The hyp. is the longest side in a right △.
6. m∠MBQ > m∠QAM	6. Ext. ∠ Th.
7. In right △QAM, m∠QAM > m∠QMB	7. A △ has at most one rt. ∠.
8. m∠MBQ > m∠QMB	8. Trans. prop. of inequality
9. QB < QM	9. If the measures of two ∠s of a △ are unequal, the longer side is opp. the larger ∠.

Conclusion: If a △ has distinct alt., ∠ bis. and median drawn from the same vertex with the foot of the ∠ bis. lying between the alt. and the median, then the lengths of these segments, in increasing order, are alt., ∠ bis., median.

Challenge:
Proof:

Statements	Reasons
1. Isos. △ABC with $\overline{AB} \cong \overline{AC}$	1. Given
2. Extend $\overrightarrow{AB}$ to D and $\overrightarrow{AC}$ to E such that $\overline{BD} \cong \overline{CE}$	2. There is exactly 1 pt. on a ray at a given distance from the endpt.
3. AB = AC; BD = CE	3. Def. of ≅ segments
4. AB + BD = AC + CE	4. Add. prop. of equality
5. AB + BD = AD; AC + CE = AE	5. Def. of betw.
6. AD = AE	6. Subst.
7. $\overline{AD} \cong \overline{AE}$	7. Def. of ≅ segments

Statements	Reasons
8. ∠A ≅ ∠A	8. Refl. prop. of ≅
9. △ACD ≅ △ABE	9. SAS
10. $\overline{CD} \cong \overline{BE}$	10. CPCTC
11. $\overline{CB} \cong \overline{BC}$	11. Refl. prop. of ≅
12. △CBD ≅ △BCE	12. SSS
13. ∠CBD ≅ ∠BCE	13. CPCTC
14. ∠CBD and ∠ABC are a linear pair; ∠BCE and ∠ACB are a linear pair	14. Def. of linear pair
15. ∠CBD and ∠ABC are supplementary; ∠BCE and ∠ACB are supplementary	15. Linear Pair Postulate
16. ∠ABC ≅ ∠ACB	16. Suppl. of ≅ ∠s are ≅.

Conclusion: Base angles of an isos. △ are ≅.

PAGE 221

22. x + 40 = 3x − 12
x = 26
m∠X = 114
m∠Y = 66
m∠Z = 114
m∠W = 66

23. 6y − 2 = 12 − y
y = 2
QS = 20

PAGE 222

27. m∠1 = m∠2 = m∠8 = m∠10 = 105
m∠3 = m∠4 = m∠6 = m∠7 = m∠9 = m∠11 = 75
∠m∠5 = 30
m∠12 = 15

28. Plan: Use the given and the properties of a ▱ to get △XWN ≅ △ZYM. Then $\overline{XN} \cong \overline{ZM}$ by CPCTC.

Proof:

Statements	Reasons
1. ▱XYZW; M is the midpt. of $\overline{XY}$; N is the midpt. of $\overline{WZ}$.	1. Given
2. $\overline{XY} \cong \overline{WZ}$; $\overline{XW} \cong \overline{ZY}$	2. Opp. sides of a ▱ are ≅.
3. $XY = WZ$	3. Def. of ≅ segs.
4. $\frac{1}{2}XY = \frac{1}{2}WZ$	4. Mult. prop.
5. $YM = \frac{1}{2}XY$, $WN = \frac{1}{2}WZ$	5. Midpt. Th.
6. $WN = YM$	6. Subst. prop.
7. $\overline{WN} \cong \overline{YM}$	7. Def. of ≅ seg.
8. $\angle W \cong \angle Y$	8. Opp. ∠s of a ▱ are ≅.
9. △XWN ≅ △ZYM	9. SAS
10. $\overline{XN} \cong \overline{ZM}$	10. CPCTC

Conclusion: Segments that join a pair of opp. ∠s to the midpts. of the opp. sides of a ▱ are ≅.

29. Plan: Show △XWN ≅ △ZYM as in Ex. 23. Then, ∠XNW ≅ ∠ZMY. Since $\overline{XY} \parallel \overline{WZ}$, ∠ZMY ≅ ∠MZN. Use the transitive prop. to get ∠XNW ≅ ∠MZN; the concl. follows because they are corr. ∠s.

Proof:

Statements	Reasons
1. ▱XYZW with M the midpt. of $\overline{XY}$ and N the midpt. of $\overline{WZ}$	1. Given
2. △XWN ≅ △ZYM	2. SAS; See Ex. 23.
3. ∠XNW ≅ ∠ZMY	3. CPCTC
4. $\overline{XY} \parallel \overline{WZ}$	4. Def. of ▱
5. ∠ZMY ≅ ∠MZN	5. If ∥ lines have a transversal, alt. int. ∠s are ≅.
6. ∠XNW ≅ ∠MZN	6. Transitive prop.
7. $\overline{XN} \parallel \overline{MZ}$	7. If corr. ∠s are ≅, then lines are ∥.

Conclusion: In the given figure, if M is the midpt. of $\overline{XY}$ and N is the midpt. of $\overline{WZ}$, then $\overline{XN} \parallel \overline{MZ}$.

30. Given: $\overleftrightarrow{AB} \parallel \overleftrightarrow{CD}$
Prove: $PQ = RS$

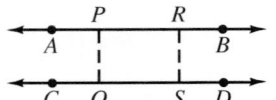

Plan: The distance between $\overleftrightarrow{AB}$ and $\overleftrightarrow{CD}$ is the length of the ⊥ segments that join them. Thus, $\overline{PQ}$ and $\overline{RS}$ are each ⊥ to $\overleftrightarrow{AB}$ and are therefore ∥. Then, PRSQ is a ▱, and the concl. follows.

Proof:

Statements	Reasons
1. $\overleftrightarrow{AB} \parallel \overleftrightarrow{CD}$; points P and R are on $\overleftrightarrow{AB}$.	1. Given
2. $\overline{PQ} \perp \overleftrightarrow{CD}$; $\overline{RS} \perp \overleftrightarrow{CD}$	2. Def. of distance between a point and a line
3. $\overline{PQ} \parallel \overline{RS}$	3. Two lines ⊥ to the same line are ∥.
4. PRSQ is a ▱.	4. Def. of ▱
5. $\overline{PQ} \cong \overline{RS}$	5. Opposite sides of a ▱ are ≅.
6. $PQ = RS$	6. Def. of ≅ segments

Conclusion: If two lines are ∥, then all points on one line are equidistant from the other line.

31. Proof:

Statements	Reasons
1. ▱OSER	1. Given
2. $\overline{RO} \parallel \overline{ES}$	2. Def. of ▱
3. ∠R and ∠E are int. ∠s on the same side of transversal $\overline{RE}$.	3. Def. of int. ∠s
4. ∠R and ∠E are supplementary.	4. If two ∥ lines have a transv., then int. ∠s on the same side of the transv. are supp.

Conclusion: Consec. ∠s in a ▱ are supplementary.

32. Proof:

Statements	Reasons
1. ▱PQRS with diagonals $\overline{PR}$ and $\overline{QS}$ intersecting in point X	1. Given

Statements	Reasons
2. $\overline{QR} \parallel \overline{SP}$	2. Def. of ▱
3. ∠1 ≅ ∠2; ∠3 ≅ ∠4	3. When ∥ lines have a transv., alt. int. ∠s are ≅.
4. $\overline{QR} \cong \overline{SP}$	4. Opp. sides of a ▱ are ≅.
5. △QRX ≅ △SPX	5. ASA
6. $\overline{RX} \cong \overline{PX}$ and $\overline{QX} \cong \overline{SX}$	6. CPCTC

Conclusion: In any ▱, the diagonals bisect each other.

33. Given: ▱ABCD
Prove: ∠B ≅ ∠D and ∠A ≅ ∠C

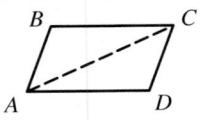

Plan: Since a diagonal of a ▱ separates the ▱ into two ≅ △, the conclusion follows immediately. (This is a proof that ∠B ≅ ∠D. Use diagonal $\overline{BD}$ and the same argument to show ∠A ≅ ∠C.)

Proof:

Statements	Reasons
1. ▱ABCD	1. Given
2. Draw diagonal $\overline{AC}$.	2. Two points determine a line.
3. △ABC ≅ △CDA	3. The diagonal of a ▱ separates it into 2 ≅ △.
4. ∠B ≅ ∠D	4. CPCTC

Conclusion: Opp. ∠s of a ▱ are ≅.

34. Given: ▱ABCD with diagonal $\overline{BD}$; E is the midpoint of $\overline{BC}$; F is the midpoint of $\overline{AD}$
Prove: G is the midpoint of $\overline{BD}$

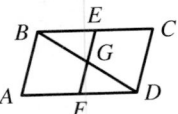

Plan: Show △BEG ≅ △DFG by AAS. Then $\overline{EG} \cong \overline{FG}$ by CPCTC, and the conclusion follows.

Proof:

Statements	Reasons
1. ▱ABCD with diagonal $\overline{BD}$; E	1. Given

is the midpt. of $\overline{BC}$; F is the midpt. of $\overline{DA}$.

Statements	Reasons
2. $\overline{BC} \cong \overline{DA}$	2. Opp. sides of $\square$ are $\cong$.
3. $BC = DA$	3. Def. of $\cong$ segments
4. $\frac{1}{2}BC = \frac{1}{2}DA$	4. Mult. prop.
5. $BE = \frac{1}{2}BC$; $DF = \frac{1}{2}DA$	5. Midpt. Th.
6. $BE = DF$	6. Subst. prop.
7. $\overline{BE} \cong \overline{DF}$	7. Def. of $\cong$ segments
8. $\overline{BC} \parallel \overline{DA}$	8. Def. of $\square$
9. $\angle EBG \cong \angle FDG$	9. If $\parallel$ lines have a transv., alt. int. $\angle$s are $\cong$.
10. $\angle BGE \cong \angle DGF$	10. Vert. $\angle$s are $\cong$
11. $\triangle BEG \cong \triangle DFG$	11. AAS
12. $\overline{BG} \cong \overline{DG}$	12. CPCTC
13. G is the midpt. of $\overline{BD}$.	13. Def. of midpt.

Conclusion: The line joining the midpoints of two opp. sides of a $\square$ bisects either diagonal of the $\square$.

35. Given: $\square TOYS$; $\overline{TP}$ bisects $\angle T$; $\overline{OR}$ bisects $\angle O$.

Prove: $\overline{TP} \perp \overline{OR}$

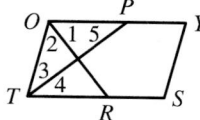

Plan: Use the given and the fact that $\angle 5$ and $\angle 4$ are alt. int. $\angle$s to get $\angle 5 \cong \angle 3$. Thus, $\triangle TOP$ is isosceles with $\overline{TO} \cong \overline{PO}$, and it follows that O is equidistant from points T and P. So, $\overline{OR}$ is the $\perp$ bisector of $\overline{TP}$.

Proof:

Statements	Reasons
1. $\square TOYS$; $\overline{TP}$ bisects $\angle T$; $\overline{OR}$ bisects $\angle O$.	1. Given
2. $\angle 3 \cong \angle 4$; $\angle 1 \cong \angle 2$	2. Def. of $\angle$ bisector
3. $\overline{OY} \parallel \overline{TS}$	3. Def. of $\square$

Statements	Reasons
4. $\angle 5 \cong \angle 4$	4. When $\parallel$ lines have a transv., alt. int. $\angle$s are $\cong$.
5. $\angle 3 \cong \angle 5$	5. Subst. prop.
6. $\overline{TO} \cong \overline{PO}$	6. Converse of Isos. $\triangle$ Th.
7. $TO = PO$	7. Def. of $\cong$ segments
8. O is equidistant from T and P.	8. Def. of equidistant
9. $\overline{OR}$ is the $\perp$ bisector of $\overline{TP}$.	9. If a point is equidistant from the endpoints of a segment, it lies on the $\perp$ bisector of the segment.
10. $\overline{TP} \perp \overline{OR}$	10. Def. of $\perp$ bisector

Conclusion: The bisectors of consecutive $\angle$s of a $\square$ are $\perp$.

36. Given: $\square PAGE$; $\overline{PM}$ bisects $\angle P$; $\overline{GN}$ bisects $\angle G$.

Prove: $\overline{PM} \parallel \overline{GN}$

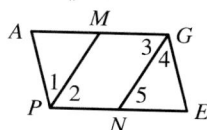

Plan: Use the given and the $\angle$ Bisector Th. to get $\angle 1 \cong \angle 3$. Since $\angle 3$ and $\angle 5$ are alt. int. $\angle$s, they are $\cong$. Use the subst. prop. to get $\angle 2 \cong \angle 5$. The conclusion follows.

Proof:

Statements	Reasons
1. $\square PAGE$; $\overline{PM}$ bisects $\angle P$; $\overline{GN}$ bisects $\angle G$.	1. Given
2. $\angle 1 \cong \angle 2$; $\angle 3 \cong \angle 4$	2. Def. of $\angle$ bisector
3. $\angle P \cong \angle G$	3. Opp. $\angle$s of a $\square$ are $\cong$.
4. $m\angle P = m\angle G$	4. Def. of $\cong \angle$s
5. $\frac{1}{2}m\angle P = \frac{1}{2}m\angle G$	5. Mult. prop.
6. $m\angle 1 = \frac{1}{2}m\angle P$; $m\angle 3 = \frac{1}{2}m\angle G$	6. $\angle$ Bisector Th.

Statements	Reasons
7. $m\angle 1 = m\angle 3$	7. Subst. prop.
8. $\angle 1 \cong \angle 3$	8. Def. of $\cong \angle$s
9. $\angle 2 \cong \angle 3$	9. Subst. prop.
10. $\overline{AG} \parallel \overline{PE}$	10. Def. of $\square$
11. $\angle 3 \cong \angle 5$	11. If $\parallel$ lines have a transv., then alt. int. $\angle$s are $\cong$.
12. $\angle 2 \cong \angle 5$	12. Trans. prop.
13. $\overline{PM} \parallel \overline{GN}$	13. If corr. $\angle$s are $\cong$, then lines are $\parallel$.

Conclusion: If the bisectors of opp. $\angle$s of a $\square$ do not coincide, the bisectors are $\parallel$.

PAGE 226

17. Proof:

Statements	Reasons
1. Quad. $OKRA$, with $\overline{KR} \parallel \overline{AO}$ and $\overline{KR} \cong \overline{AO}$	1. Given
2. Draw diagonal $\overline{OR}$.	2. Two points determine a line.
3. $\angle 1 \cong \angle 3$	3. If $\parallel$ lines have a transv., alt. int. $\angle$s are $\cong$.
4. $\overline{RO} \cong \overline{OR}$	4. Reflexive prop.
5. $\triangle KRO \cong \triangle AOR$	5. SAS
6. $\angle 4 \cong \angle 2$	6. CPCTC
7. $\overline{OK} \parallel \overline{RA}$	7. If two lines have a transv. and a pair of $\cong$ alt. int. $\angle$s, the lines are $\parallel$.
8. $OKRA$ is a $\square$.	8. Def. of $\square$

Conclusion: If a pair of opp. sides of a quad. is both $\cong$ and $\parallel$, the quad. is a $\square$.

18. Plan: Since $\square MNRP$ and $\square MOSP$ share a common side, use the properties of $\square$ to show that $\overline{NR}$ is $\parallel$ and $\cong$ to $\overline{OS}$. The concl. follows.

Proof:

Statements	Reasons
1. Parallelograms $MNRP$ and $MOSP$	1. Given
2. $\overline{MP} \parallel \overline{NR}$; $\overline{MP} \parallel \overline{OS}$	2. Def. of $\square$

Statements	Reasons
3. $\overline{NR} \parallel \overline{OS}$	3. 2 lines $\parallel$ to the same line are $\parallel$.
4. $\overline{MP} \cong \overline{NR}$; $\overline{MP} \cong \overline{OS}$	4. Opp. sides of a $\square$ are $\cong$.
5. $\overline{NR} \cong \overline{OS}$	5. Subst. prop.
6. $NOSR$ is a $\square$.	6. If a quad. has a pair of opp. sides $\cong$ and $\parallel$, the quad. is a $\square$.

Conclusion: In the figure, if $MNRP$ and $MOSP$ are $\square$s, then $NOSR$ is a $\square$.

19. Plan: Since $\angle WST \cong \angle SZY$, it follows that $\overline{ST} \parallel \overline{WX}$. Since $WXYZ$ is a $\square$, $\overline{WS} \parallel \overline{XT}$. The concl. follows from the def. of a $\square$.

Proof:

Statements	Reasons
1. $\square WXYZ$; $\angle WST \cong \angle SZY$	1. Given
2. $\overline{ST} \parallel \overline{ZY}$	2. If two lines have a trans. with corr. $\angle$s $\cong$, the lines are $\parallel$.
3. $\overline{ZY} \parallel \overline{WX}$	3. Def. of $\square$
4. $\overline{ST} \parallel \overline{WX}$	4. 2 lines $\parallel$ to the same line are $\parallel$.
5. $\overline{WZ} \parallel \overline{XY}$; hence, $\overline{WS} \parallel \overline{XT}$	5. Def. of $\square$ ($\square WXYZ$)
6. $XTSW$ is a $\square$.	6. Def. of $\square$

Conclusion: In $\square WXYZ$, if $\angle WST \cong \angle SZY$, then $XTSW$ is a $\square$.

20. Plan: Use the given to show that $RSPQ$ is a quadrilateral having a pair of opp. sides ($\overline{RQ}$ and $\overline{SP}$) $\cong$ and $\parallel$.

Proof:

Statements	Reasons
1. $\square MNPQ$; R is the midpt. of $\overline{MQ}$; S is the midpt. of $\overline{NP}$.	1. Given
2. $\overline{MQ} \parallel \overline{NP}$; hence $\overline{RQ} \parallel \overline{SP}$	2. Def. of $\square$ ($\square MNPQ$)
3. $\overline{MQ} \cong \overline{NP}$	3. Opp. sides of a $\square$ are $\cong$.
4. $MQ = NP$	4. Def. of $\cong$ segments
5. $\frac{1}{2}MQ = \frac{1}{2}NP$	5. Mult. prop.
6. $RQ = \frac{1}{2}MQ$;	6. Midpt. Th.
$SP = \frac{1}{2}NP$	
7. $RQ = SP$	7. Subst. prop.
8. $\overline{RQ} \cong \overline{SP}$	8. Def. of $\cong$ segments
9. $RSPQ$ is a $\square$.	9. If a quad. has a pair of opp. sides $\cong$ and $\parallel$, the quad. is a $\square$.

Conclusion: In $\square MNPQ$, if R is the midpoint of $\overline{MQ}$ and S is the midpoint of $\overline{NP}$, then $RSPQ$ is a $\square$.

21. Plan: Since $\overline{JT}$ and $\overline{ES}$ are $\perp$ to the same line, $\overline{JT} \parallel \overline{ES}$. Show that $\overline{JT}$ and $\overline{ES}$ are corr. parts of $\cong$ $\triangle$. The concl. follows because $\overline{JT}$ and $\overline{ES}$ are opp. sides of a quadrilateral.

Proof:

Statements	Reasons
1. $YEOJ$ is a $\square$; $\overline{JT} \perp \overline{YO}$; $\overline{ES} \perp \overline{YO}$.	1. Given
2. $\overline{JT} \parallel \overline{ES}$	2. Lines $\perp$ to the same line are $\parallel$.
3. $\angle JTY$ and $\angle ESO$ are rt. $\angle$s.	3. Def. of $\perp$ lines
4. $\triangle JTY$ and $\triangle ESO$ are rt. $\triangle$.	4. Def. of rt. $\triangle$
5. $\overline{JY} \cong \overline{EO}$	5. Opp. sides of a $\square$ are $\cong$.
6. $\angle JYT \cong \angle EOS$	6. If $\parallel$ lines have a transv., alt. int. $\angle$s are $\cong$.
7. $\triangle JYT \cong \triangle EOS$	7. HA
8. $\overline{JT} \cong \overline{ES}$	8. CPCTC
9. $JSET$ is a $\square$.	9. If a pair of opp. sides of a quad. are $\parallel$ and $\cong$, the quad. is a $\square$.

Conclusion: If $\square YEOJ$ has diagonal $\overline{OY}$ and $\overline{JT} \perp \overline{YO}$ and $\overline{ES} \perp \overline{YO}$, then $JSET$ is a $\square$.

PAGE 227

22. Plan: Since $\angle MEO \cong \angle MFN$, $\overline{JO} \parallel \overline{NH}$. Use the given and vert. $\angle$s to show $\triangle JEM \cong \triangle HFM$. Thus, $\overline{JE} \cong \overline{HF}$, from which it can be shown that $\overline{JO} \cong \overline{NH}$.

Proof:

Statements	Reasons
1. $\overline{JE} \cong \overline{EO}$; $\overline{NF} \cong$	1. Given
$\overline{FH}$; $\overline{JM} \cong \overline{HM}$; $\angle MEO \cong \angle MFN$	
2. $\overline{JO} \parallel \overline{NH}$	2. If lines have a transv. and alt. int. $\angle$s $\cong$, then the lines are $\parallel$.
3. $\angle JEM \cong \angle HFM$	3. If $\parallel$ lines have a transv., alt. int. $\angle$s are $\cong$.
4. $\angle JME \cong \angle HMF$	4. Vert. $\angle$s are $\cong$.
5. $\triangle JEM \cong \triangle HFM$	5. AAS
6. $\overline{JE} \cong \overline{HF}$	6. CPCTC
7. $JE = HF$	7. Def. of $\cong$ segments
8. E is the midpoint of $\overline{JO}$; F is the midpoint of $\overline{HN}$.	8. Def. of midpt.
9. $JO = 2 \cdot JE$; $HN = 2 \cdot HF$	9. Midpt. Th.
10. $JO = 2 \cdot HF$	10. Subst. prop.
11. $JO = HN$	11. Subst. prop.
12. $\overline{JO} \cong \overline{HN}$	12. Def. of $\cong$ segments
13. $JNHO$ is a $\square$.	13. If a quad. has a pair of opp. sides $\cong$ and $\parallel$, the quad. is a $\square$.

Conclusion: In the given figure, if $\overline{JE} \cong \overline{EO}$, $\overline{NF} \cong \overline{FH}$, $\overline{JM} \cong \overline{HM}$, and $\angle MEO \cong \angle MFN$, then $JNHO$ is a $\square$.

23. Plan: Show $\triangle ADE \cong \triangle CBF$ by ASA. Then $\overline{DE} \cong \overline{BF}$ and $\angle AED \cong \angle CFB$ by CPCTC. Since $\angle CFB \cong \angle FBE$, $\angle AED \cong \angle FBE$. Hence $\overline{DE} \parallel \overline{BF}$ and the concl. follows.

Proof:

Statements	Reasons
1. $\square ABCD$ with $\angle ADE \cong \angle CBF$	1. Given
2. $\angle A \cong \angle C$	2. Opp. $\angle$s of a $\square$ are $\cong$.
3. $\overline{AD} \cong \overline{CB}$	3. Opp. sides of a $\square$ are $\cong$.
4. $\triangle ADE \cong \triangle CBF$	4. ASA

5. $\overline{DE} \cong \overline{BF}$; $\angle AED \cong \angle CFB$ | 5. CPCTC

6. $\overline{AB} \parallel \overline{CD}$ | 6. Def. of ▱

7. $\angle CFB \cong \angle FBE$ | 7. If ∥ lines have a transv., alt. int. ∠s are ≅.

8. $\angle AED \cong \angle FBE$ | 8. Trans. prop.

9. $\overline{DE} \parallel \overline{BF}$ | 9. If 2 lines have a transv. and corr. ∠s ≅, the lines are ∥.

10. *DEBF* is a ▱. | 10. If a quad. has a pair of opp. sides ≅ and ∥, the quad. is a ▱.

Conclusion: In the figure, if *ABCD* is a ▱ with $\angle ADE \cong \angle CBF$, then *DEBF* is a ▱.

24. Given: Quad. *HARP* with $\angle H \cong \angle R$ and $\angle A \cong \angle P$
Prove: *HARP* is a ▱.

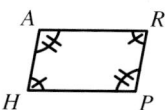

Plan: Use the given and the fact that the sum of the measures of the ∠s of a quad. = 360 to show that ∠H and ∠A are supp. and that ∠A and ∠R are supp. The concl. follows.

Proof:

Statements	Reasons
1. Quad. *HARP* with $\angle H \cong \angle R$ and $\angle A \cong \angle P$	1. Given
2. $m\angle H = m\angle R$; $m\angle A = m\angle P$	2. Def. of ≅ ∠s
3. $m\angle H + m\angle A + m\angle R + m\angle P = 360$	3. Sum of the measures of the ∠s of a quad. is 360.
4. $2 \cdot m\angle H + 2 \cdot m\angle A = 360$; $2 \cdot m\angle A + 2 \cdot m\angle R = 360$	4. Subst. prop.
5. $m\angle H + m\angle A = 180$; $m\angle A + m\angle R = 180$	5. Division property

6. ∠H and ∠A are supp.; ∠A and ∠R are supp. | 6. Def. of supp. ∠s

7. $\overline{HP} \parallel \overline{AR}$; $\overline{HA} \parallel \overline{RP}$ | 7. If two lines have a transv. and int. ∠s on the same side of the transv. supp., the lines are ∥.

8. *HARP* is a ▱. | 8. Def. of ▱

Conclusion: If both pairs of opp. ∠s of a quad. are ≅, then the quad. is a ▱.

25. Given: Quad. *TACK* with diagonals $\overline{AK}$ and $\overline{TC}$ intersecting in *Y*; $\overline{TY} \cong \overline{CY}$ and $\overline{AY} \cong \overline{KY}$
Prove: *TACK* is a ▱.

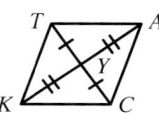

Plan: Show $\triangle TAY \cong \triangle CKY$. Then use CPCTC to show $\overline{TA}$ and $\overline{CK} \cong$ and ∥.

Proof:

Statements	Reasons
1. Quad. *TACK* with diag. $\overline{AK}$ and $\overline{TC}$; $\overline{TY} \cong \overline{CY}$; $\overline{AY} \cong \overline{KY}$	1. Given
2. $\angle TYA \cong \angle CYK$	2. Vert. ∠s are ≅.
3. $\triangle TAY \cong \triangle CKY$	3. SAS
4. $\overline{TA} \cong \overline{CK}$; $\angle YTA \cong \angle YCK$	4. CPCTC
5. $\overline{TA} \parallel \overline{CK}$	5. If 2 lines have a transv. and alt. int. ∠s ≅, the lines are ∥.
6. *TACK* is a ▱.	6. If a quad. has a pair of opp. sides ≅ and ∥, the quad. is a ▱.

Conclusion: If the diagonals of a quad. bisect each other, the quad. is a ▱.

26. Plan: Use the sum of the measures of the ∠s of a △ and algebra to show $\overline{MW} \perp \overline{NX}$, $\overline{MW} \perp \overline{WQ}$, and $\overline{WQ} \perp \overline{PX}$. It follows that $\overline{NX} \parallel \overline{WQ}$ and $\overline{PX} \parallel \overline{WM}$ and *XYWZ* is a ▱.

Proof:

Statements	Reasons
1. ▱*MNPQ*; $\overline{MW}$ bis. ∠M; $\overline{NX}$ bis. ∠N; $\overline{PX}$ bis. ∠P; $\overline{QW}$ bis. ∠Q.	1. Given
2. $m\angle NMY = \frac{1}{2}m\angle M = m\angle YMX$ $m\angle MNY = \frac{1}{2}m\angle N = m\angle YNW$ $m\angle PQZ = \frac{1}{2}m\angle Q = m\angle ZQX$ $m\angle QPZ = \frac{1}{2}m\angle P = m\angle ZPW$	2. ∠ Bisector Th.
3. $\overline{MN} \parallel \overline{PQ}$; $\overline{NP} \parallel \overline{MQ}$	3. Def. of ▱
4. $m\angle M + m\angle N = 180$ $m\angle Q + m\angle P = 180$ $m\angle M + m\angle Q = 180$	4. Consec. ∠s of a ▱ are supp.
5. $\frac{1}{2}m\angle M + \frac{1}{2}m\angle N = 90$ $\frac{1}{2}m\angle Q + \frac{1}{2}m\angle P = 90$ $\frac{1}{2}m\angle M + \frac{1}{2}m\angle Q = 90$	5. Mult. prop.
6. $m\angle NMY + m\angle MNY + m\angle MYN = 180$ $m\angle PQZ + m\angle QPZ + m\angle PZQ = 180$ $m\angle YMX + m\angle ZQX + m\angle MWQ = 180$	6. Sum of the measures of the ∠s of a △ = 180.
7. $m\angle NMY + m\angle MNY = 90$ $m\angle PQZ + m\angle QPZ = 90$ $m\angle YMX + m\angle ZQX = 90$	7. Subst. prop.
8. $m\angle MYN = 90$ $m\angle PZQ = 90$ $m\angle MWQ = 90$	8. Subtraction prop.
9. *MYN*, *PZQ*, and *MWQ* are rt. ∠s	9. Def. rt. ∠
10. $\overline{MW} \perp \overline{NX}$; $\overline{MW} \perp \overline{WQ}$; $\overline{WQ} \perp \overline{PX}$	10. Def. of ⊥ lines
11. $\overline{NX} \parallel \overline{WQ}$; $\overline{PX} \parallel \overline{WM}$	11. 2 lines ⊥ to the same line are ∥.
12. *XYWZ* is a ▱.	12. Def. of ▱

Conclusion: The quad. formed by the ∠ bisectors of a ▱ is a ▱.

27. Plan: Show $\triangle ALN \cong \triangle ISM$ to get $\overline{LN} \cong \overline{SM}$. Show $\triangle ASN \cong \triangle ILM$ to get $\overline{SN} \cong \overline{LM}$. The conclusion follows.

Proof:

Statements	Reasons
1. $\square ALIS$; $\overline{AN} \cong \overline{IM}$	1. Given
2. $\overline{AL} \cong \overline{IS}$; $\overline{AS} \cong \overline{IL}$	2. Opp. sides of a $\square$ are $\cong$.
3. $\overline{AL} \parallel \overline{IS}$; $\overline{AS} \parallel \overline{IL}$	3. Def. of $\square$
4. $\angle LAN \cong \angle SIM$; $\angle SAN \cong \angle LIM$	4. If $\parallel$ lines have a transv., alt. int. $\angle$s are $\cong$.
5. $\triangle ALN \cong \triangle ISM$; $\triangle ASN \cong \triangle ILM$	5. SAS
6. $\overline{LN} \cong \overline{SM}$; $\overline{SN} \cong \overline{LM}$	6. CPCTC
7. $LMSN$ is a $\square$.	7. If a quad. has both pairs of opp. sides $\cong$, then the quad. is a $\square$.

Conclusion: In $\square ALIS$, if $\overline{AN} \cong \overline{IM}$, then $LMSN$ is a $\square$.

28. Plan: Since $\overline{RN} \parallel \overline{SY}$, show $\overline{RY} \parallel \overline{NS}$ to conclude that $RNSY$ is a $\square$. Do this by showing that $\angle YRA$ and $\angle SNP$ are $\cong$ corr. $\angle$s of $\overline{RY}$ and $\overline{NS}$.

Proof:

Statements	Reasons
1. $\square AYDN$ with $\overline{AN}$ and $\overline{YD}$ extended; $\overline{YR}$ bisects $\angle AYQ$ and $\overline{NS}$ bisects $\angle DNP$.	1. Given
2. $\overline{AN} \parallel \overline{DY}$	2. Def. of $\square$
3. $\overline{RN} \parallel \overline{SY}$	3. $\overline{RN}$ contains $\overline{AN}$; $\overline{SY}$ contains $\overline{DY}$.
4. $\angle AYD \cong \angle AND$	4. Opp. $\angle$s of a $\square$ are $\cong$.
5. $\angle QYA$ and $\angle AYD$ are a linear pair, as are $\angle AND$ and $\angle DNP$.	5. Def. of linear pair
6. $\angle QYA$ and $\angle AYD$ are suppl., as are	6. Linear Pair Postulate

$\angle AND$ and $\angle DNP$.

7. $\angle QYA \cong \angle DNP$	7. Supp. of $\cong$ $\angle$s are $\cong$.
8. $m\angle QYA = m\angle DNP$	8. Def. of $\cong$ $\angle$s
9. $\frac{1}{2}m\angle QYA = \frac{1}{2}m\angle DNP$	9. Mult. prop.
10. $m\angle QYR = (\frac{1}{2})m\angle QYA$; $m\angle SNP = (\frac{1}{2})m\angle DNP$	10. $\angle$ Bisector Th.
11. $m\angle QYR = m\angle SNP$	11. Subst. prop.
12. $\angle QYR \cong \angle SNP$	12. Def. of $\cong$ $\angle$s
13. $\angle QYR \cong \angle YRA$	13. If $\parallel$ lines have a transv., alt. int. $\angle$s are $\cong$.
14. $\angle YRA \cong \angle SNP$	14. Subst. prop.
15. $\overline{RY} \parallel \overline{NS}$	15. If 2 lines have a transv. and corr. $\angle$s are $\cong$, the lines are $\parallel$.
16. $RNSY$ is a $\square$.	16. Def. of $\square$

Conclusion: If the bisectors of a pair of ext. opp. $\angle$s of a $\square$ are extended to meet the opp. sides, a $\square$ is formed.

PAGE 231

21. Proof:

Statements	Reasons
1. $\triangle ABC$ with D the midpoint of $\overline{AB}$; $\overline{DE} \parallel \overline{BC}$	1. Given
2. $\overline{AD} \cong \overline{DB}$	2. Def. of midpoint
3. Construct $\overleftrightarrow{AF}$ through point A such that $\overleftrightarrow{AF} \parallel \overleftrightarrow{BC}$.	3. Through a pt. not on a line, one and only one line can be drawn $\parallel$ to the given line.
4. $\overline{AE} \cong \overline{EC}$	4. If 3 or more $\parallel$ lines cut off $\cong$ segments on one transv., they cut off $\cong$ segments on every transv.
5. E is the midpoint of $\overline{AC}$.	5. Def. of midpoint
6. $\overline{DE}$ bisects $\overline{AC}$.	6. Def. of bisect

Conclusion: A line that contains the

midpoint of one side of a $\triangle$ and is $\parallel$ to another side bisects the third side.

22. Plan: Show that $\overline{ST} \parallel \overline{QR}$ and then apply the corollary of Th. 6.9.

Proof:

Statements	Reasons
1. $\triangle PQR$ with S the midpoint of $\overline{PQ}$; $\angle PST \cong \angle SQR$	1. Given
2. $\overline{ST} \parallel \overline{QR}$	2. If 2 lines have a transv. and corr. $\angle$s $\cong$, the lines are $\parallel$.
3. $\overline{ST}$ bisects $\overline{PR}$.	3. A line that contains the midpoint of one side of a $\triangle$ and is $\parallel$ to another side bisects the third side.
4. T is the midpoint of $\overline{PR}$.	4. Def. of bisect
5. $\overline{PT} \cong \overline{TR}$	5. Def. of midpoint

Conclusion: In $\triangle PQR$, with S the midpoint of $\overline{PQ}$ and $\angle PST \cong \angle SQR$, $\overline{PT} \cong \overline{TR}$.

23. Plan: Use the given to deduce that $\overline{BL} \parallel \overline{AN}$. Then $\overline{OL}$ contains the midpt. of one side of a $\triangle$ and is $\parallel$ to another side; hence, $\overline{OL}$ bisects side $\overline{AI}$ of $\triangle AIN$. The concl. follows.

Proof:

Statements	Reasons
1. $\angle GBL \cong \angle BAN$; L is the midpoint of $\overline{IN}$.	1. Given
2. $\overline{BL} \parallel \overline{AN}$	2. If 2 lines have a transv. and corr. $\angle$s $\cong$, the lines are $\parallel$.
3. $\overline{OL}$ bisects $\overline{AI}$.	3. A line that contains the midpoint of one side of a $\triangle$ and is $\parallel$ to another side bisects the third side.
4. O is the midpoint of $\overline{AI}$.	4. Def. of bisect
5. $\overline{AO} \cong \overline{OI}$	5. Def. of midpoint

Conclusion: If $\angle GBL \cong \angle BAN$ and L is the midpoint of $\overline{IN}$, then $\overline{AO} \cong \overline{OI}$.

24. Plan: Since three ∥ lines cut off ≅ segments on transv. $\overline{IN}$, they cut off ≅ segments on transv. $\overline{GA}$. The concl. follows.

Proof:

Statements	Reasons
1. $\overline{GI} \parallel \overline{BL} \parallel \overline{AN}$; L is the midpoint of $\overline{IN}$.	1. Given
2. $\overline{IL} \cong \overline{LN}$	2. Def. of midpoint
3. $\overline{GB} \cong \overline{BA}$	3. If 3 or more ∥ lines cut off ≅ segments on one transv., they cut off ≅ segments on every transv.
4. B is the midpoint of $\overline{GA}$.	4. Def. of midpoint

Conclusion: If $\overline{GI} \parallel \overline{BL} \parallel \overline{AN}$, and L is the midpoint of $\overline{IN}$, then B is the midpoint of $\overline{GA}$.

25. Plan: If $\overline{YZ} \parallel \overline{ER}$ then, since Y is the midpoint of $\overline{ME}$, the cor. to Th. 6.9 shows that $\overline{YX}$ bisects $\overline{MR}$. To show $\overline{YZ} \parallel \overline{ER}$, show that $YZRE$ has a pair of ≅ ∥ sides ($\overline{YE}$ and $\overline{ZR}$).

Proof:

Statements	Reasons
1. Consider ▱$MARE$; Y and Z are the midpoints of $\overline{ME}$ and $\overline{AR}$, respectively.	1. Given
2. $\overline{ME} \cong \overline{AR}$	2. Opp. sides of a ▱ are ≅.
3. $ME = AR$	3. Def. of ≅ segments
4. $\frac{1}{2}ME = \frac{1}{2}AR$	4. Mult. prop.
5. $YE = \frac{1}{2}ME$; $ZR = \frac{1}{2}AR$	5. Midpoint Th.
6. $YE = ZR$	6. Subst. prop.
7. $\overline{YE} \cong \overline{ZR}$	7. Def. of ≅ segs.
8. $\overline{ME} \parallel \overline{AR}$; hence $\overline{YE} \parallel \overline{ZR}$	8. Def. of ▱
9. $YZRE$ is a ▱.	9. If a quad. has a pair of opp. sides ≅ and ∥, the quad. is a ▱.
10. $\overline{YZ} \parallel \overline{ER}$; $\overline{YX} \parallel \overline{ER}$	10. Def. of ▱

11. $\overline{YX}$ bisects $\overline{MR}$. (△MER) — **11.** A line that contains the midpoint of one side of a △ and is ∥ of another side bisects the third side.

12. X is the midpoint of $\overline{MR}$. — **12.** Def. of bisect

Conclusion: A line joining the midpoints of opp. sides of a ▱ bisects a diagonal of the ▱.

26. Plan: Use the fact that $\overline{MA}$ is ∥ to both $\overline{YZ}$ and $\overline{RE}$ to show that the hypothesis of Theorem 6.9 is satisfied. The concl. follows.

Proof:

Statements	Reasons
1. ▱$MARE$; Y is the midpoint of $\overline{ME}$; $\overline{YZ} \parallel \overline{MA}$.	1. Given
2. $\overline{MA} \parallel \overline{ER}$	2. Def. of ▱
3. $\overline{YZ} \parallel \overline{ER}$	3. If two lines are ∥ to the same line, they are ∥ to each other.
4. $\overline{MY} \cong \overline{YE}$	4. Def. of midpoint
5. $\overline{AZ} \cong \overline{ZR}$	5. If 3 or more ∥ lines cut off ≅ segments on one transv., they cut of ≅ segments on every transv.
6. Z is the midpoint of $\overline{AR}$.	6. Def. of midpoint

Conclusion: A line that is ∥ to one side of a ▱ and contains the midpoint of a side of the ▱ contains the midpoint of the opp. side as well.

PAGE 232

27. Plan: Since △ABC is isosceles, ∠ABC ≅ ∠C. Hence, ∠ADE ≅ ∠ABC and $\overline{DE} \parallel \overline{BC}$. Using cor. to Th 6.9, it follows that $\overline{DE}$ bisects $\overline{AC}$. The concl. follows.

Proof:

Statements	Reasons
1. Isosceles △ABC with base $\overline{BC}$; D is the midpoint of $\overline{AB}$; ∠ADE ≅ ∠C.	1. Given
2. ∠ABC ≅ ∠C	2. Isos. △ Th.
3. ∠ADE ≅ ∠ABC	3. Subst. prop.
4. $\overline{DE} \parallel \overline{BC}$	4. If 2 lines have a transv. and corr. ∠s ≅, the lines are ∥.
5. $\overline{DE}$ bisects $\overline{AC}$.	5. A line that contains the midpoint of one side of a △ and is ∥ to another side bisects the third side.
6. E is the midpoint of $\overline{AC}$.	6. Def. of bisect
7. $\overline{BE}$ is a median of △ABC.	7. Def. of median

Conclusion: If △ABC is isosceles with base $\overline{BC}$, and if D is the midpoint of $\overline{AB}$ and ∠ADE ≅ ∠C, then $\overline{BE}$ is a median of △ABC.

28. Plan: Use the cor. to Th. 6.9 to show E is the midpoint of $\overline{AC}$. Then, by the def. of bisect and algebraic properties, it follows that $\overline{DB} \cong \overline{EC}$.

Proof:

Statements	Reasons
1. Isosceles △ABC with $\overline{AB} \cong \overline{AC}$; D is the midpoint of $\overline{AB}$; $\overline{DE} \parallel \overline{BC}$.	1. Given
2. $\overline{DE}$ bisects $\overline{AC}$.	2. A line that contains the midpoint of one side of a △ and is ∥ to another side bisects the third side.
3. E is the midpoint of $\overline{AC}$.	3. Def. of bisect
4. $AB = AC$	4. Def. of ≅ segments
5. $\frac{1}{2}AB = \frac{1}{2}AC$	5. Mult. prop.
6. $DB = \frac{1}{2}AB$; $EC = \frac{1}{2}AC$	6. Midpoint Th.
7. $DB = EC$	7. Subst. prop.
8. $\overline{DB} \cong \overline{EC}$	8. Def. of ≅ segments

731

Conclusion: In isosceles $\triangle ABC$, if D is the midpoint of $\overline{AB}$ and $\overline{DE} \parallel \overline{BC}$, then $\overline{DB} \cong \overline{EC}$.

29. Plan: Show $\triangle FMD \cong \triangle ENR$ and that $\angle FMD \cong \angle ENR$. Use alt. int. $\angle$s ENR and MRN and the transitive prop. to get $\angle FMD \cong \angle MRN$. Thus, $\overline{MD} \parallel \overline{RN}$, and the concl. follows.

Proof:

Statements	Reasons
1. $\square FDER$; M is the midpoint of $\overline{FR}$; N is the midpoint of $\overline{DE}$.	1. Given
2. $\overline{FD} \cong \overline{ER}$; $\overline{FR} \cong \overline{ED}$	2. Opp. sides of a $\square$ are $\cong$.
3. $FR = ED$	3. Def. of $\cong$ segments
4. $\frac{1}{2}FR = \frac{1}{2}ED$	4. Mult. prop.
5. $FM = \frac{1}{2}FR$; $EN = \frac{1}{2}ED$	5. Midpoint Th.
6. $FM = EN$	6. Subst. prop.
7. $\overline{FM} \cong \overline{EN}$	7. Def. of $\cong$ segments
8. $\angle DFM \cong \angle REN$	8. Opp. $\angle$s of a $\square$ are $\cong$.
9. $\triangle FMD \cong \triangle ENR$	9. SAS
10. $\angle FMD \cong \angle ENR$	10. CPCTC
11. $\overline{FR} \parallel \overline{ED}$	11. Def. of $\square$
12. $\angle ENR \cong \angle MRN$	12. If $\parallel$ lines have a transv., alt. int. $\angle$s are $\cong$.
13. $\angle FMD \cong \angle MRN$	13. Transitive prop.
14. $\overline{MD} \parallel \overline{RN}$	14. If 2 lines have a transv. and corr. $\angle$s $\cong$, the lines are $\parallel$.
15. In $\triangle FRS$, $\overline{MI}$ bisects $\overline{FS}$; in $\triangle DIE$, $\overline{NS}$ bisects $\overline{IE}$.	15. A line that contains the midpoint of one side of a $\triangle$ and is $\parallel$ to another side bisects the third side.
16. I is the midpoint of $\overline{FS}$; S is the midpoint of $\overline{IE}$.	16. Def. of bisect
17. $\overline{FI} \cong \overline{IS}$; $\overline{IS} \cong \overline{SE}$	17. Def. of midpoint
18. $\overline{FI} \cong \overline{IS} \cong \overline{SE}$	18. Subst. prop.

Conclusion: In $\square FDER$, with M the midpoint of $\overline{FR}$ and N the midpoint of $\overline{DE}$, $\overline{FI} \cong \overline{IS} \cong \overline{SE}$.

30. Plan: Show $\triangle MNS \cong \triangle PQS$. Then $\overline{MN}$ and $\overline{PQ}$ are $\cong$ corr. parts.

Proof:

Statements	Reasons
1. $\overline{MN} \parallel \overline{TS} \parallel \overline{RP}$; T is the midpoint of $\overline{MR}$.	1. Given
2. $\overline{MT} \cong \overline{TR}$	2. Def. of midpoint
3. $\overline{NS} \cong \overline{QS}$	3. If 3 or more $\parallel$ lines cut off $\cong$ segments on one transv., they cut off $\cong$ segments on every transv.
4. $\angle MSN \cong \angle PSQ$	4. Vert. $\angle$s are $\cong$.
5. $\angle MNS \cong \angle PQS$	5. If $\parallel$ lines have a transv., alt. int. $\angle$s are $\cong$.
6. $\triangle MNS \cong \triangle PQS$	6. ASA
7. $\overline{MN} \cong \overline{PQ}$	7. CPCTC

Conclusion: In the figure, if $\overline{MN} \parallel \overline{TS} \parallel \overline{RP}$ and if T is the midpoint of $\overline{MR}$, then $\overline{MN} \cong \overline{PQ}$.

PAGE 237

20. Proof:

Statements	Reasons
1. Rhombus $RANF$ with diagonals $\overline{FA}$ and $\overline{NR}$	1. Given
2. $\overline{FA} \perp \overline{NR}$	2. Diagonals of a rhombus are $\perp$
3. Angles $\angle FKR$, $\angle AKR$, $\angle AKN$, and $\angle FKN$ are right $\angle$s.	3. Def. of $\perp$ lines
4. $\triangle FKR$, $\triangle AKR$, $\triangle AKN$, and $\triangle FKN$ are right $\triangle$.	4. Def. of rt. $\triangle$
5. $\overline{FR} \cong \overline{AR} \cong \overline{AN} \cong \overline{FN}$	5. Def. of rhombus
6. $RANF$ is a $\square$.	6. Def. of rhombus
7. $\overline{KR} \cong \overline{KN}$; $\overline{FK} \cong \overline{AK}$	7. Diagonals of a $\square$ bisect each other.
8. $\triangle FKR \cong \triangle AKR \cong \triangle AKN \cong \triangle FKN$	8. HL
9. $\angle FRK \cong \angle ARK$; $\angle ANK \cong \angle FNK$; $\angle NFK \cong \angle RFK$; $\angle RAK \cong \angle NAK$	9. CPCTC
10. $\overline{NR}$ bisects $\angle R$ and $\angle N$; $\overline{FA}$ bisects $\angle F$ and $\angle A$.	10. Def. of $\angle$ bisector

Conclusion: Each diagonal of a rhombus bisects 2 $\angle$s of the rhombus.

21. Plan: Show $\triangle KSM \cong \triangle KIL$ to get $\overline{SM} \cong \overline{IL}$. Since $ASIL$ is a $\square$, $\overline{IL} \cong \overline{SA}$. Then $\overline{SM} \cong \overline{SA}$, and the concl. follows.

Proof:

Statements	Reasons
1. Rect. $ASIL$; K is the midpt. of $\overline{IS}$.	1. Given
2. $\angle KIL$ is a rt. $\angle$.	2. Def. of rect.
3. $\angle KIL \cong \angle KSM$	3. If $\parallel$ lines have a transv., alt. int. $\angle$s are $\cong$.
4. $\angle KSM$ is a right $\angle$.	4. Subst. prop.
5. $\triangle KIL$ and $\triangle KSM$ are rt. $\triangle$.	5. Def. of rt. $\triangle$
6. $\overline{KS} \cong \overline{KI}$	6. Def. of midpoint
7. $\angle SKM \cong \angle IKL$	7. Vert. $\angle$s are $\cong$
8. $\triangle KSM \cong \triangle KIL$	8. LA
9. $\overline{SM} \cong \overline{IL}$	9. CPCTC
10. $LISA$ is a $\square$.	10. Def. of rectangle
11. $\overline{IL} \cong \overline{SA}$	11. Opp. sides of a $\square$ are $\cong$.
12. $\overline{SM} \cong \overline{SA}$	12. Trans. prop.
13. S is the midpoint of $\overline{AM}$.	13. Def. of midpoint

Conclusion: In rectangle $ASIL$, if K is the midpoint of $\overline{IS}$, then S is the midpoint of $\overline{AM}$.

22. Plan: Show $\triangle AKS \cong \triangle LKI$ by LL. The concl. follows by CPCTC.

Proof:

Statements	Reasons
1. Rect. $ASIL$; K is the midpt. of $\overline{IS}$.	1. Given
2. $ASIL$ is a $\square$.	2. Def. of rectangle
3. $\overline{AS} \cong \overline{LI}$	3. Opp. sides of a $\square$ are $\cong$.

Statements	Reasons
4. $\angle S$ and $\angle I$ are right $\angle$s.	4. A rectangle has 4 rt. $\angle$s.
5. $\triangle AKS$ and $\triangle LKI$ are rt. $\triangle$s.	5. Def. of rt. $\triangle$
6. $\overline{KS} \cong \overline{KI}$	6. Def. of midpoint
7. $\triangle AKS \cong \triangle LKI$	7. LL
8. $\overline{AK} \cong \overline{LK}$	8. CPCTC

Conclusion: In rectangle $ASIL$, if K is the midpoint of $\overline{IS}$, then $\overline{AK} \cong \overline{LK}$.

23. Plan: Use the information about $GORF$ to deduce that rt. triangles FAL, RAK, OEK, and GEL are all $\cong$. Use CPCTC to show that $ALEK$ is a ▱ with a pair of $\cong$ adj. sides.

Proof:

Statements	Reasons
1. Rect. $GORF$; L, A, K, and E are the respective midpoints of $\overline{GF}$, $\overline{FR}$, $\overline{RO}$, and $\overline{OG}$.	1. Given
2. $\angle$s F, R, O, and G are rt $\angle$s.	2. A rectangle has 4 right $\angle$s.
3. $\triangle$s FAL, RAK, OEK, and GEL are rt. $\triangle$s.	3. Def. of rt. $\triangle$
4. $GORF$ is a ▱.	4. Def. of rect.
5. $\overline{FR} \cong \overline{OG}$; $\overline{FG} \cong \overline{RO}$	5. Opp. sides of a ▱ are $\cong$.
6. $FR = OG$; $FG = RO$	6. Def. of $\cong$ segments
7. $\frac{1}{2}FR = \frac{1}{2}OG$; $\frac{1}{2}FG = \frac{1}{2}RO$	7. Mult. prop.
8. $FA = (\frac{1}{2})FR$; $RA = (\frac{1}{2})FR$; $GE = (\frac{1}{2})OG$; $OE = (\frac{1}{2})OG$; $FL = (\frac{1}{2})FG$; $GL = (\frac{1}{2})FG$; $RK = (\frac{1}{2})RO$; $OK = (\frac{1}{2})RO$	8. Midpoint Th.
9. $FA = RA = GE = OE$; $FL = GL = RK = OK$	9. Subst. prop.
10. $\overline{FA} \cong \overline{RA} \cong \overline{GE} \cong \overline{OE}$; $\overline{FL} \cong \overline{GL} \cong \overline{RK} \cong \overline{OK}$	10. Def. of $\cong$ segments
11. $\triangle FAL \cong \triangle RAK \cong \triangle OEK \cong \triangle GEL$	11. LL
12. $\overline{AL} \cong \overline{EK}$; $\overline{EL} \cong \overline{AK}$	12. CPCTC
13. $ALEK$ is a ▱.	13. If a quad. has both pairs of opp. sides $\cong$, then the quad. is a ▱.
14. $\overline{AL} \cong \overline{AK}$	14. CPCTC
15. $ALEK$ is a rhombus.	15. Def. of rhombus

Conclusion: The figure formed by joining the successive midpoints of the sides of a rectangle is a rhombus.

24. Plan: From Ex. 20, $ALEK$ is a rhombus; hence, it is a ▱. Thus, $\overline{AL} \parallel \overline{KE}$, and the concl. follows by alt. int. $\angle$s.

Proof:

Statements	Reasons
1. Rect. $GORF$; L, A K, and E are the respective midpoints of $\overline{GF}$, $\overline{FR}$, $\overline{RO}$, and $\overline{OG}$.	1. Given
2. $ALEK$ is a rhombus.	2. Exercise 20
3. $ALEK$ is a ▱.	3. Def. of rhombus
4. $\overline{AL} \parallel \overline{KE}$	4. Def. of ▱
5. $\angle LAQ \cong \angle KEQ$	5. If $\parallel$ lines have a transv., alt. int. $\angle$s are $\cong$.

Conclusion: In rect. $GORF$ having L, A, K, and E as the respective midpoints of $\overline{GF}$, $\overline{FR}$, $\overline{RO}$, and $\overline{OG}$, $\angle LAQ \cong \angle KEQ$.

25. Given: Right $\triangle ABD$; E is the midpoint of $\overline{BD}$.

Prove: E is equidistant from A, B, and D; i.e., $AE = BE = DE$

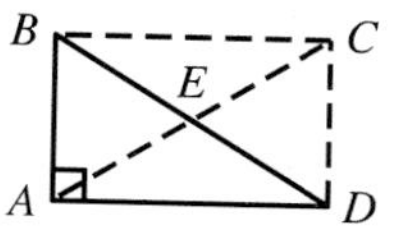

Plan: Since E is the midpoint of $\overline{BD}$, $\overline{BE} \cong \overline{DE}$. To get $AE = BE$, add auxiliary segments $\overline{BC}$ and $\overline{CD}$, so that $ABCD$ is a rectangle. Draw $\overline{EC}$. Use the props. of ▱s and alg. to reach concl.

Proof:

Statements	Reasons
1. Right $\triangle ABD$; E is the midpoint of $\overline{BD}$.	1. Given
2. $\overline{BE} \cong \overline{DE}$	2. Def. of midpoint
3. $BE = DE$	3. Def. of $\cong$ segs.
4. Construct auxiliary figure $\triangle BCD$ such that $\overline{BC} \parallel \overline{AD}$, and $\overline{CD} \parallel \overline{BA}$. Also note that $\overline{BC} \cong \overline{AD}$, and $\overline{CD} \cong \overline{AB}$.	4. Through a pt. not on a given line, there is one and only one line $\parallel$ to the given line through the given pt.
5. $ABCD$ is a rectangle.	5. Def. of rectangle
6. $\overline{AC} \cong \overline{BD}$	6. Diagonals of a rectangle are $\cong$.
7. $AC = BD$	7. Def. of $\cong$ segments
8. $(\frac{1}{2})AC = (\frac{1}{2})BD$	8. Multiplication prop.
9. $\overline{AE} \cong \overline{EC}$	9. Diagonals of a ▱ bisect each other.
10. E is the midpoint of $\overline{AC}$.	10. Def. of midpoint
11. $AE = (\frac{1}{2})AC$; $BE = (\frac{1}{2})BD$	11. Midpoint Th.
12. $AE = BE$	12. Subst. prop.
13. $AE = BE = DE$	13. Subst. prop.

Conclusion: If E is the midpoint of the hypotenuse of right $\triangle ABD$, then E is equidistant from A, B, and D.

26. Given: Rectangle $ABCD$ with rt. $\angle A$

Prove: $\angle B$, $\angle C$, and $\angle D$ are rt. $\angle$s.

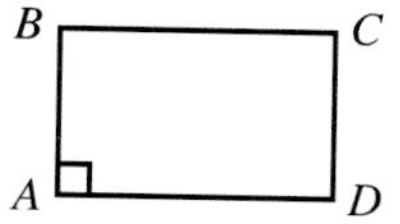

Plan: Since $ABCD$ is a rectangle, it is a ▱. Since both pairs of opp. $\angle$s of a ▱ are $\cong$, the conclusion follows.

Proof:

Statements	Reasons
1. Rect. $ABCD$ with rt. $\angle A$	1. Given
2. $m\angle A = 90$	2. Def. of rt. $\angle$
3. $ABCD$ is a ▱.	3. Def. of rect.

4. ∠A ≅ ∠C; ∠B ≅ ∠D
4. Opp. ∠s of a ▱ are ≅.

5. m∠A = m∠C; m∠B = m∠D
5. Def. of ≅ ∠s

6. m∠C = 90
6. Subst. prop.

7. ∠A and ∠B are supp.; ∠C and ∠D are supp.
7. Consecutive ∠s of a ▱ are supplementary.

8. m∠A + m∠B = 180; m∠C + m∠D = 180
8. Def. of supp. ∠s

9. 90 + m∠B = 180; 90 + m∠D = 180
9. Subst. prop.

10. m∠B = 90; m∠D = 90
10. Subtraction prop.

11. ∠B, ∠C, ∠D are rt. ∠s.
11. Def. of rt. ∠

Conclusion: All 4 ∠s of a rect. are rt. ∠s.

27. Given: Square PQRS with diagonals PR and QS
Prove: PR ⊥ QS

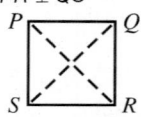

Plan: Since a square is a rhombus, the conclusion is immediate.

Proof:

Statements	Reasons
1. Square PQRS with diagonals PR and QS	1. Given
2. PQRS is a rhombus.	2. Def. of rhombus
3. PR ⊥ QS	3. Diagonals of a rhombus are ⊥.

Conclusion: The diagonals of a square are ⊥.

28. Given: Rhombus MNPQ with MN ≅ NP
Prove: MN ≅ NP ≅ PQ ≅ QM

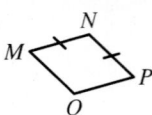

Plan: Use the given and the fact that MNPQ is a ▱ to verify the concl.

Proof:

Statements	Reasons
1. Rhombus MNPQ with MN ≅ NP	1. Given
2. MNPQ is a ▱.	2. Def. of rhombus
3. MN ≅ PQ; NP ≅ QM	3. Opp. sides of a ▱ are ≅.
4. MN ≅ NP ≅ PQ ≅ QM	4. Subst. prop.

Conclusion: A rhombus has 4 ≅ sides.

29. Given: Square ABCD with diagonals AC and BD
Prove: AC ≅ BD

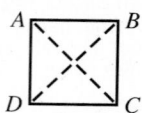

Plan: Since a square is also a rect., and since the diags. of a rect. are ≅, the concl. follows.

Proof:

Statements	Reasons
1. Square ABCD with diagonals AC and BD	1. Given
2. ABCD is a rectangle.	2. Def. of square
3. AC ≅ BD	3. Diagonals of a rectangle are ≅.

Conclusion: The diagonals of a square are congruent.

30. Theorem: If the diags. of a ▱ are ≅, the ▱ is a rect. (Conv. of Th. 6.10)
Given: ▱ GOLD with GL ≅ OD
Prove: GOLD is a rect.

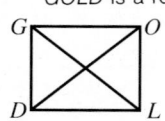

Plan: Show △GLD ≅ △ODL by SSS. Then show ∠D ≅ ∠L by CPCTC. Since ∠D and ∠L are supp., each measures 90. The concl. follows.

Proof:

Statements	Reasons
1. ▱ GOLD with GL ≅ OD	1. Given
2. GD ≅ OL	2. Opp. sides of a ▱ are ≅.
3. LD ≅ DL	3. Reflexive prop.
4. △GLD ≅ △ODL	4. SSS
5. ∠D ≅ ∠L	5. CPCTC
6. m∠D = m∠L	6. Def. of ≅ ∠s
7. ∠D and ∠L are suppl.	7. Consecutive ∠s of a ▱ are supp.
8. m∠D + m∠L = 180	8. Def. of supp. ∠s
9. 2m∠D = 180	9. Subst. and Distrib. prop.
10. m∠D = 90	10. Div. prop. of =
11. ∠D is a rt. ∠.	11. Def. of rt. ∠
12. GOLD is a rect.	12. Def. of rect.

Conclusion: If the diags. of a ▱ are ≅, the ▱ is a rect.

31. Theorem: If the diagonals of a ▱ are ⊥, the ▱ is a rhombus. (Converse of Theorem 6.11)
Given: ▱ JOHN with JH ⊥ ON
Prove: JOHN is a rhombus.

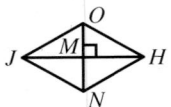

Plan: Show that JOHN has a pair of consecutive ≅ sides, HO and HN. Prove △JOM ≅ △HNM and △HOM ≅ △HNM. Use ≅ corr. parts.

Proof:

Statements	Reasons
1. ▱ JOHN with JH ⊥ ON	1. Given
2. Angles JMO, OMH, and HMN are rt. ∠s.	2. Def. of ⊥
3. △JOM, △HNM, △HMO are rt. △s.	3. Def. of rt. △
4. JO ≅ HN	4. Opp. sides of a ▱ are ≅.
5. JO ∥ HN	5. Def. of ▱

6. ∠JOM ≅ ∠HNM	6. If ∥ lines have a transv., alt. int. ∠s are ≅.
7. △JOM ≅ △HNM	7. HA
8. $\overline{OM} ≅ \overline{NM}$	8. CPCTC
9. $\overline{HM} ≅ \overline{HM}$	9. Reflexive prop.
10. △HOM ≅ △HNM	10. LL
11. $\overline{HO} ≅ \overline{HN}$	11. CPCTC
12. JOHN is a rhombus.	12. Def. of rhombus

Conclusion: If the diagonals of a ▱ are ⊥, the ▱ is a rhombus.

32. Theorem: If each diagonal of a ▱ bisects a pair of opp. ∠s, the ▱ is a rhombus.

Given: ▱ RIDE; $\overline{IE}$ bisects ∠RID and ∠DER; $\overline{RD}$ bisects ∠ERI and ∠IDE.

Prove: RIDE is a rhombus.

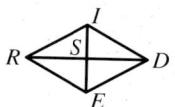

Plan: Show that consecutive sides $\overline{IR}$ and $\overline{ID}$ are ≅. First, show △RIS ≅ △DES to get $\overline{RS} ≅ \overline{DS}$. Then, show ∠IRS ≅ ∠IDS and use the converse of the Isosceles △ Th. to demonstrate the concl.

Proof:

Statements	Reasons
1. ▱ RIDE; $\overline{IE}$ bisects ∠RID and ∠DER; $\overline{RD}$ bisects ∠ERI and ∠IDE.	1. Given
2. $\overline{RI} ∥ \overline{DE}$	2. Def. of ▱
3. $\overline{RI} ≅ \overline{DE}$	3. Opp. sides of a ▱ are ≅.
4. ∠IRS ≅ ∠EDS; ∠RIS ≅ ∠DES	4. If ∥ lines have a transv., alt. int. ∠s are ≅.
5. △RIS ≅ △DES	5. ASA
6. $\overline{RS} ≅ \overline{DS}$	6. CPCTC
7. ∠R ≅ ∠D	7. Opp. ∠s of a ▱ are ≅.
8. m∠R = m∠D	8. Def. of ≅ ∠s

9. $\frac{1}{2}m∠R = \frac{1}{2}m∠D$	9. Mult. prop.
10. $m∠IRS = (\frac{1}{2})m∠R$; $m∠IDS = (\frac{1}{2})m∠D$.	10. ∠ Bis. Th.
11. $m∠IRS = m∠IDS$	11. Subst. prop.
12. ∠IRS ≅ ∠IDS	12. Def. of ≅ ∠s
13. $\overline{IR} ≅ \overline{ID}$ (△RID)	13. If 2 ∠s of a △ are ≅, the sides opp. them are ≅.
14. RIDE is a rhombus.	14. Def. of rhombus

Conclusion: If each diagonal of a ▱ bisects 2 ∠s of the ▱, the ▱ is a rhombus.

33. Theorem: If the median to one side of a △ is half the length of that side, then the △ is a rt. △.

Given: △ABC with median $\overline{CM}$; $CM = (\frac{1}{2})AB$

Prove: △ABC is a rt. △; i.e., ∠C is a rt. ∠.

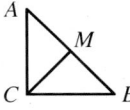

Plan: Use the given to show that $\overline{AM} ≅ \overline{CM}$ and $\overline{CM} ≅ \overline{BM}$. Then, ∠MAC ≅ ∠MCA and ∠MCB ≅ ∠MBC. Since m∠MAC + m∠ACB + m∠MBC = 180, show that m∠ACB = 90. The conclusion follows.

Proof:

Statements	Reasons
1. △ABC with median $\overline{CM}$; $CM = (\frac{1}{2})AB$	1. Given
2. M is the midpoint of $\overline{AB}$.	2. Def. of median
3. $AM = (\frac{1}{2})AB$; $BM = (\frac{1}{2})AB$	3. Midpoint Th.
4. $AM = CM$; $CM = BM$	4. Substitution
5. $\overline{AM} ≅ \overline{CM}$; $\overline{CM} ≅ \overline{BM}$	5. Def. of ≅ segments
6. ∠MAC ≅ ∠MCA;	6. Isos. △Th.

∠MCB ≅ ∠MBC	
7. m∠MAC = m∠MCA; m∠MCB = m∠MBC	7. Def. of ≅ ∠s
8. m∠MCA + m∠MCB = m∠ACB	8. Def. of betweenness
9. m∠MAC + m∠ACB + m∠MBC 180	9. The sum of the measures of the ∠s of a △ is 180.
10. m∠MAC + m∠MCA + m∠MCB + m∠MBC = 180	10. Subst. prop.
11. 2·m∠MCA + 2·m∠MCB = 180	11. Subst. prop.
12. m∠MCA + m∠MCB = 90	12. Division prop.
13. ∠ACB is a rt. ∠.	13. Def. of rt. ∠.
14. △ABC is a rt. △	14. Def. of rt. △

Conclusion: If the median to one side of a △ is half the length of that side, then the △ is a rt. △.

PAGE 238, TEST YOURSELF

7. Plan: Show △JEI ≅ △ASI. The conclusion follows by CPCTC.

Proof:

Statements	Reasons
1. ▱NOAJ with diagonal $\overline{JA}$; I is the midpoint of $\overline{JA}$.	1. Given
2. $\overline{JI} ≅ \overline{AI}$	2. Def. of midpoint
3. $\overline{JO} ∥ \overline{AN}$	3. Def. of ▱
4. ∠EJI ≅ ∠SAI ∠JEI ≅ ∠ASI	4. If ∥ lines have a transv., alt. int. ∠s are ≅.
5. △JEI ≅ △ASI	5. AAS
6. $\overline{EI} ≅ \overline{SI}$	6. CPCTC
7. I is the midpt. of $\overline{ES}$.	7. Def. of midpt.

Conclusion: In ▱NAOJ with diagonal $\overline{JA}$ having midpoint I, I is the midpoint of $\overline{ES}$.

8. Plan: Show △AED ≅ △CGB to get ∠ADE ≅ ∠CBG. Then, deduce that ∠EDG ≅ ∠GBE and that ∠AED ≅ ∠GBE. Thus, $\overline{DE} ∥ \overline{GB}$. Use a similar argument to demonstrate that $\overline{AG} ∥ \overline{EC}$.

735

Proof:

Statements	Reasons
1. □ABCD; E and G are the respective midpoints of $\overline{AB}$ and $\overline{CD}$.	1. Given
2. $\overline{AB} \cong \overline{CD}$; $\overline{DA} \cong \overline{BC}$	2. Opp. sides of a □ are ≅.
3. $AB = CD$	3. Def. of ≅ segments
4. $\frac{1}{2}AB = \frac{1}{2}CD$	4. Mult. prop.
5. $AE = \frac{1}{2}AB$; $BE = \frac{1}{2}AB$; $GD = \frac{1}{2}CD$; $CG = \frac{1}{2}CD$	5. Midpoint Th.
6. $AE = BE = DG = CG$	6. Subst. prop.
7. $\overline{AE} \cong \overline{BE} \cong \overline{DG} \cong \overline{CG}$	7. Def. of ≅ segments
8. $\angle A \cong \angle C$; $\angle B \cong \angle D$	8. Opp. ∠s of a □ are ≅.
9. $\triangle AED \cong \triangle CGB$; $\triangle ADG \cong \triangle CBE$	9. SAS
10. $\angle ADE \cong \angle CBG$; $\angle DAG \cong \angle BCE$	10. CPCTC
11. $m\angle ADE = m\angle CBG$; $m\angle DAG = m\angle BCE$	11. Def. of ≅ ∠s
12. $m\angle D = m\angle ADE + m\angle EDG$; $m\angle B = m\angle EBG + m\angle CBG$; $m\angle A = m\angle DAG + m\angle GAE$; $m\angle C = m\angle BCE + m\angle ECG$	12. Def. of betweenness
13. $m\angle ADE + m\angle EDG = m\angle EBG + m\angle CBG$; $m\angle DAG + m\angle GAE = m\angle BCE + m\angle ECG$	13. Subst. prop.
14. $m\angle EDG = m\angle EBG$; $m\angle GAE = m\angle ECG$	14. Subtraction prop.
15. $\angle EDG \cong \angle EBG$; $\angle GAE \cong \angle ECG$	15. Def. of ≅ ∠s
16. $\overline{AB} \parallel \overline{CD}$; $\overline{DA} \parallel \overline{BC}$	16. Def. of □
17. $\angle AED \cong \angle EDG$; $\angle GAE \cong \angle AGD$	17. If ∥ lines have a transv., alt. int. ∠s are ≅.
18. $\angle AED \cong \angle EBG$; $\angle AGD \cong \angle ECG$	18. Subst. prop.
19. $\overline{DE} \parallel \overline{GB}$; $\overline{AG} \parallel \overline{EC}$	19. If 2 lines have a transv. and corr. ∠s =, the lines are ∥.
20. EFGH is a □.	20. Def. of □

Conclusion: In □ABCD, if E and G are the respective midpoints of $\overline{AB}$ and $\overline{CD}$, then EFGH is a □.

9. Plan: Show $\triangle MRQ \cong \triangle PRS$ by SAS, and so $\overline{MQ} \cong \overline{PS}$. Then $\overline{NQ} \cong \overline{PS}$. Since $\angle QMR \cong \angle SPR$, then $\overline{MN} \parallel \overline{PS}$. Hence, $\overline{NQ} \parallel \overline{PS}$, and the concl. follows.

Proof:

Statements	Reasons
1. Q is the midpt. of $\overline{MN}$; R is the midpt. of $\overline{MP}$ and $\overline{QS}$.	1. Given
2. $\overline{MQ} \cong \overline{NQ}$; $\overline{RQ} \cong \overline{RS}$; $\overline{RM} \cong \overline{RP}$	2. Def. of midpt.
3. $\angle MRQ \cong \angle PRS$	3. Vert. ∠s are ≅.
4. $\triangle MRQ \cong \triangle PRS$	4. SAS
5. $\overline{MQ} \cong \overline{PS}$; $\angle QMR \cong \angle SPR$	5. CPCTC
6. $\overline{NQ} \cong \overline{PS}$	6. Subst. prop.
7. $\overline{MN} \parallel \overline{PS}$	7. If two lines have a transv. and alt. int. ∠s ≅, the lines are ∥.
8. NQSP is a □.	8. If a quad. has a pair of opp. sides ≅ and ∥, the quad. is a □.

Conclusion: If Q is the midpt. of $\overline{MN}$ and R is the midpt. of $\overline{MP}$ and $\overline{QS}$, then NQSP is a □.

PAGE 242

19. Plan: Since ACKJ is isos., $\overline{AJ} \cong \overline{CK}$. Also diags. $\overline{CJ}$ and $\overline{AK}$ are ≅. Thus, $\triangle CAJ \cong \triangle ACK$ and $\angle XAC \cong \angle XCA$. These are base ∠s of $\triangle CAX$, so the concl. follows.

Proof:

Statements	Reasons
1. Isos. trap. ACKJ with diags. $\overline{JC}$ and $\overline{AK}$	1. Given
2. $\overline{JA} \cong \overline{KC}$	2. Def. of isos. trap.
3. $\overline{CJ} \cong \overline{AK}$	3. Diags. of an isos. trap. are ≅.
4. $\overline{CA} \cong \overline{AC}$	4. Reflexive prop.
5. $\triangle CAJ \cong \triangle ACK$	5. SSS
6. $\angle XAC \cong \angle XCA$	6. CPCTC
7. $\overline{XA} \cong \overline{XC}$	7. If 2 ∠s of a △ are ≅, then the sides opp. those ∠s are ≅.
8. $\triangle CAX$ is isos.	8. Def. of isos. △.

Conclusion: If isos. trap. ACKJ has diags. that intersect in point X, then $\triangle CAX$ is isos.

PAGE 243

23. Proof:

Statements	Reasons
1. Isos. trap. ARYG	1. Given
2. $\overline{GY} \parallel \overline{AR}$; $\overline{AG} \cong \overline{RY}$	2. Def. of isos. trap.
3. Through R construct $\overrightarrow{RS}$ such that $\overrightarrow{RS} \parallel \overline{AG}$.	3. Through a point not on a line, there exists one and only one line that is ∥ to the given line.
4. GARS is a □.	4. Def. of □
5. $\angle G \cong \angle RSY$	5. If ∥ lines have a transv., corr. ∠s are ≅.
6. $\overline{AG} \cong \overline{RS}$	6. Opp. sides of a □ are ≅.
7. $\overline{RS} \cong \overline{RY}$	7. Subst. prop.
8. $\angle RSY \cong \angle Y$	8. Isos. △ Th.
9. $\angle G \cong \angle Y$	9. Trans. prop.
10. $\angle A$ and $\angle G$ are supp.; $\angle Y$ and $\angle ARY$ are supp.	10. If two ∥ lines have a transv., int. ∠s on the same side of the transv. are supp.
11. $\angle A \cong \angle ARY$	11. Supplements of ≅ ∠s are ≅.

Conclusion: Base ∠s of an isos. trap. are ≅.

24. Proof:

Statements	Reasons
1. △ABC; E is the midpoint of $\overline{AB}$; F is the midpoint of $\overline{BC}$.	1. Given
2. $\overline{BE} \cong \overline{AE}$; $\overline{BF} \cong \overline{CF}$	2. Def. of midpt.
3. Extend $\overrightarrow{EF}$ through F to G so that FE = FG.	3. On a ray, there is exactly 1 point at a given distance from the ray.
4. $\overline{FE} \cong \overline{FG}$	4. Def. of ≅ segments
5. Draw $\overline{CG}$.	5. Two points determine a line.
6. ∠BFE ≅ ∠CFG	6. Vert. ∠s are ≅.
7. △BFE ≅ △CFG	7. SAS
8. $\overline{BE} \cong \overline{CG}$; ∠BEF ≅ ∠CGF	8. CPCTC
9. $\overline{AE} \cong \overline{CG}$	9. Subst. prop.
10. $\overline{AB} \parallel \overline{CG}$	10. If 2 lines have a transv. and alt. int. ∠s ≅, the lines are ∥.
11. AEGC is a ▱.	11. If a quad. has a pair of opp. sides ≅ and ∥, the quad. is a ▱.
12. $\overline{EG} \parallel \overline{AC}$	12. Def. of ▱
13. $\overline{EF} \parallel \overline{AC}$	13. $\overline{EG}$ contains $\overline{EF}$
14. F is the midpt. of $\overline{EG}$.	14. Def. of midpt.
15. $EF = (\frac{1}{2})EG$	15. Midpt. Th.
16. $\overline{EG} \cong \overline{AC}$	16. Opp. sides of a ▱ are ≅.
17. EG = AC	17. Def. of ≅ segments
18. $EF = (\frac{1}{2})AC$	18. Subst. prop.

Conclusion: The segment that joins the midpoints of two sides of a △ is ∥ to the third side, and its length is half the length of the third side.

25. Given: ∠A ≇ ∠D
Prove: ABCD is not isosceles.

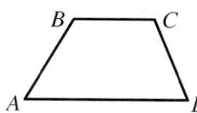

Plan: Assume the negation of the Prove and show that it leads to a contradiction.

Proof:
Assume:

| ABCD is isosceles | Negation of the conclusion |
| ∠A ≅ ∠D | Base ∠s of an isos. trap. are ≅. |

Contradiction: ∠A ≇ ∠D
Conclusion: Since the assumption leads to a contradiction of the given information, the assumption is false. Therefore, ABCD is not isosceles.

26. Given: Trapezoid ABCD is not isosceles.
Prove: $\overline{AC} \not\cong \overline{BD}$

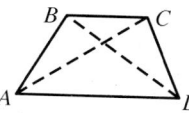

Plan: Assume the negation of $\overline{AC} \not\cong \overline{BD}$ and show that it leads to a contradiction.

Proof:
Assume:

| $\overline{AC} \cong \overline{BD}$ | Negation of the conclusion |
| ABCD is isos. | If the diags. of a trap. are ≅, the trap. is isos. |

Contradiction: ABCD is not isosceles.
Conclusion: Since the assumption leads to a contradiction of the given information, the assumption is false. Therefore, $\overline{AC} \not\cong \overline{BD}$.

27. Given: Quad. ABCD; E, F, G, and H are the respective midpts. of $\overline{AB}$, $\overline{BC}$, $\overline{CD}$, and $\overline{DA}$.
Prove: EFGH is a ▱.

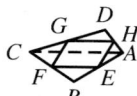

Plan: Draw diagonal $\overline{AC}$. Then $\overline{EF} \parallel \overline{AC}$ and $EF = (\frac{1}{2})AC$ by the Midsegment Th. Similarly, $\overline{GH} \parallel \overline{AC}$ and $GH = \frac{1}{2}AC$. Thus, EFGH has a pair of opposite sides ≅ and ∥.

Proof:

Statements	Reasons
1. Quad ABCD; E, F, G, and H are the respective midpoints of $\overline{AB}$, $\overline{BC}$, $\overline{CD}$, and $\overline{DA}$.	1. Given
2. Draw $\overline{AC}$.	2. Two points determine a line.
3. $\overline{EF} \parallel \overline{AC}$; $EF = (\frac{1}{2})AC$; $\overline{GH} \parallel \overline{AC}$; $GH = (\frac{1}{2})AC$	3. Midsegment Th.
4. $\overline{EF} \parallel \overline{GH}$	4. If 2 lines are ∥ to the same line, they are ∥ to each other.
5. EF = GH	5. Subst. prop.
6. $\overline{EF} \cong \overline{GH}$	6. Def. of ≅ segments
7. EFGH is a ▱.	7. If a quad. has a pair of opp. sides ≅ and ∥, the quad. is a ▱.

Conclusion: The figure formed by joining in order the midpoints of the sides of any quad. is a ▱.

28. Given: Trap. TRAP; ∠T ≅ ∠P; ∠R ≅ ∠A
Prove: TRAP is isos.; i.e., $\overline{RT} \cong \overline{AP}$

Plan: Since $\overline{RT} \not\parallel \overline{AP}$, they can be extended until they intersect. Then △STP is isos. with $\overline{ST} \cong \overline{SP}$. Since ∠TRA ≅ ∠PAR, ∠SRA ≅ ∠SAR; hence, △SRA is isos. with $\overline{SR} \cong \overline{SA}$. The concl. follows.

Proof:

Statements	Reasons
1. Trap. TRAP; ∠T ≅ ∠P;	1. Given

$\angle TRA \cong \angle PAR$

2. $\overline{TR}$ is not parallel to $\overline{PA}$.   2. Def. of trap.

3. Extend $\overrightarrow{TR}$ and $\overrightarrow{PA}$ to intersect in point S 3. If 2 coplanar lines are not ∥, then they intersect.

4. $\overline{ST} \cong \overline{SP}$ 4. If two ∠s of a △ are ≅, the sides opp. them are ≅.

5. $ST = SP$ 5. Def. of ≅ segments

6. $\angle SRA$ and $\angle TRA$ are a linear pair; $\angle SAR$ and $\angle PAR$ are a linear pair.   6. Def. of linear pair

7. $\angle SRA$ and $\angle TRA$ are supplementary; $\angle SAR$ and $\angle PAR$ are supplementary.   7. Linear Pair Post.

8. $\angle SRA \cong \angle SAR$ 8. Supplements of ≅ ∠s are ≅.

9. $\overline{SR} \cong \overline{SA}$ 9. If 2 ∠s of a △ are ≅, the sides opp. them are ≅.

10. $SR = SA$ 10. Def. of ≅ segments

11. $ST = SR + RT$; $SP = SA + AP$ 11. Def. of betweenness

12. $SR + RT = SA + AP$ 12. Subst. prop.

13. $RT = AP$ 13. Subtr. prop.

14. $\overline{RT} \cong \overline{AP}$ 14. Def. of ≅ segments

15. $TRAP$ is isos.   15. Def. of isos. trap.

Conclusion: If the base angles of a trap. are ≅, the trap. is isosceles.

29. Given: Isosceles trapezoid $GINA$
Prove: $\overline{NG} \cong \overline{AI}$

Plan: Use the given to show $\triangle ANG \cong \triangle NAI$. The conclusion follows by CPCTC.

Proof:

Statements	Reasons
1. Isos. trap. $GINA$	1. Given
2. $\overline{AG} \cong \overline{NI}$	2. Def. of isos. trap.
3. $\angle A \cong \angle N$	3. Base ∠s of an isos. trap. are ≅.
4. $\overline{AN} \cong \overline{NA}$	4. Refl. prop.
5. $\triangle ANG \cong \triangle NAI$	5. SAS
6. $\overline{NG} \cong \overline{AI}$	6. CPCTC

Conclusion: Diagonals of an isos. trap. are ≅.

30. Given: Trapezoid $ZACK$; $\overline{AK} \cong \overline{CZ}$
Prove: $ZACK$ is isos.; i.e., $\overline{AZ} \cong \overline{CK}$.

Plan: Draw ⊥ line segments from A and C to $\overline{ZK}$ and call them $\overline{AS}$ and $\overline{CT}$. Show $\triangle AKS \cong \triangle CZT$. Then, use ≅ corr. parts to show $\triangle AKZ \cong \triangle CZK$. Conc. follows by CPCTC.

Proof:

Statements	Reasons
1. Trap. $ZACK$; $\overline{AK} \cong \overline{CZ}$	1. Given
2. Through A construct $\overline{AS} \perp \overline{ZK}$; through C construct $\overline{CT} \perp \overline{ZK}$.	2. From a pt. not on a line, one and only one line can be drawn that is ⊥ to the given line.
3. $\angle ASK$ and $\angle CTZ$ are rt. ∠s.	3. Def. of ⊥ lines
4. $\triangle ASK$ and $\triangle CTZ$ are rt. △.	4. Def. of rt. △
5. $\overline{AC} \parallel \overline{ZK}$	5. Def. of trap.
6. $AS = CT$	6. If two lines are ∥, then all points on one line are equidistant from the other line.
7. $\overline{AS} \cong \overline{CT}$	7. Def. of ≅ segments
8. $\triangle AKS \cong \triangle CZT$	8. HL
9. $\angle AKZ \cong \angle CZK$	9. CPCTC
10. $\overline{KZ} \cong \overline{ZK}$	10. Reflexive prop.
11. $\triangle AKZ \cong \triangle CZK$	11. SAS
12. $\overline{AZ} \cong \overline{CK}$	12. CPCTC
13. $ZACK$ is isos.	13. Def. of isos. trap.

Conclusion: If the diagonals of a trapezoid are ≅, the trapezoid is isosceles.

31. Given: Trap. $ABCD$ with median $\overline{EF}$
Prove: $\overline{EF} \parallel \overline{BC}$; $\overline{EF} \parallel \overline{AD}$; $EF = (\frac{1}{2})(AD + BC)$

Plan: Extend $\overrightarrow{AD}$ and draw a segment through B and F that intersects $\overrightarrow{AD}$ in pt. G. Show $\triangle FBC \cong \triangle FGD$ to get $\overline{BC} \cong \overline{GD}$. Since $AG = AD + DG$, $AG = AD + BC$. Apply the Midsegment Theorem to $\triangle ABG$ to verify the concl.

Proof:

Statements	Reasons
1. Trap. $ABCD$ with median $\overline{EF}$	1. Given
2. E is the midpoint of $\overline{AB}$; F is the midpoint of $\overline{CD}$.	2. Def. of median of trap.
3. $\overline{FC} \cong \overline{FD}$	3. Def. of midpt.
4. Draw $\overline{BF}$ to intersect $\overrightarrow{AD}$ in G.	4. Two points determine a line.
5. $\overline{BC} \parallel \overline{AD}$	5. Def. of trap.
6. $\angle BCF \cong \angle GDF$	6. If ∥ lines have a transv., alt. int. ∠s are ≅.
7. $\angle CFB \cong \angle DFG$	7. Vert. ∠s are ≅
8. $\triangle FBC \cong \triangle FGD$	8. ASA
9. $\overline{BC} \cong \overline{GD}$	9. CPCTC
10. $BC = GD$	10. Def. of ≅ segs.
11. $AG = AD + GD$	11. Def. of betweenness
12. $AG = AD + BC$	12. Subst. prop.
13. $\overline{EF} \parallel \overline{AG}$ $EF = (\frac{1}{2})AG$	13. Midsegment Th.
14. $\overline{EF} \parallel \overline{AD}$	14. $\overline{AG}$ contains $\overline{AD}$.

738

15. $\overline{EF} \parallel \overline{BC}$ | 15. If two lines are ∥ to the same line, they are ∥ to each other.
16. $EF = (\frac{1}{2})(AD + BC)$ | 16. Subst. prop.

Conclusion: The median of a trapezoid is ∥ to the bases and has a length = half the sum of the lengths of the bases.

PAGE 247

3.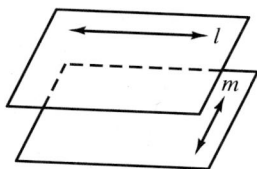

4.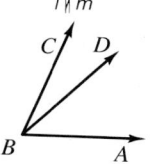

∠ABC and ∠ABD are not adjacent.

5.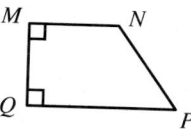

MNPQ is not a rectangle.

6.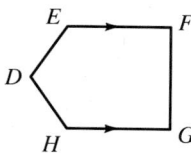

DEFGH is not a trapezoid.

7.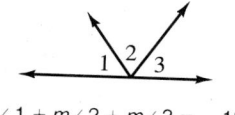

$m\angle 1 + m\angle 2 + m\angle 3 = $ 180

8.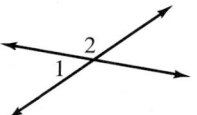

∠1 and ∠2 are not vertical ∠s.

9.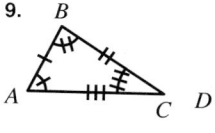

△ABC ≇ △DFE

10.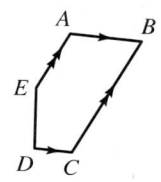

ABCDE is not a ▱

11.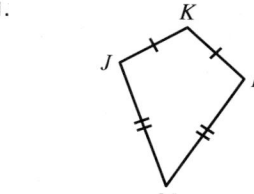

JKLM is not a rhombus.

12.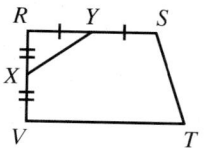

$\overline{XY}$ is not a median of trap. RSTV.

PAGE 252

31. Proof:

Statements	Reasons
1. $\overline{AB} \cong \overline{EF}$; $\overline{BC} \cong \overline{FG}$, $\overline{CD} \cong \overline{GH}$; ∠B ≅ ∠F; ∠C ≅ ∠G	1. Given
2. Draw $\overline{AC}$ and $\overline{EG}$.	2. Two points determine a line.
3. △ABC ≅ △EFG	3. SAS
4. $\overline{AC} \cong \overline{EG}$; ∠BCA ≅ ∠FGE; ∠BAC ≅ ∠FEG	4. CPCTC

Statements	Reasons
5. m∠BCA = m∠FGE; m∠BAC = m∠FEG; m∠C = m∠G	5. Def. of ≅ ∠s
6. m∠C = m∠BCA + m∠DCA; m∠G = m∠FGE + m∠HGE	6. Betweenness of rays
7. m∠BCA + m∠DCA = m∠FGE + m∠HGE	7. Subst. prop.
8. m∠DCA = m∠HGE	8. Subtraction prop.
9. ∠DCA ≅ ∠HGE	9. Def. of ≅ ∠s
10. △DCA ≅ △HGE	10. SAS
11. $\overline{DA} \cong \overline{HE}$; ∠D ≅ ∠H ∠CAD ≅ ∠GEH	11. CPCTC
12. m∠CAD = m∠GEH	12. Def. of ≅ ∠s
13. m∠CAD + m∠BAC = m∠GEH + m∠FEG	13. Addition prop.
14. m∠CAD + m∠BAC = m∠A; m∠GEH + m∠FEG = m∠E	14. Betweenness of rays
15. m∠A = m∠E	15. Subst. prop.
16. ∠A ≅ ∠E	16. Def. of ≅ ∠s
17. Quad ABCD ≅ Quad EFGH	17. Def. of ≅ quadrilaterals

Conclusion: Two quad. are ≅ if any three sides and the included ∠s of one are ≅, respectively, to the corresponding three sides and the included ∠s of the other.

32. Plan: Since △MNQ is isos., $\overline{NM} \cong \overline{QM}$ and ∠QNM ≅ ∠NQM. Thus, ∠NMT ≅ ∠QMP. The other needed congruences follow because TRAP is isos.

Proof:

Statements	Reasons
1. Isos. trap. TRAP; M is the midpoint of $\overline{TP}$; △MNQ is isos. with base $\overline{NQ}$.	1. Given
2. $\overline{NM} \cong \overline{QM}$	2. Def. of isos. △

3. ∠QNM ≅ ∠NQM	3. Isos. △Th.
4. $\overline{RA} \parallel \overline{TP}$	4. Def. of trapezoid
5. ∠QNM ≅ ∠NMT; ∠NQM ≅ ∠QMP	5. If ∥ lines have a transv., alt. int. ∠s are ≅.
6. ∠NMT ≅ ∠QMP	6. Subst. prop.
7. ∠T ≅ ∠P	7. Base ∠s of an isos. trap. are ≅.
8. $\overline{TR} ≅ \overline{PA}$	8. Def. of isos. trap.
9. $\overline{TM} ≅ \overline{PM}$	9. Def. of midpoint
10. Quad. TRNM ≅ quad. PAQM	10. SASAS

Conclusion: If TRAP is an isosceles trapezoid having M as the midpoint of $\overline{TP}$ and △MNQ isosceles, then quad. TRNM ≅ quad. PAQM.

33. Plan: Since △MNQ is isos., ∠QNM ≅ ∠NQM, and ∠RNM ≅ ∠AQM by supp. ∠s. The given provides the remaining needed congruences.

Proof:

Statements	Reasons
1. Trap. TRAP: ∠R ≅ ∠A; △MNQ is isos.; $\overline{RN} ≅ \overline{AQ}$.	1. Given
2. $\overline{NM} ≅ \overline{QM}$	2. Def. of isos. △
3. ∠QNM ≅ ∠NQM	3. Isos. △ Th.
4. ∠RNM and ∠QNM are a linear pair, as are ∠AQM and ∠NQM.	4. Def. of linear pair
5. ∠RNM and ∠QNM are supp.; ∠AQM and ∠NQM are supp.	5. Linear Pair Postulate
6. ∠RNM ≅ ∠AQM	6. Supplements of ≅ ∠s are ≅.
7. Trap. TRAP is isos.	7. If base∠s of a trap. are ≅, then trap. is isos.
8. $\overline{TR} ≅ \overline{PA}$	8. Def. of isos. trap.
9. Quad. TRNM ≅ quad. PAQM	9. SASAS

Conclusion: In trapezoid TRAP, if ∠R ≅ ∠A, △MNQ is isosceles, and $\overline{RN} ≅ \overline{AQ}$, then quad. TRNM ≅ quad. PAQM.

34. Given: ∠M ≅ ∠R; ∠N ≅ ∠S; ∠P ≅ ∠T; $\overline{MN} ≅ \overline{RS}$; $\overline{NP} ≅ \overline{ST}$

Prove: Quad. MNPQ ≅ quad. RSTU

Plan: Draw diagonals $\overline{MP}$ and $\overline{RT}$. △MNP ≅ △RST by SAS, so $\overline{MP} ≅ \overline{RT}$, ∠NMP ≅ ∠SRT, and ∠NPM ≅ ∠STR. Deduce that ∠MPQ ≅ ∠RTU and ∠PMQ ≅ ∠TRU to get △MPQ ≅ △RTU. Thus, ∠Q ≅ ∠U, $\overline{PQ} ≅ \overline{TU}$, and $\overline{QM} ≅ \overline{UR}$.

Proof:

Statements	Reasons
1. ∠M ≅ ∠R; ∠N ≅ ∠S; ∠P ≅ ∠T; $\overline{MN} ≅ \overline{RS}$; $\overline{NP} ≅ \overline{ST}$	1. Given
2. Draw $\overline{MP}$ and $\overline{RT}$.	2. Two points determine a line.
3. △MNP ≅ △RST	3. SAS
4. $\overline{MP} ≅ \overline{RT}$; ∠NPM ≅ ∠STR; ∠NMP ≅ ∠SRT	4. CPCTC
5. m∠NPM = m∠STR; m∠NMP = m∠SRT	5. Def. of ≅ ∠s
6. m∠P = m∠NPM + m∠MPQ; m∠T = m∠STR + m∠RTU; m∠M = m∠NMP + m∠PMQ; m∠R = m∠SRT + m∠TRU	6. Betweenness of rays
7. m∠NPM + m∠MPQ = m∠STR + m∠RTU; m∠NMP + m∠PMQ = m∠SRT + m∠TRU	7. Subst. prop.
8. m∠MPQ = m∠RTU; m∠PMQ = m∠TRU	8. Subtraction prop.
9. ∠MPQ ≅ ∠RTU; ∠PMQ ≅ ∠TRU	9. Def. of ≅ ∠s
10. △MPQ ≅ △RTU	10. ASA
11. $\overline{PQ} ≅ \overline{TU}$; $\overline{QM} ≅ \overline{UR}$; ∠Q ≅ ∠U	11. CPCTC
12. Quad. MNPQ ≅ quad. RSTU	12. Def. of ≅ quad.

Conclusion: Two quad. are ≅ if any three ∠s and the included sides of one are ≅, respectively, to the three corresponding ∠s and the included sides of the other.

35. Given: Quadrilaterals MNPQ and RSTU with ∠M ≅ ∠R; ∠N ≅ ∠S; ∠P ≅ ∠T

Prove: ∠Q ≅ ∠U

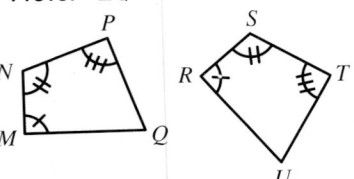

Plan: Use the fact that the sum of the measures of the interior angles of a quadrilateral is 360 to reach the conclusion.

Proof:

Statements	Reasons
1. ∠M ≅ ∠R; ∠N ≅ ∠S; ∠P ≅ ∠T	1. Given
2. m∠M = m∠R; m∠N = m∠S; m∠P = m∠T	2. Def. of ≅ ∠s
3. m∠M + m∠N + m∠P + m∠Q = 360; m∠R + m∠S + m∠T + m∠U = 360	3. Sum of the measures of the int. ∠s of a quad. is 360.
4. m∠M + m∠N + m∠P + m∠Q = m∠R + m∠S + m∠T + m∠U	4. Subst. prop.
5. m∠Q = m∠U	5. Subtr. prop.
6. ∠Q ≅ ∠U	6. Def. of ≅ ∠s

Conclusion: If three ∠s of one quad. are ≅ to the corresponding ∠s of another quad., the remaining ∠s are ≅.

36. Given: Square *ABCD* and square *EFGH*; $\overline{AB} \cong \overline{EF}$

Prove: Square *ABCD* ≅ square *EFGH*

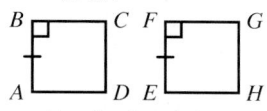

Plan: Use the fact that squares contain rt. ∠s and that all rt. ∠s are ≅, along with the fact that the sides of a square are ≅, and the given, to reach the conclusion.

Proof:

Statements	Reasons
1. Squares *ABCD* and *EFGH*; $\overline{AB} \cong \overline{EF}$	1. Given
2. $\overline{AB} \cong \overline{BC} \cong \overline{CD}$; $\overline{EF} \cong \overline{FG} \cong \overline{GH}$	2. A square has 4 ≅ sides.
3. $\overline{BC} \cong \overline{FG}$; $\overline{CD} \cong \overline{GH}$	3. Subst. prop.
4. ∠*B*, ∠*C*, ∠*F*, and ∠*G* are rt. ∠s.	4. A square has 4 rt. ∠s.
5. ∠*B* ≅ ∠*F*; ∠*C* ≅ ∠*G*	5. All rt. ∠s are ≅.
6. Square *ABCD* ≅ Square *EFGH*	6. SASAS

Conclusion: Two squares are ≅ if a side of the first square is ≅ to a side of the second square.

37. Given: Rectangles *ABCD* and *EFGH*; $\overline{AB} \cong \overline{EF}$; $\overline{BC} \cong \overline{FG}$

Prove: Rect. *ABCD* ≅ rect. *EFGH*

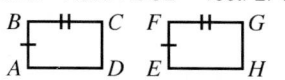

Plan: Use the fact that opposite sides of a ▱ are ≅ and the fact that a rect. has 4 rt. ∠s to verify the congruence.

Proof:

Statements	Reasons
1. Rectangles *ABCD* and *EFGH*; $\overline{AB} \cong \overline{EF}$; $\overline{BC} \cong \overline{FG}$	1. Given
2. ∠s *B*, *C*, *F*, and *G* are rt. ∠s.	2. A rect. has 4 rt. ∠s.
3. ∠*B* ≅ ∠*F*; ∠*C* ≅ ∠*G*	3. All rt. ∠s are ≅.

---

4. *ABCD* and *EFGH* are Ⓢ.	4. Def. of rect.
5. $\overline{AB} \cong \overline{CD}$; $\overline{EF} \cong \overline{GH}$	5. Opp. sides of a ▱ are ≅.
6. $\overline{CD} \cong \overline{GH}$	6. Subst. prop.
7. Rect. *ABCD* ≅ Rect. *EFGH*	7. SASAS

Conclusion: Two rectangles are ≅ if a pair of consecutive sides of one rectangle is ≅ to the corresponding sides of the other.

38. Given: Rectangles *MNPQ* and *HIJK*; $\overline{MN} \cong \overline{HI}$; $\overline{MP} \cong \overline{HJ}$

Prove: Rect. *MNPQ* ≅ rect. *HIJK*

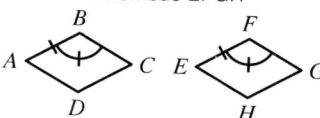

Plan: Show right △*MNP* ≅ △*HIJ* by HL. Then, $\overline{NP} \cong \overline{IJ}$, and the conclusion follows from Exercise 37.

Proof:

Statements	Reasons
1. Rectangles *MNPQ* and *HIJK*; $\overline{MN} \cong \overline{HI}$; $\overline{MP} \cong \overline{HJ}$	1. Given
2. ∠*N* and ∠*I* are rt. ∠s.	2. Def. of rectangle
3. △*MNP* and △*HIJ* are rt. Ⓢ.	3. Def. of rt. △
4. △*MNP* ≅ △*HIJ*	4. HL
5. $\overline{NP} \cong \overline{IJ}$	5. CPCTC
6. Rectangle *MNPQ* ≅ Rectangle *HIJI*	6. Result of Exercise 37

Conclusion: Two rectangles are ≅ if a side and diagonal of one are ≅ to the corresponding parts of the other.

39. Given: Rhombuses *ABCD* and *EFGH*; $\overline{AB} \cong \overline{EF}$; ∠*B* ≅ ∠*F*

Prove: Rhombus *ABCD* ≅ Rhombus *EFGH*

Plan: Use the given and the fact that all sides of a rhombus are ≅.

Proof:

Statements	Reasons
1. Rhombuses *ABCD* and *EFGH*; $\overline{AB} \cong \overline{EF}$; ∠*B* ≅ ∠*F*	1. Given
2. $\overline{AB} \cong \overline{BC} \cong \overline{CD}$; $\overline{EF} \cong \overline{FG} \cong \overline{GH}$	2. A rhombus has 4 ≅ sides.
3. $\overline{BC} \cong \overline{FG}$; $\overline{CD} \cong \overline{GH}$	3. Subst. prop.
4. *ABCD* and *EFGH* are Ⓢ.	4. Def. of rhombus
5. ∠*B* and ∠*C* are supp.; ∠*F* and ∠*G* are supp.	5. Consecutive ∠s in a ▱ are supp.
6. m∠*B* + m∠*C* = 180; m∠*F* + m∠*G* = 180	6. Def. of supp. ∠s
7. m∠*B* + m∠*C* = m∠*F* + m∠*G*	7. Subst. prop.
8. m∠*B* = m∠*F*	8. Def. of ≅ ∠s
9. m∠*C* = m∠*G*	9. Subtr. prop.
10. ∠*C* ≅ ∠*G*	10. Def. of ≅ ∠s
11. Rhombus *ABCD* ≅ Rhombus *EFGH*	11. SASAS

Conclusion: Two rhombuses are ≅ if a side and one ∠ of one rhombus are ≅ to the corr. parts of the other.

PAGE 253

6. Plan: Since *QUAD* is a ▱, its opp. sides and opp. ∠s are ≅. Also, ∠*URI* ≅ ∠*DIR*. The concl. follows by ASASA.

Proof:

Statements	Reasons
1. ▱*QUAD*; $\overline{UR} \cong \overline{DI}$	1. Given
2. ∠*Q* ≅ ∠*A*; ∠*U* ≅ ∠*D*	2. Opp. ∠s of a ▱ are ≅.
3. $\overline{UA} \parallel \overline{QD}$	3. Def. of ▱
4. ∠*URI* ≅ ∠*DIR*	4. If ∥ lines have a transv., alt. int. ∠s are ≅.
5. $\overline{QU} \cong \overline{AD}$	5. Opp. sides of a ▱ are ≅.
6. Quad. *QURI* ≅ quad. *ADIR*	6. ASASA

Conclusion: In $\square QUAD$, if $\overline{UR} \cong \overline{DI}$, then quad. $QURI \cong$ quad. $ADIR$.

PAGE 258

9. Plan: Show $\triangle ROL \cong \triangle GFP$ by SAS. Hence, $\angle RLE \cong \angle GPA$. Use alt. int. $\angle$s to get $\angle LRE \cong \angle PGA$. Thus, $\triangle RLE \cong \triangle GPA$ by ASA. The concl. follows.

Proof:

Statements	Reasons
1. $\square ROGF$ has a diagonal $\overline{RG}$; L and P are the respective midpts. of $\overline{RF}$ and $\overline{OG}$.	1. Given
2. $\overline{RF} \cong \overline{OG}$; $\overline{RO} \cong \overline{GF}$	2. Opp. sides of a $\square$ are $\cong$.
3. $RF = OG$	3. Def. of $\cong$ segments
4. $\frac{1}{2}RF = \frac{1}{2}OG$	4. Mult. prop.
5. $RL = \frac{1}{2}RF$; $GP = \frac{1}{2}OG$	5. Midpoint Th.
6. $RL = GP$	6. Subst. prop.
7. $\overline{RL} \cong \overline{GP}$	7. Def. of $\cong$ segments
8. $\angle R \cong \angle G$	8. Opp. $\angle$s of a $\square$ are $\cong$.
9. $\triangle ROL \cong \triangle GFP$	9. SAS
10. $\angle RLE \cong \angle GPA$	10. CPCTC
11. $\overline{RF} \parallel \overline{OG}$	11. Def. of $\square$
12. $\angle LRE \cong \angle PGA$	12. If $\parallel$ lines have a transv., alt. int. $\angle$s are $\cong$.
13. $\triangle RLE \cong \triangle GPA$	13. ASA
14. $\overline{RE} \cong \overline{GA}$	14. CPCTC

Conclusion: In $\square ROGF$, if L and P are the respective midpoints of $\overline{RF}$ and $\overline{OG}$, then $\overline{RE} \cong \overline{GA}$.

10. Plan: Use the theorem proven in Lesson 5, Exercise 27: *The figure formed by joining in order the midpoints of the sides of any quad. is a $\square$.* Complete the proof by showing $\overline{EF} \cong \overline{GF}$.

Proof:

Statements	Reasons
1. Isos. trap. $MNPQ$; E, F, G, and H are the midpoints of $\overline{MN}$, $\overline{NP}$, $\overline{PQ}$, and $\overline{QM}$.	1. Given
2. $EFGH$ is a $\square$.	2. The figure formed by joining in order the midpoints of the sides of a quad. is a $\square$.
3. $\overline{NM} \cong \overline{PQ}$	3. Def. of isos. trap.
4. $NM = PQ$	4. Def. of $\cong$ segments
5. $\frac{1}{2}NM = \frac{1}{2}PQ$	5. Mult. prop.
6. $NE = \frac{1}{2}NM$; $PG = \frac{1}{2}PQ$	6. Midpoint Th.
7. $NE = PG$	7. Subst. prop.
8. $\overline{NE} \cong \overline{PG}$	8. Def. of $\cong$ segments
9. $\overline{NF} \cong \overline{PF}$	9. Def. of midpt.
10. $\angle N \cong \angle P$	10. Base $\angle$s of an isos. trap. are $\cong$.
11. $\triangle NEF \cong \triangle PGF$	11. SAS
12. $\overline{EF} \cong \overline{GF}$	12. CPCTC
13. $EFGH$ is a rhombus.	13. Def. of rhombus

Conclusion: The figure formed by joining in order the midpoints of the sides of an isos. trap. is a rhombus.

PAGE 273

Class Exercise
4. Pent. $ABCDE$
$\sim$ Pent. $KLMNO$;
Scale factor: $\frac{3}{5}$;
$BA = 21$;
$AE = 9$;
$ED = 18$;
$NM = 15$

PAGE 280

14. Plan: Use the $\perp$ lines to show that $\angle B$ and $\angle D$ are rt. $\angle$s. $\angle 1 \cong \angle 3$, because they are comp. of $\cong \angle$s 2 and 4. The concl. follows by the AA Post.

Proof:

Statements	Reasons
1. $\overline{AB} \perp \overline{BD}$; $\overline{ED} \perp \overline{BD}$	1. Given
2. $\angle B$ and $\angle D$ are rt. $\angle$s.	2. Def. of $\perp$
3. $\angle B \cong \angle D$	3. All rt. $\angle$s are $\cong$.
4. $\angle 2 \cong \angle 4$; $\angle 2$ is comp to $\angle 1$; $\angle 4$ is comp. to $\angle 3$.	4. Given
5. $\angle 1 \cong \angle 3$	5. Comp. of $\cong \angle$s are $\cong$.
6. $\triangle ABC \sim \triangle EDC$	6. AA Post.

Conclusion: In the given figure, if $\overline{AB} \perp \overline{BD}$, $\overline{ED} \perp \overline{BD}$, $\angle 2 \cong \angle 4$, and $\angle 2$ and $\angle 4$ are complements of $\angle 1$ and $\angle 3$, respectively, then $\triangle ABC \sim \triangle EDC$.

15. Plan: Show $\triangle QMS \sim \triangle RMP$. Use corr. side lengths of $\sim \triangle$ are in proportion and propor. prop. 2 to get concl.

Proof:

Statements	Reasons
1. $\overline{SR} \perp \overline{TP}$; $\overline{PQ} \perp \overline{ST}$	1. Given
2. $\angle PRS$ and $\angle SQP$ are rt. $\angle$s.	2. Def. of $\perp$
3. $\angle PRS \cong \angle SQP$	3. All rt. $\angle$s are $\cong$.
4. $\angle QMS \cong \angle RMP$	4. Vert. $\angle$s are $\cong$.
5. $\triangle QMS \sim \triangle RMP$	5. AA Post.
6. $\frac{SM}{PM} = \frac{MQ}{MR}$	6. Corr. side lengths of $\sim \triangle$ are in proportion.
7. $\frac{SM}{MQ} = \frac{PM}{MR}$	7. Means of a proportion can be interchanged.

Conclusion: In the given figure, if $\overline{SR} \perp \overline{TP}$ and $\overline{PQ} \perp \overline{ST}$, then $\frac{SM}{MQ} = \frac{PM}{MR}$.

16. Plan: Show $\triangle TQP \sim \triangle TRS$. Concl. follows because corr. side lengths of $\sim \triangle$ are in proportion, and the means-extremes prop. of proportions.

Proof:

Statements	Reasons
1. $\overline{SR} \perp \overline{TP}$; $\overline{PQ} \perp \overline{ST}$	1. Given
2. $\angle TRS$ and $\angle TQP$ are rt. $\angle$s.	2. Def. of $\perp$ lines
3. $\angle TRS \cong \angle TQP$	3. All rt. $\angle$s are $\cong$.
4. $\angle T \cong \angle T$	4. Reflexive prop.
5. $\triangle TQP \sim \triangle TRS$	5. AA Post.
6. $\frac{QT}{TR} = \frac{TP}{TS}$	6. Corr. side lengths of $\sim$ △ are in proportion.
7. $QT \cdot TS = TR \cdot TP$	7. Means-extremes prop.

Conclusion: In the given figure, if $\overline{SR} \perp \overline{TP}$ and $\overline{PQ} \perp \overline{ST}$, then $QT \cdot TS = TP \cdot RT$.

17. Plan: Use the $\parallel$ line segments to show alt. int. $\angle$s $\cong$. Thus, $\triangle WVT \sim \triangle TRS$, and the concl. follows.

Proof:

Statements	Reasons
1. $\overline{WV} \parallel \overline{RT}$; $\overline{RS} \parallel \overline{TV}$	1. Given
2. $\angle VWT \cong \angle STR$; $\angle WTV \cong \angle TSR$	2. If $\parallel$ lines have a transv., alt. int. $\angle$s are $\cong$.
3. $\triangle WVT \sim \triangle TRS$	3. AA Post.
4. $\frac{RT}{VW} = \frac{RS}{TV}$	4. Corr. side lengths of $\sim$ △ are in proportion.
5. $RS \cdot VW = VT \cdot RT$	5. Means-extremes prop.

Conclusion: In the given figure, if $WV \parallel \overline{RT}$ and $\overline{RS} \parallel \overline{TV}$, then $RS \cdot VW = VT \cdot RT$.

18. Plan: Use the $\perp$ s to show $\angle WAV$ and $\angle ZBY$ are rt. $\angle$s. Use the given $\triangle$ similarity to show $\angle V \cong \angle Y$. The concl. follows by the AA Post.

Proof:

Statements	Reasons
1. $\overline{ZB} \perp \overline{XY}$; $\overline{WA} \perp \overline{UV}$	1. Given
2. $\angle ZBY$ and $\angle WAV$ are rt. $\angle$s.	2. Def. of $\perp$ lines
3. $\angle ZBY \cong \angle WAV$	3. All rt. $\angle$s are $\cong$.
4. $\triangle UVW \sim \triangle XYZ$	4. Given
5. $\angle V \cong \angle Y$	5. Corr. $\angle$s of $\sim$ △ are $\cong$.
6. $\triangle ZBY \sim \triangle WAV$	6. AA Post.

Conclusion: In the given figures, when $\overline{ZB} \perp \overline{XY}$, $\overline{WA} \perp \overline{UV}$, and $\triangle UVW \sim \triangle XYZ$, then $\triangle ZBY \sim \triangle WAV$.

PAGE 281

20. Plan: Use the def. of altitude and the reflex. prop. to apply the AA Post. to △ PAX and OYX.

Proof:

Statements	Reasons
1. $\overline{WP}$ and $\overline{XO}$ are altitudes.	1. Given
2. $\overline{WP} \perp \overline{XY}$; $\overline{XO} \perp \overline{YW}$	2. Def. of altitude
3. $\angle XPW$ and $\angle XOY$ are rt $\angle$s.	3. Def. of $\perp$ lines
4. $\angle XPW \cong \angle XOY$	4. All rt $\angle$s are $\cong$.
5. $\angle X \cong \angle X$	5. Reflexive prop.
6. $\triangle PAX \sim \triangle OYX$	6. AA Post.

Conclusion: In the given figure, if $\overline{WP}$ and $\overline{XO}$ are altitudes, then $\triangle PAX \sim \triangle OYX$.

21. Plan: Show $\triangle PAX \sim \triangle OAW$. The concl. follows from the fact that corr. side lengths of $\sim$ △ are in proportion and from the means-extremes prop.

Proof:

Statements	Reasons
1. $\overline{WP}$ and $\overline{XO}$ are altitudes.	1. Given
2. $\overline{WP} \perp \overline{XY}$; $\overline{XO} \perp \overline{YW}$	2. Def. of altitude
3. $\angle XPA$ and $\angle WOA$ are rt. $\angle$s.	3. Def. of $\perp$ lines
4. $\angle XPA \cong \angle WOA$	4. All rt. $\angle$s are $\cong$.
5. $\angle PAX \cong \angle OAW$	5. Vert. $\angle$s are $\cong$.
6. $\triangle PAX \sim \triangle OAW$	6. AA Post.
7. $\frac{PA}{AO} = \frac{XA}{AW}$	7. Corr. side lengths of $\sim$ △ are in proportion.
8. $PA \cdot AW = AO \cdot XA$	8. Means-extremes prop.

Conclusion: In the given figure, if $\overline{WP}$ and $\overline{XO}$ are altitudes, then $PA \cdot AW = AO \cdot XA$.

22. Plan: Since $\angle APC \cong \angle BPA$, $\overline{AP} \perp \overline{BC}$, and the conclusion follows.

Proof:

Statements	Reasons
1. $\triangle ACP \sim \triangle BAP$	1. Given
2. $\angle APC \cong \angle BPA$	2. Corr. $\angle$s of $\sim$ △ are $\cong$.
3. $\overline{AP} \perp \overline{BC}$	3. If 2 lines intersect to form $\cong$ adj. $\angle$s, then the lines are $\perp$.
4. $\overline{AP}$ is an altitude of $\triangle ACB$.	4. Def. of altitude

Conclusion: In the given figure, if $\triangle ACP \sim \triangle BAP$, $\overline{AP}$ is an altitude of $\triangle ACB$.

PAGE 285

19. Plan: Show $\triangle JMN \sim \triangle TCN$ by the SAS Th. The concl. follows because $\angle J$ and $\angle T$ are corr. parts of $\sim$ △.

Proof:

Statements	Reasons
1. $\frac{JM}{TC} = \frac{MN}{CN}$; $\angle 1 \cong \angle 2$	1. Given
2. $\angle 1$ and $\angle JMN$ form a linear pair; $\angle 2$ and $\angle TCN$ form a linear pair.	2. Def. of linear pair
3. $\angle 1$ and $\angle JMN$ are supp.; $\angle 2$ and $\angle TCN$ are supp.	3. Linear Pair Post.
4. $\angle JMN \cong \angle TCN$	4. Supp. of $\cong$ $\angle$s are $\cong$.
5. $\triangle JMN \sim \triangle TCN$	5. SAS Th.
6. $\angle J \cong \angle T$	6. Corr. $\angle$s of $\sim$ △ are $\cong$.

Conclusion: In the given figure, if $\angle 1 \cong \angle 2$ and $\frac{JM}{TC} = \frac{MN}{CN}$, then $\angle J \cong \angle T$.

20. Plan: Show $\triangle JMN \sim \triangle TCN$ by the SAS Th. Then, apply a prop. of proportions to the corr. segment lengths of the △.

Proof:

Statements	Reasons
1. $\angle J \cong \angle T$; $\frac{JM}{TC} = \frac{NJ}{NT}$	1. Given
2. $\triangle JMN \sim \triangle TCN$	2. SAS Th.

743

3. $\dfrac{JM}{TC} = \dfrac{MN}{CN} = \dfrac{NJ}{NT}$

3. Corr. side lengths of $\sim$ △ are in proportion.

4. $\dfrac{JM + MN + NJ}{TC + CN + NT} = \dfrac{MN}{CN}$

4. In a proportion, when the numerators are added and the denominators are added, a ratio will result equivalent to any of the ratios in the proportion.

Conclusion: In the given figure, if $\angle J \cong \angle T$ and $\dfrac{JM}{TC} = \dfrac{NJ}{NT}$, then $\dfrac{JM + MN + NJ}{TC + CN + NT} = \dfrac{MN}{CN}$.

PAGE 286

21. Plan: Use the given $\sim$ and the def. of median to get a proportion involving the side lengths of △ APC and DXF. The concl. follows by the SAS Th.

Proof:

Statements	Reasons
1. $\triangle ABC \sim \triangle DEF$; AP and DX are medians.	1. Given
2. $\angle C \cong \angle F$; $\dfrac{DF}{AC} = \dfrac{EF}{BC}$	2. Def. of $\sim$ △
3. $\dfrac{EF}{BC} = \dfrac{\frac{1}{2}EF}{\frac{1}{2}BC}$	3. Multiplying both parts of a ratio by the same nonzero number gives an equivalent ratio.
4. P is the midpoint of $\overline{CB}$; X is the midpoint of $\overline{EF}$.	4. Def. of median
5. $FX = \frac{1}{2}EF$; $CP = \frac{1}{2}CB$	5. Midpoint Th.
6. $\dfrac{EF}{BC} = \dfrac{FX}{CP}$	6. Subst. prop.
7. $\dfrac{DF}{AC} = \dfrac{FX}{CP}$	7. Transitive prop.
8. $\triangle APC \sim \triangle DXF$	8. SAS Th.

Conclusion: In the given figure, if $\triangle ABC \sim \triangle DEF$ and AP and DX are medians, then $\triangle APC \sim \triangle DXF$.

22. Plan: Use the given $\sim$ △ and the def. of altitude to show the △ $\sim$ by the AA Post.

Proof:

Statements	Reasons
1. $\triangle RST \sim \triangle JKM$	1. Given
2. $\angle T \cong \angle M$	2. Def. of $\sim$ △
3. $\overline{SP}$ and $\overline{KV}$ are altitudes.	3. Given
4. $\overline{SP} \perp \overline{RT}$; $\overline{KV} \perp \overline{JM}$	4. Def. of altitude
5. $\angle SPT$ and $\angle KVM$ are rt. $\angle$s.	5. Def. of $\perp$ lines
6. $\angle SPT \cong \angle KVM$	6. All rt. $\angle$s are $\cong$.
7. $\triangle SPT \sim \triangle KVM$	7. AA Post.

Conclusion: In the given △, if $\overline{SP}$ and $\overline{KV}$ are altitudes, then $\triangle SPT \sim \triangle KVM$.

25. Proof:

Statements	Reasons
1. $\angle A \cong \angle P$	1. Given
2. Locate X on $\overrightarrow{PQ}$ such that $PX = AB$.	2. On a ray, there is exactly one point that is a given distance from the endpoint of the ray.
3. $\overline{PX} \cong \overline{AB}$	3. Def. of $\cong$ seg.
4. Through X, draw $k \parallel \overline{QR}$.	4. Through a point not on a line, there is exactly one line $\parallel$ to the given line.
5. $\angle PXY \cong \angle Q$	5. If lines are $\parallel$, corr. $\angle$s are $\cong$.
6. $\angle P \cong \angle P$	6. Reflexive prop.
7. $\triangle PXY \sim \triangle PQR$	7. AA Post.
8. $\dfrac{PX}{PQ} = \dfrac{PY}{PR}$	8. Corr. side lengths of $\sim$ △ are in proportion.
9. $PY = \dfrac{PX \cdot PR}{PQ}$	9. Algebraic prop.
10. $\dfrac{AB}{PQ} = \dfrac{AC}{PR}$	10. Given
11. $AC = \dfrac{AB \cdot PR}{PQ}$	11. Algebraic prop.
12. $AC = \dfrac{PX \cdot PR}{PQ}$	12. Subst. prop.
13. $PY \cong AC$	13. Trans. prop.
14. $\overline{PY} \cong \overline{AC}$	14. Def. of $\cong$ segments
15. $\triangle ABC \cong \triangle PXY$	15. SAS Post.
16. $\angle B \cong \angle PXY$	16. CPCTC
17. $\angle B \cong \angle Q$	17. Trans. prop. (Steps 5 and 16)
18. $\triangle ABC \sim \triangle PQR$	18. AA Post.

Conclusion: If an $\angle$ of $\triangle ABC$ is $\cong$ to an $\angle$ of $\triangle PQR$, and the lengths of the sides that include those $\angle$s are in proportion, then $\triangle ABC \sim \triangle PQR$.

26. Proof:

Statements	Reasons
1. Locate V on $\overline{TS}$, such that $TV = DE$.	1. On a ray, there is exactly one point that is a given distance from the endpoint of the ray.
2. $\overline{TV} \cong \overline{DE}$	2. Def. of $\cong$ segments
3. Through V, draw $m \parallel \overline{SW}$.	3. Through a point not on a line, there is exactly one line $\parallel$ to the given line.
4. $\angle TVU \cong \angle TSW$	4. If lines are $\parallel$, corr. $\angle$s are $\cong$.
5. $\angle T \cong \angle T$	5. Reflexive prop.
6. $\triangle TVU \sim \triangle TSW$	6. AA Post.
7. $\dfrac{TV}{TS} = \dfrac{TU}{TW} = \dfrac{UV}{WS}$	7. Corr. side lengths of $\sim$ △ are in proportion.
8. $TU = \dfrac{TV \cdot TW}{TS}$; $UV = \dfrac{WS \cdot TV}{TS}$	8. Algebraic prop.
9. $\dfrac{ED}{TS} = \dfrac{DF}{TW}$; $\dfrac{ED}{TS} = \dfrac{FE}{WS}$	9. Given
10. $DF = \dfrac{ED \cdot TW}{TS}$; $FE = \dfrac{ED \cdot WS}{TS}$	10. Algebraic prop.
11. $DF = \dfrac{TV \cdot TW}{TS}$; $FE = \dfrac{TV \cdot WS}{TS}$	11. Subst. prop.
12. $DF = TU$; $FE = UV$	12. Trans. prop. (Step 8)
13. $\overline{DF} \cong \overline{TU}$; $\overline{FE} \cong \overline{UV}$	13. Def. of $\cong$ segments
14. $\triangle DEF \cong \triangle TVU$	14. SSS Post.
15. $\angle D \cong \angle T$; $\angle DEF \cong \angle TVU$	15. CPCTC

16. $\angle DEF \cong \angle TSW$ | 16. Transitive prop. (Step 4)
17. $\triangle DEF \sim \triangle TSW$ | 17. AA Post.

Conclusion: If in $\triangle$ DEF and TSW, $\dfrac{ED}{ST} = \dfrac{DF}{TW} = \dfrac{FE}{WS}$, then $\triangle DEF \sim \triangle TSW$.

27. Plan: Use pairs of $\sim$ $\triangle$ to show corr. $\angle$s $\cong$ and corr. side lengths in proportion for the 2 quads.

Proof:

Statements	Reasons
1. $\dfrac{PE}{PA} = \dfrac{PF}{PB} = \dfrac{PG}{PC} = \dfrac{PH}{PD}$	1. Given
2. $\angle APD \cong \angle EPH$; $\angle DPC \cong \angle HPG$; $\angle CPB \cong \angle GPF$; $\angle BPA \cong \angle FPE$	2. Reflexive prop.
3. $\triangle APD \sim \triangle EPH$; $\triangle DPC \sim \triangle HPG$; $\triangle CPB \sim \triangle GPF$; $\triangle BPA \sim \triangle FPE$	3. SAS Th.
4. $\angle DAP \cong \angle HEP$; $\angle ADP \cong \angle EHP$; $\angle CDP \cong \angle GHP$; $\angle DCP \cong \angle HGP$; $\angle BCP \cong \angle FGP$; $\angle CBP \cong \angle GFP$; $\angle PBA \cong \angle PFE$; $\angle PAB \cong \angle PEF$	4. Corr. $\angle$s of $\sim$ $\triangle$ are $\cong$.
5. $m\angle DAP = m\angle HEP$; $m\angle ADP = m\angle EHP$; $m\angle CDP = m\angle GHP$; $m\angle DCP = m\angle HGP$; $m\angle BCP = m\angle FGP$; $m\angle CBP = m\angle GFP$; $m\angle PBA = m\angle PFE$; $m\angle PAB = m\angle PEF$	5. Def. of $\cong$ $\angle$s
6. $m\angle DAP + m\angle PAB = m\angle HEP + m\angle PEF$; $m\angle ADP + m\angle CDP = m\angle EHP + m\angle GHP$; $m\angle DCP + m\angle BCP = m\angle HGP + m\angle FGP$; $m\angle CBP + m\angle PBA = m\angle GFP + m\angle PFE$	6. Addition prop.
7. $m\angle DAB = m\angle HEF$; $m\angle ADC = m\angle EHG$; $m\angle DCB = m\angle HGF$; $m\angle CBA = m\angle GFE$	7. Def. of betweenness and Subst.
8. $\angle DAB \cong \angle HEF$; $\angle ADC \cong \angle EHG$; $\angle DCB \cong \angle HGF$; $\angle CBA \cong \angle GFE$	8. Def. of $\cong$ $\angle$s
9. $\dfrac{AD}{HE} = \dfrac{DC}{HG} = \dfrac{CB}{GF} = \dfrac{BA}{FE}$	9. Corr. side lengths of $\sim$ $\triangle$s are in proportion.
10. $EFGH \sim ABCD$	10. Def. of $\sim$ polygons

Conclusion: In the given figure, if $\dfrac{PE}{PA} = \dfrac{PF}{PB} = \dfrac{PG}{PC} = \dfrac{PH}{PD}$, then $EFGH \sim ABCD$.

28. Plan: Use the reflexive property and given relationship of the side lengths to show the $\triangle$ similar by the SAS Th.

Proof:

Statements	Reasons
1. $\dfrac{DP}{DF} = \dfrac{QF}{DF} = \dfrac{1}{3}$; $\dfrac{DU}{DE} = \dfrac{TE}{DE} = \dfrac{1}{3}$; $\dfrac{FR}{FE} = \dfrac{SE}{FE} = \dfrac{1}{3}$	1. Given
2. $\dfrac{DP}{DF} = \dfrac{DU}{DE}$; $\dfrac{TE}{DE} = \dfrac{SE}{FE}$; $\dfrac{FR}{FE} = \dfrac{QF}{FD}$	2. Transitive prop.
3. $\angle D \cong \angle D$; $\angle E \cong \angle E$; $\angle F \cong \angle F$	3. Reflexive prop.
4. $\triangle DPU \sim \triangle DFE$; $\triangle TSE \sim \triangle DFE$; $\triangle QFR \sim \triangle DFE$	4. SAS Th.

Conclusion: In the given figure, if P, Q, R, S, T, and U separate $\overline{DF}$, $\overline{FE}$, and $\overline{ED}$ into thirds, then the 3 $\triangle$ formed are $\sim$ $\triangle DFE$.

29. Plan: Show that pairs of corr. $\triangle$ are $\sim$. Then, use the corr. parts and the defs. of linear pair and supp. to arrive at the concl.

Proof:

Statements	Reasons
1. $\triangle GHI \sim \triangle DFE$	1. Given
2. $\angle G \cong \angle D$; $\angle H \cong \angle F$; $\angle I \cong \angle E$	2. Def. of $\sim$ $\triangle$

3. $\dfrac{DP}{DF} = \dfrac{DU}{DE} = \dfrac{1}{3}$;
$\dfrac{FQ}{FD} = \dfrac{FR}{FE} = \dfrac{1}{3}$;
$\dfrac{ET}{ED} = \dfrac{ES}{EF} = \dfrac{1}{3}$;
$\dfrac{GJ}{GH} = \dfrac{GO}{GI} = \dfrac{1}{3}$;
$\dfrac{HK}{GH} = \dfrac{HL}{HI} = \dfrac{1}{3}$;
$\dfrac{IM}{IH} = \dfrac{IN}{IG} = \dfrac{1}{3}$ | 3. Given

4. $\triangle DPU \sim \triangle GJO$;
$\triangle FRQ \sim \triangle HLK$;
$\triangle SET \sim \triangle MIN$ | 4. SAS Th.

5. $\dfrac{PU}{JO} = \dfrac{RQ}{LK} = \dfrac{ST}{MN}$ | 5. Def. of $\sim$ $\triangle$

6. $\dfrac{PQ}{DF} = \dfrac{UT}{DE} = \dfrac{RS}{FE} = \dfrac{1}{3}$;
$\dfrac{JK}{GH} = \dfrac{LM}{HI} = \dfrac{ON}{GI} = \dfrac{1}{3}$ | 6. Given

7. $\dfrac{PQ}{DF} = \dfrac{JK}{GH} = \dfrac{1}{3}$;
$\dfrac{UT}{DE} = \dfrac{ON}{GI} = \dfrac{1}{3}$;
$\dfrac{RS}{DF} = \dfrac{LM}{HI} = \dfrac{1}{3}$ | 7. Transitive prop.

8. $\dfrac{PQ}{JK} = \dfrac{DF}{GH} = \dfrac{1}{3}$;
$\dfrac{UT}{ON} = \dfrac{DE}{GI} = \dfrac{1}{3}$;
$\dfrac{RS}{LM} = \dfrac{DF}{HI} = \dfrac{1}{3}$ | 8. Proportion prop. (interchange the means)

9. $\dfrac{PQ}{JK} = \dfrac{1}{3}$;
$\dfrac{UT}{ON} = \dfrac{1}{3}$;
$\dfrac{RS}{LM} = \dfrac{1}{3}$ | 9. Transitive prop.

10. $\angle DPU \cong \angle GJO$;
$\angle DUP \cong \angle GOJ$;
$\angle FQR \cong \angle HKL$;
$\angle FRQ \cong \angle HLK$;
$\angle EST \cong \angle IMN$;
$\angle ETS \cong \angle INM$ | 10. Def. of $\sim$ $\triangle$

11. The following are linear pairs and, therefore, supplementary:
$\angle DPU$ and $\angle QPU$; $\angle GJO$ and $\angle KJO$;
$\angle DUP$ and $\angle TUP$; $\angle GOJ$ and $\angle JON$;
$\angle FQR$ and $\angle PQR$; $\angle HKL$ and $\angle JKL$;
$\angle FRQ$ and $\angle SRQ$; $\angle HLK$ and $\angle MLK$;
$\angle EST$ and $\angle RST$; $\angle IMN$ and $\angle LMN$. | 11. Def. of linear pair and Linear Pair Post.

12. ∠QPU ≅ ∠KJO;
∠PUT ≅ ∠JON;
∠UTS ≅ ∠ONM;
∠TSR ≅ ∠NML;
∠SRQ ≅ ∠MLK;
∠RQP ≅ ∠LKJ

12. Supplements of ≅ ∠s are ≅

13. Hexagon PQRSTU ~ hexagon JKLMNO

13. Def. of ~ polygons

Conclusion: If $\overline{PU}$, $\overline{TS}$, and $\overline{QR}$ divide the sides of ∠DEF into thirds and $\overline{JO}$, $\overline{NM}$, and $\overline{KL}$ do the same to △GHI, and △DFE ~ △GHI, then the hexagons formed are ~.

PAGE 296

18. Given: △ABC ~ △DEF; $\overline{BR}$ and $\overline{ES}$ are corr. altitudes.

Prove: $\dfrac{BR}{ES} = \dfrac{AB}{DE}$

Plan: Use the definitions of ~ △ and altitudes to show △ARB ~ △DSE. The concl. follows from def. of ~ △.

Proof:

Statements	Reasons
1. △ABC ~ △DEF; $\overline{BR}$ and $\overline{ES}$ are corr. altitudes.	1. Given
2. ∠A ≅ ∠D	2. Def. of ~ △
3. $\overline{BR} \perp \overline{AC}$; $\overline{ES} \perp \overline{DF}$	3. Def. of altitude
4. ∠ARB and ∠DSE are rt. ∠s.	4. Def of ⊥
5. ∠ARB ≅ ∠DSE	5. All rt. ∠s are ≅.
6. △ARB ~ △DSE	6. AA Post.
7. $\dfrac{BR}{ES} = \dfrac{AB}{DE}$	7. Def. of ~ △

Conclusion: If ~ △ ABC and DEF have corr. altitudes $\overline{BR}$ and $\overline{ES}$, then $\dfrac{BR}{ES} = \dfrac{AB}{DE}$.

24. Proof:

Statements	Reasons
1. $\dfrac{QN}{NR} = \dfrac{PM}{MR}$	1. Given
2. $\dfrac{QN + NR}{NR} = \dfrac{PM + MR}{MR}$	2. Propor. prop.
3. QN + NR = QR; PM + MR = PR	3. Def. of betweenness
4. $\dfrac{QR}{NR} = \dfrac{PR}{MR}$	4. Subst. prop.
5. ∠R ≅ ∠R	5. Reflexive prop.
6. △QRP ~ △NRM	6. SAS Th.
7. ∠P ≅ ∠RMN	7. Def. of ~ △

---

8. $\overline{NM} \parallel \overline{PQ}$

8. If 2 lines have a transv. and ≅ corr. ∠s, then the lines are ∥.

Conclusion: In the given figure, if $\dfrac{QN}{NR} = \dfrac{PM}{MR}$, then $\overline{NM} \parallel \overline{PQ}$.

25. Proof:

Statements	Reasons
1. Through B, draw line k ∥ $\overrightarrow{AX}$.	1. Through a point not on a line, there is exactly one line ∥ to the given line.
2. Extend $\overrightarrow{CA}$ so that it intersects k at Y.	2. Two coplanar non-∥ lines intersect.
3. $\overrightarrow{AX}$ bisects ∠A of △ABC.	3. Given
4. $\dfrac{BX}{XC} = \dfrac{AY}{AC}$	4. △ Propor. Th.
5. ∠1 ≅ ∠3	5. If ∥ lines have a transv., alt. int. ∠s are ≅.
6. ∠2 ≅ ∠4	6. If ∥ lines have a transv., corr. ∠s are ≅.
7. ∠1 ≅ ∠2	7. Def. of ∠ bis.
8. ∠3 ≅ ∠4	8. Subst. prop.
9. $\overline{AY} ≅ \overline{AB}$	9. Converse of Isos. △ Th.
10. AY = AB	10. Def. of ≅ segments
11. $\dfrac{BX}{XC} = \dfrac{AB}{AC}$	11. Subst. prop.

Conclusion: If $\overrightarrow{AX}$ bisects ∠A of △ABC, then $\dfrac{BX}{XC} = \dfrac{AB}{AC}$.

26. Given: $\overleftrightarrow{AD} \parallel \overleftrightarrow{XY} \parallel \overleftrightarrow{BC}$; transv. $\overleftrightarrow{AB}$ and $\overleftrightarrow{DC}$

Prove: $\dfrac{AX}{XB} = \dfrac{DY}{YC}$

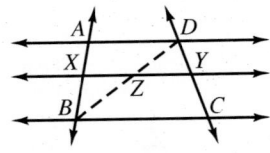

Plan: Draw $\overline{BD}$ and apply the △ Propor. Th. to each of the △ formed. The concl. follows by the transitive prop.

Proof:

Statements	Reasons
1. $\overleftrightarrow{AD} \parallel \overleftrightarrow{XY} \parallel \overleftrightarrow{BC}$; transv. $\overleftrightarrow{AB}$ and $\overleftrightarrow{DC}$	1. Given

---

2. Draw $\overline{BD}$.

2. Two points determine a unique line.

3. $\dfrac{AX}{XB} = \dfrac{DZ}{ZB}$; $\dfrac{DZ}{ZB} = \dfrac{DY}{YC}$

3. △ Propor. Th.

4. $\dfrac{AX}{XB} = \dfrac{DY}{YC}$

4. Transitive prop.

Conclusion: In the given figure, if $\overleftrightarrow{AD} \parallel \overleftrightarrow{XY} \parallel \overleftrightarrow{BC}$, then $\dfrac{AX}{XB} = \dfrac{DY}{YC}$.

28. Given: △RPQ with exterior ∠QPW; $\overrightarrow{PA}$ bisects ∠QPW.

Prove: $\dfrac{RX}{QX} = \dfrac{RP}{PQ}$

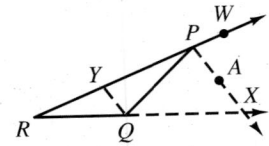

Plan: Draw $\overline{QY} \parallel \overline{PX}$. Then, apply the △ Propor. Th. and the Converse of the Isosceles △ Th to reach the desired proportion.

Proof:

Statements	Reasons
1. △RPQ with exterior ∠QPW; $\overrightarrow{PA}$ bisects ∠QPW.	1. Given
2. Extend $\overrightarrow{RQ}$.	2. A ray can be extended infinitely.
3. Extend $\overrightarrow{PA}$ to intersect $\overrightarrow{RQ}$ at X.	3. If 2 coplanar lines are not ∥, then they intersect.
4. Draw $\overline{QY} \parallel \overline{PX}$.	4. Through a point not on a line there is exactly one ∥ line.
5. $\dfrac{RY}{YP} = \dfrac{RQ}{QX}$	5. △ Propor. Th.
6. $\dfrac{RY + YP}{YP} = \dfrac{RQ + QX}{QX}$	6. Proportion props.
7. $\dfrac{RP}{YP} = \dfrac{RX}{QX}$	7. Def. of betw. and Subst.
8. ∠XPQ ≅ ∠PQY	8. If lines are ∥, alt. int. ∠s are ≅.
9. ∠XPW ≅ ∠QYP	9. If lines are ∥, corr. ∠s are ≅.
10. ∠XPQ ≅ ∠XPW	10. Def. of ∠ bis.
11. ∠PQY ≅ ∠QYP	11. Subst. prop.

12. $\overline{PQ} \cong \overline{PY}$ | 12. Converse of Isos. △ Th.
13. $PQ = PY$ | 13. Def. of ≅ seg.
14. $\dfrac{RP}{PQ} = \dfrac{RX}{QX}$ | 14. Subst. prop. (line 7)

Conclusion: In the given figure, if $\overrightarrow{PA}$ bisects exterior $\angle QPW$ and intersects $\overrightarrow{RQ}$ at X, then $\dfrac{RX}{QX} = \dfrac{RP}{PQ}$.

PAGE 297, TEST YOURSELF

1. If 2 sides of one △ are respectively proportional to 2 corr. sides of a 2nd △, and the included ∠s are ≅, then the △s are ~.

2. If a ray bisects an ∠ of a △, then it separates the opp. side into segments proportional to the other 2 sides of the △.

3. $\overline{DY} \parallel \overline{CB}$ (2 lines ⊥ to the same line are ∥); $\angle C \cong \angle DYX$ (alt. int. ∠s of ∥ lines are ≅); $\angle D \cong \angle B$ (all rt. ∠s are ≅) △CBA ~ △YDX; (AA Postulate). $\dfrac{CB}{YD} = \dfrac{BA}{DX} = \dfrac{AC}{XY}$.

CHALLENGE: PAGE 302

Given: $\overline{RA} \parallel \overline{SB}$; $\overline{XA} \parallel \overline{YB}$; $\overline{RX} \parallel \overline{SY}$
Prove: △RXA ~ △SYB
Plan: Use the ∥ sides to show corr. ∠s ≅. The concl. follows by the AA Post.

Proof:

Statements	Reasons
1. $\overline{RA} \parallel \overline{SB}$; $\overline{XA} \parallel \overline{YB}$; $\overline{RX} \parallel \overline{SY}$	1. Given
2. $\angle A \cong \angle PQX$; $\angle PQX \cong \angle B$; $\angle R \cong \angle XPQ$; $\angle XPQ \cong \angle S$	2. If ∥ lines have a transv., corr. ∠s are ≅.
3. $\angle A \cong \angle B$; $\angle R \cong \angle S$	3. Transitive prop.
4. △RXA ~ △SYB	4. AA Post.

Conclusion: If the corr. sides of △RXA and △SYB are ∥, then △RXA ~ △SYB.

PAGE 309

38. Given: Rt. △ACB with alt. $\overline{CD}$
Prove: $\dfrac{BD}{BC} = \dfrac{BC}{BA}$ and $\dfrac{AD}{AC} = \dfrac{AC}{BA}$

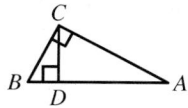

Plan: Use Th. 8.1 to prove △CBD ~ △ABC and △ACD ~ △ABC. The concl. follows by def. of ~ △.

Proof:

Statements	Reasons
1. Rt. △ACB with altitude $\overline{CD}$	1. Given
2. △CBD ~ △ABC; △ACD ~ △ABC	2. Th. 8.1
3. $\dfrac{BD}{BC} = \dfrac{BC}{BA}$ and $\dfrac{AD}{AC} = \dfrac{AC}{BA}$	3. Def. of ~ △.

Conclusion: In rt. △ACB, if $\overline{CD}$ is the alt. to the hyp., then $\dfrac{BD}{BC} = \dfrac{BC}{BA}$ and $\dfrac{AD}{AC} = \dfrac{AC}{BA}$.

PAGE 310

40. Given: Rt. △BCA with alt. $\overline{CD}$
Prove: $BC \cdot AC = AB \cdot CD$

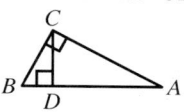

Plan: Use Th. 8.1 to show △CBD ~ △ABC. The concl. follows by the def. of ~ △ and the Means-extremes property.

Proof:

Statements	Reasons
1. Rt. △BCA with alt. $\overline{CD}$	1. Given
2. △CBD ~ △ABC	2. Th. 8.1
3. $\dfrac{BC}{AB} = \dfrac{CD}{AC}$	3. Def. of ~ △
4. $BC \cdot AC = AB \cdot CD$	4. Means-extremes prop.

Conclusion: If rt. △BCA has alt. $\overline{CD}$ drawn to the hyp., then $BC \cdot AC = AB \cdot CD$.

42. Given: Rt. △BCA with altitude $\overline{CP}$ to the hyp.; $\overrightarrow{CQ}$ bisects $\angle C$.
Prove: $\dfrac{BP}{AP} = \left(\dfrac{BQ}{QA}\right)^2$

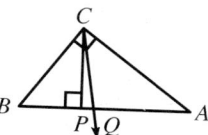

Plan: Apply the properties of algebra to proportions resulting when the altitude is drawn to the hypotenuse and when an ∠ of a △ is bisected.

Proof:

Statements	Reasons
1. Rt. △BCA with altitude $\overline{CP}$ to the hyp. and $\overrightarrow{CQ}$ bisecting $\angle C$	1. Given
2. $\dfrac{BP}{CB} = \dfrac{CB}{AB}$; $\dfrac{AP}{CA} = \dfrac{CA}{AB}$	2. Th. 8.1, Cor. 2
3. $(CB)^2 = BP \cdot AB$; $(CA)^2 = AP \cdot AB$	3. Means-extremes prop.
4. $\dfrac{(CB)^2}{(CA)^2} = \dfrac{BP \cdot AB}{AP \cdot AB}$	4. Div. prop.
5. $\dfrac{BP \cdot AB}{AP \cdot AB} = \dfrac{BP}{AP}$	5. Dividing the num. and denom. by the same non-0 number produces an equiv. ratio.
6. $\dfrac{(CB)^2}{(CA)^2} = \dfrac{BP}{AP}$	6. Transitive prop.
7. $\dfrac{CB}{CA} = \dfrac{BQ}{QA}$	7. The bisector of an ∠ of a △ divides the opp. side into lengths proportional to the lengths of the adj. sides.
8. $\left(\dfrac{CB}{CA}\right)^2 = \left(\dfrac{BQ}{QA}\right)^2$	8. Mult. prop.
9. $\dfrac{BP}{AP} = \left(\dfrac{BQ}{QA}\right)^2$	9. Transitive prop.

Conclusion: If △BCA has rt. ∠C, alt. $\overrightarrow{CP}$ and ∠ bisector $\overrightarrow{CQ}$, then $\dfrac{BP}{AP} = \left(\dfrac{BQ}{QA}\right)^2$.

PAGE 319

28. Proof:

Statements	Reasons
1. △ABC with side lengths a, b, and c	1. Given
2. Draw rt. △DEF with rt. $\angle F$ and legs of lengths a and b.	2. In a plane, there is exactly one line ⊥ to a line through a given pt. on the line (rt. ∠F); on a ray there is exactly one pt. that is a given distance from the endpt. of the ray (FE and FD); two pts. determine a line (ED).
3. $(DE)^2 = a^2 + b^2$	3. Pyth. Th.
4. $c^2 > a^2 + b^2$	4. Given
5. $c^2 > (DE)^2$	5. Subst. prop.

6. $c > DE$ | 6. Square root prop.
7. $m\angle C > m\angle F$ | 7. Conv. of Hinge Th.
8. $m\angle F = 90$ | 8. Def. of rt. $\angle$
9. $m\angle C > 90$ | 9. Subst. prop.
10. $\angle C$ is obt. | 10. Def. of obt. $\angle$
11. $\triangle ABC$ is obt. | 11. Def. of obt. $\triangle$

Conclusion: In $\triangle ABC$ with side lengths a, b, and c, if $c^2 > a^2 + b^2$, then $\triangle ABC$ is obt.

29. Given: $\triangle ABC$ with longest side length c; $c^2 < a^2 + b^2$
Prove: $\triangle ABC$ is acute.

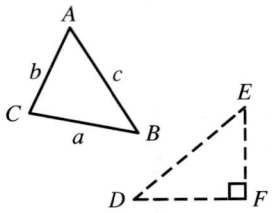

Plan: Introduce auxiliary $\triangle DEF$ with rt. $\angle F$ and legs of length a and b. By the Pyth. Th., $(DE)^2 = a^2 + b^2$. Since $c^2 < (DE)^2$, by the conv. of Hinge Th., $m\angle C < m\angle F$, and the concl. follows.

Proof:

Statements	Reasons
1. $\triangle ABC$ with side lengths a, b, and c; longest side length c	1. Given
2. Draw rt. $\triangle DEF$ with rt. $\angle F$ and legs of length a and b.	2. In a plane, there is exactly one line $\perp$ to a line through a given pt. on the line (rt. $\angle F$); on a ray, there is exactly one pt. that is a given distance from the endpt. of the ray (FE and FD); two pts. determine a line (ED).
3. $(DE)^2 = a^2 + b^2$	3. Pyth. Th.
4. $c^2 < a^2 + b^2$	4. Given
5. $c^2 < (DE)^2$	5. Subst. prop.
6. $c < DE$	6. Square root prop.

748

---

7. $m\angle C < m\angle F$ | 7. Conv. of Hinge Th.
8. $m\angle F = 90$ | 8. Def. of rt. $\angle$
9. $m\angle C < 90$ | 9. Subst. prop.
10. $\angle C$ is acute. | 10. Def. of acute $\angle$
11. $m\angle C > m\angle A$; $m\angle C > m\angle B$ | 11. $\triangle$ Ineq. Th.
12. $\triangle ABC$ is acute. | 12. Def. of acute $\triangle$

Conclusion: In $\triangle ABC$ with side lengths a, b, and c with longest side length c, if $c^2 < a^2 + b^2$, then $\triangle ABC$ is acute.

30. Plan: Use the given and the Pyth. Th. to relate the side lengths of $\triangle ACP$ and $\triangle CBP$. The concl. follows by the trans. prop. and the conv. of the Pyth. Th.

Proof:

Statements	Reasons
1. CP is the geom. mean between BP and AP.	1. Given
2. $\dfrac{BP}{h} = \dfrac{h}{AP}$	2. Def. of geom. mean
3. $h^2 = BP \cdot AP$	3. Means-extremes prop.
4. $AP + PB = AB = c$	4. Def. of betweenness
5. $c^2 = (AP + PB)^2$	5. Squaring prop.
6. $c^2 = AP^2 + 2(AP \cdot PB) + PB^2$	6. Squaring a binomial
7. $c^2 = AP^2 + 2h^2 + PB^2$	7. Subst. prop.
8. $a^2 = h^2 + PB^2$; $b^2 = h^2 + AP^2$	8. Pyth. Th.
9. $a^2 + b^2 = AP^2 + 2h^2 + PB^2$	9. Add. prop.
10. $a^2 + b^2 = c^2$	10. Trans. prop.
11. $\triangle ABC$ is a rt. $\triangle$.	11. Conv. of Pyth. Th.

Conclusion: In the given figure, if CP is the geom. mean between BP and AP, then $\triangle ABC$ is a rt. $\triangle$.

31. Let $a = m^2 - n^2$, $b = 2mn$, and $c = m^2 + n^2$ where $m > n \geq 1$. Then $a^2 = (m^2 - n^2)^2$, $b^2 = (2mn)^2$, and $c^2 = (m^2 + n^2)^2$
$a^2 + b^2 = (m^2 - n^2)^2 + (2mn)^2$
$\qquad = m^4 - 2m^2n^2 + n^4 + 4m^2n^2$
$\qquad = m^4 + 2m^2n^2 + n^4$
$\qquad = (m^2 + n^2)^2$
$\qquad = c^2$
By the Conv. of Pyth. Th., $m^2 - n^2$, $2mn$, and $m^2 + n^2$ are side lengths of a rt. $\triangle$.

PAGE 325

23. Proof:

Statements	Reasons
1. $\triangle ABC$ is a 45°-45°-90° $\triangle$.	1. Given
2. $AC = BC = s$	2. Conv. of Isos. $\triangle$ Th.
3. $AB^2 = s^2 + s^2$	3. Pyth. Th.
4. $AB^2 = 2s^2$	4. Dist. prop.
5. $AB = s\sqrt{2}$	5. Square root prop.

Conclusion: If $\triangle ABC$ is a 45°-45°-90° $\triangle$ with rt. $\angle C$, then when $AC = BC = s$, $AB = s\sqrt{2}$.

24. Proof:

Statements	Reasons
1. $\triangle ABC$ is a 30°-60°-90° $\triangle$; $BC = s$.	1. Given
2. Extend $\overrightarrow{BC}$ to D such that $CD = BC$.	2. On a ray, exactly one pt. is at a given distance from the endpt. of the ray.
3. $CD = s$	3. Subst.
4. $BC + CD = BD$	4. Def. of betw.
5. $s + s = BD$	5. Subst. prop.
6. $2s = BD$	6. Dist. prop.
7. $\overline{CD} \cong \overline{BC}$	7. Def. $\cong$ seg.
8. Draw $\overline{AD}$.	8. Two pts. determine a line.
9. $\overline{AC} \cong \overline{AC}$	9. Reflexive prop.
10. $\angle BCA$ and $\angle DCA$ form a linear pair.	10. Def. of linear pair
11. $m\angle BCA + m\angle DCA = 180$	11. Linear Pair Post. and def. of suppl.
12. $m\angle BCA = 90$	12. Def. of rt. $\angle$
13. $90 + m\angle DCA = 180$	13. Subst. prop.
14. $m\angle DCA = 90$	14. Subt. prop.
15. $m\angle BCA = m\angle DCA$	15. Trans. prop.
16. $\angle BCA \cong \angle DCA$	16. Def. $\cong \angle$s
17. $\triangle BCA \cong \triangle DCA$	17. SAS Post.
18. $\angle B \cong \angle D$	18. CPCTC
19. $m\angle B = m\angle D$	19. Def. $\cong \angle$s
20. $m\angle D = 60$	20. Subst. prop.
21. $m\angle B + m\angle D + m\angle BAD = 180$	21. Sum of measures of $\angle$s of a $\triangle = 180$.
22. $m\angle BAD = 60$	22. Subtr. prop.

23. $\triangle ABD$ is equiangular.	23. Def. of equiangular $\triangle$
24. $\triangle ABD$ is equilateral.	24. An equiangular $\triangle$ is equilateral.
25. $\overline{AB} \cong \overline{BD}$	25. Def. of equilateral $\triangle$
26. $AB = BD$	26. Def. of $\cong$ segments
27. $AB = 2s$	27. Trans. prop. (Step 6)
28. $(AC)^2 + s^2 = (2s)^2$	28. Pyth. Th.
29. $(AC)^2 = 3s^2$	29. Subtr. prop.
30. $AC = s\sqrt{3}$	30. Square root prop.

Conclusion: If $\triangle ABC$ is a 30°-60°-90° $\triangle$ with $m\angle C = 90$ and $m\angle B = 60$ and $BC = s$, then $AB = 2s$ and $AC = s\sqrt{3}$.

PAGE 336

29. Let $\sin x = \dfrac{a}{c}$ and $\cos x = \dfrac{b}{c}$

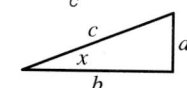

$$\sin^2 x + \cos^2 x = \left(\frac{a}{c}\right)^2 + \left(\frac{b}{c}\right)^2$$
$$= \frac{a^2}{c^2} + \frac{b^2}{c^2}$$
$$= \frac{a^2 + b^2}{c^2}$$
$$= \frac{c^2}{c^2}$$
$$= 1$$

30. Let $\sin x = \dfrac{a}{c}$, $\cos x = \dfrac{b}{c}$, and $\tan x = \dfrac{a}{b}$.

$$\frac{\sin x}{\cos x} = \frac{a}{c} \div \frac{b}{c}$$
$$= \frac{a}{c} \cdot \frac{c}{b}$$
$$= \frac{a}{b}$$
$$= \tan x$$

34. $\dfrac{\sin^2 x}{\cos^2 x} + \dfrac{\cos^2 x}{\cos^2 x} = \dfrac{1}{\cos^2 x}$

$\tan^2 x + 1 = \sec^2 x$

$\dfrac{\sin^2 x}{\sin^2 x} + \dfrac{\cos^2 x}{\sin^2 x} = \dfrac{1}{\sin^2 x}$

$1 + \cot^2 x = \csc^2 x$

PAGE 350

50. Plan: Show $\triangle ADM \cong \triangle ABN$ by SAS. Then $\overline{AM} \cong \overline{AN}$ by CPCTC.

Proof:

Statements	Reasons
1. $ABCD$ is a rhombus.	1. Given
2. $\overline{AD} \cong \overline{AB}$; $\overline{DC} \cong \overline{BC}$	2. Def. of rhombus
3. $DC = BC$	3. Def. of $\cong$ seg.
4. $\frac{1}{2}DC = \frac{1}{2}BC$	4. Mult. prop.
5. $\overline{AM}$ is a median of $\triangle DAC$; $\overline{AN}$ is a median of $\triangle BAC$	5. Given
6. M is the midpt. of $\overline{DC}$; N is the midpt. of $\overline{BC}$.	6. Def. of median
7. $DM = \frac{1}{2}DC$; $BN = \frac{1}{2}BC$	7. Midpt. Th.
8. $DM = BN$	8. Subst. prop.
9. $\overline{DM} \cong \overline{BN}$	9. Def. of $\cong$ seg.
10. $\angle D \cong \angle B$	10. Opp. $\angle$s of a $\square$ are $\cong$.
11. $\triangle ADM \cong \triangle ABN$	11. SAS
12. $\overline{AM} \cong \overline{AN}$	12. CPCTC

Concl.: If $ABCD$ is a rhombus and $\overline{AM}$ and $\overline{AN}$ are the respective medians of $\triangle DAC$ and $\triangle BAC$, then $\overline{AM} \cong \overline{AN}$.

51. Plan: Use the $\parallel$ line segments to show pairs of alt. int. $\angle$s $\cong$. Then $\triangle XYW \sim \triangle TSW$ by AA.

Proof:

Statements	Reasons
1. $\overline{XY} \parallel \overline{ST}$	1. Given
2. $\angle X \cong \angle T$; $\angle Y \cong \angle S$	2. If lines are $\parallel$, alt., int. $\angle$s are $\cong$.
3. $\triangle XYW \sim \triangle TSW$	3. AA

Concl.: In the given figure, if $\overline{XY} \parallel \overline{ST}$, then $\triangle XYW \sim \triangle TSW$.

52. Plan: Since $\triangle XYW \sim \triangle VZW$, $\dfrac{XW}{VW} = \dfrac{YW}{ZW}$. The concl. follows by the means-extremes prop.

Proof:

Statements	Reasons
1. $\triangle XYW \sim \triangle VZW$	1. Given
2. $\dfrac{XW}{VW} = \dfrac{YW}{ZW}$	2. If 2 $\triangle$ are $\sim$, corr. side lengths are in proportion.
3. $XW \cdot ZW = YW \cdot VW$	3. Means-extremes prop.

Concl.: In the given figure, if $\triangle XYW \sim \triangle VZW$, then $XW \cdot ZW = YW \cdot VW$.

PAGE 356

27. Plan: Use the *Given* and vert. $\angle$s to show $\triangle POQ \cong \triangle SOR$. Concl. follows by CPCTC.

Proof:

Statements	Reasons
1. $\overline{PR}$ and $\overline{QS}$ are diam.	1. Given
2. $\overline{OP}, \overline{OQ}, \overline{OS}, \overline{OR}$ are radii of $\odot O$.	2. Def. of radius
3. $\overline{OP} \cong \overline{OS}$, $\overline{OQ} \cong \overline{OR}$	3. Radii of the same $\odot$ are $\cong$.
4. $\angle POQ \cong \angle SOR$	4. Vert. $\angle$s are $\cong$.
5. $\triangle POQ \cong \triangle SOR$	5. SAS
6. $\overline{PQ} \cong \overline{SR}$	6. CPCTC

Conclusion: If $\overline{PR}$ and $\overline{QS}$ are diam. of the same $\odot$, then $\overline{PQ} \cong \overline{SR}$.

28. Plan: Draw $\overline{OB}$ and $\overline{OC}$. Then show $\triangle OBM \cong \triangle OCM$. Thus, $\overline{BM} \cong \overline{CM}$ by CPCTC and concl. follows.

Proof:

Statements	Reasons
1. Draw $\overline{OB}$ and $\overline{OC}$.	1. 2 pts. determine a line.
2. $\overline{OA} \perp \overline{BC}$	2. Given
3. $\angle OMB$ and $\angle OMC$ are rt. $\angle$s.	3. Def. of $\perp$
4. $\triangle OBM$ and $\triangle OCM$ are rt. $\triangle$	4. Def. of rt. $\triangle$
5. $\overline{OB} \cong \overline{OC}$	5. Radii of same $\odot$ are $\cong$.
6. $\overline{OM} \cong \overline{OM}$	6. Refl. prop.
7. $\triangle OBM \cong \triangle OCM$	7. HL Th.
8. $\overline{BM} \cong \overline{CM}$	8. CPCTC
9. $\overline{OA}$ bis. $\overline{BC}$.	9. Def. of bis.

Conclusion: If a radius is $\perp$ to a chord that is not a diam., then the radius bis. the chord.

29. Given: $\odot O$ with diam. $\overline{AB}$ and chord $\overline{CD}$

Prove: $AB > CD$

Plan: Use the $\triangle$ Ineq. Th. to show that $OC + OD > CD$. Since $OC = OD = OA = \frac{1}{2}AB$, the concl. follows by subst.

Proof:

Statements	Reasons
1. Draw $\overline{OC}$ and $\overline{OD}$.	1. Two pts. determine a line.
2. $OC + OD > CD$	2. △ Ineq. Th.
3. $OC = OD =$ $OA = OB$	3. All radii of a ⊙ have = lengths.
4. $OA + OB > CD$	4. Subst. prop.
5. $OA + OB = AB$	5. Betw. of pts.
6. $AB > CD$	6. Subst.

Conclusion: A diam. of a ⊙ is longer than any other chord that does not contain the center of that ⊙.

PAGE 360

21. Plan: Since $\overline{QR} \perp \overline{PR}$ and $\overline{QS} \perp \overline{PS}$, ∠R and ∠S meas. 90°. ∠s R and S are also opp. ∠s of quad. QRPS. Use the fact that the sum of the ∠ meas. of a quad. is 360 and algebraic props. to reach concl.

Proof:

Statements	Reasons
1. $\overline{PR}$ and $\overline{PS}$ are tangents.	1. Given
2. $\overline{QR} \perp \overline{PR}$; $\overline{QS} \perp \overline{PS}$	2. Th. 9.1
3. ∠QRP and ∠QSP are rt. ∠s.	3. Def. of ⊥
4. $m\angle QRP = 90$; $m\angle QSP = 90$	4. Def. of rt. ∠
5. $m\angle QRP +$ $m\angle QSP +$ $m\angle RQS +$ $m\angle RPS = 360$	5. Sum of meas. of ∠s of a quad = 360.
6. $90 + 90 +$ $m\angle RQS +$ $m\angle RPS = 360$	6. Subst. prop.
7. $m\angle RQS +$ $m\angle RPS = 180$	7. Subtr. prop.
8. ∠RPS and ∠RQS are supp.	8. Def. of supp.

Conclusion: In the quad. formed by 2 tan. segs. and 2 radii, the opp. ∠s are supp.

PAGE 361

22. Given: $\overline{SP}$ and $\overline{SR}$ are tan. to ⊙Q.
Prove: $\overline{SP} \cong \overline{SR}$
Plan: Draw $\overline{QP}$, $\overline{QR}$, and $\overline{SQ}$. Show △SPQ ≅ △SRQ by HL. Then by CPCTC, $\overline{SP} \cong \overline{SR}$.

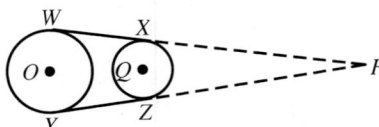

Proof:

Statements	Reasons
1. Draw $\overline{QP}$, $\overline{QR}$, and $\overline{SQ}$.	1. 2 pts. determine a line.
2. $\overline{SP}$ and $\overline{SR}$ are tan. segs.	2. Given
3. $\overline{QP} \perp \overline{PS}$; $\overline{QR} \perp \overline{RS}$	3. A tan. is ⊥ to a radius at the pt. of tangency.
4. ∠QPS and ∠QRS are rt. ∠s.	4. Def. of ⊥
5. △QPS and △QRS are rt. △s.	5. Def. of rt. △
6. $\overline{QP} \cong \overline{QR}$	6. Radii of same ⊙are ≅.
7. $\overline{SQ} \cong \overline{SQ}$	7. Refl. prop.
8. △SPQ ≅ △SRQ	8. HL
9. $\overline{SP} \cong \overline{SR}$	9. CPCTC

Conclusion: Two tans. from a common external pt. are ≅.

23. Given: $\overrightarrow{SP}$ and $\overrightarrow{SR}$ are tans. from S to ⊙Q; $\overrightarrow{SQ}$ is a ray from S to center of ⊙Q.
Prove: $\overrightarrow{SQ}$ bis. ∠PSR.
Plan: Draw $\overline{QP}$ and $\overline{QR}$. Show △SPQ ≅ △SRQ. Then ∠PSQ ≅ ∠RSQ by CPCTC and the concl. follows.

Proof:

Statements	Reasons
1. ⊙Q with tans. $\overrightarrow{SP}$ and $\overrightarrow{SR}$, and $\overrightarrow{SQ}$ through the center	1. Given
2. Draw $\overline{QP}$ and $\overline{QR}$.	2. 2 pts. determine a line.
3. $\overline{QP} \cong \overline{QR}$	3. Radii of the same ⊙ are ≅.
4. $\overline{PS} \cong \overline{RS}$	4. Cor. 1 of Th. 9.1
5. $\overline{QS} \cong \overline{QS}$	5. Refl. prop.
6. △PSQ ≅ △RSQ	6. SSS
7. ∠PSQ ≅ ∠RSQ	7. CPCTC
8. $\overrightarrow{SQ}$ bis. ∠PSR.	8. Def. of bis.

Conclusion: Two tan. rays from a common external pt. determine an ∠ that is bis. by the ray from the external pt. to the center of the ⊙.

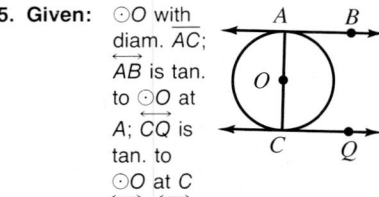

24. Plan: Extend $\overrightarrow{WX}$ and $\overrightarrow{YZ}$ to intersect at P. Then $\overline{PW} \cong \overline{PY}$ and $\overline{PX} \cong \overline{PZ}$. Use betweenness and alg. prop. to arrive at concl.

Proof:

Statements	Reasons
1. $\overline{WX}$ and $\overline{YZ}$ are common tan. to noncongruent ⊙s O and Q.	1. Given
2. Extend $\overrightarrow{WX}$ and $\overrightarrow{YZ}$ to intersect at P.	2. 2 coplanar non-‖ lines intersect in exactly 1 point.
3. $\overline{PX} \cong \overline{PZ}$; $\overline{PW} \cong \overline{PY}$	3. Cor. 1 of Th. 9.1
4. $PX = PZ$; $PW = PY$	4. Def. of ≅ segs.
5. $PW = PX + WX$ $PY = PZ + YZ$	5. Def. of betweenness
6. $PX + WX =$ $PZ + YZ$	6. Subst. prop.
7. $WX = YZ$	7. Subtr. prop.
8. $\overline{WX} \cong \overline{YZ}$	8. Def. of ≅ segs.

Conclusion: Common tan. segs. to noncongruent ⊙s are ≅.

25. Given: ⊙O with diam. $\overline{AC}$; $\overleftrightarrow{AB}$ is tan. to ⊙O at A; $\overleftrightarrow{CQ}$ is tan. to ⊙O at C
Prove: $\overleftrightarrow{AB} \parallel \overleftrightarrow{CQ}$
Plan: Since $\overline{AC}$ is a diam., $\overline{OA}$ and $\overline{OC}$ are radii and are ⊥ to $\overleftrightarrow{AB}$ and $\overleftrightarrow{CQ}$, respectively. Concl. follows because 2 lines ⊥ to the same line are ‖.

Proof:

Statements	Reasons
1. ⊙O with diam. $\overline{AC}$ and tang. $\overleftrightarrow{AB}$ and $\overleftrightarrow{CQ}$	1. Given
2. $\overleftrightarrow{AC} \perp \overleftrightarrow{AB}$; $\overleftrightarrow{AC} \perp \overleftrightarrow{CQ}$	2. Th. 9.1
3. $\overleftrightarrow{AB} \parallel \overleftrightarrow{CQ}$	3. 2 lines ⊥ to the same line are ∥.

Conclusion: If 2 lines are tan. to a ⊙ at opp. endpts. of a diam., then the lines are ∥.

28. Proof:
Assume:

l is not tan. to ⊙O.	Negation of concl.
l intersects ⊙O at X and at A.	A ⊙ and a secant have 2 common points.
$OX = OA$	All pts. of a ⊙ are equidistant from center.
$\overline{OX} \cong \overline{OA}$	Def. of ≅ segs.
$\angle OAX \cong \angle OXA$	Isos. △ Th.
$m\angle OAX = m\angle OXA$	Def. of ≅ ∠s.
$l \perp \overline{OA}$ at A	Given
$\angle OAX$ is a rt. ∠.	Def. of ⊥
$m\angle OAX = 90$	Def. of rt. ∠
$m\angle OXA = 90$	Subst. prop.

Contradiction: A △ cannot have 2 90° ∠s.
Conclusion: The assumption is false. Therefore, l is tan. to ⊙O.

29. Given: Quad. ABCD is circumscribed about ⊙O.

Prove: $AB + DC = AD + BC$
Plan: Use the def. of circumscribed quad. to show $\overline{AB}$, $\overline{BC}$, $\overline{DC}$, and $\overline{AD}$ are tans. to ⊙O at P, Q, R, and S, respectively. Since tan. segs. from a common external pt. are ≅, betweenness and alg. props. can be used to reach the concl.

Proof:

Statements	Reasons
1. ABCD is circumscribed about ⊙O.	1. Given
2. $\overline{AB}$, $\overline{BC}$, $\overline{DC}$, and $\overline{AD}$ are tans. to ⊙O at P, Q, R, and S, respectively.	2. Def. of circumscribed polygon
3. $\overline{AP} \cong \overline{AS}$; $\overline{BP} \cong \overline{BQ}$; $\overline{CQ} \cong \overline{CR}$; $\overline{DR} \cong \overline{DS}$	3. Cor. 1 of Th. 1
4. $AP = AS$; $BP = BQ$; $CQ = CR$; $DR = DS$	4. Def. of ≅ segs.
5. $AP + BP + CR + DR = AS + DS + BQ + QC$	5. Add. prop.
6. $AP + BP = AB$; $CR + DR = CD$; $AS + SD = AD$; $BQ + QC = BC$	6. Def. of betweenness
7. $AB + DC = AD + BC$	7. Subst. prop.

Conclusion: The sums of the lengths of the opp. sides of a circumscribed quad. are =

PAGE 366

27. Plan: Since △ABC is equilateral, $\overline{AB} \cong \overline{BC} \cong \overline{AC}$. Since ≅ chords of a ⊙ have ≅ arcs, the solution follows by the def. of ≅ arcs.

Proof:

Statements	Reasons
1. △ABC is equilateral.	1. Given
2. $\overline{AB} \cong \overline{BC} \cong \overline{CA}$	2. Def. of equilateral
3. $\overset{\frown}{AB} \cong \overset{\frown}{BC} \cong \overset{\frown}{CA}$	3. If chords of a ⊙ are ≅, then their arcs are ≅.
4. $m\overset{\frown}{AB} = m\overset{\frown}{BC} = m\overset{\frown}{CA}$	4. Def. of ≅ arcs

Conclusion: If an equilateral △ is inscribed in a ⊙, then the arcs of the sides have the same meas.

28. Plan: Since $\overline{AB} \cong \overline{CD}$, $\overset{\frown}{AB} \cong \overset{\frown}{CD}$ and $m\overset{\frown}{AB} = m\overset{\frown}{CD}$. Add $m\overset{\frown}{BC}$ to each side of the equation. Then $m\overset{\frown}{AC} = m\overset{\frown}{BD}$, and the concl. follows by the def. of ≅ arcs and the fact that ≅ arcs of the same ⊙ have ≅ chords.

Proof:

Statements	Reasons
1. $\overline{AB} \cong \overline{CD}$	1. Given
2. $\overset{\frown}{AB} \cong \overset{\frown}{CD}$	2. ≅ chords have ≅ arcs.
3. $m\overset{\frown}{AB} = m\overset{\frown}{CD}$	3. Def. of ≅ arcs
4. $m\overset{\frown}{BC} = m\overset{\frown}{BC}$	4. Refl. prop.
5. $m\overset{\frown}{AB} + m\overset{\frown}{BC} = m\overset{\frown}{CD} + m\overset{\frown}{BC}$	5. Add. prop.
6. $m\overset{\frown}{AB} + m\overset{\frown}{BC} = m\overset{\frown}{AC}$; $m\overset{\frown}{CD} + m\overset{\frown}{BC} = m\overset{\frown}{BD}$	6. Arc Add. Post.
7. $m\overset{\frown}{AC} = m\overset{\frown}{BD}$	7. Subst. prop.
8. $\overset{\frown}{AC} \cong \overset{\frown}{BD}$	8. Def. of ≅ arcs
9. $\overline{AC} \cong \overline{BD}$	9. ≅ arcs have ≅ chords.
10. $AC = BD$	10. Def. of ≅ segs.

Conclusion: In the given fig., if chords $\overline{AB}$ and $\overline{CD}$ are ≅, then $AC = BD$.

29. There are 2 parts to Th. 9.4:
(1) In the same ⊙ or ≅ ⊙'s, if 2 chords are ≅, then their arcs are ≅.
(2) In the same ⊙ or ≅ ⊙'s, if 2 arcs are ≅, then their chords are ≅.

(1) Given: ⊙O; chord $\overline{AB}$ ≅ chord $\overline{CD}$
Prove: $\overset{\frown}{AB} \cong \overset{\frown}{CD}$
Plan: Draw $\overline{OA}$, $\overline{OB}$, $\overline{OC}$, and $\overline{OD}$. Show that $\triangle AOB \cong \triangle COD$. Then $\angle AOB \cong \angle COD$ by CPCTC and the concl. follows.

Proof:

Statements	Reasons
1. $\overline{AB} \cong \overline{CD}$ in ⊙O.	1. Given
2. Draw $\overline{OA}$, $\overline{OB}$, $\overline{OC}$, and $\overline{OD}$.	2. 2 pts. determine 1 line.
3. $\overline{OA} \cong \overline{OC}$; $\overline{OB} \cong \overline{OD}$	3. Radii of the same ⊙ are ≅.
4. $\triangle AOB \cong \triangle COD$	4. SSS
5. $\angle AOB \cong \angle COD$	5. CPCTC
6. $\overset{\frown}{AB} \cong \overset{\frown}{CD}$	6. Th. 9.3

Conclusion: In ⊙O, if chords $\overline{AB}$ and $\overline{CD}$ are ≅, then $\overset{\frown}{AB} \cong \overset{\frown}{CD}$.

(2) Given: ⊙O; $\overset{\frown}{AB} \cong \overset{\frown}{CD}$
Prove: $\overline{AB} \cong \overline{CD}$
Plan: Draw $\overline{OA}$, $\overline{OB}$, $\overline{OC}$, and $\overline{OD}$. Show $\triangle AOB \cong \triangle COD$. Then by CPCTC, $\overline{AB} \cong \overline{CD}$.

Proof:

Statements	Reasons
1. $\overline{AB} \cong \overline{CD}$ in $\odot O$.	1. Given
2. Draw $\overline{OA}$, $\overline{OB}$, $\overline{OC}$, and $\overline{OD}$.	2. 2 pts. determine 1 line.
3. $\overline{OA} \cong \overline{OC}$; $\overline{OB} \cong \overline{OD}$	3. Radii of the same $\odot$ are $\cong$.
4. $\angle AOB \cong \angle COD$	4. Th. 9.3
5. $\triangle AOB \cong \triangle COD$	5. SAS
6. $\overline{AB} \cong \overline{CD}$	6. CPCTC

Conclusion: In $\odot O$, if $\overline{AB} \cong \overline{CD}$, then chords $\overline{AB}$ and $\overline{CD}$ are $\cong$.

30. There are 2 parts to Th. 9.6:
(1) In the same $\odot$ or $\cong \odot$s, if 2 chords are $\cong$, then they are equidistant from the center(s).
(2) In the same $\odot$ or $\odot$s, if 2 chords are equidistant from the center(s), then they are $\cong$.

(1) **Given:** In $\odot O$, $\overline{AB} \cong \overline{CD}$.
Prove: From the center, the distance to $\overline{AB}$ = the distance to $\overline{CD}$ ($OX = OY$).
Plan: Draw $\overline{OX}$ and $\overline{OY}$. Draw $\overline{OA}$ and $\overline{OC}$. Show $\triangle AOX \cong \triangle COY$. Concl. follows by CPCTC and def. of $\cong$ segs.

Proof:

Statements	Reasons
1. $\overline{AB} \cong \overline{CD}$	1. Given
2. Draw $\overline{OX} \perp \overline{AB}$. Draw $\overline{OY} \perp \overline{CD}$.	2. From a pt. not on a line, exactly 1 $\perp$ can be drawn to that line.
3. Draw $\overline{OA}$ and $\overline{OC}$.	3. 2 pts. determine 1 line.
4. $\overline{OA} \cong \overline{OC}$	4. Radii of the same $\odot$ are $\cong$.
5. $\angle AXO$ and $\angle CYO$ are rt. $\angle$s.	5. Def. of $\perp$
6. $\triangle AXO$ and $\triangle CYO$ are rt. $\triangle$s.	6. Def. of rt. $\triangle$
7. $AB = CD$	7. Def. of $\cong$ segs.
8. $\frac{1}{2}AB = \frac{1}{2}CD$	8. Mult. prop.
9. $\overline{OX}$ bisects $\overline{AB}$; $\overline{OY}$ bisects $\overline{CD}$.	9. Th. 9.5
10. $AX = \frac{1}{2}AB$; $CY = \frac{1}{2}CD$	10. Midpt. Th.
11. $AX = CY$	11. Subst. prop.
12. $\overline{AX} \cong \overline{CY}$	12. Def. of $\cong$ segs.
13. $\triangle AOX \cong \triangle COY$	13. HL
14. $\overline{OX} \cong \overline{OY}$	14. CPCTC
15. $OX = OY$	15. Def. of $\cong$ segs.

Conclusion: If 2 chords of a $\odot$ are $\cong$, then they are equidistant from the center.

(2) **Given:** In $\odot O$, chords $\overline{AB}$ and $\overline{CD}$; $\overline{OX} \perp \overline{AB}$; $\overline{OY} \perp \overline{CD}$; $OX = OY$
Prove: $\overline{AB} \cong \overline{CD}$
Plan: Draw $\overline{OA}$ and $\overline{OC}$. Show $\triangle AOX \cong \triangle COY$. Then $\overline{AX} \cong \overline{CY}$ by CPCTC. Concl. follows from the fact that a diam. $\perp$ to a chord bis. the chord and from alg. props.

Proof:

Statements	Reasons
1. $\overline{OX} \perp \overline{AB}$; $\overline{OY} \perp \overline{CD}$; $OX = OY$	1. Given
2. $\angle AXO$ and $\angle CYO$ are rt. $\angle$s.	2. Def. of $\perp$
3. $\triangle AXO$ and $\triangle CYO$ are rt. $\triangle$s.	3. Def. of rt. $\triangle$
4. $\overline{OX} \cong \overline{OY}$	4. Def. of $\cong$ segs.
5. Draw $\overline{OA}$ and $\overline{OC}$.	5. 2 pts determine 1 line.
6. $\overline{OA} \cong \overline{OC}$	6. Radii of the same $\odot$ are $\cong$.
7. $\triangle AOX \cong \triangle COY$	7. HL
8. $\overline{AX} \cong \overline{CY}$	8. CPCTC
9. $AX = CY$	9. Def. of $\cong$ segs.
10. $\overline{OX}$ bis. $\overline{AB}$; $\overline{OY}$ bis. $\overline{CD}$.	10. Th. 9.5
11. $AX = \frac{1}{2}AB$; $CY = \frac{1}{2}CD$	11. Midpt. Th.
12. $\frac{1}{2}AB = \frac{1}{2}CD$	12. Subst. prop.
13. $AB = CD$	13. Mult. prop.
14. $\overline{AB} \cong \overline{CD}$	14. Def. of $\cong$ segs.

Conclusion: If 2 chords of a $\odot$ are equidistant from the center, then they are $\cong$.

31. Given: $\odot O$ with chords $\overline{AB}$ and $\overline{CD}$; $AB > CD$
Prove: The distance from the center to $\overline{AB}$ < distance from the center to $\overline{CD}$ ($OX < OY$).
Plan: Draw $\overline{OX}$ and $\overline{OY}$. Draw $\overline{OA}$ and $\overline{OC}$. Use the Pyth. Th. to write equations involving the lengths of the sides of $\triangle AOX$ and $\triangle COY$. The concl. follows by applying alg. props.

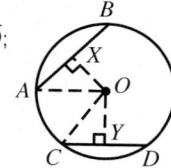

Proof:

Statements	Reasons
1. $AB > CD$	1. Given
2. Draw $\overline{OX} \perp \overline{AB}$. Draw $\overline{OY} \perp \overline{CD}$.	2. From a pt. not on a line, exactly 1 $\perp$ can be drawn to that line.
3. $\frac{1}{2}AB > \frac{1}{2}CD$	3. Mult. prop.
4. $\overline{OX}$ bis. $\overline{AB}$; $\overline{OY}$ bis. $\overline{CD}$.	4. Th. 9.5
5. $AX = \frac{1}{2}AB$; $CY = \frac{1}{2}CD$	5. Midpt. Th.
6. $AX > CY$	6. Subst. prop.
7. $(AX)^2 > (CY)^2$	7. Mult. prop.
8. Draw $\overline{OA}$ and $\overline{OC}$.	8. 2 pts. determine 1 line.
9. $\overline{OA} \cong \overline{OC}$	9. Radii of the same $\odot$ are $\cong$.
10. $OA = OC$	10. Def. of $\cong$ segs.
11. $(OA)^2 = (OC)^2$	11. Squaring prop.
12. $\angle AXO$ and $\angle CYO$ are rt. $\angle$s.	12. Def. of $\perp$
13. $\triangle AOX$ and $\triangle COY$ are rt. $\triangle$s.	13. Def. of rt. $\triangle$
14. $(OA)^2 = (OX)^2 + (AX)^2$ $(OC)^2 = (OY)^2 + (CY)^2$	14. Pyth. Th.
15. $(OX)^2 + (AX)^2 = (OY)^2 + (CY)^2$	15. Subst. prop.
16. $(OX)^2 < (OY)^2$	16. Subtr. prop. of ineq.
17. $OX < OY$	17. Square roots of unequals are $\neq$ in the same order.

Conclusion: If 2 chords of a $\odot$ are $\neq$ in length, the longer chord is nearer to the center.

32. Given: $\odot O$ with chords $\overline{AB}$ and $\overline{CD}$;
$\overline{OX} \perp \overline{AB}$,
$\overline{OY} \perp \overline{CD}$,
$OX < OY$
Prove: $AB > CD$

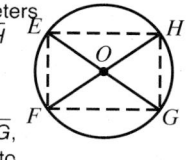

Plan: Draw $\overline{OA}$ and $\overline{OC}$. Use the Pythagorean Th. to write equations involving the lengths of the sides of $\triangle AOX$ and $\triangle COY$. The concl. follows by applying alg. props.

Proof:

Statements	Reasons
1. $\overline{OX} \perp \overline{AB}$; $\overline{OY} \perp \overline{CD}$; $OX < OY$	1. Given
2. Draw $\overline{OA}$ and $\overline{OC}$.	2. 2 pts. determine 1 line.
3. $\overline{OA} \cong \overline{OC}$	3. Radii of the same $\odot$ are $\cong$.
4. $OA = OC$	4. Def. of $\cong$ segments
5. $(OA)^2 = (OC)^2$	5. Mult. prop.
6. $\angle AXO$ and $\angle CYO$ are rt. $\angle$s.	6. Def. of $\perp$
7. $\triangle AOX$ and $\triangle COY$ are rt. $\triangle$.	7. Def. of rt. $\triangle$
8. $(OA)^2 = (AX)^2 + (OX)^2$ $(OC)^2 = (CY)^2 + (OY)^2$	8. Pyth. Th.
9. $(AX)^2 + (OX)^2 = (CY)^2 + (OY)^2$	9. Subst. prop.
10. $(OX)^2 < (OY)^2$	10. Squares of positive unequals are $\neq$ in the same order.
11. $(AX)^2 > (CY)^2$	11. Subt. prop. of ineq.
12. $AX > CY$	12. Square roots of unequals are $\neq$ in the same order.
13. $\overline{OX}$ bis. $\overline{AB}$; $\overline{OY}$ bis. $\overline{CD}$.	13. Th. 9.5
14. $AX = \frac{1}{2}AB$; $CY = \frac{1}{2}CD$	14. Midpt. Th.
15. $\frac{1}{2}AB > \frac{1}{2}CD$	15. Subst. prop.
16. $AB > CD$	16. Mult. prop.

Conclusion: If 2 chords of a $\odot$ are not equidistant from the center, then the chord closer to the center is longer.

33. Given: $\odot O$; diameters $\overline{EG}$ and $\overline{FH}$
Prove: Quad. $EFGH$ is a $\square$.

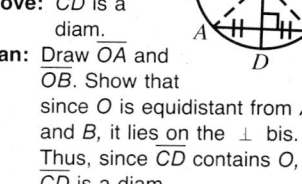

Plan: Draw $\overline{EH}$, $\overline{HG}$, $\overline{GF}$, and $\overline{FE}$ to form quad. $EFGH$. Since the radii are all $\cong$, the diams. bis. each other. The concl. follows since the diams. are diags. of quad. $EFGH$.

Proof:

Statements	Reasons
1. $\overline{EG}$ and $\overline{FH}$ are diams. of $\odot O$.	1. Given
2. Draw $\overline{EH}$, $\overline{HG}$, $\overline{GF}$, and $\overline{FE}$.	2. 2 pts. determine 1 line.
3. $\overline{OE} \cong \overline{OG}$; $\overline{OF} \cong \overline{OH}$	3. Radii of the same $\odot$ are $\cong$.
4. $\overline{EG}$ bis. $\overline{FH}$; $\overline{FH}$ bis. $\overline{EG}$.	4. Def. of bis.
5. $EFGH$ is a $\square$.	5. If the diags. of a quad. bis. each other, the quad. is a $\square$.

Conclusion: The quad. formed by the endpts. of 2 diams. of a $\odot$ is a $\square$.

34. Given: $\odot O$; chord $\overline{AB}$; $\overline{CD}$ is the $\perp$ bis. of $\overline{AB}$.
Prove: $\overline{CD}$ is a diam.

Plan: Draw $\overline{OA}$ and $\overline{OB}$. Show that since O is equidistant from A and B, it lies on the $\perp$ bis. Thus, since $\overline{CD}$ contains O, $\overline{CD}$ is a diam.

Proof:

Statements	Reasons
1. In $\odot O$, $\overline{CD}$ is the $\perp$ bis. of $\overline{AB}$.	1. Given
2. Draw $\overline{OA}$ and $\overline{OB}$.	2. 2 pts. determine 1 line.
3. $\overline{OA} \cong \overline{OB}$	3. Radii of the same $\odot$ are $\cong$.
4. $OA = OB$	4. Def. of $\cong$ segs.
5. O lies on $\overline{CD}$.	5. If a pt. is equidistant from the endpts. of a segment, then it lies on the $\perp$ bis. of the seg.
6. $\overline{CD}$ is a diam.	6. Def. of diam.

Conclusion: If a chord is the $\perp$ bis. of another chord, then the first chord is a diam.

PAGE 370

12. Plan (Case 2): Draw diam. $\overline{SA}$. By Case 1, $m\angle RSA = \frac{1}{2}m\widehat{RA}$ and $m\angle TSA = \frac{1}{2}m\widehat{TA}$. By betweenness of rays, $m\angle RST = m\angle RSA + m\angle TSA$. Thus, $m\angle RST = \frac{1}{2}m\widehat{RA} + \frac{1}{2}m\widehat{TA}$, and the concl. follows by arc add.

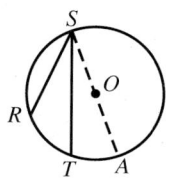

Plan (Case 3): Draw diam. $\overline{SA}$. By Case 1, $m\angle RSA = \frac{1}{2}m\widehat{RA}$ and $m\angle TSA = \frac{1}{2}m\widehat{TA}$. By betweenness of rays, $m\angle RST + m\angle TSA = m\angle RSA$. By subst., $m\angle RST + \frac{1}{2}m\widehat{TA} = \frac{1}{2}m\widehat{RA}$. Then use alg. props. and arc add. to reach the concl.

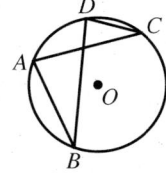

PAGE 371

25. Given: $\odot O$; inscribed $\angle$s A and D
Prove: $\angle A \cong \angle D$
Plan: Since $\angle A$ and $\angle D$ both intercept $\widehat{BC}$, use the trans. prop. and the def. of $\cong$ to reach the concl.

Proof:

Statements	Reasons
1. $\odot O$; inscribed $\angle$s A and D	1. Given
2. $m\angle A = \frac{1}{2}m\widehat{BC}$; $m\angle D = \frac{1}{2}m\widehat{BC}$	2. Th. 9.9
3. $m\angle A = m\angle D$	3. Trans. prop.
4. $\angle A \cong \angle D$	4. Def. of $\cong$ $\angle$s

Conclusion: In the same $\odot$, if $\angle A$ and $\angle D$ intercept the same arc, then $\angle A \cong \angle D$.

26. Given: Quad. *ABCD* inscribed in ⊙*O*

Prove: $m\angle A + m\angle C = 180°$

Plan: Use Th. 9.9 and props. of algebra to write an equation involving $\angle A$ and $\angle C$. Concl. follows by def. of arc degrees and the subst. prop.

Proof:

Statements	Reasons
1. Quad *ABCD* inscribed in ⊙*O*	1. Given
2. $m\angle A = \frac{1}{2}\overarc{BCD}$; $m\angle C = \frac{1}{2}\overarc{BAD}$	2. Th. 9.9
3. $m\angle A + m\angle C = \frac{1}{2}\overarc{mBCD} + \frac{1}{2}\overarc{mBAD}$	3. Add. prop.
4. $m\angle A + m\angle C = \frac{1}{2}(\overarc{mBCD} + \overarc{mBAD})$	4. Distrib. prop.
5. $\overarc{mBCD} + \overarc{mBAD} = 360$	5. Post. 18 and 360° in a ⊙
6. $m\angle A + m\angle C = \frac{1}{2}(360) = 180$	6. Subst. prop.

Conclusion: The opp. $\angle$s of a quad. inscribed in a ⊙ are supp.

27. Given: ⊙*O*; inscribed $\angle A$; $\overarc{BC}$ is a semicircle

Prove: $\angle A$ is a rt. $\angle$.

Plan: Use Th. 9.9 to write the equation $m\angle A = \frac{1}{2}\overarc{BC}$. Concl. follows by the def. of a semicircle and the def. of rt. $\angle$.

Proof:

Statements	Reasons
1. $\overarc{BC}$ is a semicircle.	1. Given
2. $m\angle A = \frac{1}{2}\overarc{mBC}$	2. Th. 9.9
3. $\overarc{mBC} = 180$	3. Semi-⊙ has meas. 180.
4. $m\angle A = \frac{1}{2}(180) = 90$	4. Subst. prop.
5. $\angle A$ is a rt. $\angle$.	5. Def. of rt. $\angle$

Conclusion: If an inscribed $\angle$ intercepts a semicircle, the $\angle$ is a rt. $\angle$.

28. Given: ⊙*O*; chords $\overline{AB}$, $\overline{CD}$; $\overline{AB} \parallel \overline{CD}$

Prove: $\overarc{AC} \cong \overarc{BD}$

Plan: Draw $\overline{BC}$. Since $\overline{AB} \parallel \overline{CD}$, $\angle ABC \cong \angle DCB$. Since $\angle ABC$ and $\angle DCB$ are also inscribed $\angle$s, the concl. follows.

Proof:

Statements	Reasons
1. $\overline{AB} \parallel \overline{CD}$	1. Given
2. Draw $\overline{BC}$.	2. 2 pts determine 1 line.
3. $\angle ABC \cong \angle DCB$	3. If lines are $\parallel$, alt. int. $\angle$s are $\cong$.
4. $m\angle ABC = m\angle DCB$	4. Def. of $\cong$ $\angle$s
5. $m\angle ABC = \frac{1}{2}\overarc{mAC}$; $m\angle DCB = \frac{1}{2}\overarc{mBD}$	5. Th. 9.9
6. $\frac{1}{2}\overarc{mAC} = \frac{1}{2}\overarc{mBD}$	6. Subst. prop.
7. $\overarc{mAC} = \overarc{mBD}$	7. Mult. prop.
8. $\overarc{AC} \cong \overarc{BD}$	8. Def. of $\cong$ arcs

Conclusion: If 2 chords are $\parallel$, then their arcs are $\cong$.

29. Given: ▱*ABCD* inscribed in ⊙*O*

Prove: *ABCD* is a rect.

Plan: Since $\angle A$ and $\angle C$ are opps. $\angle$s of a ▱, $\angle A \cong \angle C$. They are also supp. Thus, the concl. follows by alg. props.

Proof:

Statements	Reasons
1. *ABCD* is a ▱.	1. Given
2. $\angle A \cong \angle C$	2. Opp. $\angle$s of a ▱ are $\cong$.
3. $m\angle A = m\angle C$	3. Def. of $\cong$ $\angle$s
4. $\angle A$ and $\angle C$ are supp.	4. Cor. 2 of Th. 9.9
5. $m\angle A + m\angle C = 180$	5. Def. of supp.
6. $m\angle A + m\angle A = 180$	6. Subst. prop.
7. $2m\angle A = 180$	7. Distrib. prop.
8. $m\angle A = 90$	8. Div. prop.
9. $\angle A$ is a rt. $\angle$.	9. Def. of rt. $\angle$
10. *ABCD* is a rect.	10. Def. of rect.

Conclusion: A ▱ inscribed in a ⊙ is a rect.

30. Plan: Since $m\angle A + m\angle C + m\angle D = 180$ and $m\angle D + m\angle 4 = 180$, the concl. follows by alg. props.

Proof:

Statements	Reasons
1. $\overline{AD}$ and $\overline{AC}$ intersect ⊙*O* in pts. *E*, *B*, *D*, and *C*.	1. Given
2. $m\angle A + m\angle C + m\angle D = 180$	2. Sum of meas. of $\angle$s of a △ = 180.
3. $\angle D$ and $\angle 4$ are supp.	3. Cor. 2 of Th. 9.9
4. $m\angle D + m\angle 4 = 180$	4. Def. of supp.
5. $m\angle D + m\angle 4 = m\angle A + m\angle C + m\angle D$	5. Trans. prop.
6. $m\angle 4 = m\angle A + m\angle C$	6. Subtr. prop.

Conclusion: In the given fig., $m\angle 4 = m\angle C + m\angle A$.

31. Given: ⊙*O*; $\overline{AD}$ bis. $\angle A$; $\overline{AB} \cong \overline{AC}$.

Prove: $\overline{AD}$ is a diam.

Plan: Draw $\overline{OX}$ and $\overline{OY} \perp$ to $\overline{AB}$ and $\overline{AC}$, respectively. Then show rt. $\triangle AOX$ and $AOY \cong$ by HL. Since $\angle XAO \cong \angle YAO$, $\overline{AO}$ bis. $\angle A$. Concl. follows because $\angle A$ can have only one bis.

Proof:

Statements	Reasons
1. $\overline{AB} \cong \overline{AC}$	1. Given
2. Draw $\overline{OX} \perp \overline{AB}$ and $\overline{OY} \perp \overline{AC}$.	2. From a pt. not on a line, exactly 1 $\perp$ can be drawn to the line.
3. $OX = OY$	3. Th. 9.6
4. $\overline{OX} \cong \overline{OY}$	4. Def. of $\cong$ segs.
5. $\angle AXO$ and $\angle AYO$ are rt. $\angle$s.	5. Def. of $\perp$
6. $\triangle AXO$ and $\triangle AYO$ are rt. $\triangle$.	6. Def. of rt. △
7. $\overline{AO} \cong \overline{AO}$	7. Refl. prop.
8. $\triangle AOX \cong \triangle AOY$	8. HL
9. $\angle XAO \cong \angle YAO$	9. CPCTC
10. $\overline{AO}$ bis. $\angle A$.	10. Def. of $\angle$ bis.

11. $\overline{AD}$ lies on $\overrightarrow{AO}$.

11. An $\angle$ has exactly 1 bis.

12. $\overline{AD}$ is a diam.

12. Def. of diam.

Conclusion: If the $\angle$ formed by the endpts. of 2 chords is bis., the bis. is a diam.

32. Given: $\odot O$ with chords $\overline{AB}$, $\overline{AD}$, and $\overline{BC}$; $\overline{AD} \perp \overline{AB}$; $\overline{BC} \perp \overline{AB}$

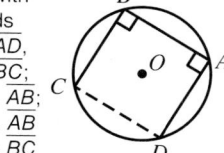

Prove: $\overline{AD} \cong \overline{BC}$

Plan: Draw $\overline{CD}$ to form quad. $ABCD$. Then apply the ths. about $\parallel$ chords and quads. inscribed in a $\odot$.

Proof:

Statements	Reasons
1. $\overline{AD} \perp \overline{AB}$; $\overline{BC} \perp \overline{AB}$	1. Given
2. $\overline{AD} \parallel \overline{BC}$	2. 2 lines $\perp$ to the same line are $\parallel$.
3. Draw $\overline{CD}$.	3. 2 pts determine 1 line.
4. $\angle A$ and $\angle C$ are supp.	4. Cor. 2 of Th. 9.9
5. $m\angle A + m\angle C = 180$	5. Def. of supp.
6. $m\angle C = 180 - m\angle A$	6. Subtr. prop.
7. $\angle A$ is a rt. $\angle$.	7. Def. of $\perp$
8. $m\angle A = 90$	8. Def. of rt. $\angle$
9. $m\angle C = 180 - 90 = 90$	9. Subst. prop.
10. $\angle C$ is a rt. $\angle$.	10. Def. of rt. $\angle$
11. $\overline{DC} \perp \overline{BC}$	11. Def. of $\perp$
12. $\overline{DC} \parallel \overline{AB}$	12. Same as reason 2
13. $\overarc{AD} \cong \overarc{BC}$	13. Cor. 4 of Th. 9.9
14. $\overline{AD} \cong \overline{BC}$	14. $\cong$ arcs of a $\odot$ have $\cong$ chords.

Conclusion: In the given fig., if chords $\overline{AD}$ and $\overline{BC}$ are $\perp$ to chord $\overline{AB}$, then $\overline{AD} \cong \overline{BC}$.

35. Proof:

Statements	Reasons
1. $\triangle DEF$ is inscribed in $\odot O$.	1. Given
2. $m\angle D = \frac{1}{2}m\overarc{FE}$; $m\angle E = \frac{1}{2}m\overarc{DF}$; $m\angle F = \frac{1}{2}m\overarc{DE}$	2. Th. 9.9

3. $m\angle D + m\angle E + m\angle F = \frac{1}{2}m\overarc{FE} + \frac{1}{2}m\overarc{DF} + \frac{1}{2}m\overarc{DE}$	3. Add. prop.
4. $m\angle D + m\angle E + m\angle F = \frac{1}{2}(m\overarc{FE} + m\overarc{DF} + m\overarc{DE})$	4. Distrib. prop.
5. $m\overarc{FE} + m\overarc{DF} + m\overarc{DE} = 360$	5. Post. 18 and 360° in a $\odot$
6. $m\angle D + m\angle E + m\angle F = \frac{1}{2}(360) = 180$	6. Subst. prop.

Conclusion: The sum of the meas. of the $\angle$s of a $\triangle$ is 180.

PAGE 376

7. Proof:

Statements	Reasons
1. $\overline{RP}$ is a chord of $\odot O$; tan $\overrightarrow{PT}$.	1. Given
2. Draw diam. $\overline{PX}$.	2. 2 pts. determine 1 line.
3. $m\angle XPT = \frac{1}{2}m\overarc{XRP}$	3. Case 1
4. $m\angle XPR = \frac{1}{2}m\overarc{XR}$	4. Th. 9.9
5. $m\angle XPT = m\angle XPR + m\angle RPT$	5. Def. of betweenness
6. $\frac{1}{2}m\overarc{XRP} = \frac{1}{2}m\overarc{XR} + m\angle RPT$	6. Subst. prop.
7. $m\overarc{XRP} = m\overarc{XR} + m\overarc{RP}$	7. Post. 18
8. $\frac{1}{2}(m\overarc{XR} + m\overarc{RP}) = \frac{1}{2}m\overarc{XR} + m\angle RPT$	8. Subst. prop.
9. $\frac{1}{2}m\overarc{XR} + \frac{1}{2}m\overarc{RP} = \frac{1}{2}m\overarc{XR} + m\angle RPT$	9. Distrib. prop.
10. $m\angle RPT = \frac{1}{2}m\overarc{RP}$	10. Subtr. prop.

Conclusion: If a tan. and a chord form an acute $\angle$, then the meas. of the $\angle = \frac{1}{2}$ the meas. of the intercepted arc.

13. Proof:

Statements	Reasons
1. $\overrightarrow{PT}$ is tan. to $\odot O$; $\overline{RP}$ is a chord.	1. Given
2. Draw diam. $\overline{XP}$.	2. 2 pts. determine 1 line
3. $m\angle XPT = \frac{1}{2}m\overarc{XP}$	3. Case 1
4. $m\angle XPR = \frac{1}{2}m\overarc{RX}$	4. Th. 9.9
5. $m\angle XPT + m\angle XPR = m\angle RPT$	5. Def. of betweenness
6. $\frac{1}{2}m\overarc{XP} + \frac{1}{2}m\overarc{RX} = m\angle RPT$	6. Subst. prop.
7. $\frac{1}{2}(m\overarc{XP} + m\overarc{RX}) = m\angle RPT$	7. Distrib. prop.
8. $m\overarc{XP} + m\overarc{RX} = m\overarc{RP}$	8. Arc Add. Post.
9. $m\angle RPT = \frac{1}{2}m\overarc{RP}$	9. Subst.

Conclusion: If a tan. and a chord form an obt. $\angle$, then the meas. of the $\angle = \frac{1}{2}$ the meas. of the intercepted arc.

14. Proof:

Statements	Reasons
1. Chords $\overline{AC}$ and $\overline{BD}$ intersect at X.	1. Given
2. Draw chord $\overline{AB}$.	2. 2 pts. determine 1 line.
3. $m\angle AXD = m\angle A + m\angle B$	3. The meas. of an ext. $\angle$ of a $\triangle$ = the sum of the meas. of the remote int. $\angle$s.
4. $m\angle A = \frac{1}{2}m\overarc{BC}$; $m\angle B = \frac{1}{2}m\overarc{DA}$	4. Th. 9.9
5. $m\angle AXD = \frac{1}{2}m\overarc{BC} + \frac{1}{2}m\overarc{DA}$	5. Subst. prop.
6. $m\angle AXD = \frac{1}{2}(m\overarc{BC} + m\overarc{DA})$	6. Distrib. prop.

Conclusion: If chords $\overline{AC}$ and $\overline{BD}$ of the same $\odot$ intersect at X, then $m\angle AXD = \frac{1}{2}(m\overarc{BC} + m\overarc{DA})$.

15. Proof:

Statements	Reasons
1. $\overrightarrow{PT}$ tan. $\odot O$; $\overline{PB}$ is a secant.	1. Given
2. Draw $\overline{AT}$.	2. 2 pts. determine 1 line.
3. $m\angle BAT = m\angle ATP + m\angle P$	3. The meas. of an ext. $\angle$ of a $\triangle =$ the sum of the meas. of the remote int. $\angle$s.
4. $m\angle BAT - m\angle ATP = m\angle P$	4. Subtr. prop.
5. $m\angle BAT = \frac{1}{2}m\widehat{BT}$	5. Th. 9.9
6. $m\angle ATP = \frac{1}{2}m\widehat{AT}$	6. Th. 9.11
7. $m\angle P = \frac{1}{2}m\widehat{BT} - \frac{1}{2}m\widehat{AT}$	7. Subst. prop.
8. $m\angle P = \frac{1}{2}(m\widehat{BT} - m\widehat{AT})$	8. Distrib. prop.

Conclusion: If a tan. and a secant intersect in the ext. of a $\odot$, then the meas. of the $\angle$ they form $= \frac{1}{2}$ the diff. of the meas. of the intercepted arcs.

16. Given: $\odot O$ with secants $\overline{AP}$ and $\overline{DP}$; C is the pt. of intersection between $\overline{PD}$ and $\odot O$.
Prove: $m\angle P = \frac{1}{2}(m\widehat{AD} - m\widehat{BC})$
Plan (Case 2): Draw $\overline{AC}$. $m\angle ACD = \frac{1}{2} = m\widehat{AD}$ and $m\angle A = \frac{1}{2}m\widehat{BC}$. Use the fact that $\angle ACD$ is an ext. $\angle$ of $\triangle APC$ to reach the concl.

Proof:

Statements	Reasons
1. $\odot O$; secants $\overline{AP}$ and $\overline{DP}$; C is pt. of intersection between $\overline{PD}$ and $\odot O$.	1. Given
2. Draw $\overline{AC}$.	2. 2 pts. determine 1 line.
3. $m\angle ACD = m\angle A + m\angle P$	3. The meas. of an ext. $\angle$ of a $\triangle =$ the sum of the meas. of the remote int. $\angle$s.
4. $m\angle ACD = \frac{1}{2}m\widehat{AD}$ $m\angle A = \frac{1}{2}m\widehat{BC}$	4. Th. 9.9
5. $\frac{1}{2}m\widehat{AD} = \frac{1}{2}m\widehat{BC} + m\angle P$	5. Subst. prop.
6. $m\angle P = \frac{1}{2}m\widehat{AD} - \frac{1}{2}m\widehat{BC}$	6. Subtr. prop.
7. $m\angle P = \frac{1}{2}(m\widehat{AD} = m\widehat{BC})$	7. Distrib. prop.

Conclusion: If 2 secants intersect in the ext. of a $\odot$, then the meas. of the $\angle$ they form $= \frac{1}{2}$ the difference of the meas. of the intercepted arcs.

17. Given: $\odot O$ with tans. $\overrightarrow{PA}$ and $\overrightarrow{PB}$
Prove: $m\angle P = \frac{1}{2}(m\widehat{ACB} - m\widehat{AB})$
Plan: Draw $\overline{AB}$. $m\angle FBA = \frac{1}{2}m\widehat{ACB}$, and $m\angle PAB = \frac{1}{2}m\widehat{AB}$. Use the fact that $\angle FBA$ is an ext. $\angle$ of $\triangle ABP$ to reach the concl.

Proof:

Statements	Reasons
1. $\overrightarrow{PA}$ and $\overrightarrow{PB}$ are tan. to $\odot O$.	1. Given
2. Draw $\overline{AB}$.	2. 2 pts. determine 1 line.
3. $m\angle FBA = m\angle A + m\angle P$	3. The meas. of an ext. $\angle$ of a $\triangle =$ the sum of the meas. of the remote int. $\angle$s.
4. $m\angle FBA = \frac{1}{2}m\widehat{ACB}$; $m\angle PAB = \frac{1}{2}m\widehat{AB}$	4. Th. 9.11
5. $\frac{1}{2}m\widehat{ACB} = \frac{1}{2}m\widehat{AB} + m\angle P$	5. Subst. prop.
6. $m\angle P = \frac{1}{2}m\widehat{ACB} - \frac{1}{2}m\widehat{AB}$	6. Subtr. prop.
7. $m\angle P = \frac{1}{2}(m\widehat{ACB} - m\widehat{AB})$	7. Distrib. prop.

Conclusion: The meas. of the $\angle$ formed by 2 tan. rays with a common endpt. $=$ the difference in the meas. of the intercepted arcs.

PAGE 377

18. Given: Trap. $ABCD$ inscribed in $\odot O$; $\overline{AB} \parallel \overline{DC}$
Prove: Trap. $ABCD$ is isos.
Plan: Since $\overline{AB} \parallel \overline{DC}$, $\overline{AD} \cong \overline{CB}$. The concl. follows because $\cong$ arcs of a $\odot$ have $\cong$ chords.

Proof:

Statements	Reasons
1. Trap. $ABCD$ is inscribed in $\odot O$, and $\overline{AB} \parallel \overline{DC}$.	1. Given
2. $\widehat{AD} \cong \widehat{CB}$	2. Cor. 4 of Th. 9.9
3. $\overline{AD} \cong \overline{CB}$	3. $\cong$ arcs have $\cong$ chords.
4. Trap. $ABCD$ is isos.	4. Def. of isos. trap.

Conclusion: Any trap. inscribed in a $\odot$ is isos.

19. Given: Equilateral $\triangle ABC$ inscribed in $\odot O$; $\overline{ED}$, $\overline{DF}$, and $\overline{FE}$ are tan. to $\odot O$.

Prove: $\triangle DEF$ is equilateral.
Plan: Use the inscribed $\angle$s to gain information about the arcs. Then write an equation involving the $\angle$ formed by intersecting tans. Thus, show that $\triangle DEF$ is equiangular and therefore equilateral.

Proof:

Statements	Reasons
1. $\triangle ABC$ is equilateral; $\overline{ED}$, $\overline{EF}$, and $\overline{DF}$ are tans.	1. Given
2. $m\angle B = m\angle C = m\angle A = 60$	2. Each $\angle$ of an equilateral $\triangle$ meas. 60°.
3. $m\angle B = \frac{1}{2}m\widehat{AC}$; $m\angle C = \frac{1}{2}m\widehat{BA}$; $m\angle A = \frac{1}{2}m\widehat{BC}$	3. Th. 9.9
4. $\frac{1}{2}m\widehat{AC} = \frac{1}{2}m\widehat{BA} = \frac{1}{2}m\widehat{BC}$	4. Subst. prop.
5. $m\widehat{AC} = m\widehat{BA} = m\widehat{BC}$	5. Mult. prop.
6. $\frac{1}{2}m\widehat{AC} = 60$	6. Subst. prop.
7. $m\widehat{AC} = 120$	7. Mult. prop.
8. $m\widehat{BA} = m\widehat{BC} = 120$	8. Trans. prop.
9. $m\angle D = \frac{1}{2}(m\widehat{BCA} - m\widehat{AB})$	9. Th. 9.12
10. $m\widehat{BCA} = m\widehat{BC} + m\widehat{CA}$	10. Post. 18
11. $m\angle D = \frac{1}{2}(m\widehat{BC} + m\widehat{CA} - m\widehat{AB})$	11. Subst. prop.
12. $m\angle D = \frac{1}{2}(120 + 120 - 120) = \frac{1}{2}\cdot 120 = 60$	12. Subst. prop.
13. Similarly, $m\angle E = 60$ and $m\angle F = 60$	13. Steps 1–12
14. $m\angle D = m\angle E = m\angle F$	14. Trans. prop.
15. $\triangle DEF$ is equilateral.	15. An equiangular $\triangle$ is equilateral.

Conclusion: If an equilateral $\triangle$ is inscribed in a $\odot$, the tans. to the vertices of the $\triangle$ form an equilateral $\triangle$.

20. Given: In $\odot O$, chords $\overline{AC}$ and $\overline{BD}$ intersect at X.

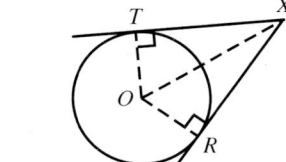

Prove: $m\angle AXD = \frac{1}{2}(m\widehat{CB} + m\widehat{AD})$

Plan: Draw $\overline{DE} \parallel \overline{AC}$. Then alt. int. $\angle$s D and AXD are $\cong$ and the arcs included between $\overline{DE}$ and $\overline{AC}$ are $\cong$. Use this information to write equations that lead to the concl.

Proof:

Statements	Reasons
1. Draw $\overline{DE} \parallel \overline{AC}$.	1. Through a pt. not on a line, exactly 1 $\parallel$ can be drawn.
2. $\angle D \cong \angle AXD$	2. If lines are $\parallel$, alt. int. $\angle$s are $\cong$.
3. $m\angle D = m\angle AXD$	3. Def. of $\cong$ $\angle$s
4. $m\angle D = \frac{1}{2}m\widehat{BCE}$	4. Th. 9.9
5. $m\widehat{BCE} = m\widehat{CB} + m\widehat{CE}$	5. Post. 18
6. $m\angle D = \frac{1}{2}(m\widehat{CB} + m\widehat{CE})$	6. Subst. prop.
7. $\widehat{AD} \cong \widehat{CE}$	7. Cor. 4 of Th. 9.9
8. $m\widehat{AD} = m\widehat{CE}$	8. Def. of $\cong$ arcs
9. $m\angle D = \frac{1}{2}(m\widehat{CB} + m\widehat{AD})$	9. Subst. prop.
10. $m\angle AXD = \frac{1}{2}(m\widehat{CB} + m\widehat{AD})$	10. Trans. prop.

Conclusion: If chords $\overline{AC}$ and $\overline{BD}$ of the same $\odot$ intersect at X, then $m\angle AXD = \frac{1}{2}(m\widehat{BC} + m\widehat{DA})$.

21. Given: $\triangle ABC$ inscribed in $\odot O$; $\overline{AB} \cong \overline{AC}$; $\overleftrightarrow{AD}$ is tan. to $\odot O$.

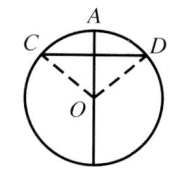

Prove: $\overleftrightarrow{AD} \parallel \overline{BC}$

Plan: Since $\angle DAC$ and $\angle B$ intercept the same arc, $\angle DAC \cong \angle B$. But $\angle B \cong \angle C$, and so the concl. follows because alt. int. $\angle$s are $\cong$.

Proof:

Statements	Reasons
1. $\overleftrightarrow{AD}$ is tan. to $\odot O$; $\overline{AB} \cong \overline{AC}$.	1. Given
2. $m\angle B = \frac{1}{2}m\widehat{AC}$	2. Th. 9.9
3. $m\angle DAC = \frac{1}{2}m\widehat{AC}$	3. Th. 9.11
4. $m\angle DAC = m\angle B$	4. Trans. prop.
5. $\angle DAC \cong \angle B$	5. Def. of $\cong$ $\angle$s
6. $\angle C \cong \angle B$	6. Isos. $\triangle$ Th.
7. $\angle DAC \cong \angle C$	7. Trans. prop.
8. $\overleftrightarrow{AD} \parallel \overline{BC}$	8. If alt. int. $\angle$s are $\cong$, lines are $\parallel$.

Conclusion: If an isos. $\triangle$ is inscribed in a $\odot$, the tan. to the $\odot$ at the vertex $\angle$ is $\parallel$ to the base of the $\triangle$.

PAGE 380

1.

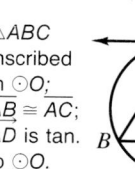

Draw $\overline{OX}$, $\overline{OT}$ and $\overline{OR}$.

2.

Draw $\overline{OC}$ and $\overline{OD}$.

PAGE 381

1.

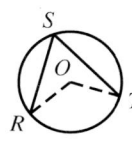 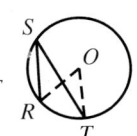 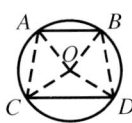

Draw $\overline{OR}$.   Draw $\overline{OR}$, $\overline{OT}$.   Draw $\overline{OR}$, $\overline{OT}$.

2.

Draw $\overline{AC}$, $\overline{BD}$, $\overline{OA}$, $\overline{OB}$, $\overline{OC}$, $\overline{OD}$.

757

3.

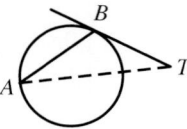

Draw $\overline{AT}$.

4.

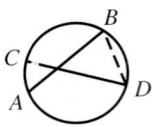

Draw $\overline{BD}$.

5. Plan: Draw auxiliary tan. $\overleftrightarrow{XY}$ through T. Then apply the th. about the $\angle$ formed by a chord and a tan. and the th. about the meas. of an inscribed $\angle$ in order to get $\angle C \cong \angle D$. Concl. follows because $\angle C$ and $\angle D$ are alt. int. $\angle$s of $\overline{AC}$ and $\overline{DB}$.

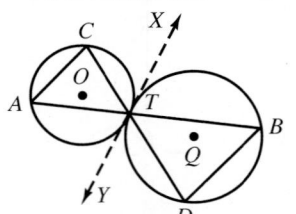

Proof:

Statements	Reasons
1. $\odot O$ and $\odot Q$ are ext. tan. at T. $\overline{AB}$ and $\overline{CD}$ are secants through T.	1. Given
2. Draw tangent $\overleftrightarrow{XY}$ through T.	2. Def. of tan.
3. $m\angle XTA = \frac{1}{2}m\widehat{AT}$ $m\angle YTB = \frac{1}{2}m\widehat{BT}$	3. Meas. of the $\angle$ formed by a chord and a tan. $= \frac{1}{2}$ the meas. of the intercepted arc.
4. $\angle XTA \cong \angle YTB$	4. Vert $\angle$s are $\cong$.
5. $m\angle XTA = m\angle YTB$	5. Def. of $\cong \angle$s
6. $\frac{1}{2}m\widehat{AT} = \frac{1}{2}m\widehat{BT}$	6. Subst. prop.
7. $m\angle C = \frac{1}{2}m\widehat{AT}$ $m\angle D = \frac{1}{2}m\widehat{BT}$	7. Meas. of an inscribed $\angle = \frac{1}{2}$ the meas. of the intercepted arc.

8. $m\angle C = m\angle D$	8. Subst. prop.
9. $\angle C \cong \angle D$	9. Def. of $\cong \angle$s
10. $\overline{AC} \parallel \overline{DB}$	10. If 2 lines have a transv. and a pair of alt. int. $\angle$s $\cong$, then the lines are $\parallel$.

Concl.: In the given figure, if $\odot O$ and $\odot Q$ are ext. tan. and $\overline{AB}$ and $\overline{CD}$ are secants through T, then $\overline{AC} \parallel \overline{DB}$.

6. Plan: Extend $\overrightarrow{OX}$ through X to intersect $\odot O$ at E. Then relate $\angle BOX$ and $\angle C$ to $\overparen{AB}$ to prove $\angle BOX \cong \angle C$.

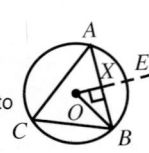

Proof:

Statements	Reasons
1. Extend $\overrightarrow{OX}$ to intersect $\overline{AB}$ at E.	1. A line can be extended indefinitely.
2. $\triangle ABC$ inscribed in $\odot O$; $\overline{OX} \perp \overline{AB}$	2. Given
3. $m\widehat{BE} = \frac{1}{2}m\widehat{AB}$	3. A diam. that is $\perp$ to a chord bisects the chord and its arc.
4. $m\widehat{BE} = m\angle EOB = m\angle BOX$	4. Meas. of an arc = the meas. of its central $\angle$.
5. $m\angle C = \frac{1}{2}m\widehat{AB}$	5. Meas. of an inscribed $\angle = \frac{1}{2}$ the meas. of its intercepted arc.
6. $m\angle C = m\widehat{BE}$	6. Trans. prop.
7. $m\angle BOX = m\angle C$	7. Trans. prop.
8. $\angle BOX \cong \angle C$	8. Def. of $\cong \angle$s

Concl.: In the given fig., if $\triangle ABC$ is inscribed in $\odot O$ and $\overline{OX} \perp \overline{AB}$, then $\angle BOX \cong \angle C$.

7. Plan: Draw $\overline{AB}$. Prove $\triangle ABC \cong \triangle ABD$ by the HA Th. Then $\overline{BC} \cong \overline{BD}$ by CPCTC and the concl. follows.

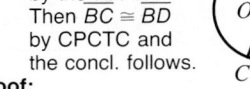

Proof:

Statements	Reasons
1. Draw $\overline{AB}$.	1. Two pts. determine a line.
2. $\overline{AC}$ is a diam. of $\odot O$.	2. Given

3. $\angle ABC$ is a rt. $\angle$.	3. An $\angle$ inscribed in a semi-$\odot$ is a rt. $\angle$.
4. $\angle ABD$ is a rt. $\angle$.	4. Supp. of a rt. $\angle$ is a rt. $\angle$.
5. $\triangle ABC$ and $\triangle ABD$ are rt. $\triangle$s.	5. Def. of rt. $\triangle$
6. $\triangle ACD$ is isos.	6. Given
7. $\overline{AC} \cong \overline{AD}$	7. Def. of isos. $\triangle$
8. $\angle C \cong \angle D$	8. Base $\angle$s of an isos. $\triangle$ are $\cong$
9. $\triangle ABC \cong \triangle ABD$	9. HA Th.
10. $\overline{BC} \cong \overline{BD}$	10. CPCTC
11. $\overline{BC}$ bis. $\overline{CD}$	11. Def. of bis.

Concl.: In the given fig., if $\triangle ABC$ is isos. and $\overline{AC}$ is a diam., then $\overline{BC}$ bis. $\overline{CD}$.

8. Plan: Draw auxiliary lines $\overline{OA}$, $\overline{BQ}$, and $\overline{OQ}$ and common tan. $\overleftrightarrow{XT}$. Relate the $\angle$s formed to $\widehat{AT}$ and $\widehat{BT}$. Since it can be shown that $\overline{AO} \parallel \overline{BQ}$ and $m\angle AOQ + m\angle BQO = 180$, an equation involving $\widehat{AT}$ and $\widehat{BT}$ can be written. Conclusion follows by alg. props.

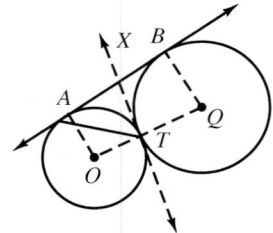

Proof:

Statements	Reasons
1. Draw $\overleftrightarrow{XT}$, a common tan. to $\odot O$ and $\odot Q$	1. Def. of tan.
2. Draw $\overline{OA}$, $\overline{BQ}$ and $\overline{OQ}$.	2. Two pts. determine a line.
3. $\odot O$ and $\odot Q$ are externally tan. at T; $\overleftrightarrow{AB}$ is their common external tan.	3. Given
4. $m\angle XTB = \frac{1}{2}m\widehat{BT}$ $m\angle XTA = \frac{1}{2}m\widehat{AT}$	4. Meas. of the $\angle$ formed by a chord and a tan. $= \frac{1}{2}$ the meas. of the intercepted arc.

5. $m\angle AOT = m\widehat{AT}$; $m\angle BQT = m\widehat{BT}$ | 5. Meas. of a central $\angle$ = the meas. of its arc.
6. $\overline{OA} \perp \overline{AB}$; $\overline{BQ} \perp \overline{AB}$ | 6. Radius and tan. are $\perp$ at the pt. of tangency.
7. $\overline{AO} \parallel \overline{BQ}$ | 7. Two lines $\perp$ to the same line are $\parallel$.
8. $m\angle AOT + m\angle BQT = 180$ | 8. If lines are $\parallel$, int. $\angle$s on the same side of the transv. are supp.
9. $m\widehat{AT} + m\widehat{BT} = 180$ | 9. Subst. prop.
10. $\frac{1}{2}m\widehat{AT} + \frac{1}{2}m\widehat{BT} = 90$ | 10. Mult. prop.
11. $m\angle XTA + m\angle XTB = 90$ | 11. Subst. prop.
12. $m\angle ATB = 90$ | 12. Def. of between ray
13. $\angle ATB$ is a rt. $\angle$. | 13. Def. of rt. $\angle$

Concl.: In the given fig., if $\odot O$ and $\odot Q$ are ext. tan. at T and $\overrightarrow{AB}$ is a common ext. tan., then $\angle ATB$ is a rt. $\angle$.

PAGE 386

15. Proof:

Statements	Reasons
1. Chords $\overline{AC}$ and $\overline{BD}$ intersect at P.	1. Given
2. Draw $\overline{DC}$ and $\overline{AB}$.	2. 2 pts. determine 1 line.
3. $\angle A \cong \angle D$; $\angle C \cong \angle B$	3. Cor. 1 of Th. 9.9
4. $\triangle APB \sim \triangle DPC$	4. AA
5. $\frac{AP}{PD} = \frac{BP}{PC}$	5. Corr. side lengths of $\sim$ $\triangle$s are in proportion.
6. $AP \cdot PC = BP \cdot PD$	6. Means-extremes prop.

Conclusion: If chords $\overline{AC}$ and $\overline{BD}$ of the same $\odot$ intersect at P, then $AP \cdot PC = BP \cdot PD$.

16. Proof:

Statements	Reasons
1. $\overline{AP}$ and $\overline{DP}$ are secants with external segments $\overline{BP}$ and $\overline{CP}$.	1. Given
2. Draw $\overline{AC}$ and $\overline{BD}$.	2. 2 pts. determine 1 line.
3. $\angle A \cong \angle D$	3. Cor. 1 of Th. 9.9
4. $\angle P \cong \angle P$	4. Refl. prop.
5. $\triangle APC \sim \triangle DPB$	5. AA
6. $\frac{AP}{DP} = \frac{PC}{PB}$	6. Corr. side lengths of $\sim$ $\triangle$s are in proportion.
7. $AP \cdot PB = DP \cdot PC$	7. Means-extremes prop.

Conclusion: If secants $\overline{AP}$ and $\overline{DP}$ intersect in the ext. of a $\odot$ and have external segs. $\overline{PB}$ and $\overline{PC}$, then $AP \cdot PB = DP \cdot PC$.

17. Plan: See Class Exercise 7.
Proof:

Statements	Reasons
1. $\overline{CP}$ is tan. to $\odot O$; $\overline{AP}$ is a secant with external seg. $\overline{BP}$.	1. Given
2. Draw $\overline{AC}$ and $\overline{BC}$.	2. 2 pts. determine 1 line.
3. $m\angle A = \frac{1}{2}m\widehat{BC}$	3. Th. 9.9
4. $m\angle PCB = \frac{1}{2}m\widehat{BC}$	4. Th. 9.11
5. $m\angle A = m\angle PCB$	5. Trans. prop.
6. $\angle A \cong \angle PCB$	6. Def. of $\cong$ $\angle$s
7. $\angle P \cong \angle P$	7. Refl. prop.
8. $\triangle APC \sim \triangle CPB$	8. AA
9. $\frac{AP}{CP} = \frac{CP}{BP}$	9. Corr. side lengths of $\sim$ $\triangle$s are in proportion.
10. $AP \cdot BP = CP^2$	10. Means-extremes prop.

Conclusion: If $\odot O$ has tan. $\overline{CP}$ and secant $\overline{AP}$ with external segment $\overline{BP}$, then $AP \cdot BP = CP^2$.

PAGE 401

10.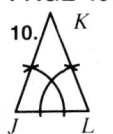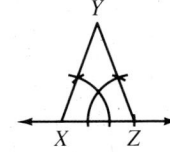

11.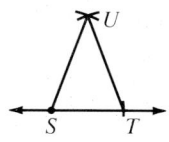

12.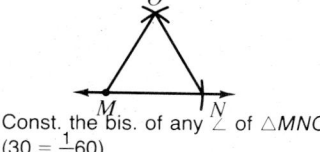

13. Const. the bis. of any $\angle$ of $\triangle MNO$. $(30 = \frac{1}{2}60)$

14. Const. the bis. of the 30° $\angle$ constructed in Ex. 15. $(15 = \frac{1}{2}(30))$

15. Answers may vary. Const. an $\angle$ whose meas. = the sum of the meas. of the $\angle$s constructed in Ex. 15 and 16. $(45 = 30 + 15)$

16. Answers may vary. Const. an $\angle$ = in meas. to 2 times any $\angle$ of $\triangle MNO$. $(120 = 60 + 60)$ or extend a side to form an exterior $\angle$.

17. Answers may vary. Const. an $\angle$ = in meas. to any $\angle$ of $\triangle MNO$ plus the $\angle$ constructed in Ex. 15. $(90 = 60 + 30)$

18. Answers may vary. Const. an $\angle$ whose meas. = the sum of the measures of the $\angle$s constructed in Ex. 19 and 17. $(135 = 90 + 45)$

19. Answers may vary. Const. an $\angle$ whose meas. equals the sum of the meas. of the $\angle$ constructed in Ex. 19 and any $\angle$ of $\triangle MNO$. $(150 = 90 + 60)$

20. Answers may vary. Const. the bis of the $\angle$ in Ex. 17. Then const. an $\angle$ = in meas. to the bisected $\angle$ of Ex. 17 plus any $\angle$ of $\triangle MNO$.

21. Since the sum of the meas. of the $\angle$s of a $\triangle$ = 180, if 2 $\angle$s are known, the 3rd is determined. No; since $\overline{PQ}$ can be any length, the $\triangle$ will be $\sim$ but not nec. $\cong$.

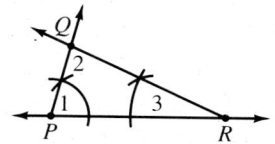

22.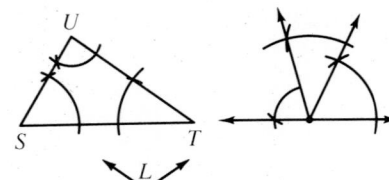

23.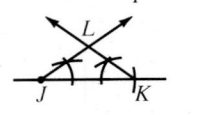

24.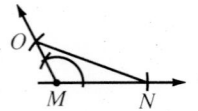

25.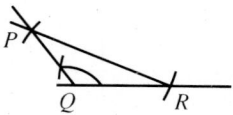

26.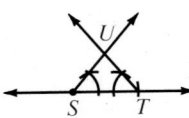

27.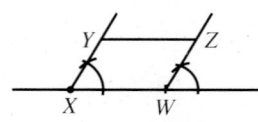

28.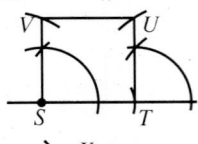

29.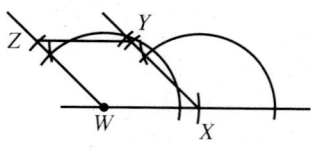

30.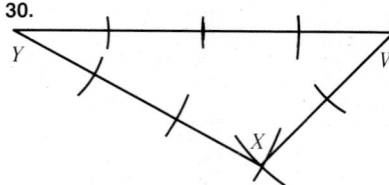

32.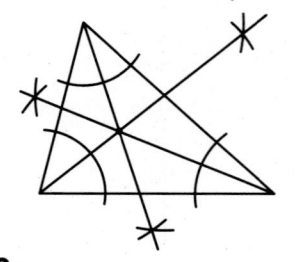

760

PAGE 402

33.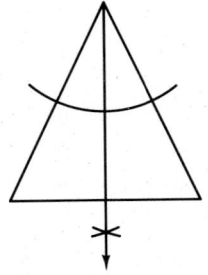

34. Extend one side of ∠A through vertex A and bis. the adj. ∠ formed. The 2 ∠s formed are the required base ∠s.
art

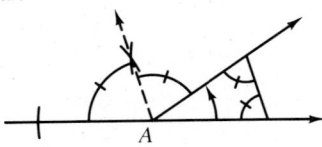

35.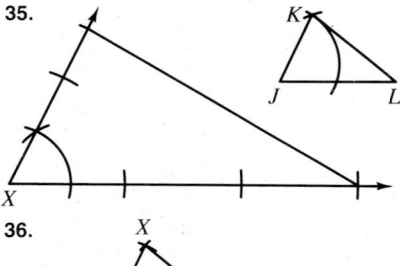

36.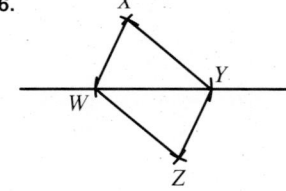

37.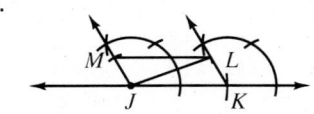

39.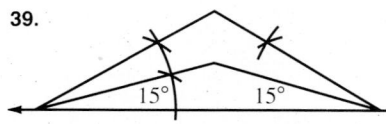

PAGE 405

4.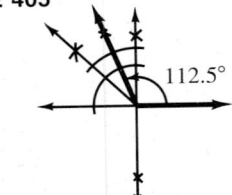
112.5°

5.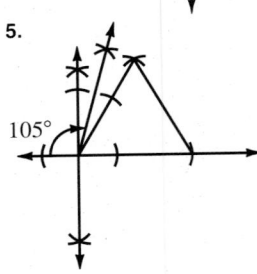
105°

6.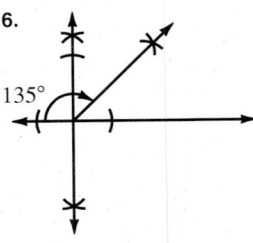
135°

7.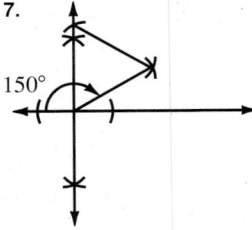
150°

8.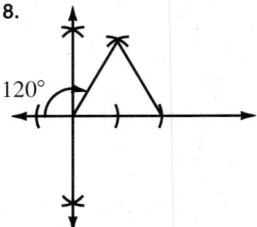
120°

9.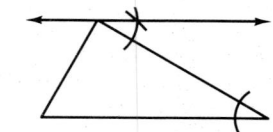

10.

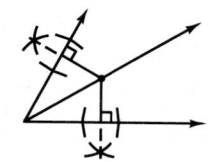

11.

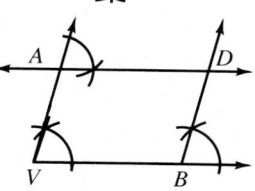

12.

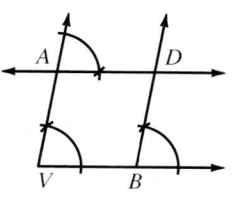

13.

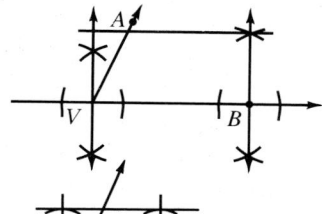

14.

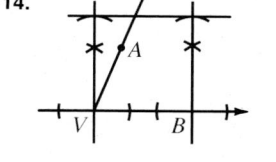

15. $\overline{XP} \cong \overline{YP}$ and $\overline{XZ} \cong \overline{YZ}$. Since Z is equidistant from the endpts. of a seg., it lies on the ⊥ bis. of the seg.

16. $PX = PY$ and $XZ = YZ$ because radii of circles are $=$. P and Z lie on the ⊥ bis. (same as 13).

17. $\angle 1 \cong \angle 2$ by construction. If 2 lines have a transv. and $\cong$ corr. $\angle$s, then the lines are $\parallel$.

18.

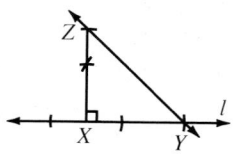

19.

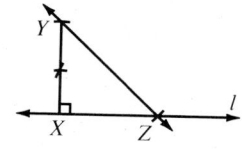

PAGE 406

20.

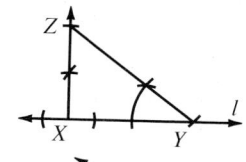

21.

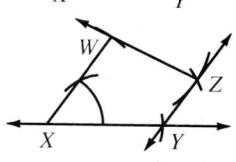

23.

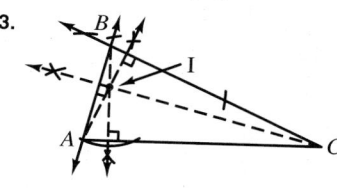

24.

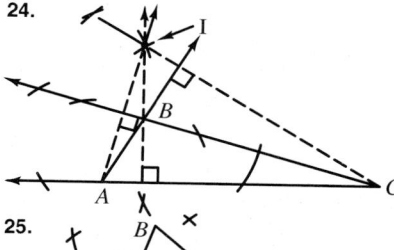

25.

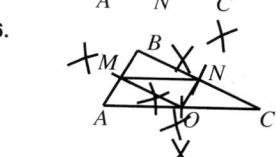

26.

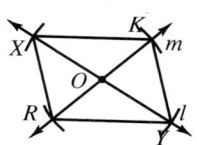

27.

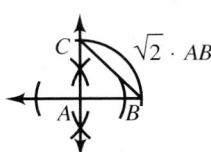

32.

$\sqrt{2} \cdot AB$

33.

$\sqrt{3}AB$

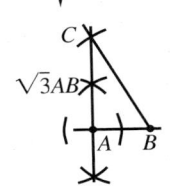

PAGE 407

1.

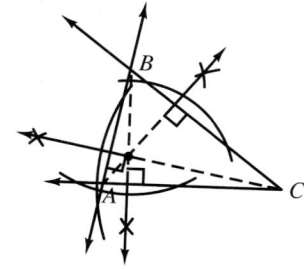

2.

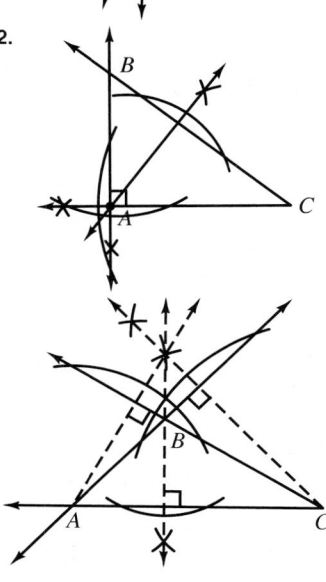

PAGE 410

21. In $\triangle PQR$, $\overline{ST} \parallel \overline{RQ}$, and in $\triangle ROQ$, $\overline{XY} \parallel \overline{RQ}$ because a line that intersects the midpts of 2 sides of a $\triangle$ is $\parallel$ to the third side. Hence, $\overline{ST} \parallel \overline{XY}$.
Also, $ST = \frac{1}{2}RQ$ and $XY = \frac{1}{2}RQ$.
Hence $\overline{ST} \cong \overline{XY}$. Since a pair of sides of $STYX$ are both $\parallel$ and $\cong$, $STYX$ is a $\square$.

22. Proof:

Statements	Reasons
1. $\triangle ABC$ with $\angle$ bis. $\overrightarrow{AO}$, $\overrightarrow{BO}$, and $\overrightarrow{CX}$	1. Given
2. Construct $\overline{OP} \perp \overline{AB}$, $\overline{OQ} \perp \overline{BC}$ and $\overline{OR} \perp \overline{AC}$.	2. Through a pt. not on a line, exactly one $\perp$ can be drawn to the line.
3. $OP = OR$; $OP = OQ$	3. If a pt. lies on the bis. of an $\angle$, then the pt. is

761

equidistant from the sides of the ∠.

4. $OR = OQ$
5. $\overrightarrow{CX}$ is concurrent at O with $\overrightarrow{AO}$ and $\overrightarrow{BO}$. That is, O lies on the bisector of $\angle C$.

4. Trans. prop.
5. If a pt. is equidistant from the sides of an ∠, then it lies on the bisector of the ∠.

Concl. Since O lies on the ∠ bis. of $\triangle ABC$ and $OP = OQ = OR$, the ∠ bisectors are concurrent and their pt. of intersection is equidistant from the 3 sides.

23. Proof:

Statements	Reasons
1. $\triangle ABC$ with ⊥ bisectors p, q, and r of its 3 sides; O is the intersection of p and q	1. Given
2. O is equidistant from A and B ($\overline{AO} \cong \overline{OB}$) and from C and B ($\overline{CO} \cong \overline{OB}$).	2. If a pt. lies on the ⊥ bis. of a seg., then the pt. is equidistant from the endpts. of the segment.
3. $\overline{AO} \cong \overline{OC}$	3. Trans. prop.
4. O lies on the ⊥ bis. of $\overline{AC}$. r is concurrent with p and q at O.	4. If a pt. is equidistant from the endpts. of a seg., then it lies on the ⊥ bis. of the seg.

Concl. Since O is the pt. of concurrency of ⊥ bis. p and q of $\triangle ABC$, it also lies on the ⊥ bis of the third side, and hence $\overline{AO} \cong \overline{OB} \cong \overline{OC}$.

PAGE 411

24. Given: isos. $\triangle ABC$; median $\overline{BD}$
Prove: $\overline{BD}$ is an alt.

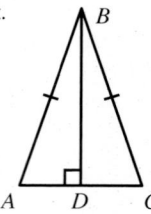

Plan: Show $\triangle ABD \cong \triangle CBD$ by SSS. Then $\angle ADB \cong \angle CDB$ by CPCTC. Since $\angle ADB$ and $\angle CDB$ also form a linear pair, it follows that they are rt. ∠s. Thus, $\overline{BD}$ is an alt.

Proof:

Statements	Reasons
1. isos. $\triangle ABC$; median $\overline{BD}$	1. Given
2. $\overline{AB} \cong \overline{CB}$	2. Def. of isos. △
3. D is the midpt. of $\overline{AC}$.	3. Def. of median
4. $\overline{AD} \cong \overline{CD}$	4. Def. of midpt.
5. $\overline{BD} \cong \overline{BD}$	5. Refl. prop.
6. $\triangle ABD \cong \triangle CBD$	6. SSS
7. $\angle ADB \cong \angle CDB$	7. CPCTC
8. $\angle ADB$ and $\angle CDB$ are a linear pair.	8. Def. of linear pair
9. $\angle ADB$ and $\angle CDB$ are supp.	9. Linear Pair Post.
10. $m\angle ADB + m\angle CDB = 180$	10. Def. of supp.
11. $m\angle ADB = m\angle CDB$	11. Def. of ≅ ∠s
12. $m\angle ADB + m\angle ADB = 180$	12. Subst. prop.
13. $2m\angle ADB = 180$	13. Distr. prop.
14. $m\angle ADB = 90$	14. Div. prop.
15. $\angle ADB$ is a rt. ∠.	15. Def. of rt. ∠
16. $\overline{BD} \perp \overline{AC}$	16. Def. of ⊥
17. $\overline{BD}$ is an alt.	17. Def. of alt.

Concl.: In isos. $\triangle ABC$ with median $\overline{BD}$ from vertex $\angle B$, $\overline{BD}$ is also an alt.

25. Given: isos. $\triangle RST$; alt. $\overline{SV}$
Prove: $\overline{SV}$ is a median.

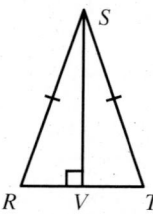

Plan: Show $\triangle SRV \cong \triangle STV$ by HL. Then $\overline{RV} \cong \overline{TV}$ by CPCTC. Thus, V is the midpt. of $\overline{RT}$, and the concl. follows by def. of median.

Proof:

Statements	Reasons
1. isos. $\triangle RST$; altitude $\overline{SV}$	1. Given
2. $\overline{SR} \cong \overline{ST}$	2. Def. of isos. △
3. $\overline{SV} \perp \overline{RT}$	3. Def. of alt.
4. $\angle RVS$ and $\angle TVS$ are rt. ∠s.	4. Def. of rt. ∠
5. $\triangle RVS$ and $\triangle TVS$ are rt. △s.	5. Def. of rt. △
6. $\overline{SV} \cong \overline{SV}$	6. Refl. prop.
7. $\triangle SRV \cong \triangle STV$	7. HL
8. $\overline{RV} \cong \overline{TV}$	8. CPCTC
9. V is the midpt. of $\overline{RT}$.	9. Def. of midpt.
10. $\overline{SV}$ is a median.	10. Def. of median

Concl.: In isos. $\triangle RST$ with alt. $\overline{SV}$ from $\angle S$, $\overline{SV}$ is also a median.

26. By the def. of altitude, X has been constructed to be the common pt. of the altitudes from A to $\overline{BC}$ and from B to $\overline{AC}$. Since, by Th. 10.3, all 3 altitudes will intersect at X, X is the orthocenter.

27. By the def. of median, X has been constructed to be the common pt. of medians $\overline{CM}$ and $\overline{AN}$. Since, by Th. 10.4, all 3 medians will intersect at X, X is the centroid.

30. Given: $\triangle ABC$ with medians $\overline{BD}$ and $\overline{CE}$; $\overline{BD} \cong \overline{CE}$
Prove: $\triangle ABC$ is isos.

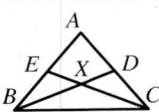

Plan: Use the Th. about the intersection of the medians of a △ and alg. prop. to prove $\triangle DXC \cong \triangle EXB$ by SAS. Then use def. of median to show $\overline{AB} \cong \overline{AC}$. The concl. follows.

Proof:

Statements	Reasons
1. $\triangle ABC$ with medians $\overline{BD}$ and $\overline{CE}$	1. Given
2. $BX = \frac{2}{3}BD$, $XD = \frac{1}{3}BD$,	2. The medians of a △ intersect in a

$CX = \frac{2}{3}CE,$ $XE = \frac{1}{3}CE$	pt. that is $\frac{2}{3}$ the distance from each vertex to the opp. side.
3. $\overline{BD} \cong \overline{CE}$	3. Given
4. $BD = CE$	4. Def. of $\cong$ segments
5. $\frac{2}{3}BD = \frac{2}{3}CE,$ $\frac{1}{3}BD = \frac{1}{3}CE$	5. Mult. prop.
6. $BX = CX,$ $XD = XE$	6. Subst. prop.
7. $\overline{BX} \cong \overline{CX},$ $\overline{XD} \cong \overline{XE}$	7. Def. of $\cong$ segments
8. $\angle DXC \cong$ $\angle EXB$	8. Vert. $\angle$s are $\cong$.
9 $\triangle DXC \cong \triangle EXB$	9. SAS
10. $\overline{EB} \cong \overline{DC}$	10. CPCTC
11. $EB = DC$	11. Def. of $\cong$ segments
12. $EB = \frac{1}{2}AB,$ $DC = \frac{1}{2}AC$	12. Def. of median and Midpt. Th.
13. $\frac{1}{2}AB = \frac{1}{2}AC$	13. Subst. prop.
14. $AB = AC$	14. Mult. prop.
15. $\overline{AB} \cong \overline{AC}$	15. Def. of $\cong$ segments
16. $\triangle ABC$ is isos.	16. Def. of isos. $\triangle$

Concl. If 2 medians of a $\triangle$ are $\cong$, then the $\triangle$ is isos.

TEST YOURSELF

4.

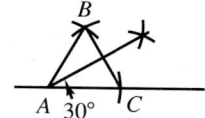

5.

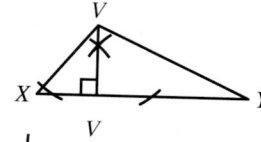

6.

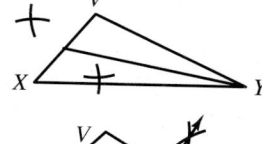

7.

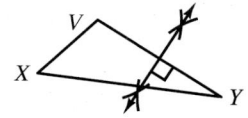

8.

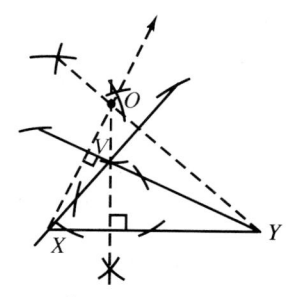

9.

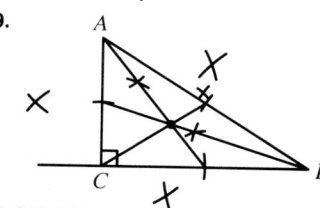

PAGE 415

2.

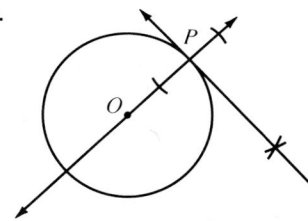

3.

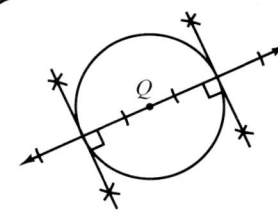

4.

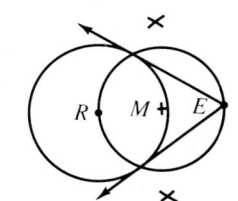

5.

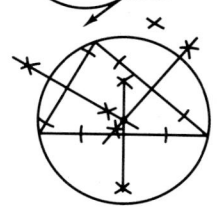

6.

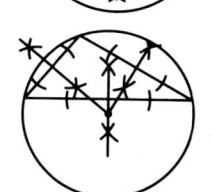

7.

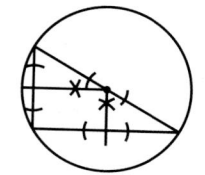

8.

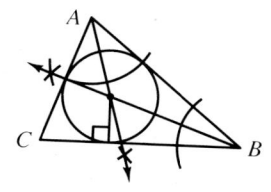

9.

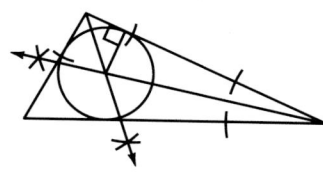

PAGE 416

11.

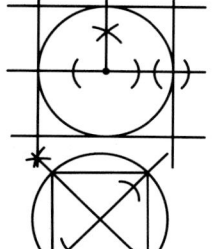

12.

15.

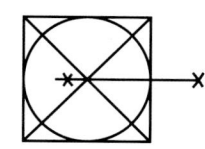

16.

18.

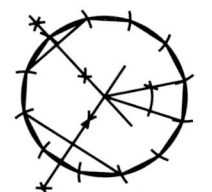

763

19.

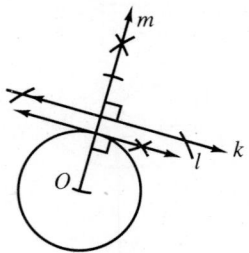

20.

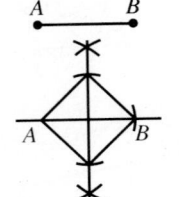

21.

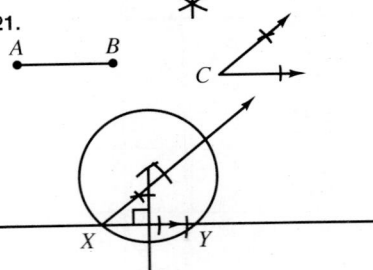

22.

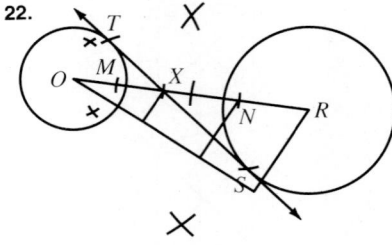

PAGE 417

2.

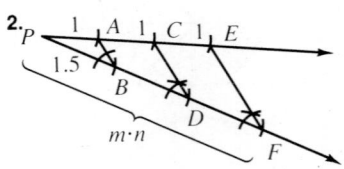

PAGE 419

1.

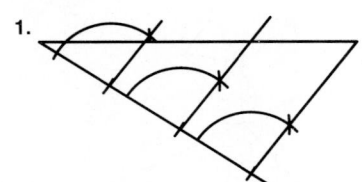

2.

3.

4.

PAGE 420

7.

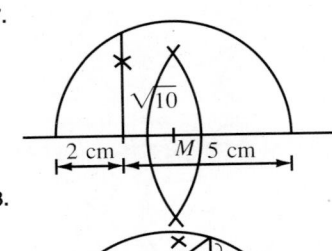

8.

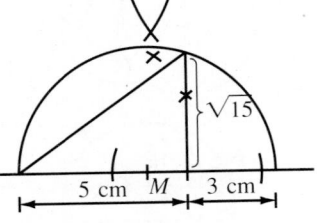

9.

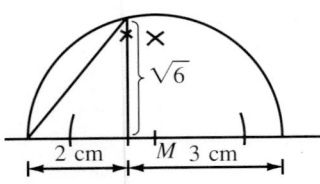

10.

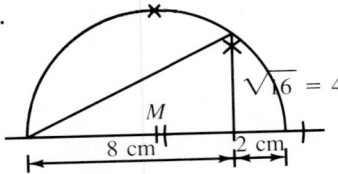

11.

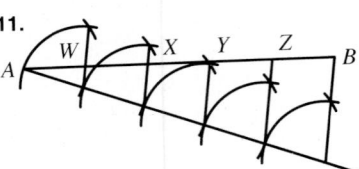

12.

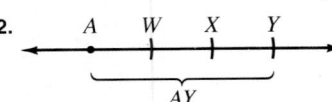

13.

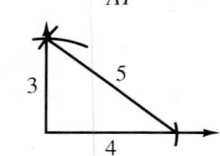

14.

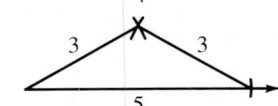

15.

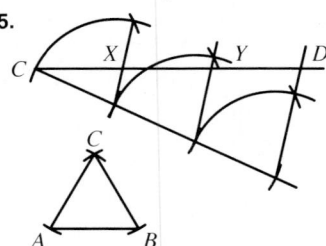

16.

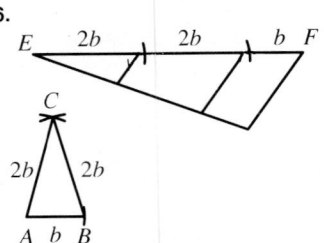

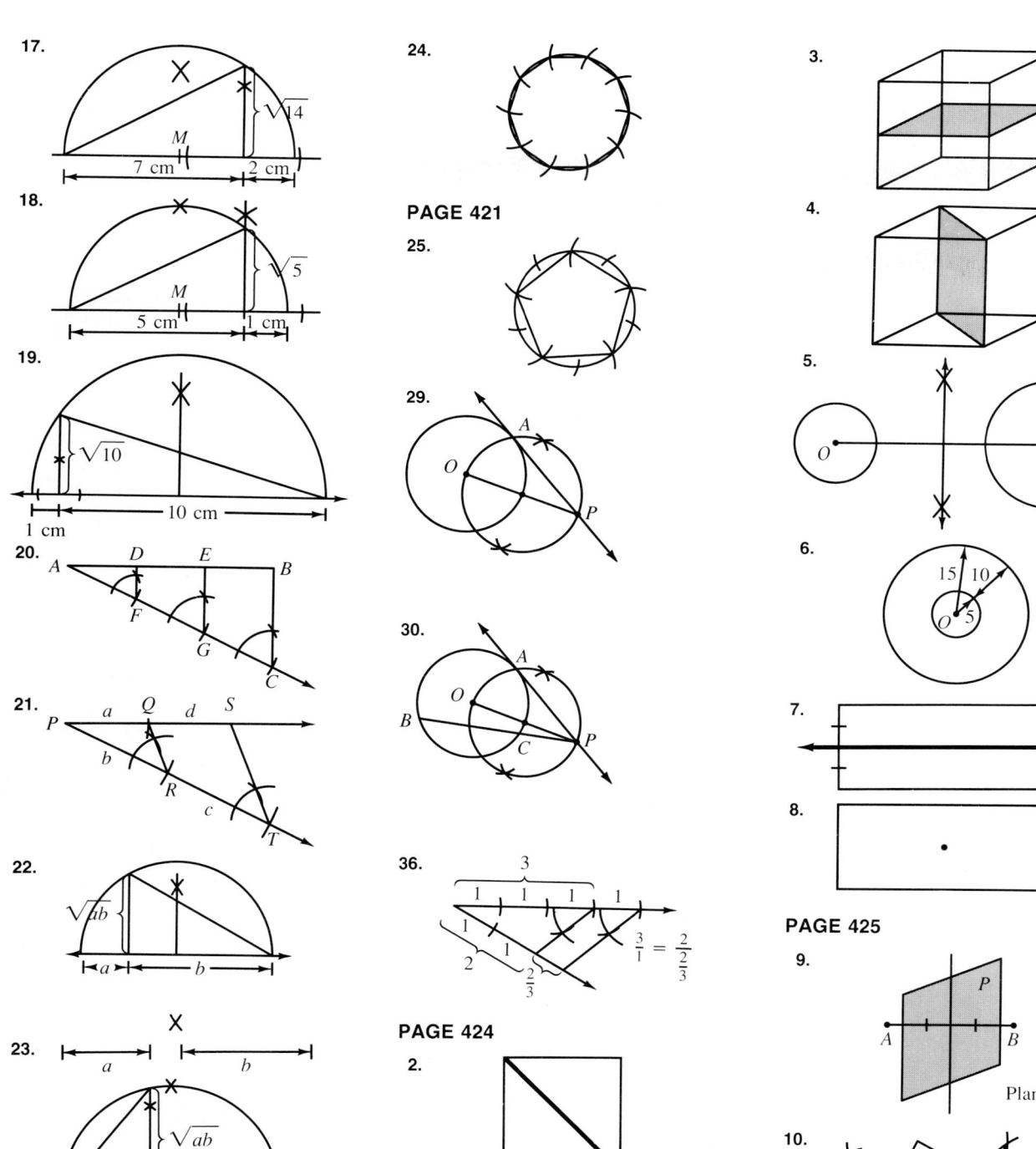

17. X $\sqrt{14}$ M 7 cm 2 cm

18. X $\sqrt{5}$ M 5 cm 1 cm

19. X $\sqrt{10}$ 10 cm 1 cm

20. A D E B F G C

21. P a Q d S b R c T

22. $\sqrt{ab}$ a b

23. X a b X $\sqrt{ab}$ M a b

24.

PAGE 421

25.

29. A O P

30. A O B C P

36. 3 1 1 1 1 1 1 1 2 $\frac{2}{3}$ $\frac{3}{1} = \frac{2}{\frac{2}{3}}$

PAGE 424

2.

3.

4.

5. O R

6. 15 10 O 5

7.

8.

PAGE 425

9. P A B
Plane $P \perp \overline{AB}$

10.

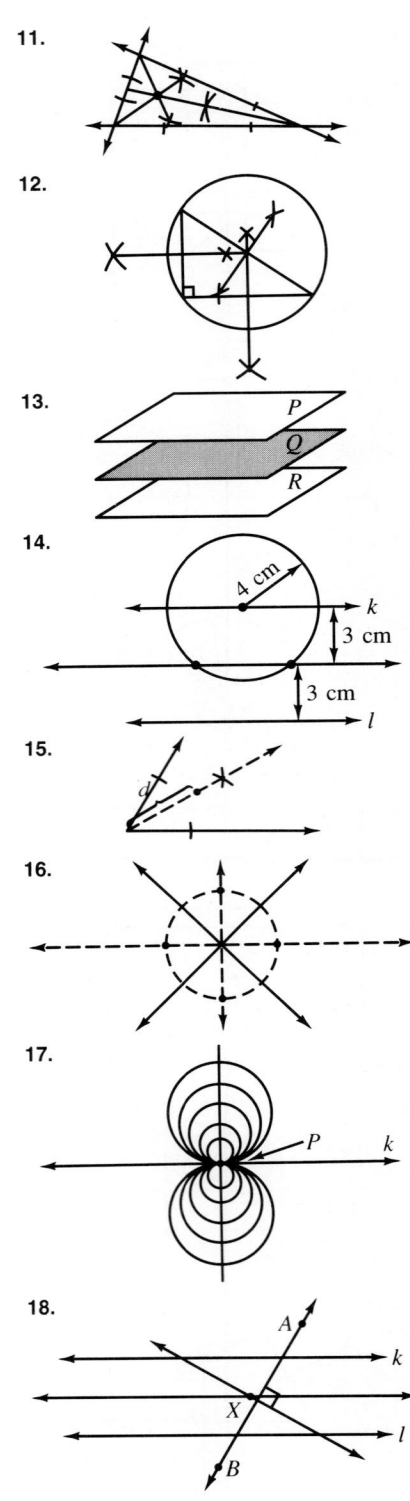

11.

12.

13. P, Q, R

14.

15.

16.

17.

18. A, k, X, l, B

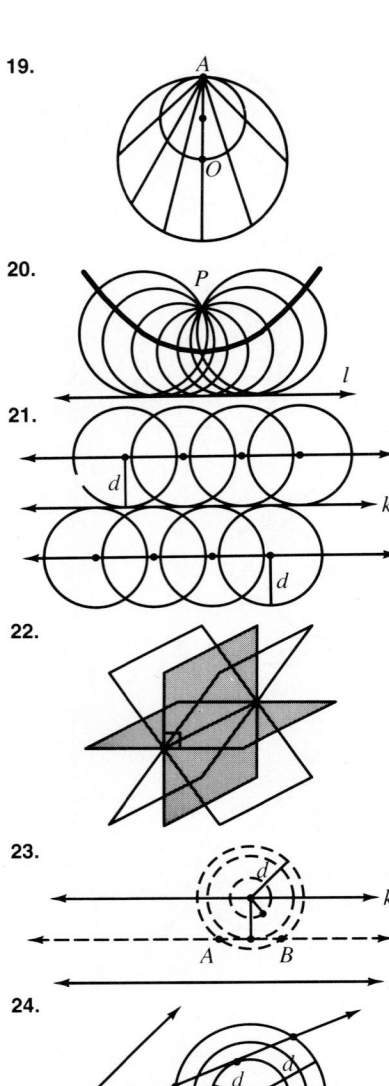

19. A, O

20. P, l

21. d, k, d

22.

23. d, k, A, B, l

24. d, d, d, P

25. Case I: If, in a plane, the locus of pts. is equidistant from 2 given pts., then the locus is the ⊥ bis. of the seg. joining the pts.
Given: locus of pts. equidistant from A and B; C and D equidistant from A and B

C, A, B, D

Prove: C and D lie on the ⊥ bis. of $\overline{AB}$.
Plan: Concl. follows immediately from Th. 4.7.
Proof:

Statements	Reasons
1. C and D are equidistant from A and B.	1. Given
2. C and D lie on the ⊥ bis. of $\overline{AB}$.	2. If a pt. is equidistant from the endpts. of a seg., then the pt. lies on the ⊥ bis. of the seg.

Case II: If, in a plane, the locus of pts. is the ⊥ bis. of the seg. joining the pts., then the locus is equidistant from the 2 given pts.
Given: C and D lie on the ⊥ bis. of $\overline{AB}$.
Prove: C and D are equidistant from pts. A and B.
Plan: Concl. follows immediately from Th. 4.6.
Proof:

Statements	Reasons
1. C and D lie on the ⊥ bis. of $\overline{AB}$.	1. Given
2. C and D are equidistant from pts. A and B.	2. If a pt. lies on the ⊥ bis. of a segment, then the pt. is equidistant from the endpts. of the segment.

26. C, Y, B, X, O, A, D

$\overline{CD}$, excluding O

27. P, O

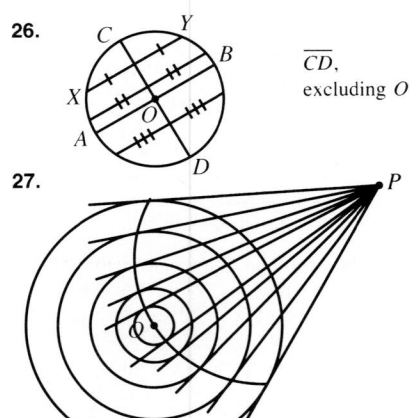

766

28. *m* is the line ∥ to and midway between *k* and *l;* if *m* is the ⊥ bis. of $\overline{AB}$, then the locus is *m;* if *m* is ⊥ $\overline{AB}$ but not the bis., the locus is empty; if $\overline{AB}$ is not ⊥ to *m,* the locus is the intersection of the ⊥ bis. of $\overline{AB}$ and line *m.*

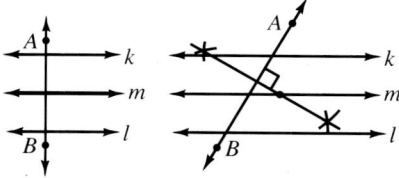

29. One case:

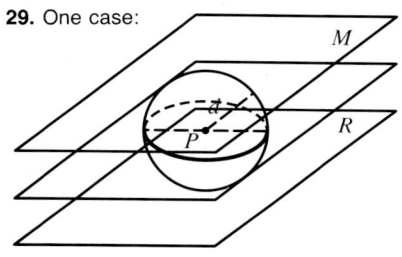

30. Answers may vary. There are 10 possible intersections for 2 ∥ planes and 2 concentric spheres: 4 circles, 3 circles, 2 circles, 1 circle, 3 circles and 1 pt., 2 circles and 1 pt., 1 circle and 1 pt., 2 pts., 1 pt., and no pts.

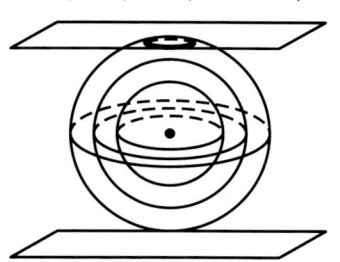

locus: 1 circle

31. Case I: If, in a plane, the locus of pts. is equidistant from the sides of an ∠, then the locus is the ∠ bis.
Given: locus of pts. equidistant from $\overrightarrow{BA}$ and $\overrightarrow{BC}$ of ∠*ABC;* *D* equidistant from $\overrightarrow{BA}$ and $\overrightarrow{BC}$

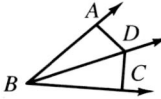

Prove: *D* lies on the ∠ bis. of ∠*ABC.*
Plan: Concl. follows immediately from Th. 4.9.
Proof:

Statements	Reasons
1. *D* is equidistant from $\overrightarrow{BA}$ and $\overrightarrow{BC}$.	1. Given
2. *D* lies on the ∠ bis. of ∠*ABC.*	2. If a pt. is equidistant from the sides of an ∠, then the pt. lies on the bis. of the ∠.

Case II: If, in a plane, the locus of pts. is the bis. of a given ∠, then the locus is equidistant from the sides of the ∠.
Given: *D* lies on the bis. of ∠*ABC.*
Prove: *D* is equidistant from $\overrightarrow{BA}$ and $\overrightarrow{BC}$.
Plan: Concl. follows immediately from Th. 4.8
Proof:

Statements	Reasons
1. *D* lies on the bis. of ∠*ABC.*	1. Given
2. *D* is equidistant from $\overrightarrow{BA}$ and $\overrightarrow{BC}$.	2. If a pt. lies on the bisector of an ∠, then the pt. is equidistant from the sides of the ∠.

32. Given: diameter $\overline{AB}$ of ⊙*O*
Prove: 1) If *M* is the midpt. of chord $\overline{XY} \parallel \overline{AB}$, then *M* is on diameter $\overline{CD} \perp \overline{AB}$.
2) If *M* is a pt. of diameter $\overline{CD} \perp \overline{AB}$, then *M* is the midpt. of chord $\overline{XY} \parallel \overline{AB}$.

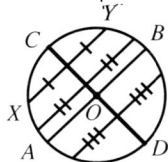

Plan: (Case 1) Show △*MXO* ≅ △*MYO* to get ∠*XMO* ≅ ∠*YMO* and, hence, $\overrightarrow{CD} \perp \overline{AB}$. (Case 2) Show that $\overline{XY} \parallel \overline{AB}$ and that $\overrightarrow{CD}$ bisects $\overline{XY}$; hence, *M* is a midpt.

Proof:

Statements	Reasons
1. *M* is midpt. of chord $\overline{XY} \parallel \overline{AB}$.	1. Given
2. $\overline{MX} \cong \overline{MY}$	2. Def. of midpt.
3. $\overline{OX} \cong \overline{OY}$	3. Radii of same ⊙ are ≅.
4. $\overline{MO} \cong \overline{MO}$	4. Refl. prop.
5. △*MXO* ≅ △*MYO*	5. SSS
6. ∠*XMO* ≅ ∠*YMO*	6. CPCTC
7. $\overline{OM} \perp \overline{XY}$	7. If 2 lines intersect so that adj. ∠s are ≅ , then the lines are ⊥
8. *M* is on the ⊥ bis. of $\overline{AB}$, a chord $\overline{CD}$ that passes through the center. Hence, $\overline{CD}$ is a diam. *M* cannot be the same as *C* or *D* since they cannot be on chords. (Case 1)	8. Def. of diam.
9. *M* is a pt. of diam. $\overline{CD}$ which is ⊥ to diam $\overline{AB}$.	9. Given
10. Consider chord $\overline{XY}$ containing *M* and ⊥ $\overline{CD}$. Then $\overline{XY} \parallel \overline{AB}$	10. Two lines ⊥ to the same line are ∥ .
11. $\overline{CD}$ bisects $\overline{XY}$.	11. A diam. ⊥ to a chord bisects that chord.
12. *M* is the midpt. of $\overline{XY}$. Also, *M* cannot be the same as *C* or *D* since no such chord $\overline{XY}$ exists on the circle. *M* cannot be the same as *O* since $\overline{AB}$ cannot be ∥ to itself.	12. Defs. of bisect and midpt.

Conclusion: The locus of the midpts. of all chords ∥ to a given diam. is another diam. excluding endpts ⊥ to given diam.

PAGE 431

7.
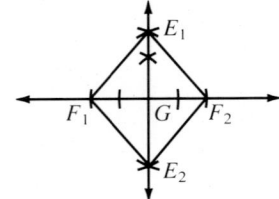

8.
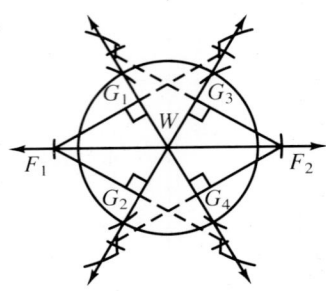

9.
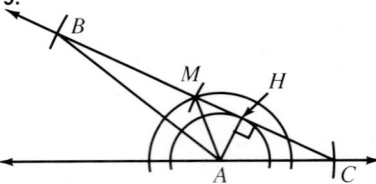

10.
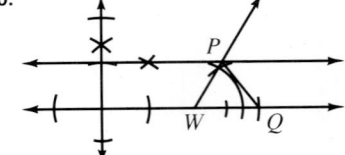

11.
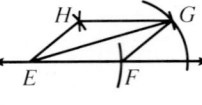

12.
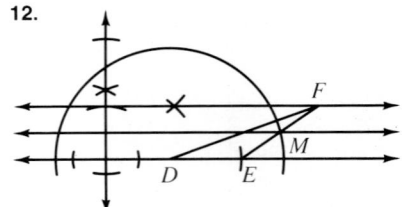

TEST YOURSELF, PAGE 431

1.

2.
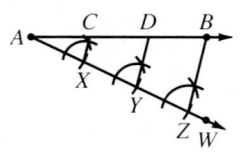

3.
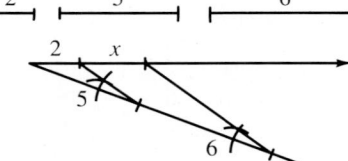

4.
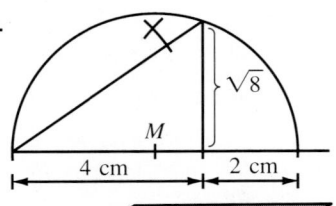

√8

4 cm   2 cm

5.
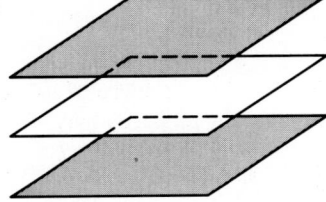

6.
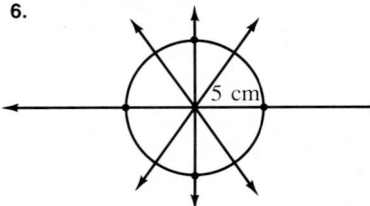

5 cm

7.
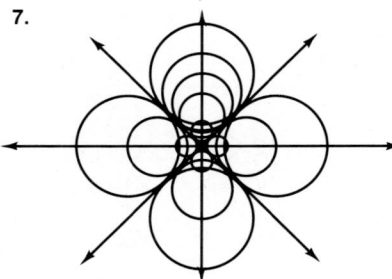

PAGE 435

12.
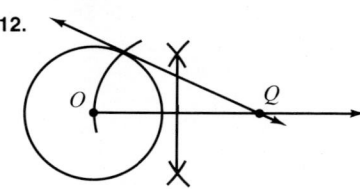

14.
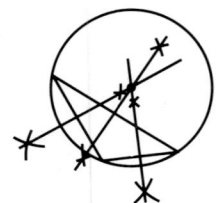

15.
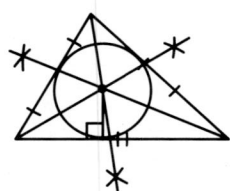

16.

17.
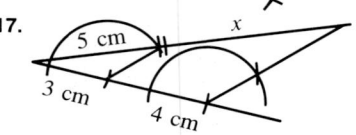

5 cm   x
3 cm   4 cm

18.
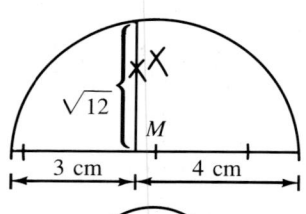

√12
3 cm   4 cm

19.
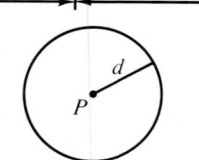

20.
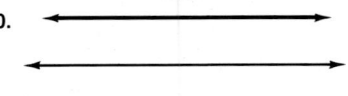

21.
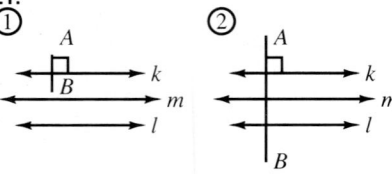

22.

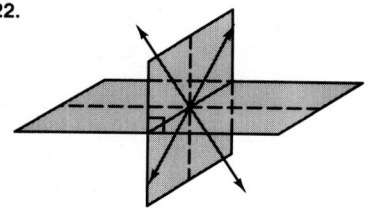

23.

infinitely many

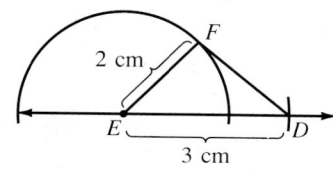

2 cm

E | D

3 cm

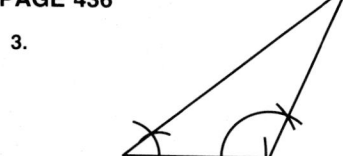

2 cm

E | D

3 cm

PAGE 436

3.

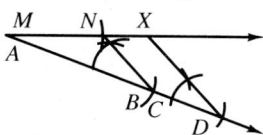

4.

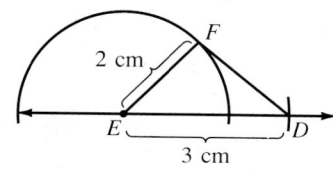

5.

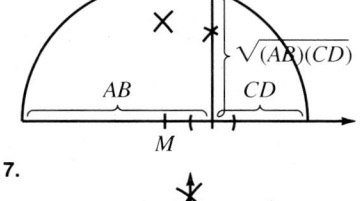

6.

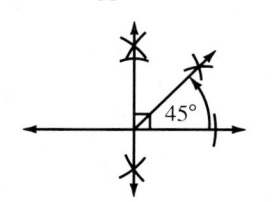

$\sqrt{(AB)(CD)}$

AB | CD

M

7.

45°

8.

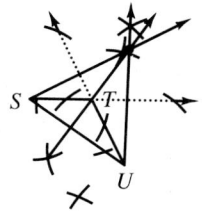

S T U

9.

O P

11.

$\frac{d}{2}$

d

12.

A B

PAGE 448

25. Proof:

Statements	Reasons
1. $\square GRAM$ with base b; $RN = h = AO$	1. Given
2. $\overline{RN} \cong \overline{AO}$	2. Def. of $\cong$ segments
3. $\overline{RN} \perp \overline{GM}$; $\overline{AO} \perp \overline{GO}$	3. Def. of alt.
4. $\angle GNR$ and $\angle MOA$ are rt. $\angle$s.	4. Def. of $\perp$
5. $\triangle RNG$ and $\triangle AOM$ are rt. $\triangle$s.	5. Def. of rt. $\triangle$
6. $\overline{RG} \cong \overline{AM}$	6. Opp. sides of a $\square$ are $\cong$.
7. $\triangle RNG \cong \triangle AOM$	7. HL
8. Area of $\triangle RNG$ = area of $\triangle AOM$	8. Area Congruence Post.
9. Area of $\triangle RNG$ + area of $RNMA$ = area of $\triangle AOM$ + area of $RNMA$	9. Add. prop.
10. Area of $\triangle RNG$ + area of $RNMA$ = area of $\square GRAM$; area of $\triangle AOM$ + area of $RNMA$ = area of rect. $NRAO$	10. Area Add. Post.
11. Area of $\square GRAM$ = area of rect. $NRAO$	11. Subst. prop.
12. Area of $NRAO = bh$	12. Area of rect. = bh
13. Area of $\square GRAM = bh$	13. Trans. prop.

Concl. If $GRAM$ is a $\square$ with base length b and height h, then the area of $\square GRAM = bh$.

28. Given: $\triangle GRM$ with base b and corr. height h

Prove: Area of $\triangle GRM = \frac{1}{2}bh$

Plan: Draw $\overleftrightarrow{RA} \parallel \overline{GM}$ and $\overleftrightarrow{MA} \parallel \overleftrightarrow{RG}$ to form $\square GRAM$ with diagonal $\overline{RM}$. Then $\triangle GRM \cong \triangle AMR$. Since area of $\triangle GRM$ + area of $\triangle AMR$ = area of $\square GRAM$, the concl. follows by subst. and alg. props.

Proof:

Statements	Reasons
1. $\triangle GRM$ with base b and height h	1. Given
2. Draw $\overleftrightarrow{RA} \parallel \overline{GM}$ and $\overleftrightarrow{MA} \parallel \overline{RG}$.	2. Through a pt. not on a line, exactly one line $\parallel$ to the given line can be drawn.
3. $GRAM$ is a $\square$.	3. Def. of $\square$
4. Area of $GRAM = bh$	4. Area of $\square = bh$

5. $\triangle GRM \cong \triangle AMR$
5. Diag. of a ▱ divides it into two $\cong$ ▵.

6. Area of $\triangle GRM$ = area of $\triangle AMR$
6. Area Congruence Post.

7. Area of $\triangle GRM$ + area of $\triangle AMR$ = area of ▱$GRAM$
7. Area Add. Post.

8. Area of $\triangle GRM$ + area of $\triangle GRM = bh$
8. Subst. prop.

9. $2 \cdot$ Area of $\triangle GRM = bh$
9. Distrib. prop.

10. Area of $\triangle GRM = \frac{1}{2}bh$
10. Mult. prop.

Concl.: If a ▵ has base b and corr. height h, then its area is $\frac{1}{2}bh$.

29. **Given:** Rhombus $ABCD$; diags. $\overline{AC}, \overline{BD}$; $AC = d_1$; $BD = d_2$

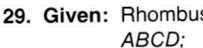

Prove: Area of $ABCD = \frac{1}{2}d_1 d_2$

Plan: Use the facts that the diags. of a rhombus are ⊥ and bisect each other to express the areas of $\triangle ABD$ and $\triangle CBD$ as $\frac{1}{2}(\frac{1}{2}d_1) \cdot d_2$. Concl. follows by alg. and the Area Add. Post.

Proof:

Statements	Reasons
1. Rhombus $ABCD$; diags. $\overline{AC}, \overline{BD}$; $AC = d_1$; $BD = d_2$	1. Given
2. $\overline{BD} \perp \overline{AC}$; $\overline{BD}$ and $\overline{AC}$ bisect each other.	2. Diags. of a rhombus bisect each other and are ⊥.
3. $\overline{AM} \cong \overline{CM}$	3. Def. of bis.
4. $AM = CM = \frac{1}{2}d_1$	4. Def. of $\cong$ seg. and Midpt. Th.
5. Area of $\triangle ABD = \frac{1}{2}AM \cdot BD$; area of $\triangle CBD = \frac{1}{2}CM \cdot BD$	5. Area of ▵ = $\frac{1}{2}b \cdot h$
6. Area of $\triangle ABD = \frac{1}{2}(\frac{1}{2}d_1)d_2$; Area of $\triangle CBD =$	6. Subst. prop.

$\frac{1}{2}(\frac{1}{2}d_1)d_2$

7. Area of $\triangle ABD$ + area of $\triangle CBD = \frac{1}{2}(\frac{1}{2}d_1)d_2 + \frac{1}{2}(\frac{1}{2}d_1)d_2$
7. Add. prop.

8. Area of $\triangle ABD$ + area of $\triangle CBD = \frac{1}{2}d_1 d_2$
8. Distrib. prop.

9. Area of $\triangle ABD$ + area of $\triangle CBD =$ area of $ABCD$
9. Area Add. Post.

10. Area of $ABCD = \frac{1}{2}d_1 d_2$
10. Subst. prop.

Conclusion: If a rhombus has diagonals of length d_1 and d_2, then its area is $\frac{1}{2}d_1 d_2$.

30. **Given:** Equilateral $\triangle ABC$ with altitude $\overline{BD}$ and side length s

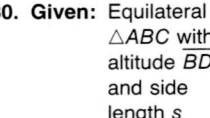

Prove: Area of $\triangle ABC = \frac{s^2\sqrt{3}}{4}$

Plan: Altitude $\overline{BD}$ forms $30°$-$60°$-$90°$ $\triangle BDC$. Since hyp. $\overline{BC}$ has length s, longer leg $\overline{BD}$ has length $\frac{s}{2}\sqrt{3}$. Concl. follows from the formula for the area of a ▵.

Proof:

Statements	Reasons
1. Equilateral $\triangle ABC$ with alt. $\overline{BD}$ and side length s	1. Given
2. $\overline{BD} \perp \overline{DC}$	2. Def. of alt.
3. $\angle BDC$ is a rt. ∠.	3. Def. of ⊥
4. $m\angle C = 60$	4. Each ∠ of an equilat. ▵ measures 60°.
5. $\triangle BDC$ is a $30°$-$60°$-$90°$ ▵.	5. Sum of ∠s of a ▵ = 180°.
6. $\overline{BC}$ is the hyp. of $\triangle BDC$.	6. Def. of hyp.
7. $BD = \frac{s}{2}\sqrt{3}$	7. Longer leg of a $30°$-$60°$-$90°$ ▵ is $\frac{1}{2}$ the hyp. times $\sqrt{3}$.

8. Area of $\triangle ABC = \frac{1}{2}BD \cdot AC$
8. Area of a ▵ = $\frac{1}{2}bh$

9. Area of $\triangle ABC = \frac{1}{2} \cdot \frac{s}{2}\sqrt{3} \cdot s$
9. Subst. prop.

10. Area of $\triangle ABC = \frac{s^2\sqrt{3}}{4}$
10. Subst. prop.

Conclusion: The area of an equilateral ▵ with side length s is $\frac{s^2}{4}\sqrt{3}$.

31. **Plan:** Construct altitude $\overline{KP}$ of both ▵. Since the bases of the ▵ are $\cong$, by the subst. prop., the ▵ will have the same area.

Proof:

Statements	Reasons
1. Construct alt. $\overline{KP}$.	1. Through a pt. not on a line, exactly one ⊥ can be drawn.
2. KP is the height of $\triangle JKM$ and $\triangle KML$.	2. Def. of height of a ▵
3. $\overline{KM}$ is a median of $\triangle JKL$.	3. Given
4. M is the midpt. of $\overline{JL}$.	4. Def. of median
5. $\overline{JM} \cong \overline{ML}$	5. Def. of midpt.
6. $JM = ML$	6. Def. of $\cong$ segments
7. Area of $\triangle JKM = \frac{1}{2}JM \cdot KP$ Area of $\triangle KML = \frac{1}{2}ML \cdot KP$	7. Area of ▵ = $\frac{1}{2}bh$
8. Area of $\triangle JKM = \frac{1}{2}ML \cdot KP$	8. Subst. prop.
9. Area of $\triangle JKM$ = area of $\triangle KML$	9. Trans. prop.

Conclusion: If a median is drawn to one side in a ▵, the areas of the ▵ formed are =.

32. **Plan:** Since $\overline{UD}$ bisects $\overline{QA}$, $\overline{UD}$ is a median of $\triangle QUA$ and $\triangle QAD$. Thus, the areas of ▵QUM and AUM are equal and so are the areas of ▵QDM and ADM (see Ex. 31). The concl. follows by Area Add. Post.

Proof:

Statements	Reasons
1. Quad. $QUAD$; $\overline{UD}$ bisects $\overline{QA}$.	1. Given
2. $\overline{QM} \cong \overline{MA}$	2. Def. of bis.
3. M is the midpt. of QA.	3. Def. of midpt.
4. $\overline{UM}$ is median of $\triangle QUA$; $\overline{DM}$ is a median of $\triangle QDA$	4. Def. of median
5. Area of $\triangle QUM$ = area of $\triangle AUM$; area of $\triangle QDM$ = area of $\triangle ADM$	5. Ex. 31
6. Area of $\triangle QUM$ + area of $\triangle QDM$ = area of $\triangle AUM$ + area of $\triangle ADM$	6. Add. prop.
7. Area of $\triangle QUM$ + area of $\triangle QDM$ = area of $\triangle DQU$; area of $\triangle AUM$ + area of $\triangle ADM$ = area of $\triangle DAU$	7. Area Add. Post.
8. Area of $\triangle DQU$ = area of $\triangle DAU$	8. Subst. prop.

Conclusion: In the given figure, if $\overline{UD}$ bisects QA, then the area of $\triangle DQU$ = area of $\triangle DAU$.

33. Plan: Draw $\overline{CD}$ to form $\square$s $BCDL$ and $CAED$. $\overline{CD}$ is also a diagonal of $BDEC$, which can be proven to be a $\square$. The diagonals of the three smaller $\square$s form $\cong$ $\triangle$. Use the transitive prop. and area postulates to relate the $\triangle$ contained in $BDEC$ to those contained in $ABLE$.

Proof:

Statements	Reasons
1. C and D are midpts. of $\overline{AB}$ and $\overline{LE}$ in $\square ABLE$.	1. Given
2. Draw $\overline{CD}$.	2. Two pts. determine exactly one line.
3. $\overline{AB} \parallel \overline{EL}$	3. Def. of $\square$
4. $\overline{AB} \cong \overline{EL}$	4. Opp. sides of a $\square$ are $\cong$.
5. $AB = EL$	5. Def. of $\cong$ seg.
6. $\frac{1}{2}AB = \frac{1}{2}EL$	6. Mult. prop.
7. $AC = \frac{1}{2}AB = BC$; $ED = \frac{1}{2}EL = DL$	7. Midpt. Th.
8. $AC = BC$ and $ED = DL$	8. Trans. prop.
9. $ACDE$, $BDEC$, and $BCDL$ are $\square$s.	9. If 2 sides of a quad. are $\parallel$ and $=$, the quad. is a $\square$.
10. $\triangle ACE \cong \triangle DEC$; $\triangle DEC \cong \triangle BCD$, $\triangle BCD \cong \triangle DLB$	10. Diag. of a $\square$ divides it into 2 $\cong$ $\triangle$.
11. $\triangle ACE \cong \triangle DEC \cong \triangle BCD \cong \triangle DLB$	11. Trans. prop.
12. Area of $\triangle ACE$ = area of $\triangle DEC$ = area of $\triangle BCD$ = area of $\triangle DLB$	12. Area Congruence Post.
13. Area of $BDEC$ = area of $\triangle DEC$ + area of $\triangle BCD$; area of $\square ABLE$ = area of $\triangle ACE$ + area of $\triangle DEC$ + area of $\triangle BCD$ + area of $\triangle DLB$	13. Area Add. Post.
14. Area of $BDEC$ = area $\triangle DEC$ + area of $\triangle DEC$; area of $\square ABLE$ = area of $\triangle DEC$ + area of $\triangle DEC$ + area of $\triangle DEC$ + area of $\triangle DEC$	14. Subst. prop.
15. Area of $BDEC$ = 2 · area of $\triangle DEC$; area of $\square ABLE$ = 4 · area of $\triangle DEC$	15. Distrib. prop.
16. $\frac{1}{2}$area of $ABLE$ = 2 · area of $\triangle DEC$	16. Mult. prop.
17. Area of $BDEC = \frac{1}{2}$area of $\square ABLE$	17. Trans. prop.

Conclusion: In $\square ABLE$, if C and D are midpoints of $\overline{AB}$ and $\overline{LE}$, respectively, then area of $BDEC = \frac{1}{2}$ area of $\square ABLE$.

34. Plan: Show $\triangle FCE \cong \triangle ABE$. Using Area Add. Post., area of $\square ABCD$ = area of $\triangle ABE$ + area of quad. $AECD$, and area of $\triangle FDA$ = area of $\triangle FCE$ + area of quad. $AECD$. Since $\triangle ABE$ and $\triangle FCE$ have equal areas, it follows that $\square ABCD$ and $\triangle FDA$ have equal areas.

Proof:

Statements	Reasons
1. $\square ABCD$ and $\triangle FDA$	1. Given
2. $\overline{AB} \parallel \overline{DF}$	2. Def. of $\square$
3. $\angle FCE \cong \angle ABE$	3. If lines are $\parallel$, alt. int $\angle$s are $\cong$.
4. E is midpt. of $\overline{BC}$	4. Given
5. $\overline{BE} \cong \overline{CE}$	5. Def. of midpt.
6. $\angle BEA \cong \angle CEF$	6. Vert. $\angle$s are $\cong$.
7. $\triangle ABE \cong \triangle FCE$	7. ASA
8. Area of $\triangle ABE$ = area of $\triangle FCE$	8. Area Congruence Post.
9. Area of $\square ABCD$ = area of $\triangle ABE$ + area of quad. $AECD$; area of $\triangle FDA$ = area of $\triangle FCE$ + area of quad. $AECD$	9. Area Add. Post.
10. Area of $\square ABCD$ = area $\triangle FCE$ + area of quad. $AECD$	10. Subst. prop.
11. Area of $\square ABCD$ = area of $\triangle FDA$	11. Trans. prop.

Conclusion: In the given figure, if $ABCD$ is a $\square$ and E is the midpoint of $\overline{BC}$, then the area of $\square ABCD$ = area of $\triangle FDA$.

PAGE 474

16. $A_1 = \pi r_1{}^2$; $A_2 = \pi r_2{}^2$. Thus, $\frac{A_1}{A_2} = \frac{\pi r_1{}^2}{\pi r_2{}^2} = \frac{r_1{}^2}{r_2{}^2}$.

17. Area of sector, $A_s = \frac{m}{360}\pi r^2$; area of circle, $A_\odot = \pi r^2$. Thus, $\frac{A_s}{A_\odot} = \frac{\frac{m}{360}\pi r^2}{\pi r^2} = \frac{m}{360}$.

18. The area A of a circle is the limit of the areas of inscribed regular n-gons as n increases. Thus apothem a has the limit r, perimeter P has limit C, and the area $\frac{1}{2}a \cdot P$ has the limit $\frac{1}{2}r \cdot C$. Then $C = 2\pi r$ gives $A = \frac{1}{2} \cdot r \cdot 2\pi r$ or $A = \pi r^2$.

PAGE 475

19. A (shaded region) $= A[\text{segment } OR + \text{sector } ROP] = \left[2 \cdot \frac{\pi r^2}{6} - \frac{r^2}{4}\sqrt{3}\right] = r^2\left(\frac{\pi}{3} - \frac{\sqrt{3}}{4}\right)$.

20. $A_1 = \pi r^2$; $A_2 = \pi(r + 1)^2 = \pi(r^2 + 2r + 1) = \pi r^2 + 2\pi r + \pi = A_1 + \pi(2r + 1)$; it is $\pi(2r + 1)$ greater.

PAGE 494

19. Theorem 12.1: The lateral area, L, of a rt. prism is the sum of the areas of the lateral faces. Using the figure, $L = s_1h + s_2h + s_3h + s_4h = h(s_1 + s_2 + s_3 + s_4)$. However, the perimeter of the base of the right prism is $P = s_1 + s_2 + s_3 + s_4$. By subst., $L = Ph$.

20. Theorem 12.2: $T = (s_1h + s_2h + s_3h + s_4h) + \text{area}_{\text{base 1}} + \text{area}_{\text{base 2}}$ However, $\text{area}_{\text{base 1}} = \text{area}_{\text{base 2}} = B$ and $s_1h + s_2h + s_3h + s_4h = h(s_1 + s_2 + s_3 + s_4) = Ph = L$. Therefore, $T = L + 2B$.

21. Theorem 12.3: The volume of an oblique prism can be equated with that of a right prism having the same base and height. The area of the base B is the number of square units it contains and the number of cubic units is B times the number of units in the height. Thus, $V = Bh$.

22. Cor.: For a cube, $B = e^2$ and $h = e$, so $V = e^2 \cdot e$ or $V = e^3$.

25. From one vertex of the upper base, draw the segment $\perp$ to the lower base. Connect the foot of the perpendicular to the lower end of the lateral edge from that vertex, forming a rt. $\triangle$ in which the lateral edge is the hypotenuse and the perpendicular is a leg. Since either leg of a rt. $\triangle$ is shorter than the hypotenuse, the height is less than the length of a lateral edge.

PAGE 510

3. a.

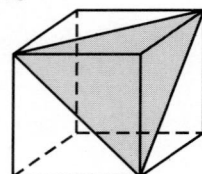

b.

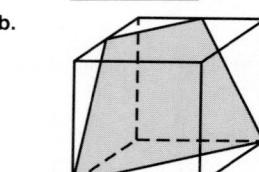

c.

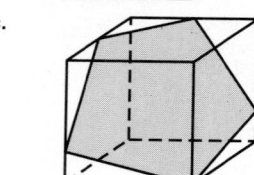

d.

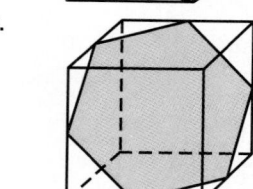

4. a.

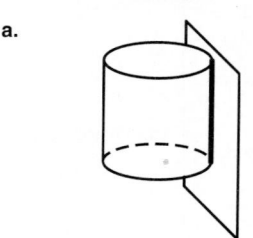

b.,c. line segment

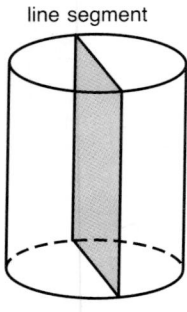

rectangle
or
parallelogram

d.

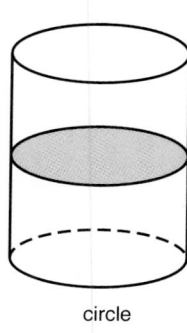

circle

5. Given: prism with faces $FBCE$ and $AFED$; lateral edges $\overline{AD}$, $\overline{FE}$, and $\overline{BC}$; cross section $ABCD$

Prove: $ABCD$ is a $\square$.

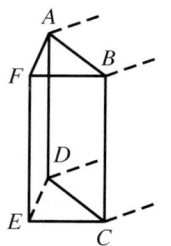

Plan: Use the prop. of a prism to show that $ABCD$ has a pair of opp. sides that are $\parallel$ and $\cong$.

Proof:

Statements	Reasons
1. prism with faces $FBCE$ and $AFED$	1. Given
2. $AFED$ and $FBCE$ are $\square$s.	2. Def. of prism
3. $\overline{AD} \parallel \overline{FE}$; $\overline{BC} \parallel \overline{FE}$	3. Def. of $\square$
4. $\overline{AD} \parallel \overline{BC}$	4. If 2 lines are $\parallel$ to a third line then they are $\parallel$ to each other.
5. $\overline{AD} \cong \overline{FE}$; $\overline{BC} \cong \overline{FE}$	5. Opp. sides of a $\square$ are $\cong$.

6. $\overline{AD} \cong \overline{BC}$ | 6. Trans. prop.
7. ABCD is a ▱. | 7. If 2 sides of a quad. are both ∥ and ≅, then the quad. is a ▱.

Concl.: In the given prism, if ABCD is a cross section as shown, then ABCD is a ▱.

6. Given: Rectangular solid with lateral edges $\overline{BC}$, $\overline{AD}$, $\overline{HE}$, and $\overline{GF}$; cross section ABCD
Prove: ABCD is a rectangle

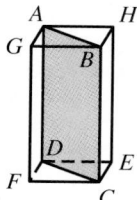

Plan: ABCD is a ▱ (see Ex. 5). Use the def. of rt. prism to show that the sides of ABCD are ⊥ to the faces of the solid. Thus, ▱ABCD has right ∠s and ABCD is a rectangle

Proof:

Statements	Reasons
1. Rectangular solid with lateral edges BC, AD, $\overline{HE}$ and $\overline{GF}$; cross section ABCD	1. Given
2. ABCD is a ▱.	2. Ex. 5
3. $\overline{AD} \perp$ plane DECF; $\overline{AD} \perp$ plane AHBG; $\overline{BC} \perp$ plane DECF; $\overline{BC} \perp$ plane AHBG	3. Def. of rt. prism
4. $\overline{AD} \perp \overline{DC}$	4. If a line is ⊥ to a plane at a pt., then it is ⊥ to every line in the plane through that pt.
5. ∠ADC is a rt. ∠.	5. Def. of ⊥
6. ABCD is a rect.	6. Def. of rect.

Concl.: In the given rectangular solid, cross section ABCD, containing a pair of nonconsecutive lateral edges, is a rect.

PAGE 524

31. Plan: Apply the props. of proportions and algebra.
Proof:

Statements	Reasons
1. Rt. circular cones C_1 and C_2 with $C_1 \sim C_2$	1. Given
2. $\dfrac{l_1}{l_2} = \dfrac{h_1}{h_2} = \dfrac{r_1}{r_2}$	2. If 2 rt. circular cones are ~, then the slant heights, heights, and radii are in the same ratio.
3. $\dfrac{r_1 l_1}{r_2 l_2} = \dfrac{r_1 r_1}{r_2 r_2}$	3. Mult. prop.
4. $\dfrac{r_1 l_1 + r_1 r_1}{r_2 l_2 + r_2 r_2} = \dfrac{r_1 l_1}{r_2 l_2}$	4. Proportion props.
5. $\dfrac{r_1(l_1 + r_1)}{r_2(l_2 + r_2)} = \dfrac{r_1 l_1}{r_2 l_2}$	5. Distrib. prop.
6. $\dfrac{\pi r_1(l_1 + r_1)}{\pi r_2(l_2 + r_2)} = \dfrac{r_1 l_1}{r_2 l_2}$	6. Mult. prop.
7. $T_1 = \pi r_1(l_1 + r_1)$; $T_2 = \pi r_2(l_2 + r_2)$	7. Th. for total area of a cone
8. $\dfrac{T_1}{T_2} = \dfrac{r_1 l_1}{r_2 l_2}$	8. Subst. prop.
9. $\dfrac{T_1}{T_2} = \dfrac{r_1 r_1}{r_2 r_2} = \dfrac{l_1 l_1}{l_2 l_2} = \dfrac{h_1 h_1}{h_2 h_2}$	9. Subst. prop.
10. $\dfrac{T_1}{T_2} = \dfrac{r_1^2}{r_2^2} = \dfrac{l_1^2}{l_2^2} = \dfrac{h_1^2}{h_2^2}$	10. Mult. prop.

Concl.: If 2 rt. circular cones are ~, then the ratios of the total areas, radii, heights, and slant heights are =.

PAGE 525

32. $V_{\text{entire pyramid}} = \dfrac{1}{3}Bh$

$V_{\text{upper pyramid}} = \dfrac{1}{3}B_u h_2$

$V_{\text{frustum}} = V_{\text{entire}} - V_{\text{upper}} = \dfrac{1}{3}Bh - \dfrac{1}{3}B_u h_2$

but $h = h_1 + h_2$

$= \dfrac{1}{3}B(h_1 + h_2) - \dfrac{1}{3}B_u h_2$

$= \dfrac{1}{3}Bh_1 + \dfrac{1}{3}Bh_2 - \dfrac{1}{3}B_u h_2$

$= \dfrac{1}{3}Bh_1 + \dfrac{1}{3}h_2(B - B_u)$

but $\dfrac{B}{B_u} = \dfrac{h^2}{h_2^2} \rightarrow B_u = \dfrac{Bh_2^2}{h^2}$

$= \dfrac{1}{3}Bh_1 + \dfrac{1}{3}h_2\left(B - \dfrac{Bh_2^2}{h^2}\right)$

$= \dfrac{1}{3}Bh_1 + \dfrac{1}{3}\dfrac{h_2 B}{h^2}(h^2 - h_2^2)$

$= \dfrac{1}{3}Bh_1 + \dfrac{1}{3}\dfrac{h_2^2 B}{h^2 h_2}$

$(h - h_2)(h + h_2)$

but $h_1 = h - h_2$, $B_u = \dfrac{h_2^2 B}{h^2}$

$= \dfrac{1}{3}Bh_1 + \dfrac{1}{3}\dfrac{B_u}{h_2}h_1(h + h_2)$

$= \dfrac{1}{3}Bh_1 + \dfrac{1}{3}B_u h_1\left(\dfrac{h}{h_2} + 1\right)$

$= \dfrac{1}{3}Bh_1 + \dfrac{1}{3}B_u h_1 + \dfrac{1}{3}B_u\dfrac{h_1 h}{h_2}$

but $\dfrac{h}{h_2} = \sqrt{\dfrac{B}{B_u}}$

$= \dfrac{1}{3}Bh_1 + \dfrac{1}{3}B_u h_1 + \dfrac{1}{3}$

$B_u h_1 \sqrt{\dfrac{B}{B_u}}$

$= \dfrac{1}{3}Bh_1 + \dfrac{1}{3}B_u h_1 + \dfrac{1}{3}h_1\sqrt{B_u B}$

$V_{\text{frustum}} = \dfrac{1}{3}h_1(B + B_u + \sqrt{B_u B})$

33.

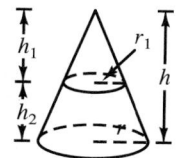

$V_{\text{entire cone}} = \dfrac{1}{3}\pi r^2 h$

$V_{\text{top cone}} = \dfrac{1}{3}\pi r_1^2 h_1$

$V_{\text{frustum}} = V_{\text{entire}} - V_{\text{top}} = \dfrac{1}{3}\pi r^2 h - \dfrac{1}{3}\pi r_1^2 h_1$

but $h = h_1 + h_2$

$= \dfrac{1}{3}\pi r^2 h_1 + \dfrac{1}{3}\pi r^2 h_2 - \dfrac{1}{3}\pi r_1^2 h_1$

$= \dfrac{1}{3}\pi r^2 h_2 + \dfrac{1}{3}\pi h_1(r^2 - r_1^2)$

$= \dfrac{1}{3}\pi r^2 h_2 + \dfrac{1}{3}\pi h_1(r - r_1)(r + r_1)$

but $\dfrac{h_1}{r_1} = \dfrac{h}{r}$ or $h_1 r = r_1 h$

and $h = h_1 + h_2$

then $h_1 r = r_1(h_1 + h_2)$
$= r_1 h_1 + r_1 h_2$

or $h_1 r - h_1 r_1 = r_1 h_2$
$h_1(r - r_1) = r_1 h_2$

also $r + r_1 = r + r_1$

using multiplication, then

$h_1(r - r_1)(r + r_1) =$

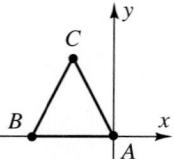

$r_1h_2(r + r_1)$
or $h_1(r^2 - r_1^2) = r_1h_2(r + r_1)$

$= \frac{1}{3}\pi r^2 h_2 + \frac{1}{3}\pi h_2 r_1$
$(r + r_1)$

$= \frac{1}{3}\pi r^2 h_2 + \frac{1}{3}\pi h_2 r r_1$
$+ \frac{1}{3}\pi h_2 r_1^2$

$V_{frustum} = \frac{1}{3}\pi h_2(r^2 + rr_1 + r_1^2)$

PAGE 539

38.

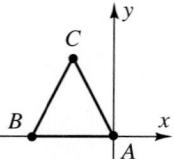

39.

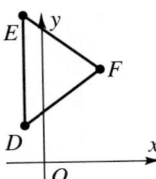

40.

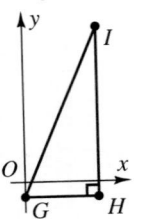

41.

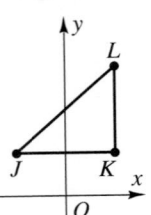

42.

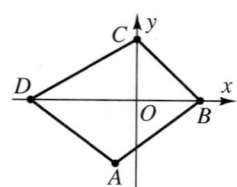

43.

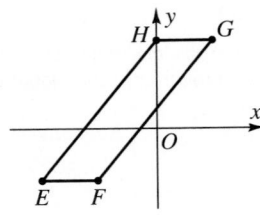

44.

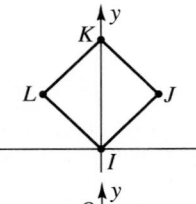

45.

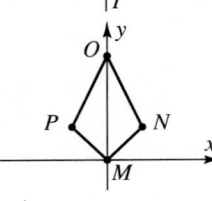

48.

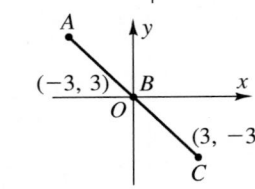

50. Proof:

Statements	Reasons
1. Pt. A (x_2, y_2); Pt. C (x_1, y_1)	1. Given
2. Draw vert. line through A and horizontal line through C that intersect at B such that $\overline{AB} \perp \overline{CB}$.	2. Coplanar vertical and horizontal lines intersect and are $\perp$.
3. $\angle ABC$ is a rt. $\angle$.	3. Def. of $\perp$
4. $\triangle ABC$ is a rt. $\triangle$.	4. Def. of rt. $\triangle$
5. $BC = |x_2 - x_1|$; $AB = |y_2 - y_1|$	5. Def. of dist. between two pts with the same y-coord. and the dist. between 2 pts. with the same x-coord.
6. $AC^2 = BC^2 + AB^2$	6. Pyth. th.
7. $AC^2 = $ $|x_2 - x_1|^2 + $ $|y_2 - y_1|^2$	7. Subst. prop.
8. $AC = $ $\sqrt{|x_2 - x_1|^2 + |y_2 - y_1|^2}$	8. Def. of square root

Concl: If the vertices of a rt. $\triangle ABC$ are A (x_2, y_2), $C(x_1, y_1)$ and $B(x_2, y_1)$ and $\overline{AC}$ is the hyp., then $AC = \sqrt{|x_2 - x_1|^2 + |y_2 - y_1|^2}$.

PAGE 557

42. Given: P_1 (x_1, y_1), P_2 (x_2, y_2), and P (x, y) on line k

Prove: Slope of $\overline{PP_2}$ = slope of $\overline{PP_1}$ = slope of $\overline{P_1P_2}$
These figures show the possibilities for P_1, P_2 and P (assuming P_2 is to the right of P_1) In each case, similar $\triangle$ have been formed by drawing parallels as shown.

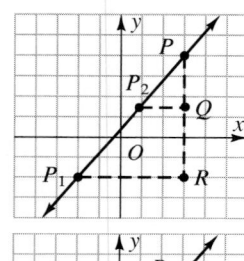

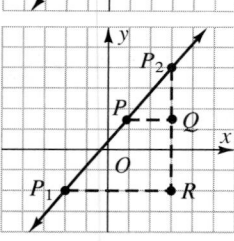

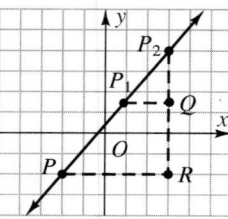

Hence $\dfrac{|y - y_2|}{|y - y_1|} = \dfrac{|x - x_2|}{|x - x_1|}$ and $\dfrac{|y - y_2|}{|x - x_2|} = \dfrac{|y - y_1|}{|x - x_1|}$.

In Fig. 1, $\dfrac{|y - y_2|}{|x - x_2|} = \dfrac{y - y_2}{x - x_2}$ and $\dfrac{|y - y_1|}{|x - x_1|} = \dfrac{y - y_1}{x - x_1}$.

Thus $\dfrac{y - y_2}{x - x_2} = \dfrac{y - y_1}{x - x_1}$ and the slopes of $\overline{PP_2}$ and $\overline{PP_1}$ are =.

In Fig. 2, $\dfrac{|y - y_2|}{|x - x_2|} = \dfrac{-(y - y_2)}{-(x - x_2)} =$

$\dfrac{y - y_2}{x - x_2}$ and $\dfrac{|y - y_1|}{|x - x_1|} = \dfrac{y - y_1}{x - x_1}$.

Thus $\dfrac{y - y_2}{x - x_2} = \dfrac{y - y_1}{x - x_1}$ and the

slopes of $\overline{PP_2}$ and $\overline{PP_1}$ are =.
A similar argument can be used for
Fig. 3 and the concl. follows.

PAGE 561

Class Ex. 8.

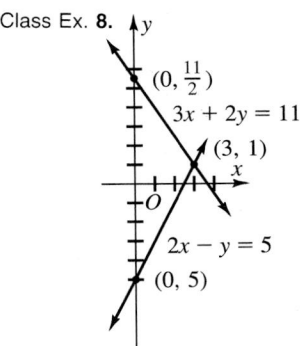

(0, $\frac{11}{2}$)
$3x + 2y = 11$
(3, 1)
$2x - y = 5$
(0, 5)

Prac. Ex. 1.

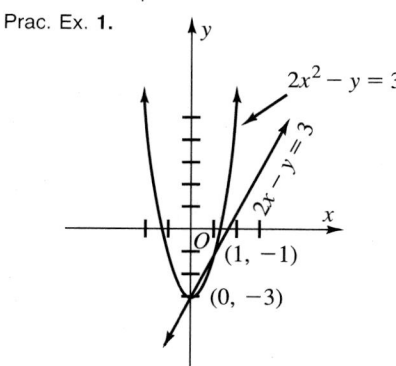

$2x^2 - y = 3$
$2x - y = 3$
(1, −1)
(0, −3)

PAGE 564

53. If you are given that line k contains
$P_1 (x_1, y_1)$ and has slope m let $P(x, y)$
be any pt. of k other than $P_1 (x_1, y_1)$.
Then, by def. of slope, $m = \dfrac{y - y_1}{x - x_1}$.
Mult. by $(x - x_1)$ gives $y - y_1 = m(x - x_1)$.

54. By Th. 13.5, $y - y_1 = m(x - x_1)$. It is
given that (x_1, y_1) is $(0, b)$. Hence,
$y - b = m(x - 0)$ by substitution and
$y = mx + b$ by addition.

PAGE 568

28. The midpt. of $\overline{AB}$ is (1, 2). The
slope of $\overleftrightarrow{BC}$ is 3. The equation of the
line through the midpt. of $\overline{AB}$ and ∥ to
$\overleftrightarrow{BC}$ is $(y - 2) = 3 (x - 1)$. The midpt.
of $\overline{AC}$ is (0, −1). By the subst. prop.,
$(-1 -2) = 3 (0 - 1)$ or $-3 = -3$,
which shows that midpt. of $\overline{AC}$ is on
the line.

PAGE 569

39. Since both lines pass through the
origin, the equations for distinct lines
k and l can be written $y = mx$ and $y = nx$. By substituting 1 for x in each
equation, the coords. of P and Q are
(1, m) and (1, n), respectively. Since
$\triangle POQ$ is a rt. $\triangle$, $PQ^2 = OP^2 + OQ^2$.
But $PQ = m - n$, $OP = \sqrt{m^2 + 1^2}$,
and $OQ = \sqrt{n^2 + 1^2}$. Then
$(m - n)^2 = (m^2 + 1^2) + (n^2 + 1^2)$
$m^2 - 2mn + n^2 = m^2 + n^2 + 2$
$\qquad -2mn = 2$
$\qquad mn = -1$

PAGE 575

8. $M\left(\dfrac{0 + (-2a)}{2}, \dfrac{2b + 0}{2}\right) = M(-a, b)$

$N\left(\dfrac{2a + 0}{2}, \dfrac{0 + 2b}{2}\right) = N(a, b)$

$EM = \sqrt{(2a - (-a))^2 + (0 - b)^2} = \sqrt{9a^2 + b^2}$

$FN = \sqrt{(-2a - a)^2 + (0 - b)^2} = \sqrt{9a^2 + b^2}$

Hence $EM = FN$.

12. Given: Coplanar lines k, l, m; $k \perp l$;
$\qquad\qquad l \parallel m$
Prove: $k \perp m$
Plan: Use the relationships of the
slopes of ∥ and ⊥ lines to write
equations to relate the slopes
of k and m.

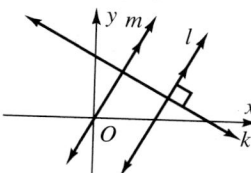

Proof:

Statements	Reasons
1. $k \perp l$; $l \parallel m$	1. Given

2. (slope of k) · (slope of l) = −1	2. Product of slopes of ⊥ lines = −1.
3. (slope of l) = (slope of m)	3. Slopes of ∥ lines are =.
4. (slope of k) · (slope of m) = −1	4. Subst. prop.
5. $k \perp m$	5. If the product of the slopes of 2 lines is −1, then the lines are ⊥.

Concl.: If a line is ⊥ to one of 2 ∥ lines,
then it is ⊥ to the other.

13. Given: $\triangle ABC$ with rt. $\angle C$; M is
$\qquad\qquad$ midpt. of BA.
$\quad$ **Prove:** $MA = MB = MC$

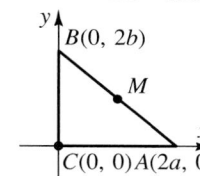

$B(0, 2b)$
M
$C(0, 0)$ $A(2a, 0)$

Plan: Use the Midpt. Formula to
write the coords. of M. Then
apply the Distance Formula.

Proof:

Statements	Reasons
1. $\triangle ABC$ with rt. $\angle C$; M is the midpt. of BA.	1. Given
2. Coords. of $M = (a, b)$	2. Midpt. Formula
3. $MC = \sqrt{a^2 + b^2}$ $MA = $ $\sqrt{(a - 2a)^2 + (b - 0)^2}$ $= \sqrt{a^2 + b^2}$ $MB = $ $\sqrt{(0 - a)^2 + (2b - b)^2}$ $= \sqrt{a^2 + b^2}$	3. Distance Formula
4. $MA = MB = MC$	4. Trans. prop.

Concl.: In rt. $\triangle ABC$, if M is the midpt. of
hyp. $\overline{BA}$, then $MA = MB = MC$.

PAGE 576

14. Given: Isos. $\triangle DEF$; $\overline{DE} \cong \overline{DF}$; $\overline{ME}$
$\qquad\qquad$ and $\overline{NF}$ are medians.
$\quad$ **Prove:** $ME = NF$

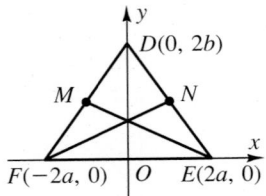

$D(0, 2b)$

M N

$F(-2a, 0)$ O $E(2a, 0)$

Plan: Use the Midpt. Formula to write the coords. of M and N. Then apply the Distance Formula.

Proof:

Statements	Reasons
1. Isos. $\triangle DEF$; $\overline{DE} \cong \overline{DF}$; $\overline{ME}$ and $\overline{NF}$ are medians.	1. Given
2. M has coords. $(-a, b)$; N has coords. (a, b)	2. Def. of median and Midpt. Formula
3. $ME = \sqrt{(-a-2a)^2 + b^2} = \sqrt{9a^2 + b^2}$ $NF = \sqrt{(a+2a)^2 + b^2} = \sqrt{9a^2 + b^2}$	3. Distance Formula
4. $ME = NF$	4. Trans. prop.

Concl.: If isos. $\triangle DEF$ with legs $\overline{DE}$ and $\overline{DF}$ has medians $\overline{ME}$ and $\overline{NF}$, then $ME = NF$.

15. Given: $\triangle ABC$ with medians $\overline{MB}$ and $\overline{NA}$; $\overline{MB} \cong \overline{NA}$

Prove: $\triangle ABC$ is isos.

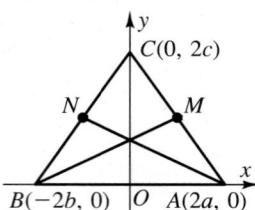

$C(0, 2c)$

N M

$B(-2b, 0)$ O $A(2a, 0)$

Plan: Use the Midpt. Formula and the Distance Formula to solve for a in terms of b. Then substitute in the Distance Formula for BC and AC.

Proof:

Statements	Reasons
1. $\triangle ABC$ with medians $\overline{MB}$ and $\overline{NA}$; $\overline{MB} \cong \overline{NA}$	1. Given

Statements	Reasons
2. M has coords. (a, c); N has coords. $(-b, c)$.	2. Midpt. Formula
3. $MB = NA$	3. Def. of $\cong$ segs.
4. $MB = \sqrt{(a+2b)^2 + c^2}$ $NA = \sqrt{(-b-2a)^2 + c^2}$	4. Distance Formula
5. $\sqrt{(a+2b)^2 + c^2} = \sqrt{(-b-2a)^2 + c^2}$	5. Subst. prop.
6. $(a+2b)^2 + c^2 = (-b-2a)^2 + c^2$ $(a+2b)^2 = (-b-2a)^2$ $a^2 + 4ab + 4b^2 = b^2 + 4ab + 4a^2$ $3a^2 = 3b^2$ $a = \pm b$	6. Alg. props.
7. B has coords. $(-2a, 0)$.	7. Subst. prop.
8. $BC = \sqrt{(0+2a)^2 + (2c)^2} = \sqrt{4a^2 + 4b^2}$ $AC = \sqrt{(0-2a)^2 + (2c)^2} = \sqrt{4a^2 + 4b^2}$	8. Distance Formula
9. $AC = BC$	9. Trans. prop.
10. $\overline{AC} \cong \overline{BC}$	10. Def. of $\cong$ segs.
11. $\triangle ABC$ is isos.	11. Def. of isos.

Concl.: If a $\triangle ABC$ has 2 $\cong$ medians, then the $\triangle$ is isos.

16. Given: Square $RSTU$

Prove: $\overline{RT} \perp \overline{US}$

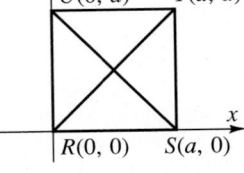

$U(0, a)$ $T(a, a)$

$R(0, 0)$ $S(a, 0)$

Plan: Compare the equations involving the products of the slopes of the segs.

Proof:

Statements	Reasons
1. Square $RSTU$	1. Given
2. Slope of $\overline{RT} = \frac{a-0}{a-0} = 1$ slope of $\overline{US} = \frac{0-a}{a-0} = -1$	2. Def. of slope
3. (slope of $\overline{RT}$)(slope of $\overline{US}$) = $1 \cdot (-1) = -1$	3. Mult. prop.

Statements	Reasons
4. $\overline{RT} \perp \overline{US}$	4. If the product of the slopes of 2 lines is -1, then the lines are $\perp$.

Concl.: In square $RSTU$, $\overline{RT} \perp \overline{US}$.

17. Given: Rectangle $ABCD$

Prove: $AC = BD$

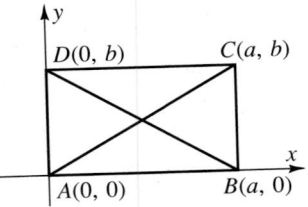

$D(0, b)$ $C(a, b)$

$A(0, 0)$ $B(a, 0)$

Plan: Use the Distance Formula

Proof:

Statements	Reasons
1. Rectangle $ABCD$	1. Given
2. $AC = \sqrt{a^2 + b^2}$ $BD = \sqrt{a^2 + b^2}$	2. Distance Formula
3. $AC = BD$	3. Trans. prop.

Concl.: In rectangle $ABCD$, $AC = BD$.

18. Given: Rhombus $STUV$

Prove: $\overline{SU} \perp \overline{TV}$

$V(b, c)$ $U(b + a, c)$

$S(0, 0)$ $T(a, 0)$

Plan: Use the def. of slope, the def. of rhombus, and the Distance Formula to relate the slopes of $\overline{SU}$ and $\overline{TV}$.

Proof:

Statements	Reasons
1. Rhombus $STUV$	1. Given
2. slope of $\overline{SU} = \frac{c}{b+a}$; slope of $\overline{TV} = \frac{c}{b-a}$	2. Def. of slope
3. $\frac{c}{b+a} \cdot \frac{c}{b-a} = \frac{c^2}{b^2-a^2}$	3. Alg. props.
4. $\overline{SV} \cong \overline{ST}$	4. Def. of rhombus

5. $SV = ST$ 5. Def. of ≅ segs.
6. $SV = \sqrt{c^2 + b^2}$;   6. Distance
    $ST = a$ Formula
7. $a = \sqrt{c^2 + b^2}$ 7. Subst. prop.
8. $a^2 = c^2 + b^2$ 8. Alg. props.
    $-c^2 = b^2 - a^2$
9. $\dfrac{c^2}{b^2 - a^2} =$ 9. Subst. prop.
    $\dfrac{-c^2}{c^2} = -1$ (Step 3) and
                   alg. props.
10. $SU \perp TV$ 10. If the product
                    of the slopes
                    of 2 lines is
                    -1, then the
                    lines are ⊥.

Concl.: In rhombus $STUV$, $SU \perp TV$.

19. Given: $\triangle ABC$; M is the midpt. of
          AC; N is the midpt. of BC.
  Prove: $MN = \frac{1}{2}AB$

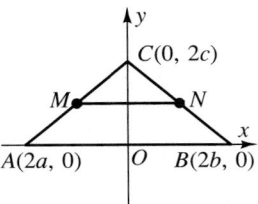

   Plan: Use the Midpt. Formula to
         write the coords. for M and N.
         Then apply the Distance
         Formula and compare MN
         and AB.
   Proof:

Statements	Reasons
1. $\triangle ABC$; M and N are the midpts. of AC and BC.	1. Given
2. M has coords. (a, c). N has coords. (b, c).	2. Midpt. Formula
3. $MN =$ $\sqrt{(a-b)^2 + (c-c)^2}$ $= \sqrt{(a-b)^2}$ $AB = \sqrt{(2a-2b)^2} =$ $= 2\sqrt{(a-b)^2}$	3. Distance Formula
4. $\dfrac{AB}{2} = \sqrt{(a-b)^2}$	4. Div. prop.
5. $MN = \dfrac{AB}{2}$	5. Subst. prop.

Concl.: In $\triangle ABC$, if AC and BC have
midpts. M and N, then $MN = \frac{1}{2}AB$.

20. Given: $\triangle RST$; $RT \cong ST$; TM bisects
          RS.
  Prove: $TM \perp RS$

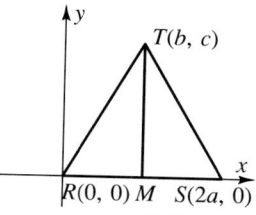

  Plan: Show that TM is ∥ to y-axis
         and hence ⊥ to RS.
  Proof:

Statements	Reasons
1. $\triangle RST$; $RT \cong ST$; TM bisects RS.	1. Given
2. M has coords. $(a, 0)$.	2. Midpt. Formula
3. $RT = ST$	3. Def. of ≅ segs.
4. $RT = \sqrt{b^2 + c^2}$ $ST =$ $\sqrt{(b-2a)^2 + c^2}$	4. Distance Formula
5. $\sqrt{b^2 + c^2} =$ $\sqrt{(b-2a)^2 + c^2}$	5. Subst. prop.
6. $a = b$	6. Alg. props.
7. M has coords. $(b, 0)$.	7. Subst. prop.
8. TM is a vertical line and hence ∥ to y-axis.	8. Def. of vert. line
9. $TM \perp RS$	9. If y-axis ⊥ RS and TM ∥ y-axis, then $TM \perp RS$.

Concl.: In isos. $\triangle RST$, if TM bisects
base RS, then $TM \perp RS$.

21. Given: $\triangle ABC$; $AB \neq BC \neq AC$;
          $CP \perp AB$

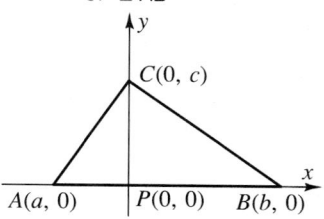

  Prove: CP does not bisect AB; or
           $AP \neq PB$
   Plan: Use the Distance Formula.
  Proof:

Statements	Reasons
1. $\triangle ABC$; $AB \neq$ $BC \neq AC$	1. Given
2. $AC = \sqrt{c^2 + a^2}$; $BC = \sqrt{c^2 + b^2}$	2. Distance Formula

---

Statements	Reasons
3. $\sqrt{c^2 + a^2} \neq$ $\sqrt{c^2 + b^2}$	3. Subst. prop.
4. $a^2 \neq b^2$; $|a| \neq |b|$	4. Alg. props.
5. $AP = |a|$; $BP = |b|$	5. Distance Formula
6. $AP \neq BP$	6. Subst. prop.

Concl.: In the given scalene △, if $CP \perp$
AB, then $AP \neq PB$.

22. Given: $\triangle ABC$; $PQ \parallel AB$;
          PQ bisects AC.
  Prove: PQ bisects BC.

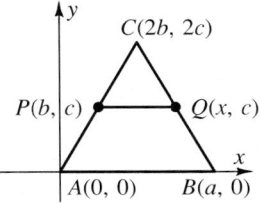

   Plan: Use the fact that slopes of ∥
         lines are equal to find the
         coords. of Q which show
         that Q is the midpt. of BC.
  Proof:

Statements	Reasons
1. $PQ \parallel AB$	1. Given
2. slope of $PQ =$ slope of $AB =$ 0	2. ∥ lines have = slopes; def. of slope
3. y-coord. of Q is c.	3. Pts. on a horizontal line have the same y-coord.
4. y-coord. of midpt. of BC is $\dfrac{2c + 0}{2} = c.$	4. Midpt. Formula
5. slope of $CQ =$ slope of QB	5. Coll. segs. have the same slope.
6. $\dfrac{2c - c}{2b - x} = \dfrac{c - 0}{x - a}$	6. Def. of slope and subst. prop.
7. $x = \dfrac{2b + a}{2}$	7. Alg. props.
8. x-coord. of the midpt. of BC is $\dfrac{2b + a}{2}$.	8. Midpt. Formula
9. Q has coords $\left(\dfrac{2b + a}{2}, c\right)$.	9. Subst. prop.
10. Q is the midpt. of BC.	10. Midpt. Formula
11. PQ bisects BC.	11. Def. of midpt.

Concl.: In $\triangle ABC$, if $PQ \parallel AB$ and PQ
bisects AC, then PQ bisects BC.

23. Given: ▱PQRS; PR = QS
Prove: PQRS is a rectangle.

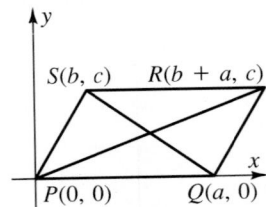

Plan: Use the Distance Formula to relate the coords and show that S and P lie on the same vertical line. Hence $\overline{SP} \perp$ horizontal $\overline{PQ}$.

Proof:

Statements	Reasons
1. PR = QS	1. Given
2. PR = $\sqrt{(b+a)^2 + c^2}$ QS = $\sqrt{(b-a)^2 + c^2}$	2. Distance Formula
3. $\sqrt{(b+a)^2 + c^2}$ = $\sqrt{(b-a)^2 + c^2}$	3. Subst. prop.
4. $(b+a)^2 + c^2 = (b-a)^2 + c^2$; $b^2 + 2ab + a^2 + c^2 = b^2 - 2ab + a^2 + c^2$; $4ab = 0$; $a = 0$ or $b = 0$	4. Alg. props.
5. But $a \neq 0$, so $b = 0$.	5. Given in figure
6. S has coords. (0, c)	6. Subst. prop.
7. S and P lie on the same vert. line.	7. Pts. with same x-coord. lie on the same vert. line.
8. $\overline{SP} \perp \overline{PQ}$	8. Vert. and horizontal lines are ⊥.
9. ∠P is a rt. ∠.	9. Def. of ⊥
10. PQRS is a rectangle.	10. Def. of rectangle

Concl.: In ▱PQRS, if PR = QS, then PQRS is a rectangle.

24. Given: Quad. ABCD; $\overline{AB} \parallel \overline{CD}$; AB = CD
Prove: ABCD is a ▱.

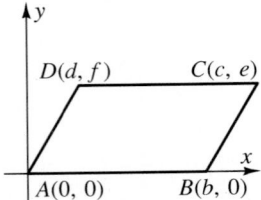

Plan: Use the def. of slope, alg. properties, and the Distance Formula to relate the coords. and show that $\overline{BC} \parallel \overline{AD}$. Concl. follows from def. of ▱.

Proof:

Statements	Reasons
1. $\overline{AB} \parallel \overline{CD}$	1. Given
2. slope of $\overline{AB}$ = slope of $\overline{CD}$	2. ∥ lines have = slopes.
3. slope of $\overline{AB}$ = $\frac{0}{b}$ slope of $\overline{CD}$ = $\frac{e-f}{c-d}$	3. Def. of slope
4. $\frac{0}{b} = \frac{e-f}{c-d}$	4. Subst. prop.
5. $e = f$	5. Alg. props.
6. D has coords. (d, e).	6. Subst. prop.
7. slope of $\overline{AD}$ = $\frac{e}{d}$; slope of $\overline{BC}$ = $\frac{e}{c-b}$	7. Def. of slope
8. AB = CD	8. Given
9. AB = b; CD = c - d	9. Distance Formula
10. b = c - d	10. Subst. prop.
11. d = c - b	11. Alg. props.
12. slope of $\overline{BC}$ = $\frac{e}{d}$	12. Subst. prop.
13. slope of $\overline{BC}$ = slope of $\overline{AD}$	13. Trans. prop.
14. $\overline{BC} \parallel \overline{AD}$	14. If 2 lines have = slopes, then the lines are ∥.
15. ABCD is a ▱.	15. Def. of ▱

Concl.: In quad. ABCD, if $\overline{AB} \parallel \overline{CD}$ and AB = CD, then ABCD is a ▱.

25. Given: ▱PQRS
Prove: $\overline{PR}$ and $\overline{QS}$ bisect each other.

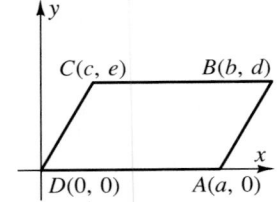

Plan: Use coords. to show that the midpts. of $\overline{PR}$ and $\overline{QS}$ coincide.

Proof: By the Midpt. Formula, the midpt. of $\overline{PR}$ is $\left(\frac{a+b}{2}, \frac{c}{2}\right)$ and the midpt. of $\overline{QS}$ is $\left(\frac{b+a}{2}, \frac{c}{2}\right)$. Thus the midpts. coincide and $\overline{PR}$ and $\overline{QR}$ bis. each other.

26. Given: Quad ABCD
$\overline{AC}$ and $\overline{BD}$ bisect each other.
Prove: ABCD is a ▱.

Plan: Use the Midpt. formula to relate the coordinates and show that $\overline{AB} \parallel \overline{CD}$ and $\overline{BC} \parallel \overline{DA}$.

Proof: Since $\overline{AC}$ and $\overline{BD}$ bisect each other, their midpts. have the same coords. Hence $\left(\frac{c+a}{2}, \frac{e}{2}\right)$ is the same as $\left(\frac{b}{2}, \frac{d}{2}\right)$. Also $b = c + a$, and $d = e$. Then slope of $\overline{DC} = \frac{e}{c}$ = slope of $\overline{AB}$ and slope of $\overline{BC} = 0$ = slope of $\overline{DA}$. Thus $\overline{DC} \parallel \overline{AB}$ and $\overline{BC} \parallel \overline{DA}$ so, by def., ABCD is a ▱.

27. Given: Trap. PQRS; M is the midpt. of $\overline{PR}$; N is the midpt of $\overline{QS}$.
Prove: $\overline{MN} \parallel \overline{SR} \parallel \overline{PQ}$; MN = $\frac{1}{2}(PQ - SR)$

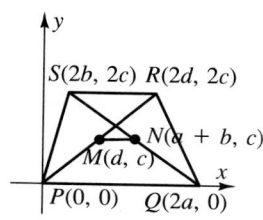

Plan: Use the Midpt. Formula to relate the coords. and show that $\overline{MN}$, $\overline{SR}$, and $\overline{PQ}$ have the same slope and so are $\parallel$. Then use the Distance Formula to relate the lengths of $\overline{MN}$, $\overline{PQ}$ and $\overline{SR}$.

Proof: The midpt. of $\overline{PR}$ is $\left(\frac{2d}{2}, \frac{2c}{2}\right)$ or (d, c); the midpt. of $\overline{QS}$ is $\left(\frac{2b + 2a}{2}, \frac{2c}{2}\right)$ or $(b + a, c)$. Thus the slope of $\overline{MN} = 0$. But the slopes of $\overline{SR}$ and $\overline{PQ}$ are also $= 0$, so $\overline{MN} \parallel \overline{SR} \parallel \overline{PQ}$. By the Distance Formula, $MN = b + a - d$, $SR = 2d - 2b$, and $PQ = 2a$. Thus $PQ - SR = 2a - (2d - 2b) = 2a + 2b - 2d$ and $\frac{1}{2}(PQ - SR) = a + b - d = MN$.

28. Given: Trap. $PQRS$; $\overline{PQ} \parallel \overline{SR}$; $\overline{MN} \parallel \overline{PQ}$; $\overline{MN}$ bisects $\overline{PS}$.
Prove: $\overline{MN}$ bisects $\overline{RQ}$

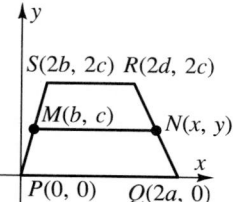

Plan: Use the slopes of $\parallel$ lines to relate the coords. Then show that the coords. of N are the coords. of the midpt. of $\overline{RQ}$.

Proof: $\overline{MN} \parallel \overline{PQ}$, so slope $\overline{MN} = 0 = \frac{y - c}{x - b}$ and $y = c$; since slope of $\overline{RN} =$ slope of $\overline{NQ}$, $\frac{2c - c}{2d - x} = \frac{c}{x - 2a}$, $\frac{c}{2d - x} = \frac{c}{x - 2a}$, $2d - x = x - 2a$, and $x = \frac{2a + 2d}{2}$. Thus the coords. of $N(x, y)$ are $\left(\frac{2a + 2d}{2}, c\right)$, which is the midpt. of $\overline{RQ}$.

29. Given: $\triangle RST$ with altitudes $\overline{RL}$, $\overline{SM}$, and $\overline{TN}$
Prove: $\overline{RL}$, $\overline{SM}$, and $\overline{TN}$ are concurrent, or P is on all 3 alts.

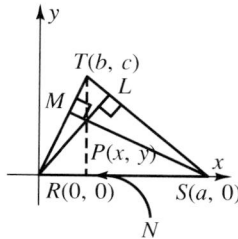

Plan: Write slope equations for $\perp$ segments $\overline{RL}$ and $\overline{ST}$ and then $\overline{SM}$ and $\overline{RT}$. Solve the system of equations and then check the equation of $\overleftrightarrow{TP}$ to see if it has a common solution.

Proof: $\overline{RL} \perp \overline{ST}$, so (slope of $\overline{RL}$) $\cdot$ (slope of $\overline{ST}$) $= -1$ or $\frac{y}{x} \cdot \frac{c}{b - a} = -1$. $\overline{SM} \perp \overline{RT}$, so (slope of $\overline{SM}$) $\cdot$ (slope $\overline{RT}$) $= -1$ or $\frac{y}{x - a} \cdot \frac{c}{b} = -1$. Solving each equation for y: $y = \frac{-x(b - a)}{c}$ and $y = \frac{-b(x - a)}{c}$. Thus $\frac{-x(b - a)}{c} = \frac{-b(x - a)}{c}$, $-bx + ax = -bx + ab$, $ax = ab$ and $x = b$. Hence P has x-coord. b and the slope of $\overleftrightarrow{TP} = \frac{c - y}{b - b} = \frac{c - y}{0}$, which is undefined. It follows that $\overleftrightarrow{TP}$ is a vert. line and so must be $\perp$ to horizontal seg. $\overline{RS}$. Thus pt. P is on all 3 alts.

30. Given: $\triangle PQR$ with medians $\overline{PM}$, $\overline{QN}$ and $\overline{RL}$
Prove: The medians are concurrent at some pt. T; $RT = \frac{2}{3}RL$, $PT = \frac{2}{3}PM$, $QT = \frac{2}{3}QN$.

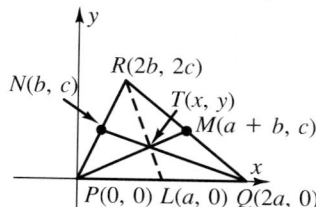

Plan: $\overline{PM}$ and $\overline{QN}$ intersect at $T(x,y)$. Show that $\overline{RL}$ contains pt. T by writing and solving equations involving the

coords. of pts. on $\overleftrightarrow{PM}$, $\overleftrightarrow{QN}$ and $\overleftrightarrow{RL}$. Use the Distance Formula to show that $RT = \frac{2}{3}RL$, etc.

Proof: Medians $\overline{PM}$ and $\overline{QN}$ intersect at a pt. $T(x,y)$. The equation for $\overleftrightarrow{PM}$ is $y = \frac{c}{a + b} \cdot x$ and the equation for $\overleftrightarrow{QN}$ is $y = \frac{c}{b - 2a} \cdot (x - 2a)$. By the Subst. prop., $\frac{cx}{a + b} = \frac{cx - 2ac}{b - 2a}$. Hence $bcx - 2acx = acx - 2a^2c + bcx - 2abc$, $3acx = 2ac(a + b)$, and $x = \frac{2}{3}(a + b)$. Subst. this expression for x in the first equation for y: $y = \frac{c}{a + b} \cdot [\frac{2}{3}(a + b)]$, or $y = \frac{2}{3}c$. So, $T(x,y)$ can be written as $T(\frac{2}{3}(a + b), \frac{2}{3}c)$. The equation for $\overleftrightarrow{RL}$ is $\frac{2c}{2b - a} = \frac{y}{x - a}$, or $y = \frac{2c(x - a)}{2b - a}$. Combine this with the equation for $\overleftrightarrow{PM}$ to get $x = \frac{2}{3}(a + b)$ and $y = \frac{2}{3}c$. This means that $\overline{RL}$ and $\overline{PM}$ also intersect at $T(\frac{2}{3}(a + b), \frac{2}{3}c)$ and so the medians are concurrent. Next, by the Distance Formula, $RL = \sqrt{(2b - a)^2 + (2c)^2}$ and $RT = \sqrt{[2b - (\frac{2a + 2b}{3})]^2 + [2c - \frac{2}{3}c]^2}$. Simplify the expression for RT to get $RT = \frac{2}{3}\sqrt{(2b - a)^2 + (2c)^2}$. Thus $RT = \frac{2}{3}RL$. Similarly, $PT = \frac{2}{3}PM$ and $QT = \frac{2}{3}QN$.

31. This theorem is a biconditional. Case I:
Given: $P(x,y)$ is equidistant from A and B or $PA = PB$.
Prove: P is on the $\perp$ bis. of $\overline{AB}$.

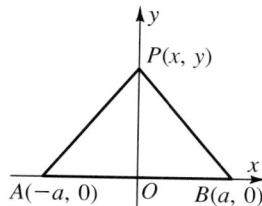

Plan: Use the Distance Formula to show that P is on the y-axis.

Proof:

$PA = \sqrt{(x + a)^2 + y^2}$ and $PB = \sqrt{(x - a)^2 + y^2}$. Since $PA = PB$, $\sqrt{(x + a)^2 + y^2} = \sqrt{(x - a)^2 + y^2}$; hence $(x + a)^2 = (x - a)^2$ and $|x + a| = |x - a|$. This means that $x = 0$ and $P(x,y)$ is on the y-axis, the $\perp$ bis. of $\overline{AB}$.

Case II:
Given: P is on the $\perp$ bis. of $\overline{AB}$.
Prove: $PA = PB$
Plan: Set P on the y-axis, which is the $\perp$ bis. of $\overline{AB}$, and use the Distance Formula to show $PA = PB$.

Proof:

Assign coords. $(0,y)$ to P, placing P on the y-axis, which is $\perp$ to the x-axis containing $A(-a,0)$ and $B(a,0)$, so that $OA = OB$. Then $PA = \sqrt{(a)^2 + y^2}$ and $PB = \sqrt{(-a)^2 + y^2}$. Thus $PA = PB$.

32. Given: $\triangle ABC$; $\overleftrightarrow{PL}$ and $\overleftrightarrow{PN}$ are the $\perp$ bisectors of $\overline{AG}$ and $\overline{AC}$, respectively.
Prove: The $\perp$ bis. of $\overline{CB}$ is concurrent with $\overleftrightarrow{PL}$ and $\overleftrightarrow{PN}$ at P.

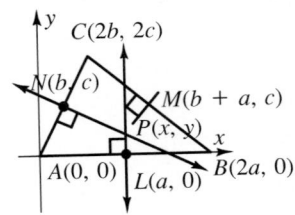

Plan: Write equations involving the slopes of the $\perp$ lines to find coords. for P in terms of a, b, and c. Then find the slope of $\overline{PM}$ and check to see if it is on the $\perp$ bis. of $\overline{CB}$.

Proof:

$\overleftrightarrow{PL}$ and $\overleftrightarrow{PN}$ are $\perp$ bisectors of $\overline{AB}$ and $\overline{AC}$; their intersection is $P(x,y)$. Since $\overleftrightarrow{PL}$ has equation $x = a$, $P(x,y)$ is $P(a,y)$. (Slope of $\overleftrightarrow{PN}$)(slope of $\overline{AC}$) $= -1$, so $\dfrac{y - c}{a - b} \cdot \dfrac{c}{b} = -1$ and $y = \dfrac{b(b - a)}{c} + c$. Thus $P(a,y)$ is $P(a, \dfrac{b(b - a)}{c} + c)$. The slope of

The slope of $\overline{PM}$ is $\dfrac{c - (\frac{b(b - a)}{c} + c)}{b + a - a} = \dfrac{a - b}{c}$.

But $\dfrac{a - b}{c} \cdot \dfrac{c}{b - a} = -1$, so $\overline{PM} \perp \overline{BC}$ at M. Thus the $\perp$ bis. of the sides are concurrent at $P(a, \dfrac{b(b - a)}{c} + c)$.

PAGE 582

14. Given: Quad. $ABCD$; P, Q, R, and S are midpts. of the sides.
Prove: $PQRS$ is a $\square$.

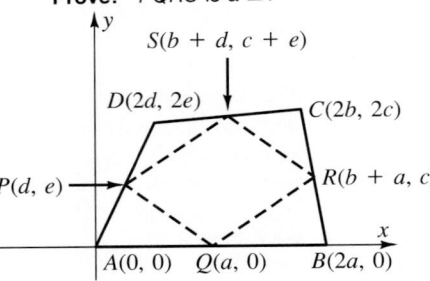

Plan: Use the def. of slope to show $\overline{PQ} \parallel \overline{RS}$ and $\overline{PS} \parallel \overline{QR}$.

Proof:

Statements	Reasons
1. Quad. $ABCD$; P, Q, R, and S are midpts. of the sides.	1. Given
2. $P(d,e)$, $Q(a,0)$, $R(b + a,c)$, and $S(b + d, c + e)$	2. Midpt. Formula
3. Slope of $\overline{PQ} = \dfrac{e}{d - a}$; slope of $\overline{RS} = \dfrac{c + e - c}{b + d - (b + a)} = \dfrac{e}{d - a}$	3. Def. of slope
4. slope of $\overline{PQ}$ = slope of $\overline{RS}$	4. Trans. prop.
5. $\overline{PQ} \parallel \overline{RS}$	5. If 2 lines have = slopes, then the lines are $\parallel$.
6. Slope of $\overline{PS} = \dfrac{c + e - e}{b + d - d} = \dfrac{c}{b}$; slope of $\overline{QR} = \dfrac{c}{b + a - a} = \dfrac{c}{b}$	6. Def. of slope
7. slope of $\overline{PS}$ = slope of $\overline{QR}$	7. Subst. prop.
8. $\overline{PS} \parallel \overline{QR}$	8. Same as 5.
9. $PQRS$ is a $\square$.	9. Def. of $\square$

Concl.: If quad. $ABCD$ has side midpts. P, Q, R and S, then $PQRS$ is a $\square$.

PAGE 590

7. a. $(-5,-4)$, $(3,-3)$, $(-2,1)$, $(0,0)$
 b. $(4,-2)$, $(-3,-4)$, $(2,3)$
 c. Yes; T preserves distance between points.
8. a. $(4,-5)$, $(3,3)$, $(-1,-2)$, $(0,0)$
 b. $(2,4)$, $(4,-3)$, $(-3,2)$
 c. Yes, distances are preserved.
9. a. $(15,12)$, $(-9,9)$, $(6,-3)$, $(0,0)$
 b. $(-\frac{4}{3},\frac{2}{3})$, $(1,\frac{4}{3})$, $(-\frac{2}{3},-1)$
 c. No; distances aren't preserved.
10. See Solutions Manual for **10a, b.**
 c. Prove that $T(x,y) = (-x, -y)$ is an isometry. Let $A = (x_1,y_1)$ and $B = (x_2,y_2)$. Then $A' = (-x_1, -y_1)$ and $B' = (-x_2, -y_2)$.
 $AB = \sqrt{(x_2 - x_1)^2 + (y_2 - y_1)^2}$
 $A'B' = \sqrt{(-x_2 - (-x_1))^2 + (-y_2 - (-y_1))^2}$
 $= \sqrt{(x_1 - x_2)^2 + (y_1 - y_2)^2}$
 $= AB$ $\therefore T$ is an isometry.

12. No; Suppose P is not on l: If Q is on $\overline{PP'}$ and Q is not P, then $M(P) = P'$ and $M(Q) = P'$. So, the distance between $M(Q)$ and $M(P)$ is zero, even though Q and P are distinct.

13.

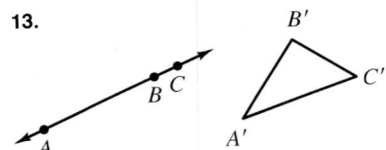

We are given that A, B, and C are on l and B is between A and C. Thus, by the definition of betweenness, $AB + BC = AC$. T is an isometry, so it is also true that $A'B' + B'C' = A'C'$. Suppose A', B', and C' are not collinear. Consider the $\triangle$ whose vertices are A', B', and C'. By the $\triangle$ Inequality Theorem, $A'B' + B'C' > A'C'$. This contradicts the fact that $A'B' + B'C' = A'C'$, however, so the assumption that A', B', and C' are not collinear must be false.

14. Suppose $k \parallel l$ and T is an isometry. Assume that $T(k) \nparallel T(l)$. Then the lines $T(k)$ and $T(l)$ must intersect in some point P'; that is, P' is on $T(k)$

and P' is on $T(l)$. Since T is an isometry, it is a one-to-one mapping of the plane onto itself, so P' is the image of exactly one point P. But this means that P is on k and P is on l, which contradicts the fact that $k \parallel l$. The assumption that $T(k) \nparallel T(l)$ must therefore be false.

PAGE 593

2. If l is the bisector of $\angle CDE$, then $R_l(\overrightarrow{DC}) = \overrightarrow{DE}$. *True* Justification:

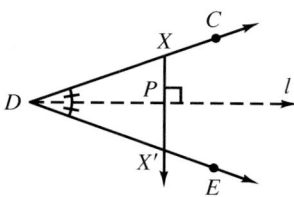

Since $D \in l$, $R_l(D) = D$. Pick any other point X on $\overrightarrow{DC}$. Let $\overrightarrow{XX'}$ intersect $\overrightarrow{DE}$ at X' such that $\overline{XX'} \perp l$ at P. Then $\triangle DXP \cong \triangle DX'P$ by LA; hence $\overline{XP} \cong \overline{X'P}$ by CPCTC. Thus l is the $\perp$-bisector of $\overline{XX'}$, from which it follows that $R_l(X) = X' \in \overrightarrow{DE}$. Since a ray is determined by its endpoint (D) and any other point (X), we have that $R_l(\overrightarrow{DC}) = \overrightarrow{DE}$.

6. Given A and l, construct $R_l(A) = A'$.

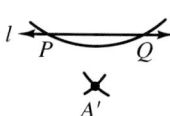

  1. With center A draw an arc that intersects l at P and Q.

  2. With the same radius and using P and Q as centers, draw intersecting arcs on the opposite side of l from A.

  3. The arcs intersect at A', the image of A under R_l.

7. Given A and A', construct l. Draw $\overline{AA'}$ and construct its $\perp$ bisector. The $\perp$ bisector is the line of reflection.

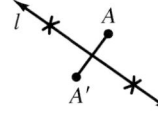

14. $A' = (-2,-1)$, $B' = (2,-4)$, $C' = (-5,2)$, $D' = (-3,0)$, $E' = (-2,5)$, $F' = (1,3)$, $G' = (2,1)$, $H' = (5,1)$, $I' = (4,3)$

15. $A' = (2,1)$, $B' = (-2,4)$, $C' = (5,-2)$, $D' = (3,0)$, $E' = (2,-5)$, $F' = (-1,-3)$, $G' = (-2,-1)$, $H' = (-5,-1)$, $I' = (-4,-3)$

16. $A' = (1,-2)$, $B' = (4,2)$, $C' = (-2,-5)$, $D' = (0,-3)$, $E' = (-5,-2)$, $F' = (-3,1)$, $G' = (-1,2)$, $H' = (-1,5)$, $I' = (-3,4)$

PAGE 595

31. The minimum length mirror is half your height.
Justification:

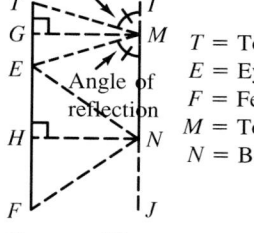

T = Top of head
E = Eyes
F = Feet
M = Top of image
N = Bottom of image

Person   Mirror
$\overline{TF}$ $\overline{MN}$

Draw $\overline{MG} \perp \overline{TF}$ and $\overline{NH} \perp \overline{TF}$, so that $MGHN$ is a rectangle. Try to show that $MN = GH = \frac{1}{2}TF$. Since $\angle TMI \cong \angle EMN$, it follows that $\angle TMG \cong \angle EMG$ because they are complements of $\cong$ $\angle$s. Thus $\triangle GMT \cong \triangle GME$ by LA; it follows that $\overline{GT} \cong \overline{GE}$, or $GE = \frac{1}{2}TE$. By a similar argument, $EH = \frac{1}{2}EF$. We have: $GH = GE + EH = \frac{1}{2}TE + \frac{1}{2}EF = \frac{1}{2}(TE + EF) = \frac{1}{2}(TF)$ Since $GH = MN$, the conclusion follows.

PAGE 600

20. Prove: If a transformation T maps any point (x,y) to $(x + a, y + b)$, then T is a translation.
  Plan: Show that if A and B are any two points, with $T(A) = A'$ and $T(B) = B'$, then $AA' = BB'$ and $AB = A'B'$.
  Proof:
Let $A(x_1, y_1)$ and $B(x_2, y_2)$. Then $A'(x_1 + a, y_1 + b)$ and $B'(x_2 + a, y_2 + b)$. (i) Show $AA' = BB'$.
$AA' = $
$\sqrt{(x_1 + a - x_1)^2 + (y_1 + b - y_1)^2} = \sqrt{a^2 + b^2}$

$BB' = $
$\sqrt{(x_2 + a - x_2)^2 + (y_2 + b - y_2)^2} = \sqrt{a^2 + b^2}$
$\therefore AA' = BB' = \sqrt{a^2 + b^2}$

(ii) Show $AB = A'B'$
$AB = \sqrt{(x_2 - x_1)^2 + (y_2 - y_1)^2}$
$A'B' = \sqrt{[(x_2 + a) - (x_1 + a)]^2 + [(y_2 + b) - (y_1 + b)]^2} = \sqrt{(x_2 - x_1)^2 + (y_2 - y_1)^2}$ $\therefore AB = A'B'$
Since (i) and (ii) hold, T is a translation.

21. A glide reflection is an isometry: Suppose $\overline{X'Y'}$ is the image of $\overline{XY}$ under $G_{AA'}$. Then

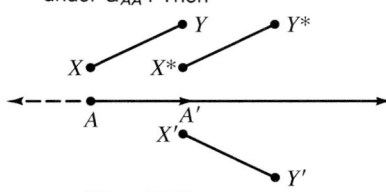

$T_{AA'}(\overline{XY}) = \overline{X^*Y^*}$ and it is true that $XY = X^*Y^*$ because a translation is an isometry. It is also true that $R_{AA'}(\overline{X^*Y^*}) = \overline{X'Y'}$, and $X^*Y^* = X'Y'$ because a reflection is an isometry. Since $XY = X^*Y^*$ and $X^*Y^* = X'Y'$, it follows that $XY = X'Y'$ (transitive property). Thus $G_{AA'}$ is an isometry.

PAGE 604

5–6.

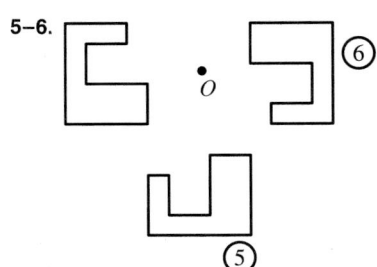

PAGE 605

26. **Given:** $\overline{AB}$ and $\mathcal{R}_{O,\alpha}(\overline{AB}) = \overline{A'B'}$
Prove: $AB = A'B'$

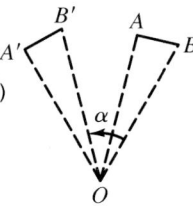

Plan: Show $\triangle OAB \cong \triangle OA'B'$ by SAS to get $\overline{AB} \cong \overline{A'B'}$. The conclusions follows.

781

Proof:

Statements	Reasons
1. $\mathcal{R}_{O,\alpha}(\overline{AB}) = \overline{A'B'}$	1. Given
2. $OA = OA'$; $OB = OB'$	2. Def. of rotation
3. $\overline{OA} \cong \overline{OA'}$; $\overline{OB} \cong \overline{OB'}$	3. Def. of $\cong$ segments
4. $m\angle AOA' = \alpha = m\angle BOB'$	4. Def. of rotation
5. $m\angle AOA' = m\angle AOB' + m\angle B'OA'$; $m\angle BOB' = m\angle BOA + m\angle AOB'$	5. Def. of a between ray
6. $m\angle AOB' + m\angle B'OA' = m\angle BOA + m\angle AOB'$	6. Subst. prop.
7. $m\angle B'OA' = m\angle BOA$	7. Subtr. prop. of =
8. $\angle B'OA' \cong \angle BOA$	8. Def. of $\cong$ $\angle$s
9. $\triangle OAB \cong \triangle OA'B'$	9. SAS
10. $\overline{AB} \cong \overline{A'B'}$	10. CPCTC
11. $AB = A'B'$	11. Def. of $\cong$ seg.

Conclusion: If $\mathcal{R}_{O,\alpha}(A) = A'$ and $\mathcal{R}_{O,\alpha}(B) = B'$, then $AB = A'B'$.

30. Plan: In quad. $A'BAO$, it can be shown that $m\angle A'BA = (180 - \alpha)$. Since $\angle A'BA$ and ABC' are suppl., the concl. follows.

Proof:

Statements	Reasons
1. $\mathcal{R}_{O,\alpha}(l) = l'$; $\mathcal{R}_{O,\alpha}(A) = A'$; $\overline{OA} \perp l$, $\overline{OA'} \perp l'$	1. Given
2. $\angle OA'B$ and $\angle BAO$ are rt. $\angle$s.	2. Def. of $\perp$ lines
3. $m\angle OA'B = m\angle BAO = 90$	3. Def. of rt. $\angle$
4. $m\angle O + m\angle OA'B + m\angle BAO + m\angle A'BA = 360$	4. The sum of the measures of the angles of a quadrilateral is 360.
5. $\alpha + 2 \cdot 90 + m\angle A'BA = 360$	5. Subst. prop.
6. $m\angle A'BA = (180 - \alpha)$	6. Subtr. prop.

Statements	Reasons
7. $\angle A'BA$ and $\angle ABC'$ are a linear pair.	7. Def. of linear pair
8. $\angle A'BA$ and $\angle ABC'$ are supplementary	8. Linear Pair Postulate
9. $m\angle A'BA + m\angle ABC' = 180$	9. Def. of supp. $\angle$s
10. $(180 - \alpha) + m\angle ABC' = 180$	10. Subst. prop.
11. $m\angle ABC' = \alpha$	11. Subtr. prop.

Conclusion: If $\mathcal{R}_{O,\alpha}(l) = l'$, then one of the angles formed by the intersection of l and l' is α.

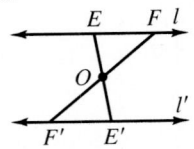

31. Plan: Pick E and F on l and consider $H_O(E) = E'$ and $H_O(F) = F'$. Since $OE = OE'$ and $OF = OF'$ by the definition of rotation, it follows that $\triangle OEF \cong \triangle OE'F'$ by SAS. Thus $\angle EFO \cong \angle E'F'O$, from which $l \parallel l'$.

Proof:

Statements	Reasons
1. $H_O(l) = l'$	1. Given
2. Pick E and F on l and consider $H_O(E) = E'$ and $H_O(F) = F'$.	2. The image points exist and can be determined.
3. $OE = OE'$; $OF = OF'$	3. Def. of rotation
4. $\overline{OE} \cong \overline{OE'}$; $\overline{OF} \cong \overline{OF'}$	4. Def. of $\cong$ segments
5. $\angle EOF \cong \angle E'OF'$	5. Vert. $\angle$s are $\cong$.
6. $\triangle OEF \cong \triangle OE'F'$	6. SAS
7. $\angle EFO \cong \angle E'F'O$	7. CPCTC
8. $l \parallel l'$	8. If two lines have a trans. such that alt. int. $\angle$s are $\cong$, the lines are $\parallel$.

Conclusion: The image of a line under a half-turn is a line that is parallel to the original.

PAGE 607

INVESTIGATION

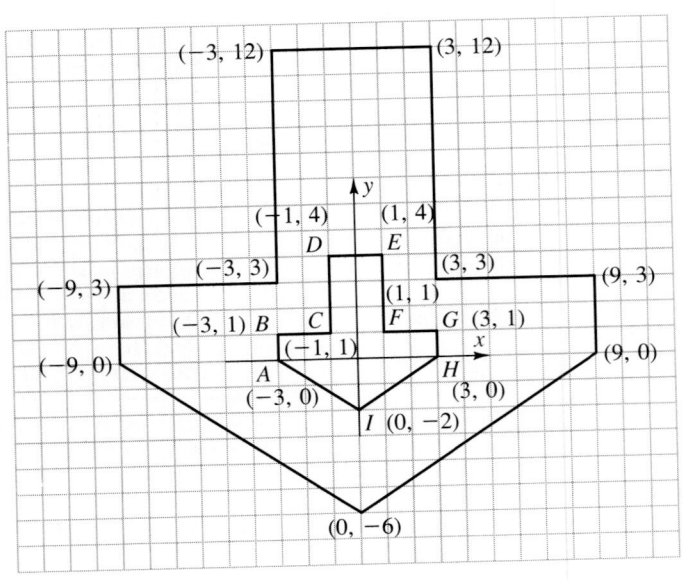

PAGE 609

7–8.

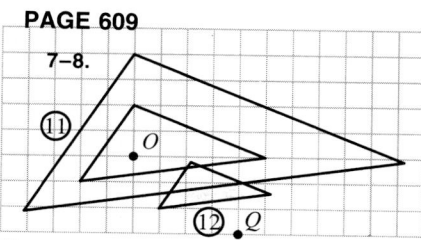

9–10.

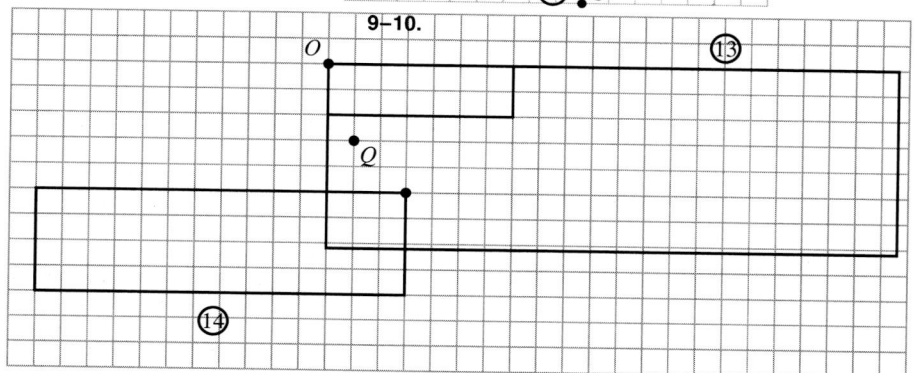

PAGE 610

25.

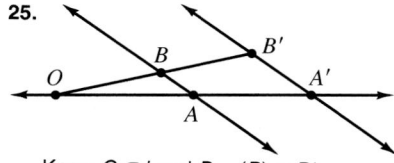

Know $O \in l$ and $D_{O,k}(B) = B'$.
1. Draw $\overline{AB}$.
Know that $\overline{AB}$ gets mapped onto $\overline{A'B'}$ where $\overline{A'B'} \parallel \overline{AB}$ and $A'B' = |k| \cdot AB$.
2. Through B', construct $\overleftrightarrow{A'B'}$ such that $\overline{A'B'} \parallel \overline{AB}$. A' is the pt. at which the line intersects l.

27. Case 1 of Theorem 14.4, $|k| > 1$
Proof:

Statements	Reasons
1. $D_{O,k}(\overline{PQ}) = \overline{P'Q'}$	1. Given
2. $\angle O \cong \angle O$	2. Refl. prop.
3. $OP' = |k| \cdot OP$, $OQ' = |k| \cdot OQ$	3. Def. of dilation
4. $\triangle POQ \sim \triangle P'OQ'$	4. SAS similarity
5. $\angle OPQ \cong \angle OP'Q'$	5. Def. of $\sim$ △s
6. $\overline{P'Q'} \parallel \overline{PQ}$	6. If 2 lines have a transv. and a pair of corr. $\angle$s are $\cong$, then the lines are $\parallel$.
7. $P'Q' = |k| \cdot PQ$	7. Def. of $\sim$ △s

28. The proof of Case 2 of Theorem 14.4, $|k| < 1$, follows that of Case 1.

PAGE 615

1.

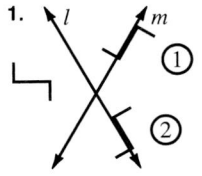

2.

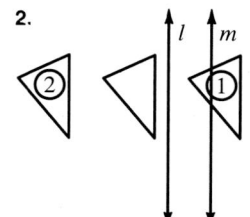

3.

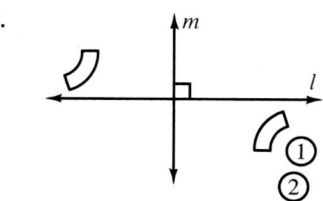

9.

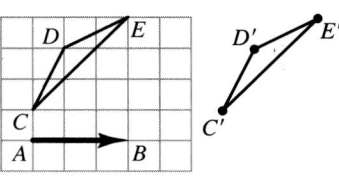

PAGE 616

20. Given: Isometries F and G with points X and Y
Prove: $G \circ F$ is an isometry.

Statements	Reasons
1. Isometries F and G with points X and Y	1. Given
2. $F(\overline{XY}) = \overline{X'Y'}$ and $G(\overline{X'Y'}) = \overline{X''Y''}$	2. Def. of transformation
3. $XY = X'Y'$; $X'Y' = X''Y''$	3. Def. of isometry
4. $XY = X''Y''$	4. Trans. prop.
5. $G \circ F$ is an isometry.	5. Def. of isometry

Conclusion: The composition of 2 isometries is an isometry.

21. Given: $l \parallel m$; distance between l and m is d; $R_m \circ R_1 (A) = A''$; $R_m \circ R_1 (B) = B''$
Prove: $R_m \circ R_1$ is a translation; $AA'' = BB'' = 2d$
Plan: It is sufficient to show that $AA''B''B$ is a $\square$ having $AA'' = BB'' = 2d$. To do so, show $\overline{AA''} \parallel \overline{BB''}$ and $\overline{AA''} \cong \overline{BB''}$.
Proof:

Statements	Reasons
1. $l \parallel m$; distance between l and m is d; $R_m \circ R_l$ $(A) = A''$; $R_m \circ R_l (B) = B''$	1. Given
2. $R_l (A) = A'$; $R_m (A') = A''$; $R_l (B) = B'$; $R_m (B') = B''$	2. Def. of composition
3. l is the $\perp$ bisector of $\overline{AA'}$ and $\overline{BB'}$; m is the $\perp$ bisector of $\overline{A'A''}$ and $\overline{B'B''}$	3. Def. of reflection

783

4. Consider $\overleftrightarrow{AA'}$ and $\overleftrightarrow{BB'}$

5. $\overleftrightarrow{AA'} \perp l$; $\overleftrightarrow{BB'} \perp l$

6. $\overleftrightarrow{AA'} \perp m$; $\overleftrightarrow{BB'} \perp m$

7. A'' is on $\overleftrightarrow{AA'}$; B'' is on $\overleftrightarrow{BB'}$

8. A, A' and A'' are collinear; B, B' and B'' are collinear

9. $AA'' = AX + XA' + A'Y + YA''$
   $BB'' = BZ + ZB' + B'W + WB''$

10. $AX = XA'$; $A'Y = YA''$; $BZ = ZB'$; $B'W = WB''$

11. $AA'' = 2 \cdot XA' + 2 \cdot A'Y$
    $BB'' = 2 \cdot ZB' + 2 \cdot B'W$

12. $AA'' = 2(XA' + A'Y)$
    $BB'' = 2(ZB' + B'W)$

13. $XA' + A'Y = ZB' + B'W = d$

14. $AA'' = 2d$; $BB'' = 2d$

15. $AA'' = BB''$

16. $\overline{AA''} \cong \overline{BB''}$

17. $\overline{AA''} \parallel \overline{BB''}$

4. Two pts. determine a line.

5. Def. of $\perp$ bis.

6. If a line intersecting two $\parallel$ lines is $\perp$ to one of the lines, it is $\perp$ to the other.

7. Through a pt. not on a line, there is one and only one line $\perp$ to the given line.

8. Def. of collinear

9. Def. of betweenness

10. A pt. on the $\perp$ bisector of a segment is equidistant from the endpts. of the segment.

11. Subst. prop.

12. Distrib. prop.

13. Def. of distance between lines

14. Subst. prop.

15. Subst. prop.

16. Def. of $\cong$ segments

17. Two lines $\perp$ to the same line are $\parallel$.

18. $AA''B''B$ is a $\square$

19. $\overline{AB} \parallel \overline{A''B''}$
20. $R_m \circ R_l$ is a translation

Conclusion: The composition of two reflections in parallel lines is a translation. Each point is translated a distance twice that of the distance between the parallel lines.

22. **Given:** Lines l and m intersecting in O; $m\angle SOR = \alpha$
    Prove: $R_m \circ R_l = \mathcal{R}_{O,2\alpha}$

Statements	Reasons
1. Lines l and m intersecting in O $m\angle SOR = \alpha$	1. Given
2. $R_l(A) = A'$ and $R_m(A') = A''$	2. Def. of reflection
3. $R_m \circ R_l$ is an isometry.	3. Composition of 2 isom. is an isom.
4. $OA = OA'$ and $OA' = OA''$	4. Def. of isometry
5. $OA = OA''$	5. Trans. prop.
6. $\angle AOS \cong \angle A'OS$ and $\angle A'OR \cong \angle A''OR$	6. Def. of isometry
7. $m\angle AOA'' = m\angle AOS + m\angle A'OS + m\angle A'OR + m\angle A''OR$	7. Def. of a between ray
8. $m\angle SOR = m\angle A'OS + m\angle A'OR$	8. Subst. prop.
9. $m\angle SOR = m\angle AOS + m\angle A''OR$	9. Subst. prop.
10. $m\angle AOA'' = 2\alpha$	10. Subst. prop.
11. $R_m \circ R_l = \mathcal{R}_{O,2\alpha}$	11. Def. of rotation

Conclusion: The composition of 2 reflections in parallel lines is a translation. Each pt. is translated a distance twice that of the distance between the parallel lines.

18. If a quad. has a pair of opp. sides $\cong$ and $\parallel$, the quad. is a $\square$.

19. Def. of $\square$
20. Def. of translation

23. **Given:** $l \perp k$ at O
    Prove: $R_k \circ R_l = H_O$

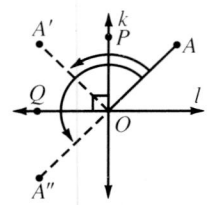

Plan: Use the def. of $\perp$ lines to reach concl.

Statements	Reasons
1. $l \perp k$ at O	1. Given
2. $\angle POQ$ is rt. $\angle$.	2. Def. of $\perp$ lines
3. $m\angle POQ = 90 = \alpha$	3. Def. of rt. $\angle$
4. $R_k \circ R_l = \mathcal{R}_{O,2\alpha}$	4. Th. 14.7
5. $R_k \circ R_l = \mathcal{R}_{O,180}$	5. Subst. prop.
6. $R_k \circ R_l = H_O$	6. Def. of half-turn

Conclusion: The composition of reflections in $\perp$ lines is a half-turn about the pts where the lines intersect.

PAGE 621

39. If $T \circ S(M) = N$, show that $S^{-1} \circ T^{-1}(N) = M$
    Let $S^{-1} \circ T^{-1}(N)$
    $= S^{-1} \circ T^{-1}(T \circ S(M))$ —substitution
    $= S^{-1} \circ (T^{-1} \circ T) \circ S(M)$ —associative prop.
    $= S^{-1} \circ I \circ S(M)$ —inverse
    $= S^{-1} \circ S(M)$ —identity
    $= I(M)$ —inverse
    $= M$ —identity

41. **Given:** H_A
    Prove: $H_A \circ H_A = I$

Plan: Apply defs. of $\frac{1}{2}$-turn, comp. and ident.

Statements	Reasons
1. H_A	1. Given
2. $H_A = \mathcal{R}_{A,180}$	2. Def. of half-turn
3. $H_A \circ H_A = \mathcal{R}_{A,360}$	3. Def. of composition
4. $\mathcal{R}_{A,360} = I$	4. Def. of identity
5. $H_A \circ H_A = I$	5. Subst. prop.

CLASS EXERCISES, PAGE 624

1. Rectangle $ABCD \ni R_l (ABCD) =$ rectangle $BADC$.
   Let l be the $\perp$-bisector of sides $\overline{AB}$ and $\overline{DC}$. Then $R_l (ABCD) = BADC$

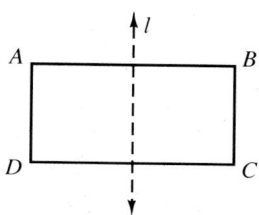

2. Pentagon *EFGHI* ∋ R_l (*EFGHI*) = *IHGFE*
Let *l* bisect ∠*G* and extend through $\overline{EI}$ (*l* is the ⊥-bis. of $\overline{EI}$). Then R_l (*EFGHI*) = *IHGFE*

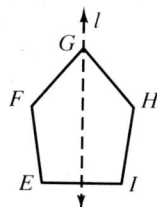

3. △*ABC* ∋ R_l (△*ABC*) = △*ACB*.
Let *l* be the bisector of vertex ∠*A* of isos. △*ABC*. Then *l* is ⊥-bis. of $\overline{BC}$, so R_l (△*ABC*) = △*ACB*.

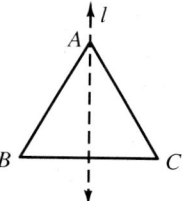

4. Nonrectangular ▱*JKLM* ∋ R_l (▱*JKLM*) = ▱*LKJM*
l contains diagonal $\overline{KM}$. R_l (▱*JKLM*) = ▱*LKJM*

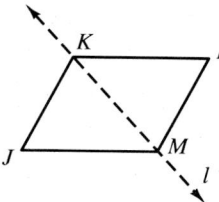

PRACTICE EXERCISES, PAGE 624

1. Choose any pt. *F* between *A* and *B*. Construct a ⊥ to $\overline{AC}$ from *F*; call the pt. where this ⊥ intersects $\overline{AC}$ pt. *E*. Also from *F*, construct a line ∥ to $\overline{AC}$; locate *G* where this line intersects $\overline{BC}$. Drop a ⊥ to $\overline{AC}$ from *G*. *EFGH* is a rectangle since it is a ▱ with a rt. ∠.

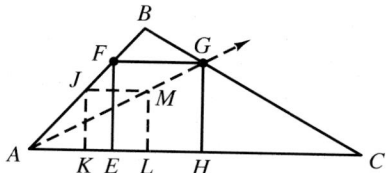

2. A square having a side on $\overline{AC}$ and a vertex on $\overline{AB}$ may not have its fourth vertex on $\overline{BC}$. However, a dilation of this square, using *A* as center, will meet all conditions.

Choose a pt. *J* on $\overline{AB}$ and construct $\overline{JK} \perp \overline{AC}$. Construct square *JKLM* having sides of length *JK*. Draw $\overrightarrow{AM}$ to intersect $\overline{BC}$ in *G*. Construct $\overline{GH} \perp \overline{AC}$. Using *GH* as side length, construct square *EFGH*.

PAGE 625

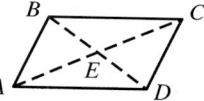

3. Given: ▱*ABCD* with diagonals intersecting in pt. *E*
Prove: $\overline{AC}$ and $\overline{BD}$ bisect each other
Plan: Find H_E (△*BEC*) = △*B'EC'*. It follows that *BE* = *B'E* and *EC* = *EC'*; hence $\overline{BB'}$ and $\overline{CC'}$ bisect each other. Since it can be shown that △*B'EC'* ≅ △*DEA* by ASA, and since *B'* is on $\overline{ED}$ and *C'* is on $\overline{EA}$, it follows that *B'* is *D* and *C'* is *A*. Substitution produces the conclusion.

Statements	Reasons
1. ▱*ABCD* with diagonals intersecting at *E*	1. Given
2. $\overline{BC} \parallel \overline{DA}$	2. Def. of ▱
3. $\overline{BC} \cong \overline{DA}$ Consider H_E (△*BEC*) = △*B'EC'*	3. Opp. sides of a ▱ are ≅.
4. △*BEC* ≅ △*B'EC'*	4. A rotation is an isometry.
5. $\overline{BE} \cong \overline{B'E}$; $\overline{EC} \cong \overline{EC'}$; $\overline{BC} \cong \overline{B'C'}$	5. CPCTC
6. *E* is the midpt. of $\overline{BB'}$ and $\overline{CC'}$	6. Def. of midpt.
7. $\overline{BB'}$ and $\overline{CC'}$ bisect each other	7. Def. of "bisect each other"
8. $\overline{BC} \parallel \overline{B'C'}$	8. A half-turn about a pt. not on a line maps a line (segment) to a parallel line (segment)
9. $\overline{B'C'} \parallel \overline{DA}$	9. Two lines ∥ to the same line are ∥ to each other.
10. ∠*EC'B'* ≅ ∠*EAD*; ∠*EB'C'* ≅ ∠*EDA*	10. If ∥ lines have a trans., corres. ∠s are ≅.
11. $\overline{B'C'} \cong \overline{DA}$	11. Substitution
12. △*B'EC'* ≅ △*DEA*	12. ASA Post.
13. $\overline{B'E} \cong \overline{DE}$; $\overline{EC'} \cong \overline{EA}$	13. CPCTC
14. *B'E* = *DE*; *EC'* = *EA*	14. Def. of ≅ segments
15. *B'* is on $\overrightarrow{ED}$; *C'* is on $\overrightarrow{EA}$	15. The image of a line under a half-turn about a pt. on the line is the line itself.
16. *B'* is *D*; *C'* is *A*	16. On a ray, there is exactly 1 pt. at a given distance from the endpt.
17. $\overline{BD}$ and $\overline{CA}$ bisect each other	17. Substitution

Conclusion: The diagonals of a ▱ bisect each other.

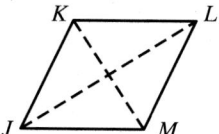

4. Given: Rhombus *JKLM*
Prove: $\overline{KM} \perp \overline{JL}$
Plan: Reflect △*MJK* in $\overline{KM}$ to get △*MJ'K*. Show that *J'* is *L* by showing that *MJKJ'* is a ▱ and that *J'* is on $\overline{KL}$. Since R_{KM} (*J*) = *L*, the conclusion follows.

Proof:

Statements	Reasons
1. Rhombus JKLM	1. Given
2. ▱JKLM with $\overline{JK} \cong \overline{KL} \cong$ $\overline{LM} \cong \overline{MJ}$	2. Def. of rhombus
3. $\overline{MJ} \parallel \overline{KL}$	3. Def. of ▱
4. $R_{KM}(K) = K$; $R_{KM}(M) = M$; $R_{KM}(J) = J'$; $R_{KM}(\triangle MJK) = \triangle MJ'K$	4. Def. of reflection
5. $\triangle MJK \cong \triangle MJ'K$	5. A reflection is an isometry.
6. $\overline{MJ} \cong \overline{MJ'}$; $\overline{JK} \cong \overline{J'K}$	6. CPCTC
7. $\overline{MJ} \cong \overline{JK} \cong \overline{KJ'} \cong \overline{J'M}$	7. Subst. prop.
8. $MJKJ'$ is a ▱.	8. If both pairs of opp. sides of a quad. are ≅, the quad. is a ▱.
9. $\overline{MJ} \parallel \overline{KJ'}$	9. Def. of ▱
10. J' is on $\overrightarrow{KL}$	10. Through a pt. not on a line there is one and only one line ∥ to the given line.
11. $\overline{KL} \cong \overline{KJ'}$	11. Subst. prop.
12. J' is L	12. On a ray there is one and only one pt. at a given dist. from the end pt.
13. $R_{KM}(J) = L$	13. Subst. prop.
14. $\overline{KM}$ is ⊥ bis. of $\overline{JL}$	14. Def. of reflection
15. $\overline{KM} \perp \overline{JL}$	15. Def. of ⊥ bis.

Conclusion: The diag. of a rhombus are ⊥

5.

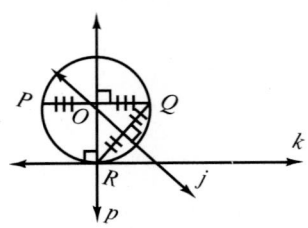

Draw $\overline{PQ}$ and construct its ⊥-bisector p. Label R where p intersects k. Draw

$\overline{QR}$ and construct its ⊥-bisector j. j and p intersect at O, the center of the desired circle. Draw ⊙O using OR as radius.

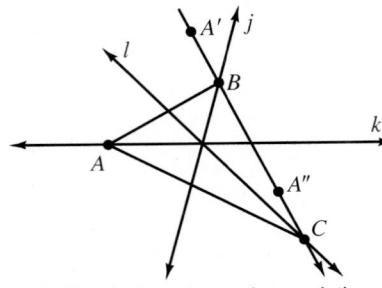

6. As drawn, there is a unique solution, found as follows: Reflect A in l to get A', and then reflect A in j to get A''. Draw $\overline{A'A''}$. $\overline{A'A''}$ intersects j and l in points B and C, the other vertices of the desired △.

If any two of j, k, and l are ⊥, there is no solution. If the lines intersect so that one lies in the *acute* angle formed by the other two, then j and k will bisect the *exterior* angles at B and C.

7. Construct △ABC so that M is the midpoint of $\overline{BC}$ and m, n, and p are the ⊥-bisectors of the sides of △ABC.

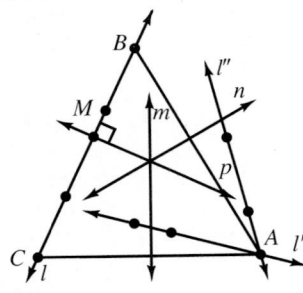

Construct a ⊥ to p at M; call it l. Reflect l in n to get l' ($R_n(l) = l'$), and reflect l in m to get l'' ($R_m(l) = l''$). l' and l'' intersect in vertex A of △ABC. Find $R_n(A) = B$ and $R_m(A) = C$ to locate vertices B and C.

Note: This problem has a unique solution provided m and n are not ⊥. If they are ⊥, then l' and l'' will either be ∥ or else they will coincide. If $l' \parallel l''$, there is no solution; if $l' = l''$, there is more than one solution.

8.

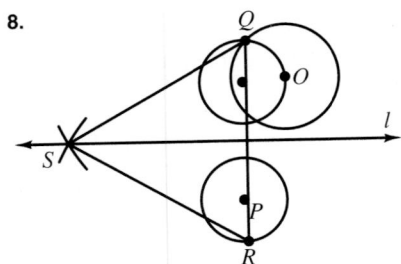

Reflect ⊙P in l. Label one of the points of intersection of the circles as Q. Find $R_l(Q) = R$. (Q and R are two of the desired vertices.) Draw $\overline{QR}$. Locate S on l by using Q and R as centers and QR as radius. △QRS is equilateral.

9.

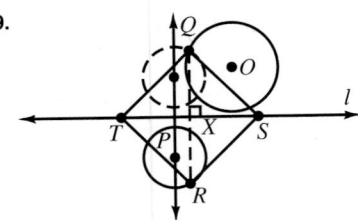

Reflect ⊙P across l, labeling one of the points of intersection as Q. Find $R_l(Q) = R$. Using X as center and QX (or XR) as radius, locate pts. T and S. Draw $QSRT$.

10. If $j \parallel k \parallel l$, construct equilateral △ABC having vertex A on j, B on k, and C on l.

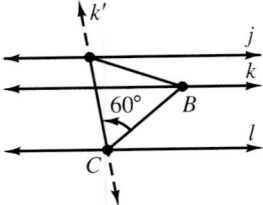

Pick arbitrary pts. C on l and B on k. Rotate k about C through an angle of 60°. ($\mathcal{R}_{c,60}(k) = k'$). The intersection of k' and j is A. Draw △ABC.

11. Use transformations to prove SAS.
  Given: △ABC and DEF; $\overline{AB} \cong \overline{DE}$; $\overline{BC} \cong \overline{EF}$; ∠B ≅ ∠E
  Prove: △ABC ≅ △DEF

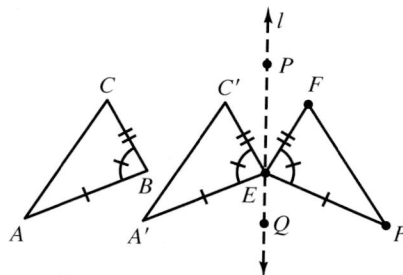

Plan: Translate △ABC so that B maps to E (i.e., T(△ABC) = △A′EC′
Reflect △A′EC′ about l, the bisector of ∠sC′EF and A′ED and show that R_l (△A′EC′) = △DEF. Since △ABC has been mapped to △DEF by a composition of isometries, it follows that △ABC ≅ △DEF.

Proof:

Statements	Reasons
1. △ABC and DEF with $\overline{AB} \cong \overline{DE}$; $\overline{BC} \cong \overline{EF}$, and ∠B ≅ ∠E Consider T (△ABC) = △A′EC′	1. Given
2. △ABC ≅ △A′EC′	2. A translation is an isometry.
3. ∠ABC ≅ ∠A′EC′	3. CPCTC
4. Let l be the bisector of ∠C′EF	4. Every ∠ has a bisector.
5. ∠C′EP ≅ ∠FEP	5. Def. of ∠ bisector
6. ∠A′EC′ ≅ ∠DEF	6. Substitution

Statements	Reasons
7. m∠A′EC′ = m∠DEF; m∠C′EP = m∠FEP	7. Def. of ≅ ∠s
8. m∠A′EC′ + m∠C′EP = m∠DEF + m∠FEP	8. Addition prop. of equality
9. m∠A′EC′ + m∠C′EP = m∠A′EP; m∠DEF + m∠FEP = m∠DEP	9. Betweenness of rays
10. m∠A′EP = m∠DEP	10. Substitution
11. ∠A′EP ≅ ∠DEP	11. Def. of ≅ ∠s
12. ∠QEA′ and ∠A′EP are a linear pair, as are ∠QED and ∠DEP	12. Def. of linear pair
13. ∠QEA′ and ∠A′EP are supp., as are ∠QED and ∠DEP	13. Linear pair postulate
14. ∠QEA′ ≅ ∠QED	14. Supp. of ≅ ∠s are ≅.
15. l bisects ∠A′ED Consider R_l (△A′EC′)	15. Def. of ∠ bisector
16. R_l (E) = E	16. Def. of reflection
17. R_l ($\overline{EC′}$) = $\overline{EF}$, R_l ($\overline{EA′}$) = $\overline{ED}$	17. Bisector of ∠ is line of reflection for sides of ∠; a reflection is an isometry.
18. R_l (△A′EC′) = △DEF	18. Steps 16 and 17
19. $R_l \circ T$(△ABC) = △DEF	19. Def. of composition

Statements	Reasons
20. $R_l \circ T$ (△ABC) is an isometry.	20. The composition of two isometries is an isometry.
21. △ABC ≅ △DEF.	21. Def. of isometry

Conclusion: If $\overline{AB} \cong \overline{DE}$, $\overline{BC} \cong \overline{EF}$, and ∠B ≅ ∠E, then △ABC ≅ △DEF.

PAGE 636

20. Given: M and N are respective midpts. of $\overline{AB}$ and $\overline{AC}$ in △ABC.
  Prove: $\overline{MN} \parallel \overline{BC}$; $MN = \frac{1}{2}BC$
  Plan: Use a dilation with center A to reach concl.
  Proof: Consider $D_{A,\frac{1}{2}}(\overline{BC}) = \overline{MN}$.
Then $\overline{MN} \parallel \overline{BC}$ and $MN = \frac{1}{2}BC$ because a dilation $D_{O,k}$ maps every line segment to a parallel line segment that is |k| times as long.

Conclusion: The segment connecting the midpts of 2 sides of a △ is ∥ to the third side and half as long.

CHALLENGE

Outline of proof: Show $\overline{EE′}$ and $\overline{FF′}$ bisect each other (follows by def. of half-turn). Thus EFE′F′ is a □. It is also true that $R_{EE′}(F) = F′$. (True, since it is known that MF = MF′ and on $\overrightarrow{MF′}$, there is only one pt. at a given distance from M.) Thus $\overline{FF′} \perp \overline{EE′} \rightarrow EFE′F′$ is a rhombus.
Note: You can actually prove that EFE′F′ is a square.

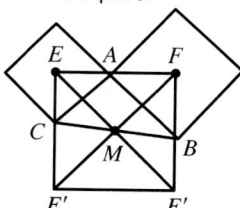